HUDSON'S

HISTORIC HOUSES
AND GARDENS

including HISTORIC SITES OF INTEREST

Forde Abbey, Dorset.

Published by:
Norman Hudson & Company
High Wardington House, Upper Wardington, Banbury, Oxon OX17 1SP
Tel: 01295 750750   Fax: 01295 750800

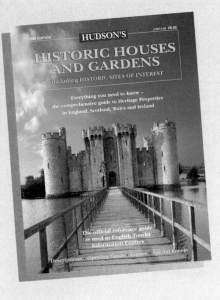

Published by:
Norman Hudson & Company,
High Wardington House, Upper Wardington,
Banbury, Oxfordshire OX17 1SP

Tel: 01295 750570   Fax: 01295 750800

ISBN: 0 9531426 1 2

Editor:.................................. Norman Hudson

Production Manager: .... Miranda Winram

Graphic Design:.......................... KC Graphics

DTP and Maps: .... Georgia Davey

Sales: .... Fiona Rolt

Editorial/Maps Consultant: .... Patrick Lane

Colour Origination:.... Spot On Reprographics

Printed in England: E T Heron & Co Ltd, Essex

Distributed in the UK & Europe by Biblios,
Partridge Green, West Sussex RH13 8LD
and in America by General Sales Agent,
SunWelcome Inc, Florida.

Find *Hudson's* illustrated properties on the
Internet incorporated on the 'Best Loved
Britain & Ireland' website at:
http://www.bestloved.com.

Cover picture: Bodiam Castle, Sussex

The garden at Coughton Court, Warwickshire.

FOREWORD

When that tireless traveller, Elizabeth, Duchess of Northumberland, visited Knole in the 1770s she noted in her diary that she and her party "had our cold loaf with us and ate it in the gateway". In the summer of 1789 John Byng was shown round Belvoir Castle by a housekeeper "of a very drunken and dawdling appearance". By contrast, 18th century visitors to Kedleston were delighted by "the uncommon politeness and attention" of Sir Nathaniel Curzon's housekeeper, Mrs Garnett, described by Boswell after his visit with Dr Johnson in 1777 as a "most distinct articulator".

Visiting country houses in the 18th century was pot luck; two hundred years later things are very different, for we now have *Hudson's* guide. This comprehensive and generously illustrated volume is the key to what we now call the heritage properties of Britain, placing in the hand of the visitor all the information he needs to plan his summer expeditions. He may not be invited to help himself to a "sword hilt and part of the blade, said to have been worn by the Vernons in the wars of France", which was the experience of John Byng after his tour of Haddon Hall, but so long as he studies his *Hudson's* with care he will certainly have no need to carry with him a "cold loaf". Many historic properties now have restaurants and gift shops and furthermore, there are a few historic houses which now accept paying guests, details of which can be found in the accommodation index.

This is one of the best and most comprehensive publications of its kind, the essential vade-mecum for the independent traveller in Britain. The Victorians had Murray, Bradshaw and Baedeker; we are now blessed with *Hudson's*.

Martin Drury

Martin Drury
Director General - The National Trust

CONTENTS

ℹ	**General information**	**P**	**Parking** Availability for cars & coaches. Courier/group leader information.
✕	**Catering/Functions** Availabilty for special functions, corporate hospitality, wedding receptions, etc.	**👪**	**Schools/Education** Special facilities for school visits or educational needs.
♿	**Disabled** Suitability of property for disabled visitors and any constraints.	**🐕**	**Dogs** Acceptability and any constraints.
♨	**Refreshments** Tearoom, café, restaurant information. Whether licensed.	**A**	**Overnight Accommodation** Provision and any constraints.
🚶	**Guided Tours** Availability and requirements for groups, etc.	**🔔**	**Civil Wedding Licence Holder** Properties at which Civil Weddings may be held.

OAP - Concessions: Use of the term OAP indicates concessionary rates for elderly people but does not necessarily coincide with State pensionable age.

All information published is supplied by owners of the properties. Every effort is made to ensure that it is correct at time of publication. Changes can occur. If long journeys or special requirements are involved, visitors are advised to telephone the properties in advance.

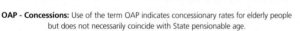

Britain and Ireland have a distinctive heritage of beautiful buildings, gardens and historic sites. Our aim has been to provide essential information on these and to give guidance for independent travellers, the travel trade, and those seeking venues for a variety of purposes.

Following the pattern of the National Trust and English Heritage we have grouped properties in England into regional sections, although within these sections we have retained the old county boundaries. This will make use of the book easier for those with an interest focused on one region and for those unfamiliar with county boundaries.

In Scotland the division is arranged so as to coincide with Area Tourist Board boundaries.

Norman Hudson

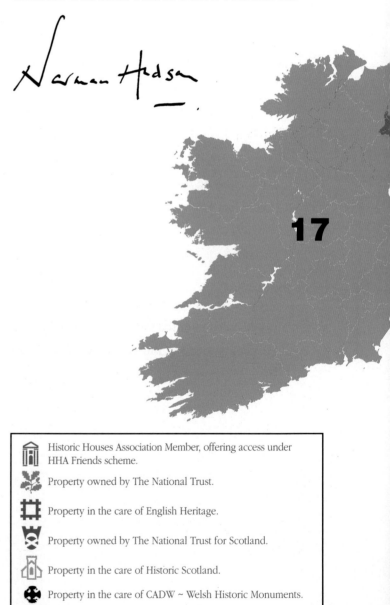

14

17

🏛	Historic Houses Association Member, offering access under HHA Friends scheme.
🌿	Property owned by The National Trust.
▦	Property in the care of English Heritage.
♛	Property owned by The National Trust for Scotland.
⌛	Property in the care of Historic Scotland.
☘	Property in the care of CADW ~ Welsh Historic Monuments.

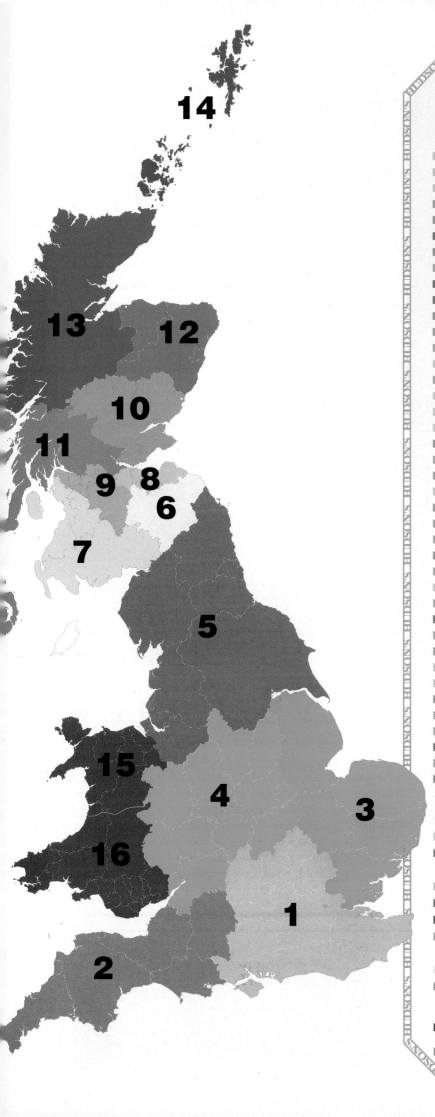

COUNTY & REGION LISTING

South East England

West Country England

Eastern Counties England

The Midlands England

Northen Counties England

Scotland

Wales

Ireland

Art Works.

Ragley Hall

Hugh, 8th Marquess of Hertford who died earlier this year was one of the first to support the establishment of the Historic Houses Association. He recognised the need more than most. In 1956 Ragley Hall was in danger of becoming a ruin. Not only did he devote his life to its restoration, but by commissioning Graham Rust to paint the vast mural '*The Temptation*' in the south staircase hall, he has also made a major 20th century contribution to one of the finest country houses (see page 229).

Garden Festival

AT HOLKER, CUMBRIA

The 1998 Holker Garden Festival, recognised as one of the friendliest early summer shows in the country, will take place at Holker Hall near Grange-over-Sands in South Cumbria, on 29 - 31 May. As in past years, many horticulturalists go to the show direct from Chelsea and high standards are expected from exhibitors and traders alike. Entry to Holker's 25 acre formal and woodland gardens is included as part of the admission (see page 252).

NORTHAMPTONSHIRE'S
PRIVATE VIEW
OPEN BY SPECIAL ARRANGEMENT

A selection of Northamptonshire's magnificent historic houses, not normally open to the public, are opened on special occasions as part of the 'Private View' experience organised by the Northamptonshire Tourism and Conference Bureau, tel: 01604 671200 (see *Hudson's* p206). One of these is Weston Hall, Northamptonshire, a charming example of the English manor house. It is probably best known over the last 70 years, as the home of Sir Sacheverall Sitwell, the youngest of the literary Sitwell trio.

Where is this?

This is not the usual view of this house, which has a 1,400 acre park with red and fallow deer. It featured in BBCs 'Pride and Prejudice'. The answer can be found on page 248.

HISTORIC HOUSES ASSOCIATION

Become a Friend of the HHA, support the Association and visit over 300 privately-owned houses, castles and gardens, many of which are listed in this Guide, for free.

DEENE PARK, NORTHAMPTONSHIRE

Privately-owned properties represent a fascinating diversity from the great treasure houses such as Blenheim and Castle Howard, to the small manor houses and many with wonderful gardens. What makes these places so special is their individuality and the fact that they are generally still lived in – often by the same family that has owned them through centuries of British history.

You can help preserve these houses in private ownership and benefit from doing so.

An integral part of the HHA is our Friends scheme. The Friends provide enlightened moral support and contribute to the funds that enable us to operate.

Richard Wilkin, Director General of the HHA, explains . . .

"It is not generally realised that two-thirds of Britain's built heritage remains in private ownership. Over 300 privately-owned houses, castles and gardens, most of which belong to this Association, are open to the public: more houses than the National Trust, English Heritage and their equivalents in Scotland and Wales put together.

Successive Governments have recognised the private owner as the most economic and effective guardian of this heritage. But the cost of maintaining these properties is colossal, and the task is daunting. The owners work enormously hard and take a pride in preserving and presenting this element of Britain's heritage. The HHA helps them do this by:

* *representing their interests in Government*

* *providing an advisory service for houses – taxation, conservation, security, regulations*

* *running charities assisting disabled visitors, conserving works of art and helping promote educational facilities*

LOSELEY PARK, SURREY

The subscription at £28.00 equates to the National Trust and English Heritage and provides access to over 300 individual member properties. You will also be able to join regional tours which include visits to houses not normally open to the public. And you will receive copies of the Association's quarterly magazine.

"The HHA Friends scheme provides amazing value for the interested house and gardens visitor . . ."

Hitherto this scheme has not been widely advertised or publicised and its overall membership has to be limited because our member houses can only absorb so many free visits. However, this year the HHA is happy to offer membership of the Friends scheme to the subscribers to Hudson's Guide.

If you do wish to become a Friend of the HHA, and I very much hope you will, then simply fill in the form below."

SUDELEY CASTLE GARDENS, GLOUCESTERSHIRE

CASTLE HOWARD, YORKSHIRE

Membership: Single £28, Double £40, £10 additional Friend at same address.

FRIENDS APPLICATION FORM

PLEASE USE BLOCK CAPITALS • DELETE AS APPROPRIATE

MR/MRS/MS or MR & MRS* INITIALS _____

SURNAME _____

ADDRESS _____

_____

_____

_____ POST CODE _____

ADDITIONAL FRIENDS AT SAME ADDRESS

_____

_____

OFFICE USE ONLY – source code ☐☐☐☐ HHHG/98

☐ I/We* enclose remittance of £ ___ payable to the Historic Houses Association.

☐ I/We* have completed the direct debit adjacent.

Please return to: Historic Houses Association, Friends Membership Department, Heritage House, PO Box 21, Baldock, Hertfordshire SG7 5SH. **Tel: (01462) 896688**

PHOTOCOPIES OF THIS FORM ARE ACCEPTABLE

INSTRUCTION TO YOUR BANK TO PAY DIRECT DEBITS

Please complete Parts 1 to 4 to instruct your Bank to make payments directly from your account. Then return the form to: Historic Houses Association, Membership Department, Heritage House, PO Box 21, Baldock, Herts, SG7 5SH.

1. Name and full postal address of your Bank

_____

_____

_____

Your Bank may decline to accept instructions to pay Direct Debits from some types of accounts.

2. Name of account holder _____

3. Account number ☐☐☐☐☐☐☐☐

4. Bank sort code ☐☐ ☐☐ ☐☐

Originator's identification number 9 3 0 5 8 7

Originator's reference Office use only ☐☐☐☐☐☐

IF COMPLETING THE DIRECT DEBIT FORM, YOU MUST ALSO COMPLETE THE APPLICATION FORM.

5. Your instructions to the Bank and signature.

■ I instruct you to pay Direct Debits for my annual subscription from my account at the request of the Historic Houses Association.

■ The amounts are variable and may be debited on various dates.

■ I understand that the Historic Houses Association may change the amounts and dates only after giving me prior notice of not less than 21 days.

■ Please cancel all previous Standing Order and Direct Debiting instructions in favour of the Historic Houses Association.

■ I will inform the Bank in writing if I wish to cancel this instruction.

■ I understand that if any Direct Debit is paid which breaks the terms of the instruction, the Bank will make a refund.

Signature(s) _____

_____

Date _____

DIRECT DEBIT Completion of the form above ensures that your subscription will be paid automatically on the date that it is due. You may cancel the order at any time. The Association guarantees that it will only use this authority to deduct annually from your account an amount equal to the annual subscription then current for your class of membership.

The NPI National Heritage

As you look through the pages of *Hudson's* spare a thought for the effort and enthusiasm that owners and managers have put in to making so many of these properties exceptionally enjoyable to visit; the unseen hands that restore, maintain and present these wonderful places, offering such a wealth of history, culture and experience. Without these committed individuals and organisations much of what we hold so valuable about the UK's heritage would not be here today.

That is why NPI, the pensions and retirement specialist, launched the NPI National Heritage Awards; to give you the opportunity to vote for your favourite heritage property, rewarding those responsible for all their effort, endeavour and enthusiasm directed to making a great day out for you.

Last year the properties you voted for not only represented the best of the past but blended these charms with today's expectations of what constitutes a worthwhile, value-packed and entertaining day out, making the NPI Awards a unique celebration of old and new.

The 1997 NPI National Heritage Award winners were:

**Best Overall Property and
Best English Heritage Property**

▼

Brodsworth Hall
South Yorkshire, see page 290.

**Best Overall Property for
Families and Best National
Trust for Scotland Property**

▼

Brodie Castle
Grampian, see page 345.

Awards

Best Historic Houses Association Member Property ▶

Pencarrow,
Cornwall,
see page 111.

◀ ### Best National Trust Property

Waddesdon Manor,
Buckinghamshire,
see page 11.

Best CADW Welsh Historic Monument ▶

Caerphilly Castle,
Mid Glamorgan,
see page 367.

◀ ### Best Historic Royal Palace

Hampton Court Palace,
Surrey, see page 78.

Glasshouses

~ a glimpse of history

Of all garden buildings, decorative or functional, glasshouses are unique because their form is the result of the needs of plants for shelter **says May Woods.**

Glasshouses have evolved over the centuries in response to the variety of sub-tropical and tropical plants that have reached northern Europe and as man's understanding of horticulture, heating and energy efficiency has increased.

At first, in Renaissance Italy, the tender oranges and lemons, oleanders, pomegranates and myrtles that flourished outside in Roman gardens were taken into cellars to escape the colder winters of Florence and

The Orangery ~ Belton House, Lincolnshire.

gardens further north. These citrus plants were a significant feature of Italian gardens, then as now, and were soon transported to the noble gardens of France and then on to England. Sir William Cecil, Lord Burghley, sent to Paris in 1562 for a lemon tree and two myrtles, and probably kept them at Cecil House in the Strand; while by the late 16th century Sir Francis Carew had a celebrated forest of orange trees at Beddington in Surrey. In winter Sir Francis' trees were protected by large wooden sheds built up around them each autumn and heated by two iron stoves.

One of the earliest brick shelters for tender plants was the Orange House at Wimbledon Manor, built for Queen Henrietta Maria in 1642. Built of brick and with a tiled roof, glass doors stretched the length of the south façade, but all was demolished in 1717 by Sarah, Duchess of Marlborough. This was a rare example however, as most tender plants were kept in frost-proof sheds or put in a dry cellar, for lack of light in the winter is no disadvantage to citrus trees, provided both temperature and humidity are low.

By the early 1700s there were many such purpose-built brick buildings which were known as greenhouses because they housed any tender evergreens as well as orange trees. Some were designed by architects and exceedingly handsome, such as Queen Anne's greenhouse at Kensington Palace by Vanbrugh and Hawksmoor, of which Daniel Defoe wrote 'the Queen oft was pleased to make the greenhouse, which is very beautiful, her summer supper house'. But there were plainer versions at Ham House in Surrey, the Chelsea Physick Garden, Lambeth Palace, and in country gardens too.

During the course of the 18th century the greenhouse became an essential feature in most important gardens, from Bowood in Wiltshire to Kenwood in Hampstead; from Blenheim in Oxfordshire to Attingham Park in Shropshire; from Hanbury Hall in Worcestershire to Norton Conyers in Yorkshire; and, in Scotland, to Arniston in Midlothian. All of these, and many more, are still in existence.

Meanwhile, inside the walls of great kitchen gardens, tropical flowers and fruit from all countries of the globe were

Norton Conyers, Yorkshire.

cherished with enthusiasm and in increasing numbers during the 18th century. They were grown in 'stove' houses which were heated by flues in the floor or, later, in the walls. The 'Exoticks' included papayas and guava fruit, which the Duchess of Beaufort produced early in the century to much acclaim at Badminton in Gloucestershire, and pineapples, which were grown at Fulham Palace by the Bishop of London, who was well known for his passion for collecting and growing horticultural rarities.

Around the beginning of the 19th century several changes took place in the design, materials, heating systems, situation and names of glasshouses. Firstly, the value of overhead light for all plants was acknowledged, so many new greenhouses tended to have glass roofs, such as Lord Brownlow's at Belton House in Lincolnshire and the Duke of Bedford's at Woburn Abbey in Bedfordshire. Secondly, improved techniques in the manufacture of cast iron meant that it could be easily moulded into any shape while retaining its strength and was, therefore, ideal for slender, curving glazing bars. This development liberated design from the constraints of brick and wood and led eventually, with improved techniques in glass manufacture developed in the 1830s, to the soaring curves of the Palm House at the Royal Botanic Gardens, Kew. Thirdly, also in the 1830s, the system of heating with hot water pipes was

The Fernery at Tatton Park, Cheshire.

perfected so that heat could be easily controlled and entirely reliable. Fourthly, the glorious profusion of tropical flowers in the kitchen garden was considered too distant from the house now that an elegant conservatory could adjoin the drawing room. So many new country houses included attached conservatories, like that at Ashridge Park in Hertfordshire, and older houses like Broughton Hall in Yorkshire had conservatories added to them.

Finally, terminology underwent a slightly confusing change. The greenhouse of the 18th century was renamed an orangery; and the term greenhouse was usually used for an all-glass house in the walled garden.

By the middle of the 19th century the well-appointed country house would have a conservatory attached to or near the house, an orangery across the lawns, greenhouses in the walled garden, plus a fernery and a peach house, hot-houses, forcing houses, melon beds, and pineries and vineries. While the former have often survived, all too many of the latter have been dismantled, or decayed into twisted skeletons during the course of the 20th century. Felbrigg Hall in Norfolk still has its handsome greenhouse in the flower garden, but the Great Stove at Chatsworth in Derbyshire and the Winter Garden at Somerleyton in Suffolk are both long gone.

A complete set of 19th century glasshouses was discovered in 1991 at Heligan in Cornwall. Brambles and ivy had broken and smothered the timber frames, the shards of glass and old heating pipes, but now nearly all are restored and in working order. Tatton Park in Cheshire, too, has recreated its old hot-beds to demonstrate the techniques of 19th century gardeners.

Glasshouses in botanic gardens have often fared better than their privately-owned counterparts. Birmingham, Sheffield, Edinburgh and Glasgow have maintained or restored their impressive 19th century heritage to display magnificent collections of plants, and Kew has virtually rebuilt the Palm House and restored the Temperate House in recent years.

The glasshouse has enjoyed a great revival in recent years, whether in public or private hands. The Royal Botanic Gardens at Kew has built the Princess of Wales Conservatory, an energy-conscious design that contains no less than 10 separate climates. Once again, a conservatory is a fashionable addition, whether tucked at the back of a town house or graciously enhancing a house in the country.

Birmingham Botanic Gardens, West Midlands.

Proportion and architectural harmony are the secrets of good design, and several companies create individually designed conservatories that integrate as successfully with the house as did those of the early 19th century. Some are added to capture sunlight, some are jungles of palms and exotic flowers, some are stately swimming pools and some are embellished with grottos in 18th century mode. By day, they have a magnetic appeal and by night they become magic places for dining by candlelight. With double-glazing and good heating, they can be a vital part of the house ~ yet still, intriguingly, part of the garden too.

Broughton Hall, Yorkshire.

May Woods is the author of *Visions in Arcadia : European Gardens from Renaissance to Rococo* (Aurum Press, 1996), and co-author with Arete Warren of *Glass Houses : A History of Orangeries, Greenhouses and Conservatories* (Aurum Press, 1988).

The Winter Garden (now demolished) at Somerleyton Hall, Suffolk.

GUERNSEY MANOR

Lying 100 miles south of the English coast but only 12 miles from the northern coast of France, the Channel Islands are not currently encompassed by *Hudson's*. Those visiting Guernsey may be interested to visit Sausmarez Manor. It is a fine example of Queen Anne colonial architecture, built at the behest of the first Governor of New York and still the seat of the Seigneurs de Sausmarez.

The contents and architecture reflect the changing fortunes of the island and family over the centuries.

OPEN: Easter – May & October, tours at 10.30am and 11.30am; June – September, tours at 10.30am, 11.30am, 2.00pm and 3.00pm. Pre-arranged groups on application at other times.

HELP US SAVE YOUR HERITAGE

There are more than 20,000 parish churches in England and Wales - many built by our forefathers over 500 years ago and passed down to us by succeeding generations. We, in turn, hold them in trust for those who will follow.

Many of our finest churches are situated in small country villages which cannot always afford to maintain them. The Historic Churches Preservation Trust, a non-denominational registered charity, depending entirely on voluntary support, exists to help preserve these churches for the future.

Please write or phone, to learn how you could help preserve our priceless heritage.

HISTORIC CHURCHES PRESERVATION TRUST

FREEPOST, Fulham Palace, London SW6 6BR. Tel: 0171-736 3054

Reg. Charity 207402

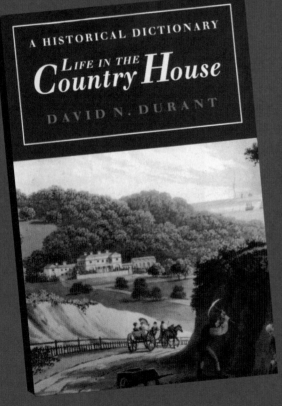

A HISTORICAL DICTIONARY

LIFE IN THE Country House

DAVID N. DURANT

When was divorce so expensive that a cheap alternative was to sell your wife?

Did you know that the fashionable time for dinner became progressively later throughout the 18th century, and that is why in the 19th century people decided to fill the gap with midday luncheon or 'nuncheon' and afternoon tea? What does it mean 'to sit below the salt'? What was the origin of being 'on the dole'? Is the term 'bounder' derived from golf, the bondage of domestic staff, or a term for an inveterate traveller?

The answers to these and many other questions which may have passed through one's mind when studying Britain's past, can be discovered in this Dictionary, extracts from which are found throughout **Hudson's** 1998.

Life in the Country House ~ a Historical Dictionary by David N Durant, is published by John Murray
(Hardback: £25.00 ISBN 0–7195–5075–0. Paperback: £15.99 ISBN 0–7195–5474–8).

Parish Churches - our forgotten heritage

Patrick Lane

Thousands flock to our cathedrals and abbeys, but few stop to enjoy the profusion of architectural treasures to be found in our parish churches.

Sadly, those that do may be disappointed, for they could find it to be one more church that has been locked to keep out thieves and vandals. Unfortunately, the sightseer and those who like to go there looking for peace and proximity to God, are also kept out.

That is what prompted Sir Andrew Lloyd-Webber in 1994 to found the Open Churches Trust, with the express purpose of promoting the opening of locked churches. Much of the

Trust's work involves funding attendants to allow doors to remain open in high-risk areas.

But churches face other dangers. Declining church attendance has taken its toll. Few people realise that the church congregation alone is responsible for maintaining these distinguished buildings for the benefit of us all. Church Authorities give very limited assistance and only the finest listed churches receive grants from English Heritage. Literally hundreds of churches fall into disrepair every year and most parishes cannot afford to pay without some outside help; some receive this from the Historic Churches Preservation Trust.

Next time you visit an historic house or

garden, remember to explore also the hidden history on its doorstep. The architectural splendour of many parish churches puts them amongst the nation's most impressive structures. In such an atmosphere you can pause for a moment of reflection and tranquillity, shielded from the outside world. And if you are frustrated at being denied this opportunity, perhaps you can help by supporting:

a) The Open Churches Trust, c/o The Really Useful Company, 22 Tower Street, London WC2H 9NS (tel: 0171 240 0880);

b) The Historic Churches Preservation Trust, Fulham Palace, London SW6 6EA (tel: 0171 736 3054).

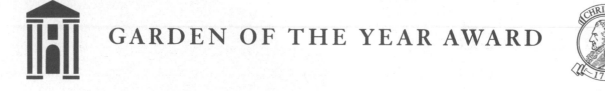

GARDEN OF THE YEAR AWARD

Hever Castle

Levens Hall

Sudeley Castle

The HHA/Christie's Garden of the Year Award, established in 1984, is an annual award designed to recognise the importance of gardens either in their own right or as settings for historic houses, and to reflect public enjoyment of gardens rather than specialised or botanical interest.

Past winners of the HHA/Christie's Garden of the Year Award: 1984 Heale House, Wiltshire; 1985 Hodnet Hall, Shropshire; 1986 Newby Hall, North Yorkshire; 1987 Arley Hall, Cheshire; 1988 Barnsley House, Gloucestershire; 1989 Brympton d'Evercy, Somerset; 1990 Parham, Sussex; 1991 Holker Hall, Cumbria; 1992 Forde Abbey, Somerset; 1993 Haddon Hall, Derbyshire; 1994 Levens Hall, Cumbria; 1995 Hever Castle, Kent; and 1996 Sudeley Castle, Gloucestershire.

CHRISTIE'S

8 King Street, St. James's, London SW1Y 6QT. Tel: (0171) 839 9060 Fax: (0171) 839 1611 *Internet:* http://www.christies.com

Christie's Fine Art Auctioneers has a network of representatives available to provide free auction estimates and advice on probate and insurance.

If you are thinking of buying or selling, please telephone your local area office to make an appointment or arrange a visit.

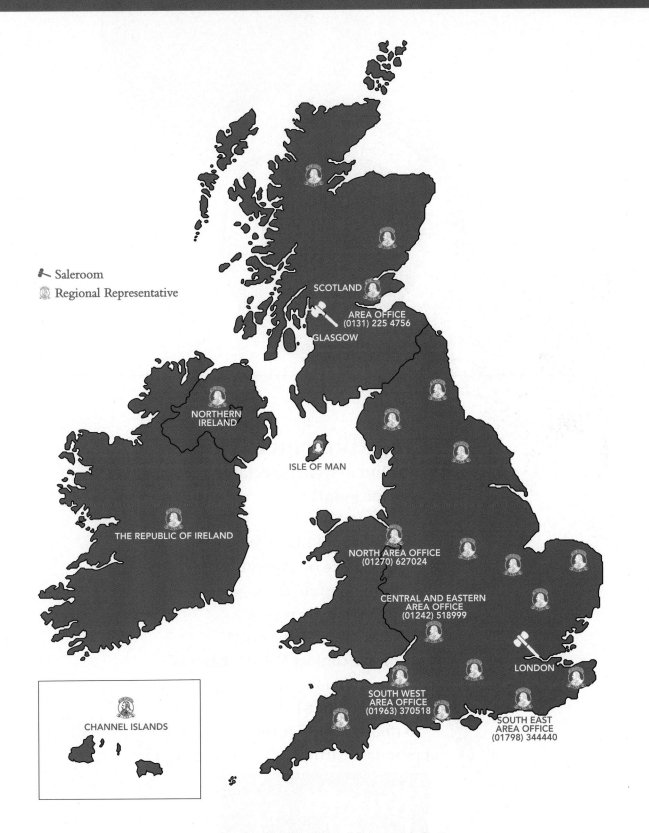

Saleroom

Regional Representative

SCOTLAND

AREA OFFICE
(0131) 225 4756

GLASGOW

NORTHERN
IRELAND

ISLE OF MAN

THE REPUBLIC OF IRELAND

NORTH AREA OFFICE
(01270) 627024

CENTRAL AND EASTERN
AREA OFFICE
(01242) 518999

LONDON

SOUTH WEST
AREA OFFICE
(01963) 370518

SOUTH EAST
AREA OFFICE
(01798) 344440

CHANNEL ISLANDS

CHRISTIE'S

Working like clockwork.
**You won't find a better specialist team
at your disposal.**

If you would like information
and advice on valuation,
farm or estate management,
or a strategic review
of your property assets
please contact Patrick Ramsay
in our Country House Department
on 0171-629 8171
so that we can put the
appropriate partner in touch with you.

Buying a Piece of England

While many of Britain's most famous historic houses have remained fundamentally unchanged over hundreds of years, even staying in the ownership of the same family that originally built them, there are many more that have changed hands, often several times.

Cricket St Thomas.

Hackwood Park .

The property pages of *Country Life* are testament to some of the most spectacular properties that have been put up for sale. Knight Frank have sold almost every type of property. It sold Stonehenge in 1915 and this last year has been offering the Hackwood Park estate, once the home of Lord Camrose; and the Cricket St Thomas estate in Somerset made famous by the popular television series, *"To the Manor Born"*.

While the sale of a magnificent house and dispersal of the contents may sometimes seem sad and represent a loss of traditional ownership, it is not always so. Some times it is the start of an exciting new era; the beginning of a new love affair and restoration of a property, as it was for Sir Winston Churchill who, when Colonial Secretary, bought Chartwell through Knight Frank & Rutley in 1922.

Winston Churchill, as he was then, had been looking for a "country basket", at least according to his wife. The large Victorian mansion at Chartwell has beautiful views over the Weald of Kent, its gardens falling dramatically away to the south to a lake fed by a spring – the Chart Well. Lady Mary Soames, Winston's daughter born at the time of the purchase wrote about it, *"this beautiful place…cast at once, and forever, its spell over Winston"*. He bought the property for £5,000 and though he quibbled over the price and was said to be cross not to have bought it for less, went on to spend another £15,000 making it into his family home. Today it is owned by the National Trust.

Other historic landmarks sold by Knight Frank in the past 101 years include: Gadshill Place in Kent, the house where Charles Dickens wrote *"Great Expectations"*; the 19,500 acre Beaufort Castle Estate, one of the most ancient of all Scottish Estates ever sold which had been in the hands of the Fraser family for over 500 years; Crystal Palace and the Royal Naval College in London; the Brecon Beacons in Wales and Fountains Abbey in Yorkshire – now a World Heritage Site.

The Saloon, Hackwood Park .

Knight Frank has recently been marketing the Hackwood Park Estate in Hampshire. This is considered one of the most important and prestigious estates to come on to the market for some time and is being sold by Lord Camrose's executors. The magnificent Grade II listed Hackwood House dates back to 1683. A sweeping drive through the 2,437 acre estate leads to the imposing front entrance of Hackwood House, built of stone with a giant curved Ionic portico from which the two wings of the house spread outwards. But it is the Park, which extends to about 800 acres around the house, that is the property's most prized possession. A real piece of classical England, it is Grade I listed. Its 80 acre Spring Wood is regarded as one of the most important garden woods in the country, offering breathtaking scenic walks.

Knight Frank KF
INTERNATIONAL

Historic Parks & Gardens

a glossary of features

by Jim Humberstone

The key objective of the design of historic parks or gardens of this and other periods was the giving of pleasure. To this end a range of structures and devices would be located in such a way that the owners and their families, together with their visitors and friends could view, visit and enjoy the features with their differing functions and impact on the landscape.

The bird's eye view sketch shows an assemblage of man-made features such as might be found in different combinations, during the eighteenth century, in country house settings. Views were central to the enjoyment of the park, whether these were panoramic 'prospects' or narrow vistas between trees. The **Terrace (1)** provided a viewing platform immediately adjoining the house. **Obelisks (8)** would sometimes be erected, as in more urban locations in order to provide structure to the layout and to serve as an aid to orientation. **Pavilions (4)** set in the landscape or **Gazebos (12)** closer to the house also acted as viewpoints. Water, either flowing or in static form, played an important part, both visually and

and linked up the various sections of footpath. Enthusiasm for classical architecture and culture, particularly that generated by the experience of the Grand Tour, encouraged the provision of **Temples (9)**, of various dedications and other elements such as the **Triumphal Arch (13)**. The **Mausoleum (3)** fulfilled the need for both a dynastic memorial and a family burial place. Horticultural needs would be met through the provision of the **Orangery (14)** which gave covered wintering space for tender orange trees. The **Ha-ha (10)** enabled clear views to be obtained of adjoining grazing land while keeping cattle at bay through the effect of its walled ditch; in a sense, a kind of 'window' on the surrounding farmed

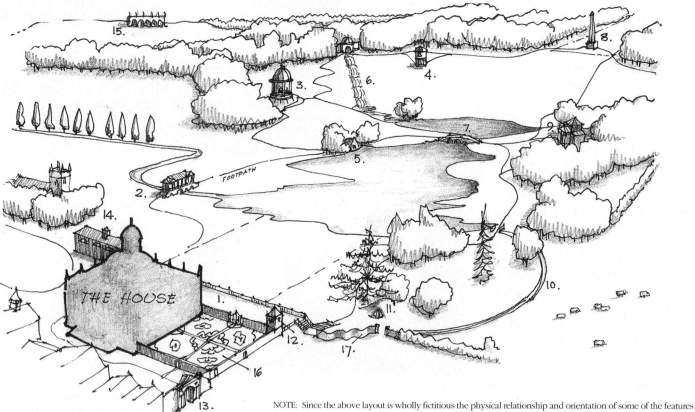

NOTE: Since the above layout is wholly fictitious the physical relationship and orientation of some of the features lacks the element of topographical authenticity that would be clearly identifiable at a real country house location.

KEY TO FEATURES

1	Terrace	10	Ha-ha
2	Palladian Bridge	11	Ice-house
3	Mausoleum	12	Gazebo
4	Pavilion	13	Triumphal Arch
5	Grotto	14	Orangery
6	Cascade	15	Eyecatcher
7	Rustic Stone Bridge	16	Parterre (walled)
8	Obelisk	17	Serpentine wall
9	Temple		

in its appeal to the other senses generally. The lakes and ponds, formed by damming watercourses, established a setting for the features located at their edges. **Cascades (6)**, that is formal, stepped waterfalls, served to bring movement and the play of light into the landscape scene. **Bridges**, both of the covered **classical style (2)** and the more **traditional form (7)**, enhanced the tributaries of the lakes

countryside. **Ice-houses (11)** were an effective but primitive device used for the storage of the material that was the only available means of refrigeration at the time. The **Grotto (5)** on the other hand was a structure, usually subterranean, which gave pleasure through the experience of its often shell-lined and cave-like interior. The 'crinkle-crankle' or **Serpentine** shape given to **walls (17)** gave stability and a certain degree of visual enjoyment. The **Eyecatcher (15)** situated usually on the skyline, at some distance from the house, helped to give depth and dimension to the intervening space. Finally, **Parterres (16)** or geometrical patterned, shrub planted spaces, reflect the tastes of a previous period with their formal intricacy and carpet-like effect of planting. It should be appreciated that the landscaped parks were for active, ie. not just passive, enjoyment. This being the case their man-made features could represent part of a sequence of 'experiences', located along a network of walks, which enabled both the natural and the artificially created environments to give inspiration to the beholder. There is a wealth of examples of the garden features mentioned above dotted about the countryside which can be visited at various historic country house sites.

The most famous and respected Mausoleum is that designed by Hawksmoor for the third Earl of Carlisle and built around 1728 at Castle Howard in Yorkshire (see p277). However, there are other examples including the fascinating pyramid structure designed as a memorial, again in the 1790s, and located at Blickling Hall, a National Trust property in Norfolk (see p165). Temples are legion. Those at Stowe (see

p14) and Stourhead (see p146) are perhaps the most visited. The latter site has two dedicated to Apollo and Hercules, both were built in the middle years of the eighteenth century. There are at least four at Stowe, two of which have clear political overtones reflecting their owner's patriotic Whig allegiance.

It should be borne in mind that the term Rotunda may be applied to a Temple feature where this is circular in form. Of Cascades there are very few still remaining. There were examples in place at Dyrham near Bath (see p187) and at Bramham Park in Yorkshire (see p290), but the only truly spectacular one available to view today is that at Chatsworth in Derbyshire (see p178).

The Palladian Bridge or versions of it can be seen at Wilton (see p141) (the prototype designed by the Earl of Pembroke) and at Prior Park (see p137) and Stowe. There are Triumphal Arches located at Holkham in Norfolk (see p164) and at Fonthill Gifford in Wiltshire. Finally the loveliest of the Pavilions must be that at Montacute in Somerset (see p136). However, many others still exist, especially in similar form to the West Country one, ie of two storeys and incorporated into a section of garden wall. There are even one or two which still bear the marks of conversion to

defensive pillboxes during the early years of World War II! Finally it should be noted that many of the terms overlap or are interchangeable. For example Pavilion and Gazebo, and Temple or Rotunda.

Prior Park, Bath.

Jim Humberstone MA ARICS DipTRP AAGrad DipCons

CHASTLETON

Chastleton House, one of England's finest and most complete Jacobean houses, has opened to the public after a six-year, £3.2 million restoration.

Continuously occupied by the same family for 400 years, it has a remarkable collection of everyday objects, furniture and textiles dating from 1612. The gardens are a rare survival of a walled Jacobean layout with interesting topiary. The rules for the game of croquet were established here in 1865.

The National Heritage Memorial Fund purchased the house for £1 million in 1991 from Mrs Clutton-Brock, the wife of Professor Alan Clutton-Brock, a direct descendant of Walter Jones who built the house. Because the house was in a very bad state of disrepair it is only now that it is being opened to the public, following a carefully planned programme of conservation over the last six years. In the roof a colony of Pipistrelle bats remained undisturbed throughout its year-long programme of repair.

The National Trust has taken care to conserve the slightly shabby condition of the interior and to enable visitors to wander at leisure through the house and enjoy its very special atmosphere. It has introduced a pre-booked, timed ticket system and visitors must phone in advance of their visit to book a time (see details on p74).

The Great Chamber (above), and the Great Parlour.

Heritage Regained:
Silver from the Gilbert Collection at Fairfax House, York

Monteith Bowl ~ *Silver-gilt. Edward Farrell, London 1820-21.*
The 'monteith', named after the Earl of Monteith, was popular during the late 17th and early 18th century for cooling glasses, suspended upside down in cold water from the notched rim.

Spectacular silver from the celebrated Gilbert Collection will be exhibited at Fairfax House, York this autumn. On view will be 40 magnificent pieces of silver from the Gilbert Collection of Decorative Arts, one of the most important collections ever to have been given to Britain. Arthur Gilbert's magnificent gift was announced in June 1996. Ultimately, the Collection will be housed permanently in Somerset House, London. Silver from the Collection will be on view at Fairfax House from 10th October to 20th December, 1998.

National Mills Day: Sunday 10th May, 1998

On National Mills Day the last remaining traditional windmills and watermills across the country will be opening to the public. These are the proud survivors of this country's early industrial and agricultural heritage. Some 300 mills across the country will welcome visitors, some only open this day each year.

The Day is designed to focus public attention the mills and the problems the owners face keeping them as living enterprises, rather than museum pieces. The Day has been encouraged by the Wind and Watermill Section of the Society for the Protection of Ancient Buildings, telephone 0171 377 1644.

The Landmark Trust

A CHARITY WHICH RESTORES HISTORIC BUILDINGS AND LETS THEM FOR HOLIDAYS

Over 165 places where you can become, for a short time, the owner of a fine historic building. No membership is required but you do need to buy The Landmark Handbook which illustrates every property with plans, location maps and black and white photographs (£8.50, refundable against your booking).

WARDEN ABBEY

NR. BIGGLESWADE, BEDFORDSHIRE

Landmarks are chosen for their historic interest or architectural importance, because they need our help, and also because many are in surroundings which give unexpected pleasure.

Warden Abbey is a fragment of a great Cistercian Abbey and a Tudor House, set in fruitful countryside, once farmed by monks.

Accommodation:
Sleeps up to 5 people.

LUNDY: OLD LIGHT

LUNDY ISLAND, BRISTOL CHANNEL

The beauty of the Landmark solution is not only that a building is saved and put to good use, but also that the restoration respects its original design. For a short time it is possible to live with rooms in surprising places. One of the light houses on Lundy Island, off the north coast of Devon, now provides unusual holiday accommodation.

Accommodation:
Flats for 4 and 5 people and a cottage for one.

LANGLEY GATEHOUSE

ACTON BURNELL, SHROPSHIRE

Landmarks often lie off the beaten track. Langley is no exception, set in a remote valley with a view to the Wrekin. In our restorations, we prefer to repair the old, and avoid renewal, to preserve the building's texture. When the building is timber framed, this can be like trying to patch a cobweb !

Accommodation:
Sleeps 6 people.

SADDELL

KINTYRE, ARGYLL

Some Landmarks, like this one, are connected with great families. Saddell Castle, a fine tower house with battlements, was in the hands of the Campbells for 400 years. Today the Castle, three cottages to the south, and the long white strand of Saddell Bay are owned by the Landmark Trust and are available for year round holidays.
Accommodation: The castle sleeps 8; the cottages sleep 4, 5 and 6 people.

The Landmark Trust Handbook Order Form

Order your copy by sending a sterling cheque drawn on a UK bank, Eurocheque or quoting your Visa or MasterCard number.

Handbooks cost £8.50 including postage and packing when they are posted to an address in the UK, otherwise they cost: - £10.50 to Europe; £20.00 to the Americas**, Central Asia, Middle East and Africa; £25.00 to Australasia and Far East.

***Residents of North America can order a copy for US$19.50 from our mailing house in the States. Contact; The Landmark Trust, RR 1 Box 510, Brattleboro, Vermont 05301. Tel: (802-254-6868).*

The cost of the Handbook is refundable against your next booking by using the voucher that comes with it.

Once you have bought a Handbook, you will automatically be put on our mailing list to receive up-to-date price lists and availability charts.

PAYMENT by credit card can be made by telephoning our Booking Office on (01628) 825925 or by filling in this order form and posting it to:
The Landmark Trust (HD), Shottesbrooke, Maidenhead, Berkshire SL6 3SW
Tel: (01628) 825925. Fax: (01628) 825417.

VISA/MASTERCARD NUMBER: HD

Expiry: Please send me   copies @   each.

Name: ....

Address:..

....

....Post Code:.................

Name and address of cardholder if different from above:

Name: ....

Address:..

....

....Post Code:.................

Charity Number: 243312

PHOTOCOPIES OF THIS FORM ARE ACCEPTABLE

Royal Connections

more people have them than you may think ...

For the historic house visitor with an interest in genealogy the inter-relationship between families can be as of much interest as the buildings and their contents. Indeed it is often these family relationships that explain how certain houses have come to be as they are now.

The possession of a noble title is not in itself indicative of Royal connections. Those without titles often have closer links. The CD Rom *Your Heritage* shows that Mr R J Berkeley of **Berkeley Castle** is descended from 250 monarchs. These include Saxon kings of England; Scottish, Welsh and Irish kings; kings of Norway, Sweden, Italy, Spain, Hungary and Kiev together with Emperors of the Holy Roman Empire and Byzantium. Another ancestor, Edward I, was father of the unfortunate Edward II who was murdered in Berkeley Castle in 1327.

Berkeley Castle

The 'Search for Monarchs' facility on the same CD showed that over 400 are to be found in the ancestry of C H Bagot Esq of **Levens Hall, Cumbria**. Mr Bagot's maternal great grandfather, Joceline Fitzroy, was a son of Charles Bagot and Louisa Percy. Their ancestry traces back to the Dukes of Somerset

and Earls of Northumberland, and these lead to such monarchs as Henry VII, Robert II, King of Scotland, Aethelread II of England and Henry I, King of France who died in 1060.

Numerous properties featured in *Hudson's* have royal associations

The title of Baron of Willoughby de Eresby has, since 1516, been vested in the owners of **Grimsthorpe Castle, Lincolnshire**. The Tudor additions were made by Charles Brandon, Duke of Suffolk, who purchased the wardship of the seven-year-old Katherine, Baroness of Willoughby de Eresby. Brandon was married to Henry VIII's sister Mary, Dowager Queen of France, but when she died in 1533 he took Katherine as his fourth wife. The Duke rebuilt and extended much of Grimsthorpe, making it ready for a visit by Henry VIII when he was en route for York.

Grimsthorpe Castle

James I said that **Audley End, Essex** was too large for a king, though it might do for a Lord Treasurer. He was referring to the home of

Audley End

Thomas Howard, Earl of Suffolk, who reportedly spent £100,000 on the building. Charles II agreed to pay half that sum when he bought the house from the Howard family after the Restoration. Not all the debt was paid however and the house was re-conveyed to the Howard family in 1701.

Bishop's Palace at Hatfield

The Banqueting Hall of the old **Bishop's Palace at Hatfield, Hertfordshire**, still stands to the west of the present house. Henry VIII acquired the palace when he dissolved the monasteries and he used it as a residence for his children. Both Queen Mary and Elizabeth I spent much of their childhood there. When James I succeeded he decided to exchange the house for Theobald's, then the home of Robert Cecil (later Earl of Salisbury). Being an enthusiastic builder,

Robert Cecil pulled down three sides of the palace and used the bricks to build the house we see today – home of his descendant, the 6th Marquess of Salisbury.

The medieval castle at **Bolsover, Derbyshire** was destroyed when Charles Cavendish and his son (later Duke of Newcastle) converted it into a mansion fit for the descendants of Bess of Hardwick. Much of the work was

Stirling Castle

Bolsover Castle

completed for a visit by Charles I. During the Civil War the King appointed William Cavendish Commander-in-Chief of the northern forces and Bolsover became a Royalist stronghold. Though he survived the War and returned to his Derbyshire estate, the fortunes of the family declined and dictated that

Bolsover would be owned by several different families before being given to the nation for safe keeping.

Major battles are a feature of *Your Heritage* and it is possible to follow the fortunes of many of the people involved. Hastings, Bosworth, Culloden and Bannockburn are amongst the sites which cater for visitors. Bannockburn, just below **Stirling Castle,** resulted in great losses for the English and independence for Scotland. Edward II escaped with his life but Gilbert de Clare,

Earl of Gloucester, and more than 60 lords were killed or taken prisoner. James IV of Scotland was not so fortunate when he met Thomas Howard of Framlingham Castle at Flodden in 1513. The King lost his life, as did many of his men and much of the Scottish nobility.

The CD-ROM *Your Heritage* contains over 50,000 names, and links many of the great European families together into a vast illustrated pedigree of monarchs and nobles.

■ Below - Mr and Mrs James Sellick at **Pashley Manor Gardens, Sussex**. These romantic gardens, enhanced by waterfalls, ponds and a moat with plantings and soft colours, were created during the last decade by the distinguished landscape architect Anthony du Gard Pasely and with careful nurturing and enhancement, continue to entrance the many visitors they receive each year.

■ Above - Lord Montagu of Beaulieu with Lady Montagu, his heir, the Hon Ralph Douglas-Scott-Montagu (standing), the Hon Jonathan Douglas-Scott-Montagu and the Hon Mary Montagu-Scott, at **Palace House, Beaulieu**. Lord Montagu is an innovator and an enthusiast who makes things happen. He is perhaps best-known in connection with motoring and his development of the National Motor Museum, but in the heritage world he was a leading force behind the creation of the Historic Houses Association, of which he was founder President. Subsequently he became the first Chairman of English Heritage, where his influence transformed the way in which ruins and monuments in the nation's care were presented. Out went the attitudes of the 'peak-capped stewards' employed by the Ministry of Works and the Department of the Environment. In came the more outgoing and welcoming Hardy Amies dressed Property Manager of today and the snappy name 'English Heritage' (it is formally called the Historic Buildings and Monuments Commission).

■ Above - The Duke and Duchess of Roxburghe, with Lady Rosanagh Innes-Ker, Charles, Marquess of Beaumont, Lord Edward Innes-Ker, Lady Isabella Innes-Ker (on her father's knee) and the youngest, Lord George Innes-Ker, photographed at **Floors Castle, Roxburghshire**. Floors was designed by William Adam and is the largest inhabited castle in Scotland, having an outstanding collection of French 17th and 18th century furniture and magnificent tapestries.

■ Left - Mr and Mrs Robin Compton with their son Mr Richard Compton, his wife Lucinda and their children Orlando, Ludovic and Sasha, at **Newby Hall, Yorkshire**. The house is one of the most exceptionally beautiful 18th century houses with wonderful contents. The 25 acres of glorious gardens with rare and beautiful shrubs and plants are even more notable. They are truly a garden for all seasons. No-one interested in such things should drive up the A1 without first considering the possibility, when near Ripon, of making only a two mile detour to see Newby.

WORDSWORTH'S LAKE DISTRICT

Rydal Water from White Moss Common

Photo: Alex Black

"Here the rainbow comes - the cloud - And mists that spread the flying shroud..."

WORDSWORTH HOUSE

Cockermouth

Birthplace of William Wordsworth in 1770.

Open: April to October. Monday to Friday and selected Saturdays. Closed remaining Saturdays and all Sundays.

Vegetarian Restaurant. Shop. Events during season. Parking in town centre car parks.

(National Trust)

TEL: 01900 824805

DOVE COTTAGE

Grasmere

Dove Cottage & Wordsworth Museum, Grasmere

Open Daily 9.30 to 5.30pm. Closed 24th - 26th December

Parking next to Dove Cottage Tearoom & Vegetarian Restaurant immediately south of Grasmere village.

TEL: 015394 35544/35547

RYDAL MOUNT

Near Ambleside

Rydal Mount Home of William Wordsworth from 1813 - 1850

**Open:
Summer: Mar - Oct 9.30 - 5.00pm
Winter: Nov - Feb 10.00 - 4.00pm**

(Closed Tuesdays in Winter)

FREE PARKING

TEL: 015394 33002

RECIPROCAL DISCOUNT OFFER - DETAILS FROM ANY OF THE ABOVE ATTRACTIONS

■ Above - Mr and Mrs William Proby with their four daughters, Alexandra, Alice, Rose and Isabella at **Elton Hall, Cambridgeshire** which has been the home of the Proby family for over 300 years. Mr Proby is currently President of the Historic Houses Association which represents over 1400 private owners of historic houses. Elton has a good collection of paintings but the visitor is afforded particular pleasure from the gardens which have been restored and expanded in recent years under the direction of Mrs Proby. The fragrance of 1000 roses is memorable.

■ Below - Lady Braye with her husband Lt Col Edward Aubrey-Fletcher and her nephew, Nicholas Fothergill and his wife Lucy, at **Stanford Hall, Leicestershire**. Stanford Hall has been the home of Lady Braye's ancestors since 1430. The existing house, built in 1690 together with its adjacent Stable Block, is exceptionally handsome. Percy Pilcher, the first man to fly in England, was killed at Stanford in 1899. He crashed while flying "the Hawk" and the full-size replica of this flying machine is on display in the Stables, where there is also an outstanding collection of racing and vintage motorcycles that attracts visitors from all over the world.

■ Above - Mr and Mrs Peter Prideaux-Brune, with Nicholas and William Prideaux-Brune, at **Prideaux Place, Cornwall**, the home of their family for 400 years. In recent years the house and gardens have been the subject of extensive and impressive restoration. Many of the thousands of visitors to Rock, Polzeath, Daymer Bay and Padstow are not always aware that this Elizabethan gem surrounded by its Deer Park, overlooking the sea, is on their doorstep – they should resolve not to miss it next time.

■ Below - The Duke and Duchess of Marlborough at **Blenheim Palace, Oxfordshire**. Bleinheim, the birthplace of Sir Winston Churchill, is an architectural masterpiece with striking interiors. The Park and Gardens are no less wonderful and the present 11th Duke has put considerable effort into restoring and enhancing them further.

CIVIL WEDDING VENUES

This index refers to those places at which the marriage ceremony itself can take place;
many of these properties will also be able to provide facilities for wedding receptions.

Full details about each property are available in the regional listings. There are numerous other properties included within *Hudson's* which do not have a Civil Wedding Licence but that can also accommodate wedding receptions. The Marriage Act 1995, which has resulted in many more wedding venues in England, has not changed the situation in Scotland.
In Scotland religious wedding ceremonies can take place anywhere subject to the Minister being prepared to perform them. Civil Weddings, however, are still confined to Registry Offices.

Ragley Hall, Warwickshire (pg.229).

Reception, Englishcombe Tithe Barn, Somerset (pg.134).

Shugborough, Staffordshire (pg.47).

This is not an exclusive list but is merely intended to draw attention to some of those properties which can host Civil Weddings.

■ Above - The Throckmorton family at **Coughton Court** (pronounced Coaton), **Warwickshire**. Clare Throckmorton (second from left) with her husband Andrew (extreme left), elder son Guy, younger son Charles, and (far right) son-in-law Benedict; (seated from left) daughter-in-law Jane with Lara, daughter Christina with Flavia, daughter-in-law Anneli with Felix, and (front row) eldest grandsons Magnus with Merlin. Over the last seven years the gardens at Coughton Court have undergone a complete transformation, with extensive reconstruction and replanting. This includes the Courtyard, the Lime Tree Walks and Sunken Gardens, the Bog Garden and the Riverside Walk, but in particular the Walled Garden, opened in 1996 by Alan Titchmarsh. This was designed by Christina Birch and is believed to be the only significant new large garden at an important historic house in the Midlands.

■ Above - Mr and Mrs Alexander Hay of Duns at **Duns Castle, Berwickshire**. The house, built round an historic 1320 Pele Tower, has been home to the Hay family since 1696. As well as being their home, Alexander and Aline Hay offer the castle as a venue for corporate hospitality.

■ Below - Mrs Patrick Gordon-Duff-Pennington, together with Mr and Mrs Peter Frost-Pennington and their son Ewan, at **Muncaster Castle, Cumbria** which has been owned by the Pennington family since 1208. Ewan is seen here holding the NPI National Heritage Award which Muncaster won in 1996.

■ Below - The Earl and Countess of Pembroke with William, Lord Herbert, Lady Jemima Herbert and Lady Alice Herbert at **Wilton House, Wiltshire**. The Abbey and lands of Wilton were given in 1544 by Henry VIII to William Herbert who had married Anne Parr, sister of Katharine, sixth wife of King Henry VIII. The house contains one of the finest art collections in Europe and is particularly well-known for its magnificent State Apartments including the famous Single and Double Cube rooms.

■ Below - Lord and Lady Cavendish in the gardens at **Holker Hall, Cumbria**. Both are passionate gardeners. The gardens at Holker cover 24 acres and have been described in some guides as "among the best in the world in terms of design and content". Holker is also home to the Great Garden and Countryside Festival held from 29–31 May 1998.

CORPORATE HOSPITALITY INDEX

Properties included in the regional listings which provide facilities for corporate functions.

Fonmon Castle, Wales (pg. 369).

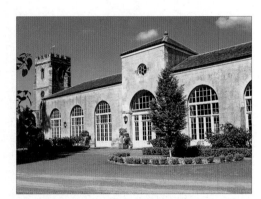
The Orangery at Settrington, Yorkshire (pg. 294).

The Banqueting House, London (pg. 52).

Naworth Castle, Cumbria (pg. 257).

This is not an exclusive list but is merely intended to draw attention to some of those properties which cater for corporate hospitality.

■ Right - The Marquess and Marchioness of Tavistock with their youngest son, Lord James Russell at **Woburn Abbey, Bedfordshire**. Woburn, richly decorated and furnished, has one of the most important private art collections in the world. The Deer Park has nine species of deer roaming freely. One of these, the Père David, was descended from the Imperial herd of China and was saved from extinction at Woburn, and is now the largest breeding herd of this species in the world.

■ Above - The Earl and Countess of Shelburne in the gardens at **Bowood, Wiltshire**. Visitors, who now see a perfectly proportioned Georgian house, find it hard to believe that the major part of Bowood was demolished in 1955. Of particular appeal is the beautiful Park, embellished with a Doric Temple, Cascade, Pinetum and an Arboretum.

■ Above - Sir Thomas and Lady Ingilby with their children Jamie, Eleanor, Jack, Joss and Richard, at **Ripley Castle, Yorkshire**. 28 generations of the Ingilby family have lived at Ripley. The current generation has helped ensure its future by skillfully exploiting the potential for it to play a contemporary role. As well as being open to the public, it is one of the most successful venues for VIP lunches, dinners and wedding receptions. Sir Thomas also founded the Stately Homes Hotline scheme to combat theft from historic houses.

■ Right - The Earl and Countess of Bradford at **Weston Park, Shropshire** with their children the Hon Benjamin Bridgeman, Alexander, Viscount Newport, the Hon Harry Bridgeman and Lady Alicia Bridgeman. Lord Bradford is well-known as an author and restaurateur who helped put Weston Park on a commercial footing. It is now one of the few stately homes offering accommodation.

ACCOMMODATION INDEX

The Historic properties listed below are not hotels. This inclusion indicates that accommodation can be made available by pre-arrangement and often for groups only. The type and standard of rooms offered vary widely from the luxurious to the utilitarian. Full details should be obtained from the individual property.

For information on hotel accommodation we recommend you consult:
Best Loved Hotels of the World 1998
Tel: 0990 862010   •   Fax: 01392 431025
or   www.bestloved.com

Castle Ashby, Northamptonshire (pg. 206).

Manderston, Borders (pg. 304).

Somerley, Hampshire (pg. 19).

This is not an exclusive list but is merely intended to draw attention to some of those properties which offer accommodation.

Weddings

now a greater choice of venues

Civil Weddings, previously confined to a Registry Office, can now be held anywhere that has been granted a licence for that purpose. Betrothed couples often decide that an historic house will provide just exactly the style and setting for the wedding that they would like. Many of the houses listed in *Hudson's*, such as Naworth, Cumbria, now have a Civil Wedding Licence (indicated by 🔔 on their entry and a mention in the Civil Weddings Index on page *twenty seven*).

In Scotland, nothing has changed. Minister willing, you can get married anywhere. That is why it has always attracted lovers, not least the thousands of eloping couples that have crossed the Border to marry at Gretna Green. Gretna Green owes its celebrity to Lord Hardwick. His Marriage Act of 1754 tightened up the marriage laws in England, making it illegal to marry without notice or without involvement of the clergy. The age of consent was also raised to 21, which led to a steady stream of young couples fleeing to Scotland, where the age of consent for marriage was (and still is) 16 and Civil Marriages were still legal.

Gretna Green was the first changing post across the Scottish Border for stagecoaches from London and, as a consequence, the Old Blacksmith's Shop at Gretna Green became notorious for impromptu weddings of eloping couples from England.

Even today young lovers of 'sweet sixteen' can marry only with parental consent in England and Scotland still sees the odd eloping couple keen to outwit disapproving parents. However, be warned – Gretna Green Registration Office is booked months in advance and modern Scottish laws require 15 days' notice, so it's no good turning up unannounced.

You can still get married at Gretna Green, where there are 5,000 plus weddings conducted annually at the Registration Office. Stately homes and castles are also a favourite choice for those looking for a memorable occasion. There are plenty to choose from – one of the most romantic is surely Lennoxlove, the home of the Duke of Hamilton (see p323). The house was originally called 'Lethington' but was renamed 'Lennoxlove' after the Duchess of Richmond and Lennox bequeathed money to her nephew Lord Blantyre to enable him to buy it, on condition that it was called 'Lennox's love to Blantyre'.

The National Trust for Scotland mentions the venues they have available in their brochure 'Historic Settings for Special Occasions' – available by phoning 0131 226 5922. Historic Scotland also has some wonderful properties for hire – including Edinburgh and Stirling Castles (further details from 0131 668 8835).

Lennoxlove House, Edinburgh.

Naworth Castle, Cumbria.

ENGLISH HERITAGE

Events 1998
Over 1000 great family days out!

Superb historical entertainments and living history, children's festivals, music, drama and guided tours ~ our events have something for everybody!

Highlights of the year include:

• History in Action III, Kirby Hall, Northamptonshire, 1–2 August
Europe's largest 2 day festival of multi-era living history and re-enactment featuring 2000 performers from 50 top groups. Major displays, historical traders' market and much more.

• Napoleonic Battle Spectacular at Battle Abbey, East Sussex, 3–4 May
Massed infantry, cavalry and cannon of the Duke of Wellington and Napoleon clash in colourful action!

• Alice in Wonderland
Magical children's fun at Audley End House and Gardens, Belsay Hall, Brodsworth Hall, Kenilworth Castle, Walmer Castle and Wrest Park Gardens.

• The Siege of Dover Castle 1216, 27-28 June
Armoured knights on foot and horseback with skills-at-arms and combat.

For our free 60 page colour 1998 events diary detailing 600 events to enjoy, please call English Heritage Customer Services on 0171 973 3396.

Dover Castle.

HUDSON'S

SPECIAL EVENTS DIARY 1998

MARCH

● 1 – 31
Brontë Parsonage Museum, Yorkshire
"No Coward Souls: Emily, Anne and Branwell Brontë".

● 1 – 31
Cecil Higgins Art Gallery, Bedfordshire
"The Loss of an East Indiaman" by Turner, The Higgins' Turners and other New Acquisitions.

● 1 – 31
The Queen's Gallery, London
"Michelangelo and His Influence".

● 5 – 8
The Tower Bridge Experience, London
Twilight Tours.

● 12 – 15
The Tower Bridge Experience, London
Twilight Tours.

● 13 – 15
Hopetoun House, Scotland
Antiques Fair.

● 18
Waddesdon Manor, Buckinghamshire
"Behind the Scenes – The Water Garden in the Spring".

● 19 – 21
The Tower Bridge Experience, London
Engineers' Evening Tours.

● 22
Waddesdon Manor, Buckinghamshire
Mothers' Day.

● 26 – 31
British Architectural Library, London
"Thomas Allom (1804–72)".

● 27 – 29
Naworth Castle, Cumbria
Galloway Antiques Fair.

● 28 – 31
Powderham Castle, Devon
Phillips Fine Art Sale.

APRIL

● 1 – 2
Powderham Castle, Devon
Phillips Fine Art Sale.

● 1 – 11
Cecil Higgins Art Gallery, Bedfordshire
"The Loss of an East Indiaman" by Turner, The Higgins' Turners and other New Acquisitions.

● 1 – 19
The Queen's Gallery, London
"Michelangelo and His Influence".

● 1 – 30
British Architectural Library, London
"Thomas Allom (1804–72)".

● 1 – 30
Brontë Parsonage Museum, Yorkshire
"No Coward Souls: Emily, Anne and Branwell Brontë".

● 1 – 30
Burford House Gardens, Shropshire
Botanical Art Show: Artist in residence, contemporary art shows.

● 4 – 5
Capesthorne Hall, Cheshire
Rainbow Craft Fair.

● 7 – 8
Painswick Rococo Gardens, Gloucestershire
Performance in Painswick House by the 'Flies on the Wall' Youth Theatre.

● 10 – 13
The Commandery, Worcestershire
"Time Travellers".

● 10 – 13
Helmsley Castle, Yorkshire
Music from the Age of Henry VIII.

● 10 – 13
Hever Castle, Kent
Easter Egg Trail.

APRIL

● 10 – 13
Sulgrave Manor, Northamptonshire
Easter Customs & Traditions.

● 11 – 13
Tatton Park, Cheshire
Easter Festival.

● 12
Fort George, Scotland
Forres Archers, 2.30pm–4.30pm.

● 12
Fulbeck Hall, Lincolnshire
Rare & Unusual Plant Fair.

● 12
Stirling Castle, Scotland
"Robert the Bruce and his Carrick Spears" Battle Re-enactment, 2.30pm.

● 12
Traquair, Scotland
Easter Egg Extravaganza.

● 12 – 13
Brodsworth Hall, Yorkshire
Easter Egg Hunt.

● 12 – 13
Chiswick House, London
Traditional Song.

● 12 – 13
Lullingstone Roman Villa, Kent
Roman Soldier and Mosaic-making.

● 12 – 13
Otley Hall, Suffolk
House and Gardens open.

● 12 – 13
Ranger's House, London
Regency Living History.

● 12 – 13
Weston Park, Shropshire
Festival of Transport.

● 13
High Beeches Gardens, Sussex
Daffodil Time.

APRIL

● 13
Swallowfield Park, Berkshire
National Garden Day 2–5pm.

● 13 – 30
Arbigland Gardens, Scotland
John Paul Jones Birthplace Museum.

● 17 – 19
Highclere Castle & Gardens, Hampshire
Country Lifestyle Fair.

● 17 – 19
Sudeley Castle, Gloucestershire
Homes & Garden Exhibition.

● 18 – 19
Audley End House, Essex
"The Soprano in Pink".

● 18 – 19
Belton House, Lincolnshire
BHTA Horse Trials.

● 18 – 19
Borde Hill, Sussex
Garden Festival, 10am–5pm.

● 18 – 19
Old Sarum Castle, Wiltshire
Medieval Entertainment.

● 18 – 19
Ragley Hall, Warwickshire
Gardeners' Weekend.

● 18 – 19
Shugborough, Staffordshire
Gamekeepers' Fair (official BASC Annual Country Fair) 10am–5pm.

● 19
Naworth Castle, Cumbria
Open Day.

● 21 – 30
Cecil Higgins Art Gallery, Bedfordshire
"People's Choice".

● 22
Waddesdon Manor, Buckinghamshire
"Adventurous Planting in Terrace Pots".

APRIL

• 25
Hatch Court, Somerset
NCCPG Rare Plant Sale.

• 25
Pashley Manor Gardens, Sussex
Spring Plant Fair.

• 25 – 26
Helmsley Castle, Yorkshire
"Skulduggery!"

• 25 – 26
Kelburn, Scotland
Woodcraft & Forestry Fair (including the
Scottish National Tree Climbing
Competition).

• 25 – 26
Richborough Castle, Kent
Fun & Fantasy Workshops for Children.

• 25 – 26
Weston Park, Shropshire
BHTA Spring Horse Trials.

• 25 – 26
Wrest Park, Bedfordshire
St George's Festival.

• 26
The Birmingham Botanical Gardens and
Glasshouses, West Midlands
Orchids Show.

• 26
Borde Hill, Sussex
Children's Animal Fair, 10am–5pm.

• 26
Great Comp Garden, Kent
Plant Fair with special guest
Roy Lancaster.

• 29
Waddesdon Manor, Buckinghamshire
"Behind the Scenes – Bulbs".

• 30
Pashley Manor Gardens, Sussex
Tulip Festival.

MAY

• 1 – 4
Pashley Manor Gardens, Sussex
Tulip Festival.

• 1 – 4
Sulgrave Manor, Northamptonshire
Georgian Living History.

• 1 – 9
British Architectural Library, London
"Thomas Allom (1804–72)".

• 1 – 31
Arbigland Gardens, Scotland
John Paul Jones Birthplace Museum.

• 1 – 31
Brontë Parsonage Museum, Yorkshire
"No Coward Souls: Emily, Anne and
Branwell Brontë".

• 1 – 31
Burford House Gardens, Shropshire
Botanical Art Show: Artist in residence,
contemporary art shows.

• 2 – 4
Corfe Castle, Dorset
Medieval Archery Weekend.

• 2 – 4
Hever Castle, Kent
May Day Music & Dance.

• 2 – 4
Leonardslee Gardens, Sussex
Bonsai Weekend.

• 2 – 4
Penshurst Place & Gardens, Kent
Craft Fair.

• 3
Gawsworth Hall, Cheshire
Classic Car Rally.

• 3 – 4
Appleby Castle, Cumbria
Historical Re-enactment.

MAY

• 3 – 4
Barnard Castle, Co Durham
A Medieval Siege.

• 3 – 4
Battle Abbey, Sussex
Napoleonic Battle Spectacular.

• 3 – 4
Eastnor Castle, Herefordshire
Spring Country Craft Festival.

• 3 – 4
Framlingham Castle, Suffolk
"The Tudor Dynasty".

• 3 – 4
Kenilworth Castle, Warwickshire
"Alice in Wonderland".

• 3 – 4
Orford Castle, Suffolk
"Wynndebagge the Piper".

• 3 – 4
Otley Hall, Suffolk
House and Gardens open.

• 3 – 4
Stokesay Castle, Shropshire
"The Bard's Best Bits".

• 3 – 4
Wroxeter Roman Site, Shropshire
"Warriors!"

• 4
Ford End Watermill, Buckinghamshire
Milling Demonstration.

• 4
Hergest Croft Gardens, Herefordshire
Flower Fair.

• 4
High Beeches Gardens, Sussex
Bluebell Time.

• 7 – 10
Hatfield House, Hertfordshire
Living Crafts.

• 8 – 10
Goodwood House, Sussex
SE Counties Antiques Fair.

• 9 – 10
Audley End House, Essex
The Victorian Kitchen.

• 9 – 10
Beaulieu, Hampshire
Spring Autojumble & Automart.

• 9 – 10
Chatsworth, Derbyshire
Angling Fair.

• 10
Appleby Castle, Cumbria
Devil's Own Classic Car Rally.

• 10
The Birmingham Botanical Gardens and
Glasshouses, West Midlands
Plant Market.

• 10
Chesters Roman Fort, Northumberland
Guided Tours.

• 10
Ford End Watermill, Buckinghamshire
Milling Demonstration.

• 10
Newby Hall, Yorkshire
Spring Plant Fair.

• 10
Wilton House, Wiltshire
"Spirit of the 60s" –
Classic Motor Cycle Rally.

• 15 – 17
Fulbeck Hall, Lincolnshire
Antiques Fair.

• 15 – 31
The Queen's Gallery, London
"The Search for Albion: Monarchy and
the Patronage of British Painting".

• 16 – 17
Leeds Castle, Kent
Festival of English Food & Wine.

MAY

• 17
Appleby Castle, Cumbria
Rolls Royce Car Owners' Club Rally.

• 17
Capesthorne Hall, Cheshire
Cheshire Kit Car Show.

• 17
Deene Park, Northamptonshire
Gardens open - National Gardens Scheme.

• 17
Eastnor Castle, Herefordshire
Steam Fair & Country Show with
Fred Dibnah.

• 17
Kingston Lacy, Dorset
Spring Plant Fair.

• 17
Montacute House, Somerset
Plant Fair.

• 17
Sherborne Castle, Dorset
Sherborne Vale Dog Training Show,
12.30pm.

• 17
Shugborough, Staffordshire
Dressage Festival.

• 17
Tatton Park, Cheshire
Dolls House & Teddies Fair.

• 18 – 22
The Chelsea Physic Garden, London
Chelsea Show Week. Exhibition: "The
Centenary of the London Sketch Club".

• 20
Dunster Castle, Somerset
Open-air Opera with Music Theatre
Kernow – "Cosi Fan Tutte", 7.30pm.

• 21 – 25
Charleston, Sussex
Charleston Festival.

• 22
Dalemain, Cumbria
Phillips International Auctioneers &
Valuers Lecture & Afternoon Tea.

• 23
Blair Castle, Scotland
Atholl Highlanders' Parade.

• 23
Dover Castle, Kent
Folk Festival.

• 23
Holkham Hall, Norfolk
Stately Car Boot Sale in aid of Norfolk
Churches Trust.

• 23
Hopetoun House, Scotland
RNIB Son et Lumière concert with BBC
Scottish Symphony Orchestra.

• 23 – 25
The Commandery, Worcestershire
"Time Travellers".

• 23 – 25
Gawsworth Hall, Cheshire
Craft Fair by Cheshire Fayre.

MAY

• 23 – 25
Hever Castle, Kent
Merrie England Weekend.

• 23 – 25
Kelburn, Scotland
Festival of Flight.

• 24
Appleby Castle, Cumbria
Teesside Yesteryear Car Club Rally

• 24
Blair Castle, Scotland
Highland Games.

• 24
Corbridge Roman Site, Northumberland
Roman Festival.

• 24 – 25
Belvoir Castle, Lincolnshire
Siege Group.

• 24 – 25
Finchcocks, Kent
Fair.

• 24 – 25
Highclere Castle & Gardens, Hampshire
Southern Counties Country Show.

• 24 – 25
Otley Hall, Suffolk
House and Gardens open.

• 24 – 25
Rockingham Castle, Northamptonshire
Antiques Fair.

• 24 – 25
Weston Park, Shropshire
English Civil War.

• 24 – 25
Wilton House, Wiltshire
Lacemakers' Demonstrations.

• 24 – 28
Athelhampton House & Gardens, Dorset
Flower Festival.

• 24
Dalemain, Cumbria
Ford RS Owners' Club Rally.

• 24 – 25
Castle Acre Priory, Norfolk
"The History Man".

• 24 – 25
Farleigh Hungerford Castle, Somerset
Medieval Combat.

• 24 – 25
Old Sarum Castle, Wiltshire
The Roman Army.

• 24 – 25
Penshurst Place & Gardens, Kent
Classic Car Show.

• 24 – 25
Ragley Hall, Warwickshire
Transport Show.

• 24 – 25
Roche Abbey, Yorkshire
Medieval Murder Mystery.

• 24 – 25
Tynemouth Castle, Tyne & Wear
"The Fury of the Norsemen".

MAY

• 25
Chesters Roman Fort, Northumberland
Roman Festival.

• 25
Ford End Watermill, Buckinghamshire
Milling Demonstration.

• 25
High Beeches Gardens, Sussex
Azalea Time.

• 25
Sherborne Castle, Dorset
Country Fair, 10am.

• 26 – 31
Lullingstone Roman Villa, Kent
Meet a Roman Soldier, Lady & Estate
Agent.

• 28
Castle Coole, Ireland
Concert: Joanna McGregor, piano.

• 29 – 31
Gawsworth Hall, Cheshire
Cheshire Area NAFAS Flower Festival.

• 29 – 31
Holker Hall, Cumbria
Holker Garden Festival.

• 29 – 31
Loseley Park, Surrey
Live Crafts.

• 30
Englishcombe Tithe Barn, Somerset
"Eden-Stell Guitar Duo".

• 30 – 31
Eastnor Castle, Herefordshire
Gardeners' Weekend.

• 30 – 31
Lyddington Bede House, Leicestershire &
Rutland
"A Tudor Hospital".

• 31
Newark Castle, Scotland
"For the Lion" – the Life of a Scottish
Knight by Alan Gault, 1, 2 & 3pm.

• 31
Stanford Hall, Leicestershire
RAC Classic Car Run.

JUNE

• 1 - 5
The Chelsea Physic Garden, London
Chelsea Festival Week, noon – 5pm.

• 1 – 30
Arbigland Gardens, Scotland
John Paul Jones Birthplace Museum.

• 1 – 30
British Architectural Library, London
"Art Nouveau Architecture of Riga".

• 1 – 30
Brontë Parsonage Museum, Yorkshire
"No Coward Souls: Emily, Anne and
Branwell Brontë".

• 1 – 30
Burford House Gardens, Shropshire
Botanical Art Show: Artist in residence,
contemporary art shows.

• 1 – 30
Cecil Higgins Art Gallery, Bedfordshire
"People's Choice".

• 1 – 30
Gainsborough's House, Suffolk
"Sculpture in the Garden".

• 1 – 30
The Queen's Gallery, London
"The Search for Albion: Monarchy and
the Patronage of British Painting".

• 2
Stirling Castle, Scotland
"Tanner's Tale", "A Braw Brave King", &
"Bell, Bat & Chuckle" - Kings Company.

• 3
Mirehouse, Cumbria
Lace-making Demonstration.

JUNE

• 4
Ardgillan Castle, Ireland
Guided Tour of Gardens at 3.30pm.

• 4 – 7
Blarney Castle, Ireland
International Horse Trials

• 5
Powderham Castle, Devon
Open Air Concert.

• 5 – 6
Hopetoun House, Scotland
Summer Concerts: "A Musical Feast".

• 5 – 7
Catton Hall, Derbyshire
Country Music Festival.

• 5 – 7
Leighton Hall, Lancashire
Antiques Fair.

• 6
Highclere Castle & Gardens, Hampshire
Shirley Bassey Concert.

• 6
Shugborough, Staffordshire
"Best of Broadway" Concert with Fireworks.

• 6
Uppark, West Sussex
"Taming of the Shrew", 8pm.

• 6 – 7
Cawdor Castle, Scotland
Gardens Weekend.

• 6 – 7
Kenilworth Castle, Warwickshire
"Famous Foes".

• 6 – 7
Leeds Castle, Kent
Balloon & Vintage Car Fiesta.

• 6 – 7
Newby Hall, Yorkshire
Rainbow Craft Fair.

• 7
Arbury Hall, Warwickshire
Motor Transport Spectacular.

• 7
Bolsover Castle, Derbyshire
Garden and Craft Fayre.

• 7
Elcho Castle, Scotland
"For the Lion" – the Life of a Scottish
Knight - Alan Gault, 1, 2 & 3pm.

• 7
Prudhoe Castle, Northumberland
Country Pastimes.

• 8
Argyll's Lodging, Scotland
"Poetic Mischief" - Frank Shiels, 1, 2 & 3pm.

• 9
Stirling Castle, Scotland
The Kings Company present "The
Tanner's Tale", "A Braw Brave King", and
"Bell, Bat & Chuckle", at 11am, 1 & 3pm.

JUNE

• 10
Mirehouse, Cumbria
Lace-making Demonstration.

• 10
Painswick Rococo Gardens,
Gloucestershire
The Festival Players Theatre Company
present "A Midsummer Night's Dream".

• 10
Stirling Castle, Scotland
Alba Adventure Company present
"A Scottish Clansman", 10am–4pm.

• 11
Ardgillan Castle, Ireland
Guided Tour of Gardens at 3.30pm.

• 11 – 13
Wolvesey Castle, Hampshire
"Merry Wives of Windsor".

• 11 – 14
Bramham Park, Yorkshire
BHTA International Horse Trials &
Yorkshire Country Fair.

• 11 – 14
Ripley Castle, Yorkshire
Homes & Gardens Magazine Grand
Summer Sale.

• 12 – 14
Goodwood House, Sussex
Festival of Speed.

• 13
How Caple Court Gardens, Herefordshire
Open Air Opera.

• 13 – 14
Arbury Hall, Warwickshire
Rainbow Craft Fair.

• 13 – 14
Beaulieu, Hampshire
Classic Boat Festival.

• 13 – 14
The Commandery, Worcestershire
"Time Travellers".

• 13 – 14
Portland Castle, Dorset
"Surgeons Through The Ages".

• 13 – 14
Tatton Park, Cheshire
Carriage Driving Event.

• 14
The Birmingham Botanical Gardens and
Glasshouses, West Midlands
Bonsai Show.

• 14
Crossraguel Abbey, Scotland
"Robert the Bruce and his Carrick
Spears" – Battle Re-enactment, 2.30pm.

• 14
East Riddlesden Hall, Yorkshire
An Evening of Jazz with the Yorkshire Post
Jazz Band, 6.30 for 7pm in the garden.

• 14
Ford End Watermill, Buckinghamshire
Milling Demonstration.

JUNE

• 14
Sherborne Castle, Dorset
RSPCA Dog Show, 11am.

• 14
Stirling Castle, Scotland
Royal Burgh of Stirling Pipe Band,
2 & 3pm. The Kings Company present
"The Tanner's Tale", "A Braw Brave King"
& "Bell, Bat and Chuckle, 10am – 2pm.

• 14 – 30
Kentwell Hall, Suffolk
"Great Annual Re-creation of Tudor Life"
(11am–5pm, Sats & Suns).

• 16
Fort George, Scotland
Alba Adventure Company present "Life of
a Redcoat Soldier", 10am–4pm.

• 17
Mirehouse, Cumbria
Lace-making Demonstration.

• 18
Ardgillan Castle, Ireland
Guided Tour of Gardens. at 3.30pm.

• 18
Weston Park, Shropshire
Balloon Nightglow Spectacular.

• 18 – 20
Fountains Abbey & Studley Royal Water
Garden, Yorkshire
Open Air Shakespeare: "The Taming of
the Shrew, 7.30pm in Abbey Cloister.

• 18 – 21
Pashley Manor Gardens, Sussex
Rose and Summer Flower Festival.

• 18 – 30
Gawsworth Hall, Cheshire
Open Air Theatre Festival.

• 19
Montacute House, Somerset
"A Midsummer Night's Dream" - The
Festival Players Theatre Co., 7.30pm.

• 19 – 21
Shaw's Corner, Hertfordshire
Summer Plays – "Pygmalion", 6.30pm.

• 20
Basildon Park, Berkshire
"Midsummer Music Al Fresco", 7.30pm.

• 20
Blickling, Norfolk
Open Air Classical Concert.

• 20
Chartwell, Kent
Music, Memories & Moonlight – 1940s
Open Air Concert with Fireworks, gates
open 6.30pm for concert at 7.30pm.

• 20
Dover Castle, Kent
Food for the Besieged.

• 20
Florence Court, Ireland
Teddy Bears' Picnic, 2.00pm–5.30pm.

• 20
Gilbert White's House & Garden,
Hampshire
Picnic to "Jazz in June" in the Park.

• 20
Lacock, Wiltshire
Opera Brava present "A Gala Opera",
7.30pm.

• 20
Nunnington Hall, Yorkshire
Outdoor Opera - Gilbert & Sullivan "The
Pirates of Penzance", 6.30pm for 7pm.

• 20
Polesden Lacey, Surrey
"Mardi Gras - with All That Jazz and
Boogie Woogie – Fireworks", 7pm (gates
open 6pm for picnics).

• 20
Stourhead, Wiltshire
"A Midsummer Night's Music", 7.30pm
(gates open 6pm).

JUNE

- 20
Wallington, Northumberland
"Elton Jones and Sounds of the Blues Brothers", 7.30pm.

- 20 – 21
Catton Hall, Derbyshire
National Forest Festival & BHTA Horse Trials.

- 20 – 21
Gilbert White's House & Garden, Hants
Unusual Plants Fair.

- 20 – 21
Hatfield House, Hertfordshire
Festival of Gardening.

- 20 – 21
Rockingham Castle, Northamptonshire
Rainbow Craft Fair.

- 20 – 2
Witley Court, Worcestershire
"World War II Living History/Battles".

- 20 – 22
Avington Park, Hampshire
Antiques Fair.

- 21
Brodsworth Hall, Yorkshire
Band Concert.

- 21
Dalemain, Cumbria
Cumbrian Classic Car Caper.

- 21
Polesden Lacey, Surrey
Children's Concert – "Tubby and Friends", 11am–1pm (gates open 10am).

- 21
Polesden Lacey, Surrey
"The Polesden Prom & Firework Spectacular", 7.45pm (gates open 6.30pm for picnics).

- 21
Ragley Hall, Warwickshire
Outdoor Concert.

- 21
Shugborough, Staffordshire
"All about Pigs" – Park Farm. Children's Literary Day – County Museum.

- 21
Waddesdon Manor, Buckinghamshire
Fathers' Day.

- 24
Mirehouse, Cumbria
Lace-making Demonstration.

- 24
Penrhyn, Wales
Concert in the Grand Hall, 7.30pm.

- 24
Quarry Bank Mill, Cheshire
Opera.

- 24 – 27
Polesden Lacey, Surrey
"King Lear", 7.45pm (plus Sat at 2pm).

- 24 – 30
Cliveden, Buckinghamshire
Cliveden Festival: Open Air Shakespeare, 2pm & 7.30pm.

- 25
Ardgillan Castle, Ireland
Guided Tour of Gardens at 3.30pm.

- 25
Naworth Castle, Cumbria
Thomson Roddick & Laurie Fine Pictures & Furniture Auction (viewing 24 June).

- 25
Quarry Bank Mill, Cheshire
Big Band Concert.

- 26
Baddesley Clinton, Warwickshire
Opera Brava, "Gala", 7.30pm (gates open 6pm).

- 26
Quarry Bank Mill, Cheshire
Mackenzie concert with the Northern Chamber Orchestra.

JUNE

- 26 – 28
Avington Park, Hampshire
Marie Curie Flower Festival.

- 26 – 28
Hever Castle, Kent
Gardeners' Weekend.

- 26 – 28
Petworth Park, Sussex
Open Air Concerts – "Gershwin Greats!", 8pm (gates open 6.30pm for picnics).

- 27
Baddesley Clinton, Warwickshire
Opera Brava, "Barber of Seville", 7.30pm (gates open 6pm).

- 27
Belton House, Lincolnshire
Open Air Concert, "A Nautical Prom", 8pm (gates open at 5pm).

- 27
Leeds Castle, Kent
Annual Open Air Concert.

- 27
Painswick Rococo Gardens, Gloucestershire
"An Evening of Outdoor Summer Entertainment".

- 27
Quarry Bank Mill, Cheshire
"Phil's Big Top".

- 27
Quarry Bank Mill, Cheshire
Jazz Concert.

- 27
Sheffield Park Garden, East Sussex
1920s Musical Evening, 6.30 for 7.30pm.

- 27
Shrewsbury Abbey, Shropshire
The Abbey Fair.

- 27 – 28
Appleby Castle, Cumbria
Historical Re-enactment.

- 27 – 28
Beaulieu, Hampshire
Motorcycle World.

- 27 – 28
Dover Castle, Kent
"The Great Siege of 1216".

- 27 – 28
Leonardslee Gardens, Sussex
Country Craft Fair.

- 27 – 28
Meols Hall, Merseyside
Southport Vintage/Yesteryear Show.

- 27 – 28
Pendennis Castle, Cornwall
"World War I Tommies".

- 27 – 28
Sudeley Castle, Gloucestershire
'Daily Telegraph' Rose Day.

- 27 – 28
Whitby Abbey, Yorkshire
"The Fury of the Norsemen".

- 27 – 30
Sulgrave Manor, Northamptonshire
Tudor Living History.

- 28
Belvoir Castle, Lincolnshire
Jousting Tournaments.

- 28
Bolsover Castle, Derbyshire
Children's Festival.

- 28
Box Hill, Surrey
Box Hill Country Day, 11am – 5.30pm.

- 28
Denny Abbey, Cambridgeshire
Sheepdog Demonstrations.

- 28
Dryburgh Abbey, Scotland
"Robert the Bruce and his Carrick Spears" – Battle Re-enactment.

JUNE

- 28
Melrose Abbey, Scotland
"Robert the Bruce and his Carrick Spears" – Battle Re-enactment.

- 28
Quarry Bank Mill, Cheshire
Brass Band Concert.

- 28
St Andrews Castle, Scotland
Edinburgh Bird of Prey Centre, 2 – 5pm (flying displays at 2.30 and 3.30pm).

- 28
Stanford Hall, Leicestershire
American Civil War Society (Battle 3pm). Rover SD1 Club Rally.

JULY

- 1
Mirehouse, Cumbria
Lace-making Demonstration.

- 1
Stirling Castle, Scotland
Alba Adventure Company present "A Scottish Clansman", 10am–4pm.

- 1
Waddesdon Manor, Buckinghamshire
"Gardens in the French Manner".

- 1 – 4
Polesden Lacey, Surrey
Franz Lehar's "The Merry Widow", 7.45pm plus Sat matinee at 2.30pm.

- 1 – 5
Cliveden, Buckinghamshire
Cliveden Festival: Open Air Shakespeare, 2 & 7.30pm.

- 1 – 5
Sulgrave Manor, Northamptonshire
Tudor Living History.

- 1 – 12
Cecil Higgins Art Gallery, Bedfordshire
"People's Choice".

- 1 – 26
British Architectural Library, London
"Art Nouveau Architecture of Riga".

- 1 – 31
Arbigland Gardens, Scotland
John Paul Jones Birthplace Museum.

- 1 – 31
Brontë Parsonage Museum, Yorkshire
"No Coward Souls: Emily, Anne and Branwell Brontë".

- 1 – 31
Burford House Gardens, Shropshire
Botanical Art Show: Artist in residence, contemporary art shows.

- 1 – 31
Gainsborough's House, Suffolk
"Sculpture in the Garden".

JULY

- 1 – 31
Gawsworth Hall, Cheshire
Open Air Theatre Festival.

- 1 – 31
The Queen's Gallery, London
"The Search for Albion: Monarchy and the Patronage of British Painting".

- 2
Ardgillan Castle, Ireland
Guided Tour of Gardens at 3.30pm.

- 2
Richborough Castle, Kent
Archaeological Walks.

- 3
Anglesey Abbey, Cambridgeshire
Open Air Music, "Berlin unter den Linden", 7.30pm.

- 3
Dyrham Park, Gloucestershire
Jazz Night, 7pm (gates open noon).

- 3
Leighton Hall, Lancashire
Concert & Fireworks.

- 3 – 5
Kentwell Hall, Suffolk
"Great Annual Re-creation of Tudor Life" (11am – 5pm).

- 4
Anglesey Abbey, Cambridgeshire
Open Air Music, "Jazz à Belles", 7.30pm (gates open 6.30pm).

- 4
Dyrham Park, Gloucestershire
60s Night, 7pm (gates open noon).

- 4
Framlingham Castle, Suffolk
Italian Renaissance Dance.

- 4
Leeds Castle, Kent
Annual Open Air Concert.

- 4
Ormesby Hall, Yorkshire
"Thank you for the Music", Bjorn Again and Beatlemania Bands, 6.30 for 7.30pm.

- 4 – 5
Borde Hill, Sussex
BHTA Borde Hill Horse Trials, 10am–5pm.

- 4 – 5
Fulbeck Hall, Lincolnshire
Garden Fair.

- 4 – 5
Powderham Castle, Devon
BHTA Horse Trials.

- 4 – 5
Shaw's Corner, Hertfordshire
Middle Plays – Oscar Wilde's "The Importance of Being Earnest", 6.30pm.

- 4 – 5
Tatton Park, Cheshire
"Stars & Stripes" American Car Show.

- 5
Anglesey Abbey, Cambridgeshire
Open Air Music, "Amadeus Boldwicket's Red Hot Peppers Jazz Band", 7.30pm (gates open 6.30pm).

- 5
Dirleton Castle, Scotland
Gaddgedlar Historical Re-enactment Society, noon – 4pm (shows 1.30 & 3pm).

- 5
Melrose Abbey, Scotland
Heritage Events Company "Scots Wha Hae" (12.30pm) & "Scott's Land" (1.30pm).

- 5
Polesden Lacey, Surrey
Polesden Fair, 11am – 5.30pm.

- 5
Polesden Lacey, Surrey
The Pasadena Roof Orchestra, 7.45 pm.

- 5
Ripley Castle, Yorkshire
Performing Arts Lakeside Concert.

- 5 – 11
Charleston, Sussex
Charleston Summer School.

- 8
Mirehouse, Cumbria
Lace-making Demonstration.

- 9
Ardgillan Castle, Ireland
Guided Tour of Gardens at 3.30pm.

- 9
Ickworth, Suffolk
Viennese Evening.

- 9 – 11
The Commandery, Worcestershire
Open Air Shakespeare "Macbeth".

- 10
Ickworth, Suffolk
"Last Night of the Proms", gardens open
from 6pm for picnic suppers.

- 10 – 11
Fountains Abbey & Studley Royal Water
Garden, Yorkshire
Music by Moonlight: "A Night in
Bohemia" with Fireworks Finale, 6pm for
6.30pm (Fri) and 5.30pm for 6pm (Sat).

- 10 – 11
Nymans Garden, Sussex
Jazz Nights in the Garden, 7.30pm
(gates open 6.30pm for picnics).

- 10 – 11
Brinkburn Priory, Northumberland
Early Music Festival.

- 10 – 12
Fulbeck Hall, Lincolnshire
Shakespeare Weekend.

- 11
Beaulieu, Hampshire
Palace House Prom.

- 11
Clumber Park, Nottinghamshire
1970s Glam Rock Concert with
Fireworks, 7pm (gates open 4pm).

- 11
Lanhydrock, Cornwall
Jazz in the Park, 7pm.

- 11
Packwood House, Warwickshire
20s Summer Follies with Fireworks,
starts 6.30pm.

- 11
Uppark, West Sussex
"Alice in Wonderland", 7pm (also at 4pm
if sufficient demand).

- 11 – 12
Borde Hill, Sussex
"Fuchsia Fanfare '98", 10am–5pm.

- 11 – 12
Claydon House, Buckinghamshire
Opera Brava: "Carmen" (Sat) and
"Opera Gala" (Sun), 7.30pm.

- 11 – 12
Penshurst Place & Gardens, Kent
Balloon Fiesta.

- 11 – 12
Powderham Castle, Devon
Historic Vehicle Gathering.

- 12
Arley Hall and Gardens, Cheshire
"Brass Spectacular!" Brass Band con-
cert in the Walled Garden.
Details: 01625 583453.

- 12
Caerlaverock Castle, Scotland
"We do the work of the Lord this
Sabbath Day" – Battle Re-enactment.

- 12
Corgarff Castle, Scotland
Bella Anderson & Charles Coutts –
traditional fiddle music, 2.30pm.

- 12
Ford End Watermill, Buckinghamshire
Milling Demonstration.

- 12
Swallowfield Park, Berkshire
National Garden Day 2–5pm.

- 12 – 31
The Chelsea Physic Garden, London
Exhibition "Art & Healing in Ghana".

- 13
Stirling Castle, Scotland
Heritage Events Company present
"Check-Mate" (11am), "A Matter of Faith"
(1pm) and "To the Last Letter" (3pm).

- 14
Basildon Park, Berkshire
Children's Open Air Theatre 'Alice in
Wonderland', 6.30pm.

- 15
Mirehouse, Cumbria
Lace-making Demonstration.

- 15
Osterley Park, Middlesex
Children's Open Air Theatre, "Alice in
Wonderland", 6.30pm.

- 15
Plas Newydd, Wales
Summer Festival Week, 7.30pm.

- 15 – 18
Claremont Landscape Garden, Surrey
Carousel – Fête Champêtre, 7–11pm.

- 15 – 25
Mottisfont Abbey Garden, Hampshire
The Maskers Theatre: "Wild Oats",
7.30pm (no performance on 20 July).

- 16
Ardgillan Castle, Ireland
Guided Tour of Gardens at 3.30pm.

- 16
Greys Court, Oxfordshire
Music Al Fresco, 7.30pm.

- 16 – 19
Scotney Castle, Kent
Opera at Scotney, 6.30pm for 7.30pm.

- 17
Gibside, Tyne & Wear
"Magic", a tribute to the music of Freddie
Mercury and Queen, 8pm.

- 17
Kingston Lacy, Dorset
Bournemouth Sinfonietta "Popular
Classics" Concert & Fireworks, 8pm
(open 5.30pm).

- 17 – 18
Blickling, Norfolk
Lakeside Jazz Festival.

- 17 – 18
The Vyne, Hampshire
Classical Music and Fireworks, 8pm
(gates open at 6.30 pm for picnics).

- 17 – 19
Castle Ashby, Northamptonshire
House Party.

- 17 – 19
Highclere Castle & Gardens, Hampshire
Porsche Club Annual Rally.

- 18
Gibside, Tyne & Wear
"Midsummer Music with Fireworks", 8pm.

- 18
Kedleston Hall, Derbyshire
"Derbyshire Prom" Open Air Classical
Concert & Fireworks, 8pm (open 6pm).

- 18
Shugborough, Staffordshire
Fireworks & Laser Symphony Concert,
5pm.

- 18 – 19
Carlisle Castle, Cumbria
Family Entertainers.

- 18 – 19
Dalemain, Cumbria
Dalemain Craft Fair.

- 18 – 19
Hatfield House, Hertfordshire
"A Tudor Revel".

- 18 – 19
Helmsley Castle, Yorkshire
"Kings and Queens".

- 18 – 19
Osterley Park, Middlesex
"The Taming of the Shrew", 7pm.

- 18
Wimpole Hall, Cambridgeshire
Concert in the Park with Fireworks, "Swing
is here again" and "Legends of Swing",
7.30pm.

- 19
Audley End House, Essex
Classic Car Show.

- 19
Corgarff Castle, Scotland
"Redcoats at Corgarff 1749", 10am–4pm.

- 19
Fort George, Scotland
Alba Adventure Company present
"Redcoat Troops of King George",
11am–4pm.

- 19
Newby Hall, Yorkshire
Historic Vehicle Rally.

- 19
Stirling Castle, Scotland
Kings Company - "Tanner's Tale", "Braw
Brave King" & "Bell, Bat & Chuckle",
10am–2pm.

- 19
Wimpole Hall, Cambridgeshire
Concert in the Park with Fireworks, "The
Blues Band", 7.30pm.

- 19
Belton House, Lincolnshire
Family Fun Day.

- 21
Cliveden, Buckinghamshire
Children's Open Air Theatre "Alice in
Wonderland", 3pm & 6.30pm.

- 21 – 22
Chiswick House, London
Antony and Cleopatra.

- 21 – 25
Painswick Rococo Gardens,
Gloucestershire
Gloucestershire Drama Association pre-
sent an outdoor Shakespeare production.

- 21 – 31
Cecil Higgins Art Gallery, Bedfordshire
"Out From Under: Land, Myth and Power
in Australian Art".

- 22
Mirehouse, Cumbria
Lace-making Demonstration.

- 22
Penrhyn, Wales
Concert in the Grand Hall, 7.30pm.

- 22
Shugborough, Staffordshire
"Last Night of the Proms", gates 5pm.

- 22
Wimpole Hall, Cambridgeshire
Concert with Fireworks, "1920s – Chaps,
Flappers, Gangsters & Molls", 8pm.

- 23
Ardgillan Castle, Ireland
Guided Tour of Gardens at 3.30pm.

- 23
Wimpole Hall, Cambridgeshire
Concert in the Garden With Fireworks,
"Alan Price & the Electric Blues Band",
8pm.

- 23 – 25
Stourhead, Wiltshire
Fête Champêtre – "Stourhead by the Sea"
with Fireworks, 7.30pm (open 5.30pm).

- 24
Fountains Abbey & Studley Royal Water
Garden, Yorkshire
Opera Gala, 6 for 7.30pm in Abbey
Cloister.

- 24 – 25
Kentwell Hall, Suffolk
Open Air Shakespeare, 7.45pm.

- 24 – 26
Loseley Park, Surrey
Garden Festival.

- 24 – 26
Shaw's Corner, Hertfordshire
Birthday Plays - Shaw's "Widower's
Houses", 6.30pm.

- 25
Fountains Abbey & Studley Royal Water
Garden, Yorkshire
"Carmen", 6 for 7.30pm - Abbey Cloister.

- 25
Hever Castle, Kent
Jousting.

- 25
Meols Hall, Merseyside
The Great North Western Line Dancing
Competition.

- 25
Stowe Landscape Gardens,
Buckinghamshire
"Music and Fireworks", 6pm.

- 25 – 26
Carisbrooke Castle, Isle of Wight
"The Rescue of King Charles, 1648".

- 25 – 26
Catton Hall, Derbyshire
Midlands Carriage Driving Trials.

- 25 – 26
Coleham Pumping Station, Shropshire
"Steam Up".

- 25 – 26
Eastnor Castle, Herefordshire
Balloon Festival in Deer Park.

JULY

- 25 – 26
Norham Castle, Northumberland
Teddy Bears' Picnic.

- 25 – 26
Richborough Castle, Kent
Roman Festival.

- 26
Beaulieu, Hampshire
Bucklers Hard Village Festival.

- 26
Belvoir Castle, Lincolnshire
Jousting Tournaments.

- 26
Bothwell Castle, Scotland
"The War Arrow" – Battle Re-enactment.

- 26
Capesthorne Hall, Cheshire
Classic Car show.

- 26
Elgin Cathedral, Scotland
Fiona Davidson – "Celtic Harp, Song & Legend", 1.30–2, 2.15–2.45 & 3–3.30pm.

- 26
Grime's Graves, Norfolk
"Stone Age Man Returns".

- 26
Hever Castle, Kent
Longbow Archery.

- 26
Hopetoun House, Scotland
Country Fair.

- 26
Meols Hall, Merseyside
"Summer Proms in the Park".

- 29
Mirehouse, Cumbria
Lace-making Demonstration.

- 30
Ardgillan Castle, Ireland
Guided Tour of Gardens at 3.30pm.

- 31
Anglesey Abbey, Cambridgeshire
Open Air Opera, "La Traviata", 7.30pm (gates open 6.30pm).

- 31
Avington Park, Hampshire
Birmingham Symphony Orchestra Open Air Concert.

- 31
Kingston Lacy, Dorset
A Traditional Ale & Jazz Evening with a Firework Finale, 8pm (gates open 5.30pm).

- 31
Mottistone Manor Garden, Isle of Wight
"Mottistone Jazz", 7.30pm (gates open 6.30pm for picnics).

- 31
Powderham Castle, Devon
Open Air Concert.

- 31
Stirling Castle, Scotland
"Stage and Film Spectacular".

AUGUST

- 1
Anglesey Abbey, Cambridgeshire
Open Air Opera, "The Barber of Seville", 7.30pm (gates open 6.30pm).

- 1
Avington Park, Hampshire
B'ham Symphony Orch. Open Air Concert.

- 1
Castle Ward, Ireland
Open Air Concert: Herb Miller Band.

- 1
Chedworth Roman Villa, Gloucestershire
Jazz Picnic, 7.30pm (picnics from 6.30pm).

- 1
Hatfield House, Hertfordshire
"The Hatfield Park Prom".

AUGUST

- 1
Hever Castle, Kent
Jousting.

- 1
Mottistone Manor Garden, Isle of Wight
"Jazz", 7.30pm (open 6.30pm for picnics).

- 1
Nostell Priory, Yorkshire
Grand Tchaikovsky Night with Firework Finale, 6pm for 8pm.

- 1
Nunnington Hall, Yorkshire
Outdoor Theatre: "Much Ado About Nothing", 6pm for 6.30pm.

- 1
Ragley Hall, Warwickshire
Outdoor Concert.

- 1
Tatton Park, Cheshire
Hallé Orch., 8.15pm (grounds open 6pm).

- 1
Trelissick, Cornwall
Promenade Concert in the Garden.

- 1
The Vyne, Hampshire
"Alice in Wonderland", 6.30pm (gates open at 5.30pm for picnics).

- 1
Waddesdon Manor, Buckinghamshire
Champagne on the Parterre 6.30–8.30pm.

- 1 – 2
Deal Castle, Kent
Tudor Printing.

- 1 – 2
Kirby Hall, Leicestershire & Rutland
"History in Action III".

- 1 – 2
Loseley Park, Surrey
QEF Classic Car Show.

- 1 – 2
Old Sarum Castle, Wiltshire
"Medieval Life".

- 1 – 15
Gawsworth Hall, Cheshire
Open Air Theatre Festival.

- 1 – 21
Tintagel Castle, Cornwall
"Legends of King Arthur".

- 1 – 31
Arbigland Gardens, Scotland
John Paul Jones Birthplace Museum open.

- 1 – 31
Brontë Parsonage Museum, Yorkshire
"No Coward Souls: Emily, Anne and Branwell Brontë".

- 1 – 31
Burford House Gardens, Shropshire
Botanical Art Show: Artist in residence, contemporary art shows.

AUGUST

- 1 – 31
Cecil Higgins Art Gallery, Bedfordshire
"Out From Under: Land, Myth and Power in Australian Art".

- 1 – 31
The Chelsea Physic Garden, London
Summer Exhibition "Art & Healing in Ghana".

- 1 – 31
Gainsborough's House, Suffolk
"Sculpture in the Garden".

- 1 – 31
The Queen's Gallery, London
"The Search for Albion: Monarchy and the Patronage of British Painting".

- 2
Anglesey Abbey, Cambridgeshire
Open Air Opera, " A Concert Gala", 7.30pm (gates open 6.30pm).

- 2
Chiswick House, London
Georgian Fun and Games.

- 2
Drummond Castle Gardens, Scotland
Open Day, 2pm–5pm.

- 2
Erddig, Wales
Opera Evening, "La Traviata", 7pm.

- 2
Fort George, Scotland
"Extravaganza", 12–4pm.

- 2
Hever Castle, Kent
Longbow Archery.

- 4
Ashridge, Hertfordshire
Children's Open Air Theatre "Alice in Wonderland", 3pm & 6.30pm.

- 6
Ardgillan Castle, Ireland
Guided Tour of Gardens at 3.30pm.

- 6 – 7
Oxburgh Hall, Norfolk
Children's Extravaganza in the Garden, 10am–5pm.

- 7
Dyrham Park, Gloucestershire
Opera Brava present "Carmen", 8pm (gates open 6.45pm).

- 7 – 8
Leighton Hall, Lancashire
Shakespeare in the Garden, "A Midsummer Night's Dream".

- 8
Bateman's, Sussex
The Bateman's Concert with Fireworks, 6pm for 7.30pm.

- 8
Claydon House, Buckinghamshire
Classical Lanternlight Concert, 7.30pm.

AUGUST

- 8
Dyrham Park, Gloucestershire
Opera Brava present "La Traviata", 8pm (gates open 6.45pm).

- 8
Fountains Abbey & Studley Royal Water Garden, Yorkshire
Fête Champêtre: "Mr Aislabie's Revels", 6pm for 7pm.

- 8
Hever Castle, Kent
Jousting.

- 8
Osterley Park, Middlesex
Big Band Concert with Fireworks, 7.30pm.

- 8
Sherborne Castle, Dorset
Medieval "Fayre".

- 8
Stanford Hall, Leicestershire
Music & Fireworks Spectacular.

- 8 – 9
Farnham Castle, Surrey
Children's Fun Days.

- 8 – 9
Old Sarum Castle, Wiltshire
"1918 – Year of Victory".

- 8 – 9
Rockingham Castle, Northamptonshire
Civil War Re-enactment.

- 8 – 9
St Augustine's Abbey, Kent
Children's Festival.

- 8 – 9
Wolvesey Castle, Hampshire
Children's Fun Day.

- 9
Bateman's, East Sussex
Sounds of the Sixties at Bateman's with Firework Finale, 6.30pm for 7.30pm.

- 9
Capesthorne Hall, Cheshire
Fireworks and Laser Symphony Concert by Performing Arts Management.

- 9
Cardoness Castle, Scotland
"We do the work of the Lord this Sabbath Day" – Battle Re-enactment.

- 9
Hever Castle, Kent
Longbow Archery.

- 9
Stirling Castle, Scotland
Fiona Davidson – "Celtic Harp, Song and Legend", 1.30 - 2, 2.15–2.45 & 3–3.30pm.

- 9 – 31
The Commandery, Worcestershire
"Time Travellers".

- 12 – 13
Carlisle Castle, Cumbria
"Arthurian Antics".

- 13
Ardgillan Castle, Ireland
Guided Tour of Gardens at 3.30pm.

- 13 – 16
Weston Park, Shropshire
Music Festival.

- 14
Basildon Park, Berkshire
Swinging 60s Concert & Fireworks, 7.30pm.

- 14
Kedleston Hall, Derbyshire
"Toad of Toad Hall", 2.30pm & 6.30pm.

- 14
Kingston Lacy, Dorset
"A Moonlight Serenade" - Palm Court Theatre Co & Firework Spectacle, 8pm (open 5.30).

- 14 – 15
Blickling, Norfolk
Firework and Laser Concert.

AUGUST

• 14 – 15
The Vyne, Hampshire
"Taming of the Shrew", 7.30pm (open 6.30).

• 15
Basildon Park, Berkshire
Annual Jazz Concert & Fireworks, 7pm.

• 15
Calke Abbey, Derbyshire
Open Air Concert with Firework Finale, 8pm (gates open at 5.45pm).

• 15
Emmetts Garden, Kent
Open Air Concert with "The Blues Band", 7.30pm (gates open 6.30pm).

• 15
Hever Castle, Kent
Jousting.

• 15 – 16
Caerlaverock Castle, Scotland
"Commission of Array", 1pm (battle at 3pm).

• 15 – 16
Farleigh Hungerford Castle, Somerset
Medieval Music.

• 15 – 16
Scarborough Castle, Yorkshire
"The Siege of Scarborough Castle, 1648".

• 16
Hever Castle, Kent
Longbow Archery.

• 16
Pashley Manor Gardens, Sussex
Summer Plant Fair.

• 16
Stirling Castle, Scotland
"Illuminating St Columba", Steve King & Kevin McCrae,1–1.30, 2–2.30 & 3–3.30pm.

• 16
Tolquhon Castle, Scotland
Forres Archers, 2.30pm–4.30pm.

• 17 – 21
Eastnor Castle, Herefordshire
Children's Fun Week.

• 20
Ardgillan Castle, Ireland
Guided Tour of Gardens at 3.30pm.

• 20
Tintagel Castle, Cornwall
Storytelling.

• 21 – 23
Kingston Lacy, Dorset
Craft Fair weekend.

• 21 – 24
Blair Castle, Scotland
Bowmore Blair Castle Int. Horse Trials.

• 22
Clumber Park, Nottinghamshire
Swinging 60s Open Air Concert with Firework Finale, 7pm (gates open 4pm).

• 22
Hatfield House, Hertfordshire
Lesley Garrett & Fireworks.

• 22
Hever Castle, Kent
Jousting.

• 22
Plas Newydd, Wales
Jazz Concert & Fireworks, 7pm (open 5pm)

• 22
Shugborough, Staffordshire
"Last Night of the Proms".

• 22 – 23
Arbury Hall, Warwickshire
Rainbow Craft Fair.

• 22 – 23
Great Comp Garden, Kent
Hardy Plant Society Annual Garden Show.

• 22 – 23
Helmsley Castle, Yorkshire
Have-a-go Archery.

AUGUST

• 22 – 23
Portland Castle, Dorset
Tudor Music.

• 22 – 23
Ragley Hall, Warwickshire
Game Fair.

• 23
Hever Castle, Kent
Longbow Archery.

• 23
High Beeches Gardens, Sussex
Gentian Time.

• 23
Wilton House, Wiltshire
Teddy Bears' Picnic.

• 24
Fort George, Scotland
"Lace Wars", 10am–4pm (firing displays at 11am, 12, 2 & 3pm).

• 25 – 26
Cobham Hall, Kent
Medway Flower & Craft Show.

• 25 – 26
Sherborne Castle, Dorset
Rainbow Craft Fair, 10am.

• 27
Ardgillan Castle, Ireland
Guided Tour of Gardens at 3.30pm.

• 28 – 31
Naworth Castle, Cumbria
Galloway Antiques Fair.

• 29
Hever Castle, Kent
Jousting.

• 29
Wallington, Northumberland
"Wallington Proms & Fireworks", 7.30pm.

• 29 – 31
Appleby Castle, Cumbria
Historical Re-enactment.

• 29 – 31
Gawsworth Hall, Cheshire
Craft Fair by Cheshire Fayre.

• 29 – 31
Highclere Castle & Gardens, Hampshire
Craft Fair.

• 29 – 31
Kedleston Hall, Derbyshire
Working Crafts Show in the Park.

• 29 – 31
Sulgrave Manor, Northamptonshire
"The 55th Infantry" – Re-enactment.

• 29 – 31
Tilbury Fort, Essex
Classical Military Vehicle Show.

• 30
Corbridge Roman Site, Northumberland
"The Roman Army".

• 30
Dalemain, Cumbria
Cumbrian Classic Car Show.

• 30
Holker Hall, Cumbria
MG Rally.

• 30
Linlithgow Palace, Scotland
Drama – "At the Royal Court of Mary", 2pm & "Linlithgow Jacobites welcome Bonnie Prince Charlie", 3pm.

• 30
Melrose Abbey, Scotland
"For the Lion" – the life of a Scottish Knight by Alan Gault, 1, 2 & 3pm.

• 30
Stirling Castle, Scotland
The Kings Company present "The Tanner's Tale", "A Braw Brave King" and "Bell, Bat and Chuckle", between 10am–2pm.

• 30 – 31
Belvoir Castle, Lincolnshire
Jousting Tournaments.

AUGUST

• 30 – 31
Bolsover Castle, Derbyshire
"The Fury of the Norsemen".

• 30 – 31
Eastnor Castle, Herefordshire
"Living History of the Wars of the Roses".

• 30 – 31
Otley Hall, Suffolk
House and gardens open.

• 30 – 31
Rockingham Castle, Northamptonshire
"The Vikings" at Rockingham.

• 30 – 31
Tatton Park, Cheshire
Steam Fair & Crafts.

• 30 – 31
Wroxeter Roman Site, Shropshire
Roman Festival.

• 31
Chesters Roman Fort, Northumberland
"The Roman Army".

SEPTEMBER

• 1 – 6
The Chelsea Physic Garden, London
Exhibition "Art & Healing in Ghana".

• 1 – 27
Gainsborough's House, Suffolk
"Sculpture in the Garden".

• 1 – 30
Arbigland Gardens, Scotland
John Paul Jones Birthplace Museum

• 1 – 30
British Architectural Library, London
The Palace of Whitehall, 1530–1698.

• 1 – 30
Brontë Parsonage Museum, Yorkshire
"No Coward Souls: Emily, Anne and Branwell Brontë".

• 1 – 30
Burford House Gardens, Shropshire
Botanical Art Show: Artist in residence, contemporary art shows.

• 1 – 30
Cecil Higgins Art Gallery, Bedfordshire
"Out From Under: Land, Myth and Power in Australian Art".

• 1 – 30
The Queen's Gallery, London
"The Search for Albion: Monarchy and the Patronage of British Painting".

• 2
Mirehouse, Cumbria
Lace-making Demonstration.

• 4
Ragley Hall, Warwickshire
Outdoor Concert.

• 4 – 6
The Commandery, Worcestershire
"Time Travellers".

• 5
Belvoir Castle, Lincolnshire
Open Air Concert.

SEPTEMBER

• 5
Tatton Park, Cheshire
Performing Arts Concert.

• 5 – 6
Carlisle Castle, Cumbria
Military Vehicles.

• 5 – 6
Chatsworth, Derbyshire.
Country Fair.

• 5 – 6
Newby Hall, Yorkshire
Rainbow Craft Fair.

• 5 – 6
Richborough Castle, Kent
"Siege Tactics for Children".

• 6
Carisbrooke Castle, Isle of Wight
Community Fun Day.

• 6
Stirling Castle, Scotland
"Extravaganza", 12.30–4.30pm.

• 9
Mirehouse, Cumbria
Lace-making Demonstration.

• 9
Penrhyn, Wales
Concert in the Grand Hall, 7.30pm.

• 9
Waddesdon Manor, Buckinghamshire
"The Art of Dining", 11am–4.30pm.

• 9 – 13
Tatton Park, Cheshire
Bailey's Quality Antiques Fair.

• 11 – 13
Fulbeck Hall, Lincolnshire
Antiques Fair.

• 11 – 13
Hatfield House, Hertfordshire
Country Lifestyle Fair.

• 11 – 13
Hever Castle, Kent
Patchwork & Quilting Exhibition.

• 11 – 13
Penshurst Place & Gardens, Kent
Craft Fair.

• 12 – 13
Bolsover Castle, Derbyshire
"Regency Duellists".

• 12 – 13
Chedworth Roman Villa, Gloucestershire
Archaeology Activity Weekend.

• 12 – 13
Framlingham Castle, Suffolk
"Crisis in the Army, 1648".

• 12 – 13
Ragley Hall, Warwickshire
Garden Weekend.

• 12 – 13
Rothesay Castle, Scotland
Special Events Weekend.

SEPTEMBER

- 12 – 13
Sulgrave Manor, Northamptonshire
"The Vikings".

- 12 – 13
Traquair, Scotland
Needlework Weekend.

- 13
Deene Park, Northamptonshire
Gardens open - National Gardens
Scheme.

- 13
Ford End Watermill, Buckinghamshire
Milling Demonstration.

- 13
Stanford Hall, Leicestershire
Mini Owners' Club National Rally.

- 16
Mirehouse, Cumbria
Lace-making Demonstration.

- 16 – 19
Leeds Castle, Kent
Flower Festival.

- 18 – 20
Avington Park, Hampshire
Home Design & Interiors Exhibition.

- 18 – 20
Castle Ashby, Northamptonshire
House Party.

- 18 – 20
Goodwood House, Sussex
Motor Circuit Revival.

- 19
Battle Abbey, Sussex
"Drums and Pipes at Battle".

- 19 – 20
Capesthorne Hall, Cheshire
Rainbow Craft Fair.

- 19 – 20
Wilton House, Wiltshire
Flowers in the Cloisters.

- 20
Arley Hall and Gardens, Cheshire
Bridal Fair.

- 20
Newby Hall, Yorkshire
Autumn Plant Fair.

- 23
Mirehouse, Cumbria
Lace-making Demonstration.

- 23
Waddesdon Manor, Buckinghamshire
"Baron Ferdinand and the Building of
Waddesdon", 11am–4.30pm.

- 27
Meols Hall, Merseyside
Churchtown Country Show.

- 30
Mirehouse, Cumbria
Lace-making Demonstration.

OCTOBER

- 1
Arley Hall and Gardens, Cheshire
Shopping Spectacular!

- 1 – 11
Cecil Higgins Art Gallery, Bedfordshire
"Out From Under: Land, Myth and Power
in Australian Art".

- 1 – 11
The Queen's Gallery, London
"The Search for Albion: Monarchy and
the Patronage of British Painting".

- 1 – 24
British Architectural Library, London
"The Palace of Whitehall, 1530–1698".

- 1 – 31
Brontë Parsonage Museum, Yorkshire
"No Coward Souls: Emily, Anne and
Branwell Brontë".

- 1 – 31
Burford House Gardens, Shropshire
Botanical Art Show: Artist in residence,
contemporary art shows.

- 2 – 4
Blair Castle, Scotland
Special Needlelace Exhibition.

- 3 – 4
Portchester Castle, Hampshire
"The Roman Army".

- 3 – 4
Stanford Hall, Leicestershire
Crafts (Lady Fayre).

- 3 – 4
Stott Park Bobbin Mill, Cumbria
Woodland Weekend.

- 9 – 11
Finchcocks, Kent
Fair.

- 9 – 11
Weston Park, Shropshire
BHTA Horse Trials.

- 10 – 11
Battle Abbey, Sussex
"1066 Living History/Skirmish".

- 10 – 31
Fairfax House, Yorkshire
Silver from the Gilbert Collection.

- 13 – 31
The Queen's Gallery, London
"Mark Catesby's Natural History of
America." Watercolours from Royal
Library.

- 17 – 18
Arley Hall and Gardens, Cheshire
The Arley Food and Drink Fair.

- 17 – 18
Rockingham Castle, Northamptonshire
Rainbow Craft Fair.

- 17 – 18
Tatton Park, Cheshire
Countrywide Fair.

- 17 – 18
Wilton House, Wiltshire
Quilters in the Cloisters.

- 18
High Beeches Gardens, Sussex
Autumn Splendour.

- 18
Leighton Hall, Lancashire
Dolls House and Miniatures Fair.

- 22
Naworth Castle, Cumbria
Fine Art & Furniture Sale (view 21 Oct).

- 23 – 25
Deene Park, Northamptonshire
Antiques Fair.

- 24
Waddesdon Manor, Buckinghamshire
"Decorations for Celebrations".

- 25
The Birmingham Botanical Gardens and
Glasshouses, West Midlands
Christmas Markets.

OCTOBER

- 30 – 31
Gainsborough's House, Suffolk
Gainsborough Drawings on display.

- 30 – 31
Shugborough, Staffordshire
Halloween.

- 31
Aydon Castle, Northumberland
"Spooky Castle".

- 31
Beaulieu, Hampshire
Fireworks Fair.

- 31
Blair Castle, Scotland
Glenfiddich World Piping Championships.

- 31
Bolsover Castle, Derbyshire
Fireworks.

- 31
Dirleton Castle, Scotland
Ghost Walks, 7.30pm.

- 31
Waddesdon Manor, Buckinghamshire
Floodlit Opening 6–9pm.

NOVEMBER

- 1
Blair Castle, Scotland
Glenfiddich World Piping Championships.

- 1 – 2
Stowe School, Buckinghamshire
Craft Fair.

- 1 – 22
Gainsborough's House, Suffolk
Gainsborough Drawings on display.

- 1 – 30
Brontë Parsonage Museum, Yorkshire
"No Coward Souls: Emily, Anne &
Branwell Brontë".

- 1 – 30
Fairfax House, Yorkshire
Silver from the Gilbert Collection.

- 1 – 30
The Queen's Gallery, London
"Mark Catesby's Natural History of
America." Watercolours from Royal Library.

- 4
Waddesdon Manor, Buckinghamshire
"The Secret Drawer", 11am–4.30pm.

- 4 – 30
British Architectural Library, London
"Alvar Aalto & House of Culture, Helsinki".

- 6 – 8
Loseley Park, Surrey
Christmas Food & Gift Fair.

- 7
Leeds Castle, Kent
Grand Firework Spectacular.

- 7
Meols Hall, Merseyside
Grand Bonfire and Firework Display.

- 13 – 15
Goodwood House, Sussex
SE Counties Antiques Fair.

- 21
Waddesdon Manor, Buckinghamshire
"The Button Collection", 11am–4.30pm.

- 27 – 29
Loseley Park, Surrey
Live Crafts.

- 28
Bolsover Castle, Derbyshire
Victorian Christmas Open Day.

- 29
The Birmingham Botanical Gardens and
Glasshouses, West Midlands
Craft Fair.

- 29
Gilbert White's House & Garden,
Hampshire
Mulled Wine & Christmas Shopping Day.

DECEMBER

- 1 – 19
British Architectural Library, London
"Alvar Aalto & House of Culture, Helsinki".

- 1 – 28
Fairfax House, Yorkshire
Silver from the Gilbert Collection.

- 1 – 31
Brontë Parsonage Museum, Yorkshire
"No Coward Souls: Emily, Anne and
Branwell Brontë".

- 1 – 31
Ford Green Hall, Staffordshire
Hall dressed in seasonal decorations.

- 1 – 31
The Queen's Gallery, London`
"Mark Catesby's Natural History of
America." Watercolours from Royal Library.

- 3
Edinburgh Castle, Scotland
Alba Adventure Company - "A Redcoat
Soldier of King George", 10am–4pm.

- 3 – 5
The Greyfriars, Worcestershire
Street Fayre.

- 3 – 31
Fairfax House, Yorkshire
Exhibition on the "Keeping of Christmas".

- 4 – 6
Highclere Castle & Gardens, Hampshire
Christmas Fair.

- 5 – 6
Sulgrave Manor, Northamptonshire
"A Tudor Christmas".

- 8 – 13
Tatton Park, Cheshire
Candlelight Tours of the Mansion.

- 12 – 13
Sulgrave Manor, Northamptonshire
"A Tudor Christmas".

- 13
Edinburgh Castle, Scotland
Fireside Stories for Christmas, 2 & 3pm.

- 13
Kenilworth Castle, Warwickshire
"Tudor Toymaker".

- 13 – 15
Powderham Castle, Devon
Phillips Fine Art Sale.

- 19 – 20
Sulgrave Manor, Northamptonshire
"A Tudor Christmas".

- 27 – 28
Dover Castle, Kent
"World War II Father Christmas".

- 27 – 31
Sulgrave Manor, Northamptonshire
"A Tudor Christmas".

- 31
Castle Ashby, Northamptonshire
New Year's Eve Gala.

Scott's View, Nr Melrose, Borders. Scottish Borders Tourist Board

OPEN ALL YEAR INDEX

Properties included on this list are open to some extent for all or most of the year. Full details are available in the regional listings.
* Park/garden only, open all year.   ** Closed for 1/2 months only.

ENGLAND

■ SOUTH & SOUTH EAST

■ WEST COUNTRY

Hever Castle, Kent

OPEN ALL YEAR INDEX

Normanby Hall, Lincolnshire.

OPEN ALL YEAR INDEX

Stokesay Castle, Shropshire.

SCOTLAND
■ BORDERS

Belsay Hall, Northumberland.

■ SOUTH WEST

■ EDINBURGH

OPEN ALL YEAR INDEX

Argyll's Lodging, Stirling.

Powerscourt, Ireland.

IRELAND

Caernarfon Castle, Wales.

This is not an exclusive list but is merely intended to draw attention to some of those properties which are open most of the year.

The Counties of
ENGLAND

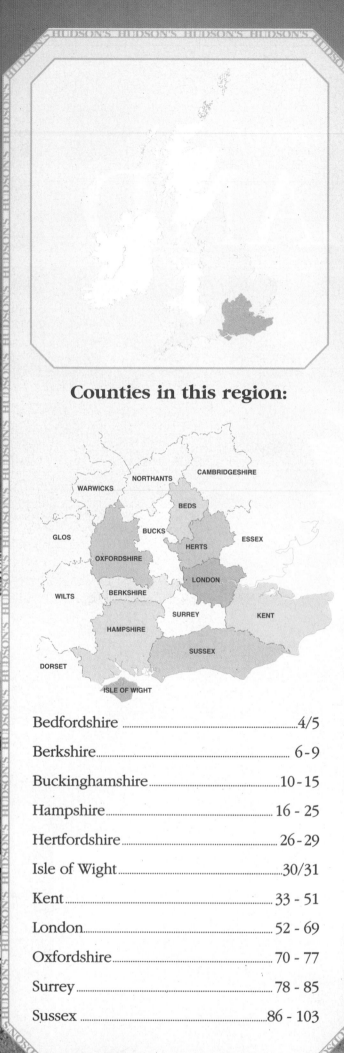

Counties in this region:

South East
England

3

South East England

WOBURN ABBEY
Woburn

CONTACT

Peter A Gregory
Woburn Abbey
Woburn
Bedfordshire
MK43 0TP

Tel: (01525) 290666

Fax: (01525) 290271

LOCATION

OS Ref. SP965 325

On A4012, midway
between M1/J13, 3m,
J14, 6m and
the A5 (turn off
at Hockliffe).
London approx. 1hr
by road 43m.
Then 4m to Woburn
Village Gate in both cases.

Rail: London Euston to
Leighton Buzzard,
Bletchley / Milton Keynes.
Kings Cross
Thameslink to Flitwick.

Air: Luton 14m.
Heathrow 39m.

Set in a beautiful 3,000 acre deer park, Woburn Abbey has been the home of the Dukes of Bedford for nearly 400 years. It is now lived in by the present Duke's heir, the Marquess of Tavistock and his family. One of the most important private art collections in the world can be seen here, including paintings by Van Dyck, Cuyp, Gainsborough, Reynolds and Velazquez. In the Venetian Room there are 21 views of Venice by Canaletto. The collection also features French and English 18th century furniture and silver. The tour of the Abbey covers three floors, including vaults, where the fabulous Sèvres dinner service presented to the 4th Duke by Louis XV of France is on display.

The deer park has nine species of deer roaming freely. One of these, the Père David, descended from the Imperial Herd of China, was saved from extinction at Woburn and is now the largest breeding herd of this species in the world. In 1985 22 Père David were given by the Family to the People's Republic of China and these are now successfully re-established in their natural habitat and number several hundred.

All catering is carried out by ourselves with banqueting, conferences, receptions and company days out our specialities in the beautiful setting of the Sculpture Gallery, overlooking the Private Gardens. It is also a popular choice for wedding receptions and a Civil Wedding Licence is held.

There are extensive picnic areas. Events are held in the Park throughout the summer including the Woburn Garden Show, Craft Fairs and the annual fly-in of the de Havilland Moth Club. The 40-shop Antique Centre is probably the most unusual such centre outside London.

Woburn Abbey and Safari Park ~ The 1998 Good Guide to Britain Family Attraction of the Year.

ℹ️	Two shops. Suitable for fashion shows, product launches, filming and company 'days out'. Use of parkland and garden. No unaccompanied children. No photography in House.
✗	Conferences, exhibitions, banqueting, luncheons, dinners in the Sculpture Gallery, Lantern and long harness rooms.
♿	Wheelchairs can be accommodated in the Abbey by prior arrangement (max. 8 per group). WC. Guide dogs in house only.
☕	Group bookings in Sculpture Gallery. Flying Duchess Pavilion Coffee Shop.

🔑	By arrangement, max 15. Tours in French, German & Dutch at an additional charge of £7.50 per guide. Audio tape tour available - £1pp. Lectures on the property, its contents, gardens and history can be arranged.
🅿️	Ample. Free.
🚶	Welcome. Special programme on request. Cost: £2.50pp. (group rate).
🐕	In park on leashes, and guide dogs in house.
💒	Civil Wedding Licence.

CONFERENCE/FUNCTION

ROOM	SIZE	MAX CAPACITY
Sculpture Gallery	130' x 25'	400 220 (sit-down)
Lantern Rm	24' x 21'	100

OPENING TIMES

SUMMER

Abbey:
22 March - 27 September
Mon - Sat: 11am - 4pm
Sun & BHs: 11am - 5pm.

Deer Park:
Mon - Sat: 10am - 4.30pm
Sun & BHs: 10am - 4.45pm

WINTER

Abbey:
1 January - 21 March
weekends only
11am - 4pm.
Deer Park:
10.30am - 3.45pm

Abbey:
3 Oct - 1 Nov
Sat: 11am - 4pm
Sun: 11am - 5pm
Deer Park:
Sat: 10.30am - 3.45pm
Sun: 10.30am - 4.45pm

Abbey closed
2 Nov - 31 Dec.

Antiques Centre open daily all year except 24 - 26 Dec.

ADMISSION

Abbey & Garden
(incl. Private Apartments)
Adult £7.50
Child (12 - 16yrs)......£3.00
OAP..........................£6.50
Groups (15+)
Adult £6.25
Child (7 - 16yrs)........£2.50
OAP £5.40

Antiques Centre £0.20

Grounds &
Deer Park only
Car £5.00
Motorcycle £2.00
Coaches ....Free
Other........................£0.50

Reduced rates apply when Private Apartments are in use by the family.

South East England

BROMHAM WATERMILL & ART GALLERY
Tel: 01234 824330

Bromham, Bedfordshire MK43 8LP
Owner: Bedfordshire County Council **Contact:** Sally Wileman
Working water mill on River Ouse.
Location: OS Ref. TL010 506. Location beside the River Ouse bridge on N side of the former A428, 2¹/₂ m W of Bedford.
Opening Times: Wed - Sat, 12 - 4pm. Sun 10.30am - 5pm. Last entry 30mins before closing.
Admission: Adult £1.50, Child 50p, Conc 75p.

BUSHMEAD PRIORY
Tel: 01234 376614

Colmworth, Bedford, Bedfordshire MK44 2LD **Regional Office:** 01604 730320
Owner: English Heritage **Contact:** The Custodian
A rare survival of the medieval refectory of an Augustinian priory, with its original timber-framed roof almost intact and containing interesting wall paintings and stained glass.
Location: OS Ref. TL115 607. On unclassified road near Colmworth, 2 m E of B660. 5m W of St. Neots (A1).
Opening Times: Jul - Aug weekends only, 10am - 6pm. Closed 1 - 2pm
Admission: Adult £1.75, Child 90p, Conc £1.30.

No dogs. P Ample.

CECIL HIGGINS ART GALLERY

CASTLE CLOSE, CASTLE LANE, BEDFORD MK40 3RP
Owner: Bedford Borough Council & Trustees of Gallery *Contact: The Curator*

Tel: 01234 211222 **Fax:** 01234 327149
An unusual combination of recreated Victorian Mansion (originally the home of the Higgins family, wealthy Bedford brewers) and adjoining modern gallery housing internationally renowned collection of watercolours, prints and drawings, ceramics and glass. Room settings include many items from the Handley-Read Collection and furniture by Victorian architect William Burges. Situated in pleasant gardens near the river embankment.
Location: OS Ref. TL052 497. Centre of Bedford, just off The Embankment. East of High Street.
Opening Times: Tue - Sat, 11am - 5pm. Sun & BH Mons, 2 - 5pm.
Admission: Free. Charge for guided tours & viewing of Reserve Collections.

i Shop. X By arrangement. House & garden suitable. WC.

By arrangement. P No parking. Guide dogs.

SPECIAL EVENTS
1998: Various exhibitions including: "People's Choice", "Out from Under" (Australian Art in English Collections) and "Turner In Focus", see the Special Events section for more details.

DE GREY MAUSOLEUM
Tel: 01799 522842 (Audley End House)

Flitton, Bedford, Bedfordshire
Owner: English Heritage **Contact:** Mr Stimpson - 01525 860094
A remarkable treasure-house of sculpted tombs and monuments from the 16th to 19th centuries dedicated to the de Grey family of nearby Wrest Park.
Location: OS Ref. TL059 359. Attached to the church on unclassified road 1¹/₂ m W of A6 at Silsoe.
Opening Times: Weekends only. Key, Mr. Stimpson, 3 Highfield Rd, Flitton.
Admission: Free.

No dogs.

HOUGHTON HOUSE
Tel: 01604 730320

Ampthill, Bedford, Bedfordshire
Owner: English Heritage **Contact:** The Midlands Regional Office
Reputedly the inspiration for "House Beautiful" in Bunyan's "Pilgrim's Progress", the remains of this early 17th century mansion still convey elements which justify the description, including work attributed to Inigo Jones.
Location: OS Ref. TL039 394. 1m NE of Ampthill off A421, 8m S of Bedford, then by footpath to NE.
Opening Times: Any reasonable time.
Admission: Free.

Suitable. On leads. P Limited.

SWISS GARDEN
Tel: 01767 627666 **Fax:** 01234 228315

Biggleswade Road, Old Warden, Bedfordshire
Owner: Bedfordshire County Council
Laid out in the early 1800s and steeped in the indulgent romanticism of the time, Swiss Garden combines all the elements of high fashion: formal walks and vistas, classical proportions, tiny thatched buildings, woodland glades and, hidden away, a fairytale grotto with a brilliant glazed fernery, magnificent trees and a network of ponds and bridges.
Location: OS Ref. TL150 447. 1¹/₂ m W of Biggleswade A1 roundabout, signposted from A1 and A600.
Opening Times: Mar - Sept: Sun & BHs, 10am - 6pm. Weekdays & Sat: 1.30 - 6pm (closed Tue). Jan, Feb & Oct: Suns & New Year's Day, 11am - 3pm. Last admission ³/₄ hr before closing. Groups at any time on request.
Admission: Adult £2.25, Conc £1.25, Family £5. Season ticket available. Special rates for groups and guided tours.

Suitable. WC. K Available . Woodland only.

WOBURN ABBEY
See page 4 for full page entry.

WREST PARK GARDENS

SILSOE, LUTON, BEDFORDSHIRE MK45 4HS
Owner: English Heritage *Contact: The Custodian*

Tel: 01525 860152
Over 90 acres of wonderful gardens originally laid out in the early 18th century, including the Great Garden. During the 18th and 19th centuries the formal parterre was introduced together with marble fountains, the Bath House and the vast Orangery, built by the Earl de Grey. The gardens form a delightful backdrop to the house, built in the style of an 18th century French chateau.
Location: OS153, Ref. TL093 356. ³/₄m E of Silsoe off A6, 10m S of Bedford.
Opening Times: 1 Apr - 1 Nov: Weekends and BHs only, 10am - 6pm or dusk in Oct.
Admission: Adult £2.95, Child £1.50, Conc £2.20. 15% discount for groups of 11+.

WC. Available.

South East England

CONTACT

Peregrine & Jill Palmer
Dorney Court
Windsor
Berkshire
SL4 6QP

Tel: (01628) 604638

Fax: (01628) 665772

LOCATION

OS Ref. SU926 791

25m W of London
W of B3026 2¹/₂ m SW of
Slough, 2m SE of
Maidenhead.

Rail: Windsor 5m
Burnham 2m.

Air: London Airport
(Heathrow) 20 mins.

CONFERENCE/FUNCTION		
ROOM	SIZE	MAX CAPACITY
Great Hall	33' x 24'	65
Dining Rm	20' x 20'	18

DORNEY COURT
Windsor

"One of the finest Tudor Manor Houses in England." Dorney Court is an enchanting, many gabled pink brick and timbered manor house with more than just a taste of history.

Grade I listed Dorney Court offers a most welcome, refreshing and fascinating experience. Built about 1440 and lived in by the present family for over 400 years.

The rooms are full of the atmosphere of history: early 15th and 16th century oak, beautiful 17th century lacquer furniture, 18th and 19th century tables, 400 years of family portraits, stained glass and needlework. Here Charles II once came to seek the charms of Barbara Palmer, Countess of Castlemaine, the most intelligent, beautiful and influential of ladies. St James' Church next door, is a lovely, cool, cheerful and very English village church.

"The approach to the house is through ancient Buckinghamshire woodland which transports the visitor into a dreamland. Suddenly the early Tudor house, a ravishing half timbered vision in gabled pinkish brick, comes into view, prettily grouped with a church. This is Dorney Court, a surprisingly little known manor house ... happily genuine ... an idyllic image." *Daily Telegraph*.

ℹ Shop and garden centre. Pick-your-own fruit, daily Jun to Aug 10% discount Mon - Wed, 10am - 5pm. Available for film/photographic shoots. Activity and family fun days, product launches, garden parties. No private family parties, wedding parties or dancing. No unaccompanied children or photography in the house.

♿ No facilities.

✗ Available, see right for further details.

☕ Available.

🚶 Available for private visits. Tour time 1¹/₂ hrs.

🅿 Ample.

👥 Welcome. £16 per guide if required. No charge for accompanying adults.

🐕 No dogs.

OPENING TIMES

SUMMER

May: BH Sun & Mon
July/August: Mon to Thur
1 - 4.30pm
Last admission 4pm.

WINTER

October - Easter
Pre-booked tours only.

ADMISSION

House and Garden

Adult £4.50
Child (10 - 16yrs) £2.50
OAP.........................£4.00
Groups* on open days
Adult £4.00
Child (10 - 16yrs) £2.50

Private Visits...............£6.00

10% discount NT, NADFAS & OAPs

* Min.10 people

✗ **CORPORATE HOSPITALITY**
Dorney Court is a privately owned and lived in family house, the perfect place for prestigious group visits or exclusive private functions. It is often matched into conferences held elsewhere, making a complete change from the work environment.
They do their own catering or use the best outside caterers, if required. They farm the land as they have for centuries, producing some of England's best lamb, strawberries, raspberries and other fruit and vegetables. Throughout the year they use their own home produce, such as lamb and asparagus in the spring, and the freshest ingredients available – summer salmon, grouse or partridge in autumn, and venison or beef in winter.
In winter the Great Hall flickers in candlelight and the large wood fires glow with warmth. In summer you can stroll the lawns with a cooling drink such as the famous Palmer cocktail, winner of the 1934 Grand Prix in Paris. The secret recipe was given to the family by a barman in Budapest, the only recognisable ingredient being champagne!

BASILDON PARK

Vera Collingwood.

LOWER BASILDON, READING RG8 9NR

Owner: *The National Trust*   **Contact:** *The Property Manager*

Tel: 0118 984 3040 **Fax:** 0118 984 1267

An elegant, classical house designed in the 18th century by Carr of York and set in rolling parkland in the Thames Valley. The house has rich interiors with fine plasterwork, pictures and furniture, and includes an unusual Octagon Room and a decorative Shell Room. Basildon Park has connections with the East through its builder and was the home of a wealthy industrialist in the 19th century. It was rescued from dereliction in the mid 20th century. Small flower garden, pleasure grounds and woodland walk.

Location: OS Ref. SU611 782. 2^1/$_2$ m NW of Pangbourne on the west side of the A329, 7m from M4/J12.

Opening Times: 1 Apr - 1 Nov: Wed - Sun & BH Mons: 1 - 5.30pm (closed Good Fri), Park, Garden & Woodland Walk: 1 - 27 Mar: Sat, Sun, 12 - 5pm; 1 Apr - 1 Nov, as house but open 11.30am - 5.30pm. House and grounds will close at 5pm on 15 Aug for Jazz Concert. Groups of 15+ £3pp, only on application to Property Manager.

Admission: House, Park & Garden: Adult £4, Child £2, Family £10. Park & Garden only: Adult £1.60, Child 80p. Family £4.

ⓘ Shop. ♿ Suitable. WC. ☕ Tearoom. 🐕 On leads in grounds only.

SPECIAL EVENTS
AUGUST 15: Open Air Jazz Concert

DONNINGTON CASTLE ⌗   **Tel:** 01732 778000

Newbury, Berkshire

Owner: English Heritage   **Contact:** The South East Regional Office

Built in the late 14th century, the twin towered gatehouse of this heroic castle survives amidst some impressive earthworks. The remainder was destroyed during one of the longest sieges of the Civil War, lasting nearly two years.

Location: OS Ref. SU463 691. 1m NW of Newbury off B4494.

Opening Times: Any reasonable time.

Admission: Free.

♿ Suitable, some steep slopes.   🐕 In grounds, on leads.

DORNEY COURT 🏛   **See page 6 for full page entry.**

ENGLEFIELD HOUSE 🏛   **Tel:** 01734 302221 **Fax:** 01734 303227

Englefield, Theale, Reading, Berkshire RG7 5EN

Owner: Sir W Benyon   **Contact:** Sir W Benyon

A seven acre garden, herbaceous and rose borders, fountain, stone balustrades and staircases, woodland and water garden, set in Deer Park.

Location: OS Ref. SU622 720. 4m W of Reading off A4. 1^1/$_4$ m of A4 at Theale.

Opening Times: Garden only: all year, Mon 10am till dusk. Apr - Jun: Mon, Tue, Wed and Thur 10am till dusk. Sat, 9 May: 2 - 6pm.

Admission: £2.

ETON COLLEGE   **Tel:** 01753 671177 **Fax:** 01753 671265

Windsor, Berkshire SL4 6DW

Owner: Eton College   **Contact:** Rebecca Hunkin

Eton College, founded in 1440 by Henry VI, is one of the oldest and best known schools in the country. The original and subsequent historic buildings of the Foundation are a part of the heritage of the British Isles and visitors are invited to experience and share the beauty of the ancient precinct which includes the magnificent College Chapel, a masterpiece of the perpendicular style.

Location: OS Ref. SU967 779. Off M4/J5. Access from Windsor by footbridge only. Vehicle access from Slough 2m N.

Opening Times: Mar - early Oct: Times vary, best to check with the Visits Office.

Admission: Ordinary admissions and daily guided tours. Groups by appointment only. Rates vary according to type of tour.

ⓘ Shop. Suitable for conferences. ✗ Catering. Functions. ♿ Ground floor suitable. WC.

🚶 Available.   Ⓟ Limited. Sometimes insufficient.   🐕 Guide dogs only.

The Savill Garden, Berkshire.

South East England

ST. GEORGE'S CHAPEL WINDSOR   **Tel:** 01753 868286

Fine example of perpendicular architecture. Open only in conjuction with Windsor Castle.
Location: OS Ref. SU968 770.
Opening Times: As Windsor Castle, closed also 25 April until 1pm, 2 May from 1pm, 5 June from 3.30pm, 4 & 25 July from 1pm, 18 Aug from 1pm, 26 Sept from 1pm, 23 Dec from 1pm. 24 Dec. Opening times subject to change at short notice.
Admission: Admission as part of Windsor Castle ticket, see below.

SWALLOWFIELD PARK   **Tel:** 0118 9883815

Swallowfield, Reading, Berkshire RG7 1TG
Owner: Country Houses Association   **Contact:** The Administrator
Built in 1678 by the second Earl of Clarendon.
Location: OS Ref. SU730 655. In Swallowfield, 6 m SE of Reading. 4m S of J11, M4. Then via Spencers Wood.
Opening Times: 1 June - 31 Aug, Mon & Fri, 2 - 5pm. Pre-booked groups any day during May - Sept.
Admission: Adult £2.50, Child £1.50, Groups by arrangement.

🐕 No dogs.   A 1 Single & 1 double with bathroom, CHA members only.

SPECIAL EVENTS
APR 13: National Garden Day, 2 - 5pm   **JUL 12:** National Garden Day, 2 - 5pm

---

THE SAVILL GARDEN

WINDSOR GREAT PARK, BERKSHIRE SL4 2HT
Owner: Crown Property   *Contact:* Jan Bartholomew

Tel: 01753 860222 **Fax:** 01753 859617

World-renowned 35 acre woodland garden, providing a wealth of beauty and interest in all seasons. Spring is heralded by hosts of daffodils, masses of rhododendrons, azaleas, camellias, magnolias and much more. Roses, herbaceous borders and countless alpines are the great features of summer, and the leaf colours and fruits of autumn rival the other seasons with a great display.
Location: OS Ref. SU977 706. Wick Lane, Englefield Green. Clearly signposted from Ascot, Bagshot, Egham and Windsor. Nearest station: Egham.
Opening Times: Mar - Oct: 10am - 6pm. Nov - Feb: 10am - 4pm.
Admission: Adult £3.80, OAP £3.30. Groups of 20+ £3.30. Accompanied under 16s free.

ℹ️ Shop. Plant centre.   ♿ Grounds suitable. WC.   ☕ Licensed restaurant.
🚶 Available.   🐕 Guide dogs only.

TAPLOW COURT

BERRY HILL, TAPLOW, NR. MAIDENHEAD, BERKS SL6 0ER
Owner: SGI-UK   *Contact:* Robert Samuels

Tel: 01628 591215 **Fax:** 01628 773055

Set high above the Thames, affording spectacular views. Remodelled mid-19th century by William Burn. Earlier neo-Norman Hall. 18th century home of Earls of Orkney and more recently of Lord and Lady Desborough who entertained "The Souls" here. Tranquil gardens & grounds. Anglo-Saxon burial mound. Permanent and temporary exhibitions.
Location: OS Ref. SU907 822. M4/J7 off Bath Road towards Maidenhead. 6m off M40/J2.
Opening Times: House & Grounds: Easter Sun & Mon, & Suns up to the end of June: 2 - 6pm. Please telephone to check for Sundays in July.
Admission: No charge. Free parking.

ℹ️ Shop.   ♿ Suitable. WCs.   ☕ Tearoom.   🚶 Available.   🐕 Guide dogs.

Historic Scotland

SPECIAL EVENTS 1998
See the front section for full list.

WELFORD PARK   **Tel:** 01488 608203

Newbury, Berkshire RG20 8HU
Owner: Mr J Puxley   **Contact:** Mr J Puxley
A Queen Anne house, with attractive gardens and grounds. Riverside walks.
Location: OS Ref. SU409 731. On Lambourn Valley Road. 6m NW of Newbury.
Opening Times: 25 May, 1 - 26 Jun, 31 Aug: 2.30 - 5pm.
Admission: House by prior arrangement. Adult £3.50, Child free, Conc. £2. Grounds free.

♿ Grounds suitable.   🐕 On leads in grounds only.

WINDSOR CASTLE   **Tel:** 01753 868286

Windsor, Berkshire SL4 1NJ
Owner: H M The Queen   **Contact:** The Information Officer
Windsor Castle has belonged to the Sovereigns of England for over 900 years.
Location: OS Ref. SU969 770. 3m S of M4/J6. In town centre.
Opening Times: Mar - Oct: daily 10am - 5.30pm (last admission 4pm). Nov - Feb: daily 10am - 4pm (last admission 3pm). Closed 10 April, 15 June, 25/26 Dec. Please telephone for additional closing dates.
Admission: Adult £9.50, OAP £7, Child under 17 £5, Family (2+2) £21.50. Sun: Adult £7.50, OAP £5.50, Child under 17 £4, Family (2+2) £17. Group rates available.

ℹ️ Shop.   ♿ Suitable, except Queen Mary's Dolls' House and Gallery. WC.
P No parking.   🐕 Guide dogs only.

Mazes:

Mazes (sometimes called labyrinths) are an attractive garden feature offering the fascination of walking into the unknown. They became fashionable in British gardens in the seventeenth century as an extension of the enthusiasm for topiary, but were known in the sixteenth century and earlier: Rosamund's 'bower' at Woodstock in Oxfordshire, made by Henry II (1154–89), was almost certainly an architectural labyrinth. A Parliamentary survey made of Wimbledon House, London, c.1650, shows a maze, but the yew Maze at Hampton Court, London (c.1699) is undoubtedly the best known. Others, all made in the nineteenth century, may be seen at Woburn Park, Bedfordshire; Somerleyton Hall, Suffolk (by William Nesfield); and Wooton Court, Warwickshire.

The concept of the labyrinth goes back many hundreds of centuries and is based on the Cretan legend of the Minotaur kept by King Minos in a labyrinth at Knossos. The idea was later taken over by the Church, as representing the difficult path of a believer, and the Cretan labyrinth pattern is to be found on the floors of many continental churches. From this it was a small step to turf mazes, and of these a number of early examples survive in Britain: at St Catherine's Hill, near Winchester, Hampshire; at Troy Farm, Somerton, Oxfordshire; and at Braemore, Hampshire. These may have had a religious significance, but an alternative theory is that they were for races, or derive from a game on horseback called The City of Troy, enjoyed by the Romans. One such turf maze survives at Trojeborg (Troy Town) in Scandinavia.

Extract from; "Life in the Country House" by David N Durant (published by John Murray), PB£15.99, see page twelve at the front of the book.

Somerleyton Hall, Suffolk.

STOWE SCHOOL
Buckingham

STOWE owes its pre-eminence to the vision and wealth of two owners. From 1715 to 1749 Viscount Cobham, one of Marlborough's Generals, continuously improved his estate, calling in the leading designers of the day to lay out the gardens, and commissioning several leading architects – Vanbrugh, Gibbs, Kent and Leoni – to decorate them with garden temples. From 1750 to 1779 Earl Temple, his nephew and successor continued to expand and embellish both Gardens and House. The House is now a major public school.

Around the mansion is one of Britain's most magnificent landscape gardens now in the ownership of the National Trust. Covering 325 acres and containing no fewer than 6 lakes and 32 garden temples, it is of the greatest historic importance. During the 1730s William Kent laid out in the Elysian Fields at Stowe, one of the first 'natural' landscapes and initiated the style known as 'the English Garden'. 'Capability' Brown worked there for 10 years, not as a consultant but as head gardener, and in 1744 was married in the little church hidden between the trees.

❖

CONTACT

The Commercial Director
Stowe School
Buckingham
MK18 5EH

Tel: (01280) 813650
House only
or (01280) 822850
Gardens

Fax: (01280) 822769

LOCATION

OS Ref. SP666 366

From London, M1 to Milton Keynes, 1^1/$_2$ hrs or Banbury 1^1/$_4$ hrs, 4m NW of Buckingham

Bus: from Buckingham 4m
Rail: Milton Keynes 15m
Air: Heathrow 50m

CONFERENCE/FUNCTION

ROOM	SIZE	MAX CAPACITY
Roxburgh Hall	–	460
Music Room	–	120
Marble Hall	–	150
State Dining Rm	–	160
Garter Room	–	180
Memorial Theatre	–	120

i Gift Shop: call for opening times. Indoor swimming pool, sports hall, tennis court, squash courts, parkland, cricket pitches and golf course.

X International conferences, private functions, weddings, and prestige exhibitions. Catering on request.

♿ Visitors may alight at entrance. Allocated parking areas. WC in garden area. 'Batricars' available.

☕ Restaurant/Tearoom for up to 100. Parties should book in advance.

🚶 Guided tours for parties of 30 at additional cost. Tour time: house and garden 2^1/$_2$ hrs. House 45 mins.

P Ample.

💒 Civil Wedding Licence

OPENING TIMES

SUMMER

House
22 March - 12 April &
6 July - 6 September
Daily: 2 - 5pm.
Sun: 12 - 5pm.

Gardens
20 March - 12 April &
6 July - 6 September
Daily: 10am - 5pm.

13 April - 5 July &
7 Sept - 1 Nov
Mon, Wed, Fri & Sun.
Daily: 10am - 5pm.

WINTER

House
Closed.
(Suns by appointment only).

Gardens
27 Dec - 4 Jan '99
Daily: 10am - 5pm/dusk.

NB: It may be necessary to close the house at times when it is being used for private functions. Please telephone first to check.

ADMISSION

SUMMER

House only

Adult	£2.00
Child	£1.00
OAP	£2.00
Student	£2.00

10% discount for groups of 30+ visiting the house.

Gardens only

Adult	£4.40
Child	£2.20
OAP	£4.20
Family	£11.00

SPECIAL EVENTS

• **Nov 1ST - 2ND:**
Craft Fair

South East England

National Trust Photographic Library.

CONTACT

Waddesdon
Nr Aylesbury
Buckinghamshire
HP18 0JH

Tel: (01296) 651211

Fax: (01296) 651293

LOCATION

OS Ref: SP740 169

Between Aylesbury &
Bicester, off A41.

NPI Award 1997:
NPI Winner

WADDESDON MANOR
Nr Aylesbury

Waddesdon Manor was built between 1874 and 1889. Its creator, Baron Ferdinand de Rothschild, intended it as a great house in which to entertain his influential guests and display his works of art. Today, this French Renaissance-style château houses one of the finest collection of French 18th century decorative arts in the world, much with Royal provenance. Rooms are lined with panelling rescued from distinguished Parisian houses in the mid 19th century and furnished with Savonnerie and Aubusson carpets, tapestries, textiles and French Royal furniture. The breadth of the collection ranges from gold boxes, majolica and rare books to English portraits by Gainsborough, Reynolds and Romney. The collection of Sèvres porcelain is amongst the finest in the world. The garden includes a fine example of a Victorian parterre, a Rococo-style aviary, shrubberies and woodland. Thousands of bottles of vintage Rothschild wines are found in the wine cellars. There are gift and wine shops and a licensed restaurant serving homemade food. Many events are organised throughout the year including floodlit openings, garden workshops, wine tastings and collection study days.

National Trust Photographic Library.

ℹ️ Shop, plant centre, conference facilities, corporate hospitality. No inside photography.

❌ Catering functions.

♿ Suitable. WCs.

☕ Tearoom, licensed restaurant.

🚶 By arrangement.

🅿️ Ample for coaches and cars.

🐕 Guide dogs only.

💒 Civil Wedding Licence.

OPENING TIMES

Grounds (including garden, aviary, restaurant and shops)
1 Mar - 20 Dec
Wed - Sun & BH Mon
10am - 5pm

House (including wine cellars)
2 Apr - 1 Nov
Thur - Sun, also BH Mon & Wed in Jul & Aug
11am - 4pm
Recommended last admission 3pm.
Bachelors' Wing open Thur.

ADMISSION

House & Grounds
Adult £9.00
Child £7.50

Grounds only
Adult £3.00
Child £1.50

Bachelors' Wing.........£1.00

National Trust members free

Timed tickets to the house can be purchased on site or reserved in advance by phoning 01296 651226 Mon - Fri, 10am - 4pm. Advance booking fee: £2.50 per transaction.

SPECIAL EVENTS

Wine Tasting, Study Days, Garden Workshops and tours, Family Events, Floodlit Evenings: Please telephone for details.

South East England

ASCOTT

Tel: 01296 688242   **Fax:** 01296 681904

Wing, Leighton Buzzard, Buckinghamshire LU7 0PS

Owner: The National Trust   **Contact:** The Administrator

Originally a Jacobean farmhouse. The garden contains unusual trees, flower borders, naturalised bulbs, water-lilies and a topiary sundial.

Location: OS Ref. SP891 230. $^{1}/_{2}$ m E of Wing, 2m SW of Leighton Buzzard, on A418.

Opening Times: House & Garden: 1 Apr - 7 May & 1 - 30 Sept: daily except Mon, 2 - 6pm. Garden only: 13 May - 30 Aug: Every Wed & last Sun in each month, 2 - 6pm.

Admission: House & Garden: £5.40. Garden: £4. Groups must book (no reduction).

  Grounds, limited access. 3 wheelchairs available. WCs.   Dogs in car park only.

BOARSTALL TOWER

Boarstall, Aylesbury, Buckinghamshire HP18 9OX

Owner: The National Trust   **Contact:** The Administrator

The stone gatehouse of a fortified house long since demolished. It dates from the 14th century, and was altered in the 16th and 17th centuries, but retains its crossloops for bows. The tower is almost entirely surrounded by a moat.

Location: OS Ref. SP624 141. Midway between Bicester and Thame, 2m W of Brill.

Opening Times: Closed in 1998.

  Ground floor & garden.   Dogs in car park only.

BUCKINGHAM CHANTRY CHAPEL

Market Hill, Buckingham, Buckinghamshire

Owner: The National Trust   **Contact:** The Administrator

Rebuilt in 1475 and retaining a fine Norman doorway. The chapel was restored by Gilbert Scott in 1875, at which time it was used as a Latin or Grammar School.

Location: OS Ref. SP693 340. In narrow lane, NW of Market Hill.

Opening Times: All year by written appointment with the Buckingham Heritage Trust, c/o Old Gaol Museum, Market Hill, Buckingham MK18 1EN. Exterior can be viewed from the lane any time.

Admission: Free.

  Suitable.

CHICHELEY HALL

Tel: 01234 391252   **Fax:** 01234 391388

Newport Pagnell, Buckinghamshire MK16 9JJ

Owner: The Hon Nicholas Beatty   **Contact:** Mrs V Child

Fine 18th century house. Naval museum, English sea paintings and furniture. Suitable for residential conferences up to 16 delegates.

Location: OS Ref. SP906 458. 2m from Milton Keynes, 5 mins from M1/J14. 10m W of Bedford.

Opening Times: Easter Sun & Mon, May BH, Sun & Mon, and all Suns and BHs in Aug: 2.30 - 5pm. Groups welcome all year by arrangement.

Admission: Adult £5, Child £1.50. Groups: Adult £4, Child £1.50.

  Conferences.   By arrangement.   Not suitable.   Tearoom.

  Compulsory.   No dogs.

CHILTERN OPEN AIR MUSEUM

Tel: 01494 871117   **Fax:** 01494 872163

Newland Park, Gorelands Lane, Chalfont St Giles, Buckinghamshire HP8 4AD

Owner: Chiltern Open Air Museum Ltd.   **Contact:** Dr. J Moir

A museum of historic buildings showing their original uses including a blacksmith's forge, stables, barns etc.

Location: OS Ref. TQ011 938. At Newland Park $1^{1}/_{2}$ m E of Chalfont St Giles, $4^{1}/_{2}$ m from Amersham. 3m from M25/J17.

Opening Times: Apr - Sept: Tue - Fri, 2 - 6pm, Sat, Sun and BHs 11am (10am in Aug) - 6pm. Oct - 1 Nov: Tue - Fri, 2 - 5pm, Sat, Sun and BHs 10am - 5pm.

Admission: Adult £4, Child (5-16yrs) £2, Child under 5 yrs free, Over 60s £3.50, Family £12. 10% discount for pre-booked groups of 15+.

  Shop.   Braille guide. WCs.   Available.

CHENIES MANOR HOUSE

CHENIES, RICKMANSWORTH, HERTS WD36 6ER

Owner: *Lt Col & Mrs MacLeod Matthews*   **Contact:** *Lt Col & Mrs MacLeod Matthews or Sue Brock*

Tel/Fax: 01494 762888

15th & 16th century Manor House with fortified tower. Original home of the Earls of Bedford, visited by Henry VIII and Elizabeth I. Home of the MacLeod Matthews family. Contains contemporary tapestries and furniture, hiding places, collection of antique dolls, medieval undercroft and well. Surrounded by beautiful gardens which have featured in many publications and on TV, a Tudor sunken garden, a white garden, herbaceous borders, a fountain court, a physic garden containing a very wide selection of medicinal and culinary herbs, a parterre and two mazes. The kitchen garden is in the Victorian style with unusual vegetables and fruit. Special exhibitions, flower drying and arrangements.

Location: OS Ref. TQ016 984. N of A404 between Amersham & Rickmansworth. M25/J18, 3m.

Opening Times: 1 Apr - 29 Oct: Wed & Thur & BH Mons, 2 - 5pm. Last entry to house 4.15pm. Groups by arrangement.

Admission: House & Garden: Adult £4.50, Child £2. Garden only: Adult £2.30, Child £1.

  Unusual plants for sale.   Corp. days, receptions.   Grounds suitable.   Tearoom.   No dogs.   Free.

CLAYDON HOUSE

Andreas Von Einsiedel.

MIDDLE CLAYDON, NR. BUCKINGHAM MK18 2EY

Owner: *The National Trust*   **Contact:** *The Custodian*

Tel: 01296 730349 or 01296 730693   **Fax:** 01296 738511

A fine 18th century house with some of the most perfect rococo decoration in England. A series of great rooms have wood carvings in Chinese and Gothic styles, and tall windows look out over parkland and a lake. The house has relics of the exploits of the Verney family in the English Civil War and also on show is the bedroom of Florence Nightingale, a relative of the Verneys and a regular visitor to this tranquil place.

Location: OS Ref. SP720 253. In Middle Claydon, 13m NW of Aylesbury, signposted from A413, A421 and A41. $3^{1}/_{2}$ m SW of Winslow.

Opening Times: 4 Apr - 1 Nov: Sat - Wed & BH Mons, 1-5pm (closed Good Fri). Last admission 4.30pm.

Admission: Adult £4, Child £2, Family £10. Groups must book; Sat & Mon - Wed £3.50pp.

  Ground floor & grounds. Braille guide. WC.   Tearoom.   In park, on leads.

South East England

CLIVEDEN

Vera Collingwood

TAPLOW, MAIDENHEAD SL6 0JA

Owner: *The National Trust*   **Contact:** *The Property Manager*

Tel: 01628 605069   **Fax:** 01628 669461

Set around a magnificent mansion of 1851, the third on the site, Cliveden gardens and woodland cover 152 hectares. Beside the magnificent parterre, cliffs fall steeply down to the River Thames, with spectacular views over the valley. There are colourful borders, a tranquil water garden, a 'secret' rose garden and the Long Garden, with its clipped hedges and statuary. A special woodland car park to the south opens in March, with access to miles of woodland walks, the 17th century 'green rides' and the towpath.

Location: OS Ref. SU915 851. 2m N of Taplow, M4/J7 onto A4 or M40/J4 onto A404 to Marlow.

Opening Times: House: Apr - Oct, Thur & Sun, 3 - 6pm (last admission 5.30pm). Entry by timed ticket from info kiosk. Estate: 28 Mar - 1 Nov, daily, 11am - 6pm. Nov & Dec, daily, 11am - 4pm. Woodlands only: 1 Mar - 1 Nov.

Admission: Grounds: Adult £4.80, Family £12. House: £1 extra. Groups must book (no groups on Sun or BH Mon). Woodland car park £2. Family ticket £5.

   Limited suitability. WC.   Licensed restaurant.

COWPER & NEWTON MUSEUM   **Tel:** 01234 711516

Home of Olney's Heritage, Orchard Side, Market Place, Olney MK46 4AJ

Owner: Board of Trustees   **Contact:** Mrs P Osborn

Once the home of 18th century poet and letter writer William Cowper and now containing furniture, paintings and belongings of both Cowper and his ex-slave trader friend, Rev John Newton (author of "Amazing Grace"). Attractions include re-creations of a Victorian country kitchen and wash-house, two peaceful gardens and Cowper's restored summerhouse. Costume gallery, important collections of dinosaur bones and bobbin lace, and local history displays.

Location: OS Ref. SP890 512. On A509, 6m N of Newport Pagnell, M1/J14.

Opening Times: 1 Mar - 23 Dec: Tue - Sat & BH Mons, 10am - 1pm & 2 - 5pm. Closed on Good Fri.

Admission: Adult £2, Conc. £1.50, Child & Students (with card) £1, Family £5.

   Shop. No photography.   Gardens suitable.   By arrangement.   Guide dogs.

DODDERSHALL PARK   **Tel:** 01296 655238

Quainton, Aylesbury, Buckinghamshire HP22 4DF

Owner: C.J Prideaux Esq   **Contact:** The Owner

A partially moated two storey Tudor building with a William and Mary wing and later additions surrounding three sides of a courtyard. There is a half-timbered Jacobean Hall and the William and Mary Drawing Room is panelled in pine imported from Lithuania. The house has been lived in by the same family for 500 years.

Location: OS Ref. SP720 202. Quainton.

Opening Times: All visits are by appointment only. Large groups are welcome to visit the house from 1 May to 1 Oct.

Admission: Please telephone for prices.

   Ground floor & grounds suitable.   By arrangement.   No dogs.

DORNEYWOOD GARDEN

Dorneywood, Burnham, Buckinghamshire SL1 8PY

Owner: The National Trust   **Contact:** The Administrator

The house was given to the National Trust as an official residence for either a Secretary of State or Minister of the Crown. Garden only open.

Location: OS Ref. SU938 848. SW of Burnham Beeches. 2m E of Cliveden.

Opening Times: Wed, 10 Jun & 1 Jul & Sat 1 and Sun 2 Aug, 2 - 5pm. By written appointment only to Dorneywood Trust at above address.

Admission: £2.70. No reduction for groups.

   Access to part of garden only.

FORD END WATERMILL   **Tel:** 01582 600391

Station Road, Ivinghoe, Buckinghamshire   **Contact:** David Lindsey

The Watermill, a listed building, was recorded in 1767 but is probably much older. Restored by members of Pitstone Local History Society, it retains all the atmosphere of a small farm mill of the late 1800s. It is the only working watermill surviving in Buckinghamshire with its original machinery.

Location: OS Ref. SP941 166. 600 metres from Ivinghoe Church along B488 (Station Road) to Leighton Buzzard.

Opening Times: 3 May - 27 Sept: Sun & BHs, 2.30 - 5.30pm. To pre-book school parties, contact 01296 668083.

Admission: Adult £1, Child 30p. School parties: 50p each adult and child.

   Shop.   Restricted.   By arrangement.   Ample for cars.

   Guided school parties by arrangement.   In grounds, on leads.

SPECIAL EVENTS

MAY & AUG BHs /2ND SUN IN MAY, JUN, JUL & SEPT: Milling demonstrations

---

HUGHENDEN MANOR

Philip Dunn

HIGH WYCOMBE HP14 4LA

Owner: *The National Trust*   **Contact:** *The Property Manager*

Tel: 01494 532580

Home of Prime Minister Benjamin Disraeli from 1847 - 1881, Hughenden has a red brick, 'gothic' exterior. The interior is a comfortable Victorian home and still holds many of Disraeli's pictures, books and furniture, as well as other fascinating mementoes of the life of the great statesman and writer. The surrounding park and woodland have lovely walks, and the formal garden has been recreated in the spirit of Mary Anne Disraeli's colourful designs.

Location: OS165 Ref. SU866 955. 1¹⁄₂ m N of High Wycombe on the W side of the A4128.

Opening Times: House: 1 - 30 Mar, Sat & Sun. 1 Apr - end Oct: Wed - Sun & BH Mons, 1 - 5pm (last admission 4.30pm). Closed Good Fri. Gardens open same days as house, 12 - 5pm. Park & Woodland: All year.

Admission: House & Garden: £4, Family £10. Garden only: £1. Park & woodland free. Groups must book, no groups on Sat, Sun or BH Mon.

   Shop. Exhibition area.   Limited. WC.   Tearoom.

   In grounds, on leads. Guide dogs in house and formal gardens.

MENTMORE TOWERS

MENTMORE, NR LEIGHTON BUZZARD, BEDFORDSHIRE LU7 0QH

Owner: *Maharishi University of Natural Law*   **Contact:** *Rodney Love*

Tel / Fax: 01296 662183

Mentmore Towers is an example of the Victorian 'Jacobethan' revival at its best. Built in 1855 for Baron Meyer Amschel de Rothschild, this grand romantic house is a reminder of the enormous wealth and power of the Rothschilds in the 19th Century. The architect was Sir Joseph Paxton, designer of the Crystal Palace. The main rooms of the House are grouped around the vast Entrance Hall dominated by the magnificent white marble Grand Staircase. The striking black and white marble fireplace in the Hall is reputed to have been designed by Rubens for his home in Antwerp. The House is now the administrative Headquarters of Maharishi University of Natural Law.

Location: OS Ref. SP902 197. M1, M25 then A41 to Tring, follow signs to Pitstone, Cheddington and Mentmore.

Opening Times: Tue - Sat: Groups by appointment. Sun: Tour of house 2.30pm only. Nov - Mar: Closed.

Admission: Adult £3, Child (under 14) £1.50, OAP / Student £2. Groups: Adult £2.50, Child (under 14) £1, OAP £2.50.

[i] Corporate hospitality.   [&] Suitable.   [k] Available.   [dog] Guide dogs.

JOHN MILTON'S COTTAGE   **Tel:** 01494 872313

21 Deanway, Chalfont St. Giles, Buckinghamshire HP8 4JH

Owner: Milton Cottage Trust   **Contact:** Mr E A Dawson

The XVIth century cottage where John Milton lived and completed 'Paradise Lost', and started 'Paradise Regained', contains many relics and exhibits of interest. Three museum rooms and attractive cottage garden open to the public. Free car park.

Location: OS Ref. SU987 933. ½ m W of A413. 3m N of M40/J2. S side of street.

Opening Times: 1 Mar - 31 Oct: Tue - Sun, 10am - 1pm & 2 - 6pm. Closed Mon (open BH Mons). Coach parking by prior arrangement only.

Admission: Adult £2 entry, under 15s 60p, Groups of 20+ £1.50.

[i] Shop.   [&] Ground floor suitable.   [k] Talk followed by free tour.   [dog] No dogs.

NETHER WINCHENDON HOUSE [icon]   **Tel:** 01844 290199

Aylesbury, Buckinghamshire HP18 0DY

Owner: Robert Spencer Bernard Esq   **Contact:** Mr R Spencer Bernard

Medieval and Tudor manor house. There is a fine 16th century frieze, ceiling and original linenfold panelling. Altered in late 18th Century in the Strawberry Hill Gothick style. Fine furniture and family portraits. Continuous family occupation since mid-16th century. Home of the last British Governor of Massachussetts Bay, 1760. Interesting garden and specimen trees.

Location: OS Ref. SP734 121. 2m N of A418 equidistant between Thame & Aylesbury.

Opening Times: 1 - 28 May & 30/31 Aug: 2.30 - 5.30pm (last party at about 4.45pm).

Admission: Adult £3 (HHA members free), Child £1.50, OAP £1.50 (not weekends or BHs). Groups by prior arrangement.

[&] Suitable.   [cup] By arrangement.

PITSTONE WINDMILL [icon]

Ivinghoe, Buckinghamshire

Owner: The National Trust   **Contact:** The Administrator

One of the oldest post mills in Britain; in view from Ivinghoe Beacon.

Location: OS Ref. SP946 158. ½m S of Ivinghoe, 3m NE of Tring. Just W of B488.

Opening Times: June - end Aug: Sun & BHs in May. 2.30 - 6pm. Last adm. 5.30pm.

Admission: Adult £1, Child 30p.

[&] Limited access.   [dog] No dogs.

PRINCES RISBOROUGH MANOR HOUSE [icon]

Princes Risborough, Aylesbury, Buckinghamshire HP17 9AW

Owner: The National Trust   **Contact:** The Administrator

A 17th century red-brick house with Jacobean oak staircase.

Location: OS Ref. SP806 035. Opposite church, off market square.

Opening Times: House and front garden by written arrangement only with tenant. Wed 2.30 - 4.30pm. Last admission 4pm. Hall, drawing room and staircase shown.

Admission: £1.10. No reduction for groups.

[P] No parking.   [dog] Grounds only by arrangement with tenant.

STOWE LANDSCAPE GARDENS [icon]

Rupert Truman

NR. BUCKINGHAM MK18 5EH

Owner: *The National Trust*   **Contact:** *The Property Manager*

Tel: 01280 822850   **Fax:** 01280 822437

One of the first and finest landscape gardens in Europe, a supreme creation of the Georgian era. Its green valleys and vistas are set with lakes, monuments and temples, created and developed throughout the 18th century by some of our greatest designers and architects including Vanbrugh, Kent, Gibbs and 'Capability' Brown, who began his career here. Finest of all the garden buildings is the great Temple of Concord and Victory which celebrates Britain's success in the Seven Years War and was recently reopened after an ambitious two year restoration by the National Trust.

Location: OS Ref. SP665 366. Off A422 Buckingham - Banbury Rd. 3m NW of Buckingham.

Opening Times: Gardens - 20 Mar - 12 Apr: daily. 13 Apr - 5 Jul: Mon, Wed, Fri, Sun. 6 Jul - 6 Sept: daily. 7 Sept - 1 Nov: Mon, Wed, Fri, Sun. 27 Dec - 5 Jan: daily, 10am - 5pm or dusk if earlier. Last admission 1 hr before closing.

Admission: Gardens: £4.40. Family £11. Groups by arrangement.

[&] Self-drive powered chairs. WC.   [cup] Tearoom.   [dog] In grounds, on leads.

STOWE SCHOOL

See page 10 for full page entry.

WADDESDON MANOR

See page 11 for full page entry.

WEST WYCOMBE PARK

Tel: 01628 488675

West Wycombe, High Wycombe, Buckinghamshire HP14 3AJ

Owner: The National Trust   **Contact:** The Administrator

A Palladian house with frescos and painted ceilings fashioned for Sir Francis Dashwood in the mid 18th century. The landscape garden and lake were laid out at the same time as the house with various classical temples including some by Nicholas Revett.

Location: OS Ref. SU828 947. At W end of West Wycombe S of the A40.

Opening Times: Grounds only: 1 Apr - end May: Sun & Wed, 2 - 6pm. Easter May & Spring BH: Sun & Mon, 2 - 6pm. House & Grounds: Jun, Jul & Aug: Sun - Thur, 2 - 6pm. Last admission 5.15pm. Weekday entry by timed ticket.

Admission: The West Wycombe Caves and adjacent café are privately owned and NT members are liable to admission fees. House & Grounds: £4.40, Family £11. Grounds only £2.60. Groups must book.

House suitable, grounds partly suitable.   Dogs on leads in car park only.

WINSLOW HALL

Tel: 01296 712323

Winslow, Buckinghamshire, MK18 3HL

Owner: Sir Edward Tomkins   **Contact:** Sir Edward Tomkins

William and Mary house generally attributed to Wren. Virtually unchanged structurally and mostly original interiors. Good period furniture, pictures and Chinese objets d'art. Attractive garden with unusual trees and shrubs.

Location: OS Ref. SP772 275. In the town of Winslow on N side of the A413.

Opening Times: BH weekends - Sat/Sun/Mon (except Christmas), Wed & Thur in Jul & Aug. 2.30 - 5.30pm. Any other time by appointment.

Admission: £5. Children under 12 free.

Chiltern Hundreds:

A principle of English parliamentary law, dating from the days when local gentry were compelled to sit in Parliament, held that a member of the House of Commons, once duly elected, could not resign; however, a statute of 1707 enacted that any member accepting an office of profit under the Crown must vacate his seat. The stewardship of the Chiltern Hundreds, a tract of Crown lands in the Chiltern Hills in Buckinghamshire, is the last surviving of an original eight such nominal offices of profit noted in the Place Act of 1742, and a Member of Parliament wishing to vacate his seat is spoken of as applying for the Chiltern Hundreds. The grant is at the discretion of the Chancellor of the Exchequer.

Extract from; "Life in the Country House" by David N Durant (published by John Murray), PB£15.99, see page twelve at the front of the book.

Jeremy Cockayne.

Waddesdon Manor, Buckinghamshire.

BEAULIEU
Beaulieu

BEAULIEU is set in the heart of the New Forest. Formerly the Great Gatehouse of Beaulieu Abbey, Palace House has been Lord Montagu's family home since 1538. Within its stately interiors you can see its monastic origins in features such as the fan vaulted ceilings as well as glimpsing many rare and fascinating family treasures. Walks amongst the gardens and by the Beaulieu River can also be enjoyed.

Beaulieu Abbey was founded in 1204 and although most of the buildings were destroyed during the Dissolution, much of the beauty and interest remains. The former Monks' Refectory is now the Parish Church of Beaulieu. The Domus, which houses an exhibition that takes the visitor back to the ages of King John and medieval monastic life, is home to beautiful wall hangings.

The fragrant surroundings of a Herb Garden in the Cloisters are close at hand.

Beaulieu is also home to the National Motor Museum. The Museum traces the story of motoring from 1894 to the present day, with many special displays and 250 cars, motorcycle and commercial vehicles. Legendary World Record breakers such as Bluebird and Golden Arrow can be seen amongst the Veteran, Vintage and Classic cars from the 30s, 40s and 50s.

In addition, there is 'Wheels' a spectacular ride through display which is a tribute to man's motoring achievements. A monorail transports visitors through the complex where rides on a replica 1912 open-topped London Bus or in miniature veteran cars can be enjoyed.

CONTACT

Special Visits Department
John Montagu Building
Beaulieu
Brockenhurst
Hampshire
SO42 7ZN

Tel: (01590) 612345

Fax: (01590) 612624

www.beaulieu.co.uk

LOCATION

OS Ref. SU387 025

From London, M3, M27 W to J2, A326, B3054 follow brown signs.

Bus: Bus stops within complex.

Rail: Stations at Brockenhurst and Beaulieu Rd both 7m away.

CONFERENCE/FUNCTION		
ROOM	SIZE	MAX CAPACITY
Brabazon (x3)	40'x40'	120 (x3)
Domus	69'x27'	170
Classic Car Theatre		200

OPENING TIMES

SUMMER
Easter - October
daily, 10am - 6pm.

WINTER
October - Easter
daily, 10am - 5pm.

ADMISSION

ALL YEAR

Individual rates upon application.

Groups (min 15)
Adult £7.50
Child (4-12).............£5.15
OAP.........................£6.25
Student (13-17) £5.50

Catering & Functions

New conference and function brochure is available for those requesting it.

The Brabazon and Domus (pictured left) banqueting halls can be hired all year round. For a fee Lord Montagu may meet groups and participate in functions.

Groups can be booked in advance for buffets, lunches, dinners and Royal Feasts. Please contact the Conference Co-ordinator for further details.

Tel: (01590) 612888.

BEAULIEU continued...

ℹ️ Information Centre, Palace House Shop and Kitchen Shop. Plus Herb Shop and Abbey Shop open Summer only. Rallies, product launches, promotions, filming, outdoor events, exhibitions. Helicopter landing point, audio-visual, lectures, hardstanding exhibition arena. Veteran and vintage cars and buses available to transport guests. Most requests considered. Allow 2 hrs or more for visits. Last adm. 40 mins before closing. Hostesses are on hand to welcome and assist you.

✕ Private dining room of Palace House available for receptions, dinners, lunches, banquets, wedding receptions etc. Domus available for banquets.

♿ Visitors may be left at entrance before parking. WC. Wheelchairs at Information Centre.

☕ The Brabazon seats 300 in a self-service Restaurant and Bar. Prices from £4 for tea and £7 for lunch. Groups can book in advance. Further details and menus from Catering Manager (01590) 612102.

🚶 Attendants on duty. Guided tours by prior arrangement.

🅿️ 1,500 cars and 30 coaches. During the season the busy period is from 11.30am to 1.30pm. Coach drivers should sign in at Information Desk. Free admission for coach drivers plus voucher which can be exchanged for food, drink and souvenirs.

👨‍👩‍👧 Professional staff available to assist in planning of visits. Services include introductory talks, films, guided tours, role play and extended projects. In general, educational services incur no additional charges and publications are sold at cost. Starter sets available free of charge to pre-booked parties. Information pack available from Education at Beaulieu, John Montagu Building, Beaulieu, Hants SO42 7ZN.

🐕 No dogs in the buildings.

SPECIAL EVENTS

- **APR 5:**
  Boat Jumble
- **MAY 9/10:**
  Spring Autojumble & Automart
- **JUN 13/14:**
  Beaulieu Classic Boat Festival

- **JUN 27/28:**
  Motorcycle World
- **JUL 11:**
  Palace House Prom
- **JUL 26:**
  Bucklers Hard Village Festival

- **SEPT 5/6:**
  Autojumble & Automart
- **OCT 31:**
  Fireworks Fair
- **DEC:**
  Festival Season of Fun Programme

The National Motor Museum

When Lord Montagu inherited Beaulieu, he displayed a handful of early vehicles in the Front Hall as a memorial to his father, one of the leading pioneers of motoring in Britain. From this beginning the now famous National Motor Museum grew.

The Museum traces the story of motoring from 1894 to the present day, with many special displays and 250 cars, commercial vehicles and motorcycles. It is especially proud to have four World Land Speed Record Breaking Cars (above).

'Wheels - The Legend of the Motor Car', is a major feature in the Museum. This spectacular ride-through display is a tribute to man's motoring achievements. 'Wheels' transports visitors in space-age 'pods' through 100 years of motoring, from the early pioneers and their problems, to fantasies of the future, and shows how the motor vehicle has revolutionised our lives.

A monorail transports visitors to the Motor Museum, entering the building at roof level. There are rides on a 1912 open-topped London Bus or in Miniature Veteran Cars; Remote Controlled Model Cars.

Entry to the museum is included in the inclusive admission price.

South East England

HIGHCLERE CASTLE & GARDENS
Newbury

Designed by Charles Barry in the 1830s at the same time as he was building the Houses of Parliament, this soaring pinnacled mansion provided a perfect setting for the 3rd Earl of Carnarvon one of the great hosts of Queen Victoria's reign. The extravagant interiors range from church Gothic through Moorish flamboyance and rococo revival to the solid masculinity in the long Library. Old master paintings mix with portraits by Van Dyck and 18th century painters. Napoleon's desk and chair rescued from St. Helena sits with other 18th and 19th century furniture.

The 5th Earl of Carnarvon, discovered the Tomb of Tutankhamun with Howard Carter. The castle houses a unique exhibition of some of his discoveries which were only rediscovered in the castle in 1988. The current Earl is the Queen's Horseracing Manager. In 1993 to celebrate his 50th year as a leading owner and breeder 'The Lord Carnarvon Racing Exhibition' was opened to the public, and offers a fascinating insight into a racing history that dates back three generations.

GARDENS

The magnificent parkland with its massive cedars was designed by 'Capability' Brown. The walled gardens also date from an earlier house at Highclere but the dark yew walks are entirely Victorian in character. The glass Orangery and Fernery add an exotic flavour. The Secret Garden has a romance of its own with a beautiful curving lawn surrounded by densely planted herbaceous gardens. A place for poets and romantics.

CONTACT

Adrian Wiley
Highclere Castle
Newbury
Berkshire
RG20 9RN

Tel: (01635) 253210

Fax: (01635) 255066

LOCATION

OS Ref. SU445 587

Approx 7m out of Newbury on A34 towards Winchester. From London: M4/J13, A34, Newbury-Winchester 20 mins. M3/J5 approx 15m.

Air: Heathrow M4 45 mins.

Rail: Paddington - Newbury 45 mins.

Taxi: 4$^{1}/_{2}$ m (01635) 40829

CONFERENCE/FUNCTION

ROOM	SIZE	MAX CAPACITY
Library	43' x 21'	120
Saloon	42' x 29'	150
Dining Rm	37' x 18'	70
Library, Saloon, Drawing Rm, Music Rm, Smoking Rm		400

i Shop. Conferences, exhibitions, filming, fairs, and concerts (cap. 8000). No photography in the house.

Receptions, dinners, corporate hospitality.

Visitors may alight at the entrance. WC.

Tearooms. Lunches for 20+ can be booked.

P Ample.

By prior arrangement. The Egyptian Collection, nature walks, beautiful old follies, Secret Garden.

In grounds, on leads.

Civil Wedding Licence.

OPENING TIMES

SUMMER

5 July - 6 September
Tue - Sun.

Castle
11am - 5pm.
Last admission 4pm,
Sat 2pm.

Castle closed over Easter and on Mon except BHs during May & August.

Grounds, Gardens & Tearooms
11am - 6pm.

WINTER

October - July
By appointment only.

ADMISSION

Adult	£6.00
Child	£3.00
Student	£4.75

Gardens only

Adult	£3.00
Child	£1.50

VIP Season Ticket

(2+3)* £25.00
Groups (min. 20)
Adult/OAP £4.75
Child £3.00

*runs from date of joining, 10% off shop, tea rooms, Watermill Theatre (Newbury) and Stubbs Restaurant at Newbury Hilton. Free admission to special events, concert discounts.

SPECIAL EVENTS

- **APR 17 /18 /19:**
Country Lifestyle Fair
- **MAY 24 / 25:**
Southern Counties Country Show
- **JUN 6:**
Shirley Bassey Concert
- **JULY 17 / 18 / 19:**
Porsche Club Annual Rally
- **AUG 29 / 30 / 31:**
Craft Fair
- **DEC 4 / 5 / 6:**
Christmas Fair

South East England

SOMERLEY
Ringwood

To visit Somerley, even briefly, is to taste the elegant lifestyle. The architectural grandeur, the elegance of its interiors and its magnificent setting on the edge of the New Forest combine to make it one of Britain's finest houses. The house was designed by Samuel Wyatt in the mid 1700s and has been the residence of the Normanton family for almost 200 years. The sixth Earl and Countess live here today with their three children.

The house is not open to the public; the magnificently proportioned rooms with high gilded ceilings house a treasure trove of fine antique furniture, porcelain, paintings and objets d'art, and can be enjoyed by guests who visit to conduct business meetings, conferences, concerts, receptions, product launches and top level corporate hospitality.

The house is $1^1/_2$ miles from the nearest road and although easily accessible, provides privacy for meetings demanding security and complete confidentiality. The 7,000 acres of parkland can be used for incentive fun days, promotions and golf events. The high standard of service and cuisine (much of the food comes from the Estate and gardens), and the warm, friendly atmosphere are very rarely found in a house of this size. The peace and tranquillity of the grounds are a sheer delight.

❖

CONTACT

Richard Horridge
Somerley
Ringwood
Hampshire
BH24 3PL

Tel: (01425) 480819

Fax: (01425) 478613

LOCATION

OS Ref. SU134 080

Off the A31 to Bournemouth 2m. London $1^3/_4$ hrs via M3, M27, A31. 2m NW of Ringwood.

Air: Bournemouth International Airport 5m.

Rail: Bournemouth Station 12m.

Taxi: A car can be arranged from the House if applicable.

CONFERENCE/FUNCTION

ROOM	SIZE	MAX-CAPACITY
Picture Gall.	80' x 30'	150
Drawing Rm	38' x 30'	50
Dining Rm	39' x 19'	50
East Library	26' x 21'	30

OPENING TIMES

Privately booked functions only.

ADMISSION

Upon application for privately booked functions only.

i No individual visits, application only. Ideal for shooting, filming, archery. Events, fashion shows, air displays, equestrian events, shows and rallies. Croquet, tennis, golf driving range and 9-hole golf course, 4 x 4 safari driving course, outdoor pool, salmon fishing.

X Dining Room available for private parties. Parties must book, menus are available on request. Meals from £23 per head. Outside caterers may be used in Grounds if requested. Garden parties and wedding receptions.

& Visitors may alight at the Front Entrance.

P 200 cars and 20+ coaches. Liaise with Richard Horridge or the Earl of Normanton: 01425 480819.

A 4 twin and 4 double with bathrooms and 1 single without bathroom. All rooms to be taken by house party. Smaller numbers negotiable.

AVINGTON PARK 🏛

WINCHESTER, HAMPSHIRE SO21 1DD
Owner: Mrs A M Hickson   Contact: Mrs S L Bullen

Tel: 01962 779260 **Fax:** 01962 779864

Avington Park, where Charles II and George IV both stayed at various times, dates back to the 11th century. The house was enlarged in 1670 by the addition of two wings and a classical Portico surmounted by three statues. The State rooms are magnificently painted and lead onto the unique pair of conservatories flanking the South Lawn. The Georgian church, St. Mary's, is in the grounds.

Location: OS Ref. SU534 324. 4m NE of Winchester ¹/₂ m S of the B3047 in Itchen Abbas.

Opening Times: May - Sept: Sun & BHs, 2.30 - 5.30pm. Last tour 5pm. Other times by arrangement, coach parties welcome by appointment.

Admission: Adult £3, Child £1.50.

ℹ️ Conferences.   ✖ Available.   ♿ Partially suitable, WC.
☕ Tearoom.   🚶 Compulsory.   🐕 In grounds, on leads. (Guide dogs in house)

SPECIAL EVENTS
FEB 21 - 23 & JUN 20 - 22: Antiques Fair   JUN 26 - 28: Marie Curie Flower Festival
JUL 31 - AUG 1: Birmingham Symphony Orchestra open air concert
SEPT: 18 - 20: Home Design & Interiors Exhibition

BASING HOUSE
Tel: 01256 467294

Redbridge Lane, Basing, Basingstoke RG24 7HB

Owner: Hampshire County Council   **Contact:** Alan Turton

Ruins, covering 10 acres, of huge Tudor palace. Recent recreation of Tudor formal garden.

Location: OS Ref. SU665 526. 2m E from Basingstoke town centre. Signposted car parks are about 5 or 10 mins walk from entrance.

Opening Times: 1 Apr - 30 Sept: Wed - Sun & BHs, 2 - 6pm.

Admission: Adult £1.50, Child 70p.

ℹ️ Shop.   ♿ Ground floor & grounds suitable. WC.   🐕 Grounds only, on leads.

BEAULIEU
See pages 16/17 for full page entry.

BISHOP'S WALTHAM PALACE ⛬
Tel: 01489 892460

Bishop's Waltham, Hampshire SO32 1DH

Owner: English Heritage   **Contact:** The Custodian

This medieval seat of the Bishops of Winchester once stood in an enormous park. There are still wooded grounds and the remains of the Great Hall and the three storey tower can still be seen. Dower House furnished as a 19th century farmhouse.

Location: OS Ref. SU552 173. In Bishop's Waltham, 5m NE from M27/J8.

Opening Times: 1 Apr - 1 Nov: daily 10am - 6pm or dusk if earlier.

Admission: Adult £2, Child £1, Conc. £1.50.

ℹ️ Shop & exhibition.   ♿ Grounds suitable.   🐕 Grounds only, on leads.

BOHUNT MANOR GARDENS
Tel: 01428 722208 **Fax:** 01428 722080

Liphook, Hampshire GU30 7DL

Owner: Worldwide Fund for Nature   **Contact:** Lady Holman

Woodland gardens with lakeside walk, collection of ornamental waterfowl, herbaceous borders and unusual trees and shrubs.

Location: OS Ref. SU839 310. W side of B2070 at S end of village.

Opening Times: All year: daily, 10am - 6pm.

Admission: Adult £1.50, Child under 14 free, Conc. £1. Group: 10% off.

♿ Grounds suitable. WC.   🐕 Guide dogs only.

BRAMDEAN HOUSE
Tel: 01962 771 214 **Fax:** 01962 771095

Bramdean, Alresford, Hampshire SO24 0JU

Owner: Mr & Mrs H Wakefield   **Contact:** Mrs H Wakefield

Famous herbaceous borders and unusual plants. Working walled kitchen garden.

Location: OS Ref. SU611 281. In Bramdean village on A272 midway between Winchester and Petersfield.

Opening Times: 12 - 13 Apr, 10 May, 14 Jun, 12 Jul, 9 Aug & 13 Sept: 2 - 5pm. Also by prior appointment.

♿ Not suitable.   🐕 No dogs.

BREAMORE HOUSE & MUSEUM 🏛
Tel: 01725 512233

Breamore, Fordingbridge, Hampshire SP6 2DF

Owner: Sir Edward Hulse Bt   **Contact:** Sir Edward Hulse Bt

Elizabethan manor with fine collections of pictures and furniture. Countryside Museum takes visitors back to the time when a village was self-sufficient.

Location: OS Ref. SU152 191. W Off the A338, between Salisbury and Ringwood.

Opening Times: Apr: Easter Holiday, Tue, Wed & Sun. May, Jun, Jul & Sept: Tue, Wed, Thur, Sat & Sun & all hols. Aug: daily. House: 2 - 5.30pm. Countryside Museum: 1 - 5.30pm.

Admission: Combined ticket for house and museum: Adult £5, Child £3.50.

ℹ️ Shop.   ♿ Ground floor & grounds suitable. WC.   ☕ Tearoom.   🐕 No dogs.

BROADLANDS

ROMSEY, HAMPSHIRE SO51 9ZD
Owner: Lord & Lady Romsey   Contact: Mrs S J Tyrrell

Tel: 01794 517888

Famous as the home of the late Lord Mountbatten, and equally well known as the country residence of Lord Palmerston, the Great Victorian Prime Minister. Broadlands is an elegant Palladian mansion in a beautiful landscaped setting on the banks of the River Test. Visitors may view the House with its art treasures and mementoes of the famous, enjoy the superb views from the Riverside Lawns or relive Lord Mountbatten's life and times in the Mountbatten Exhibition and spectacular Mountbatten audio-visual presentation.

Location: OS Ref. SU355 204. On A31 at Romsey.

Opening Times: 13 Jun - 6 Sept: daily 12 - 5.30pm. Last admission 4pm.

Admission: All inclusive admission charges. Accompanied child under 12, free.

ℹ️ Shop.   ✖ Available.   ♿ Ground floor & grounds suitable.WC.
☕ Tearoom.   🚶 Compulsory.   🐕 Guide dogs only.

CALSHOT CASTLE ⛬
Tel: 01703 892023

Calshot, Fawley, Hampshire SO45 1BR

Owner: English Heritage   **Contact:** Hampshire County Council

Henry VIII built this coastal fort in an excellent position, commanding the sea passage to Southampton. The fort houses an exhibition and recreated pre-World War I barrack room.

Location: OS Ref. SU488 025. On spit 2m SE of Fawley off B3053.

Opening Times: 1 Apr - 31 Oct: daily 10am - 6pm or dusk if earlier.

Admission: Adult £1.80, Child 90p, Conc. £1.40.

ℹ️ Shop.   ♿ Keep & ground floor suitable. WC.   🐕 Guide dogs only.

South East England

ELING TIDE MILL

Tel: 01703 869575

The Toll Bridge, Eling, Totton, Hampshire SO40 9HF

Contact: Mr David Blackwell-Eaton

Owner: Eling Tide Mill Trust Ltd & New Forest District Council

Location: OS Ref. SU365 126. 4m W of Southampton. ½ m S of the A35.

Opening Times: Wed - Sun and BH Mons, 10am - 4pm.

Admission: Adult £1.50, Child 80p, Family £4.10, OAP £1.15. Discounts for groups and joint entry with Totton and Eling Heritage Centre.

ⓘ Shop.   ♿ Ground floor suitable.   ☕ Tearoom.   👥 By arrangement.

🚶 By prior arrangement for groups.   🅿 Ample.   🐕 No dogs.

EXBURY GARDENS 🏛

Tel: 01703 891203   **Fax:** 01703 243 380

Exbury, Southampton, Hampshire SO45 1AZ.

Owner: Edmund de Rothschild Esq   **Contact:** Sebastian Green

Extensive landscaped woodland gardens overlooking the Beaulieu River. World famous Rothschild plant collection (rhododendrons, azaleas etc.) as well as many rare and wonderful trees: Rock Garden, Cascades, Ponds, River Walk, Rose Garden, Water Garden, Heather Gardens, seasonal trails and themed walks. Ample seating throughout. Gardens spectacular in Spring and Autumn. Ask about Special Events.

Location: OS Ref. SU425 005. 11m SE of Totton (A35) via A326 & B3054 & minor road.

Opening Times: 1 Mar - 1 Nov: daily, 10am - 5pm or dusk if earlier.

Admission: Please telephone for details.

ⓘ Shop.   ♿ Grounds suitable. WC.   ☕ Tearoom/restaurant.   🐕 In grounds, on leads.

FORT BROCKHURST ⚜

Tel: 01705 581059

Gunner's Way, Gosport, Hampshire PO12 4DS

Owner: English Heritage   **Contact:** The Head Custodian

This 19th century fort was built to protect Portsmouth, today its parade ground moated keep and sergeants' mess are available to hire as an exciting setting for functions and events of all types. The fort is also open to visitors at weekends when tours will explain the exciting history of the site and the legend behind the ghostly activity in cell 3.

Location: OS196, Ref. SU596 020. Off A32, in Gunner's Way, Elson on N side of Gosport.

Opening Times: 1 Apr - 1 Nov: weekends only, 10am - 6pm.

Admission: Adult £2, Child £1, Conc. £1.50.

ⓘ Shop.   ♿ Ground floor & grounds suitable. WC.   🐕 In grounds, on leads.

FURZEY GARDENS

Tel: 01703 812464   **Fax:** 01703 812297

Minstead, Lyndhurst, Hampshire SO43 7GL

Owner: Furzey Gardens Charitable Trust   **Contact:** Stephen Cole

Set in the heart of the New Forest this is a peaceful and informal garden of about 8 acres offering all year round botanical interest. There is ample seating, a lake, restored 16th century cottage, large art and craft galleries with refreshments, children's play log cabins and a nursery shop.

Location: OS Ref. SU273 114. Minstead village ½m N of M27/A31 junction off A337 to Lyndhurst.

Opening Times: All year (except 25/26 Dec): 10am - 5pm.

Admission: Mar - Oct: Adult £3, Child £1.50, OAP £2.50, Student £1.50, Family £8. Nov - Feb: Adult £1.50, Child 50p, OAP £1, Student 50p, Family £4. Pre-arranged Groups (max 80): Adult £2.55, Child £1.27, OAP £2.12, Student £1.27.

ⓘ Shop. Plant centre. Art & craft gallery.   ☕ Tearoom.   🐕 Guide dogs only.

🅿 Ample.

SPECIAL EVENTS 1998

See the front section for full list.

Historic Scotland

GILBERT WHITE'S HOUSE & GARDEN

THE WAKES, HIGH STREET, SELBORNE, ALTON GU34 3JH

Owner: Oates Memorial Trust   *Contact:* Mrs Anna Jackson

Tel: 01420 511275

Charming 18th century house in heart of old Selborne, home of Rev Gilbert White, author of *The Natural History of Selborne*. Lovely garden with many plants of the 18th century. Museum devoted to Captain Oates of Antarctic fame. Tea parlour with 18th century fare.

Location: OS Ref. SU741 336. On W side of B3006, in village of Selborne 4m NW of the A3.

Opening Times: Mid-Mar - Christmas: daily, 11am - 5pm. Jan, Feb & early Mar: weekends, 11am - 5pm. Summer evenings and winter weekdays also for groups by arrangement.

Admission: Adult £3.50, Child £1, OAP £3. Group: Adult £3, Child 75p, OAP £2.50.

ⓘ Shop & plant sales.   ♿ Ground floor & grounds suitable.

☕ Tearoom.   🐕 Guide dogs only.

SPECIAL EVENTS

JUN 20 / 21: Unusual Plants Fair.   JUN 20: Picnic to 'Jazz in June' in the park.
NOV 29: Mulled wine & Christmas shopping day.

GREAT HALL

Tel: 01962 846476

Winchester Castle, Winchester, Hampshire SO23 8PJ

Owner: Hampshire County Council   **Contact:** Miss Chalke

Part of Henry III's Castle built in 1222/36. Home of King Arthur's famous round table.

Location: OS Ref. SU477 295. Central Winchester. SE of Westgate archway.

Opening Times: All year: daily 10am - 5pm (except weekends Nov - Feb, 10am - 4pm). Note: Queen Eleanor's Garden is closed until further notice due to work being carried out.

Admission: Free.

GREATHAM MILL

Tel: 01420 538245   **Fax:** 01420 538219

Greatham, Liss, Hampshire GU33 6HH

Owner: Mr and Mrs E Groves   **Contact:** Mr E Groves

Interesting garden with large variety of plants surrounding a mill house.

Location: OS Ref. SU765 304. 2m from Liss; 7m from Alton. On small lane, W of B3006, ¼ m W of A325.

Opening Times: Feb - Sept: daily. Tearoom open Sat, Sun and BHs.

Admission: Adult £2, Child free. Organised tours by appointment.

ⓘ Plant centre.   ♿ Grounds suitable. WC.   ☕ Tearoom.   🐕 Guide dogs only.

GUILDHALL GALLERY

Tel: 01962 848289   **Fax:** 01962 848299

The Broadway, Winchester, Hampshire SO23 9LJ

Owner: Winchester City Council   **Contact:** Mr C Wardman Bradbury

19th century Guild Hall. Changing contemporary exhibitions.

Location: OS Ref. SU485 293. Winchester - city centre.

Opening Times: Tue - Sat: 10am - 5pm, Sun & Mon: 2 - 5pm. Closed Mon Oct - Mar.

Admission: Free.

♿ Suitable.

SIR HAROLD HILLIER GARDENS

JERMYNS LANE, AMPFIELD, NR ROMSEY SO51 0QA

Owner: Hampshire County Council   *Contact: Mrs Wendy Pidduck*

Tel: 01794 368787 **Fax:** 01794 368027

These beautiful 184 acre gardens are home to one of the best 20th century collections of plants to be found anywhere in the world. They were begun in 1953 by the famous nurseryman Sir Harold Hillier and since 1977 have been held in trust by Hampshire County Council, earning a reputation as a garden for all seasons. From the magnificent spring blossoms to the bark and witch hazels of mid-winter, there is always something to delight visitors.

Location: OS Ref. SU380 236. 3m NE of Romsey off A3090 (A31).

Opening times: Apr - Oct: daily, 10.30am - 6pm. Nov - Mar: daily, 10.30am - 5pm or dusk if earlier. Closed on BHs over Christmas.

Admission: Apr - Oct: Adult £4, Child £1, OAP £3.50; Nov - Mar: Adult £3, Child £1, OAP £2.50. Groups: Apr - Oct, £3; Nov - Mar, £2.

ℹ️ Plant centre.   ♿ Partially suitable. WC.   ☕ Licensed tearoom.

🚶 By arrangement.   🐕 Guide dogs only.

HIGHCLERE CASTLE & GARDENS 🏛️   See page 18 for full page entry.

Highclere Castle, Hampshire.

HINTON AMPNER GARDEN 🌺

Stephen Robson.

BRAMDEAN, NR. ALRESFORD, HAMPSHIRE SO24 0LA

Owner: The National Trust   *Contact: The Administrator*

Tel: 01962 771305 **Fax:** 01962 771305

The garden is set in superb countryside and combines formal design with informal planting, producing delightful walks with many unexpected vistas. There is colour and scent throughout the season and highlights include a dell and a sunken garden. The house, restored after a fire in 1960, has a fine collection of Regency furniture and Italian paintings. It is privately tenanted and is open by arrangement with the tenant.

Location: OS Ref. SU597 275. On A272, 1m W of Bramdean village, 8m E of Winchester.

Opening times: Garden: 15 & 22 Mar then 28 Mar - end of Sept: Tue, Wed, Sat, Sun & BH Mon. House: 31 Mar - end of Sept, Tue & Wed, plus Sat & Sun in Aug, 1.30 - 5.30pm.

Admission: House & Garden: £4. Garden only: £3. Groups £3.50 (must book).

♿ Garden suitable.   ☕ Tearooms.   🐕 No dogs.

HOUGHTON LODGE 🏛️

STOCKBRIDGE, HAMPSHIRE, SO20 6LQ

Owner: Captain M W Busk   *Contact: Captain M W Busk*

Tel: 01264 810177 or 01264 810502 **Fax:** 01794 388072

Landscaped pleasure grounds and fine trees surround this enchanting and rare 18th century 'Cottage Ornée' which overlooks the tranquil beauty of the River Test. Featured in *The Buccaneers* (BBC TV) and the film *Wilde*. In the traditional kitchen garden old espaliered fruit trees are protected by one of the few remaining complete chalk cob boundary walls. Greenhouses contain many tender plants protected by biological control of pests and there is a growing collection of fuchsias. The **Hydroponicum** is a living exhibition of horticulture without soil and demonstrates the many applications of this fascinating form of gardening from window sill to space capsule: a garden of the future in a garden of the past.

Location: OS Ref. SU344 332. 1½ m S of Stockbridge (A30) on minor road to Houghton village.

Opening times: Garden: 1 Mar - 30 Sept: Sat, Sun & BHs, 10am - 5pm also Mon, Tue, Thur & Fri, 2 - 5pm. Other times by appointment. House: Groups welcome by arrangement.

Admission: Adult £2.50, Hydroponicum £1, Accompanied child free.

ℹ️ Plant centre.   ♿ Grounds suitable. WC.   🐕 In grounds, on leads.

HURST CASTLE ⛫

Tel: 01590 642344

Keyhaven, Lymington, Hampshire PO41 0PB

Owner: English Heritage   **Contact:** (Managed by) Hurst Castle Services

This was one of the most sophisticated fortresses built by Henry VIII, and later strengthened in the 19th and 20th centuries, to command the narrow entrance to the Solent. There is an exhibition in the Castle, and two huge 38-ton guns form the fort's armaments.

Location: OS196 Ref. SZ319 898. On Pebble Spit S of Keyhaven. Best approach by ferry from Keyhaven. 4m SW of Lymington.

Opening times: 1 Apr - 31 Oct: daily, 10am - 5.30pm (July & Aug until 6pm). Café: open Apr - May weekends & Jun - Sept: daily.

Admission: Adult £2, Child £1, Conc. £1.50.

ℹ️ Shop.   ♿ Not suitable.   ☕ Café.

JANE AUSTEN'S HOUSE

CHAWTON, ALTON, HAMPSHIRE GU34 1SD

Owner: *Jane Austen Memorial Trust*   **Contact:** *The Curator*

Tel/Fax: 01420 83262

17th century house where Jane Austen wrote or revised her six great novels. Contains many items associated with her and her family, documents and letters, first editions of the novels, pictures, portraits and furniture. Pleasant garden, suitable for picnics, bakehouse with brick oven and wash tub, houses Jane's donkey carriage.

Location: OS Ref. SU708 376. Just S of A31, 1m SW of Alton, signposted Chawton.

Opening times: 1 Mar - 1 Jan: daily, 11am - 4.30pm. Jan & Feb: Sat & Sun and half term in Feb (ring for dates). Closed 25 & 26 Dec.

Admission: Adult £2.50, Conc/Groups (15+) £2, Child (8-18yrs) 50p.

ℹ️ Bookshop.   ♿ Grounds floor & grounds suitable. WC.   🐕 Guide dogs only.

MANOR HOUSE GARDEN

Tel: 01256 862827   **Fax:** 01256 861035

Upton Grey, Basingstoke, Hampshire RG25 2RD

Owner: Mrs J Wallinger   **Contact:** Mrs J Wallinger

4 acre garden designed by Gertrude Jekyll in 1908, meticulously restored to original plans.

Location: OS Ref. SU697 485. 6m SE of Basingstoke.

Opening Times: By appointment for groups May - Jul.

Admission: Standard £3.50. Groups £3pp.

🚶 By arrangement.   🅿 No parking.   🐕 No dogs.

MEDIEVAL MERCHANTS HOUSE ⛫

Tel: 01703 221503

58 French Street, Southampton, Hampshire SO1 0AT

Owner: English Heritage   **Contact:** The Custodian

The life of the prosperous merchant in the Middle Ages is vividly evoked in this recreated, faithfully restored 13th century townhouse.

Location: OS Ref. SU419 112. 58 French Street. ¼m S of Bargate off Castle Way. 150yds SE of Tudor House.

Opening Times: 1 Apr - 1 Nov: daily, 10am - 6pm (dusk if earlier in Oct).

Admission: Adult £2, Child £1, Conc. £1.50.

ℹ️ Shop.   ♿ Suitable. WC.   🚶 Free audio tour.   🅿 No parking.

🐕 Guide dogs only.

MOTTISFONT ABBEY GARDEN, HOUSE & ESTATE 🌿

National Trust Photographic Library.

MOTTISFONT, NR ROMSEY, HAMPSHIRE SO51 0LP

Owner: *The National Trust*   **Contact:** *The Property Manager*

Tel: 01794 340757   **Fax:** 01794 341492

The Abbey and Garden form the central point of an 809 ha estate including most of the village of Mottisfont, farmland and woods. A tributary of the River Test flows through the garden forming a superb and tranquil setting for a 12th century Augustinian priory which, after the Dissolution, became a house. It contains the spring or "font" from which the place name is derived. The magnificent trees, walled gardens and the Nnational Collection of Old-fashioned Roses combine to provide interest throughout the seasons. The Abbey contains a drawing room decorated by Rex Whistler and the cellarium of the old Priory. In 1996 the Trust acquired Derek Hill's 20th century picture collection.

Location: OS Ref. SU327 270. 4½m NW of Romsey, ¾m W of A3057.

Opening times: Garden & Grounds: 28 Mar - 28 Oct: Sat - Wed, 12 - 6pm (or dusk if earlier). During peak rose season (13 Jun - 28 Jun: check recorded message for state of roses) open daily 11am - 8.30pm. Last admission to grounds 1 hr before closing. House & Cellarium: same days as garden, 1 - 5pm. Derek Hill picture collection: Sun & Mon, 1 - 5pm.

Admission: Garden, Grounds & Whistler Room: £4, Family £10. During rose season £5, Family £12. No reduction for groups. Coaches must book.

ℹ️ Shop.   ☕ Available.   🐕 Guide dogs only.   💍 Civil Wedding Licence.

NETLEY ABBEY ⛫

Tel: 01705 378291

Netley, Southampton, Hampshire

Owner: English Heritage   **Contact:** The South East Regional Office

A peaceful and beautiful setting for the extensive ruins of this 13th century Cistercian abbey converted in Tudor times for use as a house.

Location: OS Ref. SU453 089. In Netley, 4m SE of Southampton, facing Southampton Water.

Opening Times: Any reasonable time.

Admission: Free.

♿ Grounds suitable.   🅿 Limited.   🐕 In grounds, on leads.

PORTCHESTER CASTLE ⛫

Tel: 01705 378291   **Fax:** 01705 378291

Portsmouth, Hampshire PO1 2HH

Owner: English Heritage   **Contact:** The Custodian

Visit the rallying point of Henry V's expedition to Agincourt and explore the ruined palace of King Richard II. This grand castle has a history going back nearly 2,000 years including the most complete Roman walls in Europe. Don't miss the interactive exhibition telling the story of the castle.

Location: OS196, Ref. SU625 046. On S side of Portchester off A27, M27/J11.

Open: 1 Apr - 1 Nov: daily, 10am - 6pm or dusk if earlier. 2 Nov - 31 Mar: daily, 10am - 4pm. Closed 24 - 26 Dec.

Admission: Adult £2.50, Child £1.30, Conc. £1.90. 15% discount for groups of 11+. One extra place free for every additional 20.

ℹ️ Shop & exhibition.   ♿ Grounds and lower levels suitable.   🐕 In grounds, on leads.

PORTSMOUTH CATHEDRAL

Tel: 01705 823300   **Fax:** 01705 295480

Portsmouth, Hampshire PO1 2HH   **Contact:** Rosemary Fairfax

Maritime Cathedral founded in 12th century and finally completed in 1991. A member of the ship's crew of Henry VIII flagship *Mary Rose* is buried in Navy Aisle.

Location: OS Ref. SZ633 994. 1½m from end of M275. Follow signs to Historic Ship and Old Portsmouth.

Opening Times: 7.45am - 6pm all year. Sun service: 8am, 9.30am, 11am, 6pm. Weekday: 7.20am, 7.45am, 6pm (Choral on Tue and Fri in term time).

Admission: Donation appreciated.

ℹ️ Shop.   ♿ House suitable. WC.   🅿 Limited.   🐕 Guide dogs only.

SANDHAM MEMORIAL CHAPEL

BURGHCLERE, NR. NEWBURY, HAMPSHIRE RG15 9JT

Owner: The National Trust   *Contact:* Sarah Hook

Tel/Fax: 01635 278394

Considered by many to be one of Stanley Spencer's greatest achievements, Sandham will intrigue anyone with an interest in 20th century art. The Chapel is a First World War memorial built in the 1920s and the paintings by Stanley Spencer of war scenes in Salonica cover the chapel walls.

Location: OS Ref. SU463 608. 4m S of Newbury, 1/2 m E of A34, W end of Burghclere.

Opening times: Apr - end Oct: Wed - Sun & BH Mon, 11.30am - 5pm (closed Wed following BH Mon). Mar - Nov: Sat & Sun, 11.30am - 4pm. Dec - Feb: by appointment.

Admission: Adult £2, Child £1. Groups by prior arrangement, no reduction.

♿ Ramped steps. W/chair users enter via side gate.   In grounds, on leads.

STRATFIELD SAYE HOUSE

STRATFIELD SAYE, BASINGSTOKE RG7 2BZ

Owner: The Duke of Wellington   *Contact:* The Comptroller

Tel: 01256 882882

Stratfield Saye House was presented to the Great Duke of Wellington by a grateful nation after the battle of Waterloo in 1815, and is still the home of the present Duke and Duchess. The house retains, with many of his personal belongings, much of the atmosphere created by the Great Duke. The Wellington Exhibition houses his magnificent 18 ton funeral carriage, and within the grounds are the American Gardens and the grave of Copenhagen, the Great Duke's favourite charger.

Location: OS Ref. SU700 615. Equidistant from Reading (M4/J11) & Basingstoke (M3/J6) 11/2 m W of the A33.

Opening times: May: Sat, Sun & BH Mon, Jun, Jul & Aug: daily except Fri. Sept: Sat & Sun and during the week by arrangement for groups. Grounds & exhibition: 11.30am - 6pm. House: 12 - 4pm. Last admission 4pm.

Admission: Adult £5, Child £2.50. Groups: Adult £4.25, Child £2.25, OAP £3.25.

ℹ Shop. Plant centre. Conference facilities, corporate hospitality.

♿ Suitable. WC.   Tearoom, licensed restaurant.   In grounds, on leads.

SOMERLEY

See page 19 for full page entry.

Portchester Castle, Hampshire.

TITCHFIELD ABBEY   **Tel:** 01329 842133

Titchfield, Southampton, Hampshire

Owner: English Heritage   **Contact:** Mr K E Groves

Remains of a 13th century abbey overshadowed by the grand Tudor gatehouse. Reputedly some of Shakespeare's plays were performed here for the first time. Under local management of Titchfield Abbey Society.

Location: OS Ref. SU544 067. 1/2 m N of Titchfield off A27.

Opening Times: 22 Mar - 31 Oct: daily, 10am - 6pm (dusk in Oct). 1 Nov - 31 Mar: daily, 10am - 4pm.

Admission: Free.

♿ Grounds suitable.   P Limited.   In grounds, on leads.

TUDOR HOUSE MUSEUM   **Tel:** 01703 635904 **Fax:** 01703 339601

Bugle Street, Southampton, Hampshire

Owner: Southampton City Council   **Contact:** Sian Jones

Late 15th century half timbered house. Unique Tudor knot garden.

Location: OS Ref. SU418 113. Follow signs to Old Town and waterfront from M27/M3. 150yds NW of Merchants House.

Opening Times: Tue - Fri, 10am - 12pm, 1 - 5pm. Sat 10am - 12pm, 1- 4pm. Sun 2 - 5pm. Closed Mon.

Admission: Free.

ℹ Shop. ♿ Ground floor & grounds suitable. WC. P No parking.   Guide dogs only.

THE VYNE

E.M. Kirk

SHERBORNE ST JOHN, BASINGSTOKE RG26 5DX

Owner: The National Trust   *Contact:* The Property Manager

Tel: 01256 881337 **Fax:** 01256 881720

Built in the early 16th century for Lord Sandys, Henry VIII's Lord Chamberlain, the house acquired a classical portico in the mid-17th century (the first of its kind in England) and contains a fascinating Tudor chapel with Renaissance glass, a Palladian staircase and a wealth of old panelling and fine furniture. The attractive grounds feature herbaceous borders and a wild garden, with lawns, lakes and woodland walks.

Location: OS Ref. SU637 566. 4m N of Basingstoke between Bramley and Sherborne St John.

Opening times: House: 3 Jun - end of Oct: Wed - Sun, 1.30 - 5.30pm. Grounds: 25 Mar - end of Oct: Wed - Sun, 12.30 - 5.30pm. Open Good Fri & BH Mon, 11am - 5.30pm.

Admission: House & Grounds: Adult £4.50, Child £2.25. Grounds only: Adult £2.50, Child £1.25. Groups: £3.50 (Wed - Fri only)

Ground floor & grounds suitable. WC.   Tearoom.   No dogs.

Print Rooms:

A charming mid-eighteenth century fashion for decorating rooms with cut-out prints pasted to the walls and often surrounded by cut-out decorative paper frames. In 1746 Lady Cardigan paid for pasting up 'Indian pictures' in her dining room. These would have been pieces of Chinese wallpaper showing views, many things Chinese being referred to at this date as 'Indian'. They were not strictly prints, but it is the earliest evidence of the beginning of a vogue. One such room survives at Erddig, Clwyd made in the 1770s. In 1750 that indefatigable correspondent, Mrs Delany, kept indoors by bad weather, was 'cutting out frames for prints'. Some eighteenth century print rooms are still extant; at Uppark in West Sussex, a dressing-room survived the fire of 1989; at Blickling Hall, Norfolk the National Trust has 'restored and recreated' the print room; Thomas Chippendale designed that at Mersham-le-Hatch, Kent; Rokeby Park, Co Durham has one with a remarkable selection of borders set on a coral background; Ston Easton Park, Somerset has one on a pale blue background. Later print rooms survive: one at Calke Abbey, Derbyshire has, uniquely, Gilray prints from c.1805; another of c.1815 is at The Vyne, Hampshire. At Stratfield Saye, Hampshire in the 1820s the Duke of Wellington created eight such rooms, each including a print of himself.

Extract from; "Life in the Country House" by David N Durant (published by John Murray), PB£15.99, see page twelve at the front of the book.

WINCHESTER CATHEDRAL   **Tel:** 01962 853137 **Fax:** 01962 841519

Winchester, Hampshire SO23 9LS   **Contact:** Mrs J George

The Cathedral was founded in 1079 on a site where Christian worship had already been offered for over 400 years. Special facilities for school visits. Guided tours available.

Location: OS Ref. SU483 293. Winchester city centre.

Opening Times: 8.30am - 5pm. East end closes 5pm. Access may be restricted during services. Weekday services:7.40am, 8am, 5.30pm. Sun services: 8am, 10am, 11.15am, 3.30pm.

Admission: Recommended donations: Adult £2.50, Child 50p, Conc. £2, Family £5, charges apply for Triforium gallery & Library - £1 & for Tower & Roof Tours £1.50. Group tours £3 should be booked through the Education centre. (Tel: 01962 866854 between 9am - 1pm).

Available.   Suitable. WC.   Licensed restaurant.   Guide dogs only.

WINCHESTER COLLEGE   **Tel:** 01962 621217 **Fax:** 01962 621218

College Street, Winchester, Hampshire SO23 9NA

Owner: Winchester College   **Contact:** Mr Maclure

One of the oldest public schools, founded by Bishop William of Wykeham in 1382.

Location: OS Ref. SU483 290. S of the Cathedral.

Opening Times: Apr - Sept: Mon - Sat, 10am - 1pm and 2 - 5pm. Oct - Mar: Mon - Sat, 10am - 1pm and 2 - 4pm. Guided tours leave Porters Lodge at 11am, 2pm and 3.15pm.. Closed Sun mornings.

Admission: Adult £2.50, Child £2, Conc. £2. Guided tours may be booked for groups 10+.

Shop.   Ground floor & grounds suitable.   Guide dogs only.

WOLVESEY CASTLE   **Tel:** 01962 854766

College Street, Wolvesey, Winchester, Hampshire SO23 8NB

Owner: English Heritage   **Contact:** The Custodian

The fortified palace of Wolvesey was the chief residence of the Bishops of Winchester and one of the greatest of all medieval buildings in England. Its extensive ruins still reflect the importance and immense wealth of the Bishops of Winchester, occupants of the richest seat in medieval England. Wolvesey was frequently visited by medieval and Tudor monarchs and was the scene of the wedding feast of Philip of Spain and Mary Tudor in 1554.

Location: OS Ref. SU484 291. 3/4 m SE of Winchester Cathedral, next to the Bishop's Palace; access from College Street.

Opening Times: 1 Apr - 1 Nov: 10am - 6pm (dusk if earlier).

Admission: Adult £1.80, Child £1, Conc. £1.40.

In grounds, on leads.

The Vyne, Hampshire.

HATFIELD HOUSE
Hatfield

This celebrated Jacobean house, which stands in its own great park, was built between 1607 and 1611 by Robert Cecil, 1st Earl of Salisbury and Chief Minister to King James I. It has been the family home of the Cecils ever since.

The main designer was Robert Lyminge helped, it is thought, by the young Inigo Jones. The interior decoration was the work of English, Flemish and French craftsmen, notably Maximilian Colt.

The State Rooms are rich in world-famous paintings including *The Rainbow Portrait of Queen Elizabeth I* and *The Ermine Portrait* by Nicholas Hilliard. Other paintings include works by Hoefnagel, Mytens, John de Critz the Elder and Sir Joshua Reynolds. Fine furniture

from the 16th, 17th and 18th centuries, rare tapestries and historic armour can be found in the State Rooms.

Within the delightful gardens stands the surviving wing of The Royal Palace of Hatfield (1497) where Elizabeth I spent much of her girlhood and held her first Council of State in November 1558. Some of her possessions can be seen in the House.

GARDENS

The West Gardens contain a formal garden, a scented garden with a herb garden at its centre, and a knot garden, planted with plants and bulbs which would have grown there in the 15th, 16th and 17th centuries.

CONTACT

The Curator
Hatfield House
Hatfield
Hertfordshire
AL9 5NQ

Tel: (01707) 262823

Fax: (01707) 275719

LOCATION

OS Ref. TL 237 084

21m N of London,
1m E of the A1(M)/J4.

Bus: Local bus services from St Albans, Hertford.

Rail: From Kings Cross every 30 mins. Hatfield Station is immediately opposite entrance to Park.

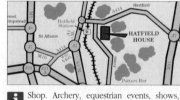

i   Shop. Archery, equestrian events, shows, filming. National collection of model soldiers, William IV Kitchen Exhibition. Nature trails, small children's Venture Play Area. Indoor and outdoor picnic areas. No photography in house.

Wedding receptions, functions. Elizabethan Banquets held in Old Palace throughout year: (01707) 262055.

Visitors may alight at entrance. WCs and lift.

Restaurant/tearoom seats 120. Pre-booked lunch and tea available for groups 10+. Tel: (01707) 262030.

Tue - Sat, no extra charge. Available in French, German, Italian or Spanish by prior arrangement. Garden tour £12.

P   Ample. Hardstanding for coaches.

1:15 ratio. Teacher free. Guide provided. Of interest: kitchen exhibition, model soldier collection, adventure playground and picnic trails.

   In park, on leads.

Civil Wedding Licence.

CONFERENCE/FUNCTION		
ROOM	SIZE	MAX CAPACITY
The Old Palace	112' x 33'	300

OPENING TIMES

25 March - 4 October

Park
Daily: 10.30am - 8pm.

Gardens
Daily: 11am - 6pm.
Last entry 5pm.

House
Closed Mon
Tue - Sat: 12 - 5pm.
Last admission 4pm
Sun: 1 - 4.30pm.

NB. Open Easter, May Day, Spring & Aug BH Mons, 11am - 4.30pm
Closed Good Fri.

ADMISSION

House, Gardens & Park
Adult £5.70
Child (5 - 15yrs)........£3.40
OAP..........................£4.80
Groups*
Adult (& OAP)........£4.80
Child (5 - 15yrs)........£2.90

Park & Gardens
Adult £3.10
Child (5 - 15yrs)........£2.30
OAP..........................£2.90
Groups (min 20, prebooked)
Adult £2.90
Child (5 - 15yrs)........£2.10

SPECIAL EVENTS

- **MAY 7 - 10:**
  Living Crafts
- **JUN 20 / 21:**
  Festival of Gardening
- **JUL 18 - 19:**
  A Tudor Revel
- **AUG 1:**
  The Hatfield Park Prom
- **AUG 7 - 9:**
  Art in Clay
- **AUG 22:**
  Lesley Garrett & Fireworks
- **SEPT 11 - 13:**
  Country Lifestyle Fair

For full listing see Special Events Section at the front of the book.

KNEBWORTH
Nr. Stevenage

CONTACT

The Estate Office
Knebworth House
Knebworth
Hertfordshire
SG3 6PY

Tel: (01438) 812661

Fax: (01438) 811908

LOCATION

OS Ref. TL230 208

Stevenage, A1(M)/J7,
30m N of Central London
and 12m N of M25.

No access from
minor local roads.

Rail: Stevenage Station 2m
(from Kings Cross).

Air: Luton Airport 8m
Landing facilities.

Taxi: (01438) 811122.

Knebworth House has been the home of the Lytton family for over 500 years. Originally a Tudor Manor House, it was transformed 150 years ago with spectacular High Gothic decoration by Victorian romantic novelist Edward Bulwer-Lytton. There are many beautiful rooms, important portraits and furniture. The magnificent Jacobean Hall, where Charles Dickens acted in private theatricals and Winston Churchill painted at his easel, recently underwent restoration work which revealed an unknown early 17th century hand-painted archway under the original panelling, now on permanent display to the public. Knebworth was the home of Constance Lytton, the suffragette, and Robert Lytton, Viceroy of India. Lord Lytton's Viceroyalty and the Great Delhi Durbar of 1877 are commemorated in a fascinating exhibition and audio-visual display.

GARDENS

The elaborate formal gardens of the Victorian era were simplified by Sir Edwin Lutyens. The unique quincunx pattern Herb Garden was designed for Knebworth in 1907 by Gertrude Jekyll and contains a delightful mixture of many herbs. A new feature is the reinstated Maze. The House stands in 250 acres of parkland, with herds of Red and Sika Deer and is the setting for many special events. Fort Knebworth (a large Adventure Playground) and a Miniature Railway are also situated in the park.

i Shop. Suitable for fashion shows, air displays, archery, shooting, equestrian events, cricket pitch, garden parties, shows, rallies, filming, helicopter landing. No pushchairs, photography, smoking or drinking in House.

X Indian Raj Evenings and Elizabethan Banquets with jousting. Full catering service.

Visitors may alight at entrance. Ground floor accessible to wheelchairs.

Restaurant in 400 year old tithe barn. Special rates for advance bookings, menus on request.

P Unlimited parking. Group visits must be booked in advance with Estate Office.

Tue - Fri at 30 min intervals or at booked times including evenings. Tour time 1hr. Shorter tours by arrangement. Room Wardens on duty at weekends. 'Gothick Visions' tour.

National Curriculum based worksheets and children's guide.

Guide dogs only in house. In park, on leads.

SUMMER

Park, Gardens, Fort Knebworth
4 - 20 April &
23 May - 7 September
(closed 7 June)
daily 11am - 5.30pm.

Plus weekends &
BHs from
25 April - 17 May
& weekends only from
12 - 27 September
11am - 5.30pm.

House
As above but closed
Mon except BH Mons
12 - 5pm.

Pre-booked groups of 20+
all year (subject to special
events).

WINTER

Closed, except to
pre-booked parties.

ADMISSION

House, Gardens, Park & Playground

Adult £5.00
Child*/OAP £4.50
Groups (min. 20)
Adult £4.00
Child*/OAP £3.60
(subject to special events)

Gardens, Park & Playground
All persons..............£4.00
Family (2 + 2)..........£14.00
Groups (min. 20)
All persons..............£3.20

Supplement tickets to House (individuals)
Adult £1.00
Child*/OAP...............50p

* Age 5 - 16yrs
Season Tickets available

CONFERENCE/FUNCTION		
ROOM	SIZE	MAX CAPACITY
Banqueting Hall	26 'x 41'	80
Dining Parlour	21' x 38'	50
Library	32' x 21'	40
Manor Barn	70' x 25'	300
Lodge Barn	75' x 30'	250

South East England

ASHRIDGE ✿

Tel: 01442 851227   **Fax:** 01442 842062

Ringshall, Berkhamsted, Hertfordshire HP4 1LT

Owner: The National Trust   **Contact:** The Property Manager

The Ashridge Estate comprises over 1619ha of woodlands, commons and downland. At the northerly end of the Estate the Ivinghoe Hills are an outstanding area of chalk downland which supports a rich variety of plants and insects. The Ivinghoe Beacon itself offers splendid views. This area may be reached from a car park at Steps Hill. The rest of Ashridge is an almost level plateau with many fine walks through woods and open commons.

Location: OS Ref. SP970 131. Between Northchurch & Ringshall, just off B4506.

Opening Times: Estate: All year. Monument, Shop & Visitor Centre: 10 Apr - 1 Nov: Mon - Thur & Good Fri, 2 - 5pm. Sat, Sun & BH Mon 2 - 5.30pm. Last adm. ¹/₂ hr before closing.

Admission: Monument: £1, Child 50p.

ⓘ Shop. Visitor Centre.

BENINGTON LORDSHIP GARDENS 🏛

STEVENAGE, HERTFORDSHIRE SG2 7BS

Owner: Mr C H A Bott   *Contact:* Mr or Mrs C H A Bott

Tel: 01438 869668   **Fax:** 01438 869622

A hilltop garden which appeals to everyone with its intimate atmosphere, ruins, Queen Anne Manor, herbaceous borders, old roses, lakes, vegetable garden, nursery and verandah teas. For films, fashion shoots etc. the gardens and estate offer excellent facilities. Mediaeval barns, cottages and other unique countryside features.

Location: OS Ref. TL296 236. In village of Benington next to the church. 4m E of Stevenage.

Opening times: Gardens only: Apr - Aug, Wed & BH Mon, 12- 5pm, Sun 2 - 5pm. Sept: Wed only. Groups any time by arrangement.

Admission: Adult £2.60, Child free.

ⓘ Air-strip. Suitable for filming & fashion shoots.   ♿ Unsuitable.

☕ Available.   🐕 No dogs.

BERKHAMSTED CASTLE ⚏

Tel: 01442 871737

Berkhamsted, St Albans, Hertfordshire

Owner: English Heritage   **Contact:** Mr Stevens - The Key Keeper

The extensive remains of a large 11th century motte and bailey castle which held a strategic position on the road to London.

Location: OS165 Ref. SP996 083. Adjacent to Berkhamsted rail station.

Opening Times: All year: daily, 10am - 4pm.

Admission: Free.

CATHEDRAL & ABBEY CHURCH OF ST ALBAN

St Albans, Hertfordshire AL1 1BY   **Tel:** 01727 860780   **Fax:** 01727 850944

e-mail: catherdra@alban.u-net.com

       Contact: Mrs Susan Evans

Abbey church of Benedictine Monastery founded 793AD. Britain's first martyr. Rebuilt 1077 became Cathedral in 1877. Many 13th century wall paintings, ecumenical shrine of St Alban (1308).

Location: OS Ref. TL145 071. Centre of St Albans.

Opening Times: All year: 9am - 5.45pm. Tel for details of services, concerts and special events Mon - Sat, 11am - 4pm.

Admission: Free of charge. (AV show, Adult £1.50, Child £1).

ⓘ Shop. Audio visual show.   ♿ Ground floor & grounds suitable. WC.   ☕ Available.

CROMER WINDMILL

Tel: 01438 861662

Ardeley, Stevenage, Hertfordshire SG2 7QA

Owner: Hertfordshire Building Preservation Trust   **Contact:** Simon Bennett

17th century Post Windmill restored to working order.

Location: OS165, Ref. TL305 286. 4m NE of Stevenage on B1037. 1m SW of Cottered.

Opening Times: 10 May - end Aug: Sun, 2nd & 4th Sat & BHs, 2.30 - 5pm.

Admission: Adult £1.25, Child 25p. Groups by arrangement.

THE GARDENS OF THE ROSE

CHISWELL GREEN, ST ALBANS, HERTFORDSHIRE AL2 3NR

Owner: The Royal National Rose Society   *Contact:* Lt Col K J Grapes

Tel: 01727 850461   **Fax:** 01727 850360   **email:** mail@rnrs.org.uk

The Royal National Rose Society Gardens provide a wonderful display of one of the best and most important collections of roses in the world. There are some 30,000 roses in 1800 different varieties. The Society has introduced many companion plants which harmonise well with roses including over 100 varieties of clematis. The garden named for the Society's Patron Her Majesty The Queen Mother contains a fascinating collection of old garden roses. Various cultivation trials show just how easy roses are to grow and new varieties can be seen in the International Trial Ground. There are excellent facilities for films and fashion photography.

Location: OS Ref. TL124 045. 2m S of St Albans, M1/J6, M25/J21A. ¹/₂ m W of B4630.

Opening times: 13 Jun - 11 Oct: Mon - Sat, 9am - 5pm. Sun & Aug BHs, 10am - 6pm.

Admission: Adult £4, Child (4+)/Student £1.50, OAP £3.50. Pre-arranged groups (min 20, max 100): Adult £3.50, Child £1.50.

ⓘ Shop. Plant centre, corporate hospitality.   ✗ Wedding receptions.

♿ Suitable. WC.   ☕ Licensed café.   🐕 In grounds, on leads.

GORHAMBURY HOUSE 🏛

Tel: 01727 854051   **Fax:** 01727 843675

St Albans, Hertfordshire AL3 6AH

Owner: The Earl Of Verulam   **Contact:** The Administrator

Late 18th century house by Sir Robert Taylor. Extensive collection of 17th century portraits.

Location: OS Ref. TL114 078. 2m W of St Albans. Only accessible via private drive from A4147 at St Albans.

Opening Times: May - Sept: Thur, 2 - 5pm.

Admission: Adult £4, Child £2.50, OAP £2, Guided tour £3.50. Other Days £5.

🚶 Guided tours.

HATFIELD HOUSE

See page 26 for full page entry.

KNEBWORTH 🏛

See page 27 for full page entry.

OLD GORHAMBURY HOUSE ⚏

Tel: 01604 730320 (Regional Office)

St Albans, Hertfordshire

Owner: English Heritage   **Contact:** The Midlands Regional Office

The remains of this Elizabethan mansion, particularly the porch of the Great Hall, illustrate the impact of the Renaissance on English architecture.

Location: OS166, Ref. TL110 077. ¹/₄m W of Gorhambury House and accessible only through private drive from A4147 at St Albans (2m).

Opening Times: Any reasonable time.

Admission: Free.

South East England

Boiserie:

Lit., wainscot, wainscoting, woodwork. Wood panels, particularly the carved rococo panelling, painted white and picked out in gold, fashionable in France from the early eighteenth century. There was also a fashion for boiseries in Britain from the mid-eighteenth century; in 1756 Norfolk House in London had a music room panelled with boiseries, now in the Victoria & Albert Museum. The Seven Years' War of 1756–63 caused a reaction against French influence, and the style was subsequently eclipsed by Robert Adam's Grotesques. The rococo saw a revival when George IV (1820–30) created rooms in Windsor Castle and Buckingham Palace in the 'Old French Style', in the 1820s. Also in the 1820s, Lord Stuart de Rothsay, British Ambassador in Paris 1815–24, brought back genuine French boiseries to put into Highclere Castle, Hampshire. At the same time, 1825, the Duchess of Rutland fitted out the Elizabethan Saloon at Belvoir Castle, Leicestershire with boiseries said to be from Mme de Maintenon's château but actually dating from c.1735 – sixteen years after her death. After the French Revolution such pieces were easy to buy in Paris, where the houses of the aristocracy had been looted. French boiseries can also be seen at Harlaxton Manor, Lincolnshire installed in the house begun in 1831 by Salvin for Gregory Gregory. The ceiling heights of French rooms were lower than English ones, so the panelling often had to be ingeniously adapted to fit. English boiseries were made for the White and Gold Room at Petworth, Sussex in 1828.

Extract from; "Life in the Country House" by David N Durant (published by John Murray), PB£15.99, see page twelve at the front of the book.

ST PAULS WALDEN BURY

Tel/Fax: 01438 871218

Hitchin, Hertfordshire   SG4 8BP

Owner: S Bowes Lyon   **Contact:** S or C Bowes Lyon

A formal landscape garden, laid out in 1730, covering 40 acres. The childhood home of Queen Elizabeth, The Queen Mother. Long rides lined with beech hedges fan out to temples, statues, lake and ponds. Grade I listed. Described in *Gardens of the Mind*.

Location: OS Ref. TL186 216. 5m S of Hitchin on B651.

Opening Times: 19 Apr, 10 May, 7 Jun: Sun, 2 - 7pm. Other days by appointment.

Admission: Adult £2, Child 50p. Visits by appointment £5. Non-commercial, proceeds to charity.

♿ Grounds suitable.   ☕ Tearoom.   In grounds, on leads.

SCOTT'S GROTTO

Tel: 01920 464131

Ware, Hertfordshire

Owner: East Hertfordshire District Council   **Contact:** J Watson

One of the finest grottos in England built in the 1760s by Quaker Poet John Scott.

Location: OS Ref. TL355 137. In Scotts Rd, S of the A119 Hertford Road.

Opening Times: 1 Apr - 30 Sept: Sat & BH Mon, 2 - 4.30pm. Also by appointment.

Admission: Suggested donation of £1 for adults. Children free. Please bring a torch.

🚶 By arrangement.

SHAW'S CORNER

National Trust Photographic Library.

AYOT ST LAWRENCE, WELWYN, HERTFORDSHIRE   AL6 9BX

Owner: The National Trust   *Contact:* The Custodian

Tel: 01438 820307

The fascinating home of playwright George Bernard Shaw until his death in 1950. The modest Edwardian villa contains many literary and personal relics, and the interior is still set out as it was in Shaw's lifetime. The garden, with its richly planted borders and views over the Hertfordshire countryside, contains the revolving summerhouse where Shaw retreated to write.

Location: OS Ref. TL194 167. At SW end of village, 2m NE of Wheathampstead, approximately 2m N from B653.

Opening times: 1 Apr - 1 Nov: Wed - Sun & BH Mon, 1 - 5pm (closed Good Fri). Parties by written appointment, Mar - Nov. Last admission 4.30pm. On busy days admission by timed ticket. On event days closes at 3.30pm. No large hand luggage inside property.

Admission: Adult £3.20, Family £8. No reduction for groups.

♿ Access to house & garden but some steps.   Car park only.

South East England

OSBORNE HOUSE
East Cowes

OSBORNE HOUSE was the peaceful, rural retreat of Queen Victoria, Prince Albert and their family, they spent some of their happiest times here.

The prince personally supervised the building, landscaping and alterations of this beautiful Italianate villa and its gardens which command a stunning view of the Solent.

Many of the apartments have a very intimate association with the Queen who died here in 1901 and have been preserved almost unaltered ever since. The nursery bedroom remains just as it was in the 1870s when Queen Victoria's first grandchildren came to stay. Children were a constant feature of life at Osborne (Victoria and Albert had nine). Don't miss the Swiss Cottage, a charming chalet in the grounds built for the Royal children to play and entertain their parents in.

❖

CONTACT

The House Administrator
Osborne House
Royal Apartments
East Cowes
Isle of Wight
PO32 6JY

Tel: (01983) 200022
Fax: (01983) 297281

LOCATION

OS Ref. SZ516 948

1m SE of East Cowes.

Ferry: Isle of Wight ferry terminals

East Cowes 1¹/₂ m
Tel: 01703 334010

Fishbourne 4m
Tel: 01705 827744

i Shop. Suitable for filming, concerts, drama. No photography in the House.

♿ Wheelchairs available, access to house via ramp, ground floor access only. WC.

☕ Teas, coffees and light snacks.

P Ample. Coach drivers and tour leaders free, one extra place for every additional 20. Group rates.

👫 Visits free, please book. Education room available.

OPENING TIMES

SUMMER

House
1 April - 1 November
daily, 10am - 5pm.

Last admission 4.30pm.

Grounds
1 April - 1 November
daily, 10am - 6pm.

Last admission 5pm.

WINTER
House only
2 November - 13 December
Sun, Mon, Wed & Thur.
Guided tours only, through booking system please call
01983 200022/281784

SPRING
7 February - 21 March
Please see winter information above.

ADMISSION

Adult	£6.50
Child*	£3.30
Conc.	£4.90

Grounds only
Adult	£3.50
Child*	£1.80
Conc.	£2.60

Winter & Spring
Adult	£4.50
Child	£2.50
Conc.	£3.50

Plus normal 15% discount for groups.

* 5 - 15 yrs. Under 5s free.

South East England

APPULDURCOMBE HOUSE ♯♯
Tel: 01983 852484

Wroxhall, Shanklin, Isle of Wight
Owner: English Heritage   **Contact:** Mr & Mrs Owen
The bleached shell of a fine 18th century Baroque style house standing in grounds landscaped by 'Capability' Brown.
Location: OS Ref. SZ543 800. 1/2m W of Wroxall off B3327.
Opening Times: 1 Apr - 1 Nov: daily, 10am - 6pm, last admission 5.30pm.
Admission: Adult £2, Child £1, Conc. £1.50.

ⓘ Shop.   ♿ Suitable. WC.   Ⓟ Limited.   In grounds, on leads.

BEMBRIDGE WINDMILL ✿
Tel: 01983 873945

Enquiries to: NT Estates Office, Strawberry Lane, Mottistone, Isle of Wight
Owner: The National Trust   **Contact:** The Custodian
Dating from around 1700, this is the only windmill to survive on the Island. Much of its original wooden machinery is still intact and there are spectacular views from the top.
Location: OS Ref. SZ639 874. 1/2m W of Bembridge off B3395.
Opening Times: 1 Apr - 30 Oct: Sun - Fri. Easter, Jul & Aug: daily, 10am - 5pm.
Admission: Adult £1.30, Child 65p. Special charge for guided tours.

ⓘ Shop. Picnic area.   ♿ Not suitable.   🚶 By arrangement.   No dogs.

CARISBROOKE CASTLE ♯♯

NEWPORT, ISLE OF WIGHT PO30 1XY
Owner: English Heritage   *Contact: The Custodian*

Tel: 01983 522107   **Fax:** 01983 528632
The Island's Royal fortress and prison of King Charles I before his execution in London in 1648. See the famous Carisbrooke donkeys treading the wheel in the Well House or meet them in the donkey centre. Don't miss the castle story in the gatehouse, the museum in the great hall and the interactive coach house museum. Costumed guided tours available.
Location: OS196 Ref. SZ486 877. Off the B3401, 1 1/4m SW of Newport.
Opening times: 1 Apr - 1 Nov: daily, 10am - 6pm (dusk in Oct). 2 Nov - 31 Mar: daily, 10am - 4pm. Closed 24 - 26 Dec.
Admission: Adult £4, Child £2, Conc. £3, Family (2+3) £10. 15% discount for groups of 11+, extra place for additional groups of 20.

ⓘ Shop.   ♿ Suitable. WC.   Tearoom.   In grounds, on leads.

HASELEY MANOR & CHILDREN'S FARM   **Tel:** 01983 865420   **Fax:** 01983 867547

Arreton, Isle of Wight PO30 3AN   **Contact:** Mr R J Young
Location: OS Ref. SZ535 867. Main Sandown to Newport Road.
Opening Times: Apr - 31 Oct: daily, 10am - 5.30pm. Last admission 4pm.
Admission: Adult £4.25, Child £3.15, Conc. £3.60, Groups £3.50, Family (2+2) £13.50.

ⓘ Shop. ♿ Ground floor & grounds suitable. WC.   Tearoom.   In grounds, on leads.

MORTON MANOR
Tel: 01983 406168

Brading, Isle of Wight
Owner: Mr J B Trzebski   **Contact:** Mr J B Trzebski
Refurbished in the Georgian period. Magnificent gardens and vineyard. *Winners of Southern England in Bloom 1996.* Guided tours available. Ample parking.
Location: OS Ref. SZ603 863 (approx.). 1/4m W of A3055 in Brading.
Opening Times: 5 Apr - 31 Oct: daily except Sat, 10am - 5.30pm.
Admission: Adult £3.50, Child £1.50, Conc. £3.25, Group £2.75.

ⓘ Shop.   ♿ Ground floor & grounds suitable.   Tearoom.   Guide dogs.

MOTTISTONE MANOR GARDEN ✿
Tel: 01983 740012

Mottistone, Isle of Wight
Owner: The National Trust   **Contact:** The Gardener
A haven of peace and tranquillity with colourful herbaceous borders and a backdrop of the sea making a perfect setting for the historic Manor House. An annual open air Jazz Concert is held in the grounds during July/August.
Location: OS Ref. SZ406 838. 2m W of Brightstone on B3399.
Opening Times: 1 Apr - 7 Oct: Wed & BH Mon also Suns in July & Aug, 2 - 5.30pm. House: Aug BH Mon only.
Admission: Adult £2, Child £1. Special charge for guided tours; 10.30am - 12 noon, NT members only.

♿ Not suitable.   In grounds, on leads.

NEEDLES OLD BATTERY ✿
Tel: 01983 754772

West High Down, Isle of Wight PO39 0JH
Owner: The National Trust   **Contact:** The Administrator
High above the sea, the Old Battery was built in the 1860s against the threat of French invasion. Original gun barrels, cartoon information panels and a tea-room with one of the finest views in Britain. A 200ft tunnel leads to a restored searchlight position from which dramatic views of the Needles rocks can be seen.
Location: OS Ref. SZ300 848. Needles Headland W of Freshwater Bay & Alum Bay (B3322).
Opening Times: 22 Mar - 29 Oct: Sun - Thur. Easter w/end, Jul & Aug: daily, 10.30am - 5pm.
Admission: Adult £2.40, Child £1.20, Family £6. Special charge for guided tours.

ⓘ Shop.   ♿ Grounds suitable.   Tearoom.   In grounds, on leads.

NUNWELL HOUSE & GARDENS
Tel: 01983 407240

Brading, Isle of Wight PO36 0JQ
Owner: Mrs J A Aylmer   **Contact:** Mrs J A Aylmer
A lived in family home with fine furniture, attractive gardens and historic connections with Charles I.
Location: OS Ref. SZ595 874. 1m NW of Brading. 3m S of Ryde signed off A3055.
Opening Times: 13 July - 23 Sept: Mon, Tue & Wed, 1 - 5pm, but closed 31 Jul - 17 Aug.
Admission: Adult £4, Pair of Adults £7.50 (incl. guide book), OAP/Student £3, Child (up to 10yrs) £1. Garden only: Adult £2.50.

♿ Not suitable.   🚶 Compulsory.   Guide dogs only.

OLD TOWN HALL ✿
Tel: 01983 741052

Newtown, Isle of Wight
Owner: The National Trust   **Contact:** The Custodian
A charming small 18th century building that was once the focal point of the 'rotten borough' of Newtown. There is also an exhibition depicting the history of the famous 'Ferguson's gang'.
Location: OS Ref. SZ424 905. Between Newport and Yarmouth, 1m N of A3054.
Opening Times: 29 Mar - 28 Oct: Sun, Mon, Wed. Easter weekend, Tue & Thur in Jul & Aug: 2 - 5pm.
Admission: Adult £1.20, Child 60p. Special charge for guided tours (written application).

♿ Not suitable.   Ⓟ Limited.   Guide dogs only.

OSBORNE HOUSE ♯♯
See page 30 for full page entry.

YARMOUTH CASTLE ♯♯
Tel: 01983 760678

Quay Street, Yarmouth, Isle of Wight PO41 0PB
Owner: English Heritage   **Contact:** The Custodian
This last addition to Henry VIII's coastal defences was completed in 1547 and is, unusually for its kind, square with a fine example of an angle bastion. It was garrisoned well into the 19th century. It houses exhibitions of paintings of the Isle of Wight and photographs of old Yarmouth.
Location: OS Ref. SZ354 898. In Yarmouth adjacent to car ferry terminal.
Opening Times: 1 Apr - 1 Nov: daily, 10am - 6pm (dusk in Oct).
Admission: Adult £2, Child £1, Conc. £1.50.

ⓘ Shop.   ♿ Ground floor suitable.   Ⓟ No parking.   In grounds, on leads.

Patrick Lane.

Hall Place, Kent.

Patrick Lane.

Dickens Centre - Eastgate House, Kent.

National Trust Photographic Library.

CHARTWELL
Westerham

The family home of Sir Winston Churchill from 1924 until the end of his life. He said of Chartwell, simply 'I love the place - a day away from Chartwell is a day wasted'. With magnificent views over the Weald of Kent it is not difficult to see why.

The rooms are left as they were in Sir Winston & Lady Churchill's lifetime with daily papers, fresh flowers grown from the garden and his famous cigars. Photographs and books evoke his career and interests, as well as happy family life. Museum and exhibition rooms contain displays and sound recordings, superb collections of memorabilia from his political career, including uniforms and a 'siren-suit'.

The garden studio contains Sir Winston's easel and paintbox, as well as many of his paintings. Terraced and water gardens descend to the lake, the gardens also include a golden rose walk, planted by Sir Winston and Lady Churchill's children on the occasion of their golden wedding anniversary, and the Marlborough Pavilion decorated with frescoes depicting the battle of Blenheim. Visitors can see the garden walls that Churchill built with his own hands, the pond stocked with the golden orfe he loved.

The Mulberry Room can be booked for meetings, conferences, dinners. Please telephone for details.

CONTACT

The Property Manager
Chartwell
Westerham
Kent
TN16 1PS

Tel: (01732) 866868
(01732) 868381

Fax: (01732) 868193

LOCATION

OS Ref. TQ455 515

2m S of Westerham,
forking left off B2026.

National Trust Photographic Library.

i   Shop. Conference facilities.

X   Wedding receptions.

  Partially suitable. WC. Please telephone before visit.

  Licensed restaurant.

  By arrangement.

P   Ample.

  In grounds, on leads.

OPENING TIMES

1 April - 1 November
Wed - Sun & BH Mon
11am - 5pm.

July & August only
Tue - Sun & BH Mon
11am - 5pm.

Last admission 4.30pm.

ADMISSION

Adult £5.20
Child........................£2.60
Family £13.00

SPECIAL EVENTS

• **JUN 20:**
Music Memories & Moonlight

South East England

CHIDDINGSTONE CASTLE
Edenbridge

The dream-child of two romantics; Squire Henry Streatfield, who c1805, had his family seat transformed into a fantasy castle by that master of the picturesque, William Atkinson, and whose money ran out; and Denys Eyre Bower, eccentric genius and inspired art collector, who never had any money at all. Enchanted by the then semi-derelict castle, he made it his home in 1956. He died in 1977, leaving the mansion and its contents to the nation. Now administered by a private charitable trust, it remains a home with its fine furnishings, Japanese lacquer and swords, Egyptian antiquities, Buddhist images, Stuart and Jacobite relics and pictures. Denys Bower wished it to be kept as a home as he had enjoyed it, not a museum but a place where works of great art are part of daily life.

An enchanting miniature 35 acre park, one of the listed historic gardens of Kent, surrounds the Castle which is uniquely integrated with its garden buildings. Paradise for photographers!

Great Hall.

CONTACT

Mrs R Vernon
Chiddingstone Castle
Edenbridge
Kent
TN8 7AD

Tel: (01892) 870347

LOCATION

OS Ref. TQ497 452

B2027, turn to Chiddingstone at Bough Beech, 1m further on to crossroads, then straight to castle.

10m from Tonbridge, Tunbridge Wells and Sevenoaks. 4m Edenbridge. Accessible from A21 and M25/J5.

Bus: 210 Tonbridge - Edenbridge, alight Bough Beech - castle 1m.

Rail: Tonbridge, Tunbridge Wells, Edenbridge then taxi.

Air: Gatwick 15m.

OPENING TIMES

SUMMER

Easter Hol, April, May & October
Sun & BHs.

June - September
Wed - Fri & Sun
Weekdays: 2 - 5.30pm
Sun & BHs
11.30am - 5.30pm
Last entry 5pm.

WINTER

Open only for specially booked groups of 20+.

ADMISSION

Weekdays
  Adult £3.50
  Child* £1.50
Sundays
  Adult £4.00
  Child* £1.50
Groups (pre-booked 20+)
  Adult £3.00

* Under 16yrs, accompanied by adult.
Under 5 yrs free.

i Shop. Available for conferences, receptions, concerts. No photography in house, no smoking.

X Available for special events. Wedding receptions

Suitable. WC.

Tearoom. Light refreshments. Licensed for functions.

By arrangement.

P Ample hardcore parking. Coaches, please book.

Teachers' pack. Educational programme.

In grounds, on leads.

Civil Wedding Licence.

CONFERENCE/FUNCTION		
ROOM	SIZE	MAX CAPACITY
Assembly Rm	14' x 35'	50
Seminar Rms	15' x 15'	

CHIDDINGSTONE CASTLE continued...

Grounds.

Orangery.

THE GOODHUGH WING, created from old domestic quarters, is an ideal meeting place for small prestige conferences (50), study groups and other functions. Opening off the coachyard, yet an integral part of the Castle, it offers an assembly room, three seminar rooms, a tea kitchen and private garden. Fine decoration and antique furnishings contribute to the 'English' atmosphere which appeals particularly to our foreign guests. Refreshments are available in the refectory by arrangement with the appointed caterers.

CIVIL MARRIAGES: Celebrated in the Great Hall or ruined orangery. During the ceremony the Castle is closed to other events. You receive your guests as in your home. The drawing room may be hired for receptions.

EDUCATION: Local schools have used, for some time, the superb collection of Egyptian antiquities for the National Curriculum. Private visits arranged for groups of 20 plus. Wider activities using Japanese and historic collections are under consideration. Enquire for details.

Assembly Room, Conference Centre.

South East England

COBHAM HALL
Cobham

'One of the largest, finest and most important houses in Kent', Cobham Hall is an outstandingly beautiful, red brick mansion in Elizabethan, Jacobean, Carolean and 18th Century styles.

It yields much of interest to the student of art, architecture and history. The Elizabethan wings were begun in 1584 whilst the central section contains the Gilt Hall, wonderfully decorated by John Webb, Inigo Jones' most celebrated pupil, 1654. Further rooms were decorated by James Wyatt in the 18th century.

Cobham Hall, now a girls' school, has been visited by several of the English monarchs from Elizabeth I to Edward VIII, later Duke of Windsor. Charles Dickens used to walk through the grounds from his house in Higham to the Leather Bottle pub in Cobham Village. In 1883, the Hon Ivo Bligh, later the 8th Earl of Darnley, led the victorious English cricket team against Australia bringing home the 'Ashes' to Cobham.

GARDENS

The gardens, landscaped for the 4th Earl by Humphry Repton, are gradually being restored by the Cobham Hall Heritage Trust. Extensive tree planting and clearing have taken place since the hurricanes of the 1980s. The Gothic Dairy and some of the classical garden buildings are being renovated. The gardens are particularly delightful in Spring, when they are resplendent with daffodils and a myriad of rare bulbs.

❖

CONTACT

Mrs Sue Anderson
Development Director
Cobham Hall
Cobham
Kent DA12 3BL

Tel: (01474) 824319
or (01474) 823371

Fax: (01474) 822995
or (01474) 824171

LOCATION

OS Ref. TQ683 689

Situated adjacent to the A2/M2. ¹/₂ m S of A2 4m W of Strood. 8m E of M25/J2 between Gravesend & Rochester

London 25m
Rochester 5m
Canterbury 30m

Rail: Meopham 3m
Gravesend 5m
Taxis at both stations.

Air: Gatwick 45 mins.
Heathrow 60 mins.
Stansted 50 mins.

CONFERENCE/FUNCTION		
ROOM	SIZE	MAX CAPACITY
Gilt Hall	41' x 34'	180
Wyatt Dining Rm	49' x 23'	135
Clifton Dining Rm	24' x 23'	75
Activities Centre	119' x 106'	300

ℹ️ Shop. Conferences, business or social functions, 150 acres of parkland for sports, corporate events, open air concerts, sports centre, indoor swimming pool, art studios, music wing, tennis courts, helicopter landing area. Filming and photography. No smoking.

✕ In-house catering team for private, corporate hospitality and wedding receptions. (cap. 200).

♿ House tour involves 2 staircases, ground floor access for w/chairs.

☕ Afternoon teas, other meals by arrangement.

🚶 All tours guided, tour time 1¹/₂ hrs. Garden tours arranged outside standard opening times.

🅿️ Ample parking. Pre-booked coach parties are welcome any time.

👫 Guide provided, Adult £3, Child / OAP £2.50.

🐕 On leads.

🅰️ 18 single and 18 double with bathroom. 22 single and 22 double without bathroom. Dormitory. Groups only.

💒 Civil Wedding Licence.

OPENING TIMES

SUMMER
March:
22, 25, 26, 29.

April:
1, 2, 5, 10, 11, 12, 13, 15, 16.

July:
8, 9, 12, 15, 16, 19, 22, 23, 25, 26, 29, 30.

August:
2, 5, 6, 9, 12, 16, 19, 23, 26, 27, 30, 31.

ADMISSION

Adult £3.00
Child (4 - 14yrs.).....£2.50
OAP.........................£2.50

Gardens & Parkland

Self-guided tour and booklet...............£1.50

Historical/Conservation tour of Grounds (by arrangement)

Per person.................£3.00

SPECIAL EVENTS

• **APRIL 10 - 13:**
Medway Craft Show

• **AUG 25 / 26:**
Medway Flower & Craft Show

South East England

DOVER CASTLE & THE SECRET WARTIME TUNNELS
Dover

CONTACT

Mr K Scott
Dover Castle
Dover
Kent
CT16 1HU

Tel: (01304) 211067

Info Line: (01304) 201628

LOCATION

OS Ref. TR326 416

Easy access from M2 and M20. Well signed from Dover centre and east side of Dover. 2 hrs from central London.

Rail: London Charing Cross or Victoria 1¹/₂ hrs.

Bus: Freephone 0800 696996.

Journey deep into the White Cliffs of Dover and discover the top secret World War II tunnels. Through sight, sound and smells relive the wartime drama of the underground hospital as a wounded Battle of Britain pilot is taken to the operating theatre in a bid to save his life. Discover how life would have been during the planning days of the Dunkirk evacuation and Operation Dynamo as you are led around the network of tunnels and casements housing the communications centre.

Above ground you can explore the magnificent mediaeval keep and inner bailey of King Henry II. Visit the evocative Princess of Wales' Royal Regiment Museum. There is also the Roman Lighthouse and Anglo-Saxon church to see or take an audio tour of the intriguing 13th century underground fortifications and medieval battlements. Enjoy magnificent views of the White Cliffs from Admiralty lookout.

Throughout the summer there are many fun events taking place, bringing the castle alive through colourful enactments and living history.

Opening in Spring 1998 is the exciting Life Under Seige exhibition. Enter the basement of the keep and discover, through a dramatic light and sound presentation, how it must have felt to be a garrison soldier defending Dover Castle on behalf of King John against the French King in 1216. The land train will help you around this huge site.

ℹ️ Two shops.

❌ For private functions telephone 01304 205830.

♿ Lift for access to tunnels. Courtyard and grounds, some very steep slopes.

☕ 2 restaurants, hot and cold food and drinks.

🚶 Tour of tunnels approx. every 20 mins, more at peak times when a 30 min wait can occur.

🅿️ Ample. Groups welcome, discounts available. Free entry for drivers. One extra place for each additional group of 20.

👨‍👩‍👧 Free visits available for schools. Education centre. Pre-booking essential.

OPENING TIMES

SUMMER
1 Apr - 1 Nov
daily
9.30am - 6pm
or dusk if earlier.

WINTER
2 November - 31 March
daily
10am - 4pm.

ADMISSION

Adult £6.60
Child......................£3.30
OAP........................£5.00
Family (2 + 3) £16.50

Groups
15% discount for groups of 11+.

South East England

GROOMBRIDGE PLACE GARDENS
Tunbridge Wells

Surrounded by acres of breathtaking parkland, Groombridge Place has an intriguing history stretching back to medieval times. Flanked by a medieval moat, with a classical 17th century manor as its backdrop, the beautiful formal gardens boast a rich variety of 'rooms', together with extensive herbaceous borders. High above the walled gardens and estate vineyard, hidden from view, lies The Enchanted Forest, where magic and fantasy await discovery. Here are secret mysterious gardens to challenge and delight your imagination and reward your mind's ingenuity.

❖

Chosen by South East England Tourist Board as 'Visitor Attraction of the Year 1997'

CONTACT

The Estate Office
Groombridge Place
Groombridge
Tunbridge Wells
Kent
TN3 9QG

Tel: (01892) 863999

Fax: (01892) 863996

LOCATION

OS Ref. TQ534 375

Groombridge Place Gardens are located on the B2110 just off the A264. 4m SW of Tunbridge Wells and 9m E of East Grinstead.

Rail: London Charing Cross to Tunbridge Wells 55 mins.

OPENING TIMES

SUMMER
Gardens

Good Friday - 25 October daily, 9am - 6pm.

The house is not open to visitors.

ADMISSION

Adult	£5.50
Child (under 17)	£3.50
Student/OAP	£4.50
Groups	
Per person	£5.00
Child	£3.00
OAP	£4.00

ℹ️ Shop. Suitable for concerts, filming and fairs.

✖️ Available for weddings.

♿ Restaurant. Some access to formal gardens. WC.

☕ Restaurant.

🚶 Must be pre-booked, additional charge. Tour time:1hr.

🅿️ Ample. Free admittance for coach drivers.

👪 Welcome

🐕 No dogs permitted in the gardens.

💒 Civil Wedding Licence.

Scotney Castle, Kent.

HEVER CASTLE
Edenbridge

HEVER CASTLE dates back to 1270, when the gatehouse, outer walls and the inner moat were first built. 200 years later the Bullen (or Boleyn) family added the comfortable Tudor manor house constructed within the walls. This was the childhood home of Anne Boleyn, Henry VIII's second wife and mother of Elizabeth I. A costume exhibition in the Long Gallery includes all the familiar characters from this royal romance. The castle was later given to Henry VIII's fourth wife, Anne of Cleves.

In 1903, the estate was bought by the American millionaire William Waldorf Astor, who became a British subject and the first Lord Astor of Hever. He invested an immense amount of time, money and imagination in restoring the castle and grounds. Master craftsmen were employed and the castle was filled with a magnificent collection of furniture, tapestries and other works of art. The Miniature Model Houses exhibition, a collection of $1/12$ scale model houses, room views and gardens, depicts life in English Country Houses from Medieval to Victorian times.

GARDENS

Between 1904-8 over 30 acres of formal gardens were laid out and planted, these have now matured into one of the most beautiful gardens in England. The unique Italian garden is a four acre walled garden containing a superb collection of statuary and sculpture. The award winning gardens include the Rose garden and Tudor garden, a traditional yew maze and a 110 metre herbaceous border. A water maze has been added to the other water features in the gardens. Visitors are challenged to reach the central folly whilst avoiding various water barriers.

❖

CONTACT

Anne-Marie
Critchley-Salmonson
Hever Castle
Hever
Edenbridge
Kent
TN8 7NG

Tel: (01732) 865224

Fax: (01732) 866796

LOCATION

OS Ref. TQ476 450

Exit M25/J5 & J6
M23/J10,
$1^1/2$ m S of B2027 at
Bough Beech,
3m SE of Edenbridge.

Rail: Hever Station
1m (no taxis),
Edenbridge Town
3m (taxis).

Taxi: Relyon Car Services,
Tel: (01732) 863800.

Beeline Taxis
Tel: (01732) 456214.

ℹ️ Gift, garden and book shop. Suitable for filming, conferences and corporate hospitality. Product launches, outdoor heated pool, tennis court and billiard room.

✖️ Wedding receptions, dinner dances, special functions.

♿ Access to gardens, ground floor only (no ramps into castle), restaurants, gift shop, book shop and water maze. Wheelchairs. WC.

🍵 Two licensed restaurants. Supper provided during open air theatre season. Pre-booked lunches and teas for groups.

🚶 Pre-booked tours in mornings. 1 Mar - 30 Nov. Tour time 1 hr. Tours in French, German, Dutch, Italian and Spanish (min 20). Garden tours in English only (min 15).

🅿️ Ample. Free admission and refreshment voucher for driver and courier. Please book, group rates for 15+.

👫 Welcome (min 5). Guide provided for groups of 20. 1:10 ratio. Free preparatory visits for teachers in normal open hours. Please book.

OPENING TIMES

SUMMER
1 March - 30 November
daily
Grounds: 11am
Castle: 12 noon
Last admission 5pm
Closes 6pm.

WINTER
March & November
Grounds: 11am - 4pm.

Castle: Noon - 4pm.

ADMISSION

Castle & Garden

Adult	£7.00
Child (5-16 yrs)	£3.80
OAP	£6.00
Family (2+2)	£17.80

Groups

Adult	£6.00
Student	£5.00
Child	£3.60

Garden only

Adult	£5.50
Child (5-16 yrs)	£3.60
OAP	£4.70
Family (2+2)	£14.60

Groups

Adult	£4.70
Student	£4.40
Child	£3.40

Pre-booked private guided tours are available between 10am & 12 noon during season.

CONFERENCE/FUNCTION

ROOM	SIZE	MAX CAPACITY
Dining Hall	35' x 20'	70
Breakfast Rm	22' x 15'	12
Sitting Rm	24' x 20'	20
Pavilion	96' x 40'	250
Moat Restaurant	25' x 60'	75

HEVER CASTLE continued...

The Tudor Village was built for William Waldorf Astor in the style of the Tudor period, but with every modern comfort and luxury.

All twenty individually decorated rooms have private bathrooms, colour televisions, direct dial telephones, tea/coffee-making facilities and hair dryers. Guests can enjoy a billiard room, outdoor heated swimming pool, tennis court and croquet lawn.

The Village is available year round for groups requiring high standards of accommodation and service, delicious foods and wines and top-level conference facilities. There are three interconnecting reception rooms which can be used for conferences, dining or meetings. There are also a number of smaller seminar rooms.

The Hever Castle Estate includes Stables House, an imposing five bedroomed property overlooking the River Eden. This is an ideal venue for smaller groups, which can also make use of the Tudor Village amenities.

The Dining Hall, Breakfast Room and Sitting Room (which together form the Tudor Suite) are available throughout the year. Smaller seminar rooms are also available. The Pavilion can be hired between November and March. Overhead projector, flip charts and screen can be provided and specialist audio-visual equipment hired. There are a number of magnificent private dining rooms available for receptions, Tudor banquets, lunches and dinners.

SPECIAL EVENTS

- **APR 10 - 13:**
  Easter Egg Trail
- **MAY 2 - 4:**
  May Day Music & Dance
- **MAY 23 - 25:**
  Merrie England Weekend
- **JUN - AUG: SUNDAYS**
  Summer Music Season
- **JUN 26 - 28:**
  Gardeners' Weekend

- **JUL 25 & AUG 1/8/15/22/29:**
  Jousting
- **JUL 26 & AUG 2/9/16/23/30/31:**
  Longbow Archery
- **SEPT 11 - 13:**
  Patchwork & Quilting Exhibition
- **OCT 24 - NOV 1:**
  Medieval Half Term Fun

In addition, the magnificent Dining Hall in the Castle is available for a truly memorable dinner. Guests can enjoy a private guided tour of the Castle and a Tudor Banquet with minstrels.

Laser clay pigeon shooting, archery, fishing, riding, golf and other pursuits can be arranged on or near the estate.

In all, the Tudor Village provides a unique and unusual venue for private meetings, receptions, product launches or corporate hospitality.

Hever Castle/Tudor Village offers the following accommodation (see picture below):

- 4 singles with bath
- 8 twins with bath
- 8 doubles with bath
- 4 twins and 1 double (in the Stables House)

Tulip Bedroom in Tudor Village.

Tudor Suite Dining Room in Tudor Village.

The Music Room in Tudor Village.

Rupert Truman

Andreas Von Einsiedel.

KNOLE
Sevenoaks

Set in an extensive deer park owned by Lord Sackville, Knole is one of the "Great" houses of England. It has been the home of the Sackville family since 1603, including four Dukes of Dorset, and houses an extensive collection of furnishings and paintings, many in the house since the 17th century.

The largest private house in England, Knole is a spectacular example of late medieval architecture overlaid with extensive Jacobean embellishments, including remarkable carving and plasterwork. The Sackville family crest of the leopard rampant recurs throughout.

An internationally renowned collection of Royal Stuart furnishings, including three state beds, celebrated silver furniture, and the prototype of the 'Knole' settee. Thirteen years were spent restoring the fabrics on the bed in the Kings' room.

The 6th Earl of Dorset played host to poets Pope and Dryden. Knole was the birthplace of the writer, Vita Sackville-West, and the setting for Virginia Woolf's novel *Orlando*.

Important collection of paintings, including works by Van Dyck, Lely, Kneller, Gainsborough, Hoppner, Wootton, and a room devoted to the works of Sir Joshua Reynolds, commissioned for the house by the 3rd Duke of Dorset, including portraits of Dr Johnson, David Garrick and Oliver Goldsmith.

The experience of visiting the house, which has been little altered since the 18th century, is like stepping back in time.

CONTACT

John Coleman
Property Manager
Knole
Sevenoaks
Kent TN15 0RP

Tel: (01732) 462100

Info: (01732) 450608

Fax: (01732) 465528

LOCATION

OS Ref. TQ532 543

25m SE of London. Just off A225 at S end of High Street, Sevenoaks.

Rail: 1/2 hr from London Charing Cross to Sevenoaks, and bus to house.

Special rail/bus and ticket admission available.

OPENING TIMES

House & Garden

1 April - 1 November
Wed - Sat, 12 - 4pm.

Last admission 3.30pm.

Sun, BH Mon & Good Fri
11am - 5pm.

Last admission 3.30/4pm.

Garden

May - September
1st Wed of month only
12 - 4pm.

Last admission 3pm.

ADMISSION

Adult	£5.00
Child	£2.50
Family	£12.50
Groups (pre-booked)	
Adult	£4.00
Parking	£2.50

National Trust Photographic Library.

Andreas Von Einsiedel.

ℹ️ Concerts and other events in Great Hall and Stone Court. Full range of National Trust goods and souvenirs of Knole.

♿ Wheelchair access to Green Court, Stone Court and Great Hall.

🍴 Brewhouse Restaurant serving morning coffee, lunch and teas. Also ice-creams and snacks in courtyard.

🚶 Pre-booked parties: Guided tours only on Thur mornings.

🅿️ Ample.

🚶‍♂️ Welcome. Special reduction for booked parties.

South East England

LEEDS CASTLE
Maidstone

Surrounded by 500 acres of magnificent parkland and gardens, and built on two small islands in the middle of a natural lake, Lord Conway christened Leeds "the loveliest Castle in the world."

The site of a manor of the Saxon royal family in the 9th century, it was then rebuilt in stone by the Normans and later converted into a Royal Palace by Henry VIII.

For some 300 years, the Castle was home to the Kings and Queens of medieval England. Now lovingly restored and beautifully furnished, it contains a magnificent collection of medieval furnishings, tapestries and paintings.

The Castle was purchased in 1926 by the late the Hon Olive, Lady Baillie, whose American Whitney inheritance helped restore the Castle and cement strong Anglo-American links. The Leeds Castle Foundation now preserves the castle for the nation, hosts important medical conferences and supports the arts.

A unique collection of Dog Collars can be viewed in the Castle Gate House.

Popular attractions within the Castle grounds include the colourful Culpeper Garden, Wood Garden, Duckery, Castle greenhouses and vineyard. An aviary houses rare and endangered species from around the world, beyond which can be found a traditional maze and underground grotto. A challenging nine hole golf course surrounds the Castle, whose moat occasionally comes into play!

CONTACT

Nick Day
Leeds Castle
Maidstone
Kent
ME17 1PL

Tel: (01622) 765400

Fax: (01622) 735616

LOCATION

OS Ref. TQ835 533

From London to A20/M20/J8, 40m, 1 hr. 6m E of Maidstone, 1/4 m S of A20.

Rail: BR Connex South Eastern train and admission. London - Bearsted.

Coach: Nat Express/ Invictaway coach and admission from Victoria.

Air: Gatwick 45m. Heathrow 65m.

Channel Tunnel: 25m.

Channel ports: 38m.

CONFERENCE/FUNCTION		
ROOM	SIZE	MAX CAPACITY
Fairfax Hall	19.8 x 1m	200
Gate Tower	9.8 x 5.2m	50
Culpeper	7.65 x 7.34m	40
Terrace	8.9 x 15.4m	80

SPECIAL EVENTS

- **JAN 1:**
  New Year's Day Treasure Trail

- **FEB 16 - 20, MAY 25 - 29 & OCT 26 - 30:**
  Half-term fun for children

- **APR 11 - 13:**
  A Celebration of Easter

- **MAY 16 - 17:**
  Festival of English Food & Wine

- **JUN 6 - 7:**
  Balloon & Vintage Car Fiesta

- **JUN 27 & JUL 4:**
  Annual Open Air Concerts

- **SEPT 16 - 19:**
  Leeds Castle Flower Festival

- **NOV 7:**
  Grand Firework Spectacular

- **DEC 12 - 24:**
  Christmas at the Castle

OPENING TIMES

OPEN ALL YEAR

SUMMER
1 March - 31 October
daily: 10am - 5pm
(last admission).

WINTER
November - February
daily: 10am - 3pm
(last admission).
(except Christmas Day).

Also special private tours for pre-booked groups at any other time by appointment

Castle & Grounds closed 27 Jun & 4 July prior to the Open Air Concerts.

ADMISSION

Proposed rates
from 1 March 1998.

Castle, Park & Gardens
Adult £8.80
Child (5 -15yrs).........£5.80
OAP/Student...........£6.80
Family (2+3)...........£24.00
Disabled Visitors
Adult £4.30
Child (5 -15yrs).........£3.10
Groups (Min 20)
Adult £6.60
Child (5 -15yrs).........£4.80
OAP/Student...........£5.60

Park & Gardens
Adult £6.80
Child (5 -15yrs).........£4.30
OAP/Student...........£5.30
Family (2+3) £20.00
Disabled Visitors
Adult £3.30
Child (5 -15yrs).........£2.10
Groups (Min 20)
Adult £5.60
Child (5 -15yrs).........£3.80
OAP/Student...........£5.60

A guidebook is published in English, French, German, Dutch, Spanish, Italian, Japanese, Mandarin and Russian. £2.50 each.

i Shops. Residential conferences, exhibitions, sporting days, clay shooting, falconry, field archery, hot air ballooning, golf, croquet and heli-pad. Talks can be arranged for horticultural, viticultural, historical and cultural groups. No radios.

X Corporate hospitality, large scale marquee events, wedding receptions, buffets and dinners.

♿ Shuttle for elderly/disabled, wheelchairs, wheelchair lift, special rates. WC.

🍴 2 restaurants, group lunch menus.

🚶 Guides in rooms. French, Spanish, Dutch, German, Italian and Russian speaking guides.

P Ample free parking. Pre-booking advisable, free entry, refreshment voucher for drivers.

👫 Welcome, outside normal opening hours, private tours. Teacher's resource pack.

🐕 No dogs.

South East England

PENSHURST PLACE & GDNS
Nr Tonbridge

PENSHURST PLACE is one of England's greatest family-owned stately homes with a history going back six and a half centuries.

In some ways time has stood still at Penshurst; the great House is still very much a medieval building with improvements and additions made over the centuries but without any substantial rebuilding. Its highlight is undoubtedly the medieval Barons' Hall, built in 1341, with its impressive 60ft-high chestnut-beamed roof.

A marvellous mix of paintings, tapestries and furniture from the 15th, 16th and 17th centuries can be seen throughout the House, including the helm carried in the state funeral procession to St Paul's Cathedral for the Elizabethan courtier and poet, Sir Philip Sidney, in 1587. This is now the family crest.

GARDENS
The Gardens, first laid out in the 14th century, have been developed over successive years by the Sidney family who first came to Penshurst in 1552. A twenty-year restoration and re-planting programme undertaken by the late Viscount De L'Isle has ensured that they retain their historic splendour. He is commemorated with a new Arboretum, planted in 1991. The gardens are divided by a mile of yew hedges into "rooms", each planted to give a succession of colour as the seasons change. There is also an Adventure Playground, Nature Trail and Toy Museum for children.

CONTACT

Bonnie Vernon
Penshurst Place
Penshurst
Nr Tonbridge
Kent
TN11 8DG

Tel: (01892) 870307
Fax: (01892) 870866

LOCATION

OS Ref. TQ527 438

From London M25/J5 then A21 to Tonbridge North, B2027 via Leigh; from Tunbridge Wells A26, B2176.

Visitors entrance at SE end of village, S of the church.

Bus: Maidstone & District 231, 232, 233 from Tunbridge Wells.

Rail: Charing Cross/Waterloo - Hildenborough, Tonbridge or Tunbridge Wells; then taxi.

CONFERENCE/FUNCTION		
ROOM	SIZE	MAX CAPACITY
Sunderland Room	45' x 18'	100
Barons' Hall	64' x 39'	250
Buttery	20' x 23'	50

i Shop. Product launches, garden parties, photography, filming, fashion shows, receptions, archery, clay pigeon shooting, falconry, parkland for hire, lectures on property, its contents and history. Conference facilities. No photography in house.

X Private banqueting, wedding receptions.

& Limited, disabled and elderly may alight at entrance.

☕ Restaurant (waitress service can be booked by groups of 20+).

🚶 Mornings only by arrangement, lunch/dinner can be arranged. Out of season tours by appointment. Guided tours of the gardens.

P Ample. Double decker buses to park from village.

👪 All year by appointment, discount rates, education room and packs.

🐕 No dogs.

💍 Civil Wedding Licence.

OPENING TIMES

SUMMER
From 28 February weekends only.

28 March - 1 November

House
Daily, 12 - 5.30pm
Last entry 5pm.

Grounds
Daily, 11am - 6pm.

WINTER
November - March open weekends.
Open to Groups by appointment only (see Guided Tours).

ADMISSION

House & Garden
Adult	£5.70
Child*	£3.20
Conc.**	£5.30
Family	£15.00
Groups***	
Adult	£5.10
Child	£2.80

Garden only
Adult	£4.20
Child*	£2.80
Conc.**	£3.70
Family	£12.00

* Aged 5-15; under 5s FREE.
** Concessions: OAP/Students/UB40
*** Min 20 people, afternoons only. Special rates for morning Guided Tours

SPECIAL EVENTS

- **MAY 2 - 4 & SEPT 11 - 13:**
  Craft Fair

- **MAY 24 - 25:**
  Classic Car Show

- **JUL 11 - 12:**
  Balloon Fiesta

Jeremy Whitaker

SQUERRYES COURT
Westerham

SQUERRYES COURT has been the home of the Wardes since 1731 and is still lived in by the family today. Although it was built in Charles II's reign in 1681 it is a typical William and Mary manor house. Squerryes is 22 miles from London and easily accessible from the M25. Surrounded by parkland, there are fine views over the lake to the hills beyond.

The house has an important collection of Italian, 18th century English and 17th century Dutch paintings acquired and commissioned by the family in the 18th century. John Warde who inherited in 1746 purchased 93 paintings in the space of 25 years. He did not go on the Grand Tour but bought from auction houses, dealers and private sales in England. This gives an insight into the taste of a man of his time and also what was available on the art market in England in the mid 18th century.

The furniture and porcelain have been in the house since the 18th century and the Tapestry Room contains a fine set of Soho tapestries made c.1720. General Wolfe of Quebec was a friend of the family and there are items connected with him in the Wolfe Room.

GARDENS

These were laid out in the formal style but were re-landscaped in the mid 18th century. Some of the original features in the 1719 Badeslade print survive. The family have restored the formal garden using this print as a guide. The garden is lovely all year round with bulbs, wild flowers and woodland walks, azaleas, summer flowering herbaceous borders and roses.

CONTACT

Curator or Mrs Warde
Squerryes Court
Westerham
Kent
TN16 1SJ

Tel: (01959) 562345
or (01959) 563118

Fax: (01959) 565949

LOCATION

OS Ref. TQ440 535

Off the M25/J6, 6m,
E along A25 $^1/_2$ m SW of
Westerham

London 1-1$^1/_2$ hrs.

Rail: Oxted Station 4m.
Sevenoaks 6m.

Air: Gatwick,
30 mins.

OPENING TIMES

SUMMER

1 April - 30 September
Wed, Sat, Sun & BH Mon

Closed: Mon (except BH Mon), Tue, Thur & Fri.

Grounds: 12 - 5.30pm
House: 1.30 - 5.30pm
last admission 5pm.

NB. Pre-booked groups welcome any day.

WINTER

October - 1 April
Closed.

ADMISSION

House & Garden
Adult £3.90
Child* £2.20
OAP........................£3.50
Groups (min 20)
Adult £3.30
Child* £1.70
OAP........................£3.30

House only
Adult £3.90
Child* £2.20
OAP........................£3.50
Groups (min 20)
Adult £3.30
Child* £1.70
OAP........................£3.30

Garden only
Adult £2.40
Child* £1.40
OAP........................£2.10
Groups (min 20, booked)
Adult £2.10
Child* £1.00
OAP........................£2.10

* Aged 14yrs and under.

CONFERENCE/FUNCTION		
ROOM	SIZE	MAX CAPACITY
Hall	32' x 32'	60
Old Library	20' x 25' 6"	40

ℹ️ Shop. Suitable for conferences, product launches, filming, photography, archery, clay pigeon shooting, garden parties. No photography in house.

🚶 Available for groups (max 55) at a small additional charge. The owner will meet groups by prior arrangement. Tour time $^3/_4$ hr.

✕ Available for exclusive entertaining and wedding receptions (marquee).

🅿️ Ample. Free teas for drivers and couriers.

♿ Limited garden access, house unsuitable, tearoom access. WC.

👪 Welcome, cost £1.50 per child, guide provided. Areas of interest: nature walk, ducks and geese.

☕ Available. Groups must book. Menus upon request.

🐕 On leads, in grounds.

South East
England

THE ARCHBISHOP'S PALACE   Tel: 01622 663006 Fax: 01622 682451

Mill Street, Maidstone, Kent ME15 6YE
Owner: Maidstone Borough Council   **Contact:** The Heritage Services Manager
Recently refurbished 14th century Palace used as a resting place for Archbishops travelling from London to Canterbury.
Location: OS Ref. TQ760 555. On the banks of River Medway SW of the centre of Maidstone.
Opening Times: Daily: 10am - 4.30pm.
Admission: Entrance to 1st floor rooms is free.

BEDGEBURY NATIONAL PINETUM   Tel: 01580 211044 Fax: 01580 212423

Goudhurst, Cranbrook, Kent TN17 2SL
Owner: Forestry Commission   **Contact:** Mr Colin Morgan
Location: OS Ref. TQ714 337 (gate on B2079). 7m E of Tunbridge Wells on A21, turn N on B2079 for 1m.
Opening Times: W/ends Jan & Feb. 1 Mar - Christmas: daily. 10am - dusk or 7pm.
Admission: Adult £2.50, OAP £2, Child £1.20 (from 1 Apr 1998).

[i] Shop. [&] Not suitable. [☕] Tearoom. [🐕] In grounds, on leads.

BELMONT

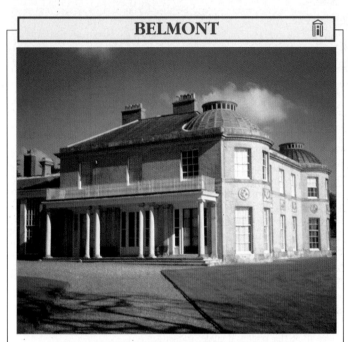

BELMONT PARK, THROWLEY, FAVERSHAM ME13 0HH
Owner: Harris (Belmont) Charity   Contact: Lt. Col F.E. Grant

Tel: 01795 890202

Charming late 18th century country mansion by Samuel Wyatt set in fine parkland. Seat of the Harris family since 1801 when it was acquired by General George Harris, the victor of Seringapatam. The mansion remains in its original state and contains interesting mementos of the family's connections with India and the colonies, plus the 5th Lord Harris' fine clock collection.
Location: OS Ref. TQ986 564. 4^1/2m SSW of Faversham, off A251.
Opening Times: 12 Apr - 27 Sept: Sat, Sun & BHs, 2 - 5pm. Last admission 4.30pm. Groups of 20+ on other days by appointment.
Admission: House & Garden: Adult £5, Child £2.50. Garden: Adult £2.75, Child £1.

[i] Shop. [&] Ground floor suitable. WC. [☕] Tearoom. [🐕] In grounds on leads.

CANTERBURY CATHEDRAL   Tel: 01227 762862 Fax: 01227 762897

Canterbury, Kent CT1 2EH   **Contact:** Lt. Col. D Earlam
Founded in 597AD, Mother Church of the Anglican Communion, Norman Crypt, 14 - 15th century Nave. Site of Becket's martyrdom. Notable stained glass.
Location: OS Ref. TR151 579. Canterbury city centre.
Opening Times: All year: Mon - Sat, 9 - 5pm. Sun, 12 30 - 2.30pm & 4.30 - 5.30pm.
Admission: £2.50, Conc. £1.50.

[i] Shop. [&] Suitable. WC. [🚶] By arrangement.

CHARTWELL 🍃   See page 33 for full page entry.

CHIDDINGSTONE CASTLE 🏛   See pages 34/35 for full page entry.

COBHAM HALL 🏛   See page 36 for full page entry.

DEAL CASTLE   ⊞

VICTORIA ROAD, DEAL, KENT CT14 7BA
Owner: English Heritage Contact: The Custodian

Tel: 01304 372762
Crouching low and menacing, the huge, rounded bastions of this austere fort, built by Henry VIII, once carried 119 guns. A fascinating castle to explore, with long, dark passages, battlements and a huge basement. New for 1988 - interactive displays and exhibition giving a fascinating insight into the Castle's history. Coach parking on main road.
Location: OS Ref. TR378 521. SW of Deal town centre.
Opening Times: 1 Apr - 1 Nov: daily, 10am - 6pm (dusk in Oct). 2 Nov - 31 Mar: Wed - Sun only, 10am - 4pm. Closed 24 - 26 Dec.
Admission: Adult £3, Child £1.50, Conc. £2.30.

[i] Shop. [&] Restricted. [🚶] Free audio tour. [🐕] Guide dogs only.

DICKENS CENTRE - EASTGATE HOUSE   Tel: 01634 844176

High Street, Rochester, Kent ME1 2EW
Owner: Rochester upon Medway City Council
Much altered late 16th century brick house, now containing the Dickens Centre, with exhibits of his life and works, including his best known characters. At the rear is Dickens' prefabricated chalet, brought from Switzerland.
Location: OS Ref. TQ746 683. N side of Rochester High Street, close to the Eastern Road. 400yds SE of the Cathedral.
Opening Times: Daily, 10am - 4.45pm (last admission).
Admission: Adult £3, Child £2 (1997 prices).

DODDINGTON PLACE GARDENS 🏛   Tel: 01795 886101

Doddington, Sittingbourne, Kent ME9 0BB
Owner: Mr & Mrs Richard Oldfield   **Contact:** Mrs Richard Oldfield
10 acres of landscaped gardens in an area of outstanding natural beauty. Woodland garden (spectacular May/Jun), Edwardian rock garden, formal terraces with mixed borders, impressive clipped yew hedges, fine trees, lawns and new folly.
Location: OS Ref. TQ944 575. 4m N from A20 at Lenham or 5m SW from A2 at Ospringe, W of Faversham. Signposted.
Opening Times: May - Sept: Sun 2 - 6pm. Wed & BHs 11am - 6pm. Other times by appointment for groups.
Admission: Adult £2.50, Child 25p.

[i] Shop. [&] Grounds suitable. [☕] Licensed tearoom. [🐕] In grounds, on leads.

DOVER CASTLE & THE SECRET WARTIME TUNNELS ⛫

See page 37 for full page entry.

DOWN HOUSE ⛫

Tel: 0171 973 3434

Luxted Road, Downe, Kent BR6 7JT

Owner: English Heritage   **Contact:** Customer Services

Down House was the home of one of the world's greatest and best known scientists, Charles Darwin. From his study he wrote the controversial *On the Origin of Species by Means of Natural Selection* in 1859.

Location: OS Ref. TQ431 611. Off A21 near Biggin Hill, Downe, Kent.

Opening Times: 10 Apr - 31 Oct: Wed - Sun, 10am - 6pm. 1 Nov - 31 Jan: Wed - Sun, 10am - 4pm. 1 Mar - 31 Mar: Wed - Sun, 10am - 4pm. Closed 24 - 26 Dec & Feb.

Admission: Timed ticketing: available on day or pre-booked on 0171 973 3399.

ℹ Shop.   ♿ Suitable. WC.   🐕 Guide dogs only.

DYMCHURCH MARTELLO TOWER ⛫

Tel: 01304 211067

Dymchurch, Kent

Owner: English Heritage   **Contact:** Area Manager

Built as one of 74 such towers to counter the threat of invasion by Napoleon, Dymchurch is perhaps the best example in the country. Fully restored. You can climb to the roof which is dominated by an original 24-pounder gun complete with traversing carriage.

Location: OS189, Ref. TR102 294. In Dymchurch, access from High Street.

Opening Times: 10 - 13 Apr: 2 - 5.30pm. 2 - 4 May: 2 - 5.30pm. 9 May - 11 Jul & 18 Jul - 31 Aug: daily, 2 - 5.30pm. 1- 30 Sept: Sat & Sun, 2 - 5.30pm.

Admission: Adult £1, Child 50p, Conc. 80p.

EMMETTS GARDEN 🌿

Jenny Harpur

IDE HILL, SEVENOAKS, KENT TN14 6AY

Owner: The National Trust   **Contact:** *The Head Gardener*

Tel: 01732 750367 or 01732 868381 (office)

This charming hill side garden boasts the highest tree top in Kent. Noted for its rare trees and shrubs, bluebells and rose and rock gardens. Wonderful views across The Weald. 18 acres open to the public.

Location: OS Ref. TQ477 524. 1^{1}/2m N of Ide Hill off B2042. M25/J5, then 4m.

Opening Times: 1 Apr - 1 Nov: Sat, Sun, Wed & BH Mon, 11am - 5.30pm, plus Good Fri, 11am - 5.30pm. Last adm. 1 hr before close.

Admission: Adult £3, Child £1.50, Family £7.50. Pre-booked groups £2.20.

ℹ Shop.   ♿ Steep in places. WC.   ☕ Tearoom.   🐕 In grounds, on leads.

FINCHCOCKS

GOUDHURST, KENT TN17 1HH

Owner: Mr Richard Burnett   *Contact: Mrs Katrina Burnett*

Tel: 01580 211702   **Fax:** 01580 211007

Finchcocks is a fine early Georgian manor with a dramatic front elevation attributed to Thomas Archer. It is set in a beautiful garden surrounded by parkland and hop gardens. It is celebrated as a museum of historic keyboard instruments and many musical events take place. Entertaining musical tours on all open days and for all group visits.

Location: OS Ref. TQ700 365. 1m A262, W of village of Goudhurst. 5m Cranbrook, 10m Tunbridge Wells, 45m from London.

Opening Times: Open days with music: Easter - Sept: Sun, BH Mons, Wed & Thur in Aug, 2 - 6pm. By appointment (with music): Apr - Oct: most days, morning, afternoon or evening.

Admission: Adult £5.50, Child £4, OAP £5.50, Student £4.50. Garden only: £2.50.

ℹ Shop. Plant centre. Corporate hospitality.   ✗ Wedding receptions.

☕ Tearoom, licensed restaurant (must book).   🚶 Compulsory.

👪 Educational programme.   🐕 Guide dogs.   💒 Civil Wedding Licence.

THE FRIARS

Tel: 01622 717272   **Fax:** 01622 715575

Aylesford Priory, Aylesford, Kent ME20 7BX

Owner: Carmelite Friars   **Contact:** Margaret Dunk

A peaceful, tranquil retreat, set in 42 acres of lovingly tended grounds. Outstanding ceramic works of art by Adam Kossowski.

Location: OS Ref. TQ724 588. W end of Aylesford village. 3m NW of Maidstone.

Opening Times: Grounds open Summer & Winter, 24 hrs, 365 days.

Admission: No charge.

✗ Available for special functions.   ♿ Suitable.   ☕ Available.   🚶 Available.

🅿 Ample.   🐕 Guide dogs only.   🅰 By arrangement.

GAD'S HILL PLACE

Tel: 01474 822366   **Fax:** 01474 822977

Gad's Hill School, Higham-by-Rochester, Kent ME3 7PA

Owner: Gad's Hill School   **Contact:** Mrs Ann Everitt

This Grade I listed building dates from 1870. Charles Dickens lived here with his family from 1857 until his death in 1870, and wrote his last four novels here. Visitors can see his study, the newly restored conservatory, other rooms, the gardens and the grounds. Rooms can be hired for parties and weddings etc.

Location: OS Ref. TQ710 708. On A226, 3m from Rochester, 4m from Gravesend.

Opening Times: Apr - Oct: 1st Sun in month and BH Suns (inc Easter), 2 - 5pm. During Rochester Dickens Festivals (May/June & Dec), 11am - 4pm. At other times by appointment. Groups welcome.

Admission: Adult £2.50, Child £1.50, OAP £2.50, Student £1.50. Groups by arrangement.

ℹ Shop. Corporate hospitality.   ✗ Wedding receptions.   ♿ Partially suitable.

☕ Café.   🚶 Compulsory.   🐕 Guide dogs.   💒 Civil Wedding Licence.

South East England

GOODNESTONE PARK GARDENS 🏛

GOODNESTONE PARK, CANTERBURY, KENT CT3 1PL

Owner: The Lord & Lady FitzWalter **Contact:** *Lady FitzWalter*

Tel/Fax: 01304 840107

The garden is approximately 14 acres, set in 18th century parkland. There are many fine trees, a woodland area and a large walled garden with a collection of old fashioned roses, clematis and herbaceous plants. Jane Austen was a frequent visitor, her brother Edward having married a daughter of the house.

Location: OS Ref. TR254 544. 8m ESE of Canterbury, 1¹/₂ m E of B2046, at S end of village. Runs from the A2 to Wingham signposted from this road.

Opening Times: 30 Mar - 23 Oct: Sun, 12 - 6pm. Mon, Wed - Fri, 11am - 5pm. Closed Tue & Sat. House open by appointment to groups of 20 at £1.50pp.

Admission: Adult £2.50, Child (under 12) 20p, OAP £2.20, Student £2. Groups (20+) Adult £2.20. Wheelchair users £1, Guided groups £3.

ℹ️ Plant centre.   ♿ Suitable. WC.   ☕ Tearoom.   🐕 No dogs.

GREAT COMP GARDEN

COMP LANE, PLATT, BOROUGH GREEN, KENT TN15 8QS

Owner: R Cameron Esq. **Contact:** *Mr W Dyson*

Tel: 01732 886154

One of the finest gardens in the country, comprising ruins, terraces, tranquil woodland walks and sweeping lawns with a breathtaking collection of trees, shrubs, heathers and perennials, many rarely seen elsewhere. The truly unique atmosphere of Great Comp is further complemented by its Festival of Chamber Music held in July/September.

Location: OS Ref. TQ635 567. 2m E of Borough Green, B2016 off A20. First right at Comp crossroads. ¹/₂ m on left.

Opening Times: 1 Apr - 31 Oct: daily, 11am - 6pm.

Admission: Adult £3, Child £1. Groups (20+) £2.50, Annual ticket: Adult £9, OAP £6.

ℹ️ Plant sales.   ♿ Suitable.   ☕ Sun, BHs & by arrangement.   🐕 Guide dogs.

SPECIAL EVENTS

APR 26: Plant Fair. Special guest Roy Lancaster.

AUG 22 - 23: Hardy Plant Society Annual Garden Show.

GREAT MAYTHAM HALL   **Tel:** 01580 421346 **Fax:** 01580 241038

Rolvenden, Cranbrook, Kent TN17 4NE

Owner: Country Houses Association   **Contact:** The Administrators

Built in 1910 by Sir Edwin Lutyens.

Location: OS Ref. TQ848 306. ¹/₂ m S of Rolvenden village, on road to Rolvenden Lane. Stations: Headcorn 10m, Staplehurst 10m.

Opening Times: 1 May - 30 Sept: Wed & Thur, 2 - 5pm.

Admission: Adult £2.50, Child £1. Groups by arrangement.

🐕 No dogs.   A 1 single & 1 double with bathroom, CHA members only.

GROOMBRIDGE PLACE GARDENS 🏛   See page 38 for full page entry.

HALL PLACE   **Tel:** 01322 526574 **Fax:** 01322 522921

Bourne Road, Bexley, Kent DA5 1PQ

Owner: Bexley Council   **Contact:** Rosemary Evans

A fine Grade I listed country house built in 1540 for Sir John Champnels, a Lord Mayor of London. The house is set in beautiful formal gardens on the banks of the River Cray. Some rooms are open to the public, including the magnificent great hall.

Location: OS Ref. TQ502 743. Near the A2 less than 5m (London bound) from the M25/J2.

Opening Times: Mon - Sat, 10am - 5pm (4.15pm in winter), Sun & BHs, 2 - 6pm (BST only).

Admission: Free. Pre-arranged groups: £1pp.

ℹ️ Shop.   ♿ Partially Suitable.   ☕ Café, licensed restaurant.

🚶 By arrangement.   P Ample for cars, limited for coaches.   🐕 Guide dogs only.

HEVER CASTLE 🏛   See pages 40/41 for full page entry.

THE HISTORIC DOCKYARD   **Tel:** 01634 812551/823800

Chatham, Kent ME4 4TE   **Contact:** Mrs T Gurr

Most complete Georgian/Early Victorian dockyard in the world. 80 acre working heritage site and museum.

Location: OS Ref. TQ756 684. ¹/₄ m from Chatham on Dock Rd, A231.

Opening Times: Apr - Oct: daily, 10am - 5pm (last admission 4pm). Feb/Mar/Nov: Wed, Sat & Sun, 10am - 4pm (last admission 3pm).

ℹ️ Shop.   ♿ Grounds suitable.   🍽 Restaurant.   🚶 Available.

P Ample.   👥 Available.   🐕 In grounds, on leads.

HOLE PARK   **Tel:** 01580 241251 **Fax:** 01580 241882

Rolvenden, Cranbrook, Kent TN17 4JB

Owner: D G W Barham   **Contact:** D G W Barham

A 15 acre garden with all year round interest, set in beautiful parkland with fine views. Trees, lawns and extensive yew hedges precisely cut are a feature. Walled garden with mixed borders, pools and water garden. Natural garden with bulbs, azaleas, rhododendrons and flowering shrubs. Woodland bluebell walk and autumn colours a speciality.

Location: OS Ref. 830 325. 1m W of Rolvenden on B2086 Cranbrook road.

Opening Times: 12, 19 Apr. 3, 10, 24, 31 May. 11, 18 Oct (Sun). Also Weds, 8 Apr - 24 Jun, 2 - 6pm. Groups other days by arrangement.

Admission: Adult £2.50, Child 50p.

♿ Suitable.   🚶 By arrangement.   🐕 Guide dogs.

IGHTHAM MOTE

Andrew Butler

IVY HATCH, SEVENOAKS, KENT TN15 0NT

Owner: The National Trust **Contact:** *The Property Manager*

Tel: 01732 810378 **Fax:** 01732 811029

Beautiful moated manor house covering 650 years of history from the Medieval Great Hall to the Victorian housekeeper's room. North-west quarter re-opens in 1998 after a major conservation programme; see the Tudor chapel, billiard room and drawing room. Exhibition details the traditional skills used. Lovely garden with lakes and woodland. Surrounding estate provides many country walks. House is busy on Sun and BH Mon, 2 - 4pm, visitors may have to wait.

Location: OS Ref. TQ584 535. 6m E of Sevenoaks off A25. $2^1/2$ m S of Ightham off A227.

Opening Times: 1 Apr - 1 Nov: Mon, Wed - Fri & Good Fri, 11am - 5.30pm, Sun & BH Mon, 11am - 5.30pm. Last adm. $^1/2$ hr before close.

Admission: Adult £4.50, Child £2.25, Family £11.25. Groups (pre-booked) £3.50.

[i] Shop.　[♿] Ground floor suitable. WC.　[☕] Tea pavilion.　[🐕] On leads.

KNOLE

See page 42 for full page entry.

LADHAM HOUSE GARDENS
Tel: 01580 211203　**Fax:** 01580 212596

Ladham Lane, Goudhurst, Kent TN17 1DB

Owner: Mr & Mrs Alastair Jessel　　　　**Contact:** Mrs Jessel

10 acre gardens with spectacular twin mixed borders, fine specimen trees and newly planted arboretum. Fine views.

Location: OS Ref. TQ732 384. $^3/4$ NE of Goudhurst off A262. 5m NW of Cranbrook.

Opening Times: 3 & 17 May, 4 Oct, 2 - 5.30pm. By appointment at other times.

Admission: Adult £2.50, Child (under 12yrs) 50p.

[☕] Available.　[🐕] In grounds, on leads.

LEEDS CASTLE
See page 43 for full page entry.

LESNES ABBEY
Tel: 0181 303 9052

Abbey Road, Abbey Wood, London DA17 5DL

Owner: Bexley Council　　　　**Contact:** TIC Manager

The Abbey was founded in 1178 by Richard de Lucy as penance for his involvement in events leading to the murder of Thomas à Becket. Today only the ruins remain.

Location: OS Ref. TQ479 788. In public park on S side of Abbey Road (B213), 500yds E of Abbey Wood Station, $^3/4$ m N of A206 Woolwich - Erith Road.

Opening Times: Any reasonable time.

Admission: Free.

LULLINGSTONE CASTLE
Tel: 01322 862114

Lullingstone Castle, Eynsford, Kent DA4 0JA

Owner: Guy Hart Dyke Esq　　　　**Contact:** Guy Hart Dyke Esq

Fine state rooms, family portraits and armour in beautiful grounds. The 15th century gatehouse was one of the first ever to be made of bricks.

Location: OS Ref. TQ530 644. 1m S Eynsford W side of A225. 600yds S of Roman Villa.

Opening Times: Apr - Jun: Sun & BHs only, 2 - 6pm. Jul - Sept: Sat, Sun & BHs, 2 - 6pm. Apr - Sept: Wed, Thur, Fri, Sat by arrangement.

Admission: Adult £3.75, Child £1.50, Conc. £3, Groups over 25 midweek 10% discount.

[i] Shop.　[♿] Ground floor & grounds suitable. WC.　[☕] Tearoom.　[🐕] No dogs.

LULLINGSTONE ROMAN VILLA

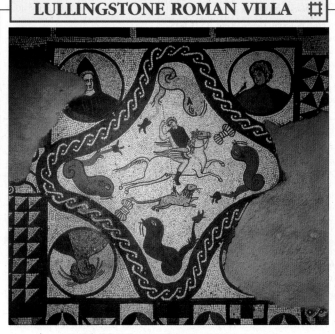

LULLINGSTONE LANE, EYNSFORD, KENT DA4 0JA

Owner: English Heritage **Contact:** *The Custodian*

Tel: 01322 863467

Recognised as one of the most exciting archaeological finds of the century, the villa has splendid mosaic floors and one of the earliest private Christian chapels. Take the free audio tour and discover how the middle-class owners lived, worked and entertained themselves.

Location: OS Ref. TQ529 651. $^1/2$ m SW of Eynsford off A225, M25/J3. Follow A20 towards Brands Hatch. 600yds N of Castle.

Opening Times: 1 Apr - 1 Nov: daily, 10am - 6pm or dusk in Oct. 2 Nov - 31 Mar: 10am - 4pm. Closed 24 - 26 Dec.

Admission: Adult £2.50, Child £1.30, Conc. £1.90.

[i] Shop.　[♿] Ground floor & grounds suitable. WC.　[🚶] Free audio tour.

LYMPNE CASTLE
Tel: 01303 267571

Hythe, Kent CT21 4LQ

Owner: H H Margary Esq　　　　**Contact:** H H Margary Esq

Ancient Castle, rebuilt 1360 and restored in 1905, situated on high ground with magnificent views.

Location: OS Ref. TR120 346. 4m W from Hythe. 9m from Folkstone, via B2067 and then by small lane southwards.

Opening Times: 25 May - mid-Sept (except 25 Aug): Mon - Thur (occasionally Sun), 10am - 5.30pm.

Admission: Adult £2, Child 50p.

[i] Shop.　[♿] Not suitable.　[🐕] On leads.　[💍] Civil Wedding Licence.

MAISON DIEU
Tel: 01795 534542

Ospringe, Faversham, Kent.

Owner: English Heritage　　　　**Contact:** The Faversham Society

This forerunner of today's hospitals remains largely as it was in the 16th century with exposed beams and an overhanging upper storey. It contains an exhibition about Ospringe in Roman times.

Location: OS Ref. TR002 608. In Ospringe on A2, $^1/2$ m W of Faversham.

Opening Times: 11 Apr - 1 Nov: Weekends & BHs, 2 - 5pm. Keykeeper in Winter.

Admission: Adult £1, Child 50p, OAP 80p.

[♿] Not suitable.　[🐕] Guide dogs only.

MILTON CHANTRY
Tel: 01474 321520

New Tavern Fort Gardens, Gravesend, Kent

Owner: English Heritage　　　　**Contact:** Gravesend Borough Council

A small 14th century building which housed the chapel of the leper hospital and the chantry of the de Valence and Montechais families and later became a tavern and in 1780 part of a fort.

Location: OS Ref.TQ652 743. In New Tavern Fort Gardens $^1/4$ m E of central Gravesend off A226.

Opening Times: 1 Apr - 30 Sept: Tue - Fri and BH, 1 - 5pm (closed Tue after BH). Sat & Sun, 10am - 5pm. 1 Oct - 31 Mar, Fri - Sun, 10am - 4pm. Closed 25 - 26 Dec & 1 Jan.

Admission: Adult £1.50, Child 75p, Conc. 75p.

[🐕] Guide dogs only.

South East
England

OLD SOAR MANOR 🌸

Tel: 01732 810378

Plaxtol, Borough Green, Kent TN15 0QX

Owner: The National Trust   **Contact:** Ightham Mote

The solar block of a late 13th century knight's dwelling.

Location: OS Ref. TQ619 541. 1m E of Plaxtol. By narrow lane. 2m S of A25 at Borough Green.

Opening Times: 1 Apr - 30 Sept: daily, 10am - 6pm.

Admission: Free.

PATTYNDENNE MANOR

Tel: 01732 810378

Goudhurst, Kent TN17 2QU

Owner: Mr & Mrs D C Spearing   **Contact:** Mr D C Spearing

One of the great timber houses of England, built of oak trees felled from the surrounding forest twenty years before Columbus discovered America. Special architectural details include the jettying, dragon beams, king post and tie beam, corner posts of upturned oaks, and an amazing wealth of timbering only to be seen in a house built before the modern iron industry destroyed England's forests. 13th century prison. Associated with Henry VIII as a hunting lodge.

Location: OS Ref. TQ720 366. 10m E of Tunbridge Wells. W side of B2079, 1m S of Goudhurst (A262).

Opening Times: By prior appointment only. Groups 20 - 55 people.

Admission: Groups only. Adult £4.25.

☕ Available.   🚶 Connoisseur tours.

PENSHURST PLACE & GARDENS

See page 44 for full page entry.

QUEBEC HOUSE 🌸

Tel: 01892 890651

Westerham, Kent TN16 1TD

Owner: The National Trust   **Contact:** Regional Office

General Wolfe spent his early years in this gabled, red-brick 17th century house. Four rooms containing portraits, prints and memorabilia relating to Wolfe's family and career are on view. In the Tudor stable block is an exhibition about the Battle of Quebec (1759) and the parts played by Wolfe and his adversary, the Marquis de Montcalm.

Location: OS Ref. TQ449 541. At E end of village, on N side of A25, facing junction with B2026, Edenbridge Road.

Opening Times: 5 Apr - 27 Oct: Sun & Tue, 2 - 6pm, last admission 5.30pm.

Admission: Adult £2.50, Child £1.25, Groups £1.80.

RECULVER TOWERS & ROMAN FORT ⌗

Tel: 01227 366444

Reculver, Herne Bay, Kent

Owner: English Heritage   **Contact:** Reculver Country Park

This 12th century landmark of twin towers has guided sailors into the Thames estuary for seven centuries, but you can also see the walls of a Roman fort, which were erected nearly 2,000 years ago.

Location: OS Ref. TR228 694. At Reculver 3m E of Herne Bay by the seashore.

Opening Times: Any reasonable time. External viewing only.

Admission: Free.

♿ Ground floor suitable, long slope from car park.   🐕 No dogs.

RICHBOROUGH ROMAN FORT ⌗

Tel: 01304 612013

Richborough, Sandwich, Kent CT13 9JW

Owner: English Heritage   **Contact:** The Custodian

This fort and township date back to the Roman landing in AD43. The fortified walls and the massive foundations of a triumphal arch which stood 80 feet high still survive. Museum giving an insight into Roman life in Richborough's heyday as a busy township.

Location: OS Ref. TR324 602. 1^1/2m NW of Sandwich off A257.

Opening Times: 1 Apr - 1 Nov: daily, 10am - 6pm or dusk in Oct. 2 Nov - 31 Mar: Wed - Sun only, 10am - 4pm. Weekends only in Dec, Jan & Feb, 10am - 4pm. Closed 24 - 26 Dec.

Admission: Adult £2.50, Child £1.30, Conc. £1.90.

ℹ Shop & museum.   ♿ Ground floor suitable.   🚶 Free audio tour.   🐕 Guide dogs only.

RIVERHILL HOUSE 🏠

Tel: 01732 458802 or 01732 452557

Sevenoaks, Kent TN15 0RR

Owner: The Rogers Family   **Contact:** Mrs Rogers

Small country house built in 1714, home of the Rogers family since 1840. Panelled rooms, portraits and interesting memorabilia. Historic hillside garden with extensive views, rare trees and shrubs. Sheltered terraces and rhododendrons and azaleas in a woodland setting. Bluebells, ancient trackway known as Harold's Road.

Location: OS Ref. TQ541 522. 2m S of Sevenoaks on E side of A225.

Opening Times: Garden: Apr, May & Jun: Wed, Sun & BH weekends. House & Garden: Apr, May & Jun: Open for pre-booked groups (adults only, 20+) on any day.

Admission: Adult £2.50, Child 50p. Pre-booked groups: £3.50.

ℹ Shop. Conferences.   ♿ Not suitable.   ☕ Tearoom.   🚶 By arrangement.   🐕 No dogs.

ROCHESTER CASTLE ⌗

Tel: 01634 402276

The Lodge, Rochester-upon Medway, Medway ME1 1SX

Owner: English Heritage   **Contact:** Head Custodian

(Managed by Rochester upon Medway City Council)

Built in the 11th century to guard the point where the Roman road of Watling Street crossed the River Medway, the size and position of this grand Norman Bishop's castle, founded on the Roman city wall, eventually made it an important royal stronghold for several hundred years. The keep is truly magnificent - over 100 feet high and with walls 12 feet thick. At the top you will be able to enjoy fine views over the river and surrounding city of Rochester.

Location: OS Ref. TQ742 686. By Rochester Bridge (A2), M2/J1 & M25/J2.

Opening Times: 1 Apr - 1 Nov: daily, 10am - 6pm. 2 Nov - 31 Mar: daily 10am - 4pm. (Closed 24 - 27 Dec).

Admission: Adult £2.60, Child £1.30, OAP £2.

ℹ Shop.   🐕 Guide dogs only.

ROCHESTER CATHEDRAL

Tel: 01634 401301 **Fax:** 01634 401410

Rochester, Kent ME1 1JY

Contact: Ms M Hawes

Founded in 604AD, Rochester Cathedral has been a place of Christian worship for nearly 1,400 years. The present building is a blend of Norman and Gothic architecture. In the cloister are the remains of the 12th century chapter house and priory. A focal point is the Doubleday statue of Christ and the Blessed Virgin.

Location: OS Ref. TQ742 686. Signposted from M20/J6 and on the A2/M2/J3. City centre.

Opening Times: 8.30am - 5pm. Visiting may be restricted during services.

Admission: Donation.

ℹ Shop.   ♿ Suitable. WC.   ☕ Tearoom.   Ⓟ No parking.

ROMAN PAINTED HOUSE

Tel: 01304 203279

New Street, Dover, Kent CT17 9AJ

Owner: Dover Roman Painted House Trust   **Contact:** Mr B Philip

Discovered in 1970. Built around 200AD as a hotel for official travellers. Well preserved impressive wall paintings, central heating systems and the Roman fort wall built through the house.

Location: OS Ref. TR318 414. Dover town centre. E of York St.

Opening Times: Apr - Sept: 10am - 5pm, except Mon.

Admission: Adult £2, Child 80p, OAP 80p.

ℹ Shop.   ♿ First floor suitable. .   🐕 Guide dogs only.

ST AUGUSTINE'S ABBEY ⌗

Tel: 01227 767345

Longport, Canterbury, Kent CT1 1TF

Owner: English Heritage   **Contact:** The Custodian

The Abbey, founded by St Augustine in 598, is a world heritage site. Take the free interactive audio tour which gives a fascinating insight into the Abbey's history and visit the new museum displaying artifacts uncovered during archaeological excavations of the site.

Location: OS Ref. TR154 578. In Canterbury ^{1}/2m E of Cathedral Close.

Opening Times: 1 Apr - 1 Nov: daily, 10am - 6pm or dusk if earlier. 2 Nov - 31 Mar: daily, 10am - 4pm. Closed 24 - 26 Dec.

Admission: Adult £2.50, Child £1.30, Conc. £1.90. 15% discount for groups of 11+. One extra place for every additional 20. Free audio tours.

ℹ Shop. ♿ Grounds suitable. WC. ☕ Available. 🚶 Audio tour. 🐕 Guide dogs only.

ST JOHN'S COMMANDERY ⌗

Tel: 01304 211067

Densole, Swingfield, Kent

Owner: English Heritage   **Contact:** The South East Regional Office

A medieval chapel built by the Knights Hospitallers, ancestors of the St John Ambulance Brigade. It has a moulded plaster ceiling and a remarkable timber roof which was converted into a farmhouse in the 16th century.

Location: OS Ref. TR232 440. 2m NE of Densole on minor road off A260.

Opening Times: Any reasonable time for exterior viewing. Internal viewing by appointment only.

Admission: Free.

♿ Not suitable.   🐕 Guide dogs only.

Bounder:

One who does not behave in the accepted manner. The term arose c.1900 with the arrival from the USA of the new-fangled rubber-core golf ball: most golfers in Britain continued to use the old gutta percha balls, but shifty players, the bounders, used the new ball, which went further and bounced.

Extract from: "Life in the Country House" by David N Durant (published by John Murray), PB£15.99, see page twelve at the front of the book.

SCOTNEY CASTLE GARDEN

Stephen Robson

LAMBERHURST, TUNBRIDGE WELLS, KENT TN3 8JN

Owner: The National Trust   Contact: Administration Assistant

Tel: 01892 891081 **Fax:** 01892 890110

One of England's most romantic gardens, surrounding the ruins of a 14th century moated castle. Rhododendrons, azaleas, water-lilies and wisteria flower in profusion. Renowned for its autumn colour. The ruined old castle with its priest hole is open for the summer. The surrounding estate has many country walks.

Location: OS Ref. TQ688 353. Signed off A21 1m S of Lamberhurst village.

Opening Times: 1 Apr - 1 Nov (old Castle May - 13 Sept): Wed - Fri, 11am - 6pm, Sat & Sun 2 - 6pm, BH Sun & Mon 12 - 6pm (closed Good Fri). Last adm. 1 hr before close.

Admission: Adult £3.80, Child £1.90, Family £9.50 Pre-booked groups £2.80.

i Shop.   Grounds (but steep parts).   In grounds, on leads.

SISSINGHURST CASTLE GARDEN   Tel: 01580 715330 Fax: 01580 713911

Sissinghurst, Cranbrook, Kent TN17 2AB

Owner: The National Trust   **Contact:** The Visitor Services Manager

The 5½ acre famous connoisseurs' garden created by Vita Sackville-West and her husband, Sir Harold Nicolson. Exhibition, woodland and lake walks.

Location: OS Ref. TQ807 383. 1m E of Sissinghurst village off A262, 2m NE of Cranbrook.

Opening Times: 1 Apr - 15 Oct: Tue - Fri, 1 - 6.30pm, Sat, Sun & Good Fri, 10am - 5.30pm. Closed all Mons including BH Mon. Last admission ½ hr before close. Timed tickets due to over-crowding, please be prepared to wait at peak times.

Admission: Adult £6, Child £3.

SMALLHYTHE PLACE   Tel/Fax: 01580 762334

Smallhythe, Tenterden, Kent TN30 7NG

Owner: The National Trust   **Contact:** The Custodian

Home of Shakespearean actress Dame Ellen Terry, containing personal and theatrical mementoes. Also garden and barn theatre.

Location: OS Ref. TQ893 300. 2m S of Tenterden on E side of the Rye road B2082.

Opening Times: 1 Apr - 28 Oct: Sat - Wed and Good Fri, 1 - 5.30pm. Last adm. 5pm.

Admission: Adult £3, Child £1.50, Family £7.50.

SQUERRYES COURT   See page 45 for full page entry.

STONEACRE   Tel: 01622 862871 Fax: 01622 862157

Otham, Maidstone, Kent ME15 8RS

Owner: The National Trust   **Contact:** The Tenant

A half-timbered mainly late 15th century yeoman's house, with great hall and crownpost, and newly restored cottage-style garden.

Location: OS Ref. TQ800 535. In narrow lane at N end of Otham village, 3m SE of Maidstone, 1m S of A20.

Opening Times: 1 Apr - 31 Oct: Wed & Sat, 2 - 6pm. Last admission 1hr before close.

Admission: Adult £2.80, Child £1.25.

TEMPLE MANOR   Tel: 01634 827980

Strood, Rochester, Kent

Owner: English Heritage   **Contact:** Rochester upon Medway City Council

The 13th century manor house of the Knights Templar which mainly provided accommodation for members of the order travelling between London and the Continent.

Location: OS Ref. TQ733 686. In Strood (Rochester) off A228.

Opening Times: 1 Apr - 30 Sept: daily, 12 - 5pm. Weekends & BHs, 10am - 6pm.

Admission: Free.

Grounds only.   Guide dogs only.

TONBRIDGE CASTLE   Tel: 01732 770929

Castle Street, Tonbridge, Kent TN9 1BG

Owner: Tonbridge & Malling Borough Council   **Contact:** Sheila Kostyrka

Location: OS Ref. TQ588 466. 300 yds NW of the Medway Bridge at town centre.

Opening Times: Mon - Sat, 9am - 4pm. Sun/BHs 10.30am - 4pm. Phone for Autumn opening times.

Admission: Adult £3.35, Conc. £1.65, Family £8.

UPNOR CASTLE   Tel: 01634 718742

Upnor, Kent

Owner: English Heritage   **Contact:** Rochester upon Medway City Council

Well preserved 16th century gun fort built to protect Queen Elizabeth I's warships. However in 1667 it failed to prevent the Dutch navy which stormed up the Medway destroying half the English fleet.

Location: OS Ref. TQ758 706. At Upnor, on unclassified road off A228. 2m NE of Strood.

Opening Times: 1 Apr - 30 Sept: daily 10am - 6pm.

Admission: Adult £2.60, Child £1.30, OAP £1.90.

Grounds suitable.   Dogs allowed in certain areas.

WALMER CASTLE & GARDENS

WALMER, DEAL, KENT CT14 7LJ

Owner: English Heritage   Contact: The Custodian

Tel: 01304 364288

A Tudor fort transformed into an elegant stately home. The residence of the Lords Warden of the Cinque Ports and still used by HM The Queen Mother today. See the Duke of Wellington's rooms and even his famous boots. Beautiful gardens including the Queen Mother's Garden. Lunches and cream teas available in the delightful Lord Warden's tearooms.

Location: OS Ref. TR378 501. S of Walmer on A258, M20/J13 or M2 to Deal.

Opening Times: 1 Apr - 1 Nov: daily, 10am - 6pm or dusk in Oct. 2 Nov - Dec: Wed - Sun only. Closed 24 - 26 Dec. Jan - Feb: Weekends only. Mar: Wed - Sun only. Closed when Lord Warden in residence.

Admission: Adult £4, Child £2, OAP/Student £3. 15% discount for groups of 11+. One extra place for each additional 20. EH members free. Free audio tour.

i Shop.   Grounds suitable.   Available.   Guide dogs only.

WILLESBOROUGH WINDMILL   Tel: 01233 661866

Mill Lane, Willesborough, Ashford, Kent

125 year old restored smock mill.

Location: OS Ref. TR031 421. Off A292 close to M20/J10. At E end of Ashford.

Opening Times: Apr - Sept; Sat, Sun and BH Mon, 2 - 5pm or dusk if earlier.

Admission: Adult £1, Child 50p, Conc. 50p. Groups 10% reduction by arrangement only.

South East
England

THE BANQUETING HOUSE
Whitehall

The Banqueting House is principally used for concerts and banqueting. It was completed in 1622, commissioned by King James I, and designed by Inigo Jones, the noted classical architect. In 1635 the main hall was further enhanced with the installation of 9 magnificent ceiling paintings by Sir Peter Paul Rubens.

King Charles I was executed just outside the entry door in 1649. The hall and ceiling paintings survive to this day (as does the atmospheric undercroft) and the whole building provides a magnificent backdrop for many of society's most glittering occasions.

❖

CONTACT

Irma Hay (day visitors)
Fiona Thompson
(functions)
The Banqueting Hall
Whitehall
London
SW1A 2ER

Tel: (0171) 930 4179
or (0171) 839 7569

Fax: (0171) 930 8268

LOCATION

OS Ref. TQ302 801

Tube Stations:
Westminster,
Embankment
and Charing Cross

Rail: Charing Cross

OPENING TIMES

All year
Mon - Sat
10am - 5pm
last admission 4.30pm.

Closed 24 December -
1 January, Good Friday
and other public holidays.

NB. Liable to close at short notice for Government functions.

ADMISSION

Adult £3.50
Child* £2.30
OAP/Conc...............£2.70
Under 5s ....FREE

Groups
Less 10% for groups
over 15

* under 16 years.

ℹ️ Shop. Concerts.

✖️ Banquets.

♿ Undercroft suitable.

☕ No catering for
day visitors.

🚶 Video and audio guide.

🅿️ Parking on the
Embankment.

👫 Welcome.

CONFERENCE/FUNCTION		
ROOM	SIZE	MAX CAPACITY
Main Hall	110' x 55'	550
Undercroft	70' x 55'	350

CHISWICK HOUSE
Chiswick

Chiswick House is internationally renowned as one of the first and finest English Palladian villas. Lord Burlington, who built the villa from 1725 - 1729, was inspired by the architecture and gardens of ancient Rome and this house is his masterpiece. His aim was to create a fit setting to show his friends his fine collection of art and library and the opulent interior features gilded decoration, velvet walls and painted ceilings. The important 18th century gardens surrounding Chiswick House have, at every turn, something to surprise and delight the visitor from the magnificent cedar trees to the beautiful Italianate gardens with their cascade, statues, temples, urns and obelisks.

CONTACT

Visits:
The Head Custodian
Chiswick House
Burlington Lane
London
W4 2RP

Tel: (0181) 995 0508

Corporate Events:
Events Manager
Room 402
429 Oxford Street
London
W1R 2HD

Tel: 0171 973 3494

LOCATION

OS Ref: TQ210 775

Burlington Lane
London W4

Rail: 1/4m NE of Chiswick Station.

Bus: LT190, 290 (Hammersmith - Richmond)

OPENING TIMES

SUMMER
1 April - 30 September
daily, 10am - 6pm.

AUTUMN
1 - 21 October
daily, 10am - 5pm.

WINTER
22 October - 31 March
Wed - Sun, 10am - 4pm.

ADMISSION

Adult £3.00
Child* £1.50
Conc.......................£2.30

* 5 - 15 years.

15% discount for groups of 11+.

---

i Shop. Filming, plays, photographic shoots. Colour guide book £2.25.

X Exclusive private & corporate hospitality.

& Wheelchair access to ground floor.

Homemade refreshments available in the summer season.

Available for pre-booked parties, tour time 1 hr. Free audio tours in English, French & German.

P Tour leader and coach driver have free entry. 1 extra place for every 20 additional people.

Free if booked in advance. Tel: 0181 348 1268/7.

Guide dogs in grounds.

Civil Wedding Licence.

KENSINGTON PALACE STATE APARTMENTS
Kensington

Please telephone for details of 1998 opening times.

CONTACT

Kensington Palace
State Apartments
London
W8 4PX

Tel: (0171) 937 9561

LOCATION

OS Ref. TQ258 801

In Kensington Gardens.

Tube Station: Queensway
on Central Line,
High Street Kensington on
Circle & District Line

The history of Kensington Palace goes back to 1689 when the newly crowned William III and Mary II commissioned Sir Christopher Wren to convert the then Nottingham House into a Royal Palace. The Palace was again altered when George I had the artist William Kent paint the magnificent and elaborate trompe l'oeil ceilings and staircases which can still be enjoyed at this most private of Royal Palaces.

This beautiful historic building has seen such momentous events as the death of George II and the birth of Princess Victoria who began her long reign as Queen in 1837, with a meeting of her Privy Council in the Red Saloon.

While the Palace remains a busy Royal residence, the State Apartments have been unoccupied since 1837 and this year marks one hundred years since they were first opened to the public. Guided tours offer an informative and anecdotal insight into the lives of those who lived there, from the last of the Stuarts to the Hanoverians and finally the young Victoria herself. Highlights of the tour include the splendid Cupola Room, where Queen Victoria was baptised, and the beautifully restored King's Gallery with its fine collection of 17th century paintings.

This year also sees the unveiling of an exciting new representation of the Royal Ceremonial Dress Collection, with court and ceremonial dress spanning the last two hundred years on show to the public.

ADMISSION

Please telephone for 1998 admission prices.

FUNCTIONS		
ROOM	SIZE	MAX CAPACITY
Orangery	55' 6" x 11' 6"	250 (receptions)
		125 (dinners)

ℹ️ Shop. No inside photography.

☕ The Orangery serves light refreshments.

🚶 Entry by guided tour for Dress Collection and sound guide for State apartments.

👨‍👩‍👧 Welcome, please book.

South East
England

KENWOOD HOUSE
Hampstead

KENWOOD, one of the treasures of London, is an idyllic country retreat close to the popular villages of Hampstead and Highgate.

The house was remodelled in the 1760s by Robert Adam, the fashionable neo-classical architect. The breathtaking library or 'Great Room' is one of his finest achievements.

Kenwood is famous for the internationally important collection of paintings bequeathed to the nation by Edward Guinness, first Earl of Iveagh. Some of the world's finest artists are represented by works such as a Rembrandt *Self Portrait*, Vermeer's *The Guitar Player, Mary,*

Countess Howe by Gainsborough and paintings by Turner, Reynolds and many others.

As if the house and its contents were not riches enough, Kenwood stands in 112 acres of landscaped grounds on the edge of Hampstead Heath, commanding a fine prospect towards central London. The meadow walks and ornamental lake of the park, designed by Humphry Repton, contrast with the wilder Heath below. The open air concerts held in the summer at Kenwood have become part of London life, combining the charms of music with the serenity of the lakeside setting.

CONTACT

The House Manager
Kenwood House
Hampstead Lane
London
NW3 7JR

Tel: 0181 348 1286

LOCATION

OS Ref. TQ271 874

Hampstead Lane, NW3.

Bus: London Transport 210.

Rail: Hampstead Heath.

Underground: Archway or Golders Green Northern Line then bus 210.

OPENING TIMES

SUMMER

1 April - 30 September
daily: 10am - 6pm.

October
daily: 10am - 5pm.

WINTER

1 November - 31 March
daily
10am - 4pm.

ADMISSION

FREE

The 45 minute tour must be booked in advance. This can be given in French as well as English.

ℹ️ Shops. Concerts, exhibitions, filming. No photography in house.

✖️ The Old Kitchen is available for wedding receptions and corporate entertainment.

♿ Ground floor access. Parking for the disabled.

☕ Available in the Brew House.

🚶 Foreign language tours by prior arrangement. Personal stereo tours.

🅿️ West Lodge car park on Hampstead Lane.

👪 Free when booked in advance on (0171) 973 3499.

South East England

QUEEN'S HOUSE
Greenwich

CONTACT

Bookings Unit
National Maritime Museum
Romney Road
Greenwich
London
SE10 9NF

Tel: (0181) 858 4422

Fax: (0181) 312 6632

Recorded Info:
0181 312 6565

LOCATION

OS Ref. TQ386 776

On the South Bank of the Thames at Greenwich. A2/A206 from London, elsewhere M25/J2 then A2.

Rail: From Charing Cross, Waterloo East or London Bridge to Maze Hill or Greenwich.

River: Cruises from Central London to Greenwich.

Air: London City Airport 4m.

At the centre of a group of splendid historical buildings lies The Queen's House, a royal palace designed by Inigo Jones. The house has been sumptuously restored to show the vibrant colours of the decoration when occupied by the dowager queen Henrietta Maria, wife of Charles I. Built in the classical style of Palladio, the house in 1635 marked a major change for English architecture, and demonstrated new rules of proportion. The Great Hall is a 40' cube, and its ceiling is a reproduction of the original by the Gentileschis.

The vaults now house a Treasury of trophies, swords and plate marking great occasions in history. The elegant Tulip Staircase leads to rooms used for audiences which are now decorated with beautifully woven silk damask and brocatelle. A quiet loggia overlooks the royal park with a view of Wren's Observatory building with its unusual red time ball that marks Greenwich time at 1 o'clock daily.

The 3-site ticket includes admission to The Old Royal Observatory and the adjacent National Maritime Museum which is filled with stories of Britain's great naval heroes and explorers, impressive oil paintings and many fascinating exhibits. A fine exhibition celebrates the life of Nelson.

A visit to all three buildings will occupy a full day or a visit can be combined with a river cruise on the Thames. The park, the oldest of the royal parks, is ideal for picnics and includes outstanding landscaping by Le Notre, flower gardens, deer park and children's playground.

❖

i Shop. Fashion photography, filming, small balls, lawns for marquees, parkland and grounds, lecture theatre in adjacent museum. No photography.

✗ Approved and recommended caterers. Corporate hospitality, wedding receptions.

♿ Accessible for wheelchairs (upper floor by 'Stairmate'). Signed and Touch tours for groups by prior arrangement. Advisory leaflet.

☕ Restaurant seating 150 in adjoining museum.

🚶 Pre-book, Tel: 0181 312 6608. Approx £40 per group.

P 115 cars within 100m and 25 coaches within 600m. Coaches can set down nearby prior to parking. Guides and coach drivers admitted free. Children's groups must pre-book.

👥 Linked to National Curriculum. Education enquiries 0181 312 6608.

💍 Civil Wedding Licence.

OPENING TIMES

ALL YEAR
January - October
possible closure
thereafter for works.

Daily
10am - 5pm
Last admission 4.30pm.

Closed 24 - 26 Dec.

ADMISSION

3 Site Ticket
Adult £5.00
Concessions*...........£4.00
Child (5 - 16yrs)......£2.50
Family (2+3) £15.00

Groups
A discount of 20% for groups of 10 or more.

* OAPs, Students, UB40, Disabled.

CONFERENCE/FUNCTION		
ROOM	SIZE	MAX CAPACITY
Great Hall	40' x 40'	200*
Orangery		150*
Private Rms		40
* Includes ante-rooms.		

ROYAL SOCIETY OF ARTS
John Adam Street

The House of the RSA (Royal Society for the encouragement of Arts, Manufactures and Commerce) was designed specially for the Society by Robert Adam in the early 1770s. Today the RSA's terrace of five 18th century houses is the finest and historically most interesting remaining section of the Adam brothers' development known as the Adelphi. A complex £4,500,000 building and refurbishment programme has brought the RSA's magnificent vaults into full use for receptions and private dining.

The Great Room. The jewel in the RSA's crown is the Great Room, one of the most spectacular and delightful lecture halls in the country. The recent refurbishment of this room, including the installation of air conditioning and a new roof light, has enhanced this spectacular setting for the series of allegorical paintings, *The Progress of Human Knowledge* by James Barry. A perfect atmosphere for meetings, press conferences, recitals and wedding ceremonies. The unique ambience of this room is suitable for groups from 50 to 200.

Benjamin Franklin Room: The classic Benjamin Franklin Room is a spacious assembly room with its chandelier and Adam fireplaces yet with a controlled ventilation system, ideal for meetings, receptions and banquets for 30-150 persons.

The Vaults: Beneath the Society's house lies the largest remaining part of the Adelphi arches. Originally built for storage and more recently used as wine cellars, the vaults have now been restored and converted to provide a unique venue for all forms of event. They feature the original 18th century brickwork, and can be dressed to enhance product launches, parties, themed events and private exhibitions.

CONTACT

Ms Y Chenaux
Conference Manager
Royal Society of Arts
8 John Adam Street
London
WC2N 6EZ

Tel: (0171) 839 5049

Fax: (0171) 321 0271

LOCATION

OS Ref. TQ305 806

Rail: Near to two mainline stations. Charing Cross, Waterloo.

Nearest underground: Embankment, Charing Cross, Covent Garden

OPENING TIMES

SUMMER

8am - 8pm

Closed during the last 2 weeks of August.

WINTER

8am - 8pm

Closed 24 Dec - 2 Jan 1998.

ADMISSION

For room hire prices, please contact the RSA Conference Office direct for a brochure.

CONFERENCE/FUNCTION		
ROOM	SIZE	MAX CAPACITY
Great Room	42' x 36'	200
Durham St Auditorium	36' x30'	60
B. Franklin	42' x 36'	150
Tavern	40' x 17'	60
Folkestone	20' x 20'	30
Gallery	40' x 20'	100
Vault 1	55' x 28'	100
Vault 2	36' x 18'	50
Vault 3	20' x 18'	30
Vault4	37' x 11'	75

i Product launches, themed parties, corporate announcements, film previews, dinner dances, private concerts, exhibitions, lectures on history of the house. All visits are by prior arrangement.

✗ Private catering, lunches, dinners and receptions.

♿ Wheelchair access to all main rooms via a lift.

🚶 Tours for groups of up to 25 may be arranged in advance. All visitors to the house must pre-book.

P Parking area is at Vauxhall, meters in John Adam Street, car parks in Savoy Place and St Martin's Lane. Coaches may only set down and pick up on John Adam Street or the Strand.

💒 Civil Wedding Licence

SPENCER HOUSE
St James's Place

CONTACT

Jane Rick
Director
Spencer House
27 St James's Place
London
SW1A 1NR

Tel: (0171) 514 1964

Fax: (0171) 409 2952

Info Line: (0171) 499 8620

LOCATION

OS Ref. TQ293 803

Central London:
off St James's Street,
overlooking Green Park.

Underground:
Green Park.

All images are copyright
of Spencer House Ltd
and may not be used
without the permission of
Spencer House Ltd

SPENCER HOUSE, built 1756 - 66 for the 1st Earl Spencer, an ancestor of Diana, Princess of Wales (1961-97), is London's finest surviving 18th century town house. The magnificent private palace has regained the full splendour of its late 18th century appearance, after a painstaking ten-year restoration programme.

Designed by John Vardy and James 'Athenian' Stuart, the nine state rooms are amongst the first neo-classical interiors in Europe. Vardy's Palm Room, with its spectacular screen of gilded palm trees and arched fronds, is a unique Palladian setpiece, while the elegant mural decorations of Stuart's Painted Room reflect the 18th century passion for classical Greece and Rome. Stuart's superb gilded furniture has been returned to its original location in the Painted Room by courtesy of the V&A and English Heritage. Visitors can also see a fine collection of 18th century paintings and furniture, specially assembled for the house, including five major Benjamin West paintings, graciously lent by Her Majesty The Queen.

The state rooms are open to the public for viewing on Sundays. They are also available on a limited number of occasions each year for private and corporate entertaining during the rest of the week.

❖

OPENING TIMES

ALL YEAR

All year
except January & August
Sun, 10.30am - 5.30pm.

Last tour 4.45pm.

Tours begin approximately every 15 mins and last 1 hr. Maximum number on each tour is 15.

Open for corporate hospitality except during January & August.

ADMISSION

To end Dec 1998

Adult £6.00
Conc.* £5.00

* Students, Friends of V&A, Tate Gallery and Royal Academy (all with cards), children under 16 (no under 10s admitted).

Prices include guided tour.

ℹ️ Board meetings, theatre-style meetings, contract signings. No photography inside House. Comprehensive colour guidebook £3.50.

✕ In-house catering for private and corporate events including wedding receptions and private parties.

♿ Ramps and lifts. WC.

☕ Not available for Sunday visitors.

🚶 All visits are by guided tour.

🅿️ No parking facilities. Coaches can drop off at door.

🐕 No dogs.

CONFERENCE/FUNCTION		
ROOM	SIZE	MAX CAPACITY
Receptions		500
Lunches & Dinners		130
Board Meetings		40
Theatre Style meetings		100

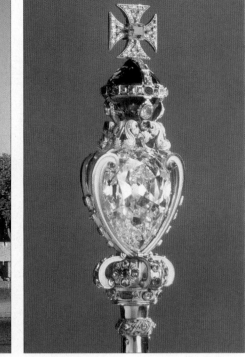

THE TOWER OF LONDON
London

The Tower of London was started by William the Conqueror in 1078. Over the ensuing 900 years the Tower has served as a Royal Palace, armoury, fortress, Royal Mint and more infamously, as a prison and place of execution.

It remains home to the magnificent Crown Jewels. To many these represent the most potent symbols of the British monarchy. The Imperial State Crown is still worn by HM The Queen at the annual State Opening of Parliament. The Crown Jewels also boast one of the largest cut diamonds in the world at 530 carats, the First Star of Africa, which is set in the Sovereign's Sceptre.

Once inside, the famous Yeoman Warders give free guided tours giving an unrivalled insight into the dark secrets of the Tower's history.

They will tell of the legend of the ravens, resident at the Tower for over 900 years. It is said that if they leave, the White Tower will fall and a great disaster befall the Kingdom.

Visitors can stand on Tower Green where two of Henry VIII's wives lost their heads, enter the Bloody Tower where Sir Walter Raleigh was imprisoned, and look down upon Traitor's Gate through which many royal visitors made their last journey.

Costumed guides give special presentations in Edward I's Medieval Palace, where the restored rooms evoke life in the 1280s. A new permanent exhibition 'Crowns and Diamonds' recalls the history of English crowns and show cases a pile of diamonds worth £2.5 million.

❖

CONTACT

The Tower of London
London
EC3N 4AB

Tel: (0171) 709 0765

LOCATION

OS Ref. TQ336 806

Tube Station: Tower Hill on Circle / District Line. Monument on Northern Line.

Docklands Light Railway: Tower Gateway Station.

Rail: Fenchurch Street Station and London Bridge Station.

Bus: 15, X15, 25, 42, 78, 100, D1, D9, D11.

Riverboat: From Charing Cross, Westminster or Greenwich to Tower Pier.

OPENING TIMES

SUMMER

1 March - 31 October
daily
Mon - Sat: 9am - 6pm
Sun: 10am - 6pm

WINTER

1 November - 28 February
Tue - Sat: 9am - 5pm
Sun & Mon: 10am - 5pm

Closed 24 - 26 December
and 1 January.

Last admission one hour
before closing.

ADMISSION

Prices are from
1 Jan '98 - 11 Jun '98

Adult..........................£9.00
Child..........................£5.90
OAP/Student..............£6.80
Family.......................£26.90

Prices from 12 Jun '98

Adult..........................£9.50
Child..........................£6.25
OAP/Student..............£7.15
Family.......................£28.40

ℹ️ Shops.

♿ WC.

☕ Available on the wharf.

🚶 Yeoman Warder tours are free and leave front entrance every ¹/₂ hr.

🅿️ No parking.

👪 Welcome. Group rates on request.

THE WALLACE COLLECTION
Manchester Square

The Wallace Collection is a national museum. It is housed in Hertford House, Manchester Square, which was originally built for the 4th Duke of Manchester in 1776-88. It is a rare survivor of a London town house occupying the whole northside of the garden square.

The museum itself houses a superb range of fine and decorative arts from the 16th - 19th centuries. It was formed largely between 1802 and 1875 by three generations of the Marquesses of Hertford and by the 4th Marquess' son, Sir Richard Wallace. Although it is probably best known for its magnificent 18th century French paintings, furniture and porcelain, the Wallace Collection also displays many other treasures such as paintings by Titian, Rembrandt, Rubens and Frans Hals (*The Laughing Cavalier*). There is also the finest collection of princely armour and arms in Britain, as well as choice and opulent displays of gold boxes, miniatures, sculpture and medieval and Renaissance works of art such as maiolica, glass and Limoges enamels.

The Wallace Collection offers some of the most spectacular rooms in London for entertaining and is available a limited number of times a year for corporate and private receptions and dinners.

❖

CONTACT

Joanne Charlton
Jane Cappabianca
The Wallace Collection
Hertford House
Manchester Square
London
W1M 6BN

Tel: (0171) 935 0687

Fax: (0171) 224 2155

LOCATION

OS Ref. TQ283 813

Central London behind Selfridges department store off Duke Street.

Tube Station: Baker Street, Marble Arch and Bond Street.

CONFERENCE/FUNCTION		
ROOM	SIZE	MAX CAPACITY
Receptions		300
Dinners		150

OPENING TIMES

ALL YEAR
Weekdays 10am - 5pm
Sunday 2 - 5pm
(April - September
Sunday 11am - 5pm).

Closed
Good Friday, May Day,
24 - 26 December and
New Year's Day.

ADMISSION

Free.

ℹ️ Shop. Corporate hospitality, launches, filming, photography, Sunday morning recitals (contact Jane Cappabianca ext. 45 or Joanne Charlton ext. 16).

✗ Approved and recommended caterers.

♿ Suitable, wheelchair at front entrance, lift to first floor. All works of art shown on ground and first floors.

🚶 Free guided tours daily. Private tours, study days (contact Stephen Duffy ext. 17).

🅿️ Coaches may set down at Hertford House, parking is at Bayswater Road, W8. Meters in Manchester Square.

👪 Welcome. Activity days, education pack linked to National Curriculum (contact Suzanne Higgott ext. 51).

2 WILLOW ROAD 🌿

Tel: 0171 435 6166

Hampstead, London NW3 1TH

Owner: The National Trust　　　**Contact:** The Custodian

The former home of Erno Goldfinger, designed and built by him in 1939. A three-storey brick and concrete rectangle, it is one of Britain's most important examples of modernist architecture and is filled with furniture also designed by Goldfinger. The interesting art collection includes works by Henry Moore and Max Ernst.

Location: OS Ref. TQ270 858. Hampstead, London.

Opening Times: 2 Apr - 31 Oct: Thur, Fri & Sat, 12 - 5pm. (Closed BH Mon). Last admission 4pm. Guided tours every 45 mins.

Admission: Adult £4.

♿ Ground floor suitable, filmed tour of whole house available.　🚶 Compulsory.

ALBERT MEMORIAL ⛫

Tel: 0171 225 1059　**Fax:** 0171 591 0036

Visitor Centre, Princes Gate, Kensington Gore SW7

Owner: English Heritage　　　**Contact:** Head Custodian

An elaborate memorial by George Gilbert Scott to commemorate the Prince Consort.

Location: OS Ref. TQ266 798. Victoria Station 1 1/2 m, South Kensington Tube 1/2 m.

Opening Times: The Visitor Centre is closed for 1998.

Admission: Free.

APSLEY HOUSE

149 Piccadilly, Hyde Park Corner, London W1V 9FA

Owner: V & A Museum & Dept. of Culture, Media & Sport　*Contact: Leah Tobin*

Tel: 0171 495 8525 / 499 5676　**Fax:** 0171 493 6576

Apsley House (No. 1, London) was designed by Robert Adam and built 1771-8. In 1817 it was bought by the Duke of Wellington and his 'London Palace' houses his magnificent collection: paintings, mainly original from the Spanish Royal Collection, by Velazquez, Goya, Rubens, Lawrence, Wilkie and Dutch masters; sculpture, silver, porcelain and furniture.

Location: OS Ref. TQ284 799. N side of Hyde Park Corner. Nearest tube station: Hyde Park Corner exit 3 Piccadilly Line.

Opening Times: Tue - Sun, 11am - 5pm, last admission 4.30pm. Closed Mon, except BHs, Good Fri, May Day BH, 24 - 26 Dec and New Year's Day.

Admission: Adult £4, Child (under 12) free, OAP/Student £2.50. Pre-arranged groups (min 10): Adult £2.50.

ℹ️ Shop. Corporate hospitality.　♿ Partially suitable.　🚶 By arrangement.

🅿️ Parking nearby in Park Lane.　🐕 Guide dogs only.

THE BANQUETING HOUSE

See page 52 for full page entry.

BLEWCOAT SCHOOL 🌿

Tel: 0171 222 2877

23 Caxton Street, Westminster, London SW1H 0PY

Owner: The National Trust　　　**Contact:** The Administrator

Built in 1709 at the expense of William Green, a local brewer, to provide an education for poor children. The building was used as a school until 1926, and is now the NT London Information Centre and shop.

Location: OS Ref. TQ295 794. Near the junction with Buckingham Gate.

Opening Times: All year: Mon - Fri, 10am - 5.30pm. Also 28 Nov & 5 & 12 & 19 Dec, 11am - 4.30pm. Closed BH Mon, Good Fri, 25 Dec - 1 Jan 1999 inclusive.

ℹ️ Shop.　♿ Suitable (some steps to shop).

BOSTON MANOR HOUSE

BOSTON MANOR ROAD, BRENTFORD TW8 9JX

Owner: London Borough of Hounslow　*Contact: Allan Downend*

Tel: 0181 560 5441　**Fax:** 0181 862 7602

A fine Jacobean House built in 1623. The rooms that can be viewed include the State Drawing Room with a magnificent ceiling and fireplace designed in 1623. The ceiling is divided into panels representing the senses and the elements. It is a rare example of a Jacobean House in the London area. The ground floor is available for hire and when not in use can be viewed. The rooms contain part of the local collection of paintings, and represent views of the locality from the 18th century to today.

Location: OS Ref. TQ168 784. 10 mins walk S of Boston Manor Station (Piccadilly Line) and 250yds N of Boston Manor Road junction with A4 - Great West Road, Brentford.

Opening Times: 4 Apr - 25 Oct: Sat, Sun & BHs, 2.30 - 5pm. Park open daily.

Admission: Free.

♿ Ground floor & grounds suitable. WC.　🐕 No dogs.　💒 Civil Wedding Licence.

BRITISH ARCHITECTURAL LIBRARY

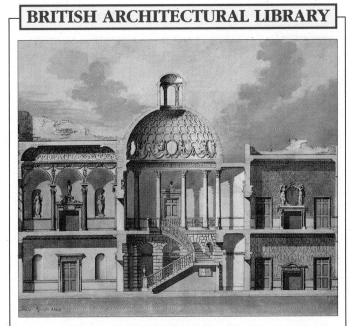

DRAWINGS COLLECTION, 21 PORTMAN SQUARE, LONDON W1H 9HF

Owner: Royal Institute of British Architects　*Contact: The Curator*

Tel: 0171 580 5533　**Fax:** 0171 486 3797

Collection of 600,000 architectural drawings from c.1500 onwards.

Location: OS Ref. TQ280 812. NE of Marble Arch.

Opening Times: Exhibitions: Weekdays 11am - 5pm. Saturdays: 11am - 2pm. The Study Collection seen by appointment.

Admission: Exhibition: Free. Fee charged to consult drawings.

SPECIAL EVENTS

JAN 22 - MAR 7: Architects & Exhibition Design 1900 - 1998.

MAR 26 - MAY 9: Thomas Allom (1804 - 72)

JUN 4 - JUL 26: Art Nouveau Architecture of Riga.

SEPT 1 - OCT 24: The Palace of Whitehall, 1530 - 1698.

NOV 4 - DEC 19: Alvar Aalto and The House of Culture, Helsinki.

BRUCE CASTLE
Tel: 0181 808 8772

Lordship Lane, London N17 8NU
Owner: London Borough of Haringey

A Tudor building. Sir Rowland Hill (inventor of the Penny Post) ran a progressive school at Bruce Castle from 1827.

Location: OS Ref. TQ335 906. Corner of Bruce Grove (A10) and Lordship Lane, 600yds NW of Bruce Grove Station.

Opening Times: All year: Wed - Sun & Summer BHs, 1 - 5pm. Organised groups by appointment.

Admission: Free.

ℹ️ Shop.　　♿ Ground floor suitable. WC.　　🅿️ Ample for cars.

BUCKINGHAM PALACE
Tel: 0171 839 1377

London SW1A 1AA
Owner: HM The Queen

Official London residence of HM The Queen. Bought for George III in 1762 and extensively remodelled by John Nash in the 1820s for George IV.

Location: OS Ref. TQ291 796. Central London.

Opening Times: 10 Aug - 30 Sept: 9.30am - 5.30pm. Ticket Office: 9am, last admission 4.30pm. Pre-booking essential for disabled visitors. Dates are provisional.

Admission: State Rooms: Adult £9.50, OAP £7, Child (under 17) £5.

ℹ️ Shop.　　♿ House suitable. WC.　　🅿️ No parking.　　🐕 Guide dogs only.

BURGH HOUSE
Tel: 0171 431 0144　Buttery: 0171 431 2516　**Fax:** 0171 435 8817

New End Square, Hampstead, London NW3 1LT
Owner: London Borough of Camden　　　　**Contact:** Ms Helen Wilton

A Grade I listed building of 1703 in the heart of old Hampstead with original panelled rooms, "barley sugar" staircase bannisters and a music room. Home of the Hampstead Museum, permanent and changing exhibitions. Prize-winning terraced garden. Regular programme of concerts, art exhibitions, and meetings. Receptions, seminars and conferences. Rooms for hire. Special facilities for schools visits. Wedding receptions.

Location: OS Ref. TQ266 859. New End Square, E of Hampstead underground station.

Opening Times: All year: Wed - Sun 12 - 5pm. Good Fri & BH Mon, 2 - 5pm. Closed Christmas week and New Year. Groups by arrangement. Buttery: Wed - Sun, 11am - 5.30pm. BHs 1 - 5.30pm. Closed Christmas fortnight.

Admission: Free.

ℹ️ Shop.　　♿ Ground floor & grounds suitable. WC.　　☕ Licensed buttery.
🅿️ No parking.　　🐕 Guide dogs only.　　💒 Civil Wedding Licence.

CAPEL MANOR GARDENS

BULLSMOOR LANE, ENFIELD EN1 4RQ
Owner: Capel Manor Charitable Organisation　　Contact: Miss Julie Ryan

Tel: 0181 366 4442　**Fax:** 01992 717544

These extensive, richly planted gardens are delightful throughout the year offering inspiration, information and relaxation. The gardens include various themes - historical, modern, walled, rock, water, sensory and disabled and an Italianate Maze, Japanese Garden and 'Gardening Which?' demonstration and model gardens. Capel Manor is a College of Horticulture and runs a training scheme for professional gardeners devised in conjunction with the Historic Houses Association. Special events throughout the year.

Location: OS Ref. TQ344 997. Minutes from M25/J25. Tourist Board signs posted (yellow signs in Summer).

Opening Times: Daily in summer: 10am - 5.30pm. Last ticket 4.30pm. Check for winter times.

Admission: Adult £4, Conc. £3.50, Child £2, Family £10. Charges alter for special show weekends and winter months.

ℹ️ Shop.　　♿ Grounds suitable. WC.　　☕ Tearoom.　　🐕 In grounds, on leads.

CARLYLE'S HOUSE 🦋
Tel: 0171 352 7087

24 Cheyne Row, Chelsea, London SW3 5HL
Owner: The National Trust　　　　**Contact:** The Custodian

This Queen Anne town house was the home of the 'Sage of Chelsea', Victorian writer and historian Thomas Carlyle and his wife Jane. The atmospheric interior has the Carlyles original furniture and decoration, together with the books, portraits and personal mementoes acquired during their 30 years here. Dickens, Chopin, Tennyson, George Eliot and Emerson were among the illustrious visitors to the house. Carlyle used to sit and enjoy the small, tranquil walled garden.

Location: OS Ref. TQ272 777. Off Cheyne Walk, between Battersea and Albert Bridges on Chelsea Embankment, or off the Kings Road and Oakley Street.

Opening Times: 1 Apr - 1 Nov: Wed - Sun & BH Mon, 11am - 5pm. Last admission 4.30pm. Closed Good Fri.

Admission: Adult £3.20, Child £1.60.

THE CHELSEA PHYSIC GARDEN
Tel: 0171 352 5646　**Fax:** 0171 376 3910

66 Royal Hospital Road, London SW3 4HS
Owner: Chelsea Physic Garden Company　　　　**Contact:** Sue Minter

The second oldest botanic garden in Britain, founded in 1673. For many years these 4 acres of peace and quiet with many rare and unusual plants were known only to a few. Specialists in medicinal plants, tender species and the history of plant introductions.

Location: OS Ref. TQ277 778. Off Embankment, between Chelsea & Albert Bridges. Entrance - Swan Walk.

Opening Times: 5 Apr - 25 Oct: Wed 12 - 5pm & Sun 2 - 6pm. Snowdrop opening & winter festival: 8 & 15 Feb 11am - 3pm.

Admission: Adult £3.50, Child £1.80, Student £1.80, OAP £3.50, carers for disabled: free.

♿ Suitable. WC.　　☕ Available.　　🐕 No dogs.

SPECIAL EVENTS
JUL 12 - SEPT 6: Summer Exhibition 'Art and Healing in Ghana'.
MAY 18 - 22: Chelsea Show Week. Exhibition: The Centenary of The London Sketch Club.
JUNE 1 - 5: Chelsea Festival Week, 12 noon - 5pm.

CHISWICK HOUSE ⌗
See page 53 for full page entry.

COLLEGE OF ARMS
Tel: 0171 248 2762　**Fax:** 0171 248 6448

Queen Victoria Street, London EC4V 4BT
Owner: Corp. of the Kings, Heralds & Pursuivants of Arms　**Contact:** The Officer in Waiting

Mansion built in 1670s to house the English Officers of Arms and their records.

Location: OS Ref. TQ320 810. On N side of Queen Victoria Street, S of St Paul's Cathedral. No coaches or indoor photography.

Opening Times: Earl Marshal's Court only; open all year (except BHs, State and special occasions) Mon - Fri 10am - 4pm. Group visits (up to 10) by arrangement only. Record Room: open for tours (groups of up to 20) by special arrangement in advance with the Officer in Waiting.

Admission: Free (parties by negotiation).

ℹ️ Shop.　　♿ Not suitable.　　🚶 By arrangement.　　🅿️ No parking.　　🐕 No dogs.

THE DICKENS HOUSE MUSEUM
Tel: 0171 405 2127　**Fax:** 0171 831 5175

48 Doughty Street, London WC1N 2LF
Owner: The Trustees　　　　**Contact:** Dr David Parker

Charles Dickens lived here as a young man, and his drawing room has been reconstructed.

Location: OS Ref. TQ308 822. W of Grays Inn Road.

Opening Times: Mon - Sat: 10am - 5pm (last admission 4.30pm). Closed Sun & some BHs.

Admission: Adult £3.50, Student £2, Child £1.50, Family £7.

DR JOHNSON'S HOUSE
Tel: 0171 353 3745

17 Gough Square, London EC4A 3DE
Owner: The Trustees

Fine 18th century house, once home to Dr Samuel Johnson, the celebrated literary figure, famous for his English dictionary.

Location: OS Ref. TQ314 813. N of Fleet Street.

Opening Times: Oct - Apr: Mon - Sat, 11am - 5pm. May - Sept: Mon - Sat, 11am - 5.30pm.

Admission: Adult £3, Child over 10 £1, Child under 10 free, Conc. £2.

EASTBURY MANOR HOUSE 🦋
Tel: 0181 507 0119

Barking IG11 9SN
Owner: The National Trust　　　　**Contact:** The Administrator

Eastbury is a rare example of a medium-sized Elizabethan Manor House, originally part of the estate of Barking Abbey and still surviving amongst 20th century housing. The interior has early wallpaintings and several rooms are being refurbished in Elizabethan style. The manor garden is being recreated. Leased to the Borough of Barking and Dagenham and used for a variety of arts and heritage activities.

Location: OS177, Ref. TQ457 838. In Eastbury Square, 10 mins walk S from Upney Station.

Opening Times: 1 Feb - 30 Nov: Mon - Fri, 10am - 5pm by appointment. Also open one Sat (Visitor Day) every month 10am - 4pm. Telephone for details.

Admission: £1.60. Group visits by prior arrangement. Rates on application.

♿ Ground floor suitable.　　☕ Tearoom.　　🅿️ No parking.　　🐕 Garden only.

ELTHAM PALACE

Tel: 0181 294 2548

Court Yard, Eltham SE9 5QE

Owner: English Heritage   **Contact:** Head Custodian

Eltham Palace provides a unique combination; a medieval palace and a Modernist country house set in magnificent moated grounds. The 1930s apartments built by the Courtauld family with their fascinating period interiors make an unusual contrast with the connecting medieval Great Hall with its magnificent hammer-beam roof.

Location: OS Ref. TQ425 740. ³/₄ m N of A20 off Court Yard, SE9. Train Stations: Eltham or Mottingham.

Opening Times: English Heritage is carrying out major conservation and building work in 1998. Please telephone for details of opening times in spring 1999.

FULHAM PALACE & MUSEUM

BISHOPS AVENUE, FULHAM, LONDON SW6 6EA

Owner: London Borough of Hammersmith & Fulham & Fulham Palace Trust

Tel: 0171 736 5821   **Museum:** 0171 736 3233

Former home of the Bishops of London (Tudor with Georgian additions and Victorian Chapel). The gardens, famous in the 17th century, now contain specimen trees and a knot garden of herbs. The museum is in part of the palace and details the history of the site. Rooms and grounds are available for private functions.

Location: OS Ref. TQ240 761.

Opening Times: Gardens: open daylight hours. Museum: Mar - Oct: Wed - Sun, 2 - 5pm. Nov - Feb: Thur - Sun, 1 - 4pm. Tours of principal rooms and gardens every 2nd Sun - contact museum, selected other Sundays contact Fulham Archaeological Rescue Group 0171 385 3723, £2. Private tours £4 each by arrangement with either organisation.

Admission: Gardens: Free. Museum: Adult 50p, Conc. 25p.

ⓘ Private & wedding receptions.   ♿ Partially suitable.   🚶 Guided tours only.

🅿 No parking.   Educational programme.   🐕 Guide dogs only.

FENTON HOUSE

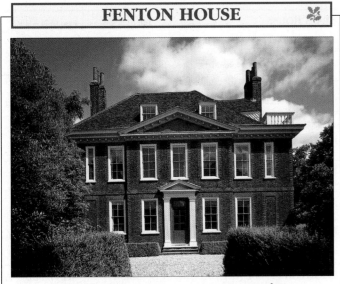

WINDMILL HILL, HAMPSTEAD, LONDON NW3 6RT

Owner: The National Trust   Contact: The Custodian

Tel: 0171 435 3471

A delightful late 17th century merchant's house, set among the winding streets of Old Hampstead. The charming interior contains an outstanding collection of Oriental and European porcelain, needlework and furniture. The Benton Fletcher Collection of beautiful early keyboard instruments is also housed at Fenton and the instruments are sometimes played by music scholars during opening hours. The walled garden has a formal lawn and walks, an orchard and vegetable garden and fine wrought-iron gates.

Location: OS Ref. TQ262 862. Visitors' entrance on W side of Hampstead Grove. Hampstead underground station 300 yds.

Opening Times: 1 - 22 Mar: Sat & Sun, 2 - 5pm. 1 Apr - 1 Nov: Sat, Sun & BH Mon, 11am - 5pm, Wed, Thur & Fri, 2 - 5pm. Last admission 30 mins before closing. Parties received at other times by appointment.

Admission: Adult £4, Family £10. No reduction for pre-booked groups. No picnics in grounds.

♿ Ground floor suitable.   🅿 No parking.   🐕 No dogs.

FORTY HALL MUSEUM

Tel: 0181 363 8196 **Fax:** 0181 367 9098

Forty Hill, Enfield, Middlesex EN2 9HA

Owner: London Borough of Enfield   **Contact:** John Griffin

Built in 1629 for Sir Nicholas Raynton, Lord Mayor of London.

Location: OS Ref. TQ336 986. W side of Forty Hill, 1¹/₂ m N of Enfield and 1¹/₂ m SW of M25/J25. ¹/₂ m W of A10 via Hoe Lane.

Opening Times: Thur - Sun, 11am - 5pm.

Admission: Free

♿ Ground floor suitable.   ☕ Café.   🅿 Ample. No coaches.   🐕 No dogs.

FREUD MUSEUM

Tel: 0171 435 2002 **Fax:** 0171 431 5452

20 Maresfield Gardens, London NW3 5SX

Contact: Ms E Davies

The Freud Museum was the home of Sigmund Freud after he escaped the Nazi annexation of Austria. The house retains its domestic atmosphere and has the character of turn of the century Vienna. The centrepiece is Freud's study which has been preserved intact, containing his remarkable collection of antiquities: Egyptian, Greek, Roman, Oriental and his large library. The Freuds brought all their furniture and household effects to London; fine Biedermeier and 19th century Austrian painted furniture. The most famous item is Freud's psychoanalytic couch, where his patients reclined. Fine Oriental rugs cover the floor and tables. Videos are shown of the Freud family in Vienna, Paris and London.

Location: OS Ref. TQ265 850. Between Swiss Cottage and Hampstead.

Opening Times: Wed - Sun (inc) 12 - 5pm.

Admission: Adult £3, Child under 12 free, Conc. £1.50. Coach parties by appointment.

ⓘ Shop.   ♿ Ground floor suitable.   🅿 Limited.   🐕 Guide dogs only.

THE GEFFRYE MUSEUM

Tel: 0171 739 9893 **Fax:** 0171 729 5647

Kingsland Road, London E2 8EA

Owner: Independent Charitable Trust   **Contact:** Ms Nancy Loader

The Geffrye Museum is one of London's most friendly and enjoyable museums, set in elegant grade I listed 18th century almshouses with delightful gardens, just north of the city. It presents the changing style of the English domestic interior from 1600 to 1950 through a series of period rooms. Innovative programme of lectures and activities.

Location: OS Ref. TQ335 833. 1m N of Liverpool St. Buses: 22A, 22B, 149, 243, 67. Underground: Liverpool St. or Old St. Parking: available in neighbouring streets.

Opening Times: Tue - Sat, 10am - 5pm. Sun & BH Mon, 2 - 5pm. Closed Mon (except BHs) Good Fri, Christmas Eve, Christmas Day, Boxing Day & New Years Day.

Admission: Free.

ⓘ Shop.   ♿ Suitable. WC.   ☕ Coffee bar.   🐕 Guide dogs only.

GEORGE INN

Tel: 0171 407 2056

77 Borough High Street, Southwark, London SE1

Owner: The National Trust

The only remaining galleried inn in London, famous as a coaching inn in the 18th and 19th centuries, and mentioned by Dickens in *Little Dorrit*. The George Inn is leased to and run by Whitbread Plc as a public house.

Location: OS Ref. TQ326 799. On E side of Borough High Street, near London Bridge station.

Opening Times: During licensing hours.

GUNNERSBURY PARK MUSEUM

Tel: 0181 992 1612 **Fax:** 0181 752 0686

Gunnersbury Park, London W3 8LQ

Owner: Hounslow and Ealing Councils   **Contact:** Mr Séan Sherman

Built in 1802 and refurbished by Sydney Smirke for the Rothschild family. Their attractive park, splendid interiors and original kitchens survive. Now a social history museum with regularly changing displays.

Location: OS Ref. TQ190 792. Acton Town underground station. ¹/₄ m N of the junction of A4, M4 North Circular.

Opening Times: Apr - Oct: daily: 1 - 5pm. (6pm weekends & BHs). Nov - Mar: daily: 1 - 4pm. Victorian kitchens summer weekends only. Closed Christmas Day and Boxing Day. Park: open dawn - dusk.

Admission: Free. Donations welcome.

HAM HOUSE

HAM, RICHMOND, SURREY TW10 7RS

Owner: The National Trust   *Contact: Mrs J Graffius*

Tel: 0181 940 1950 **Fax:** 0181 332 6903 **e-mail:** shhgen@smtp.ntrust.org.uk

Ham House, on the banks of the River Thames, is perhaps the most remarkable Stuart house in the country. Apart from the fact that its architectural fabric has survived virtually unchanged since the 1670s, it still retains many of the furnishings from that period. Ham is presented today principally as the late 17th century Lauderdale residence with overlays of the 18th and 19th centuries. Visitors view the rooms in the sequence intended at the time, progressing through a hierarchy of apartments towards the Queen's Closet - the culmination of the sequence. The gardens are being restored using plans and images which were found in the house and were laid out in compartments, reflecting the ordered symmetry of the house and together they present the modern visitor with a complete picture of 17th century aristocratic life.

Location: OS Ref. TQ172 732. 1½ m from Richmond and 2m from Kingston. On the S bank of the River Thames, W of A307 at Petersham.

Opening times: 28 Mar - 1 Nov: daily except Thur & Fri . House: 1 - 5pm, last adm.4.30pm. Gardens: 10.30am - 6pm/dusk if earlier. Closed 25 - 26 Dec & 1 Jan.

Admission: House & Garden: Adult £5, Child £2.50, Family £12.50. Garden only: Adult £1.50, Child 75p. Pre-booked groups (min 15): Adult £4, Child £2.

Partially suitable. WC. Tearoom. Guide dogs. Civil Wedding Licence.

HOGARTH'S HOUSE

HOGARTH LANE, GREAT WEST ROAD, CHISWICK W4 2QN

Owner: London Borough of Hounslow   **Contact:** Allan Downend

Tel: 0181 994 6757 **Fax:** 0181 862 7602

This late 17th century house was the country home of William Hogarth, the famous painter, engraver, satirist and social reformer between 1749 and his death in 1764. It contains a collection of his engravings and prints, and the house is surrounded by an extensive garden which is in the process of restoration. The house is now a gallery, which describes Hogarth's life and work and also his wide range of interests, together with a display of his prints.

Location: OS Ref. TQ213 778. 100 yds W of Hogarth roundabout on the Great West Road - junction of Burlington Lane. Car park in named spaces in Axis Business Centre behind house and Chiswick House grounds.

Opening Times: Apr - Oct: Tue - Fri, 1 - 5pm, Sat & Sun 1 - 6pm. Nov - Mar: Tue - Fri, 1 - 4pm, Sat & Sun, 1 - 5pm. Closed Jan, Good Fri, 25 & 26 Dec. Closed Mons except BHs.

Admission: Free.

Ground floor suitable. No dogs.

JEWEL TOWER

Tel: 0171 222 2219

Abingdon Street, Westminster, London SW1P 3JY

Owner: English Heritage   **Contact:** Head Custodian

Built c1365 to house the personal treasure of Edward III and one of two surviving parts of the Palace of Westminster. It was used to house valuables which formed part of the King's 'wardrobe' and subsequently used as a storehouse and government office. Exhibition, 'Parliament Past and Present', with a new touch screen computer giving a virtual reality tour of the Houses of Parliament.

Location: OS Ref. TQ302 794. Opposite S end of Houses of Parliament (Victoria Tower).

Opening Times: 22 Mar - 30 Sept: daily 10am - 6pm. 1 - 31 Oct: daily 10am - 6pm or dusk if earlier. 1 Nov - 21 Mar: daily 10am - 4pm.

Admission: Adult £1.50, Child 80p, Conc. £1.10.

Shop. Ground floor suitable. In grounds, on leads.

KEATS HOUSE

Tel: 0171 435 2062 **Fax:** 0171 431 9293

Keats Grove, Hampstead, London NW3 2RR

Owner: Corporation of London   **Contact:** Mrs C M Gee

Regency home of the poet John Keats (1795 - 1821).

Location: OS Ref. TQ272 856. Hampstead, NW3. Nearest underground: Belsize Park & Hampstead.

Opening Times: The House will be closed to the public from Dec 1997 until further notice for urgent repairs. Please telephone for further details.

Admission: Free.

Shop. Not suitable. No parking. Guide dogs only.

KENSINGTON PALACE STATE APARTMENTS

See page 54 for full page entry.

KENWOOD HOUSE

See page 55 for full page entry.

LEIGHTON HOUSE ART GALLERY & MUSEUM

Tel: 0171 602 3316

12 Holland Park Road, Kensington, London W14 8LZ

Fax: 0171 371 2467

Owner: Royal Borough of Kensington & Chelsea   **Contact:** Curator

Leighton House was the home of Frederic, Lord Leighton 1830 - 1896, painter and President of the Royal Academy, built between 1864 - 1879. It was a palace of art designed for entertaining and to provide a magnificent working space in the studio, with great north windows and a gilded apse. The Arab Hall is the centrepiece of the house, containing Leighton's collection of Persian tiles, a gilt mosaic frieze and a fountain. Victorian paintings by Leighton, Millais and Burne-Jones are on display.

Location: OS Ref. TQ247 793. N of High Street Kensington, off Melbury Rd, close to Commonwealth Institute.

Opening Times: Daily, except Sun & BHs, 11am - 5.30pm.

Admission: Free. £1.50 per head for pre-booked tour.

LINDSEY HOUSE

Tel: 01494 528051

99 -100 Cheyne Walk, London SW10 0DQ

Owner: The National Trust   **Contact:** NT Regional Office

Part of Lindsey House was built in 1674 on the site of Sir Thomas More's garden, overlooking the River Thames. It has one of the finest 17th century exteriors in London.

Location: OS Ref. TQ268 775. On Cheyne Walk, W of Battersea Bridge near junction with Milman's Street on Chelsea Embankment.

Opening Times: By written appointment only. Please write to: R Bourne, 100 Cheyne Walk, London SW10 0DQ.

Not suitable. No parking. No dogs.

Louis XV (Louis Quinze) Style (1715–1774):

Much French furniture of this period is to be seen in the great houses of Britain. The style is rococo at its most frivolous, easily distinguished by heavy ormolu decoration, beautiful marquetry and sensuous curves, particularly in the legs. The best is undoubtedly in the Wallace Collection in London, but there are a number of exquisite pieces at Boughton House, Northamptonshire and the Rothschilds' collection at Waddesdon Manor, Buckinghamshire is well worth seeing.

Extract from; "Life in the Country House" by David N Durant (published by John Murray), PB£15.99, see page twelve at the front of the book.

LINLEY SAMBOURNE HOUSE

18 STAFFORD TERRACE, LONDON W8 7BH

Owner: *Administered by The Victorian Society*   **Contact:** *The Administrator*

Recorded Message: 0181 937 0663 **Info:** 0171 602 3316 **Fax:** 0171 371 2467

The home of Linley Sambourne (1844 - 1910) chief political cartoonist at Punch. A unique example of a late Victorian town house. The original decoration and furnishings have been largely preserved together with many of Sambourne's own cartoons and photographs, as well as works by other artists of the period.

Location: OS Ref. TQ252 794. Bus: 9, 10, 27, 28, 31, 49, 52, 70 & C1. Tube: Kensington High Street. Parking on Sun in nearby streets.

Opening Times: Mar - Oct: Wed, 10am - 4pm & Sun 2 - 5pm, last admission 30 mins before close. Groups at other times by appointment. Closed Nov - Feb.

Admission: Adult £3, Child (under 16) £1.50, OAP £2.50. Group: Adult £2.50, Child £1.50, OAP £2.50. Extra charge for groups at other times, Wed & Sun.

[i] Shop.   Not suitable.   By arrangement.   No dogs.

MARBLE HILL HOUSE

RICHMOND ROAD, TWICKENHAM TW1 2NL

Owner: *English Heritage*   **Contact:** *House Manager*

Tel: 0181 892 5115

This beautiful villa beside the Thames was built in 1724 - 29 for Henrietta Howard, mistress of George II. Here she entertained many of the poets and wits of the Augustan age including Alexander Pope and Horace Walpole. The perfect proportions of the villa were inspired by the work of the 16th century Italian architect, Palladio. Today this beautifully presented house contains an important collection of paintings and furniture, including some pieces commissioned for the villa when it was built.

Location: OS Ref. TQ174 736. A305, 600yds E of Orleans House.

Opening Times: 1 Apr - 30 Sept: daily, 10am - 6pm. 1 Oct - 21 Oct: daily, 10am - 5pm. 22 Oct - 31 Mar, Wed - Sun, 10am - 4pm.

Admission: Adult £3, Child £1.50, Conc. £2.30.

[i] Shop.   Ground floor & grounds suitable. WC.   Café.

MUSEUM OF GARDEN HISTORY   **Tel:** 0171 261 1891

Lambeth Palace Road, Lambeth, London SE1 7LB   **Tel enquiry:** 0171 401 8865

Owner: The Tradescant Trust   **Contact:** Mrs J Battersby

Location: OS Ref. TQ306 791. At Lambeth parish church, next to Lambeth Palace, at E end of Lambeth bridge.

Opening Times: All year: daily Mon - Fri: 10.30am - 4pm. Sun 10.30am - 5pm. Closed Sat.

Admission: Free. Donations appreciated.

THE OCTAGON, ORLEANS HOUSE GALLERY   **Tel:** 0181 892 0221

Riverside, Twickenham, Middlesex TW1 3DJ   **Fax:** 0181 744 0501

Owner: London Borough of Richmond upon Thames

Outstanding example of baroque architecture built by James Gibbs c.1720. Adjacent wing now converted to an art gallery.

Location: OS Ref. TQ168 734. On N side of Riverside, 700yds E of Twickenham town centre, 400yds S of Richmond Road, A305 via Lebanon Park Road and 500yds W of Marble Hill House.

Opening Times: Tue - Sat, 1 - 5.30pm. Sun & BH, 2 - 5.30pm. Closed Mon. Garden: open daily, 9am - sunset.

Admission: Adult £1, Leisure card holders 80p. Child under 16yrs free.

 Ground floor suitable.   Schools/education services.   Civil Wedding Licence.

OLD BATTERSEA HOUSE   **Tel:** 0181 785 6450

30 Vicarage Crescent, Battersea, London SW11 3LD

Owner: Forbes Magazine   **Contact:** J. Catleugh

Built 1699. Houses collection of paintings by Evelyn De Morgan and ceramics by William De Morgan.

Location: OS Ref. TQ267 767. Close to S shore of River Thames, 1/2 m SW of S end of Battersea Bridge, via Battersea Church Road and Vicarage Crescent.

Opening Times: By appointment, generally on Wed afternoons.

Admission: £2.

OLD ROYAL OBSERVATORY   **Tel:** 0181 312 6565 (24hr) **Fax:** 0181 312 6632

Greenwich Park, London SE10 9NF

Owner: c/o National Maritime Museum   **Contact:** Robin Scates, Visitor Services

Built by Wren in 1675. Famous for 'Greenwich Mean Time' and the Meridian Line (Longitude 0°), datum point for world time and the Millennium. See the timeball drop at 1 o' clock, the Astronomer Royal's apartments, famous Harrison timekeepers (1735-60) and the largest refracting telescope in Britain. Ticket includes National Maritime Museum and Queen's House. Astronomy days during school holidays.

Location: OS Ref. TQ388 773. In Greenwich Park, off A2, 1/2m S of town centre.

Opening Times: All year: daily 10am - 5pm. (not 24 - 26 Dec).

Admission: Adult £5, Child £2.50, OAP/Student £4, Family £15. Pre-arranged groups (10+) 20% discount.

[i] Shop. No photography.   Partially suitable. WC.   Café.   By arrangement.
[P] Coach park 625 metres.   Education programme.   Guide dogs only.

SPECIAL EVENTS 1998 See the front section for full list.

Historic Scotland

South East England

OSTERLEY PARK

ISLEWORTH TW7 4RB

Owner: *The National Trust*　**Contact:** *The Property Manager*

Tel: 0181 560 3918

Osterley's four turrets look out across one of the last great landscaped parks in suburban London, its trees and lakes an unexpected haven of green. Originally built in 1575, the mansion was transformed in the 18th century into an elegant villa by architect Robert Adam. The classical interior, designed for entertaining on a grand scale, still impresses with its specially made tapestries, furniture and plasterwork.

Location: OS Ref. TQ146 780. Access via Thornbury Road on N side of A4.

Opening Times: 1 Apr - 1 Nov: Wed - Sat, 2 - 5pm. BH Mon & Sun: 11am - 5pm. Closed Good Fri. Last admission: 4.30pm. Grand Stable: Sun afternoon in summer. Park & Pleasure Grounds: All year, 9am - 7.30pm or sunset if earlier. Park will be closed early during major events. Car park closed 25 - 26 Dec.

Admission: £4, Family £10. Group: Wed - Sat £3.50, pre-booking required. £1 off adult tickets for holders of valid LT travelcard. Car Park: £2 (refundable when house ticket purchased).

[i] Shop.　[&] Suitable, phone for details.　[☕] Tearoom.　[P] Ample.

THE RANGER'S HOUSE

CHESTERFIELD WALK, BLACKHEATH, LONDON SE10 8QX

Owner: *English Heritage*　**Contact:** *House Manager*

Tel: 0181 853 0035

A handsome, red-brick house which lies between two of London's great open spaces, Greenwich Park and Blackheath. The house was built for a successful seafarer, Admiral Francis Hosier around 1700 who sited the house within view of the Thames estuary and used to boast that the grand bow-windowed gallery commanded the three finest views in the world. Today Ranger's House is home to the Suffolk collection of paintings including elegant full-length Jacobean portraits.

Location: OS Ref. TQ388 768. N of Shooters Hill Road.

Opening Times: 1 Apr - 30 Sept: daily, 10am - 6pm. 1 - 21 Oct: daily 10am - 5pm. 22 Oct - 31 Mar: Wed - Sun, 10am - 4pm.

Admission: Adult £2.50, Child £1.30, Conc. £1.90.

[i] Shop.　[&] Limited, lift available.　[🐕] Guide dogs only.

[👥] School facilities available.　[💒] Civil Wedding Licence.

THE QUEEN'S GALLERY　　　　**Tel:** 0171 839 1377

Buckingham Palace, London SW1A 1AA

Owner: HM The Queen　　　　　　**Contact:** The Visitor Office

Location: OS Ref. TQ290 795. Buckingham Palace

Opening Times: 9.30am - 4.30pm. Last admission 4pm.

Admission: Adult £4, OAP £3, Child (under 17) £2.

[i] Shop, open between exhibitions.　[&] Not suitable.　[🐕] Guide dogs only.

SPECIAL EVENTS

JAN 23 - APR 19: Michelangelo and His Influence.

MAY 15 - OCT 11: The Search for Albion: Monarchy and the Patronage of British Painting.

OCT 13 - JAN 10: Mark Catesby's Natural History of America. The watercolours from the Royal Library.

THE QUEEN'S HOUSE　　　See page 56 for full page entry.

Ham House, London.

THE ROYAL MEWS　　　　**Tel:** 0171 839 1377

Buckingham Palace, London SW1A 1AA

Owner: HM The Queen　　　　　　**Contact:** The Visitor Officer

Location: OS Ref. TQ289 794. Entrance in Buckingham Palace Road, W of The Queen's Gallery.

Opening Times: 1 Jan - 23 Mar: Wed. 24 Mar - 2 Aug: Tue - Thur. 3 Aug - 1 Oct: Mon - Thur. 2 Oct - 31 Dec: Wed. All days 12 - 4pm (last adm. 3.30pm), except 3 Aug - 1 Oct when 10.30am - 4.30pm (last adm. 4pm).

Admission: Adult £4, OAP £3, Child (under 17) £2.

[i] Shop.　[&] Suitable. WC.　[P] No parking.　[🐕] Guide dogs only.

ROYAL SOCIETY OF ARTS　　　See page 57 for full page entry.

ST GEORGE'S CATHEDRAL　　**Tel:** 0171 928 5256 **Fax:** 0171 787 8923

Westminster Bridge Road, London SE1 7HY　　　**Contact:** James Cronin

Neo-Gothic rebuilt Pugin Cathedral bombed during the last war and rebuilt by Romily Craze in 1958.

Location: OS Ref. TQ315 794. Near Imperial War Museum. 1/2 m SE of Waterloo Stn.

Opening Times: 8am - 8pm, every day, except BHs.

Admission: Free.

ST JOHN'S GATE
THE MUSEUM OF THE ORDER OF ST JOHN

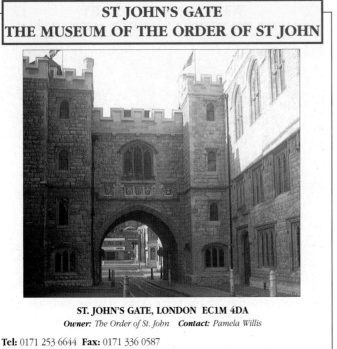

ST. JOHN'S GATE, LONDON EC1M 4DA

Owner: The Order of St. John　　*Contact:* Pamela Willis

Tel: 0171 253 6644 **Fax:** 0171 336 0587

Tudor Gatehouse to 12th century Priory of Clerkenwell, English home of Crusading Knights Hospitaller and St. John Ambulance. Grand Priory Church, and 12th century crypt survive (despite Wat Tyler and Peasants' Revolt). Also Hogarth's home and Dr Johnson's workplace. Museum collections represent the Order from Crusade to First-Aid, including Arms & Armour, pharmacy jars, paintings, Maltese silver and furniture, and historic First-Aid collections.

Location: OS Ref. TQ317 821. St. John's Lane, Clerkenwell. Nearest underground: Farringdon, Barbican.

Opening Times: Mon - Fri: 10am - 5pm. Sat: 10am - 4pm. Closed BHs. Tours: Tue, Fri & Sat at 11am & 2.30pm. Ref. Library: Open by appointment. Guided tours Tue, Fri & Sat, 11am and 2.30pm.

Admission: Free but donations are welcome.

[i] Shop. [&] Ground floor suitable. WC. [K] Available. [dog] Guide dogs only.

SIR JOHN SOANE'S MUSEUM　　　　**Tel:** 0171 4052107 **Fax:** 0171 8313957

13 Lincoln's Inn Fields, London WC2A 3BP

Owner: Trustees of Sir John Soane's Museum　　**Contact:** Ms S Palmer

The celebrated architect Sir John Soane built this in 1812 as his own house. It now contains his collection of antiquities, sculpture and paintings. included among which are The Rake's Progress paintings by William Hogarth.

Location: OS Ref. TQ308 816. E of Kingsway, S of High Holborn.

Opening Times: Tue - Sat, 10am - 5pm. 6pm - 9pm on first Tue of the month. Closed BHs and Christmas Eve.

Admission: Free. Groups must book.

[&] Not suitable. [P] No parking. [dog] No dogs.

SOUTHSIDE HOUSE 🏛　　　　　　　**Tel:** 0181 946 7643

Wimbledon Common, London SW19 4RJ

Owner: The Pennington-Mellor-Munthe Charity Trust　　**Contact:** Desmond Sanford

One of the few houses open only during the winter. The house originated as a Tudor farmhouse and has been in the same family for 310 years. Late 17th and 18th century house with intriguing contents and collections.

Location: OS Ref. TQ234 706. Near King's College School on Wimbledon Common.

Opening Times: 3 Jan - 21 Jun: BH Mon, Tue, Thur & Sat, 2 - 4pm. Guided tours at 2pm, 3pm & 4pm lasting approx 1½ hrs. Groups upon written application.

Admission: Adult £5, Child (11 - 18 years) £3.

SOUTHWARK CATHEDRAL　　　　**Tel:** 0171 407 3708 **Fax:** 0171 357 7389

Southwark, London SE1 9DA　　　　　　**Contact:** Mrs A Lovell

Location: OS Ref. TQ327 803. South side of London Bridge.

Opening Times: Daily: 8.30am - 6pm. Sun services: 9am, 11am and 3pm. Weekday services: 8am, 12.30pm, 12.45pm and 5.30pm.

Admission: Donation.

[i] Shop. [&] Ground floor & grounds suitable. [café] Restaurant. [dog] Guide dogs only.

SPENCER HOUSE　　　　　　　**See page 58 for full page entry.**

STRAWBERRY HILL

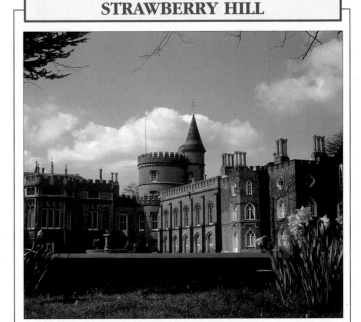

**ST MARY'S UNIVERSITY COLLEGE, WALDEGRAVE ROAD,
TWICKENHAM TW1 4SX**

Contact: Noreen Evans

Tel: 0181 240 4114 **Fax:** 0181 255 6174

Horace Walpole converted a modest house at Strawberry Hill into his own version of a Gothic fantasy. It is widely regarded as the first substantial building of the Gothic Revival and as such is internationally known and admired. A century later Lady Frances Waldegrave added a magnificent wing to Walpole's original structure. Please telephone for details of special events to celebrate Walpole's Bicentenary.

Location: OS Ref. TQ158 722. Off A310 between Twickenham & Teddington.

Opening Times: Easter - Oct: Sun, 2 - 3.30pm or by appointment.

Admission: Adult £4.50, OAP £3.50. Groups: Adult £4.

[i] Shop. [café] Available. [dog] No dogs.

SUTTON HOUSE 🦌　　　　　　　　**Tel:** 0181 986 2264

2 & 4 Homerton High Street, Hackney, London E9 6JQ

Owner: The National Trust　　　　**Contact:** The Administrator

A rare example of a Tudor red-brick house, built in 1535 by Sir Rafe Sadleir, Principal Secretary of State for Henry VIII, with 18th century alterations and later additions. Recent restoration has revealed many 16th century details, even in rooms of later periods. Notable features include original linenfold panelling and 17th century wall paintings.

Location: OS Ref. TQ352 851. At the corner of Isabella Road and Homerton High St.

Opening Times: 4 Feb - 25 Nov ('98) & 3 Feb - end of Oct ('99): Wed, Sun & BH Mon 11.30am - 5.30pm, Sat 2 - 5.30pm. Last admission 5pm. Café Bar: All year except 21 Dec - 12 Jan ('99): Wed - Fri 11am - 5pm, Sat & Sun & BH 11am - 5pm.

Admission: £1.90. Family £4.50. Group visits by prior arrangement.

[i] Shop. [&] Ground floor only. WC. [café] Café. [P] No parking.
[🦌] Civil Wedding Licence.

CIVIL WEDDING VENUES

South East England

SYON PARK

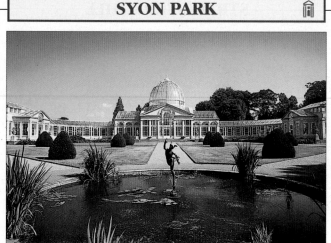

BRENTFORD, TW8 8JF

Owner: *The Duke of Northumberland*   *Contact:* *Louise Taylor*

Tel: 0181 560 0881   **Fax:** 0181 568 0936

Described by John Betjeman as 'the Grand Architectural Walk', Syon House and its 200 acre park is the London home of the Duke of Northumberland, whose family, the Percys, have lived here since the late 16th century. Originally the site of a late medieval monastery, Syon Park has a fascinating history. The present house has Tudor origins but contains some of Robert Adam's finest interiors, which were commissioned by the first Duke in the 1760s. The 30 acres of gardens, landscaped by 'Capability' Brown, contain the spectacular Great Conservatory designed by Charles Fowler in the 1820s. The House and Great Conservatory are available for hire for functions and events.

Location: OS Ref. TQ173 767. Between Brentford & Twickenham, off the A4, A310 in SW London.

Opening Times: House: Apr - Oct: Wed - Sun & BHs, 11am - 5pm (Closed at 3.30pm on Fri and Sat). House closed Nov - Mar. Open other times by appointment for groups. Gardens: daily except 25 & 26 Dec, 10am - 6pm or dusk.

Admission: Adult £5.50, Child £4, Conc. £4, Family (2+2) £13. Groups: Adult £5, Child £2, OAP £3.50, Student £2.

| i | Shop. | X | Full catering facilities. | ♿ | Grounds suitable. | ☕ | Restaurant. |
| 🐕 | No dogs. | 💒 | Civil Wedding Licence. | | | | |

WESTMINSTER ABBEY
CHAPTER HOUSE, PYX CHAMBER & ABBEY MUSEUM

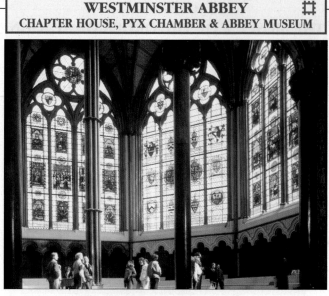

EAST CLOISTERS, WESTMINSTER ABBEY, LONDON SW1P 3PE

Owner: *English Heritage*   *Contact:* *Head Custodian*

Tel: 0171 222 5897

The Chapter House, built by the Royal masons in 1250 and faithfully restored in the 19th century, contains some of the finest examples of medieval English sculpture to be seen. The building is octagonal, with a central column, and still has its original floor of glazed tiles, which have been newly conserved. Its uses have varied, but in the 14th century it was used as a meeting place for the Benedictine monks of the Abbey, and for Members of Parliament. The 11th century Pyx Chamber now houses the Abbey treasures, reflecting its use as the strongroom of the exchequer from the 14th to 19th centuries. The Abbey museum contains medieval Royal effigies.

Location: OS Ref. TQ301 795. Approach either through the Abbey or through Dean's Yard and the cloister.

Opening Times: 1 Apr - 1 Nov: daily, 10am - 5.30pm. 2 Nov - 31 Mar: daily, 10am - 4pm.

Admission: Adult £2.50, Child £1.30, Conc. £1.90.

THE TOWER BRIDGE EXPERIENCE   Tel: 0891 600 210   Fax: 0171 357 7935

Tower Bridge, London SE1 2UP

Owner: Corporation of London   **Contact:** Amanda Moring

One of London's most unusual and exciting exhibitions is situated inside Tower Bridge. Animatronic characters from the Bridge's past guide you through a series of audio-visual presentations, which tell the story of this world-famous London landmark. From the high level walkways which link the two towers, you'll also enjoy one of the most memorable panoramic views of London.

Location: OS Ref. TQ337 804. Adjacent to Tower of London, nearest Tube: Tower Hill.

Opening Times: Nov - Mar: 9.30am - 6pm. Apr - Oct: 10am - 6.30pm (last entry 1¼ hrs before closing). Closed 1 & 28 Jan, 24 - 26 Dec (not 22 Jan).

Admission: Adult £5.95, OAP/Student/Child (5-15) £3.95, Family (2+2) £14.95.

| i | Shop. | X | Full catering service. | ♿ | House suitable. WC. |
| 👨‍🏫 | Teachers' pack & education centre. | | | 🐕 | Guide dogs only. |

SPECIAL EVENTS

FEB 16 - 20: Half term quiz.   **FEB 21 - 22:** Scouts' 90th Anniversary Celebrations.
MAR 5 - 8 & 12 - 15: Twilight Tours.
MAR 19 - 21: Engineers' Evening Tours.

THE TOWER OF LONDON   See page 59 for full page entry.

THE WALLACE COLLECTION   See page 60 for full page entry.

WESTMINSTER ABBEY   Tel: 0171 222 5152   Fax: 0171 233 2072

London SW1P 3PA   **Contact:** Miss E St John Smith

Location: OS Ref. TQ301 795. Westminster.

Opening Times: Mon - Fri, 9am - 4.45pm (last admission 3.45pm), Sat, 9am - 2.45pm (last admission 1.45pm).

Admission: Adult £5, Child (11 - 16yrs) £2, Child under 11yrs free, Student & OAP £3, Family (2+2) £10.

| i | Shop. Enquiry desk in Abbey. | ♿ | Mostly suitable. | P | No parking. |
| 🐕 | Guide dogs only. | | | | |

WESTMINSTER CATHEDRAL   Tel: 0171 798 9055   Fax: 0171 798 9090

Victoria, London SW1P 1QW

Owner: Diocese of Westminster   **Contact:** Rev Mgr George Stack

The Roman Catholic Cathedral of the Archbishop of Westminster. Spectacular building in the Byzantine style, designed by J F Bentley, opened in 1903, famous for its mosaics, marble and music. Westminster Cathedral celebrated the Centenary of its foundation in 1995.

Location: OS Ref. TQ293 791. On Victoria Street, between Victoria Station and Westminster Abbey.

Opening Times: All year: 7am - 7pm. Please telephone for times at Easter & Christmas.

Admission: Free. Lift charge: Adult £2. Child £1. Family (2 + 4) £5.

| i | Shop. | ♿ | Ground floor suitable. | 🧍 | Available. Prior booking required. |
| 👨‍🏫 | Worksheets & tours available. | P | No parking. | 🐕 | Guide dogs only. |

WILLIAM MORRIS GALLERY   Tel/Fax: 0181 527 7070

Lloyd Park, Forest Road, Walthamstow, London E17 4PP

Owner: London Borough of Waltham Forest   **Contact:** Ms Nora Gillow

Location: OS Ref. SQ372 899. 15 mins walk from Walthamstow tube (Victoria line). 5 - 10 mins from M11/A406.

Opening Times: Tue - Sat and first Sun each month, 10am - 1pm and 2 - 5pm.

Admission: Admission is free for all visitors but a charge is made for guided tours which must be booked in advance.

| i | Shop. | ♿ | Ground floor & grounds only. | 🐕 | Guide dogs only. |

Ham House, Richmond, Surrey (see London within M25).

Furniture arrangement:

Until the end of the eighteenth century, furniture in rooms where company was received was arranged round the walls, which left space for numbers of guests to move about and to be seen. If a chair was needed, then servants were at hand to bring one instantly. By the 1780s a new fashion had evolved, of placing furniture out in the room and especially round the fireplace, with sofas placed at right-angles to the hearth instead of alongside. This fashion brought with it the need for various light pieces of furniture which could be carried and placed by members of the family, such as work-boxes, games-tables, occasional tables – and the sofa-table, which was placed before the sofa and not behind it, as we do now. The convention, in use, of the arrangement in front of the hearth was that the women sat in a semicircle on the sofas and light chairs, the hostess occupying a seat next to the fire, while the men stood in the middle, sparkling with witty conversation. It proved neither convivial nor social; in 1782 Fanny Burney tells us that some hostesses were trying to get rid of 'the circle'. 'My whole care is to prevent a circle,' exclaimed one hostess as she moved the chairs into conversational groupings. Once the old formality had been broken, the new conversational arrangement was quickly adopted. Nineteenth century photographs of grand interiors show what appears to be a complete muddle of furniture, but careful observers will be able to see that the chairs and sofas are arranged so that two, three or four people can sit together and converse. Today, when there is little entertaining on the grand scale, the need for large rooms filled with many conversational groupings has passed, and we are back to informal seating around the hearth.

Extract from; "Life in the Country House" by David N Durant (published by John Murray), PB£15.99, see page twelve at the front of the book.

BLENHEIM PALACE
Woodstock

BLENHEIM PALACE, home of the 11th Duke of Marlborough and birthplace of Sir Winston Churchill, was built between 1705-1722 for John Churchill, 1st Duke of Marlborough, in grateful recognition of his magnificent victory at the Battle of Blenheim in 1704. One of England's largest private houses, Blenheim was built in the Baroque style by Sir John Vanbrugh and is considered his masterpiece. The land and £240,000 were given by Queen Anne and a grateful nation.

Blenheim's wonderful interior reveals striking contrasts – from the lofty Great Hall to gilded state rooms and the majestic Long Library. The superb collection includes fine paintings, furniture, bronzes and the famous Marlborough Victories tapestries. The five-room Churchill Exhibition includes his birth room.

GARDENS

The Palace grounds reflect the evolution of grand garden design. Of the original work by Queen Anne's gardener, Henry Wise, only the Walled Garden remains; but dominating all is the superb landscaping of 'Capability' Brown. Dating from 1764, his work includes the lake, park and gardens. Achille Duchêne, employed by the 9th Duke, subsequently recreated the Great Court and built the Italian Garden on the east and the Water Terraces on the west of the Palace. Recently the Pleasure Gardens complex has been developed. This includes the Marlborough Maze, Herb Garden, Adventure Playground, Butterfly House and Putting Greens.

CONTACT

Paul F D Duffie FTS
Blenheim Palace
Woodstock
Oxon
OX20 1PX

Tel: (01993) 811091

Fax: (01993) 813527

LOCATION

OS Ref. SP441 161

From London, M40, A44 (1½ hrs), 8m NW of Oxford. London 63m Birmingham 54.

Air: Heathrow 60m. Birmingham 54m.

Coach: From London (Victoria) to Oxford.

Rail: Oxford Station.

Bus: Oxford (Cornmarket) - Woodstock.

CONFERENCE/FUNCTION

ROOM	SIZE	MAX CAPACITY
Orangery		200
Great Hall	70' x 40'	150
Saloon	50' x 30'	72
with Great Hall		450
with Great Hall & Library		750
Library	180' x 30'	300

OPENING TIMES

SUMMER
Palace
Mid March - 31 October daily: 10.30am-5.30pm
Last admission 4.45pm.

WINTER
Park only
1 November - Mid March.
The Duke of Marlborough reserves the right to close the Palace or Park or to amend admission prices without notice.

ADMISSION

- Palace Tour and Churchill Exhibition
- Park
- Garden
- Butterfly House
- Adventure Play Area
- Motor Launch
- Train
- Car or Coach Parking, but not entry to the maze or rowing boat hire.

  Adult £8.00
  Child (5 - 15 yrs.)......£4.00
  Child (16 & 17 yrs.)...£6.00
  OAP.........................£6.00
  Family £21.00
  Groups
  Adult £6.80
  OAP/Student...........£5.80
  Child (5 - 15 yrs.)......£3.50
  Child (16 & 17 yrs.)...£5.80

- Blenheim Park, Butterfly House, Adventure Play Area, Train, Parking, but not entry to the maze or rowing boat hire.
  Coaches* £20.00
  Cars*.......................£5.00
  Adult** £1.00
  Child** £0.50

- Private visits† £15.00

* Including occupants.
** Pedestrians.
† By appointment only.
Min. charge of £300 (mornings and £500 (evenings)

BLENHEIM PALACE continued …

The second State Room.

The Mermaid Fountain in the Italian Garden.

i Five Shops. Filming, Equestrian Events, Craft Fairs. Will consider any proposals (contact Admin Office). Lake (Rowing Boats for hire), Motor Launch trips, Train rides. Photography outside only.

X Corporate hospitality, including dinners and receptions. The Orangery seats 200 for luncheon or dinner, throughout the year together with the Spencer Churchill Conference Room. For the Palace contact the Administrator, or for catering details contact Town and County Catering tel: 01993 813874/811274.

Visitors may alight at the Palace entrance then park in allocated area. WCs.

P Unlimited for cars and coaches. Advise Administrator for groups of over 100. Coaches/groups welcome without pre-booking. 'Notes for Party Organisers' available by post.

2 Restaurants, 2 Cafeterias. Group capacity 150. Groups can book for afternoon tea, buffets and luncheon. Menus on request. Contact Town and County Catering for further info: 01993 813874/811274.

Included in the cost of entry. Private and language tours may be pre-booked.

Blenheim has held the Sandford Award for an outstanding contribution to Heritage Education since 1982. Operated by a very experienced headmaster, education groups may study virtually all subjects at all four stages of the National Curriculum as well as have general interest or leisure visits. Tourism Studies (all levels) available.

Dogs on leads in Park. Guide dogs for the blind & hearing dogs for the deaf only in house and garden.

BROGHTON CASTLE

Banbury

BROUGHTON CASTLE is essentially a family home lived in by Lord and Lady Saye and Sele and their family.

The original medieval Manor House, of which much remains today, was built in about 1300 by Sir John de Broughton. It stands on an island site surrounded by a 3-acre moat. The Castle was greatly enlarged between 1550 and 1600, at which time it was embellished with magnificent plaster ceilings, splendid panelling and fine fireplaces.

In the 17th century William 8th Lord Saye and Sele, played a leading role in national affairs. He opposed Charles I's efforts to rule without Parliament and Broughton became a secret meeting place for the King's opponents.

During the Civil War William raised a regiment and he and his 4 sons all fought at the nearby Battle of Edgehill. After the battle the Castle was besieged and captured.

Arms and armour for the Civil War and from other periods are displayed in the Great Hall. Visitors may also see the gatehouse, gardens and park together with the nearby 14th century Church of St Mary, in which there are many family tombs, memorials and hatchments.

GARDENS

The garden area consists of mixed herbaceous and shrub borders containing many old roses. In addition, there is a formal walled garden with beds of roses surrounded by box hedging and lined by more mixed borders.

CONTACT

Mrs G M Cozens
Broughton Castle
Banbury
Oxfordshire
OX15 5EB

Tel: (01295) 262624
Tel / Fax: (01869) 337126

LOCATION

OS Ref. SP418 382

Broughton Castle is 2^1/2m SW of Banbury Cross on the B4035, Shipston-on-Stour - Banbury Road. Easily accessible from Stratford-on-Avon, Warwick, Oxford, Burford and the Cotswolds. M40/J11.

Rail: From London/ Birmingham to Banbury.

OPENING TIMES

SUMMER

18 May - 14 September
Wed & Sun.

Also in July and August
Thur and BH Sun and
BH Mon (including Easter)
2 - 5pm.

Groups welcome on any day and at any time throughout the year by appointment.

ADMISSION

Adult £3.90
Child (5-15).............£2.00
OAP.........................£3.40
Groups*
Adult £3.40
Child (5-15).............£1.75
OAP.........................£3.40

* Min payment: adults £65, children £35.

ℹ️ Shop. Filming, product launches, advertising features, corporate events in park. Photography permitted for personal use. Brief guidance notes available in French, Spanish, Dutch, Italian, Japanese, German, Polish, Greek & Russian.

♿ Visitors allowed vehicle access to main entrance.

☕ Tearoom. Tea/coffee for guided groups if pre-booked. Other meals by arrangement.

🚶 Available to pre-booked groups at no extra charge. Not available on open days.

🅿️ Ample, 300 yards from the castle.

👪 Welcome.

🐕 No dogs inside House.

STONOR
Henley-on-Thames

Stonor, family home of Lord and Lady Camoys and the Stonor family for over 800 years, is set in a valley in the beautiful woods of the Chiltern Hills and surrounded by an extensive deer park.

The earliest part of the house dates from the 12th century, whilst most of the house was built in the 14th century. Early use of brick in Tudor times resulted in a more uniform façade concealing the earlier buildings, and changes to the windows and the roof in the 18th century reflect the Georgian appearance still apparent today.

Inside, the house shows strong Gothic decoration, also from the 18th century, and contains many items of rare furniture, sculptures, bronzes, tapestries, paintings and portraits of the family from Britain, Europe and America.

The Catholic Chapel used continuously through the Reformation is sited close by a pagan stone circle. In 1581 Stonor served as a sanctuary for St Edmund Campion, and an exhibition at the house features his life and work.

GARDENS

Extensive gardens enclosed at the rear of the house face south and have fine views over the park. The springtime display of daffodils is particularly outstanding.

CONTACT

The Administrator
Stonor Park
Henley-on-Thames
Oxfordshire
RG9 6HF

Tel: (01491) 638587

Fax: (01491) 638587

LOCATION

OS Ref. SU743 893

1 hr from London, M4/J8/9. A4130 to Henley-on-Thames. On B480 NW of Henley. A4130/B480 to Stonor.

Bus: 3m along the Oxford - London route.

Rail: Henley-on-Thames Station 5m.

i Shop. Filming, craft fairs, car displays, product promotion, clay pigeon shooting. Evening tours and buffet suppers by prior arrangement. Lectures can be given on the property, its contents and history. No smoking and no photography.

♿ Visitors may alight at the entrance before parking. Ramp access to gardens, tearoom & shop.

☕ By arrangement. for groups.

🚶 Outside normal hours for 20 - 60 people per tour. Tour time: $1\frac{1}{4}$ hrs. Single payments for group bookings on arrival unless prior arrangements are made for payment with vouchers

P Ample, 100 yds away.

👨‍👩‍👧 Welcome. Lectures and guided tours by arrangement.

🐕 On leads but not in the House, tearoom or shop.

OPENING TIMES

SUMMER

April - September
Sun: 2 - 5.30pm.

Mon: 2 - 5.30pm
BHs only.

Tue: Closed.

Wed: (not April):
2 - 5.30pm.

Thur: July & August only
2 - 5.30pm.

Fri: Closed

Sat 29 August only:
2 - 5.30pm.

Groups by appointment on Wed & Thur on the occasions the house is not open to the public.

WINTER

October - March Closed.

ADMISSION

House & Garden
Adult £4.50
Child (under 14) ......Free
Groups** £4.00

Garden and Chapel
Adult £2.50

** Min 12 persons, in a single payment. Visits outside normal hours at £5pp. Min. 20 persons and single payment.

School groups £2.50 per head, 1 teacher for every 10 children admitted free.

HHA members free.

ARDINGTON HOUSE 🏛

Tel: 01235 833244

Wantage, Oxfordshire OX12 8QA

Owner: Mrs D C N Baring   **Contact:** Mrs D C N Baring

Early 18th century exceptionally fine brickwork, hall with imperial staircase, panelled dining room with plasterwork ceiling. Attractive garden and stable yard. Small supper parties.

Location: OS Ref. SU432 883. 12m S of Oxford, 12m N of Newbury, 2½ m E of Wantage.

Opening Times: May - Sept: Mon & all BHs 2.30 - 4.30pm. Groups welcome appointment.

Admission: House and Gardens £2.50.

♿ Not suitable.   ☕ By arrangement.   🚶 By members of the family.   🐕 Guide dogs only.

BLENHEIM PALACE 🏛

See page 70/71 for full page entry.

BROOK COTTAGE

Tel: 01295 670303 / 670590

Well Lane, Alkerton, Nr. Banbury OX15 6NL

Owner: Mr & Mrs David Hodges   **Contact:** Mr & Mrs David Hodges

4 acre hillside garden. Wide variety of trees, shrubs and herbaceous plants in areas of differing character, water garden, alpine scree, one-colour borders, over 200 shrub and climbing roses, many clematis.

Location: OS Ref. SP378 428. 6m NW of Banbury, ½ m SW of A422 Banbury to Stratford-upon-Avon road.

Opening Times: 13 Apr - 30 Oct: Mon - Fri, 9am - 6pm. Evenings, weekends and all group visits by appointment.

Admission: Adult £2.50, OAP £2, Child free. In aid of National Garden Scheme.

ℹ Plant sales.   ☕ By arrangement for groups, otherwise DIY coffee/tea.

BROUGHTON CASTLE 🏛

See page 72 for full page entry.

BUSCOT OLD PARSONAGE 🌿

Tel: 01793 762209

Buscot, Faringdon, Oxfordshire SN7 8DQ

Owner: The National Trust   **Contact:** Estate Office

An early 18th century house of Cotswold stone on the bank of the Thames with a small garden.

Location: OS Ref. SU231 973. 2m from Lechlade, 4m N of Faringdon on A417.

Opening Times: Apr - end Oct, Wed only 2 - 6pm by written appointment.

Admission: £1.10. Not suitable for parties.

BUSCOT PARK 🌿

Tel: 01367 240786

Buscot, Faringdon, Oxfordshire SN7 8BU

Owner: The National Trust   **Contact:** Lord Faringdon

A late 18th century house with pleasure gardens, set within a park.

Location: OS Ref. SU239 973. Between Lechlade and Faringdon on A417.

Opening Times: House & Grounds: 1 Apr - end Sept (including Good Fri, Easter Sat & Sun): Wed - Fri 2 - 6pm. Also open every 2nd and 4th Sat & immediately following Sun, 2 - 6pm. Grounds only 1 Apr - end Sept: open as house but also Mon (but not BH Mons) & Tue, 2 - 6pm.

Admission: House & Grounds £4.40, Grounds only £3.30. No reduction for groups, which must book in advance.

♿ Not suitable.   ☕ Tearoom.

CHASTLETON HOUSE 🌿

Tel: 01608 674355

Chastleton, Moreton-in-Marsh, Gloucestershire GL56 0SU

Owner: The National Trust   **Contact:** The Custodian

One of England's finest and most complete Jacobean houses, dating from 1612. It is filled with a mixture of rare and everyday objects and the atmosphere of four hundred years of continuous occupation by one family. The gardens have a Jacobean layout and the rules of modern croquet were codified here.

Location: OS Ref. SP248 291. 6m ENE of Stow-on-Wold. 1½ m NW of A436. Approach only from A436 between the A44 (W of Chipping Norton) and Stow.

Opening Times: 1 Apr - end Oct: Wed to Sat, 12 - 4pm. Last admission 3.30pm or dusk if earlier. Admission for all visitors (including NT members) by pre-booked timed tickets only. Bookings can be made by letter to the ticket office or tel: 01608 674284 Mon - Fri, 2 - 5pm from 3 Feb 1998.

Admission: Adult £4.80, Child £2.40. Family £12.

♿ Not suitable.   P Coaches limited to 25 seat minibuses.   🐕 Guide dogs only.

CHRIST CHURCH CATHEDRAL

Tel: 01865 276154

The Sacristy, The Cathedral, Oxford OX1 1DP   **Contact:** Mr Jim Godfrey

12th century Norman Church, formerly an Augustinian monastery, given Cathedral status in 16th century by Henry VIII. Also the college chapel for Christ Church, the largest of the Oxford Colleges.

Location: OS Ref. SP515 059. Just S of city centre, off St Aldates. Entry via Meadow Gate visitors' entrance on S side of college.

Opening Times: Mon - Sat: 9am - 5pm. Sun: 1 - 5pm, closed Christmas Day. Services: weekdays 7.20am, 6pm. Sun 8am, 10am, 11.15am & 6pm.

Admission: Adult £3, Child under 5 free, Conc. £2, Family £6.

COGGES MANOR FARM MUSEUM

Tel: 01993 772602   Fax: 01993 703056

Church Lane, Witney, Oxfordshire OX8 6LA

Owner: Oxfordshire County Council   **Contact:** Ms Catherine Mason

The Manor House dates from the 13th century, rooms are furnished to show life at the end of the 19th century. Daily cooking on the Victorian range. On the first floor, samples of original wallpapers and finds from under the floorboards accompany the story of the history of the house. In one of the rooms, rare 17th century painted panelling survives. Farm buildings including two 18th century barns, stables and a thatched ox byre, display farm implements. Traditional breeds of farm animals, hand-milking demonstration each day. Seasonal produce from the walled kitchen garden sold in the museum shop.

Location: OS Ref. SP362 097. Just off A40 Oxford - Burford Road. Access by footbridge from centre of Witney, 600 yds. Vehicle access from S side of B4022 near E end of Witney.

Opening Times: 31 Mar - 1 Nov: Tue - Fri & BH Mon, 10.30am - 5.30pm; Sat & Sun, 12 - 5.30pm. Closed Good Fri. Early closing in Oct.

Admission: Adult £3.25, Child £1.75, Conc. £2, Family £9.

ℹ Shop.   ♿ Ground floor suitable. WCs.   ☕ Café.   P Ample.   🐕 In grounds, on leads.

DEDDINGTON CASTLE ⚜

Tel: 01732 778000

Deddington, Oxfordshire

Owner: English Heritage   **Contact:** The South East Regional Office

Extensive earthworks concealing the remains of a 12th century castle which was ruined as early as the 14th century.

Location: OS Ref. SP471 316. S of B4031 on E side of Deddington, 17m N of Oxford on A423. 5m S of Banbury.

Opening Times: Any reasonable time.

Admission: Free.

DITCHLEY PARK

Tel: 01608 677346

Enstone, Oxfordshire OX7 4ER

Owner: Ditchley Foundation   **Contact:** Brigadier Christopher Galloway

The most important house by James Gibbs with most distinguished interiors by Henry Flitcroft and William Kent. Ditchley was a regular weekend retreat for Churchill during the Second World War.

Location: OS Ref. SP391 214. 2m NE from Charlbury. 13m NW of Oxford.

Opening Times: Visits only by prior arrangement with the Bursar.

Admission: House opening fee £30. Entry fee £4pp.

♿ Ground floor suitable. WCs.   🚶 Compulsory by arrangement.   🐕 No dogs.

FAWLEY COURT

HISTORIC HOUSE & MUSEUM, HENLEY-ON-THAMES RG9 3AE

Owner: Marian Fathers   *Contact:* The Secretary

Tel: 01491 574917   Fax: 01491 411587

Designed by Christopher Wren, built in 1684 for Col W Freeman, decorated by Grinling Gibbons and by James Wyatt. The Museum consists of a library, various documents of the Polish Kings, a very well-preserved collection of historical sabres and many memorable military objects of the Polish army. Paintings, early books, numismatic collections, arms and armour are also housed in a part of 12th century manor house.

Location: OS Ref. SU765 842. 1m N of Henley-on-Thames E to A4155 to Marlow.

Opening Times: Mar - Oct: Wed, Thur & Sun, 2 - 5pm. Other dates by arrangement. Closed Easter and Whitsuntide weeks and Nov - Feb.

Admission: House, Museum & Gardens: Adult £3, Child £1, Conc. £2. Groups (min 15) £2pp.

ℹ Shop.   ♿ Ground floor & grounds suitable. WC.

☕ Tearoom.   🐕 Guide dogs only.

GREAT COXWELL BARN

Tel: 01793 762209

Great Coxwell, Faringdon, Oxfordshire

Owner: The National Trust   **Contact:** The Administrator

A 13th century monastic barn, stone built with stone tiled roof, which has an interesting timber construction.

Location: OS Ref. SU269 940. 2m SW of Faringdon between A420 and B4019.

Opening Times: All year: daily at reasonable hours.

Admission: 50p.

In grounds, on leads.

GREYS COURT

Tel: 01491 628529

Rotherfield Greys, Henley-on-Thames, Oxfordshire RG9 4PG

Owner: The National Trust   **Contact:** The Custodian

Rebuilt in the 16th century and added to in the 17th, 18th and 19th centuries, the house is set amid the remains of the courtyard walls and towers of a 14th century fortified house. A Tudor donkey wheel, well-house and an ice house are still intact, and the garden contains Archbishop's Maze, inspired by Archbishop Runcie's enthronement speech in 1980.

Location: OS Ref. SU725 834. 3m W of Henley-on-Thames, E of B481.

Opening Times: 1 Apr - end Sept: House; Mon, Wed & Fri, 2 - 6pm (closed Good Fri) Garden: daily except Thur & Sun 2 - 6pm (closed Good Fri) Last admission 5.30pm.

Admission: House & Garden: £4.40, Family £11. Garden only: £3.20, Family £8. No reduction for coach parties who must book.

Grounds partly suitable. WCs.   Tearoom.   In car park only, on leads.

KINGSTON BAGPUIZE HOUSE

ABINGDON, OXFORDSHIRE OX13 5AX

Owner: Mr & Mrs Francis Grant   *Contact: Mrs Francis Grant*

Tel: 01865 820259   **Fax:** 01865 821659

Beautiful manor house and family home. It has a cantilevered staircase and panelled rooms with some good furniture and pictures. Set in mature parkland, the gardens including shrub border and woodland garden, contain a notable collection of trees, shrubs, perennials and bulbs. Available for functions and other events. Facilities for small conferences.

Location: OS Ref. SU408 981. In Kingston Bagpuize village, off A415 Abingdon to Witney road S of A415/A420 intersection. Abingdon 5m, Oxford 9m.

Opening Times: 8 Mar - 11 Oct: BH weekends (Sat, Sun, Mon), Wed, Sat & Sun. Mar: 8. Apr: 5, 11, 12, 13, 25, 26. May: 2, 3, 4, 23, 24, 25. Jun: 13, 14. Jul: 15, 18, 19. Aug: 5, 8, 9, 29, 30, 31. Sept: 9, 12, 13, 23, 26, 27. Oct: 11. 2.30 - 5.30pm. Last entry to garden 5pm. House: Guided tours only, last tour 4.45pm.

Admission: House & Garden: Adult £3.50, Child £2.50, (children under 5 not admitted to house), OAP £3. Gardens: £1.50. (child under 5 free). Groups by appointment throughout the year, min 15, max 100, prices on request.

Shop. No photography.   Available.   Ample.

Grounds suitable. WCs.   Tearoom.   Compulsory.   No dogs.

KINGSTONE LISLE PARK

KINGSTONE LISLE PARK, WANTAGE, OXON OX12 9QG

Owner: Mr James Lonsdale   *Contact: The Secretary*

Tel: 01367 820599   **Fax:** 01367 820749

A sensational Palladian house, home of the Lonsdale family, set in 140 acres of parkland. Superb views up to the Lambourn Downs. Three spring-fed lakes beside the house complete this very attractive landscape. Built in 1677, the house is on the site of a fortified castle which burnt down in 1620. The nearby Blowing Stone, which according to legend, was blown by King Alfred to muster his armies on the Downs is still in the village and can be blown by visitors during daylight hours. The hall, in the style of Sir John Soane, gives a strong impression of entering an Italian palazzo with beautiful ornate plaster ceilings, columns and figurines. In complete contrast the inner hall becomes the classical English country house, the most exciting feature being the Flying Staircase winding its way up, totally unsupported. A fine collection of art, furniture, clocks, glass and needlework, together with the architecture, evoke admiration for the craftsmanship that has existed in Britain over the centuries. 12 acres of gardens include a shrubbery, pleached limes, an avenue leading up to an ornamental pond. Suitable for films, wedding receptions, functions and fundays.

Location: OS Ref. SU326 876. M4/J14.

Opening Times: Only on Family Fun Day in aid of FSID on Sun, 7 Jun.

Admission: Telephone for details.

Suitable.   In grounds, on leads.

MAPLEDURHAM HOUSE & WATERMILL

MAPLEDURHAM, READING RG4 7TR

Owner: The Mapledurham Trust   *Contact: Mrs Lola Andrews*

Tel: 01189 723350   **Fax:** 01189 724016

Late 16th century Elizabethan home of the Blount family. Original plaster ceilings, great oak staircase, fine collection of paintings and a private chapel in Strawberry Hill Gothic added in 1797. Interesting literary connections with Alexander Pope, Galsworthy's *Forsyte Saga* and Kenneth Graham's *Wind in the Willows*. 15th century watermill fully restored producing flour and bran which is sold in the giftshop.

Location: OS Ref. SU670 767. N of River Thames. 4m NW of Reading, 1 1/2 m W of A4074.

Opening Times: Easter - Sept: Sat, Sun & BHs. Midweek parties by arrangement only (Tue, Wed, Thur).

Admission: Please call 01189 723350 for details.

Shop.   Grounds suitable. WCs.   Tearoom.   Guide dogs only.

10 holiday cottages available all year.

South East England

MILTON MANOR HOUSE

MILTON, ABINGDON, OXFORDSHIRE OX14 4EN

Owner: Anthony Mockler-Barrett   *Contact: Gwendoline Marsh*

Tel: 01235 862321 or 01235 831287

Extraordinarily beautiful family house traditionally designed by Inigo Jones, with a celebrated Gothick library and a beautiful Catholic chapel. Pleasant and relaxed atmosphere. Park with fine old trees, attractive walled garden, two lakes, stables (pony rides often available), shire horse cart-rides, rare-breed pigs, two llamas, other animals. Woodland Wigwam walk. Plenty to see and enjoy for all ages. Also wedding receptions, filming, select conferences. etc.

Location: OS Ref. SU485 924. Just off A34, village and house signposted, 9m S of Oxford, 15m N of Newbury. 3m from Abingdon and Didcot.

Opening Times: Aug: daily: 11am - 5pm. Guided tours of the house: 11am, 12 noon, 2pm, 3pm, 4pm. Also BH Sat, Sun, Mon (i.e. Easter, May BHs) same times.

Admission: House & Gardens: Adult £4, Child £2. House: Guided tours only. Grounds only: Adult £2.50, Child £1. Free parking. Groups by arrangement throughout the year.

🅇 Available.   ♿ Grounds suitable.   ☕ Tearoom.   🐕 Guide dogs only.

MINSTER LOVELL HALL & DOVECOTE ⌗   **Tel:** 01732 778000

Witney, Oxfordshire

Owner: English Heritage   **Contact:** The South East Regional Office

The ruins of Lord Lovell's 15th century manor house stand in a lovely setting on the banks of the River Windrush.

Location: OS Ref. SP324 114. Adjacent to Minster Lovell Church, 1/2 m NE of village. 3m W of Witney off A40.

Opening Times: Any reasonable time.

Admission: Free.

PRIORY COTTAGES 🌿   **Tel:** 01793 762209

1 Mill Street, Steventon, Abingdon, Oxfordshire OX13 6SP

Owner: The National Trust   **Contact:** Coleshill Office

Former monastic buildings, converted into two houses. South Cottage contains the Great Hall of the original priory.

Location: OS Ref. SU466 914. 4m S of Abingdon, on B4017 off A34 at Abingdon West or Milton interchange on corner of The Causeway and Mill Street, entrance in Mill Street.

Opening Times: The Great Hall in South Cottage only: Apr - end Sept: Wed, 2 - 6pm by written appointment.

Admission: £1, no reduction for groups.

ROUSHAM HOUSE   **Tel:** 01869 347110 / 0860 360407

Nr. Steeple Aston, Bicester, Oxfordshire OX6 3QX

Owner: Charles Cottrell-Dormer Esq   **Contact:** Charles Cottrell-Dormer Esq

Rousham represents the first stage of English landscape design and remains almost as William Kent (1685 - 1748) left it. One of the few gardens of this date to have escaped alteration. Includes Venus' Vale, Townesend's Building, seven-arched Praeneste, the Temple of the Mill and a sham ruin known as the 'Eyecatcher'. The house was built in 1635 by Sir Robert Dormer.

Location: OS Ref. SP477 242. E of A4260, 12m N of Oxford, S of B4030, 7m W of Bicester.

Opening Times: House: Apr - Sept: Wed, Sun and BH Mon 2 - 4.30pm. Garden: All year: daily, 10am - 4.30pm.

Admission: House: £3. Garden: Adult £3. No children under 15.

🚶 Compulsory.   🐕 No dogs.

RYCOTE CHAPEL ⌗   **Tel:** 01732 778000 (regional office)

Rycote, Oxfordshire

Owner: English Heritage   **Contact:** South East Regional Office

A 15th century chapel with exquisitely carved and painted woodwork. It has many intriguing features, including two roofed pews and a musicians' gallery.

Location: OS165 Ref. SP667 046. 3m SW of Thame, off A329. 1 1/2 m NE of M40/J7.

Opening Times: 1 Apr - 30 Sept: Fri - Sun & BHs, 2 - 6pm.

Admission: Adult £1.60, Child 80p, Conc. £1.20. 15% discount for groups of 11+.

♿ Ground floor & grounds suitable.   📞 Limited.   🐕 No dogs.

STANTON HARCOURT MANOR 🏛

STANTON HARCOURT, NR. WITNEY, OXFORDSHIRE OX8 1RJ

Owner: The Hon Mrs Gascoigne   *Contact: The Hon Mrs Gascoigne*

Tel: 01865 881928

12 acres of garden with Great Fish Pond and Stew Ponds provide tranquil surroundings for the unique mediaeval buildings, Old Kitchen (Alexander) Pope's Tower and Domestic Chapel. The house, a fine example of a very early unfortified house built to house the Harcourt family and its retainers, is still maintained as the family home.

Location: OS Ref. SP416 056. 9m W of Oxford, 5m SE of Witney off B4449 between Eynsham and Standlake.

Opening Times: Thur, Sun and BH Mon. Apr: 12, 13, 23, 26. May: 3, 4, 14, 17, 24, 25. Jun: 4, 7, 18, 21. Jul: 2, 5, 16, 19, 30. Aug: 2, 13, 16, 30, 31. Sept: 10, 13, 24, 27.

Admission: House & Garden: Adult £4, Child (under 12) /OAP £2. Garden: Adult £2.50, Child (under 12) /OAP £1.50. Group visits by prior arrangement.

♿ Suitable.   ☕ Teas available.   📞 Limited.   🐕 Guide dogs in grounds.

STONOR 🏛   See page 73 for full page entry.

UNIVERSITY OF OXFORD BOTANIC GARDEN   **Tel:** 01865 276920

Rose Lane, Oxford, Oxfordshire OX1 4AX   **Contact:** Timothy Walker Esq

Location: OS Ref. SP520 061. E end of High St, on the banks of River Cherwell.

Opening Times: 1 Apr - 31 Aug: 9am - 5pm (4.30pm in winter). Greenhouses 2 - 4pm.

Admission: £2 during opening times above, otherwise free. Guided tours by appointment only at £3.50 per person (min 15).

🚶 Guided tours.

WATERPERRY GARDENS   **Tel:** 01844 339254/226   **Fax:** 01844 339883

Wheatley, Oxford, Oxfordshire OX33 1JL   **Contact:** The Administrator

Location: OS Ref. SP630 063. M40/J8, follow A40 W for 1 1/2 m to Wheatley, then 2m NE.

Opening Times: Apr - Oct: Mon - Fri, 9am - 5pm. Sat & Sun, 9am - 5.30pm. Nov - Mar: 9am - 5pm. 16 - 19 Jul open only for visitors to Art in Action. Closed Christmas & New Year.

Admission: Apr - Oct: Adult £3, Child 10 - 16 £1.50 (under 16 free), OAP £2.50. Groups of 20+ £2.50. Nov - Mar: £1.

ℹ️ Shop.   ♿ Grounds suitable.   ☕ Licensed restaurant.   🐕 Guide dogs only.

Chastleton House, Oxfordshire
Nadia MacKenzie
Please note: Limited visiting. Pre-booked tickets only. See entry.

HAMPTON COURT PALACE
Surrey

CONTACT

Hampton Court Palace
Surrey
KT8 9AU

For all enquiries
please telephone:

Tel: (0181) 781 9500

LOCATION

OS Ref. TQ155 686

From M25/J15 and A312,
or M25/J12 and A308, or
M25/J10 and A307.

Rail: From London
Waterloo direct to
Hampton Court (32 mins)

The splendour of Cardinal Wolsey's house, begun in 1514, surpasses that of many a Royal Palace, so it was not surprising that Henry VIII at first coveted, then obtained it prior to Wolsey's fall from power.

Henry VIII enlarged it; Charles I lived in it as a prisoner; Charles II repaired it; William III and Mary II rebuilt it to a design by Sir Christopher Wren, and Queen Victoria opened it to the public. Today the beauty of Wren's building is combined with the finest Tudor architecture in Britain.

Costumed guides give lively and informative tours of the sumptuous interiors of the Kings' Apartments, giving a unique insight into the daily lives of the Kings and their courtiers, and entertaining with tales of the etiquette and gossip of court life throughout the centuries.

The Chapel Royal is a stunning example of the Palace's rich interiors, while the Great Hall is still decorated with Henry VIII's priceless Flemish tapestries. Hampton Court is also home to important Renaissance paintings from the collection of HM The Queen.

The 16th century Tudor kitchens are the finest of their date anywhere in the world. They once cooked for over a thousand people a day, and are laid out as if a feast is being prepared, with a roaring log fire and boiling cauldrons.

Hampton Court is set in sixty acres of beautiful Tudor, Baroque and Victorian gardens, which feature the famous maze, and the Great Vine, the oldest and largest grapevine in the world, believed to have been planted in 1768 by 'Capability' Brown.

With its five hundred years of Royal history Hampton Court Palace is a living tapestry portraying the life and times from Henry VIII to George II. It is both visually and historically interesting, and a visit here has something for everyone.

❖

OPENING TIMES

SUMMER
Mid March - mid October
Daily, Tue - Sun
9.30am - 6pm
Mon: 10.15am - 6pm.

WINTER
Mid October - mid March
Tue - Sun: 9.30am - 4.30pm
Mon: 10.15am - 4.30pm

Closed 24 - 26 December.

Last admission 1hr
before closing.

ADMISSION

Adult £9.25
Child (under 16yrs) £6.00
Child (under 5yrs) ......Free
OAP/Conc...............£7.00
Family (2+3) £27.65

ℹ Shops and Information Centre.

♿ Motorised buggies are available upon request at main entrance. WCs.

☕ Tiltyard tearooms and Queen Elizabeth's Privy Kitchen.

🚶 Costumed guides give tours of the State Apartments.

🅿 Available.

👪 Welcome. Rates on request.

South East England

Hatchlands Park.

Clandon Park.

HATCHLANDS PARK/CLANDON
Guildford

Clandon Park and Hatchlands Park were built during the 18th century and are set amid beautiful parklands. They are two of the most outstanding country houses in the country and are only five minutes' drive apart.

Hatchlands Park was built in 1758 for Admiral Boscawen and is set in a beautiful Repton park offering a variety of park and woodland walks. Hatchlands contains splendid interiors by Robert Adam, decorated in appropriately nautical style. It houses the Cobbe collection, the world's largest group of early keyboard instruments associated with famous composers, eg. Purcell, J C Bach, Mozart, Chopin, Mahler and Elgar. There is

also a small garden by Gertrude Jekyll flowering from late May to early July.

Clandon Park is a Palladian house of dramatic contrasts; from the neo-classical marble hall to the Maori Meeting House in the garden; the opulent saloon to the old kitchen, complete with original range, below stairs. All this adds up to a fascinating insight into the different lifestyles of the ruling and serving classes in the 18th century. The house is rightly acclaimed for its remarkable collection of ceramics, textiles, furniture and its excellent restaurant. Clandon is also home to the Queen's Royal Surrey Regiment Museum.

CONTACT

The Property Manager
Clandon Park/
Hatchlands Park
West Clandon
Guildford
Surrey
GU4 7RQ

Tel: (01483) 222482

Info Line: (01483) 223479

Fax: (01483) 223479

LOCATION

HATCHLANDS

OS Ref. TQ063 516
E of East Clandon
on the A246 Guildford -
Leatherhead road.

Rail: Clandon BR
2¹/₂ m,
Horsley 3m.

CLANDON

OS Ref. TQ042 512
At West Clandon on
the A247, 3m E of
Guildford.

Rail: Clandon BR 1m.

Hatchlands Park

Hatchlands Park

OPENING TIMES

HATCHLANDS
House
1 April - 29 October
Tue, Wed, Thur,
Sun & BH Mon.
Fri in August only.
2 - 5.30pm.

Park Walks
Daily (April - October)
11.30am - 6pm.

CLANDON
House
1 April - 29 October
Tue - Thur, Sun &
BH Mon, Good Fri &
Easter Sat
11.30am - 4.30pm.

Garden
Daily, 9am - dusk.

Museum
1 April - 29 October
Tue - Thur & Sat, Sun,
BH Mon, Good Fri &
Easter Sat
12 noon - 5pm.

ADMISSION

Clandon
Adult £4.20
Child £2.10
Family £10.50
Groups (Tue - Thur only)
Adult £3.50

Hatchlands
Adult £4.20
Park Walks & Garden
.............................£1.70
Child £2.10
Park Walks & Garden
.............................85p
Family £10.50
Groups (Tue - Thur only)
Adult £3.50

Combined ticket
Clandon/Hatchlands...£6.00

South East England

LOSELEY PARK
Guildford

LOSELEY PARK, built in 1562 by Sir William More, is a fine example of Elizabethan architecture, its mellow stone brought from the ruins of Waverley Abbey now over 850 years old. The house is set amid magnificent parkland grazed by the Loseley Jersey herd. Many visitors comment on the very friendly atmosphere of the house, it is a country house, the family home of descendants of the builder.

Furniture has been acquired by the family and includes an early 16th century Wrangelschrank beautifully inlaid with many different woods, a Queen Anne cabinet, Georgian armchairs and settee, a Hepplewhite four-poster bed and King George IV's coronation chair. The King's bedroom has Oudenarde tapestry and a carpet commemorating James I's visit.

The Christian pictures include the Henri Met de Bles triptych of the Nativity and modern mystical pictures of the living Christ, St Francis and St Bernadette. A Christian Cancer Help Centre meets twice monthly. Loseley House is available for dinners and functions.

GARDEN

A magnificent Cedar of Lebanon presides over the front lawn. Parkland adjoins the lawn and a small lake adds to the beauty of Front Park. In the Walled Garden are mulberry trees, yew hedges, a grass terrace and the moat walk with herbaceous borders including rose, herb, fruit and vegetable gardens.

CONTACT

Miss Vicky Owen
Loseley Park
Guildford
Surrey
GU3 1HS

Tel: (01483) 304440

Telex: 859972 LOSELG

Fax: (01483) 302036

LOCATION

OS Ref. SU975 471

30m from London, A3 leave at Compton, South of Guildford, on B3000 for 2m, signposted.

Bus: 1¼ m from House.

Rail: Guildford Station 2m, Godalming 3m.

Air: Heathrow 30m, Gatwick 30m.

CONFERENCE/FUNCTION		
ROOM	SIZE	MAX CAPACITY
Tithe Barn	100' x 18'	200
Marquee	sites available	
Great Hall	70' x 40'	100
Drawing Rm	40' x 30'	50
Walled Gdn	Marquee	sites

i Shop. Business launches and promotions. 10 - 12 acre field can be hired in addition to the lawns. Fashion shows, air displays, archery, garden parties, shows, rallies, filming, parkland, moat walk and terrace. Lectures can be arranged on the property, its contents, gardens and history. Loseley Christian Trust Exhibition, children's play area, picnic area, home to Jersey Herd since 1916; traditional working dairy farm, tractor and trailer ride across estate. No unaccompanied children, no photography in house, no videos on estate.

✗ Special functions, banquets and conference catering. Additional marquees for hire. Wedding receptions.

♿ Visitors may alight at entrance to property. WCs. Ground floor suitable.

☕ Tearoom.

🚶 Tour time for house, ¾ hr.

P 150 cars, 6 coaches. Summer overflow car park. Coaches approach from B3000 only, as other roads too narrow. All group visits must be booked in advance.

👥 School visits by prior arrangement. Loseley Park Farm Education Centre.

🐕 No dogs.

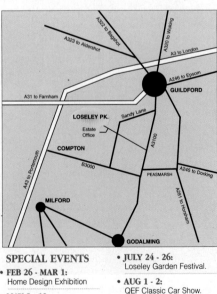

SPECIAL EVENTS

- **FEB 26 - MAR 1:**
  Home Design Exhibition

- **MAY 8 - 10:**
  Surrey Advertiser Motor Show.

- **MAY 29 - 31:**
  Live Crafts.

- **JULY 24 - 26:**
  Loseley Garden Festival.

- **AUG 1 - 2:**
  QEF Classic Car Show.

- **NOV 6 - 8:**
  Christmas Food & Gift Fair.

- **NOV 27 - 29:**
  Live Crafts.

OPENING TIMES

SUMMER

Garden, Shop & Tea Room
4 May - 26 September
Wed - Sat & BH Mon
11am - 5pm.
Last entry 4.30pm to all attractions.

House Tours
25 May - 29 August
(inc. BH Mon) 2 - 5pm.

Trailer Rides
25 May - 29 August
(inc. BH Mon) Sat only.
12 - 5pm.

ALL YEAR
Tithe Barn, House and Grounds available for private/business functions and wedding receptions.

ADMISSION

House & Gardens
Adult £4.50
Child (3-16yrs)........£2.75
OAP/Disabled.........£3.75
Child (under 3) ....FREE

All-in-one (Sats only)
(House, gardens, trailer ride and farm visit)
Adult £6.75
Child (3-16yrs)........£3.75
OAP/Disabled.........£5.75
Child (under 3) ....FREE

Trailer ride (Sats only)
Adult £2.75
Child (3-16yrs)........£1.25
OAP/Disabled.........£2.25
Child (under 3) ....FREE

Group rates available for 20+.

LOSELEY PARK continued ...

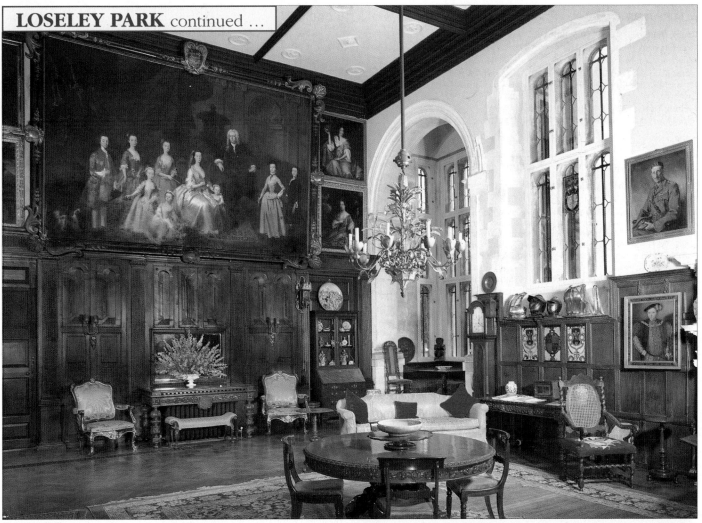

The Great Hall.

THE TITHE BARN AT LOSELEY PARK

The Tithe Barn (originally 1635) is situated on the sweeping lawns of Loseley House and offers unrivalled views of the surrounding parkland and a magnificent Cedar of Lebanon.

It is adaptable for a wide range of functions and will comfortably accommodate 50-150 people for a full sit-down meal, or up to 200 for a cocktail reception. Should a larger group be envisaged, our permanent marquee may be used and further marquees erected. The South Room of the Tithe Barn is ideal for small meetings and private lunches.

The location is ideal for business and corporate hospitality events. It is within easy reach of the A3 and M25, an hour from London and some 40 minutes from Heathrow and Gatwick Airports. Ample car parking is available.

Garden.

The Tithe Barn

ALBURY PARK

Tel: 01483 202964 **Fax:** 01483 205023

Albury, Guildford, Surrey GU5 9BB

Owner: Country Houses Association   **Contact:** The Administrators

Country mansion by Pugin.

Location: OS Ref. TQ058 479 (gate). 1^1/$_2$ m E of Albury off A25 Guildford to Dorking Road. Stations: Chilworth Clandon 3m, Gomshall 2m. Bus route: Tillingbourne No.25 Guildford - Cranley 2m.

Opening Times: 1 May - 30 Sept: Wed & Thur, 2 - 5pm.

Admission: Adult £2.50, Child £1, OAP/Student £2.50. Groups by arrangement.

No dogs.   A 1 single & 1 double with bathroom, CHA members only.

CARSHALTON HOUSE

Tel: 0181 770 4781 **Fax:** 0181 770 4666

Pound Street, Carshalton, Surrey SM5 3PN

Owner: St Philomena's Catholic High School for Girls   **Contact:** Ms V Murphy

A Queen Anne mansion built c1707, now in use as a school, with grounds originally laid out by Charles Bridgeman. The principal rooms contain 18th century decoration including the 'Adam' room and the Painted Parlour, attributed to Robert Robinson. Garden buildings include the unique Water Tower. Publications, souvenirs and home made refreshments available. Open to the public twice a year by Sutton Heritage Service in conjunction with the Water Tower Trust.

Location: OS Ref. TQ275 644. On A232 just S of junction with B278.

Opening Times: Easter BH Mon, 13 Apr and BH Mon, 31 Aug: 10am - 5pm. Last admission 4.15pm.

Admission: Adult £3, Child under 16/Full-time students £1.50.

Grounds & ground floor suitable.   Tearoom.   Available.   P Available.

Guide dogs only.

CLANDON/HATCHLANDS PARK

See page 79 for full page entry.

CLAREMONT LANDSCAPE GARDEN

Tel: 01372 467806/469421

Portsmouth Road, Esher, Surrey KT10 9JG

Owner: The National Trust   **Contact:** The Property Manager

One of the earliest surviving English landscape gardens, restored to its former glory. Begun by Sir John Vanbrugh and Charles Bridgeman before 1720, the gardens were extended and naturalised by William Kent. 'Capability' Brown also made improvements. Features include a lake, island with pavilion, grotto, turf amphitheatre, viewpoints and avenues.

Location: OS Ref. TQ128 634. On S edge of Esher, on E side of A307 (no access from Esher bypass).

Opening Times: Jan - 31 Mar: daily except Mon, 10am - 5pm or sunset if earlier. Apr - 31 Oct: Mon - Fri, 10am - 6pm. Sat, Sun & BH Mon, 10am - 7pm. Garden closed 14 Jul all day and at 2pm on 15 - 19 Jul. Nov - end Mar: daily except Mon, 10am - 5pm or sunset if earlier. Last adm. ^{1}/$_2$ hr before closing. Closed 25 Dec. Open 1 Jan: 1 - 4pm (for NGS).

Admission: Adult £3, Child £1.50. Coach parties must book; no coach parties on Sun. Family (2+2) £8. Groups of 15+, £2.50. 50p discount if using public transport.

i Shop.   Limited suitability. WC.   Tearoom.   No dogs (Apr - Oct).

CROYDON PALACE

Tel: 0181 688 2027

Old Palace Road, Croydon, Surrey CR0 1AX

Owner: The Whitgift Foundation   **Contact:** The Whitgift Foundation

One thousand year old residence of former Archbishops of Canterbury.

Location: OS Ref. TQ320 654. 200 yds S of Croydon parish church, 400 yds W of Croydon High St.

Opening Times: 14 - 18 April, 25 - 29 May, 13 - 18 July, 20 - 25 July.

Admission: £4.

FARNHAM CASTLE KEEP

Tel: 01252 713393

Castle Hill, Farnham, Surrey GU6 0AG

Owner: English Heritage   **Contact:** The Head Custodian

Used as a fortified manor by the medieval Bishops of Winchester, this motte and bailey castle has been in continuous occupation since the 12th century. You can visit the large shell-keep enclosing a mound in which are massive foundations of a Norman tower.

Location: OS Ref. SU839 474. ^{1}/$_2$ m N of Farnham town centre on A287.

Opening Times: 1 Apr - 1 Nov: 10am - 6pm or dusk if earlier.

Admission: Adult £2, Child, £1, Conc. £1.50.

Ground floor & grounds.   Free audio tour.   In grounds, on leads.

GODDARDS

Tel: 01628 825920

Abinger Common, Dorking, Surrey RH5 6TH

Owner: The Lutyens Trust, leased to The Landmark Trust   **Contact:** The Landmark Trust

Built by Sir Edwin Lutyens in 1898 - 1900 and enlarged by him in 1910. Garden by Gertrude Jekyll. Given to the Lutyens Trust in 1991 and now managed and maintained by the Landmark Trust, which let buildings for self-catering holidays. The whole house, apart from the library, is available for up to 12 people. Full details of Goddards and 163 other historic buildings available for holidays are featured in The Landmark handbook (price £8.50 refundable against booking), from The Landmark Trust, Shottesbrooke, Maidenhead, Berkshire SL6 3SW.

Location: OS Ref. TQ120 450. 4^1/$_2$ m SW of Dorking on the village green in Abinger Common. Signposted Abinger Common, Friday Street and Leith Hill from A25.

Opening Times: Strictly by appointment. Must be booked in advance, including parking, which is very limited. Visits booked for Wed afternoons from the Wed after Easter until the last Wed of Oct between 2 - 6pm. Only those with pre-booked tickets will be admitted.

Admission: £3. Tickets available from Mrs Baker on 01306 730871, Mon - Fri, 9am & 6pm. Visitors will have access to part of the garden and house only.

A Available.

GREATHED MANOR

Tel: 01342 832577 **Fax:** 01342 836207

Ford Manor Road, Dormansland, Lingfield, Surrey RH7 6PA

Owner: Country Houses Association   **Contact:** The Administrator

Victorian Manor House.

Location: OS Ref. TQ414 423. 2m SE of Lingfield off the B2028 Edenbridge Road, take Ford Manor Road beside Plough Inn. Dormansland for final mile.

Opening Times: 1 May - 30 Sept: Wed & Thur, 2 - 5pm.

Admission: Adult £2.50, Child £1, Groups by arrangement.

Not suitable.   P Limited for cars. No coaches.   No dogs.

A 1 single & 1 double with bathroom, CHA members only.

GUILDFORD HOUSE GALLERY

Tel: 01483 444740 **Fax:** 01483 444742

155 High Street, Guildford, Surrey GU1 3AJ

Owner: Guildford Borough Council   **Contact:** Curator

Fascinating Grade I listed town house dating from 1660. Finely decorated plaster ceilings, panelled rooms, wrought iron work and richly carved staircase. A wide range of changing exhibitions on display together with selections from Guildford Borough's collection which includes topographical pictures over 200 years, prints and contemporary craftwork. Pastel portraits by Guildford-born artist John Russell RA (1745-1806) are often on show. Workshops and free lunchtime talks.

Location: OS Ref. SU996 494. Central Guildford.

Opening Times: All year: Tue - Sat, 10am - 4.45pm.

Admission: Free.

i Gallery shop.   Not suitable.   Tearoom.   P No parking.   Guide dogs only.

HAMPTON COURT PALACE

See page 78 for full page entry.

HATCHLANDS PARK/CLANDON

See page 79 for full page entry.

HONEYWOOD HERITAGE CENTRE

Tel: 0181 773 4555 **Fax:** 0181 770 4666

Honeywood Walk, Carshalton, Surrey SM5 3NX

Owner: London Borough of Sutton   **Contact:** The Curator

A 17th century listed building next to the picturesque Carshalton Ponds, containing displays on many aspects of the history of the London Borough of Sutton plus a changing programme of exhibitions and events on a wide range of subjects. Attractive garden at rear.

Location: OS Ref. TQ279 646. On A232 approximately 4m W of Croydon.

Opening Times: Wed - Fri, 10am - 5pm. Sat, Sun & BH Mon, 10am - 5.30pm. Tea rooms open Tue - Sun, 10am - 5pm.

Admission: Adult £1, Child 50p, under 5 free. Groups by arrangement.

i Shop.   Ground floor only. WC.   Tearoom.   Available.   P Limited.

Available.   Guide dogs only.

LITTLE HOLLAND HOUSE

Tel: 0181 770 4781 **Fax:** 0181 770 4666

40 Beeches Avenue, Carshalton, Surrey SM5 3LW

Owner: London Borough of Sutton   **Contact:** Ms V Murphy

The home of Frank Dickinson (1874 - 1961) artist, designer and craftsman, who dreamt of a house that would follow the philosophy and theories of William Morris and John Ruskin. Dickinson designed, built and furnished the house himself from 1902 onwards. The Grade II* listed interior features handmade furniture, metal work, carvings and paintings produced by Dickinson in the Arts and Crafts style.

Location: OS Ref. TQ275 634. On B278 1m S of junction with A232.

Opening Times: First Sun of each month and BH Sun & Mon excluding New Year, 1.30 - 5.30pm.

Admission: Free. Groups by arrangement, £2pp (includes talk and guided tour).

Ground floor only.   By arrangement.   P No parking.   Guide dogs only.

LOSELEY PARK

See page 80/81 for full page entry.

OAKHURST COTTAGE

Tel: 01428 683207

Hambledon, Godalming, Surrey

Owner: The National Trust **Contact:** Witley Common Information Centre

A very small 16th century timber-framed cottage, restored and furnished as a simple cottager's dwelling. Delightful cottage garden with contemporary plant species.

Location: OS Ref. SU965 385. Hambledon, Surrey.

Opening Times: 30 Mar - end Oct: Wed, Thur, Sat, Sun & BH Mon, 2 - 5pm. Strictly by appointment only (48 hrs notice required)

Admission: Adult £2.50, Child £1.25 (including guided tour). No reduction for parties.

Not suitable. Compulsory, by arrangement. Limited. No dogs.

PAINSHILL LANDSCAPE GARDEN

Tel: 01932 868113 **Fax:** 01932 868001

Portsmouth Road, Cobham, Surrey KT11 1JE

Owner: Painshill Park Trust **Contact:** Visitor Manager

This is one of the finest 18th century landscape gardens, created by the Hon Charles Hamilton (1704 - 86). Situated in 158 acres, visitors can take a circuit walk through a series of emerging scenes, each one more surprising than the last. A 14-acre lake fed by a massive water wheel gives a breathtaking setting for a variety of spectacular features including a Gothic temple, ruined abbey, Turkish tent, crystal grotto, magnificent Cedars of Lebanon, replanted 18th century shrubberies and vineyard. Available for corporate and private hire, location filming, wedding receptions, etc.

Location: OS Ref. TQ099 605. M25/J10 to London. W of Cobham on A245. Entrance opposite Territorial Army Centre, 200 yds E of A245/A307 roundabout.

Opening Times: Apr - Oct: Tue - Sun and BH Mon, 10.30am - 4.30pm (last admission). Gates close 6pm. Nov - Mar: daily except Mon & Fri, 11am - 4pm or dusk if earlier. Closed Christmas and Boxing Day.

Admission: Adult £3.80, Child over 5 £1.50, under 5 free, Conc. £3.30, Groups (min 20) £3pp.

Shop. Marquee site. Grounds suitable. WCs.

Tearoom. Guide dogs only.

RHS GARDEN WISLEY

NR. WOKING, SURREY

Owner: *The Royal Horticultural Society* ***Contact:*** *The Royal Horticultural Society*

Tel: 01483 224234 **Fax:** 01483 211750

A world famous garden which extends to 240 acres and provides the chance to glean new ideas and inspiration. Highlights include the azaleas and rhododendrons in spring, the glasshouses and the model gardens. The visitor centre offers the world's finest collection of horticultural books and over 10,000 varieties of plants for sale.

Location: OS Ref. TQ066 583. NW side of A3 1/2 m SW of M25/J10.

Opening Times: All year: Mon - Fri (except Christmas Day), 10am - sunset or 6pm during the summer; Sat 9am - sunset or 6pm during summer.

Admission: Adult £5, Child (up to 6) free, Child (6-16yrs) £2. Groups 10+ £4. Companion for disabled or blind visitors, free.

Plants for sale. Wheelchairs available tel: 01483 211113 & special map.

Restaurant. Guide dogs only.

POLESDEN LACEY

GREAT BOOKHAM, NR DORKING, SURREY RH5 6BD

Owner: *The National Trust* ***Contact:*** *The Property Manager*

Tel: 01372 452048 **Infoline:** 01372 458203 **Fax:** 01372 452023

Originally an elegant 1820s Regency villa in magnificent landscape setting. The house was remodelled after 1906 by the Hon Mrs Ronald Greville, a well-known Edwardian hostess. Her collection of fine paintings, furniture, porcelain and silver are still displayed in the reception rooms, and corridors, which surround an inner courtyard. Extensive grounds, walled rose garden, lawns and landscaped walks. King George VI and Queen Elizabeth, The Queen Mother spent part of their honeymoon here.

Location: OS Ref. TQ136 522. 5m NW of Dorking, 2m S of Great Bookham, off A246.

Opening Times: House: 1 Apr - 1 Nov: Wed - Sun, 1.30 - 5.30pm also BH Mon starting with Easter, 11am - 5.30pm. Grounds: All year: daily, 11am - 6pm/dusk. Last admission to house 1/2 hr before closing.

Admission: Garden, grounds & landscape walks: Adult £3, Family £7.50. House: £3 extra. Family £7.50 extra. All year pre-booked parties £5pp (house, garden & walks).

Shop. Suitable. WC. Restaurant. In grounds on leads.

RAMSTER GARDENS

Tel: 01428 654167

Ramster, Chiddingfold, Surrey GU8 4SN

Owner: Mrs M Gunn **Contact:** Mrs M Gunn

20 acres of woodland and flowering shrub garden laid out in 1904. Well maintained with lake and bog garden.

Location: OS Ref. SU950 333. 1 1/2 m S of Chiddingfold on A283.

Opening Times: 18 Apr 12 Jul: 11am 5.30pm.

Admission: £2.50, Child free.

Plants for sale. Wedding receptions. Grounds suitable. Tearoom (in May).

In grounds, on leads. Civil Wedding Licence.

ROYAL BOTANIC GARDENS

Tel: 0181 940 1171 **Fax:** 0181 332 5610

Kew, Richmond, Surrey TW9 3AB **Contact:** Enquiry Unit

Location: OS Ref. TQ188 776. A307. Junction A305 and A205 (1m Chiswick roundabout M4).

Opening Times: 9.30am, daily except Christmas Day and New Year's Day.

Admission: Adult £4.50, Child £2.50, Conc. £3, Family £12. Groups 20% discount when pre-booked and paid. (1997 prices)

Shop. Suitable. Restaurant. 2/day. £1 charge.

Teacher's pack & tours. Guide dogs only. Civil Wedding Licence.

SHALFORD MILL

Tel: 01483 561617

Shalford, Guildford, Surrey

Owner: The National Trust   **Contact:** Mr Bagnall

18th century watermill on the Tillingbourne, given in 1932 by "Ferguson's Gang".

Location: OS Ref. TQ000 476. 1$\frac{1}{2}$ m S of Guildford on A281, opposite Sea Horse Inn.

Opening Times: Daily, 10am - 5pm.

Admission: Free. No unaccompanied children.

WHITEHALL

Tel: 0181 643 1236   **Fax:** 0181 770 4666

1 Malden Road, Cheam, Surrey SM3 8QD

Owner: London Borough of Sutton   **Contact:** The Curator

A Tudor, timber-framed house, c1500 with later additions, in the heart of Cheam village conservation area. Twelve rooms open to view with displays on Nonsuch Palace, timber-framed buildings, Cheam pottery, Cheam school and William Gilpin. Changing exhibition programme and special event days throughout the year. Attractive rear garden features medieval well from c1400.

Location: OS Ref. TQ242 638. Approx. 2m S of A3 on A2043 just N of junction with A232.

Opening Times: 1 Oct - 31 Mar: Wed, Thur, Sun, 2 - 5.30pm; Sat, 10am - 5.30pm. 1 Apr - 30 Sept: Tue - Fri, Sun, 2 - 5.30pm; Sat, 10am - 5.30pm; BH Mon, 2 - 5.30pm. Closed Christmas and New Year.

Admission: Adult £1, Child (under 16) 50p, children under 5 free.

ℹ️ Shop.   ♿ Ground floor only.   ☕ Tearoom.   🚶 Available.

👥 Available.   🐕 Guide dogs only.

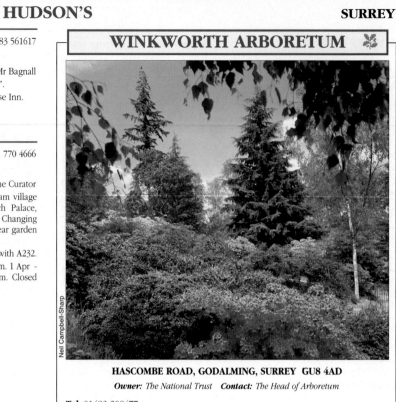

WINKWORTH ARBORETUM

Neil Campbell-Sharp

HASCOMBE ROAD, GODALMING, SURREY GU8 4AD

Owner: The National Trust   *Contact:* The Head of Arboretum

Tel: 01483 208477

Hillside woodland with two lakes, many rare trees and shrubs and fine views. The most impressive displays are in spring for bluebells and azaleas, autumn for colour and wildlife.

Location: OS Ref. SU990 412. Near Hascombe, 2m SE of Godalming on E side of B2130.

Opening times: All year: daily during daylight hours. May be closed during bad weather.

Admission: Adult £2.70, Child (5-16) £1.35, Family (2+2) £6.75 additional family member £1.25.

ℹ️ Shop.   ♿ Limited. WC.   ☕ Tearoom.   🐕 In grounds, on leads.

Winkworth Arboretum, Surrey.

Hatchlands Park, Surrey.

South East England

ARUNDEL CASTLE
Arundel

This great castle, home of the Dukes of Norfolk, dates from the Norman Conquest. Containing a very fine collection of furniture and paintings, Arundel Castle is still a family home, reflecting the changes of nearly a thousand years.

In 1643, during the Civil War, the original castle was very badly damaged and it was later restored by the 8th, 11th and 15th Dukes in the 18th and 19th centuries. Amongst its treasures are personal possessions of Mary Queen of Scots and a selection of historical, religious and heraldic items from the Duke of Norfolk's collection.

The Duke of Norfolk is the Premier Duke, the title having been conferred on Sir John Howard in 1483 by his friend King Richard III. The Dukedom also carries with it the hereditary office of Earl Marshal of England. Among the historically famous members of the Howard family are Lord Howard of Effingham who, with Drake, repelled the Spanish Armada; the Earl of Surrey, the Tudor poet and courtier and the 3rd Duke of Norfolk, uncle of Anne Boleyn and Catherine Howard, both of whom became wives of King Henry VIII.

CONTACT

The Comptroller
Arundel Castle
Arundel
West Sussex
BN18 9AB

Tel: (01903) 883136
or (01903) 882173

Fax: (01903) 884581

LOCATION

OS Ref. TQ018 072

1m Arundel, N of A27
Brighton 40 mins,
Worthing 15 mins,
Chichester 15 mins.
From London A3 or A24,
1$^{1}/_{2}$ hrs.
M25 motorway, 30m.

Bus: Bus stop 100 yds.

Rail: Station $^{1}/_{2}$ m.

Air: Gatwick 25m.

OPENING TIMES

SUMMER
1 April - 30 October
daily
except Sat & Good Fri
12 - 5pm
Last admission 4pm.

WINTER
1 November - 31 March
Pre-booked parties only.

ADMISSION

SUMMER
Adult £5.70
Child (5-15).............£4.20
OAP £5.20
Family £15.50

Grounds only £2.00

Groups (min 20)
Adult £5.20
Child (5-15).............£3.70
OAP.........................£4.70

WINTER
Pre-booked parties
Mornings.................£7.00
(Min Fee ....£350.00)
Evenings, Sat &
Sun £8.00
(Min Fee ....£400.00)

ℹ️ Shop. No unaccompanied children or photography inside the Castle. Guide book translations in English, French and German.

♿ Visitors may alight at the entrance, before parking in the allocated areas. WCs.

☕ The Restaurant seats 140. Special rates for pre-booked groups. Self-service restaurant in the Castle serves home-made food. Groups need to book in advance for afternoon tea, lunch or dinner.

🚶 Available for pre-booked parties only, £7pp. Also available in French and German. Tour time 1$^{1}/_{2}$ hrs.

🅿️ Ample. Coaches can park opposite the Castle entrance.

👪 Items of particular interest include a Norman Keep and Armoury. Special rates for schoolchildren (aged 5-15) and teachers.

🐕 No dogs.

CHARLESTON
Lewes

CONTACT

Emma Whelan
Charleston
Nr. Firle
Lewes
East Sussex
BN8 6LL

Tel: (01323) 811265
(Visitor information)
(01323) 811626
(Admin.)

Fax: (01323) 811628

LOCATION

OS Ref. TQ490 069

6m E of Lewes
on A27 between Firle
and Selmeston.
The lane to Charleston
leads off the A27, 2m
beyond the Firle turning.

London 60m. Brighton
15m. Monk's House,
Rodmell (Leonard and
Virginia Woolf's
house) 11m.

Air: Gatwick 35m .

Rail: London (Victoria)
hourly to Lewes
(65 mins).
Occasional train
to Berwick.
Bus: Rider 125 Route
on A27.
Taxi: George & Graham,
Lewes 473692.

A mile or so from Firle village, near the end of a track leading to the foot of the Downs, lies Charleston. It was discovered in 1916 by Virginia and Leonard Woolf when Virginia's sister, the painter Vanessa Bell, was looking for a place in the country. Vanessa moved here with fellow artist Duncan Grant, the writer David Garnett, her two young sons and an assortment of animals. It was an unconventional and creative household which became the focal point for artists and intellectuals later to be known as the Bloomsbury set, among them Roger Fry, Lytton Strachey and Maynard Keynes.

Over the years the artists decorated the walls, furniture and ceramics with their own designs, influenced by Italian fresco painting and post-impressionist art. Creativity extended to the garden too. Mosaics were made in the piazza, sculpture was cleverly positioned to intrigue and subtle masses of colour were used in the planting.

After Duncan Grant's death in 1978, the Charleston Trust was formed to save and restore the house to its former glory. The task has been described as "one of the most difficult and imaginative feats of restoration current in Britain".

❖

ℹ Shop. Filming and photography contact Shaun Romain: 01323 811626. Small lecture room available by special arrangement. No filming, video or photography in house.

♿ Visitors may alight at entrance. Wheelchair visitors by prior arrangement. Ground floor only suitable. WCs.

☕ Available most afternoons during the season.

🚶 Compulsory.

🅿 50 spaces. Mini coaches and cars only. Mini coaches may use the lane to the property. It is essential to arrange group visits (up to 50) in advance and out of public hours. All group visits to the house are guided. Large coaches may set down at the start of the lane, 10 mins walk.

👪 Student pack and a teacher's guide suitable for KS I & II.

🐕 No dogs.

OPENING TIMES

1 April - 31 October
Wed - Sun: 2 - 5pm.

July & August
Wed - Sat: 11.30am - 5pm
Sun: 2 - 5pm.

September & October
Wed - Sun: 2 - 5pm.

November - December
Christmas shopping
Sat & Sun, 2 - 5pm.

Guided visits
Wed - Sat,
unguided on Suns.

House closed Mon & Tue
except BH Mons.

Connoisseur Fridays
April - June, September
and October, in-depth tour
of the house, including
Vanessa Bell's studio and
the kitchen.

ADMISSION

House & Garden
Adult £5.00
Child (5+)/Conc*. £3.50
Child (under 5)............Free
Disabled..................£3.50

Groups
Adult £4.50
Child/Student..........£3.50
OAP........................£4.50

Connoisseur Fridays
Adult £6.50

* OAPs, Students &
UB40 Wed & Thur
only throughout season.
Organised tours should
telephone for group rates.

SPECIAL EVENTS

• **MAY 21 - 25:**
Charleston Festival

• **JUL 5 - 11:**
Charleston Summer School

South East England

GOODWOOD HOUSE
Chichester

Nestling at the foot of the Sussex Downs surrounded by a patchwork of rolling green, Goodwood, the country home of the Dukes of Richmond since 1697, is one of Europe's great estates.

The son of King Charles II and his French mistress Louise de Keroualle, the 1st Duke was renowned for his love of life and brilliance at entertaining - a tradition which continues to this day.

The original Jacobean house, enlarged in the 18th century by James Wyatt, was used by the 1st Duke as a hunting lodge. Three famous hunting scenes by Stubbs grace the Front Hall. The 2nd Duke, patron of the Venetian artist

Canaletto, was responsible for commissioning the two great views of London which today hang with many other Italian Old Masters in one of the many beautiful rooms. Goodwood also has a magnificent collection of Sèvres porcelain and French furniture collected by the 3rd Duke whilst Ambassador to the Court of King Louis XV.

Now refurbished by the Earl and Countess of March, Goodwood is not only a beautiful house to visit, but has also established a worldwide reputation for excellence as the perfect location for all manner of corporate, private and incentive entertainment requirements.

❖

CONTACT

Valerie Lambirth
Goodwood House
Goodwood
Chichester
West Sussex
PO18 0PX

Tel: (01243) 755040
Fax: (01243) 755005

LOCATION

OS Ref. SU888 088

4m NE of Chichester. A3 from London then A286 or A285. M27/A27 from Portsmouth or Brighton.

Rail: Chichester 4m
Arundel 9m.

Air: Heathrow 1½ hrs
Gatwick ¾ hr.

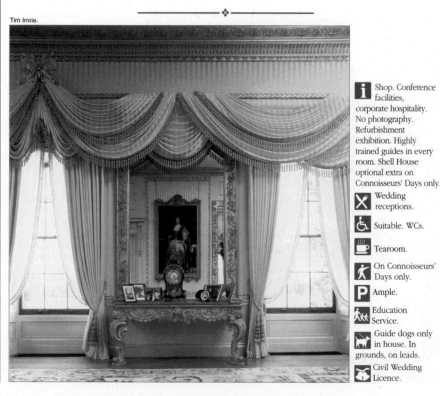

Tim Imrie.

i Shop. Conference facilities, corporate hospitality. No photography. Refurbishment exhibition. Highly trained guides in every room. Shell House optional extra on Connoisseurs' Days only.

✗ Wedding receptions.

♿ Suitable. WCs.

☕ Tearoom.

🚶 On Connoisseurs' Days only.

P Ample.

Education Service.

Guide dogs only in house. In grounds, on leads.

Civil Wedding Licence.

OPENING TIMES

SUMMER
From Easter Sun & Mon, 12 & 13 April, the House will be open on Suns & Mons until 28 September, Sun - Thur in August.
1 - 5pm.

Closed on occasional Event Days: 19, 20 April, 10 May, 7, 14, 15 June and 20 Sept.

Connoisseurs' Days
Group visits with special guided tours can be booked on 5 & 12 May, 1 Jul and 10 Nov. Refreshments available: light lunches and famous Goodwood teas.

ADMISSION

House
Adult	£5.50
Child*	£2.00

Groups (25 - 200)
Economy	£4.50
Connoisseur	£7.50

* 12 - 18 years, under 12 Free

SPECIAL EVENTS

• **FEB 13 - 15, MAY 8 - 10 & NOV 13 - 15:**
SE Counties Antiques Fair

• **MAY - SEPT:**
Goodwood Horserace Meetings
19, 20, 21 May
3, 28 June,
5, 12, 19, 26 June (evenings)
28 July - 1 August (Festival Meeting)
28, 29 August
11, 12, 23, 24 September

• **JUN 12 - 14:**
Goodwood Festival of Speed

• **SEPT 18 - 20:**
Goodwood Motor Circuit Revival

CONFERENCE/FUNCTION

ROOM	SIZE	MAX CAPACITY
Ballroom	79' x 23'	200
11 other rooms also available		

South East
England

LEONARDSLEE GARDENS
Horsham

LEONARDSLEE GARDENS represent one of the largest and most spectacular woodland gardens in England with one of the finest collections of mature rhododendrons, azaleas, choice trees and shrubs to be seen anywhere. It is doubly fortunate in having one of the most magnificent settings, within easy reach of London, only a few miles from the M23. Laid out by Sir Edmund Loder since 1889, the gardens are still maintained by the Loder family today. The 240 acre (100 hectare) valley is world famous for its spring display of azaleas and rhododendrons around the 7 lakes, giving superb views and reflections.

The delightful Rock Garden, a photographer's paradise, is a kaleidoscope of colour in May. The superb exhibition of Bonsai in a walled courtyard shows the fascinating living art-form of Bonsai to perfection. The Alpine House has 400 different alpine plants growing in a natural rocky setting. Wallabies (used as mowing machines!) have lived wild in part of the garden for over 100 years, and deer (Sika, Fallow & Axis) may be seen in the parklands.

Many superb rhododendrons have been raised at Leonardslee. The most famous is *rhododendron loderi* raised by Sir Edmund Loder in 1901. The original plants can still be seen in the garden. In May the fragrance of their huge blooms pervades the air throughout the valley.

The Loder family collection of Victorian motorcars (1895 - 1900) provides a fascinating view of the different designs adopted on the first auto-mobile constructors.

CONTACT

R Loder
Leonardslee Gardens
Lower Beeding
Horsham
West Sussex
RH13 6PP

Tel: (01403) 891212

Fax: (01403) 891305

LOCATION

OS Ref. TQ222 260

M23 to Handcross then B2110 (signposted Cowfold) for 4m. From London: 1 hr 15 mins.

Rail: Horsham Station 4$\frac{1}{2}$ m

Bus: No. 107 from Horsham and Brighton

CONFERENCE/FUNCTION		
ROOM	SIZE	MAX CAPACITY
Clock Tower		100

OPENING TIMES

SUMMER

1 April - 31 October
daily 9.30am - 6pm

May: 9.30am - 8pm

WINTER

1 November - 31 March
Closed to the general public.

Available for functions.

ADMISSION

May
  Adult £4.50
  Child £2.00

April, June - October
  Adult £3.50
  Child £2.00

Season Ticket...........£10.00

Groups
May: Mon - Fri £4.00
Sat, Sun &
BH Mon:.....................£4.50

April, June - October
  Adult £3.00
  Child £2.00

i Shop. photography - landscape and fashion, film location.

X Restaurant available for private and corporate function in the evenings and out of season.

♿ Not suitable.

☕ Restaurant and café. Morning coffee, lunch and teas.

P Ample. Refreshments free to coach drivers. Average length of visit 2 - 4 hours.

🚶 Not available.

🐕 No dogs.

SPECIAL EVENTS

• **MAY 2 - 4:**
  Bonsai weekend

• **JUN 27 - 28:**
  Country Craft Fair.

South East England

Oliver Benn

CONTACT

The Administration Office
Petworth House
Petworth
West Sussex
GU28 0AE

Tel: (01798) 342207

Info Line: (01798) 343929

Fax: (01798) 342963

LOCATION

OS Ref. SU976 218

In the centre of Petworth
town (approach roads
A272/A283/A285)
Car park signposted.

Rail: Pulborough
BR 5¼ m.

Andreas Von Einsiedel

PETWORTH HOUSE
Petworth

Petworth House is one of the finest houses in the care of the National Trust and is home to an art collection that rivals many London galleries. Assembled by one family over 350 years, it includes works by Turner, Van Dyck, Titian, Claude, Gainsborough, Bosch, Reynolds and William Blake.

The state rooms contain sculpture, furniture and porcelain of the highest quality and are complemented by the opening of the old kitchens in the servants' block.

A continuing programme of repairs and restoration brings new interest for the visitor each year. Petworth House is also the home of Lord and Lady Egremont and extra family rooms are open on weekdays by kind permission (not Bank Holidays).

Petworth Park is a 700 acre park landscaped by 'Capability' Brown and is open to the public all year free of charge. Spring and autumn are particularly breathtaking and the summer sunsets over the lake are spectacular.

❖

i Shop. Events throughout the year. Large musical concerts in the park. Baby feeding and changing facilities, highchairs. Pushchairs admitted in house but no prams, please.

✗ Contact Retail & Catering Manager on 01798 344080.

♿ As car park is 800 yards from house there is a vehicle available to take less able visitors to house.

☕ Licensed tearoom 12-5pm.

🚶 Available by arrangement with the Administration Officer on variety of subjects, tailor-made to suit your group (additional charge).

P Car park 800 yards from house. Coach parties alight at Church Lodge entrance, coaches then park in NT car park. Coaches must book in advance.

👫 Welcome. Must pre-book. Teachers' pack available.

🐕 Guide dogs only in house. Dogs in park only.

OPENING TIMES

House
28 March - 1 November
daily except
Thur & Fri but open
Good Fri
1 - 5.30pm.

Last admission to
house 4.30pm,
old kitchen 5pm.

Extra rooms shown on
weekdays, not BH Mon.

**Pleasure Grounds
and Car Park**
Dates as above
12 - 6pm.
BH Mon, July and August
11am - 6pm.

Park
All year: Daily
8am - sunset.

Closed 26 - 28 June
from 12 noon.

ADMISSION

House
Adult	£5.00
Child*	£2.50
Family**	£12.50
Park Only	Free

Groups (pre-booked 15+)
Adult	£4.50
Child	£2.50

Pleasure Grounds
	Free

* 5 - 17 years.
** 2 adults & 2 children

SPECIAL EVENTS

• **MAY 17:**
Spring Plant Fair

• **MAY 23 - 25:**
Craft Festival

• **JUN 26 - 28:**
Open Air Concerts

THE ROYAL PAVILION
Brighton

CONTACT

Visitor Services
The Royal Pavilion
Brighton
East Sussex
BN1 1EE

Tel: (01273) 290900

Fax: (01273) 292871

LOCATION

OS Ref. TQ313 043

The Royal Pavilion is in the centre of Brighton easily reached by road and rail. From London M25, M23, A23 - 1 hr 30 mins.

Rail: Victoria to Brighton station 55 mins. 15 mins walk from Brighton station.

Air: Gatwick 20 mins.

Universally acclaimed as one of the most beautiful buildings in the British Isles, the Royal Pavilion was the famous seaside residence of King George IV.

Originally a simple farmhouse, in 1787 architect Henry Holland created a neo-classical villa on the site. It was later transformed into its current Indian style by John Nash between 1815 and 1822. With interiors decorated in the Chinese style and an astonishingly exotic exterior, this Regency Palace is quite breathtaking.

Magnificent decorations and fantastic furnishings have been re-created in the recent extensive restoration programme. From the opulence of the main state rooms to the charm of the first floor bedroom suites, the Royal Pavilion is filled with astonishing colours and superb craftsmanship.

Witness the magnificence of the Music Room with its domed ceiling of gilded scallop-shaped shells and hand-knotted carpet, and promenade through the Chinese bamboo grove of the Long Gallery.

Lavish menus were created in the Great Kitchen, with its cast iron palm trees and dazzling collection of copperware, and then served in the dramatic setting of the Banqueting Room, lit by a huge crystal chandelier held by a silvered dragon.

With the quiet grace of the galleries, the elegance of the King's private apartments and much more, the Royal Pavilion is an unforgettable experience.

Following the successful restoration of the exterior of the Royal Pavilion, the surrounding gardens have now been returned to their original 1826 appearance. The picturesque Regency gardens, replanted to John Nash's elegant design, are a truly fitting setting for the magical Royal Pavilion.

CONFERENCE/FUNCTION

ROOM	SIZE	MAX CAPACITY
Banqueting Room		200
Great Kitchen		90
Music Rm		180
Queen Adelaide Suite		100
Small Adelaide		40
William IV		80

ℹ️ Gift shop. Popular location for filming and photography, including feature films, fashion shoots and corporate videos.

✕ Spectacular rooms available for prestigious corporate entertaining and wedding receptions..

♿ Access to ground floor. Free admission. Guided tours, including tactile and signed tours, are free of charge to those with disabilities but must be booked in advance with Visitor Services Tel: (01273) 292820/2/3.

☕ Tearooms with a balcony providing sweeping views across the restored Regency gardens.

🚶 Renowned in-house guiding section offer tours in English, French and German by prior arrangement. General introduction and specialist tours provided.

🅿️ Close to NCP car parks, town centre voucher parking. Coach drop-off point in Church Street, parking in Madeira Drive. Free entry for coach drivers.

👫 Specialist tours relating to all levels of National Curriculum, must be booked in advance with Visitor Services. Special winter student rates. Slide lecture presentations by arrangement.

Civil Wedding Licence.

OPENING TIMES

SUMMER
June - September
daily 10am - 6pm
Last entry at 6pm.

WINTER
October - May
daily 10am - 5pm
Last entry at 5pm.

Closed 25 & 26 December.

ADMISSION

Adult £4.10
Child £2.50
Conc.......................£3.00

Groups (20+)
Adult £3.60

Prices valid until 31.3.98

SPECIAL EVENTS

• **SPRING & AUTUMN HALF TERM:**
  Half term Fun at the Palace.

• **OCT - MAR:**
  Winter programme of events – call for details.

South East England

CONTACT

Peter Thorogood or
Roger Linton (Curator)
St Mary's House
Bramber
West Sussex
BN44 3WE

Tel: (01903) 816205

Fax: (01903) 816205

LOCATION

OS Ref. TQ189 105

Bramber village off A283
From London 56m via
M23/A23 or A24.

Bus: From Shoreham to
Steyning, alight Bramber.

Train: To Shoreham-by-
Sea with connecting
bus 20 (4m).

Taxi: Southern Taxis
(01273) 461655, Access
Cars (01273) 452424.

ST. MARY'S
Bramber

FAMOUS historic house in the downland village of Bramber. Built in 1470 by William Waynflete, Bishop of Winchester, founder of Magdalen College, Oxford. Classified (Grade I) as "the best example of late 15th century timber-framing in Sussex." Fine panelled rooms, including the unique trompe l'oeil 'Painted Room', decorated for the visit of Elizabeth I. The 'Kings Room' has connections with Charles II's escape to France in 1651. Rare 16th century painted wall leather. English furniture, ceramics, manuscripts and fine English costume-doll collection. The Library houses an important private collection of works by Victorian poet and artist Thomas Hood. Still a lived in family home, St. Mary's was awarded the 'Warmest Welcome' Commendation by the S.E. Tourist Board.

GARDENS

Charming gardens with amusing topiary as seen on BBC TV. Features include an exceptional example of the Living Fossil Tree, Ginkgo Biloba, a magnificently tall magnolia grandiflora and the mysterious ivy-clad Monks' Walk. Rediscover the lost Victorian walled and pleasure gardens, hidden for half a century, rescued in April 1997 and now under restoration.

CONFERENCE/FUNCTION

ROOM	SIZE	MAX CAPACITY
Music Rm	60' x 30'	80
Monks' Parlour	26' x 22'	25
Painted Rm	26' x 15'	20

i Shop. Film location, lecture/demonstration facilities for up to 70, grand piano. No photography in House.

✗ Exclusive corporate or private functions, promotional product launches, wedding receptions. Quality catering by both in-house and top London caterers.

☕ Superb Victorian music room seats up to 70. Groups can pre-book for morning coffee or afternoon teas.

✦ The owner/family usually meet groups. Larger parties, max 60 are divided into smaller groups. Tour time 1 hr.

P Gravel car park, 30 cars or 2 coaches, 20 yds from house, also a village car park 50 yds. Groups must pre-book. Allow 2½ hrs for your visit. Free tour and tea for coach driver.

♿ Groups welcome by prior arrangement.

🐕 Dogs on leads in car park only.

OPENING TIMES

General Public
Easter - end September
Sun, Thur, 2 - 6pm.

BH Mon, 2 - 6pm.

Last admission 5pm.

Groups
Easter - end October
daily by appointment,
avoiding public
opening times.

ADMISSION

SUMMER
House & Garden
Adult £4.00
Child £2.00
OAP.........................£3.70
Student...................£3.50
Groups
Adult/OAP
25 or more £3.70
Less than 25 ....£4.00
Child £2.00
Student...................£3.00

Gardens only
Adult £2.00
Child £0.50

Secret Garden
Adult/OAP £1.50
Child £0.50

ALFRISTON CLERGY HOUSE 🌿

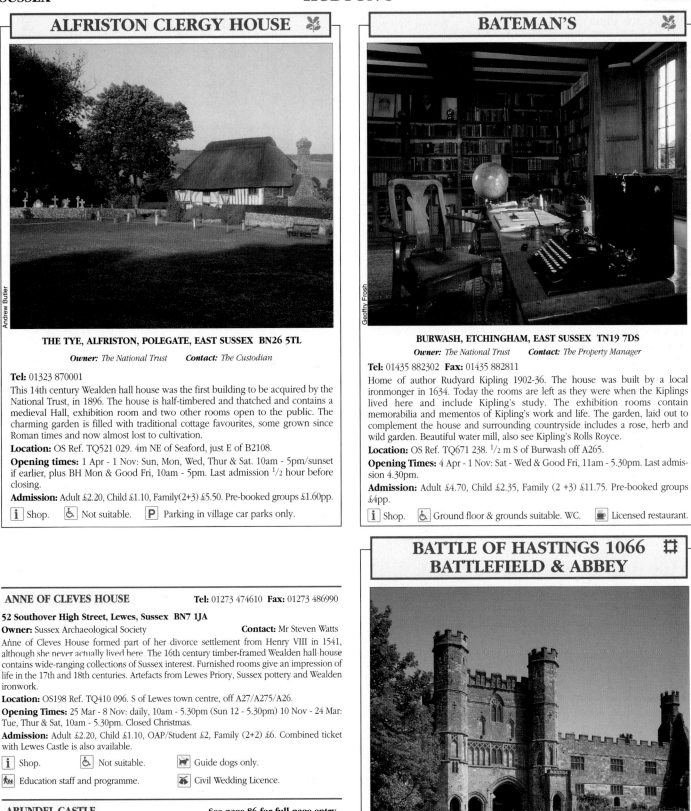

Andrew Butler

THE TYE, ALFRISTON, POLEGATE, EAST SUSSEX BN26 5TL

Owner: The National Trust   *Contact:* The Custodian

Tel: 01323 870001

This 14th century Wealden hall house was the first building to be acquired by the National Trust, in 1896. The house is half-timbered and thatched and contains a medieval Hall, exhibition room and two other rooms open to the public. The charming garden is filled with traditional cottage favourites, some grown since Roman times and now almost lost to cultivation.

Location: OS Ref. TQ521 029. 4m NE of Seaford, just E of B2108.

Opening times: 1 Apr - 1 Nov: Sun, Mon, Wed, Thur & Sat. 10am - 5pm/sunset if earlier, plus BH Mon & Good Fri, 10am - 5pm. Last admission $^1/_2$ hour before closing.

Admission: Adult £2.20, Child £1.10, Family(2+3) £5.50. Pre-booked groups £1.60pp.

ⓘ Shop.   ♿ Not suitable.   🅿 Parking in village car parks only.

ANNE OF CLEVES HOUSE   **Tel:** 01273 474610 **Fax:** 01273 486990

52 Southover High Street, Lewes, Sussex BN7 1JA

Owner: Sussex Archaeological Society   **Contact:** Mr Steven Watts

Anne of Cleves House formed part of her divorce settlement from Henry VIII in 1541, although she never actually lived here. The 16th century timber-framed Wealden hall-house contains wide-ranging collections of Sussex interest. Furnished rooms give an impression of life in the 17th and 18th centuries. Artefacts from Lewes Priory, Sussex pottery and Wealden ironwork.

Location: OS198 Ref. TQ410 096. S of Lewes town centre, off A27/A275/A26.

Opening Times: 25 Mar - 8 Nov: daily, 10am - 5.30pm (Sun 12 - 5.30pm) 10 Nov - 24 Mar: Tue, Thur & Sat, 10am - 5.30pm. Closed Christmas.

Admission: Adult £2.20, Child £1.10, OAP/Student £2, Family (2+2) £6. Combined ticket with Lewes Castle is also available.

ⓘ Shop.   ♿ Not suitable.   🐕 Guide dogs only.

👫 Education staff and programme.   💍 Civil Wedding Licence.

ARUNDEL CASTLE   **See page 86 for full page entry.**

ARUNDEL CATHEDRAL   **Tel:** 01903 882297 **Fax:** 01903 885335

Parsons Hill, Arundel, Sussex BN18 9AY   **Contact:** Rev A Whale

French Gothic Cathedral, church of the RC Diocese of Arundel and Brighton built by Henry, 15th Duke of Norfolk and opened 1873. Carpet of Flowers and Floral Festival held annually on the Feast of Corpus Christi (60 days after Easter) and day preceding.

Location: OS Ref. TQ015 072. Above junction of A27 and A284.

Opening Times: Summer: 9am - 6pm. Winter: 9am - dusk. Mass at 10am each day. Sun Masses: 8am, 9.30am & 11am, Vigil Sat evening: 6.30pm. Shop opened after services and on special occasions and otherwise at request.

Admission: Free.

ⓘ Shop.

BATEMAN'S 🌿

BURWASH, ETCHINGHAM, EAST SUSSEX TN19 7DS

Owner: The National Trust   *Contact:* The Property Manager

Tel: 01435 882302 **Fax:** 01435 882811

Home of author Rudyard Kipling 1902-36. The house was built by a local ironmonger in 1634. Today the rooms are left as they were when the Kiplings lived here and include Kipling's study. The exhibition rooms contain memorabilia and mementos of Kipling's work and life. The garden, laid out to complement the house and surrounding countryside includes a rose, herb and wild garden. Beautiful water mill, also see Kipling's Rolls Royce.

Location: OS Ref. TQ671 238. $^1/_2$ m S of Burwash off A265.

Opening Times: 4 Apr - 1 Nov: Sat - Wed & Good Fri, 11am - 5.30pm. Last admission 4.30pm.

Admission: Adult £4.70, Child £2.35, Family (2 +3) £11.75. Pre-booked groups £4pp.

ⓘ Shop.   ♿ Ground floor & grounds suitable. WC.   ☕ Licensed restaurant.

BATTLE OF HASTINGS 1066 ⌗
BATTLEFIELD & ABBEY

BATTLE, SUSSEX TN33 0AD

Owner: English Heritage   *Contact:* The Custodian

Tel: 01424 773792 **Fax:** 01424 775059

Visit the site of the 1066 Battle of Hastings. New for 1988 is an exciting exhibition which sets the scene for this momentous event in English history. A free interactive audio tour will lead you around the battlefield and to the exact spot where Harold fell. Explore the magnificent Abbey ruins and see the fascinating exhibition in the gate house. Children's themed play area.

Location: OS Ref. TQ749 157. Top of Battle High Street. Turn off A2100 to Battle.

Opening Times: 1 Apr - 1 Nov: daily, 10am - 6pm, dusk in Oct. 2 Nov - 31 Mar, daily 10am - 4pm. Closed 24 - 26 Dec.

Admission: Adult £4, Child £2, Conc. £3, Family £10. 15% discount on parties of 11+. EH members free.

ⓘ Shop.   ♿ Ground floor & grounds suitable.   🚶 Free audio tour.

🐕 In grounds, on leads.

BAYHAM OLD ABBEY ⛩

Tel/Fax: 01892 890381

Lamberhurst, Sussex

Owner: English Heritage   **Contact:** The Custodian

These riverside ruins are of a house of 'white' canons, founded c1208 and preserved in the 18th century, when its surroundings were landscaped to create the delightful setting in which you will find the ruins today.

Location: OS Ref. TQ651 366. 1¾ m W of Lamberhurst off B2169.

Opening Times: 1 Apr - 1 Nov: daily, 10am - 6pm, dusk in Oct. 2 Nov - 31 Mar: w/ends only 10am - 4pm.

Admission: Adult £2, Child £1, Conc. £1.50.

ℹ️ Shop. ♿ Grounds suitable. WC. 🐕 In grounds, on leads. 🎎 Civil Wedding Licence.

BENTLEY WILDFOWL & MOTOR MUSEUM

Tel: 01825 840573

Halland, Lewes, East Sussex BN8 5AF   **Fax:** 01825 841322

Owner: East Sussex County Council   **Contact:** Mr Barry Sutherland - Manager

Early 18th century farmhouse with a large reception room of Palladian proportions added on either end in the 1960s by the architect Raymond Erith, each lit by large Venetian windows. Furnished to form a grand 20th century evocation of a mid-Georgian house.

Location: OS Ref. TQ485 160. 7m NE from Lewes, signposted off A22, A26 & B2192.

Opening Times: Estate: 16 Mar - 31 Oct: daily, 10.30am - 4.30pm (last adm.). Nov, Feb - 16 Mar: weekends only, 10.30am - 4pm (last adm.). House: 1 Apr - 31 Oct: daily 12 noon - 5pm. Estate closed Dec & Jan.

Admission: (1997 prices). Adult £4.10 (£3.10 in winter), Child (4 - 15) £2.50, OAPs /Students £3.10, Family (2 + 4) £12. Coach drivers free admission & refreshment ticket. 10% discount for groups of 11+. Special rates for the disabled. Call to verify prices.

ℹ️ Shop. ✖️ Wedding receptions. ♿ Suitable. WC. ☕ Licensed tearoom.
🧑‍🏫 Education programme & teacher's pack. 🐕 Guide dogs. 🎎 Civil Wedding Licence.

BODIAM CASTLE 🍃

Alasdair Ogilvie

BODIAM, NR ROBERTSBRIDGE, EAST SUSSEX TN32 5UA

Owner: The National Trust   *Contact:* The Administrator

Tel: 01580 830436 **Fax:** 01580 830398

Built in 1385 against a French invasion that never came and as a comfortable dwelling for a rich nobleman, Bodiam Castle is one of the finest examples of medieval military architecture. The virtual completeness of its exterior makes it a popular filming location. Inside, although a ruin, floors have been replaced in some of the towers and visitors can climb the spiral staircase to enjoy superb views from the battlements. Audio-visual presentations of life in a castle and museum room.

Location: OS Ref. TQ782 256. 3m S of Hawkhurst, 2m E of A21 Hurst Green.

Opening Times: 14 Feb - 1 Nov: daily 10am - 6pm/dusk. 3 Nov - 3 Jan: Tue - Sun, 10am - 4pm or dusk, (closed 24 - 26 Dec, open New Year's Day). Last admission 1 hr before close.

Admission: Adult £3.30, Child £1.65, Family ticket (2+3) £8.25. Groups £2.80.

ℹ️ Shop. Small museum. ♿ Ground floor & grounds suitable. ☕ Restaurant.
🧑‍🏫 Teacher and Student packs and education base.

BORDE HILL GARDEN 🏛

BALCOMBE ROAD, HAYWARDS HEATH, WEST SUSSEX RH16 1XP

Owner: Mr & Mrs A P Stephenson Clarke   *Contact:* Sarah Brook

Tel: 01444 450326 **Fax:** 01444 440427 **email:** info@bordehill.co.uk

Borde Hill renowned botanical garden set in 200 acres of spectacular Sussex parkland and woods. Rich variety of seasonal colour with breathtaking displays of rhododendrons, camellias and azaleas. Extensive planting with new rose and herbaceous garden for summer. Blaze of autumnal hues of crocuses and shrubs. New Bressingham plant centre.

Location: OS Ref. TQ324 265. 1½m N of Haywards Heath on Balcombe Road, 3m from A23.

Opening Times: Every day of the year, 10am - 6pm.

Admission: Adult £3, Child £1.50, OAP/Student £3. Groups (min 20): Adult £2.50, Child £1.25.

ℹ️ Shop. Plant centre. Corporate hospitality. ♿ Suitable. WCs.
☕ Tearoom & restaurant. 🚶 By arrangement. 🐕 In grounds, on leads.

BOXGROVE PRIORY ⛩

Tel: 01732 778000

Boxgrove, Chichester, Sussex

Owner: English Heritage   **Contact:** The South East Regional Office

Remains of the Guest House, Chapter House and Church of this 12th century priory, which was the cell of a French abbey until Richard II confirmed its independence in 1383.

Location: OS Ref. SU909 076. N of Boxgrove, 4m E of Chichester on minor road N of A27.

Opening Times: Any reasonable time.

Admission: Free.

♿ Not suitable. 🐕 Guide dogs only.

BRAMBER CASTLE ⛩

Tel: 01732 778000

Bramber, Sussex

Owner: English Heritage   **Contact:** The South East Regional Office

The remains of a Norman castle gatehouse, walls and earthworks in a splendid setting overlooking the Adur valley.

Location: OS Ref. TQ187 107. On W side of Bramber village NE of A283.

Opening Times: Any reasonable time.

Admission: Free.

♿ Not suitable. 🅿️ Limited. 🐕 In grounds, on leads.

BRICKWALL HOUSE & GARDENS

Tel: 01797 253388 **Fax:** 01797 252567

Northiam, Rye, Sussex TN31 6NL

Owner: Frewen Educational Trust   **Contact:** The Curator

Impressive timber-framed house. 17th century drawing room with magnificent plaster ceilings and good portraits including by Lely, Kneller and Vereist. Topiary, chess garden.

Location: OS Ref. TQ831 241. S side of Northiam village at junction of A28 and B2088.

Opening Times: By appointment only.

Admission: Free.

♿ Ground floor & grounds suitable. WC. 🐕 In grounds, on leads.

CAMBER CASTLE

Tel: 01797 223862

Camber, Nr. Rye, East Sussex

Owner: English Heritage   **Contact:** Rye Harbour Nature Reserve

A fine example of one of many coastal fortresses built by Henry VIII to counter the threat of invasion during the 16th century. Monthly guided walks of Rye Nature Reserve including Camber Castle, telephone for details.

Location: OS189, Ref. TQ922 185. Across fields off A259, 1m S of Rye off harbour road.

Opening Times: 1 Jul - 30 Sept: Sat only, 2 - 5pm.

Admission: Adult £2, Child £1, Conc. £1.50.

  Not suitable. By arrangement. No parking. Guide dogs only.

CHARLESTON

See page 87 for full page entry.

CHICHESTER CATHEDRAL

Tel: 01243 782595   **Fax:** 01243 536190

Chichester, Sussex PO19 1PX

Contact: Mrs J Thom

The beauty of the 900 year old cathedral, site of the Shrine of St Richard, is enhanced by many art treasures, ancient and modern.

Location: OS Ref. SU860 047. West Street, Chichester.

Opening Times: Summer: 7.30am - 7pm, Winter: 7.30am - 5pm. Sun services: 8am, 10am, 11am and 3.30pm. Weekday services: 7.30am, 8am and 5.30pm.

Admission: Donation.

  Suitable. Available. Pre-book, out of season. Education programme.

DANNY

Tel: 01273 833000

Hurstpierpoint, Sussex BN6 9BB

Owner: Country Houses Association   **Contact:** The Administrator

A late Elizabethan E-shaped house in red brick, part modernised in 1728.

Location: OS Ref. TQ285 149. 1m SE of Hurstpierpoint S of the Hassocks road.

Opening Times: May - Sept: Wed and Thur, 2 - 5pm.

Admission: Adult £2.50, Child under 16 £1, Groups by arrangement.

  No dogs. **A** 1 single & 1 double with bathroom, CHA members only.

Nymans Garden, Sussex.

FIRLE PLACE

FIRLE, NR. LEWES, EAST SUSSEX BN8 6LP

Owner: *The Rt Hon Viscount Gage*   **Contact:** *Mrs Brig Davies*

Tel: 01273 858335 **Tel/Fax:** 01273 858188 (Group & Corporate Enquiries)

Tel: 01273 858307 (Restaurant)

Discover the civilised atmosphere of Firle Place, the beautiful home of the Gage family for over 500 years. Admire and enjoy the magnificent collections of Old Master paintings; the fine English and European furniture; plus the notable collection of Sèvres porcelain. Learn fascinating facts about the Gage family. This welcoming house which connoisseurs will appreciate is set in parkland in an Area of Outstanding Natural Beauty at the foot of the South Downs. There is a delightful Tea Terrace and Restaurant for lunch or cream teas.

Location: OS Ref. TQ473 071. SE of Lewes on A27 Brighton/Eastbourne Road. Station: Lewes.

Opening Times: 24 May - end Sept: plus BHs except Christmas. Wed, Thur, Sun, 11.30am - last tickets at 4.30pm. House closes 5.30pm. Unguided tours BH Mons and Connoisseurs' Day - first Wed of months Jun - Sept.

Admission: Adult £4, Child £2, Disabled £2.95. Connoisseurs' Day £4.85. Group tours (min 25 people): Apr - end Sept by arrangement with Events Secretary tel: 01273 858188 Admission: General Open Days £3.55; Exclusive Private Group Tour: Adult £6, Child £2. No reduction on Connoisseurs' Day.

Car park adjacent to House. Catering for groups must be pre-arranged with Catering Manager tel: 01273 858307.

  Shop. Corporate hospitality

  Ground floor & grounds suitable. Tearoom & licensed restaurant.

  Ample In grounds on leads.

FISHBOURNE ROMAN PALACE

SALTHILL ROAD, FISHBOURNE, CHICHESTER, SUSSEX PO19 3QR

Owner: Sussex Archaeological Society   *Contact:* David Rudkin

Tel: 01243 785859 **Fax:** 01243 539266

A Roman site built around AD75. A modern building houses part of the extensive remains including a large number of Britain's finest in-situ mosaics. The museum displays many objects discovered during excavations and an audio-visual programme tells Fishbourne's remarkable story. Roman gardens have been reconstructed. A museum of Roman gardening.

Location: OS Ref. SU837 057. 1^1/$_2$ m W of Chichester in Fishbourne village off A27/A259.

Opening Times: Feb, Nov - Dec: daily, 10am - 4pm. Mar - Jul & Sept - Oct: daily, 10am - 5pm. Aug: daily, 10am - 6pm. 14 Dec - 7 Feb: Sun, 10am - 4pm. Closed Christmas.

Admission: Adult £4, Child £2.20, OAP/Student £3.40, Family (2+2): £10.50, Registered disabled £3.30. Groups: Adult £3.20, Child £2.

[i] Shop.   [&] Suitable. WCs.   [☕] Tearoom.   [🐕] Guide dogs only.

GLYNDE PLACE

GLYNDE, LEWES, SUSSEX BN8 6SX

Owners: Viscount & Viscountess Hampden   *Contact:* Viscount Hampden

Tel: 01273 858224   **Fax:** 01273 858224

Glynde Place is a magnificent example of Elizabethan architecture commanding exceptionally fine views of the South Downs. Amongst the collections of 400 years of family living can be seen a fine collection of 17th and 18th century portraits of the Trevors and a room dedicated to Sir Henry Brand, Speaker of the House of Commons 1872 - 1884 and an exhibition of 'Harbert Morley and the Great Rebellion 1638 - 1660' the story of the part played by the owner of Glynde Place in the Civil War. Plus a collection of 18th century Italian masterpieces.

Location: OS Ref. TQ457 093. In Glynde village 4m SE of Lewes on A27.

Opening Times: Gardens: Easter & Sun in Apr. House: May: Sun & BH only. Jun - Sept: Wed & Sun, 2 - 5pm. Last admission 4.45pm.

Admission: Adult £4, Child £2.

[☕] Available.   [P] Free.   [💍] Civil Wedding Licence.

GOODWOOD HOUSE   See page 88 for full page entry.

GREAT DIXTER HOUSE & GARDENS 🏛

NORTHIAM, RYE, SUSSEX TN31 6PH

Owner: Christopher Lloyd   *Contact:* The Administrator

Tel: 01797 252878 **Fax:** 01797 252879 **email:** greatdixter@compuserve.com

Built in the 1450s, the manor of Dixter was bought in 1910 by Nathaniel Lloyd. He employed Lutyens to renovate and extend the medieval hall house, creating a very impressive property. The house forms a splendid backdrop to Christopher Lloyd's acclaimed gardens. His style is always bold and his use of plants and colour give a garden which has something to delight and inspire whatever the season. Of particular note are the Long Border and the Exotic Garden.

Location: OS Ref. TQ817 251. Signposted off the A28 in Northiam.

Opening Times: 1 Apr - 25 Oct: Tue - Sun, 2 - 5pm (last admission).

Admission: House & garden: Adult £4, Child £1. Garden only: Adult £3, Child 50p. Groups by appointment, house & garden: £3.50pp.

[i] Shop. Plant centre.   [&] Not suitable.   [🚶] Compulsory.   [🐕] No dogs.

Andreas von Einseidel

Uppark, Sussex.

HAMMERWOOD PARK

EAST GRINSTEAD, SUSSEX RH19 3QE

Owner: David Pinnegar   *Contact: David Pinnegar*

Tel: 01342 850594 **Fax:** 01342 850864

www: http://there.is/hammerwood **e-mail:** latrobe@mistral.co.uk

Built in 1792 as an Apollo's hunting lodge by Benjamin Latrobe, architect of the Capitol and the White House, Washington DC. Owned by Led Zepplin in the 1970s, rescued from dereliction in 1982. Cream teas in the Organ Room; mural by French artists in the hall; and a derelict dining room still shocks the unwary. Guided tours (said by many to be the most interesting in Sussex) by the family.

Location: OS Ref. TQ442 390. $3^{1}/_{2}$ m E of East Grinstead on A264 to Tunbridge Wells, 1m W of Holtye.

Opening Times: Easter Mon - Sept: Wed, Sat & BH Mon, 2 - 5.30pm. Guided tour starts 2.05pm. Coaches strictly by appointment. Small groups any time throughout the year by appointment.

Admission: House & Park: Adult £3.50, Child £1.50. Private viewing by arrangement.

[i] Conferences, corporate hospitality.   [X] Available.   [☕] Tearoom.

[🚶] Compulsory.   [♿] Educational programme.   [🐕] In grounds.   [A] B&B.

SPECIAL EVENTS
Monthly concerts: please telephone, fax or e-mail for details.

HERSTMONCEUX CASTLE GARDEN   Tel: 01323 833816 Fax: 01323 834499

Hailsham, Sussex BN27 1RP

Owner: Queen's University, Canada   **Contact:** Mrs Ruth Wilson

Magnificent 15th century moated castle set among superb formal gardens and parkland.

Location: OS Ref. TQ646 104. 2m S of Herstmonceux village (A271) by minor road. 10m WNW of Bexhill.

Opening Times: Easter - 1 Nov: daily 10am - 6pm (last adm. 5pm) Closes pm from Oct.

Admission: Grounds and Gardens: Adults £3, Child under 5 free, Conc. £2. Castle Tour: Adult £2.50, Child £1 (under 5s free). Group rates available.

[i] Visitor Centre.   [♿] Suitable, limited for Castle Tour.   [☕] Tearoom.

[🚶] Available.   [P] Ample.   [🐕] On leads.   [A] B&B (Bader Hall in Castle grounds).

[💍] Civil Wedding Licence.

HIGH BEECHES GARDENS   Tel: 01444 400589

High Beeches, Handcross, Sussex RH17 6HQ

Owner: High Beeches Gardens Conservation Trust (Reg. Charity)   **Contact:** Sarah Bray

Help preserve these 20 acres of magically beautiful, peaceful woodland and water gardens. Daffodils, bluebells, azaleas, naturalised gentians, autumn colours. Rippling streams, enchanting vistas. Four acres of natural wildflower meadows. Rare plants. Tree trail. Recommended by Christopher Lloyd. Picnic area. Gardens may be booked for photographic sessions.

Location: OS Ref. TQ275 308. S side of B2110. 1m NE of Handcross.

Opening Times: Spring & Autumn: daily, 1 - 5pm. Closed Wed. Also open Jul & Aug: Mon & Tue. Enjoy our Event Days: 13 Apr, 4 & 25 May, 23 Aug, 18 Oct, 10.30am - 5pm.

Admission: Adult £3.50, Child free. Groups: £3.50pp. (£15 extra outside normal opening hours). Privileged guest tour £4.50 inclusive.

[i] Plants for sale on Events Days.   [♿] Not suitable.   [☕] Available.   [🐕] Guide dogs.

HIGHDOWN GARDENS   Tel: 01903 501054

Littlehampton Road, Goring by Sea, Worthing, Sussex BN12 6PE

Owner: Worthing Borough Council   **Contact:** C Beardsley Esq

Unique gardens in disused chalk pit, begun in 1909.

Location: OS Ref. TQ098 040. 3m NNW of Worthing on N side of A259, just W of the Goring roundabout.

Opening Times: 1 Apr - 30 Sept: Mon - Fri, 10am - 6pm. W/ends & BHs, 10am - 6pm. 1 Oct - 30 Nov: Mon - Fri, 10am - 4.30pm. 1 Dec - 31 Jan: 10am - 4pm. 1 Feb - 31 Mar: Mon - Fri, 10am - 4.30pm.

Admission: Free.

LAMB HOUSE 🦋   Tel: 01892 890651   Fax: 01892 890110

West Street, Rye, Sussex TN31 7ES

Owner: The National Trust   **Contact:** Regional Office

The home of the writer Henry James from 1898 to 1916 where he wrote the best novels of his later period. The walled garden, staircase, hall and three rooms on the ground floor containing some of James' personal possessions are on view. Also once home to the author E F Benson.

Location: OS Ref. TQ920 202. In West Street, facing W end of church.

Opening Times: 1 Apr - 31 Oct: Wed & Sat only 2 - 6pm. Last admission 5.30pm.

Admission: Adult £2.50, Child £1.25.

LEONARDSLEE GARDENS   See page 89 for full page entry.

LEWES CASTLE & BARBICAN HOUSE

169 HIGH STREET, LEWES, SUSSEX BN7 1YE

Owner: Sussex Archaeological Society   *Contact: Mrs Helen Poole*

Tel: 01273 486290 **Fax:** 01273 486990

Lewes's imposing Norman castle offers magnificent views across the town and surrounding downland. Barbican House towered over by the Barbican Gate is home to the Museum of Sussex Archaeology; a superb scale model of Victorian Lewes provides the centrepiece of a 25 minute audio visual presentation telling the story of the county town of Sussex.

Location: OS198 Ref. TQ412 101. Lewes town centre off A27/A26/A275.

Opening Times: All year (except 25 & 26 Dec): Mon - Sat: 10am - 5.30pm; Sun & BHs, 11am - 5.30pm. Castle closes at dusk in winter.

Admission: Adult £3.40, Child £1.80, OAP/Student £2.90. Family (2 + 2) £9.50. Groups: Adult £3, Child £1.50, OAP/Student £2.60. Combined ticket with Anne of Cleves House available.

[i] Shop.   [♿] Not suitable.   [🚶] By arrangement.   [♿] Education programme.

MARLIPINS MUSEUM   Tel: 01273 462994

High Street, Shoreham-by-Sea, Sussex BN43 5DA

Owner: Sussex Archaeological Society   **Contact:** David Rudkin

Shoreham's local and especially maritime history is explored at Marlipins, an important historic building of Norman origin. The maritime gallery contains many fine paintings and models while the museum houses exhibits dating back to man's earliest occupation of the area. Formerly an old customs house, the building has a superb chequer-work façade of knapped flint and Caen stone.

Location: OS198 Ref. TQ214 051. Shoreham town centre on A259, W of Brighton.

Opening Times: 1 May - 30 Sept: Tue - Sat, 10am - 1pm & 2pm - 4.30pm. Sun, 2 - 4.30pm.

Admission: Adult £1.50, Child 75p (accompanied children free), OAP/Student £1.

[i] Shop.   [♿] Not suitable.   [🚶] By arrangement.   [🐕] Guide dogs only.

MERRIMENTS GARDENS

HAWKHURST ROAD, HURST GREEN, EAST SUSSEX TN19 7RA

Owner: Family owned   *Contact:* Mark Buchele

Tel: 01580 860666   **Fax:** 01580 860324

'Gardened naturally, free from restriction of institute, experimenting continuously, and always permitting nature to have its say'.

Set in 4 acres of gently sloping Weald farmland, a naturalistic garden which never fails to delight. Deep curved borders richly planted and colour themed. An abundance of rare plants will startle the visitor with sheer originality.

The garden is planted according to prevailing conditions and only using plants suited for naturalising and colonising their environment. This natural approach to gardening harks back to the days of William Robinson and is growing in popularity, especially in Northern Europe..Alternatively many borders are colour themed and planted in the great tradition of English gardening. These borders use a rich mix of trees, shrubs, perennials and grasses and give an arresting display from spring to autumn.

There is a new entrance garden in the style of Monet's 'Grande Allée' at Giverny, France. Other new ventures include a rock and scree garden, a foliage border and further development of the woodland.

Location: OS198, Ref. TQ412 101. Signposted off A21 London - Hastings road, at Hurst Green.

Opening Times: 10 Apr - 30 Sept: daily, 10am - 5pm.

Admission: Adult £2.50, Child £1, OAP/Student £2.50. Group size min. 5.

ℹ️ Shop. Plant centre.	♿ Partially suitable.	☕ Licensed café.
🚶 By arrangement.	🅿️ Ample.	🐕 In grounds, on leads.

MICHELHAM PRIORY

UPPER DICKER, HAILSHAM, SUSSEX BN27 3QS

Owner: Sussex Archaeological Society   *Contact:* Ms. Allex Jenkinson

Tel: 01323 844224   **Fax:** 01323 844030

Set on a medieval moated island surrounded by superb gardens, the Priory was founded in 1229. The remains after the Dissolution were incorporated into a Tudor farm and country house that now contains a fascinating array of exhibits. Grounds include 14th century gatehouse, watermill, physic and cloister gardens and Elizabethan great barn.

Location: OS Ref. TQ557 093. 8m NW of Eastbourne off A22 / A27. 3m W of Hailsham.

Opening Times: 15 Mar - 31Oct: Wed - Sun & BH Mon & daily in Aug. Mar & Oct: 11am - 4pm. Apr - Jul & Sept: 10.30am - 5pm. Aug: 10.30am - 5.30pm.

Admission: Adult £4, Child £2.20, OAP/Student £3.40, Family (2+2) £10.50, Registered disabled / Carer £2. Groups Adult £3.20, Child £2.

ℹ️ Shop.	♿ Suitable. WC.	☕ Licensed restaurant.	🐕 Guide dogs only.

MOORLANDS   **Tel:** 01892 652474

Friar's Gate, Crowborough, East Sussex TN6 1XF

Owner: Dr & Mrs Steven Smith   **Contact:** Dr Steven Smith

4 acre garden set in a lush valley adjoining Ashdown Forest. Primulas, azaleas and rhododendrons flourish by streams and a small lake. New river walk with views over garden. Many unusual trees and shrubs. Good autumn colour. Featured in Meridien TV programme.

Location: OS Ref. TQ498 329. 2m NW of Crowborough. From B2188 at Friar's Gate, take left fork signposted 'Crowborough Narrow Road', entrance 100yds on left. From Crowborough crossroads take St Johns Road to Friar's Gate.

Opening Times: 1 Apr - 1 Oct: Wed, 11am - 5pm. 24 May, 7 Jun, 19 Jul: Sun 2 - 6pm. Other times by appointment only.

Admission: Adult £2, Child free.

☕ Tearoom.

SPECIAL EVENTS 1998

See the front section for full list.

Historic Scotland

South East England

NYMANS GARDEN

Nick Meers

HANDCROSS, HAYWARDS HEATH, SUSSEX RH17 6EB

Owners: The National Trust   *Contact:* The Property Manager

Tel: 01444 400321/400777 **Fax:** 01444 400253

One of the great gardens of the Sussex Weald, with rare and beautiful plants, shrubs and trees from all over the world. Wall garden, hidden sunken garden, pinetum, laurel walk and romantic ruins. Lady Rosse's library, drawing room and forecourt garden now also open. Woodland walks and Wild Garden.

Location: OS Ref. TQ265 294. On B2114 at Handcross, 4^1/$_2$ m S of Crawley, just off London - Brighton M23 / A23.

Opening Times: 1 Mar - 1 Nov: daily except Mon & Tue but open BHs, 11am - 6pm or sunset if earlier. House open 12 - 4pm same days as garden.

Admission: Adult £5, Child £2.50, Family £12.50. Groups £4. Joint group ticket which includes same day entry to Standen £7 available Wed - Fri only.

ℹ️ Shop. Plant centre.   ♿ Grounds suitable. WC.   ☕ Licensed restaurant.

PARHAM HOUSE & GARDENS 🏛️

PARHAM PARK, NR. PULBOROUGH, WEST SUSSEX RH20 4HS

Owners: Parham Park Trust   *Contact:* Patricia Kennedy

Tel: 01903 744888 **Fax:** 01903 746557

A great favourite with all the family, this beautiful Elizabethan house with award-winning gardens is idyllically situated in an ancient deer park under the South Downs. Enjoy the important collection of paintings, furniture and needlework in panelled rooms, including Long Gallery. Light lunches and cream teas served in the 16th century big kitchen.

Location: OS Ref. TQ060 143. Midway between Pulborough & Storrington on A283.

Opening Times: 1 Apr - 29 Oct: Wed, Thur, Sun & BH Mon. Picnic area and gardens: 12 - 6pm. House: 2 - 6pm. Last entry 5pm.

Admission: House & Gardens: Adult £5, OAP £4, Child £1, Family (2+2) £10. Groups 20+ £4. Garden only: Adult/OAP £3, Child 50p.

ℹ️ Shop. Plant centre.   ♿ Partially suitable.   ☕ Tearoom.   🚶 Available.
🅿️ Ample   📽️ Slide lectures by arrangement.   🐕 In grounds, on leads.

PASHLEY MANOR GARDENS

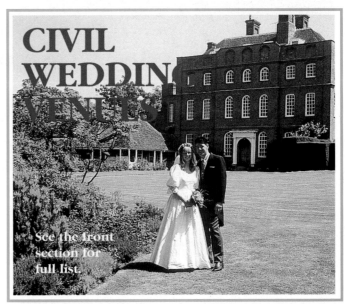

Ian Shaw

TICEHURST, WADHURST, EAST SUSSEX TN5 7HE

Owner: Mr & Mrs James Sellick   *Contact:* Mr & Mrs James Sellick

Tel: 01580 200692 **Fax:** 01580 200102

Pashley Manor Gardens, a Grade I listed timber-framed house dating from 1550 and enlarged in 1720, stands in a well timbered park with magnificent views. Its gardens are laid out in true English romantic style enhanced by waterfalls, ponds and a moat, with plantings in soft colours, created during the last decade by distinguished landscape architect Antony du Gard Pasley. A garden of great age, steeped in romance, where all you can hear is the sound of splashing water and birdsong.

Location: OS Ref. TQ707 291. Between Ticehurst and A21 on B2099. Wadhurst 5m.

Opening Times: Gardens only: 11 Apr - 30 Sept (Oct Garden only): Tue, Wed, Thur, Sat and all BH Mon, 11am - 5pm.

Admission: Adult £4.50, OAP £4. Coaches by appointment only.

ℹ️ Plants for sale.   ☕ Licensed tearoom.   🚶 By arrangement.   🐕 No dogs.

SPECIAL EVENTS
Special events include Flower festivals and Plant fairs, please telephone for details.

PETWORTH HOUSE 🦌   **See page 90 for full page entry.**

PEVENSEY CASTLE ⚔️   **Tel:** 01323 762604

Pevensey, Sussex BN24 5LE

Owner: English Heritage   **Contact:** The Custodian

Originally a 4th century Roman Fort, Pevensey was the place where William the Conqueror landed in 1066 and established his first stronghold. The Norman castle included the remains of an unusual keep within the massive walls. Free audio tour tells the story of the Castle's 2,000 year history.

Location: OS Ref. TQ645 048. In Pevensey off A259.

Opening Times: 1 Apr - 1 Nov: daily, 10am - 6pm, dusk in Oct. 2 Nov - 31 Mar: Wed - Sun only, 10am - 4pm. Closed 24 - 26 Dec.

Admission: Adult £2.50, Child £1.30, Conc. £1.90. 15% discount for groups of 11+.

♿ Grounds suitable.   ☕ Tearoom.   🚶 Audio tour.   🐕 In grounds, on leads.

PRESTON MANOR

PRESTON DROVE, BRIGHTON, EAST SUSSEX BN1 6SD

Owner: Brighton & Hove Council   *Contact:* David Beevers

Tel: 01273 292770 **Fax:** 01273 292871

A delightful Manor House which powerfully evokes the atmosphere of an Edwardian gentry home both 'upstairs' and 'downstairs'. Explore more than twenty rooms over four floors – from the servants' quarters, kitchens and butler's pantry in the basement to the attic bedrooms and nursery on the top floor. Walled gardens, pet cemetery, 13th century parish church.

Location: OS Ref. TQ303 064. 2m N of Brighton on the A23 London road.

Opening Times: Tue - Sat 10am - 5pm, Sun 2 - 5pm, Mon 1 - 5pm (BHs 10am - 5pm). Closed Good Fri & 25 - 26 Dec.

Admission: Adult £2.95, Child £1.80, Conc. £2.45. Groups (min 20) £2.45. Prices valid until 31 Mar 1998.

ℹ️ Shop. Corporate hospitality. No photography. ✖️ Wedding receptions.

♿ Not suitable. 🚶 By arrangement. 👫 Education programme. 🐕 No dogs.

THE PRIEST HOUSE   **Tel:** 01342 810479

North Lane, West Hoathly, Sussex RH19 4PP

Owner: Sussex Archaeological Society   **Contact:** Antony Smith

Standing in the beautiful surroundings of a traditional cottage garden on the edge of Ashdown Forest, the Priest House is an early 15th century timber-framed hall-house. In Elizabethan times it was modernised into a substantial yeoman's dwelling. Its furnished rooms contain 17th and 18th century furniture, kitchen equipment, needlework and household items. Formal herb garden.

Location: OS187 Ref. TQ362 325. In triangle formed by Crawley, East Grinstead and Haywards Heath, 4m off A22, 6m off M23.

Opening Times: 1 Mar - 31 Oct: Mon - Sat, 11am - 5.30pm, Sun 2 - 5.30pm.

Admission: Adults £2.20, Child £1.10, OAP/Student £2.20. Groups (min 20): Adult £2, Child £1, Conc. £2.

ℹ️ Shop. ♿ Partially suitable. 🚶 By arrangement. 🅿️ Limited.

👫 Education programme. 🐕 Guide dogs only.

THE ROYAL PAVILION   See page 91 for full page entry.

ST. MARY'S BRAMBER 🏛   See page 92 for full page entry.

SAINT HILL MANOR

SAINT HILL ROAD, EAST GRINSTEAD, WEST SUSSEX RH19 4JY

Contact: Mrs Liz Nyegaard

Tel: 01342 326711

Fine Sussex sandstone house built in 1792 and situated near the breathtaking Ashdown Forest. Saint Hill Manor's final owner, acclaimed author and humanitarian L Ron Hubbard lived there for many years with his family. Oak wood panelling, marble fireplaces, Georgian windows and plasterwork ceilings have been expertly restored to their original beauty. Outstanding features of this lovely house include an impressive library of Mr Hubbard's works, elegant winter garden, and the delightful monkey room housing John Spencer Churchill's 100 foot mural depicting many famous characters as monkeys, including his uncle, Winston Churchill. 59 acres of landscaped gardens, lake and woodlands.

Location: OS Ref. TQ382 359. 2m SW of East Grinstead, turn off A22, down Imberhorne Lane, and over crossroads into St Hill Road, 200 yds on right.

Opening Times: Daily, 2 - 5pm, on the hour or by appointment. Groups welcome.

Admission: Free.

♿ Not suitable. ☕ Tearoom. 🚶 Compulsory. 🐕 No dogs.

South East England

SHEFFIELD PARK GARDEN

NR UCKFIELD, EAST SUSSEX TN22 3QX

Owner: *The National Trust*   **Contact:** *The Property Manager*

Tel: 01825 790231 **Fax:** 01825 791264

A magnificent 100 acre landscape garden, with 5 lakes linked by cascades, laid out in the 18th century by 'Capability' Brown. Carpeted with daffodils and bluebells in spring, its rhododendrons, azaleas and spring garden are spectacular in early summer. Cool tree-lined paths and lake reflections make it perfect for a stroll in high summer and the garden is ablaze with colour from its rare trees and shrubs in autumn.

Location: OS Ref. TQ415 240. Midway between East Grinstead and Lewes, 5m NW of Uckfield on E side of A275.

Opening Times: Mar: Sat & Sun only, 11am - 6pm. 1 Apr - 15 Nov: Tue - Sun & BH Mon: 11am - 6pm or sunset if earlier. 18 Nov - 20 Dec: Wed - Sun, 11am - 4pm. Last admission 1 hr before closing.

Admission: Adult £4.20, Child £2.10, Family (2+3) £10.50. Pre-booked groups £3.20pp. No reduction for groups on Sat, Sun & BH Mon.

| i | Shop. | ♿ | Grounds suitable. WC. | ☕ | Available. | | Guide dogs only. |

STANSTED PARK

ROWLANDS CASTLE, HAMPSHIRE PO9 6DX

Owner: *Trustees of Stansted Park Foundation*   **Contact:** *James Cooper*

One of the South's most elegant stately homes, Stansted House is set in 1,250 acres of glorious parkland. Situated on the Hampshire/Sussex border it is an exceptional location with a unique range of facilities. The Wren-style house with its adjacent buildings offers many options for conferences, business meetings, exhibitions and corporate hospitality including a theatre with tiered seating for up to 100. Now licensed for Civil Marriage Ceremonies and the perfect venue for wedding receptions. Also a very versatile location for filming and commercial photography. The House contains the Bessborough collection of paintings and family furnishings. Below stairs the Victorian kitchen, housekeeper's room and pantries give insight into life in days gone by. The ancient chapel inspired some of Keat's finest verse and visitors can enjoy the Victorian walled gardens, arboretum and the enchanted forest which is rich in wildlife and famous for its peace and tranquillity.

Location: OS Ref. SU761 104. Follow brown heritage signs from A3 (Rowlands Castle) or A27 (Havant).

Opening Times: Gardens, Grounds & Chapel: Easter - end Sept: Sun & Mon, 2 - 5.30pm. House: BH Sun & Mon, Jul & Aug: Sun & Mon, 2 - 5.30pm plus all summer event days. Groups by appointment Apr - Sept (except Sat). Contact the Estate Office for the full Events Programme and details of corporate hospitality, wedding and business facilities.

| i | Shop. | ♿ | Partially suitable. WC. | ☕ | Tearoom. | | Civil Wedding Licence. |

STANDEN

EAST GRINSTEAD, WEST SUSSEX RH19 4NE

Owner: *The National Trust*   **Contact:** *The Property Manager*

Tel: 01342 323029 **Fax:** 01342 316424

Dating from the 1890s and containing original Morris & Co furnishings and decorations, Standen survives today as a remarkable testimony to the ideals of the Arts and Crafts movement. The property was built as a family home by the influential architect Phillip Webb and retains a warm, welcoming atmosphere. Details of Webb's designs can be found everywhere from the fireplaces to the original electric light fittings.

Location: OS Ref. TQ389 356. 2m S of East Grinstead, signposted from B2110.

Opening Times: 25 Mar - 1 Nov: Wed - Sun & BH Mon. Garden: 12.30 - 6pm House: 12.30 - 4pm (last adm). 6 Nov - 20 Dec: garden only: Fri - Sun, 1 - 4pm.

Admission: House & Garden: £5. Garden only: £3 (£2 Nov/Dec), Children half price, Family £12.50. Joint ticket which includes same day entry to Nymans Garden £7, available Wed - Fri.

| i | Shop. | ♿ | Partially suitable. WC. | ☕ | Licensed restaurant. |
| 🚶 | By arrangement. | | In grounds on leads, not in garden. |

UPPARK

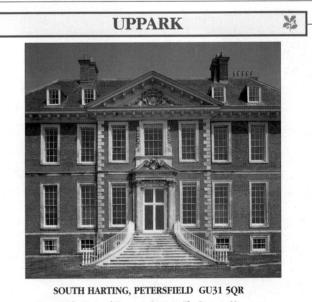

SOUTH HARTING, PETERSFIELD GU31 5QR

Owner: *The National Trust*   **Contact:** *The Property Manager*

Tel: 01730 825415 or 01730 825857 (Info Line) **Fax:** 01730 825873

Fine pictures, furniture and ceramics all rescued from the disastrous 1989 fire and now returned to successfully and fully restored exquisite 18th century interior. Award winning multi-media fire/restoration exhibition. Evocative 'below stairs' rooms. H G Wells connections. Garden in the picturesque style. Wonderful setting high on the South Downs.

Location: OS Ref. SU775 177. 5m SE of Petersfield on B2146.

Opening Times: 1 Apr - 29 Oct: Sun - Thur. House: 1 - 5pm. Last admission 4.15pm. Woodland Walk, Ticket Office, Shop, Restaurant, Garden & Exhibition: 11.30am - 5.30pm.

Admission: House, Garden and Exhibition: £5.50, Family £13.75. Garden, exhibition etc. half price. All entry by timed ticket. Some advance booking available, tel: 01730 825415 (during office hours Mon - Thur), giving a week's notice. Groups by arrangement only.

| i | Shop. | ♿ | Partially suitable. WC. | ☕ | Licensed tearoom. |
| P | Coaches must pre-book. | | In grounds, on leads. |

WAKEHURST PLACE

Tel: 01444 894066

Ardingly, Haywards Heath, Sussex RH17 6TN

Owner: The National Trust (managed by Royal Botanic Gdns) **Contact:** The Administrator
A superb collection of exotic trees, shrubs and other plants, many displayed in a geographic manner. Extensive water gardens, a winter garden, a rock walk and many other features. The Loder Valley Nature Reserve can be visited by prior arrangement.

Location: OS Ref. TQ339 314. 1½ m N of Ardingly, on B2028.

Opening Times: Daily (not 25 Dec & 1 Jan). Opens 10am, closing times vary according to season. Mansion closes 1 hr before gardens.

Admission: Adult £4.50, Child (5 - 16): £2.50, Conc. £3, Family (2+4) £12. Reductions for pre-paid booked groups. (1997 prices, please telephone for 1998 prices).

[i] Shop.   [&] Ground floor & grounds suitable.   [☕] Restaurant.   [🐕] Guide dogs only.

WEALD & DOWNLAND OPEN AIR MUSEUM

Tel: 01243 811348

Singleton, Chichester, Sussex PO18 0EU

Collection of over 35 historic buildings rescued from destruction, including working watermill and various timber-framed houses.

Location: OS Ref. SU876 127. 6m N of Chichester. SE side of A286. W of Singleton.

Opening Times: 1 Mar - 31 Oct: daily. Nov - Feb: Wed & w/ends only. 10.30am - 4pm.

Admission: Adult £5.10, Child/Student £2.50, Family £13.

[i] Shop.   [☕] Tearoom.   [🐕] In grounds, on leads.

WEST DEAN GARDENS

Tel: 01243 811301/818210

West Dean, Chichester, Sussex PO18 0QZ

Owner: The Edward James Foundation   **Contact:** J D Buckland
Extensive Victorian walled kitchen garden located in downland overlooking the beautiful West Dean Park and surrounding West Dean College.

Location: OS Ref. SU863 128. SE side of A286 Midhurst Road, 6m N of Chichester.

Opening Times: March - October: daily 11am - 5pm.

Admission: Adult £3.50, Child £1.50, Over 60's £3.

[☕] Licensed Restaurant.   [P] Ample for cars.   [🎒] Educational visits.   [🐕] Guide dogs only.

Mews:

A mew was originally a cage or place for keeping hawks, particularly while they were 'mewing' or moulting; the royal stables, built on the site at Charing Cross in London where the royal hawks had formerly been mewed, were still known as 'The Mews', and thus began the word's association with stabling. The first private mews to be built were those behind the houses in Grosvenor Square, in the 1720s. Parallel rows of houses were served by common back-streets, called mews, lined all along with stables having accommodation above them for stable-hands. Each mews was at the bottom of the gardens it served.

Extract from; "Life in the Country House" by David N Durant (published by John Murray), PB£15.99, see page twelve at the front of the book.

National Trust Photo Library.

Petworth House, Sussex.

Counties in this region:

GLOS

OXON

BERKS

WILTSHIRE

SOMERSET

HAMPSHIRE

DEVON

DORSET

CORNWALL

ISLES OF
SCILLY

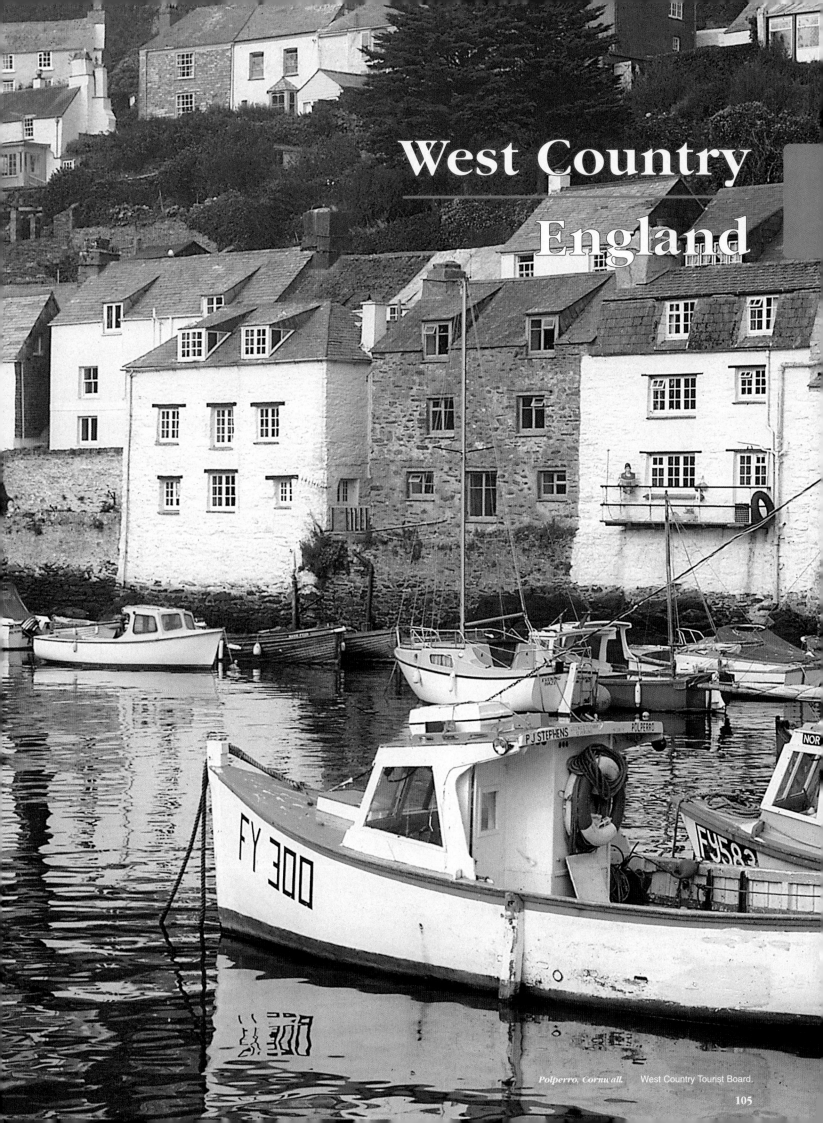

West Country
England

Polperro, Cornwall. West Country Tourist Board.

National Trust Photographic Library.

ANTONY HOUSE & GDN. & ANTONY WOODLAND GDN.
Torpoint

Antony House and Garden: A superb example of an early 18th century mansion. The main block is faced in lustrous silver-grey stone, flanked by mellow brick pavilions. The ancestral home of the Carew family for nearly 600 years, the house contains a wealth of paintings, tapestries, furniture and embroideries, many linking the great families of Cornwall – set in parkland and fine gardens (including the National Collection of day lilies), overlooking the Lynher river. An 18th century Bath House can be viewed by arrangement.

Antony Woodland Garden: The woodland garden was established in the late 18th century with the assistance of Humphrey Repton. It features numerous varieties of camellias, together with magnolias, rhododendrons, azaleas and other flowering shrubs, interspersed with many fine species of indigenous and exotic trees. A further 50 acres of natural woods bordering the tidal waters of the Lynher provide a number of delightful walks. The Woodland Garden is at its finest in the spring and autumn months.

CONTACT

Antony House
(The National Trust)
The Administrator
Antony House & Gdn
Torpoint
Cornwall
PL11 2QA
Tel: (01752) 812191

Antony Woodland Garden
(Carew Pole Gdn. Trust)
Mrs Valerie Anderson
Torpoint
Cornwall
PL11 2QA
Tel: (01752) 812364

LOCATION

OS Ref. SX418 564

Antony House and Antony Woodland Garden
5m W of Plymouth via Torpoint car ferry, 2m NW of Torpoint.

OPENING TIMES

Antony House and Garden
1 April - 29 October
Tue, Wed, Thur &
BH Mon
plus Sun in June,
July & August
1.30 - 5.30pm.

Guided tours at less busy times.

Last admission 4.45pm

Antony Woodland Garden
1 March - 31 October
Daily
11am - 5.30pm.

ADMISSION

Antony House & Garden
Adult £4.00
Parties £3.00

Antony Woodland Garden:
Adult £2.50

Joint Gardens only ticket to NT-owned garden and Antony Woodland Garden
Adult £3.00
Child £1.50
Parties £2.40

NB. Entrance to the Woodland Garden is free to NT members on days when the house is open.

National Trust Photographic Library.

i Shop.　& Braille guide.　Tearoom.　No dogs.

West Country England

National Trust Photographic Library.

COTEHELE
Saltash

CONTACT

Lewis Eynon
Property Manager
Cotehele
St Dominick
Saltash
Cornwall
PL12 6TA

Tel: (01579) 351346

Fax: (01579) 351222

e-mail:
cctlce@smtp.ntrust.org.uk

LOCATION

OS Ref. SX422 685

1m SW of Calstock by foot.
8m S of Tavistock,
4m E of Callington,
15m from Plymouth via the
Tamar bridge at Saltash

Trains: Limited service
from Plymouth to Calstock
(1¼ m uphill)

Boats: Limited (tidal)
service from Plymouth to
Calstock Quay (Plymouth
Boat Cruises)
Tel: (01752) 822797

Buses: Western National
(seasonal variations)
Tel: (01752) 222666

Cotehele, owned by the Edgcumbe family for nearly 600 years, is a fascinating and enchanting estate set on the steep wooded slopes of the River Tamar. Exploring Cotehele's many and various charms provides a full day out for the family and leaves everyone longing to return.

The steep valley garden contains exotic and tender plants which thrive in the mild climate. Remnants of an earlier age include a mediaeval stewpond and domed dovecote, a 15th century chapel and 18th century tower with fine views over the surrounding countryside. A series of more formal gardens, terraces, an orchard and a daffodil meadow surround Cotehele House.

One of the least altered medieval houses in the country, Cotehele is built in local granite, slate and sandstone. Inside the ancient rooms, unlit by electricity, is a fine collection of textiles, tapestries, armour and early dark oak furniture. The chapel contains the oldest working domestic clock in England, still in its original position.

A walk through the garden and along the river leads to the quay, a busy river port in Victorian times. The National Maritime Museum worked with the National Trust to set up a museum here which explains the vital role that the Tamar played in the local economy. As a living reminder, the restored Tamar sailing barge *Shamrock* (owned jointly by the Trust and the National Maritime Museum) is moored here.

A further walk through woodland along the Morden stream leads to the old estate corn mill which has been restored to working order.

This large estate with many footpaths offers a variety of woodland and countryside walks, opening up new views and hidden places. The Danescombe Valley, with its history of mining and milling, is of particular interest.

National Trust Photographic Library.

ℹ️ NT Shop. Cotehele Quay Gallery offers a wide range of local hand-made arts and crafts. No photography in house. *Winner of 1996 Merit Award for Excellence, Times/NPI National Heritage Awards.*

✗ Available for up to 90 people.

♿ 2 wheelchairs at Reception. Hall and kitchen accessible to wheelchairs. Ramps at house, restaurant and shop. Most of garden is very steep with loose gravel. Riverside walks are flatter (from Cotehele Quay) and Edgcumbe Arms is accessible. WCs near house and at Quay. Parking near house and mill by prior arrangement.

🍴 In Barn restaurant (can be pre-booked) daily (except Fri, Apr - Oct). At the Quay, Edgcumbe Arms offers lighter meals (daily, Apr - Oct). Both licensed.

🅿️ Near house and garden and at Cotehele Quay. No parking at Mill.

🚶 All groups (15+) must pre-book with Property Manager and receive a coach route which must be followed. These are limited to two per day. No group bookings Sun and BH weekends. Visitors to house limited to 80 at any one time. Please arrive early and be prepared to queue at busy times. Avoid dull days early and late in the season. Allow a full day to see estate.

🐕 No dogs, but dogs under control welcome on woodland walks.

OPENING TIMES

SUMMER
1 April - 1 November
Garden
Daily 11am - dusk
House
Daily except Fri
(but incl. Good Fri)
11am - 5pm
(4.30pm in October)
Last admission 30 mins
before closing.
Mill
Daily except Fri
(but open Good Fri
& Fri in July & August)
1.30 - 5.30pm
(6pm in July & August
4.30pm in October)
Last admission 30 mins
before closing.

WINTER
October - March
Garden
Open daily 11am - dusk.

ADMISSION

House, Garden & Mill
Adult £5.60
Child (5-17yrs) £2.80
Groups*...................£4.50
Family (2+3)...........£14.00

Garden & Mill only
Adult £2.80
Child (5-17yrs) £1.40
Family (2+3) £7.00

*Groups must book in
advance with the
Property Manager.

NT members free.
You may join here.

TREBAH GARDEN
Mawnan Smith

The Enchanted Garden

'Like a corner of the Himalayas only better cared for', Trebah is the home of Tony and Eira Hibbert. It was planted in the 1820s by Charles Fox of the celebrated family which created Glendurgan, Penjerrick and Rosehill. During the 19th century it received plants and seeds from the great Victorian plant hunting expeditions and is now as celebrated for its sub-tropical botanical collections as for its beauty.

Here is a magnificent, old, wild, enchanted Cornish garden, the end product of 100 years of inspired and dedicated creation, followed by 40 years of mellowing neglect and 16 years of love and restoration. Like a great wine it is now drinking at its best. The 26 acre sub-tropical ravine garden runs down to the private beach on the Helford River.

A stream winding down through water gardens with waterfalls and Koi Carp is flanked with carpets of arums and primula candelabra and two acres of blue and white hydrangeas. 100 year old rhododendrons and magnolias overhang glades of giant gunnera and tree ferns. The side curtains of magnificent beeches and copper beeches climbing the steep walls of the ravine, and the back-curtain of the Helford River with the distant Bosahan hills, form a theatrical set of extraordinary beauty.

In 1990 Trebah was donated to a registered charity, the Trebah Garden Trust, to ensure that the garden will remain open to the public for ever. A new Curator has been appointed and Tony Hibbert, who has worked on the restoration of the garden since 1980, is retiring on his 81st birthday.

CONTACT

Barbara Pascoe
Trebah Garden Trust
Mawnan Smith
Nr. Falmouth
Cornwall
TR11 5JZ

Tel: (01326) 250448

Fax: (01326) 250781

LOCATION

OS Ref. SW768 275

4m SW of Falmouth

Follow brown and white tourism signs from junction of A394 and A39 at Treliever Cross Roundabout. From Falmouth, follow signs from Hillhead Roundabout on A39.

OPENING TIMES

ALL YEAR
Open every day
10.30am - 5pm
(last admission)

ADMISSION

1 March - 31 October*
Adult £3.20
OAP.........................£3.00
Disabled.................£1.00
Child (5 - 15) £1.00
Child under 5 ....Free

Reduced winter rates
1 November - 28 February

Groups of 12+
Adult £2.70
OAP.........................£2.70
Disabled.................£0.80
Child (5 - 15) £0.80
Child under 5 ....Free

Free entry for groups
1 November - 28 February

*RHS & NT Members
RHS members have free entry to Trebah throughout the year. NT members have free entry from 1 Nov - end of Feb.

Derek Harris.

ℹ️ Shop. Gifts, books, etc. Unique collection of hardy and exotic plants on sale in the sunken garden.

🍴 Coffee shop, seats 65. Light lunches and cream teas. Adjacent picnic area seats a further 100.

🚶 Garden tours for groups of 12. Pre-booking required.

🅿️ Free. 3 coaches, 140 cars. Free entrance and meal for couriers and coach drivers.

🐕 Dogs on leads.

ANTONY HOUSE & GARDEN
ANTONY WOODLAND GARDEN

See page 106 for full page entry.

BOSVIGO

Tel: 01872 275774 **Fax:** 01872 275774

Bosvigo Lane, Truro, Cornwall TR1 3NH

Owner: Michael & Wendy Perry   **Contact:** Mr Michael Perry

Series of walled and enclosed gardens surrounding Georgian House (not open).

Location: OS Ref. SW815 452. ³/₄ m W from city centre. Turn down Dobbs Lane near Sainsbury roundabout.

Opening Times: Mar - end Sept: Wed - Sat, 11am - 6pm.

Admission: Adult £2, Child 50p.

ⓘ Plant centre.   ♿ Partially suitable.   🐕 No dogs.

BURNCOOSE NURSERIES & GARDEN

Gwennap, Redruth, Cornwall TR16 6BJ   **Tel:** 01209 861112 **Fax:** 01209 860011

Owner: C H Williams   **Contact:** C H Williams

The Nurseries are set in the 30 acre woodland gardens of Burncoose.

Location: OS Ref. SW742 395. 2m SE of Redruth on main A393 Redruth to Falmouth road between the villages of Lanner and Ponsanooth.

Opening Times: Mon – Sat: 9am - 5pm, Sun 11am - 5pm. Gardens and Tearooms open all year (except Christmas Day).

Admission: Nurseries: Free. Gardens: Adult/OAP/Student £2. Children free. Group tours: £2.50pp by arrangement.

ⓘ Shop.   ♿ Grounds suitable. WCs.   ☕ Tearoom.   🐕 In grounds, on leads.

CAERHAYS CASTLE & GARDEN

Tel: 01872 501310 **Fax:** 01872 501870

Caerhays, Gorran, St Austell, Cornwall PL26 6LY

Owner: F J Williams Esq   **Contact:** Mrs Sarah Rundle

One of the very few Nash built castles still left standing - situated within approximately 60 acres of informal woodland gardens created by J C Williams, who sponsored plant hunting expeditions to China at the turn of the century. Noted for its camellias, magnolias, rhododendrons and oaks. English Heritage listing - Grade I: Outstanding.

Location: OS Ref. SW972 415. S coast of Cornwall – between Mevagissey and Portloe. 9m SW of St. Austell.

Opening Times: House: 23 Mar - 1 May, Mon - Fri (excluding BHs) 2 - 4pm. Gardens: 16 Mar - 8 May: Mon - Fri, 11am - 4pm also Sat 25 & Sun 26 Apr.

Admission: House £3.50. Gardens: £3.50, Child £1.50. House & Gardens £6. Guided group tours by Head Gardener £4pp and can be arranged outside normal opening times.

ⓘ Plant centre.   ♿ Not suitable.   ☕ Tearoom.   🐕 In grounds, on leads.

CHYSAUSTER ANCIENT VILLAGE ⌗

Tel: 0831 757934

Nr. Newmill, Penzance, Cornwall TR20 8XA

Owner: English Heritage   **Contact:** The Custodian

On a windy hillside, overlooking the wild and spectacular coast, is this deserted Romano-Cornish village with a 'street' of eight well preserved houses, each comprising a number of rooms around an open court.

Location: OS203 Ref. SW473 350. 2¹/₂ m NW of Gulval off B3311.

Opening Times: 1 Apr - 31 Oct: daily, 10am 6pm (dusk if earlier). Winter: closed.

Admission: Adult £1.60, Child 80p, Conc. £1.20. 15% discount for groups of 11+.

🚶 Available if booked in advance.   🐕 On leads.   Ⓟ Ample for cars. No coaches.

COTEHELE

See page 107 for full page entry.

SPECIAL EVENTS 1998

See the front section for full list.

Historic Scotland

GLENDURGAN GARDEN

MAWNAN SMITH, FALMOUTH, CORNWALL TR11 5JZ

Owner: The National Trust   *Contact: Reception*

Tel: 01326 250906 (opening hours only) or 01208 74281

A valley garden of great beauty with fine trees, shrubs and water gardens. The laurel maze, recently restored, is an unusual and popular feature. The garden runs down to the tiny village of Durgan and its beach on the Helford River.

Location: OS Ref. SW772 277. 4m SW of Falmouth, ¹/₂ m SW of Mawnan Smith, on road to Helford Passage. 1m E of Trebah Garden.

Opening Times: 3 Mar - 31 Oct: Tue - Sat & BH Mon, 10.30am - 5.30pm. (closed Good Fri): Last admission 4.30pm.

Admission: £3.20. Pre-arranged groups: £2.70. Family £8.

ⓘ Shop & plant sales.   ♿ Braille guide.   ☕ Tearoom.   🐕 No dogs.

GODOLPHIN 🏛

BREAGE, HELSTON, CORNWALL TR13 9RE

Owner: Mrs M Schofield   *Contact: Mrs M Schofield*

Tel: 01736 762409

Godolphin is a Tudor and Stuart house with original Elizabethan stables. The recently discovered gardens show the ancient raised walks and carp ponds and are at present undergoing clearance. The most eminent Godolphins were Sidney the poet, killed in the Civil War fighting for the King, and Sidney the 1st Earl, who was Queen Anne's Lord High Treasurer. His son, the 2nd Earl, owned the famous Godolphin Arabian and a painting of the stallion by John Wootton hangs in the dining room.

Location: OS Ref. SW602 318. Breage, Helston. On minor road from Breage to Townshend.

Opening Times: 1 May - 30 Sept. May & Jun: Thur, 2 - 5pm. Jul & Sept: Tue & Thur: 2 - 5pm. Aug: Tue: 2 - 5pm, Thur: 10am - 1pm & 2 - 5pm. Open BH Mon (not Christmas). Groups and tours by arrangement.

Admission: Adult: £3. Child £1. Reductions for groups of 20+ by prior arrangement.

ⓘ Plant sales.   ♿ Suitable. WC.   ☕ Tearoom.   🐕 Guide dogs only.

LANHYDROCK

E J Spear

BODMIN, CORNWALL PL30 5AD

Owner: The National Trust *Contact:* The Property Manager

Tel: 01208 73320 **Fax:** 01208 74084 **e-mail:** clhlan@smtp.ntrust.org.uk

The grandest and most welcoming house in Cornwall, Lanhydrock is superbly set in 450 acres of woods and parkland and encircled by a garden of rare shrubs and trees, lovely in all seasons. Although dating from the 17th century, Lanhydrock was largely rebuilt after a fire in 1881 and now exemplifies the great Victorian country house. A total of 49 rooms are open to the public.

Location: OS Ref. SX085 636. $2^1/_2$ m SE of Bodmin, follow signposts from either A30, A38 or B3268.

Opening Times: Garden: All year, daily 11am - 5.30pm. House: 1 Apr - 1 Nov, daily except Mon (but open BHMon) 11am - 5.30pm. Closes 5pm in Oct. Last admission $^1/_2$ hr before closing.

Admission: House, Gdn & Grnds: Adult £6.20, Child £3.10. Gdn & Grnds: £3.10. Pre-booked groups (15+): Adult £5.50, Child £2.75. Family £15.50.

i Shop. Plant centre.	✗ By arrangement.	♿ Suitable. Braille guide. WC.
🍴 Licensed restaurant	🐾 In grounds, on leads. Guide dogs only in house.	

THE LOST GARDENS OF HELIGAN

PENTEWAN, ST AUSTELL, CORNWALL PL26 6EN

Owner: Mr. T Smit *Contact:* Mr. C.A. Howlett

Tel: 01726 844157 **Fax:** 01726 843023

These award winning Gardens are 80 acres of superb pleasure grounds together with a magnificent complex of four walled gardens and kitchen garden, all being restored to their former glory as a living museum of 19th century horticulture. An Italian Garden, Fern Ravine, Crystal Grotto, Summerhouses, Rides, Lawns and a 20 acre sub-tropical "Jungle Garden" are just some of the delights of this "Sleeping Beauty".

Location: OS Ref. SX000 465. 5m SW of St. Austell. 2m NW of Mevagissey. Take the B3273 to Mevagissey – follow tourist signs.

Opening Times: Daily except Christmas Day. 10am - 6pm. Last adm. 4.30pm.

Admission: Adult £4.50. Child (5-15) £2, OAPs £4. Family £12. Groups and tours by prior arrangement.

i Shop. Plant centre.	♿ Suitable. WC.	☕ Tearoom.	🐾 On leads only.

LAUNCESTON CASTLE

Tel: 01566 772365

Castle Lodge, Launceston, Cornwall PL15 7DR

Owner: English Heritage **Contact:** The Custodian

Set on the motte of the original Norman castle and commanding the town and surrounding countryside, the shell keep and tower survive of this medieval castle which controlled the main route into Cornwall.

Location: OS201 Ref. SX330 846. In Launceston.

Opening Times: 1 Apr - 31 Oct: daily, 10am - 6pm (dusk if earlier). Winter: closed.

Admission: Adult £1.60, Child 80p, Conc. £1.20. 15% discount for groups of 11+.

i Shop.	♿ Grounds suitable.	☕ Kiosk.	P Limited.	🐾 In grounds, on leads.

CIVIL WEDDING VENUES

See the front section for full list.

MOUNT EDGCUMBE HOUSE & COUNTRY PARK

CREMYLL, TORPOINT, CORNWALL PL10 IHZ

Owner: Cornwall County & Plymouth City Councils *Contact:* Cynthia Gaskell Brown

Tel: 01752 822236 **Fax:** 01752 822199

Tudor home of Earls of Mount Edgcumbe, set in historic 18th century gardens on the dramatic sea-girt Rame peninsula. Wild fallow deer, follies, forts; national camellia collection. One of the Great Gardens of Cornwall.

Location: OS Ref. SX452 527. 10m W of Plymouth via Torpoint.

Opening Times: 8 Apr - 18 Oct, Wed - Sun, 11am - 5pm. Country Park: All year, daily 8am - dusk.

Admission: Adult £3.50, Child £1.70, OAP £2.50.

i Shop.	♿ Suitable. WCs.	🍴 Licensed restaurant.	P Ample.	🐾 Grounds only.

West Country England

PENCARROW 🏛

NPI Award 1997: NPI Winner

BODMIN, CORNWALL PL30 3AG
Owner: Molesworth-St Aubyn family   *Contact:* The Administrator

Tel: 01208 841369

Still owned and lived in by the family. Georgian house and listed gardens. Superb collection of pictures, furniture and porcelain. Marked walks through 50 acres of beautiful formal and woodland gardens, Victorian rockery, Italian garden, over 700 different varieties of rhododendrons, lake and ice house.

Location: OS Ref. SX040 711. Between Bodmin and Wadebridge. 4m NW of Bodmin off A389 & B3266 at Washaway.

Opening Times: Easter - 15 Oct: Sun - Thur, 1.30 - 5pm. 1 Jun - 10 Sept & BH Mon opens 11am.

Admission: House & Garden: Adult £4, Child £2. Garden only: Adult £2 (garden free for children). Groups: House & Garden: £3.75pp.

ℹ️ Craft centre, plant shop, small childrens' play area, self-pick soft fruit.
♿ Suitable. WC. ☕ Licensed tearoom. 🐕 Grounds only.

PENDENNIS CASTLE ⊞

FALMOUTH, CORNWALL TR11 4LP
Owner: English Heritage   *Contact:* The Head Custodian

Tel: 01326 316594

Pendennis and its neighbour, St Mawes Castle face each other across the mouth of the estuary of the River Fal. Built by Henry VIII in 16th century as protection against threat of attack and invasion from France. Extended and adapted over the years to meet the changing threats to national security from the French and Spanish and continued right through to World War II. It withstood five months of siege during the Civil War before becoming the penultimate Royalist Garrison to surrender on the mainland. Pendennis today stands as a landmark, with fine sea views and excellent site facilities including exhibitions, a museum and guardhouse.

Location: OS204, Ref SW824 318. On Pendennis Head.

Opening Times: 1 Apr - 31 Oct: daily, 10am - 6pm or dusk if earlier. 1 Nov - 31 Mar: daily, 10am - 4pm. Closed 24 - 26 Dec.

Admission: Adult £3, Child £1.50, Conc. £2.30. 15% discount for groups of 11+.

ℹ️ Shop. ✖️ By arrangement. ♿ Ground floor & grounds suitable.
☕ Tearoom. 🅿️ Ample. 🐕 In grounds, on leads.

PENJERRICK GARDEN   **Tel:** 01872 870105

Budock, Falmouth, Cornwall TR11 5ED
Owner: Mrs Rachel T. Morin   **Contact:** Mrs Rachel T. Morin

A peaceful 15 acre natural, Spring-flowering garden of historical and botanic interest. Home of Penjerrick and Barclayi hybrid rhododendrons. The upper garden, with a lovely view to the sea, contains many rhododendrons, camellias, magnolias, azaleas, bamboos and tree ferns. The lower luxuriant valley garden, reached by a wooden bridge, features ponds in a wilder, somewhat jungle-like woodland setting with a tropical feel. A quiet and peaceful non-commercialised garden.

Location: OS10 Ref. SW780 307. 3m SW of Falmouth opp. Penmorvah Manor Hotel nr Budock.

Opening Times: 1 Mar - 30 Sept: Wed, Fri & Sun, 1.30 - 4.30pm.

Admission: Adult/OAP/Student £1.50, Child 50p.

♿ Not suitable for the disabled.   🐕 Dogs on leads welcome.

PRIDEAUX PLACE 🏛

PADSTOW, CORNWALL PL28 8RP
Owner: Peter Prideaux-Brune   *Contact:* Peter Prideaux-Brune

Tel: 01841 532411

Tucked away in the busy port of Padstow, the home of the Prideaux family for the past 400 years, is surrounded by gardens and wooded grounds overlooking a deer park and the Camel estuary to the moors beyond. The house still retains its 'E' shape Elizabethan front, contains fine paintings and furniture and an exhibition reflecting its emergence as a major international film location. The impressive outbuildings have been restored in recent years and the 16th century plaster ceiling in the great chamber has been uncovered for the first time since 1760.

Location: OS Ref. SW913 756. 5m from A39 Newquay / Wadebridge link road. Signposted by Historic House signs.

Opening Times: Easter Sun - 1 Oct: Sun - Thur, 1.30 - 5pm. Late Spring & Aug BH Mons: 11am - 5pm. Open all year round for groups 15+ by arrangement.

Admission: Adult £4, Accompanied children £1. Grounds only: £2. Groups £3.50.

ℹ️ Shop. ✖️ By arrangement. ♿ Ground floor & grounds suitable.
☕ Tearoom. 👥 By arrangement. 🐕 In grounds, on leads.

PROBUS GARDENS   **Tel:** 01726 882597 **Fax:** 01726 883868

Probus, Nr. Truro, Cornwall TR2 4HQ
Owner: Cornwall County Council   **Contact:** Mr Alistair Rivers

Seven and a half acre garden with displays of annuals, herbaceous, perennials, shrubs, trees, conifers and hedges.

Location: OS Ref. SW903 478. East of Probus village on A390. 8m W of St Austell. 1m W of Trewithin.

Opening Times: 11 Mar - 11 Oct: daily 10am - 5pm. 14 Oct - 14 Mar: Mon - Fri 10am - 4pm.

Admission: Adult £2.80, Child free, Groups of 20+ £2.50pp. Guided tours for 15+ £3.50pp, pre-booking is essential.

ℹ️ Shop. Plant centre. Conferences.   ♿ Suitable. WC.   ☕ Tearoom.   🐕 No dogs.

RESTORMEL CASTLE ⊞   **Tel:** 01208 872687

Lostwithiel, Cornwall PL22 0BD
Owner: English Heritage   **Contact:** The Custodian

Perched on a high mound, surrounded by a deep moat, the huge circular keep of this splendid Norman castle survives in remarkably good condition. It is still possible to make out the ruins of Restormel's Keep, Gate, Great Hall and even the kitchens and private rooms.

Location: OS200 Ref. SX104 614. 1½ m N of Lostwithiel off A390.

Opening Times: 1 Apr - 31 Oct: daily, 10am - 6pm (dusk if earlier). Winter: closed.

Admission: Adult £1.60, Child 80p, Conc. £1.20. 15% discount for groups of 11+.

ℹ️ Shop. ♿ Grounds suitable. ☕ Kiosk. 🅿️ Ample for cars, limited for coaches.
🐕 In grounds, on leads.

West Country England

ST. CATHERINE'S CASTLE
Tel: 01179 750700

Fowey, Cornwall

Owner: English Heritage   **Contact:** The South West Regional Office

A small fort built by Henry VIII to defend Fowey harbour, with fine views of the coastline and river estuary.

Location: OS200 Ref. SX118 508. ³/₄ m SW of Fowey along footpath off A3082.

Opening Times: Any reasonable time.

Admission: Free.

ST MAWES CASTLE

ST MAWES, CORNWALL TR2 3AA

Owner: English Heritage   *Contact: The Head Custodian*

Tel: 01326 270526

The pretty fishing village of St Mawes is home to this castle. On the opposite headland to Pendennis Castle, St Mawes shares the task of watching over the mouth of the River Fal as it has done since Henry VIII built it as a defence against the French. With three huge circular bastions shaped like clover leaves, St Mawes was designed to cover every possible angle of approach. It is the finest example of Tudor military architecture. The castle offers views of St Mawes little boat-filled harbour, the passenger ferry tracking across the Fal, and the splendid coastline which featured in the *Poldark* TV series. Also the start of some delightful walks along the coastal path.

Location: OS204 Ref. SW842 328. W of St Mawes on A3078.

Opening Times: 1 Apr - 31 Oct: daily, 10am - 6pm or dusk if earlier. Winter: 1 Nov - 31 Mar: Fri - Tue, 10am - 4pm. Closed 1 - 2pm & 24 - 26 Dec.

Admission: Adult £2.50, Child £1.30, Conc. £1.90. 15% discount for groups of 11+.

ℹ️ Shop.   ♿ Grounds suitable. WC.   ☕ Kiosk.   🅿️ Limited.   🐕 Guide dogs only.

Posh:

The dictionary definition is 'stylish, smart, first-rate'. The word is widely believed to be an acronym for Port Out, Starboard Home, arising in the days when the Peninsular & Oriental Steam Navigation Company ran a passenger service from Britain to India (from 1840 until after the Second World War). On the voyage east to India the cabins on the port side were shaded from the blistering tropical sun, and therefore more expensive, as were those on the starboard side on the voyage west and home. The posh were those who could afford the shaded cabins. But 'posh' was also late nineteenth century slang for a dandy, perhaps derived from the Romany posh, half, used in criminal cant to mean 'money'.

Extract from; "Life in the Country House" by David N Durant (published by John Murray), PB£15.99, see page twelve at the front of the book.

ST MICHAEL'S MOUNT

National Trust Photographic Library.

MARAZION, NR PENZANCE, CORNWALL TR17 0EF

Owner: The National Trust   *Contact: The Manor Office*

Tel: 01736 710507 (710265 tide & ferry information) **Fax:** 01736 711544

This magical island is the jewel in Cornwall's crown. The great granite crag which rises from the waters of Mount's Bay is surmounted by an embattled medieval castle, home of the St. Aubyn family for over 300 years. The Mount's flanks are softened by lush sub-tropical vegetation and on the water's edge there is a harbourside community which features shops and restaurants.

Location: OS Ref. SW515 300. At Marazion there is access on foot over causeway at low tide. In summer months there is a ferry at high tide. 4m E of Penzance.

Opening Times: 1 Apr - 30 Oct: Mon - Fri 10.30am - 5.30pm. Last admission 4.45pm. Shops & restaurants open daily. Nov - end Mar: It is essential to telephone before setting out in order to ascertain the opening arrangements for that day. The castle & grounds are open most weekends during the season. These are special charity days when National Trust members are asked to pay admission.

Admission: £3.90. Pre-arranged groups £3.50. Family £10.

ℹ️ Shops.   ♿ Braille and taped guides.   ☕ Restaurants.   🐕 Guide dogs only.

TINTAGEL CASTLE

TINTAGEL, CORNWALL PL34 0HE

Owner: English Heritage   *Contact: The Head Custodian*

Tel: 01840 770328

The spectacular setting for the legendary castle of King Arthur is the wild and windswept Cornish coast. Clinging precariously to the edge of the cliff face are the extensive ruins of a medieval royal castle, built by Richard, Earl of Cornwall, younger brother of Henry III. Also used as a Cornish stronghold by subsequent Earls of Cornwall. Despite extensive excavations since the 1930s, Tintagel Castle remains one of the most spectacular and romantic spots in the entire British Isles. Destined to remain a place of mystery and romance, Tintagel will always jealously guard its marvellous secrets.

Location: OS200 Ref. SX048 891. On Tintagel Head, ¹/₂ m along uneven track from Tintagel. No vehicles.

Opening Times: 1 Apr - 31 Oct: daily, 10am - 6pm or dusk if earlier. 1 Nov - 31 Mar, daily, 10am - 4pm. Closed 24 - 26 Dec.

Admission: Adult £2.80, Child £1.40, Conc. £2.10. 15% discount for groups of 11+.

ℹ️ Shop. No vehicles.   ♿ Ground floor suitable.   🐕 No dogs.

West Country England

TINTAGEL OLD POST OFFICE   **Tel:** 01840 770024 or 01208 74281

Tintagel, Cornwall PL34 0DB

Owner: The National Trust   **Contact:** The Custodian

One of the most characterful buildings in Cornwall, and a house of great antiquity, this small 14th century manor is full of charm and interest.

Location: OS Ref. SX056 884. In the centre of Tintagel.

Opening Times: 1 Apr - 1 Nov: daily 11am - 5.30pm. Closes 5pm in October.

Admission: £2.20. Family £5. Pre-arranged groups £1.60.

ℹ️ Shop.   ♿ Ground floor suitable. Braille guide.   🐕 No dogs.

TREBAH GARDEN   See page 108 for full page entry.

TREGREHAN   **Tel:** 01726 814389 **Fax:** 01726 814389

Par, Cornwall PL24 2SJ   **Contact:** Mr T C Hudson

Large woodland garden created since early 19th century by the Carlyon family, concentrating on species from warm-temperate regions.

Location: OS Ref. SX053 533. 2m E of St. Austell. 1/2 m W of St. Blazey on A390.

Opening Times: Mid Mar - mid Jun (closed Easter Sun): 10.30am - 5pm.

Admission: Adult £2.50, Child free.

☕ Available.   🅿️ Ample.   🅰️ Self-catering.

TRELISSICK GARDEN

FEOCK, TRURO, CORNWALL TR3 6QL

Owner: *The National Trust*   **Contact:** *The Property Manager*

Tel: 01872 862090

A garden and estate of rare tranquil beauty with glorious maritime views over Carrick Roads to Falmouth Harbour. The tender and exotic shrubs make this garden attractive in all seasons. Extensive park and woodland walks beside the river. There is an Art and Craft Gallery.

Location: OS Ref. SW837 396. 4m S of Truro by road, on both sides of B3289 above King Harry Ferry.

Opening Times: 1 Mar - 1 Nov: Mon - Sat, 10.30am - 5.30pm, Sun 12.30 - 5.30pm (restaurant opens noon). Closes 5pm Mar & Oct. Nov/Dec: Shop, Gallery & Restaurant open 10.30am - 4pm. Sun, 12 noon - 4pm. Woodland walk open all year. Guided tours by arrangement.

Admission: £4. Pre-arranged group £3.40. Family £10. £1.50 car park fee (refundable on admission).

ℹ️ Shop.   ✖️ By arrangement.   ♿ Suitable. WC.   ☕ Restaurant.

🐕 In park on leads; only guide dogs allowed in garden.

TRELOWARREN HOUSE & CHAPEL   **Tel:** 01326 221366

Mawgan-in-Meneage, Helston, Cornwall TR12 6AD

Owner: Sir Ferrers Vyvyan Bt   **Contact:** Sir Ferrers Vyvyan Bt

Tudor and 17th century house. Chapel and main rooms of house are open to the public.

Location: OS Ref. SW721 238. 6m S of Helston, off B3293 to St Keverne.

Opening Times: House & Chapel: 31 Mar - 24 Sept: Wed & BH Mon, 2 - 5.15pm.

Admission: Adult £1.50, Child 50p (under 12 free). Entry fee includes admittance to exhibitions.

♿ Partially suitable.

TRENGWAINTON GARDEN   **Tel:** 01736 362297 **Fax:** 01736 368142

Penzance, Cornwall TR20 8RZ

Owner: The National Trust   **Contact:** The Sub-Agent

This large shrub garden, with views over Mount's Bay, is a beautiful place throughout the year and a plantsman's delight. The walled gardens have many tender plants which cannot be grown in the open anywhere else in England.

Location: OS Ref. SW445 315. 2m NW of Penzance, 1/2 m W of Heamoor on Penzance - Morvah road (B3312), 1/2 m off St. Just road (A3071).

Opening Times: 1 Mar - 29 Oct: Sun - Thur & Good Fri,10.30am - 5.30pm. N.B.Closes 5pm in Mar & Oct. Last admission 1/2 hr before closing.

Admission: Adult £3. Family £7.50.

TRERICE

NEWQUAY, CORNWALL TR8 4PG

Owner: *The National Trust*   **Contact:** *The Property Manager*

Tel: 01637 875404

Trerice is an architectural gem and something of a rarity – a small Elizabethan manor house hidden away in a web of narrow lanes and still somehow caught in the spirit of its age. An old Arundell house, it contains much fine furniture, ceramics, glasses and a wonderful clock collection. A small barn museum traces the development of the lawn mower.

Location: OS Ref. SW841 585. 3m SE of Newquay via the A392 & A3058 (right at Kestle Mill).

Opening Times: 1 Apr - 1 Nov: daily except Tue & Sat, but open every day from 27 Jul - 6 Sept, 11am- 5.30pm. Closes 5pm in Oct. Last adm.1/2 hr before closing.

Admission: £4. Pre-arranged groups £3.40. Family £10.

ℹ️ Shop. Plant centre.   ♿ Suitable. Braille & taped guides. WC.

☕ Licensed tearoom.   🐕 Guide dogs only.

Trelissick Garden, Cornwall.

West Country
England

TRESCO ABBEY GARDENS

ISLES OF SCILLY, CORNWALL TR24 0QQ

Owner: *Mr R A and Mrs L A Dorrien-Smith*   **Contact:** *Mr M.A Nelhams*

Tel: 01720 424105 or **Tel/Fax:** 01720 422868

Tresco Abbey built by Augustus Smith has been the family home since 1834. The garden here flourishes on the small island. Nowhere else in the British Isles does such an exotic collection of plants grow in the open. Agaves, aloes, proteas and acacias from such places as Australia, South Africa, Mexico and the Mediterranean grow within the secure embrace of massive Holm Oak hedges. Valhalla Ships Figurehead Museum.

Location: OS Ref. SV895 143. Isles of Scilly. Isles of Scilly Steamship 0345 105555. B.I.H. Helicopters 01736 363871. Details of day trips on application.

Opening Times: All year: 10am - 4pm.

Admission: Adult £5, (under 14yrs free). Weekly ticket £10. Guided group tours available.

[i] Shop.   [&] Grounds suitable.   [☕] Tearoom.   [🐕] In grounds, on leads.

TREVARNO ESTATE & GARDENS

HELSTON, CORNWALL TR13 0RU

Contact: *Yvonne Ashmore*

Tel: 01326 574274   **Fax:** 01326 574282

An historic and tranquil haven protected and unspoilt for 700 years. Experience the magical atmosphere of Trevarno, an original and fascinating Cornish Estate. Beautiful Victorian and Georgian gardens, extensive collection of rare shrubs and trees, numerous garden features and follies, fascinating Gardening Museum including an intriguing collection of tools and implements. Splendid Fountain Garden Conservatory – enjoy the plants and refreshments whatever the weather. Walled gardens, woodland walks, and abundant wildlife. Follow the progress of major restoration and conservation projects.

Location: OS Ref. SW642 302. Leave Helston on Penzance road, signed from B3302 junction.

Opening Times: All year, 10.30am - 5pm. Groups welcome by prior arrangement.

Admission: Adult £3, Child (5-14yrs) £1.25, Child under 5 free, OAP £2.50

[X] Available.   [&] Partially suitable.   [☕] Tearoom.   [P] Ample.
[👥] Education programme available.   [🐕] On leads.   [💒] Civil Wedding Licence.

TREWITHEN

GRAMPOUND ROAD, TRURO, CORNWALL TR2 4DD

Owner: *A M J Galsworthy*   **Contact:** *The Estate Office*

Tel: 01726 883647   **Fax:** 01726 882301

Trewithen means 'house of the trees' and the name truly describes this fine early Georgian House in its splendid setting of wood and parkland. *Country Life* described the house as 'one of the outstanding West Country houses of the 18th century'.

The gardens at Trewithen are outstanding and of international fame. Created since the beginning of the century by George Johnstone, they contain a wide and rare collection of flowering shrubs. Some of the magnolias and rhododendron species in the garden are known throughout the world. They are one of two attractions in this country awarded three stars by Michelin.

Location: OS Ref. SW914 476. S of A390 between Grampound and Probus villages. 7m WSW of St Austell.

Opening Times: Gardens: 1 Mar - 30 Sept: Mon - Sat, 10am - 4.30pm. Sun in Apr & May only. Walled Garden: Apr - Jul, Mon & Tue only. House: Apr - Jul & Aug: BH Mon, Mon & Tue, 2 - 4pm.

Admission: Adult £3, Child £1.50. Groups (pre-arranged, 12+): Adult £2.80, Child £1.50.

[i] Plant centre. No photography in house.   [☕] Tearoom.   [🐎] By arrangement.
[P] Ample.   [🐕] In grounds, on leads.

Trelissick Garden, Cornwall.

115

West Country England

POWDERHAM CASTLE
Exeter

Historic family home of the Earl of Devon, Powderham Castle was built between 1390 and 1420 by Sir Philip Courtenay. The present Earl is his direct descendant. The Castle was extensively damaged during the Civil War and fell to the Parliamentary Forces after a protracted siege. When the family returned to the Castle seventy years later they embarked on a series of rebuilding and restoration which continued into the 19th century.

The Castle contains a large collection of portraits by many famous artists, including Cosway, Reynolds, Kneller and Hudson as well as some charming paintings by gifted members of the family. The 14ft high Stumbels Clock and the magnificent rosewood and brass inlaid bookcases by John Channon are particularly fine. One of the most spectacular rooms on view is the Music Room, designed for the 3rd Viscount by James Wyatt. It contains an exceptional Axminster carpet upon which sits recently commissioned carved gilt wood furniture.

GARDENS
The Castle is set within an ancient deer park beside the Estuary of the River Exe and the Gardens and grounds are informally laid out. The Rose Garden is planted mostly with older sweet scented varieties and enjoys fine views from its terraces across the Park. Timothy, a 150 year old tortoise, lives here and keeps the lawns weed free. The woodland garden is being restored and is open to visitors in the spring and early summer. Children will love the new 'Secret Garden' an imaginative adaption of the Victorian Walled Garden into a magical house for pets, birds and friendly animals.

CONTACT

Mr Tim Faulkner
The Estate Office
Powderham Castle
Kenton
Exeter
Devon
EX6 8JQ

Tel: (01626) 890243

Fax: (01626) 890729

LOCATION

OS Ref. SX965 832

6m SW of Exeter,
4m S M5/J30.
Access from A379 in
Kenton village.

Air: Exeter Airport 9m.

Rail: Starcross
Station 2m

Bus: Devon General
No: 85, 85A, 85B to
Castle Gate.

CONFERENCE/FUNCTION

ROOM	SIZE	MAX CAPACITY
Music Room	56' x 25'	170
Dining Room	42' x 22'	100
Ante Room	28' x 18'	25
Library 1	32' x 18'	85
Library 2	31"x18'	85

i   Shop. Filming and car launches including 4WD vehicle rallies, open air concerts, etc. Grand piano in Music Room, 3800 acre estate, tennis court, cricket pitch, horse trials course. Deer park safari. Guide book available in French, Dutch and German translations.

X   Conferences, dinners, corporate entertainment.

  Facilities limited. Some ramps. WC.

  Fully licensed restaurant and coach room access.

  Fully inclusive. Tour time: 1 hr.

P   Unlimited free parking. Commission and complimentary drinks / meals for drivers. Advance warning of group bookings preferred but not essential.

  Welcome. Fascinating tour and useful insight into the life of one of England's Great Houses over the centuries. Victorian School Room and teacher pack.

  Civil Wedding Licence.

OPENING TIMES

SUMMER

5 April - 1 November

Daily*: 10am - 5.30pm
*Except Sat: closed to public, but available for private hire.

WINTER

Available for hire for conferences, receptions and functions, tel. for details.

ADMISSION

ALL YEAR

(1997 prices)
Adult......................£4.95
OAP £4.45
Child......................£2.85
Group Rates
Adult......................£3.95
OAP £3.75
Child......................£2.35
Family.................£12.45
2 adults + 2 children or
1 adult + 3 children.

SPECIAL EVENTS

- **MAR 28 - 2 APR:**
  Phillips Fine Art Sale.

- **JUN 5:**
  Open Air Concert

- **JUN 27 - 30:**
  Phillips Fine Art Sale

- **JUL 4 - 5:**
  Powderham Horse Trials

- **JUL 11 - 12:**
  Historic Vehicle Gathering

- **JUL 31:**
  Open Air Concert

- **SEPT 26 - 29:**
  Phillips Fine Art Sale

- **DEC 13 - 15:**
  Phillips Fine Art Sale

A LA RONDE

Tel: 01395 265514

Summer Lane, Exmouth, Devon EX8 5BD

Owner: The National Trust   **Contact:** The Custodian

A unique 16-sided house built in 1796 for two spinsters, Jane and Mary Parminter. The fascinating interior decoration includes a shell-encrusted room, a feather frieze, and many 18th century contents and collections brought back by the two women from a European Grand Tour.

Location: OS Ref. SY004 834. 2m N of Exmouth on A376.

Opening Times: 1 Apr - 1 Nov: daily except Fri & Sat, 11am - 5.30pm. Last admission $^1/_2$ hr before closing.

Admission: Adult £3.20, Child £1.60, no reduction for groups.

[i] Shop.   Available.

BERRY POMEROY CASTLE

Tel: 01803 866618

Totnes, Devon TQ9 6NJ

Owner: The Duke of Somerset   **Contact:** English Heritage

A romantic late medieval castle, dramatically sited half-way up a wooded hillside, looking out over a deep ravine and stream. It is unusual in combining the remains of a large castle with a flamboyant courtier's mansion. Reputed to be one of the most haunted castles in the country.

Location: OS202 Ref. SX839 623. 2$^1/_2$m E of Totnes off A385. Entrance gate $^1/_2$m NE of Berry Pomeroy village, then $^1/_2$m drive. Narrow approach, unsuitable for coaches.

Opening Times: 1 Apr - 31 Oct: daily, 10am - 6pm or dusk if earlier.

Admission: Adult £2.10, Child £1.10, Conc £1.60. 15% discount for groups of 11+.

[&] Ground floor & grounds suitable.   Kiosk (not EH)   [P] Not suitable for coaches.

ARLINGTON COURT

Andreas Von Einsiedel

NPI Award 1997: Runner up

NR BARNSTAPLE, NORTH DEVON EX31 4LP

Owner: *The National Trust*   **Contact:** *James Stout - Property Manager*

Tel: 01271 850296   **Fax:** 01271 850711

The house, built for the Chichesters in 1822 and still with much original furniture, is full of collections for every taste, including model ships, costume, pewter, shells and many other fascinating objects. Housed in the stables is the Trust's large collection of horse drawn carriages. Carriage rides through the 30 acres of peaceful informal gardens and past the formal terraced Victorian garden, start from the front of the house. Miles of walks through woods. Parks grazed by Shetland ponies and Jacob sheep.

Location: OS180 Ref. SS611 405. 7m NE of Barnstaple on A39.

Opening Times: 1 Apr - 1 Nov: Sun - Fri (& BH Sats), 11am - 5.30pm. Paths through park and woods open during daylight hours from Nov - Mar.

Admission: House & Garden: Adult £5.10, Child £2.50, Family £12.80. Groups: Adult £4.30, Child £2.10. Garden & Carriage Museum only: Adult £2.80, Child £1.40.

[i] Shop.   [&] Ground floor & grounds suitable. WC.   Licensed restaurant.

[P] Ample.   Teacher's pack.   In grounds, on leads.

BICKLEIGH CASTLE

BICKLEIGH, NR. TIVERTON, DEVON EX16 8RP

Owner: *M J Boxall Esq*   **Contact:** *M J Boxall Esq*

Tel: 01884 855363

Royalist stronghold: 900 years of history and architecture. 11th century detached Chapel; 14th century Gatehouse – Armoury (Cromwellian), Guard Room – Tudor furniture and fine oil paintings, Great Hall – 52' long and 'Tudor' Bedroom, massive fourposter. 17th century Farmhouse: inglenook fireplaces, bread ovens, oak beams. The Museum, Spooky Tower, Great Hall and picturesque moated garden make Bickleigh a favoured venue for functions, particularly wedding receptions.

Location: OS Ref. SS936 068. Off the A396 Exeter-Tiverton road. Follow signs SW from Bickleigh Bridge 1m.

Opening Times: Easter week (Good Fri - Fri, then Wed, Sun & BHs until late May BH, then daily (except Sat) until 1st Sun in Oct, 2 - 5pm. Coaches & pre-booked groups welcome anytime.

Admission: Adult £4, Child (5 - 15) £2, Family £11.

[i] Shop. Plant centre. Conferences.   [&] Ground floor suitable.   Tearoom.

[*] Compulsory.   No dogs.   Civil Wedding Licence.

AVENUE COTTAGE GARDENS

Tel: 01803 732769

Ashprington, Totnes, Devon TQ9 7UT

Owner: R J Pitts Esq & R C H Soans Esq   **Contact:** R J Pitts Esq & R C H Soans Esq

A completely secluded and secret garden, yet one which has been in existence for over 200 years. For the last 10 years it has been undergoing restoration and recreation by the present owners. In this lovely valley site there is a large and fascinating collection of plants which is full of interest from spring until autumn.

Location: OS Ref. SX821 574. 3m SE of Totnes, from centre of village, up hill past church for 400 yds.

Opening Times: 1 Apr - 30 Sept, Tue - Sat, 11am - 5pm. Other times by appointment.

Admission: Adult £1.50, Child 25p. Entrance, guided tour & tea £3.50.

[&] Wheelchairs in grounds.   [*] Available, please book.   In grounds, on leads.

BAYARD'S COVE FORT

Tel: 01803 861234

Dartmouth, Devon

Owner: English Heritage   **Contact:** South Hams District Council

Set among the picturesque gabled houses of Dartmouth, on the waterfront at the end of the quay, this is a small artillery fort built 1509 - 10 to defend the harbour entrance.

Location: OS Ref. SX879 510. In Dartmouth, on riverfront 200 yds, S of S ferry.

Opening Times: Any reasonable time.

Admission: Free.

[P] No parking within 400 yds.   No dogs.

SPECIAL EVENTS 1998

See the front section for full list

BOWDEN HOUSE

Tel: 01803 863664

Totnes, Devon TQ9 7PW

Owner: Mrs Belinda Petersen   **Contact:** Mrs Belinda Petersen

Elizabethan mansion with Queen Anne façade.

Location: OS Ref. SX800 600. Follow signs from Totnes. 1¹/₂ m S of Totnes, E of A381.

Opening Times: 25 Mar - 31 Oct: Mon - Thur plus BH Sun. Museum opens 12 noon, Tours start at 2pm, or 1.30pm in high season, with ghost stories.

Admission: Adult £4.50, Child: (10-13 yrs) £2.60, (6-9 yrs) £1.60, under 6 free. Tickets include Photo Museum and old film shows.

ℹ Museum & shop.   ♿ Museum suitable. WCs.   ☕ Tearoom.   🐕 Guide dogs only.

BRADLEY MANOR

Tel: 01626 54513

Newton Abbot, Devon TQ12 6BN

Owner: The National Trust   **Contact:** Mrs A H Woolner

A small medieval manor house set in woodland and meadows.

Location: OS Ref. SX848 709. On Totnes road A381. ³/₄ m SW of Newton Abbot.

Opening Times: Apr - end Sept: Wed 2 - 5 pm: also Thur 2 & 9 Apr, 17 & 24 Sept. Last admission 4.30pm.

Admission: £2.60, no reduction for groups.

🐕 No dogs.

BUCKFAST ABBEY

BUCKFASTLEIGH, DEVON TQ11 0EE

Owner: Buckfast Abbey Trust   *Contact: Robin Clutterbuck*

Tel: 01364 642519   **Fax:** 01364 643891

The Benedictine monks of Buckfast welcome visitors to their Abbey, which they rebuilt themselves on its medieval foundations. The Abbey is famous today for its pioneering work in beekeeping, its tonic wine and spectacular modern stained glass. Tranquil precinct with 'physic' and 'pleasure' gardens. Restaurant, video, exhibition and shops selling the products of Buckfast and other European monasteries. Facilities for conferences and accommodation for guests and retreats. Few visitors leave untouched by the peace and serenity of Buckfast.

Location: OS Ref. SX741 674. ¹/₂ m from A38 Plymouth - Exeter route at Buckfastleigh turn off.

Opening Times: Church & Grounds: All year, 5.30am - 7pm. Shops/Rest/Video, Exhibition: Easter - Oct: 9am - 5pm. Nov - Easter: 10am - 4pm. Shops closed Good Fri & Xmas Day. Restaurant closed 24/25 Dec.

Admission: Free. Exhibition: 75p / 30p.

ℹ Shops.   ✗ Full catering service.   ♿ Suitable. Braille plan. WC.   ☕ Restaurant.

🚶 By arrangement for groups.   👪 Educational programme. Pre-book, ext. 225.

🐕 Guide dogs only.   A 8 single. 4 Twin.

BUCKLAND ABBEY

George Wright

YELVERTON, DEVON PL20 6EY

Owner: The National Trust   *Contact: Michael Coxson*

Tel: 01822 853607   **Fax:** 01822 855448

The spirit of Sir Francis Drake is rekindled at his home with exhibitions of his courageous adventures and achievements throughout the world. One of the Trust's most interesting historical buildings and originally a 13th century monastery, the abbey was transformed into a family residence before Sir Francis bought it in 1581. Outside there are monastic farm buildings, herb garden, craft workshops and country walks. Introductory video presentation.

Location: OS201 Ref. SX487 667. 6m S of Tavistock; 11m N of Plymouth off A386.

Opening Times: 1 Apr - 1 Nov: daily except Thur, 10.30am - 5.30pm (last adm. 4.45pm). 7 Nov - end Mar 1999: Sat & Sun, 2 - 5pm, (last adm. 4.15pm). Other days for pre-booked groups. Closed 4 - 22 Jan 1999.

Admission: Abbey & Grounds: Adult £4.30, Child £2.10, Family £10.70. Group: £3.50. Grounds only: Adult £2.20, Child £1. Winter: half price Abbey admission.

♿ Ground floor & grounds suitable. Wheelchair stairclimber may be available. WC.

☕ Restaurant.   🐕 Guide dogs only.

CADHAY

OTTERY ST MARY, DEVON EX11 1QT

Owner: Mr O N W William-Powlett   *Contact: Mr O William-Powlett*

Tel: 01404 812432

Cadhay is approached by an avenue of lime-trees, and stands in a pleasant listed garden, with herbaceous borders and yew hedges, with excellent views over the original medieval fish ponds. The main part of the house was built about 1550 by John Haydon who had married the de Cadhay heiress. He retained the Great Hall of an earlier house, of which the fine timber roof (about 1420) can be seen. An Elizabethan Long Gallery was added by John's successor at the end of the 16th century, thereby forming a unique and lovely courtyard.

Location: OS Ref. SY090.962. ³/₄ m S of A30 at Fairmile. 5m W of Honiton, 9m E of Exeter.

Opening Times: Jul & Aug: Tue, Wed & Thur, also Sun & Mon in late Spring & Summer BHs, 2 - 5.30pm. Groups by appointment only.

Admission: Adult £3, Child £1.50.

♿ Ground floor & grounds suitable.   ✗ By arrangement.   🐕 No dogs.

West Country
England

CASTLE DROGO

David Cripps.

DREWSTEIGNTON, EXETER EX6 6PB

Owner: The National Trust   *Contact: Pat Harris, Property Manager*

Tel: 01647 433306 **Fax:** 01647 433186

Extraordinary granite and oak castle, designed by Sir Edwin Lutyens, which combines the comforts of the 20th century with the grandeur of a Baronial castle. Elegant dining and drawing rooms and fascinating kitchen and scullery. Terraced formal garden with colourful herbaceous borders and rose beds. Panoramic views over Dartmoor and delightful walks in the 300ft Teign Gorge.

Location: OS191 Ref. SX721 900. 5m S of A30 Exeter - Okehampton road.

Opening Times: 1 Apr - 1 Nov: not Fri but open Good Fri, 11am - 5.30pm (last admission 5pm). Garden, shop and tearooms open daily at same times.

Admission: House & Garden: Adult £5.20, Child £2.60, Family £13, Party £4.30. Garden only: Adult £2.40, Child £1.20.

ℹ Shop.   ♿ Grounds floor & grounds suitable. WCs.   ☕ Licensed restaurant.

🎎 By arrangement.   🐕 Guide dogs only in certain areas.

COLETON FISHACRE GARDEN

BROWNSTONE ROAD, KINGSWEAR, DARTMOUTH TQ6 0EQ

Owner: The National Trust   *Contact: David Mason, Property Manager*

Tel/Fax: 01803 752466

A 9 hectare garden in a stream-fed valley within the spectacular scenery of the South Devon coast. The garden was created by Rupert and Lady Dorothy D'Oyly Carte between 1925 and 1948 and is planted with a wide range of rare and exotic plants for all seasons from around the world. Extensively replanted and developed by the National Trust over the past fifteen years.

Location: OS202 Ref. SX910 508. 3m E of Kingswear, follow brown tourist signs.

Opening Times: Mar: Sun only, 2 - 5pm. 1 Apr - 1 Nov: Wed, Thur, Fri, Sun & BH Mon, 10.30am - 5.30pm.

Admission: Adult £3.50, Child £1.70. Pre-booked groups (15+) £2.80

ℹ Shop. Plant centre.   ♿ Limited access to grounds.   ☕ Tea garden.

🅿 Limited.   🐕 Guide dogs only in garden.

COMPTON CASTLE   **Tel:** 01803 872112

Marldon, Paignton TQ3 1TA

Owner: The National Trust   **Contact:** The Administrator

A fortified manor house with curtain wall, built at three periods: 1340, 1450 and 1520 by the Gilbert family. It was the home of Sir Humphrey Gilbert (1539-1583), coloniser of Newfoundland and half-brother of Sir Walter Raleigh; the family still lives here.

Location: OS Ref. SX865 648. At Compton, 3m W of Torquay.

Opening Times: 1 Apr - 29 Oct: Mon, Wed & Thur, 10am - 12.15pm & 2 - 5pm. The courtyard, restored great hall, solar, chapel, rose garden and old kitchen are shown. Last admission ½ hr before closing.

Admission: £2.80, pre-arranged groups £2.20.

🐕 No dogs.

DARTINGTON HALL GARDENS   **Tel/Fax:** 01803 862367

Dartington, Totnes, Devon TQ9 6EL

Owner: Dartington Hall Trust   **Contact:** Mr G Gammin

28 acre gardens surrounds 14th century Hall.

Location: OS Ref. SX798 628. 30 mins from M5 at Exeter (off A38 at Buckfastleigh).

Opening Times: All year. Groups by appointment only. Guided tours by arrangement £4pp.

Admission: £2 donation welcome.

ℹ Shop. Conferences.   ♿ Grounds suitable. WC.   ☕ Tearoom.   🐕 Guide dogs only.

DARTMOUTH CASTLE

CASTLE ROAD, DARTMOUTH, DEVON TQ6 0JH

Owner: English Heritage   *Contact: The Custodian*

Tel: 01803 833588

This brilliantly positioned defensive castle juts out into the narrow entrance to the Dart estuary, with the sea lapping at its foot. When begun in 1480s it was one of the most advanced fortifications in England, and was the first castle designed specifically with artillery in mind. For nearly 500 years it kept its defences up-to-date in preparation for war. Today the castle is in a remarkably good state of repair, along with excellent exhibitions, the history of the castle comes to life. A picnic spot of exceptional beauty.

Location: OS202 Ref. SX887 503. 1m SE of Dartmouth off B3205, narrow approach road.

Opening Times: 1 Apr - 31 Oct: Daily, 10am - 6pm dusk if earlier. 1 Nov - 31 Mar: Wed - Sun, 10am - 4pm. Closed 24 - 26 Dec.

Admission: Adult £2.50, Child £1.30, Conc. £1.90. 15% discount for groups of 11+.

ℹ Shop.   ♿ Ground floor suitable.   ☕ Kiosk.   🅿 Limited.   🐕 No dogs.

West Country England

DOCTON MILL & GARDEN   Tel/Fax: 01237 441369

Spekes Valley, Hartland, Devon EX39 6EA

Owner: Martin G Bourcier Esq   **Contact:** Martin G Bourcier Esq
Garden for all seasons in 8 acres of sheltered wooded valley.

Location: OS Ref. SS244 213. 3m Hartland Quay. 15m N of Bude. 3m W of A39, 3m S of Hartland.

Opening Times: Mar - Oct: 10am - 5pm. No coaches.

Admission: Adult £2.50, Child 50p.

☕ Tearoom.   🚶 By arrangement.   🐕 In grounds, on leads.   **A** Available.

ESCOT HOUSE, PARK & GARDENS 🏛   Tel: 01404 822188   Fax: 01404 822903

Parklands Farm, Escot, Ottery St Mary, Devon EX11 1LU

Owner: Mr J M Kennaway   **Contact:** Mr J M Kennaway
Otters, wild boar, 2 acre walled Victorian rose garden, 25 acres of shrubbery, rhododendrons and azaleas. 'Capability' Brown parkland, pet and aquatic centre, wetlands and waterfowl park, Coach House Restaurant (all home cooking). The Kennaway family estate for over 200 years.

Location: OS Ref. SY080 977 (gate). 9m E of Exeter on A30 at Fairmile.

Opening Times: Easter - 1 Oct: 10am - 6pm. 1 Oct - Easter: 11am - 4pm. Closed Christmas Day and Boxing Day.

Admission: Adult £2.95, Child £2.55 (under 5 free), Family of 5 £12, OAP £2.55.

ℹ️ Craft & gift shop.   ♿ WC.   ☕ Licensed restaurant.   🐕 Dogs on leads only.

EXETER CATHEDRAL   Tel: 01392 55573   Fax: 01392 498769

Exeter, Devon EX1 1HS

                 Contact: Mrs Juliet Dymoke-Marr
The Exeter Rondels - 333 ft of Tapestry on the plinth around the walls of the Nave. This depicts national, local and Cathedral history from Roman times to the present day.

Location: OS Ref. SX921 925. Central to the City - between High Street and Southernhay. Groups may be put down in South Street.

Opening Times: All year: Mon - Fri 7.30am - 6.30pm, Sat 7.30am - 5pm, Sun 8am - 7.30pm.

Admission: No formal charge – donation requested of £2 per person.

ℹ️ Shop.   ♿ Suitable.   ☕ Refectory.   **P** Within 1/2 mile.

FLETE   Tel: 01752 830308   Fax: 01752 830309

Ermington, Ivybridge, Devon PL21 9NZ

Owner: Country Houses Association   **Contact:** The Administrators
Built around an Elizabethan Manor with alterations in 1879 by Norman Shaw.

Location: OS Ref. SX631 519. 11m E of Plymouth at junction of A379 & B3121. Stations: Plymouth 12m, Totnes 14m. Bus route: No 93 Plymouth - Dartmouth.

Opening Times: 1 May - 30 Sept: Wed & Thur, 2 - 5pm. Groups by arrangement.

Admission: Adult £2.50, Child £1.

🐕 No dogs.   **A** 1 single & 1 double with bathroom, CHA members only.

FURSDON HOUSE 🏛   Tel/Fax: 01392 860860   e-mail: fursdon@eclipse.co.uk

Cadbury, Thorverton, Exeter, Devon EX5 5JS   **www:** http//eclipse.co.uk/fursdon/

Owner: E D Fursdon Esq   **Contact:** Mrs C Fursdon
The Fursdon family have lived here for over 700 years. The house is set in parkland with views stretching south to Dartmoor and the grounds include a walled and terraced garden.

Location: OS Ref. SS922 046. 1 1/2 m S of A3072 between Tiverton & Crediton, 9m N of Exeter. 2m N of Thorverton by narrow lane.

Opening Times: Easter - end Sept, Thur & BH Mon. Tours at 2.30 & 3.30pm.

Admission: Adult £3.50, Child (under 16) £1.75, Child under 10 free. Groups 20+ £3.25pp.

ℹ️ Conferences.   ✖ Available.   ♿ Not suitable.   ☕ Tearoom.
🚶 By arrangement.   **P** Ample.   🐕 No dogs.   **A** Self-catering.

THE GARDEN HOUSE   Tel: 01822 854769

Buckland Monachorum, Yelverton, Devon PL20 7LQ

Owner: Fortescue Garden Trust   **Contact:** Mr K Wiley
An 8-acre garden of interest throughout the year including a romantic terraced, walled garden around the ruins of a 16th century vicarage.

Location: OS Ref. SX490 682. Signposted W off A386 near Yelverton, 10m N of Plymouth.

Opening Times: 1 Mar - 31 Oct: daily, 10.30am - 5pm. Last admission 4.40pm.

Admission: Adult £3.50, Child £1, OAP £3, pre-booked groups 15+ £2.75 (if deposit paid).

ℹ️ Plant sales.   ♿ Not suitable.   ☕ Available.   🐕 No dogs.

HARTLAND ABBEY 🏛

HARTLAND, BIDEFORD, DEVON EX39 6DT

Owner: Sir Hugh Stucley Bt   *Contact: The Administrator*

Tel: 01884 860225   **Fax:** 01884 861134

Founded as an Augustinian Monastery in 1157 in a beautiful valley only 1 mile's walk from a spectacular Atlantic Cove, the Abbey was given by Henry VIII in 1539 to the Sergeant of his Wine Cellar, whose descendants live here today. Extensively remodelled in the 18th century, it contains spectacular architecture and murals. Paintings, furniture, porcelain collected over many generations. Documents from 1160, early photographs, museum, dairy. Shrub and walled gardens of camellias, rhododendrons, azaleas, tender and rare plants. Peacocks, donkeys and Jacob's Sheep in the park.

Location: OS Ref. SS240 249. 15m W of Bideford, 15m N of Bude off A39 between Hartland and Hartland Quay.

Opening Times: May - Sept (including Easter Sun & Mon): Wed, Thur, Sun & BHs, plus Tue in Jul & Aug, 2 - 5.30pm.

Admission: House, Gardens & Grounds: Adults £4, Child (5 - 15) £1.75. Gardens & Grounds only: Adult £2, Child £1. Groups (20+): Adult £3.50, Child £1.50.

✖ Wedding receptions.   ♿ Partially suitable. WC.   ☕ Tearoom.
🚶 By arrangement.   **P** Ample.   🐕 In grounds, on leads.

HEMERDON HOUSE 🏛   Tel: w/days 01752 841410   w/ends 01752 337350

Sparkwell, Plympton, Plymouth, Devon PL7 5BZ   **Fax:** 01752 331477

Owner: J H G Woollcombe Esq   **Contact:** Paul Williams & Partners
Late 18th century family house, rich in local history.

Location: OS Ref. SX564 575. 3m E of Plympton off A38.

Opening Times: 1 May - 30 Sept: for only 30 days including May & Aug BHs, 2 - 5.30pm. Last admission 5pm. Please contact the Administrator for opening dates.

Admission: £2.50.

♿ Ground floor suitable.   🚶 Compulsory.   **P** Ample.

HEMYOCK CASTLE   Tel: 01823 680745

Hemyock, Cullompton, Devon EX15 3RJ

Owner: Capt Sheppard   **Contact:** Miss M Sheppard
Former medieval moated castle, displays show site's history as fortified manor house, castle and farm. Medieval, civil war and Victorian tableaux, archaeological finds, cider press and cow parlour.

Location: OS Ref. ST135 134. M5/J26, Wellington then 5m S over the Blackdown Hills.

Opening Times: BH Mons 2 - 5pm. Other times by appointment. Groups and private parties welcome.

Admission: Adult £1, Child 50p. Group rates available.

♿ Grounds suitable.   🚶 By arrangement.   **P** Ample.   🐕 In grounds, on leads.

HOUND TOR DESERTED MEDIEVAL VILLAGE ⛨   Tel: 01179 750700

Ashburton Road, Manaton, Dartmoor, Devon

Owner: English Heritage   **Contact:** Dartmoor National Park
The remains of the dwellings.

Location: OS191 Ref. SX746 788. 1 1/2 m S of Manaton off Ashburton road. 6m N of Ashburton.

Opening Times: Any reasonable time.

Admission: Free.

KILLERTON HOUSE & GARDEN

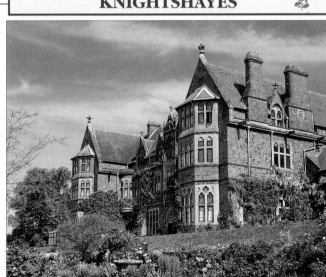

Chris Vile.

BROADCLYST, EXETER EX5 3LE

Owner: *The National Trust*   **Contact:** *Denise Melhuish*

Tel: 01392 881345

The spectacular hillside garden is beautiful throughout the year with spring flowering bulbs and shrubs, colourful herbaceous borders and fine trees. The garden is surrounded by parkland and woods offering lovely walks. The house is furnished as a family home and includes a costume collection dating from the 18th century in a series of period rooms and a Victorian laundry.

Location: OS Ref. SS977 001. Off Exeter – Cullompton Rd (B3181). M5 N'bound J29, M5 S'bound J28.

Opening Times: House: 14 Mar - 1 Nov: daily (closed Tue), 11am - 5.30pm (last adm. 5pm). Park & Garden: daily, 10.30am to dusk.

Admission: House & Garden: Adult £5, Child £2.50, Family £12.50, Group £4. Garden only: Adult £3.50, Child £1.70. Reduced Nov - Feb.

[i] Shop.   Suitable. WC.   Restaurant.   Guide dogs only in house.

KNIGHTSHAYES

BOLHAM, TIVERTON, DEVON EX16 7RQ

Owner: *The National Trust*   **Contact:** *Penny Woollams*

Tel: 01884 254665   **Fax:** 01884 243050

The striking Victorian Gothic house is a rare survival of the work of William Burges with ornate patterns in many rooms. One of the finest gardens in Devon, mainly woodland and shrubs with something of interest throughout the seasons. Drifts of spring bulbs, summer flowering shrubs, pool garden and amusing animal topiary.

Location: OS Ref. SS960 151. 2m N of Tiverton (A396) at Bolham.

Opening Times: House: 1 Apr - 1 Nov: daily except Fri (but open Good Fri), 11am - 5.30pm. Nov/Dec: Sun, 2 - 4pm, pre-booked groups only. Garden & park: 1 Apr - 1 Nov: daily, 11am - 5.30pm.

Admission: House & Garden: Adult £5.10, Child £2.50, Family £12.70. Group £4.40pp. Garden only: Adult £3.50, Child £1.70.

[i] Shop. Plant centre.   Available.   Ground floor & grounds suitable. WC.   Restaurant.   Guide dogs in park.

LYDFORD CASTLES & SAXON TOWN   **Tel:** 01392 881691

Lydford, Okehampton, Devon

Owner: English Heritage   **Contact:** The National Trust

Standing above the lovely gorge of the River Lyd, this 12th century tower was notorious as a prison. The earthworks of the original Norman fort are to the south. A Saxon town once stood nearby and its layout is still discernible.

Location: OS191 Castle Ref. SX510 848, Fort Ref. SX509 847. In Lydford off A386 8m SW of Okehampton.

Opening Times: Any reasonable time.

On leads.

MARKERS COTTAGE   **Tel:** 01392 461546

Broadclyst, Exeter, Devon EX5 3HR

Owner: The National Trust   **Contact:** The Custodian

Fascinating medieval cob house which contains a cross-passage screen decorated with a painting of St Andrew and his attributes.

Location: OS Ref. SX985 973. 1/4 E of B3181 in village of Broadclyst.

Opening Times: 29 Mar - 1 Nov: Sun, Mon and Tue, 2 - 5pm.

Admission: £1.

MARWOOD HILL   **Tel:** 01271 342528

Barnstaple, Devon EX31 4EB

Owner: Dr J A Smart   **Contact:** Dr J A Smart

20 acre garden with 3 small lakes. Extensive collection of camellias, bog garden. National collection of astilbes.

Location: OS Ref. SS545 375. 4m N of Barnstaple. 1/2 m W of B3230. Signs off A361 Barnstaple - Braunton road.

Opening Times: Dawn to dusk throughout the year.

Admission: Adult £2, Child free under 12.

[i] Garden centre.   Grounds suitable.   Tearoom.   In grounds, on leads.

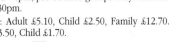

West Country England

MORWELLHAM QUAY
Tel: 01822 832766   **Fax:** 01822 833808

Morwellham, Tavistock, Devon PL19 8JL

Owner: The Morwellham & Tamar Valley Trust   **Contact:** Anne Emerson

Award winning visitor centre at historic river port. Train ride into old mine workings. Horse-drawn carriage ride, staff in costume, costumes to try on. Museums, workshops, cottages, woodland walks in beautiful Tamar Valley. Average visit length 5 - 6 hours.

Location: OS Ref. SX446 697. Off A390 about 15 mins drive from Tavistock, Devon. 5m SW of Tavistock. 3m S of A390 at Gulworthy.

Opening Times: Summer: daily, 10am - 5.30pm, last adm. 3.30pm. Winter: daily, 10am - 4.30pm, last adm. 2.30pm.

Admission: Adult £7.95, Child £5.60, Conc. £7, Family (2+2) £26. Group rate please apply for details.

ℹ️ Shop.   ♿ WC.   ☕ Café & licensed restaurant.   🐕 In grounds, on leads.

OKEHAMPTON CASTLE
Tel: 01837 52844

Okehampton, Devon EX20 1JB

Owner: English Heritage   **Contact:** The Custodian

The ruins of the largest castle in Devon stand above a river surrounded by splendid woodland. There is still plenty to see, including the Norman motte and the jagged remains of the Keep. There is a picnic area and lovely woodland walks.

Location: OS191 Ref. SX584 942. 1m SW of Okehampton town centre off A30 bypass.

Opening Times: 1 Apr - 31 Oct: daily, 10am - 6pm or dusk if earlier. Winter: Closed.

Admission: Adult £2.30, Child £1.20, Conc. £1.70. 15% discount for groups of 11+.

ℹ️ Shop. ♿ Grounds suitable. WC. ☕ Available. 🅿️ Ample. 🐕 In grounds, on leads.

OLD BAKERY
Tel: 01297 680333

Branscombe, Seaton, Devon EX12 3DB

Owner: The National Trust

A traditional stone built and partially rendered building beneath a thatch roof which was, until 1987, the last traditional bakery in use in Devon. The baking room has been preserved and houses traditional baking equipment. The remainder of the building is used as tearooms.

Location: OS Ref. SY198 887. In Branscombe ½ m S off A3052, by steep narrow lane.

Opening Times: Easter - Oct: daily and weekends in winter, 11am - 5pm.

☕ Tearoom.

OVERBECKS MUSEUM & GARDEN
Tel: 01548 842893

Sharpitor, Salcombe, Devon TQ8 8LW

Owner: The National Trust   **Contact:** The Property Manager

Spectacular views over Salcombe estuary can be enjoyed from the beautiful 2.4ha garden, with its many rare plants, shrubs and trees. The elegant Edwardian house contains collections of local photographs taken at the end of the last century, local ship building tools, model boats, toys, shells, birds, animals and other collections.

Location: OS Ref. SX728 374. 1½ m S of Salcombe, signposted from Malborough and Salcombe (single track roads).

Opening Times: Museum: 1 Apr - 31 Jul, Sun - Fri, 11am - 5.30pm; Aug: daily 11am - 5.30pm. Sept: Sun - Fri, 11am - 5.30pm Oct: Sun - Thur, 11am - 5pm. Garden: All year, daily 10am - 8pm/dusk if earlier.

Admission: Museum & Garden: £3.80, Garden only: £2.60. No reductions for groups.

ℹ️ Shop. No coaches. ☕ Available. 🐕 No dogs.

POWDERHAM CASTLE
See page 116 for full page entry.

ROSEMOOR RHS GARDEN
Tel: 01805 624067   **Fax:** 01805 624717

Great Torrington, Devon

Owner: The Royal Horticultural Society   **Contact:** The Royal Horticultural Society
40 acres of gardens.

Location: OS Ref. SS500 183. 1m S of Great Torrington on B3220.

Opening Times: Apr - Sept:10am - 6pm. Oct - Mar:10am - 5pm.

Admission: Adult £4, Child £1. Groups of 10+ £3.25pp. Companion for disabled visitor £4.

ℹ️ Shop. ♿ Suitable. ☕ Licensed restaurant. 🐕 Guide dogs only.

ROYAL CITADEL
Tel: 01752 775841

Plymouth Hoe, Plymouth, Devon

Owner: English Heritage   **Contact:** Blue Badge Guides

A large, dramatic 17th century fortress, with walls up to 70 feet high, built to defend the coastline from the Dutch and still in use today.

Location: OS201 Ref. SX480 538. At E end of Plymouth Hoe. SE of city centre.

Opening Times: By guided tour only (1½ hrs) at 2 and 3.30pm. 1 May - 30 Sept. Tickets at Plymouth Dome below Smeaton's Tower on the Hoe.

Admission: Adult £3, Child £2, OAP £2.50.

🐕 No dogs.

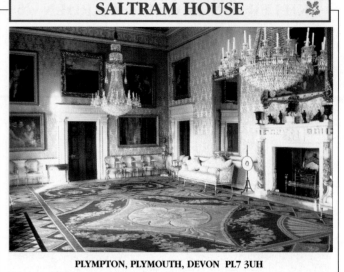

SALTRAM HOUSE

PLYMPTON, PLYMOUTH, DEVON PL7 3UH

Owner: The National Trust   *Contact:* The Property Manager

Tel: 01752 336546   **Fax:** 01752 336474

A magnificent George II mansion set in beautiful gardens and surrounded by landscaped park overlooking the Plym estuary. Visitors can see the original contents including important work by Robert Adam, Chippendale, Wedgwood and Sir Joshua Reynolds. You can explore the garden follies including Fanny's Bower and The Castle, follow the tree trail in the garden and enjoy fascinating walks beside the river, through the parkland and in the woods. Saltram starred as Norland Park in the award winning film *Sense & Sensibility.*

Location: OS Ref. SX520 557. 3½ m E of Plymouth city centre. ¾ m S of A38.

Opening Times: House: 1 Apr - 30 Sept: daily except Fri & Sat (open Good Fri). 12.30 - 5.30pm (open 11.30am on Sun & BHs). 1 Oct - 1 Nov: daily except Fri & Sat 12.30 - 4.30pm. Art Gallery & Great Kitchen open as house but from 10.30am. Garden: 2 - 23 Mar: Sat & Sun only 11am - 4pm; from 1 Apr as house but from 10.30am.

Admission: House & Garden: Adult £5.60, Child £2.70, Family £13.90. Group £4.80. Garden only: Adult £2.60, Child £1.30.

ℹ️ Shop. Conferences.   ♿ House & garden access. WC. Audio visual tape.

☕ Licensed restaurant.   🐕 In grounds, on leads. Guide dogs in house.

SAND
Tel: 01395 597230

Sidbury, Sidmouth, Devon EX10 0QN

Owner: Lt Col P Huyshe   **Contact:** Lt Col P Huyshe

Lived in house, owned by Huyshe family from 1560, rebuilt 1592 - 94 in unspoilt valley. Screens passage, heraldry, family documents. Also Sand Lodge roof structure of late 15th century hall house.

Location: OS Ref. SY146 925. ¼ m off A375 Honiton to Sidmouth.

Opening Times: Sun, Mon: Apr: 12 & 13. May: 3, 4, 24, 25. Aug: 16, 17, 30, 31. 2 - 6pm. Last tour 4.45pm.

Admission: Adult £3. Child/full time student 60p.

✖️ By arrangement. ☕ Tearoom. 🚶 Compulsory. 🅿️ Ample. 🐕 In grounds, on leads.

SHOBROOKE PARK
Tel: 01363 775153   **Fax:** 01363 775153

Crediton, Devon EX17 1DG

Owner: Dr J R Shelley   **Contact:** Dr J R Shelley

A classical English 180-acre park. The lime avenue dates from about 1800 and the cascade of four lakes was completed in the 1840s. The southern third of the Park is open to the public under the Countryside Commission Access Scheme. The 15 acre garden, created c1845 with Portland stone terraces, roses and rhododendrons is being restored.

Location: OS Ref. SS848 010. 1m E of Crediton. Access to park by kissing gate at SW end of park, just S of A3072. Garden access on A3072.

Opening Times: South Park: All daylight hours. Gardens: Sats 4 Apr, 16 May & 27 Jun, 2 - 5.30pm.

Admission: Park: No charge. Gardens: NGS £2, accompanied children under 14 free.

♿ Limited, wheelchairs in garden only.   🐕 Guide dogs only in garden.

SHUTE BARTON
Tel: 01297 34692

Shute, Axminster, Devon EX13 7PT

Owner: The National Trust

One of the most important surviving non-fortified manor houses of the Middle Ages. Commenced in 1380 and completed in the late 16th century, then partly demolished in the late 18th century, the house has battlemented turrets, late Gothic windows and a Tudor gatehouse.

Location: OS Ref. SY253 974. 3m SW of Axminster, 2m N of Colyton, 1m S of A35.

Opening Times: 1 Apr - 31 Oct: Wed & Sat, 2 - 5.30pm. Last admission 5pm.

Admission: £1.60, No group reductions.

TIVERTON CASTLE

Tel: 01884 253200/255200 **Fax:** 01884 254200

Tiverton, Devon EX16 6RP

Owner: Mr A K Gordon

Contact: Mrs A K Gordon

Architecture from medieval to modern. Civil War and Napoleonic displays.

Location: OS Ref. SS954 130. Just N of Tiverton town centre.

Opening Times: Easter - end of Jun. Sept: Sun & Thur only. Jul & Aug: Sun - Thur. BH Mon, 2.30 - 5.30pm. Open to groups (12+) by prior arrangement at any time.

Admission: Adult £3, Child (7-16) £2, Children under 7 free.

i Shop.   & Suitable. WC.   In grounds, on leads.   Civil Wedding Licence.

TORRE ABBEY

THE KINGS DRIVE, TORQUAY, DEVON TQ2 5JX

Owner: Torbay Borough Council   Contact: L Retallick

Tel: 01803 293593 **Fax:** 01803 215948 **e-mail:** michael.rhodes@torbay.gov.uk

Torre Abbey was founded as a monastery in 1196. Later adapted as a country house and in 1741-3 remodelled by the Cary family. Bought by the Council in 1930 for an art gallery. Visitors can see monastic remains, historic rooms, family chapel, mementoes of Agatha Christie, Victorian paintings including Holman Hunt & Burne-Jones & Torquay terracotta. Torre Abbey overlooks the sea and is surrounded by parkland and gardens. Teas served in Victorian Kitchen.

Location: OS Ref. SX907 638. On Torquay sea front. Between station and town centre.

Opening Times: Apr - 1 Nov: daily, 9.30am - 6pm, last adm. 5pm. Free access to members of the National Art Collections Fund.

Admission: Adult £2.75, Child £1.50, OAP/student £2.25, Family £6.50. Groups (pre-booked, min 10): Adult £2, Child £1.30.

i Shop. Conferences.   & Not suitable.   Tearoom.   By arrangement.

Schools' programme, apply for details.   Guide dogs only.

TOTNES CASTLE

Tel: 01803 864406

Castle Street, Totnes, Devon TQ9 5NU

Owner: English Heritage

Contact: The Custodian

By the North Gate of the hill town of Totnes you will find a superb motte and bailey castle, with splendid views across the roof tops and down to the River Dart. It is a symbol of lordly feudal life and a fine example of Norman fortification.

Location: OS202 Ref. SX800 605. In Totnes, on hill overlooking the town. Access in Castle St. off W end of High St.

Opening Times: 1 Apr - 31 Oct: daily 10am - 6pm or dusk if earlier. 1 Nov - 31 Mar: Wed - Sun, 10am - 4 pm. Closed: 24 - 26 Dec.

Admission: Adult £1.60, Child 80p, Conc. £1.20. 15% discount for groups of 11+.

i Shop.   & Not suitable.   Kiosk.   In grounds, on leads.

YARDE MEDIEVAL FARMHOUSE

Tel: 01548 842367

Malborough, Kingsbridge, Devon TQ7 3BY

Owner: John R Ayre Esq

Contact: John R Ayre Esq

Location: OS Ref. SX718 400. 5m S of Kingsbridge ¼ m N of A381. ½ m E of Malborough. 1½ m W of Salcombe. Coaches only by appointment.

Opening Times: Easter - 30 Sept: Wed, Fri, Sun, 2 - 5pm.

Admission: Adult £2, Child 50p, Child under 5 free. Groups by appointment only.

& Ground floor & grounds suitable.   Available.   P Ample for cars.

Guide dogs only.

Markets and fairs:

It is suggested that fairs grew out of truces between warring tribes, and that markets evolved from fairs. Whatever their origins, they are linked together. A prohibition in 1285 of the early medieval custom of holding fairs in churchyards was largely ignored. In Henry VI's reign (1422–71) it was prohibited to hold fairs on various feast days and Sundays. Any merchant who continued to sell after a fair closed was liable to a heavy fine of double the value of what he had sold.

Local landlords greedily collected charters to hold fairs and markets. In Northumberland in the fourteenth century, for example, the Percies were licensed to hold fairs in nine market towns; the Scropes had four, and the Nevilles had three. By the fifteenth century, most towns held at least a weekly market. It was the tolls on goods sold and fees for the use of stalls that made fairs so profitable, together with the fines that might accrue from the Court of Piepowder, the summary court held at fairs and markets to administer justice among the hawkers and pedlars.

Medieval fairs and markets were a vital part of the economy. Although a large household was largely self-sufficient, it could not be so in all things. Cloth, dried fruits and jewellery, for example, often readily available in London, were not so in the provinces: for their supply, and that of other unusual items, fairs and markets answered a need. Sturbridge Fair in Cambridgeshire, held in September and by tradition a Roman foundation, was the greatest of all British fairs and the prototype of Bunyan's 'Vanity Fair'. In 1720 one Sturbridge warehouse seen by the writer Daniel Defoe (1661–1731) held £20,000 worth of goods. The last Sturbridge Fair was held in the 1930s.

Bartholomew Fair, held in West Smithfield in London on St Bartholomew's Day (24 August) for two weeks (shortened to four days in 1691), was another great event, held regularly until 1854. Other notably important fairs were held at Winchester in Hampshire – the chief cloth fair in the kingdom – Boston in Lincolnshire, and St Ives in Cambridgeshire; many other, smaller fairs were held up and down the country, mainly in May and June. Widecombe Fair in Devon is perhaps the best known, from being celebrated in popular song – but the first recorded date for it is as late as 1850.

Although fairs and markets gradually lost their attraction as the efficiency of distribution and retailing increased, they still linger on locally, for household goods and for the sale of livestock. Some are now no more than amusement fairs, like the famous Nottingham Goose Fair held in the autumn, which today has nothing to do with the sale of anything other than candyfloss, and with having a good time.

Extract from; "Life in the Country House" by David N Durant (published by John Murray), PB£15.99, see page twelve at the front of the book.

ATHELHAMPTON HOUSE & GARDENS 🏛

Winner of the HHA/Christie's Garden of the Year Award 1997.

ATHELHAMPTON, DORCHESTER DT2 7LG

Owner: Patrick Cooke   *Contact:* Patrick Cooke

Tel: 01305 848363 **Fax:** 01305 848135 **www:** http://www.athelhampton.co.uk

Athelhampton is one of the finest 15th century manor houses and is surrounded by one of the great architectural gardens of England. Enjoy the Tudor Great Hall, Great Chamber, Wine Cellar and the East Wing restored after the fire in Nov 1992. Wander through 20 acres of beautiful grounds dating from 1891, including the Great Court with 12 giant yew pyramids. The walled gardens include collections of tulips, magnolias, roses, clematis and lilies in season. This glorious garden of vistas is full of surprises and gains much from the fountains and River Piddle flowing through.

Location: OS Ref. SY771 942. On A35, 5m E of Dorchester.

Opening Times: 1 Mar - 1 Nov: daily, 10.30am - 5pm (except Sat). 2 Nov - 30 Apr: Suns only.

Admission: House & Gardens: Adult £4.80, OAP £4.50, Child £1.50, Family £11. Grounds only: Adult/OAP £3, Child free.

  ℹ️ Shop.   ✖ By arrangement.   ♿ Ground floor & grounds only. WC.

  ☕ Licensed restaurant.   🅿 Ample.   👥 Education programme.

  🐕 Guide dogs only.

SPECIAL EVENTS
MAY 24 – 28: Flower Festival.

BROWNSEA ISLAND 🌿

Joe Cornish.

POOLE HARBOUR, DORSET BH15 1EE

Owner: The National Trust   *Contact:* The Property Manager

Tel: 01202 707744

A 202.42 ha island of heath and woodland, with wide views of Dorset coast, the island includes a 80.97 ha nature reserve leased to the Dorset Wildlife Trust. Boats run from Poole Quay, Swanage and Bournemouth. Visitors may land from own boat at Pottery Pier at west end of island. Accessible at all stages of the tide.

Location: OS Ref. SZ032 878. In Poole Harbour. Boats run from Poole Quay, Swanage, Bournemouth and Sandbanks. Visitors may land on the beach with a dinghy.

Opening Times: 1 Apr - 4 Oct: daily, 10am - 5pm. Jul & Aug: 10am - 6pm.

Admission: Adult £2.40, Child £1.20, Groups £2.10 (Child 95p), Family (2 +2) £6.

  ℹ️ Shop.   ♿ Limited. WC.   ☕ Café.   🐕 No dogs.

CHETTLE HOUSE

Tel: 01258 830209 **Fax:** 01258 830380

Chettle, Blandford Forum, Dorset DT11 8DB

Owner: Patrick Bourke Esq   **Contact:** Patrick Bourke Esq

A fine Queen Anne manor house designed by Thomas Archer and a fine example of English baroque architecture. The house features a basement with the typical north-south passage set just off centre with barrel-vaulted ceilings and a magnificent stone staircase. The house is set in 5 acres of peaceful gardens and there is a new rose garden.

Location: OS Ref. ST952 132. 6m NE of Blandford NW of A354.

Opening Times: 10 Apr - 4 Oct: Mon, Wed, Thur, Fri & Sun, 11am - 5pm. Closed 23 - 25 May.

Admission: Adult £2, Child free (under 16yrs).

  ℹ️ Plant centre.   ♿ Grounds suitable.   ☕ Tearoom.   🐕 No dogs.

CHRISTCHURCH CASTLE & NORMAN HOUSE ⊞   **Tel:** 01179 750700

Christchurch, Dorset

Owner: English Heritage   **Contact:** The South West Office

Early 12th century Norman keep and Constable's house, built c.1160.

Location: OS195. Ref. SZ160 927. In Christchurch, near the Priory.

Opening Times: Any reasonable time.

Admission: Contact The South West Office.

  🐕 On leads only.

CLOUDS HILL 🌿   **Tel:** 01929 405616

Wareham, Dorset BH20 7NQ

Owner: The National Trust   **Contact:** The Administrator

T E Lawrence (Lawrence of Arabia) bought this cottage in 1925 as a retreat; it contains his furniture.

Location: OS Ref. SY824 909. 9m E of Dorchester, 1½ m E of Waddock crossroads B3390.

Opening Times: 5 Apr - 1 Nov: Wed, Thur, Fri, Sun & BH Mon, 12 - 5pm (dusk if earlier).

Admission: £2.30, no reduction for children or groups.

  ♿ Braille guide.   🅿 No coaches due to restricted parking area.

COMPTON ACRES GARDENS   **Tel:** 01202 700778 **Fax:** 01202 707537

Canford Cliffs Road, Poole , Dorset BH13 7ES

Owner: Compton Acres Ltd.   **Contact:** P Willsher Esq

Nine different gardens of the world over-looking Poole Harbour and the Purbeck Hills beyond. Grounds include Italian and Japanese heather gardens, rock and water gardens and a woodland walk, plus a fabulous collection of bronze and marble statuary.

Location: OS Ref. SZ054 896. Off the B3065 on to Canford Cliffs Road.

Opening Times: 1 March - 31 Oct: daily, 10am - 6pm or dusk if earlier. Last entry 5.15pm.

Admission: Adult £4.75, Child £1, OAP/Student £3.70, Family £10. Groups: Adult £4, OAP £3.

  ℹ️ Shop. Plant centre.   ♿ Suitable. WCs.   ☕ Tearoom. Licensed restaurant.

  🅿 Ample.   🐕 Guide dogs only.

CORFE CASTLE

Joe Cornish

WAREHAM, DORSET BH20 5EZ

Owner: *The National Trust*   **Contact:** *The Property Manager*

Tel: 01929 481294

One of the most impressive medieval ruins in England, this former royal castle was besieged and slighted by parliamentary forces in 1646. Visitor centre at castle view on A351 north of castle.

Location: OS Ref. SY959 824. On A351 Wareham - Swanage Rd. NW of the village.

Opening Times: 1 Mar - 1 Nov: daily, 10am - 5.30pm (10am - 4.30pm in early Mar & late Oct). 2 Nov - 28 Feb: daily, 11am - 3.30pm.

Admission: Adult £3.80, Child £2. Groups £3.50pp (Child £1.80). Family £9.60 / £5.80.

ℹ️ Shop.   ♿ Limited. WC.   ☕ Tearoom.   🐕 On leads.

CRANBORNE MANOR GARDEN
Tel: 01725 517248   **Fax:** 01725 517862

Cranborne, Wimborne, Dorset BH21 5PP

Owner: The Viscount & Viscountess Cranborne   **Contact:** The Manor Garden Centre

The beautiful and historic gardens of yew hedges, walled, herb, mount and wild gardens originate from the 17th century – originally laid out by Mounten Jennings with John Tradescant supplying many of the original plants. Spring time is particularly good with displays of spring bulbs and crab apple orchard in the wild garden.

Location: OS Ref. SU054 133. On B3078 N of Bournemouth (18m), S of Salisbury (16m).

Opening Times: Mar - Sept: Weds, 9am - 5pm. Occasional weekends, phone for details. Entrance, parking and tearoom via the Garden Centre.

Admission: Adult £3, Child 50p, OAP £2.50.

ℹ️ Shop. Garden centre.   ♿ Partially suitable.   ☕ Tearoom.   🚶 By arrangement.
🅿️ Ample.   🐕 Strictly no dogs.

DEANS COURT 🏛️
Tel: 01202 886116

Wimborne, Dorset BH21 1EE

Owner: Sir Michael & Lady Hanham   **Contact:** Wimborne Tourist Information Centre

A partly wild garden with specimen trees, monastery fishpond, peacocks, herb garden (over 200 species), walled kitchen garden. Produce and herb plants for sale – all chemical free. The house, formerly the Deanery is open by prior written appointment. Wholefood teas and coffee on Bank Holiday mornings.

Location: OS Ref. SZ010 997. 2 mins walk S from centre of Wimborne Minster.

Opening Times: 12 Apr, 24 May, 30 Aug & 20 Sept: daily 2 - 6pm. 13 Apr, 25 May & 31 Aug 10am - 6pm. Other days may be arranged contact Tourist Information Centre.

Admission: Adult £2, Child 50p, OAP £1.50. Groups by prior arrangement 70p. During Sculpture Exhibition: Adult £3, Child (5 - 16) / Students £1.50, Child under 5 free, Groups (15+) £1.50.

ℹ️ Garden produce sales.   ☕ Available.   🐕 Guide dogs only.

EDMONDSHAM HOUSE & GARDENS
Tel: 01725 517207

Cranborne, Wimborne, Dorset BH21 5RE

Owner: Mrs Julia E Smith   **Contact:** Mrs Julia E Smith

Charming blend of Tudor and Georgian architecture with interesting contents. Organic walled garden, dower house garden, 6 acre garden with unusual trees and spring bulbs. 12th century church nearby.

Location: OS Ref. SU062 116. Off B3081 between Cranborne and Verwood, NW from Ringwood 9m, Wimborne 9m.

Opening Times: House & Gardens: All BH Mons & Weds in April & Oct 2 - 5pm. Gardens: April - Oct, Suns & Weds 2 - 5pm.

Admission: Adult £2.50, Child £1 (under 5 free). Garden only: Adult £1, Child 50p. Groups by arrangement, teas for groups.

ℹ️ Plant shop.   ♿ Suitable.   ❌ Available if booked, max 35 persons.
🚶 Compulsory.   🐄 Car park only.   🔲 Civil Wedding Licence (max 50).

FIDDLEFORD MANOR 🏛️
Tel: 01179 750700

Sturminster Newton, Dorset

Owner: English Heritage   **Contact:** The South West Regional Office

Part of a medieval manor house, with a remarkable interior. The splendid roof structures in the hall and upper living room are the best in Dorset.

Location: OS194 Ref. ST801 136. 1m E of Sturminster Newton off A357.

Opening Times: 1 Apr - 30 Sept & 1 - 31 Oct: 10am - 6pm or dusk in Oct. 1 Nov - 31 Mar, 10am - 4pm.

Admission: Contact South West Regional Office.

♿ Ground floor suitable.   🐕 No dogs.

FORDE ABBEY 🏛️

NR. CHARD, SOMERSET TA20 4LU

Owner: *Mark Roper Esq*   **Contact:** *Mark Roper Esq*

Tel: 01460 221290   **Fax:** 01460 220296

Winners of Christie's/HHA Garden of the Year Award (1992). Founded by Cistercian monks almost 900 years ago. Today it remains a genuine family home, unchanged since the middle of the 17th century. Situated in some of the most beautiful countryside in west Dorset. 30 acres of gardens with herbaceous borders, arboretum, magnificent trees and shrubs, 5 lakes, bog garden. Here you can enjoy the peace and beauty of a past age. There are no ropes or barriers in the house and no sideshows in the gardens.

Location: OS Ref. ST362 052. Just off the B3167 4m S of Chard.

Opening Times: House: 1 Apr - end Oct, Sun, Wed & BHs, 1 - 4.30pm last admission. Garden: All year: daily, 10am - 4.30pm (last admission).

Admission: House & Gardens: Adult £5, OAP £4.70, Groups £3.80, Child free. Gardens: Adult £3.75, OAP £3.50, Groups £3.30 Child free.

ℹ️ Shop. Plant centre. Conferences.   ❌ Wedding receptions.
♿ Ground floor & gardens suitable. WC. Wheelchair available, please telephone.
☕ Licensed tearoom.   🚶 By arrangement.   🐕 In grounds, on leads.

HARDY'S COTTAGE

Tel: 01305 262366

Higher Bockhampton, Dorchester, Dorset DT2 8QJ
Owner: The National Trust　　　　　**Contact:** The National Trust
A small thatched cottage where the novelist and poet Thomas Hardy was born in 1840. It was built by his great grandfather and little altered, furnished by the Trust.
Location: OS Ref. SY728 925. 3m NE of Dorchester, ¹/₂ m S of A35.
Opening Times: 5 Apr - 1 Nov: daily except Fri & Sat, 11am - 5pm or dusk if earlier. Open Good Fri.
Admission: £2.60.

Garden suitable.　　　No dogs.

HORN PARK

Tel: 01308 862212　**Fax:** 01308 863778

Beaminster, Dorset DT8 3HB
Owner: John Kirkpatrick Esq　　　　**Contact:** John Kirkpatrick Esq
Extensive garden with good views. Wildflower meadow.
Location: OS Ref. ST468 030. ¹/₂ m NW of Beaminster, just S of the tunnel on the A3066.
Opening Times: 1 Apr - 31 Oct: Sun - Thur, 2 - 6pm.
Admission: Adult £3, Child under 14 free. Groups £3pp.

ⓘ Plant sales.　　　Teas by arrangement.　　　Dogs on leads.

KINGSTON LACY

Rupert Truman

WIMBORNE MINSTER, DORSET BH21 4EA

Owner: The National Trust　　*Contact:* The Property Manager

Tel: 01202 883402　**Fax:** 01202 882402

A fine 17th century house designed for Sir Ralph Bankes by Sir Roger Pratt and altered by Sir Charles Barry in the 19th century. The house contains an outstanding collection of paintings, including works by Rubens, Titian, Van Dyck and Velásquez. Fascinating interiors include the fabulous gilded leather Spanish Room and the elegant grand Saloon, both with lavishly decorated ceilings. Fine collection of Egyptian artefacts from 3000BC. The house and garden are set in a wooded park, which is home to a herd of magnificent Red Devon cattle.
Location: OS Ref. ST978 013. On B3082 - Blandford / Wimborne road, 1¹/₂ m NW of Wimborne.
Opening Times: House: 28 Mar - 1 Nov: Sat - Wed, 12 - 5.30pm. Last admission 4.30pm. Garden & Park: 28 Mar - 1 Nov: daily, 11am - 6pm. Closed on Fri 17 & 31 Jul and 14 Aug during preparation for events. 2 Nov - 20 Dec: house closed but park, garden shop and restaurant open Fri, Sat and Sun, 11am - 4pm.
Admission: House, Garden & Park: Adult £6, Child £3. Park & Garden only: Adult £2.50, Child £1.25, Family (2+5) £15. Pre-booked groups of 15: £5pp.

ⓘ Shop.　　Garden only. Braille guide. WC.　　Restaurant.
By arrangement.　　Available.　　P Ample.　　In park only.

SPECIAL EVENTS
See Special Events section for a full listing.

KINGSTON MAURWARD GARDENS

DORCHESTER, DORSET DT2 8PY

Contact: Mike Hancock

Tel: 01305 215000　**Fax:** 01305 215001　**e-mail:** Administration@kmc.ac.uk
Classical Georgian Mansion set in 35 acres of 18th century gardens including 5 acre lake. Restored Edwardian gardens with dividing hedges, stone balustrading features. Walled demonstration garden, National collections of penstemons and salvias. Animal park, nature and tree trails. Visitors' centre.
Location: OS Ref. SY713 911. 1m E of Dorchester. Roundabout off A35 by-pass.
Opening Times: 14 Mar - 31 Oct: daily, 10am - 5.30pm.
Admission: Adult £3.75, Child £2.

ⓘ Shop. Plant centre. Conferences.　　X Wedding receptions.
Garden/restaurant. WCs.　　Restaurant.　　By arrangement.　　P Ample.
Schools' education programme.　　Guide dogs only.　　A Available.

KNOLL GARDENS & NURSERY

Tel: 01202 873931　**Fax:** 01202 810842

Stapehill Road, Hampreston, Wimborne BH21 7ND
Owner: J & J Flude & N R Lucas　　　　　**Contact:** Mr John Flude
Award winning 6 acre gardens, with 6000+ named plants from the world over.
Location: OS Ref. SU059 001. Between Wimborne & Ferndown. Exit A31 Canford Bottom roundabout, B3073 Hampreston. Signposted 1¹/₂ m.
Opening Times: Mar: Wed - Sun, 10am - 4pm. 1 Apr - 31 Oct: daily 10am - 5.30pm (Oct 4.30pm). Nov/Dec: Tue - Thur, 10am - 4pm. Closed Christmas - Feb.
Admission: Adult £3.40, Child (5 - 15) £1.70, OAP £2.90, Student £2.40. Groups: Adult £2.95, Child £1.50, OAP £2.60, Student £2.10. Family (2+2) £8.20.

ⓘ Shop.　　X Wedding receptions.　　Suitable.　　Licensed café.
Available.　　P Ample.　　Guide dogs only.

LULWORTH CASTLE

Tel: 01929 400483

East Lulworth, Wareham, Dorset
Owner: The Weld Estate　　　　　**Contact:** The Custodian
Built in the early 16th century as a romantic hunting lodge, Lulworth Castle was changed into a fashionable country house set in beautiful parkland during the 18th century. Gutted by fire in 1929 the exterior of the castle is now being restored by English Heritage.
Location: OS194 Ref. SY853 822. In East Lulworth off the B3070, 3m NE of Lulworth Cove.
Opening Times: 1 Apr - 31 Oct: daily, 10am - 6pm. 1 Nov - 31 Mar: daily 10am - 6pm or dusk. 1 Nov - 22 Dec: daily, 10am - 4pm.
Admission: Prices on application. Separate charges for grounds and castle.

Suitable.　　On leads.

West Country England

MAPPERTON 🏛

BEAMINSTER, DORSET DT8 3NR

Owner: Earl & Countess of Sandwich   *Contact: Earl & Countess of Sandwich*

Tel: 01308 862645   **Fax:** 01308 863348

Jacobean 1660s manor with Tudor features and classical north front. Italianate upper garden with orangery, topiary and formal borders descending to fish ponds and shrub gardens. All Saints Church forms south wing opening to courtyard and stables. Area of outstanding natural beauty with fine views of Dorset hills and woodlands. Featured in *Restoration*, *Emma* and *Tom Jones*.

Location: OS Ref. SY503 997. 1m S of B3163, 2m NE of B3066, 2m SE Beaminster, 5m NE Bridport.

Opening Times: Gardens: 1 Mar - 31 Oct: daily, 2 - 6pm. House: Open only to groups by appointment (times as for gardens, not Sun).

Admission: Gardens: £3, House (tour) £3. Under 18 £1.50, child under 5 free.

ℹ️ Shop. Plants for sale.   🚶 All visits of house are by guided tour.

MAX GATE 🌿   **Tel:** 01305 262538   **Fax:** 01305 250978

Alington Avenue, Dorchester, Dorset DT1 2AA

Owner: The National Trust   **Contact:** The Tenant

Poet and novelist Thomas Hardy designed and lived in the house from 1885 until his death in 1928. The house is leased to tenants and contains several pieces of Hardy's furniture.

Location: OS Ref. SY704 897. 1m E of Dorchester just N of the A352 to Wareham. From Dorchester follow A352 signs to the roundabout named Max Gate (at Jct. of A35 Dorchester bypass). Turn left and left again into cul-de-sac outside Max Gate.

Opening Times: Garden & Drawing Room: 5 Apr - 30 Sept: Mon, Wed, Sat & Sun. 2 - 5pm.

Admission: Adult £2.10, Child £1.10.

♿ Limited access to ground floor for wheelchairs.   🅿️ Limited.   🐕 No dogs.

MILTON ABBEY CHURCH   **Tel:** 01258 880489

Milton Abbas, Blandford, Dorset DT11 0BP

Owner: Diocese of Salisbury   **Contact:** Mrs D Illingworth

A church has stood here for over 1,000 years. Present Abbey dates from 14/15th century. 18th century Gothic style house built to complement Abbey and Abbots Hall. Exterior by Sir William Chambers, interior in classic style by James Wyatt. Beautiful tranquil setting in heart of Dorset 1/2 mile from 200 yr old "New" village of Milton Abbas with its identical cottages. Abbey situated in grounds of Milton Abbey School.

Location: OS Ref. ST798 022. 3 1/2 m N of A354 Puddletown to Blandford Road.

Opening Times: Abbey Church: daily. House & Grounds:(Council of Milton Abbey School) mid-Jul - end Aug: Daily 10am - 6pm. Groups by arrangement only, please.

Admission: By donation except Easter & mid-Jul - end Aug. Adult £1.75, Child free.

ℹ️ Shop.   ☕ Tearoom.   🚶 By arrangement.   🐕 In grounds, on leads.

MINTERNE GARDENS 🏛   **Tel:** 01300 341370   **Fax:** 01300 341747

Minterne Magna, Nr. Dorchester, Dorset DT2 7AU

Owner: The Lord Digby   **Contact:** The Lord Digby

Important Rhododendron Garden. The home of the Churchill and Digby families for 330 years. The valley was landscaped after the manner of 'Capability' Brown in the 18th century. Over 1 mile of wild woodland walks with rhododendrons and magnolias, towering over small lakes, cascades and streams. Brilliant autumn colouring.

Location: OS Ref. ST660 042. On A352 Dorchester/Sherborne Road, 2m N of Cerne Abbas.

Opening Times: 28 Mar - 10 Nov: daily, 10am - 7pm.

Admission: Adult £3, accompanied children free.

♿ Not suitable.   🐕 In grounds on leads.

PARNHAM HOUSE 🏛

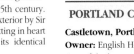

BEAMINSTER, DORSET DT8 3NA

Owner: John Makepeace   *Contact: The House Manager - Cdr Bruce Hunter-Inglis*

Tel: 01308 862204   **Fax:** 01308 863494

Inspiring 20th century craftsmanship displayed in the home of John and Jennie Makepeace, who have restored and enlivened this fascinating Tudor Manor House. Exhibitions of exciting contemporary work in glass, wood, textiles and ceramics. Romantic terraces and topiary in 14 acres of fine gardens and woodland walks.

Location: OS Ref. ST478 002. On A3066 5m N of Bridport, 1/2 m S of Beaminster.

Opening Times: 1 Apr - 29 Oct: Tue, Wed, Thur, Sun and BHs, 10am - 5pm. Tue & Thur groups only.

Admission: Adult £5, Child (5-15 yrs) £2, Child under 5 free.

ℹ️ Shop & furniture workshop. Conferences.   🚶 By arrangement (max 150).   ♿ Suitable. WCs.   ☕ Licensed Oak Café.   🐕 In grounds, on leads.

PORTLAND CASTLE ⚏   **Tel:** 01305 820539

Castletown, Portland, Weymouth, Dorset DT5 1AZ

Owner: English Heritage   **Contact:** The Custodian

One of the best preserved of Henry VIII's coastal forts, built of white Portland stone. Now standing quietly overlooking the harbour, it was originally intended to thwart attack by the Spanish and French, and changed hands several times during the Civil War.

Location: OS194 Ref. SY684 743. Overlooking Portland harbour adjacent to RN base.

Opening Times: 1 Apr - 31 Oct: daily 10am - 6pm (dusk if earlier). Winter: Closed.

Admission: Adult £2.30, Child £1.20, Conc. £1.70. 15% discount for groups of 11+.

ℹ️ Shop.   ♿ Ground floor suitable. WCs.   ☕ Kiosk.   🅿️ Limited.   🐕 No dogs.

PURSE CAUNDLE MANOR 🏛   **Tel:** 01963 250400

Purse Caundle, Sherborne, Dorset DT9 5DY

Owner: Michael de Pelet Esq   **Contact:** Michael de Pelet Esq

15th & 16th century manor house. Great Hall with minstrels gallery. Upstairs great chamber with barrel ceiling and oriel window. Family home.

Location: OS Ref. ST695 177. 4m E of Sherborne, just S of the A30.

Opening Times: Easter Mon and then 1 May - 27 Sept: Thur, Sun and BHs, 2 - 5pm.

Admission: Adult £2.50, Child free. Groups by appointment. Tea for groups.

ST CATHERINE'S CHAPEL ⊞

Tel: 01179 750700

Abbotsbury, Dorset

Owner: English Heritage   **Contact:** The South West Regional Office

A small stone chapel, set on a hilltop, with an unusual roof and small turret used as a lighthouse.

Location: OS194 Ref. SY572 848. $^1/_2$ m S of Abbotsbury by pedestrian track to the hilltop.

Opening Times: Any reasonable time.

Admission: Contact the South West Regional Office.

🐕 No dogs.

SANDFORD ORCAS MANOR HOUSE

Tel: 01963 220206

Sandford Orcas, Sherborne, Dorset DT9 4SB

Owner: Sir Mervyn Medlycott Bt   **Contact:** Sir Mervyn Medlycott Bt

Tudor Manor House with gatehouse, fine panelling, furniture, pictures. Terraced gardens with topiary and herb garden. Personal conducted tour by owner.

Location: OS Ref. ST623 210. $2^1/_2$ m N of Sherborne, Dorset 4m S of A303 at Sparkford. Entrance next to church.

Opening Times: Easter Mon, 10am - 6pm. May - Sept: Sun, 2 - 6pm, Mon, 10am - 6pm.

Admission: Adult £2.50, Child £1. Group: Adult £2, Child 80p.

♿ Not suitable.   🚶 Compulsory.   🐕 In grounds, on leads.

SHERBORNE CASTLE 🏛

SHERBORNE, DORSET DT9 3PY

Owner: *Mr Simon Wingfield Digby*   ***Contact:*** *The Administrator*

Tel: 01935 813182   **Fax:** 01935 816727

A fully furnished Historic House built by Sir Walter Raleigh in 1594 and home of the Digby family since 1617, reflecting various styles from the Elizabethan Hall to the Victorian Solarium. Splendid collections of art, furniture and porcelain. Well informed guides are happy to answer questions. Set in beautiful parkland with lawns, wooded walks and a 50 acre lake.

Location: OS Ref. ST649 164. $^3/_4$ m SE of Sherborne town centre. Follow brown signs from A30 or A352. $^1/_2$ m S of the old castle.

Opening Times: Easter Sat - Sept: Thur, Sat, Sun & BH Mon. Castle: 1.30 - 4.30pm. Grounds & Tearoom: 12.30 - 5pm. Last admission 4.30pm.

Admission: Grounds & Castle: Adult £4.80, OAP £4, Child £2.40, Family £12. Grounds: Adult / OAP £2.40, Child £1.20.

ℹ️ Shop.   ♿ Partially suitable.   ☕ Tearoom.   🚶 By arrangement.

🐕 In grounds, on leads. Guide dogs in house.

SPECIAL EVENTS

See the Special Events section for a full listing.

SHERBORNE OLD CASTLE ⊞

Tel: 01935 812730

Castleton, Sherborne, Dorset DT9 3SA

Owner: English Heritage   **Contact:** The Custodian

The ruins of this early 12th century castle are a testament to the 16 days it took Cromwell to capture it during the Civil War, after which it was abandoned. A gatehouse, some graceful arcading and decorative windows survive.

Location: OS183 Ref ST647 167. $^1/_2$ m E of Sherborne off B3145. $^1/_2$ m N of the 1594 castle.

Opening Times: 1 Apr - 31 Oct: daily, 10am - 6pm or dusk if earlier. 1 Nov - 31 Mar: Wed - Sun, 10am - 4pm. Closed 24 - 26 Dec.

Admission: Adult £1.60, Child 80p, Conc. £1.20. 15% discount for groups of 11+.

ℹ️ Shop.   ♿ Grounds suitable.   🏪 Kiosk.   🅿 Limited for cars. No coach parking.

🐕 No dogs.

SMEDMORE HOUSE 🏛

SMEDMORE, KIMMERIDGE, WAREHAM BH20 5BG

Owner: *Dr Philip Mansel*   ***Contact:*** *Mr. T Gargett*

Tel/Fax: 01929 480702

The home of the Mansel family for nearly 400 years nestles at the foot of the Purbeck hills looking across Kimmeridge Bay to Portland Bill. Originally built in 1620 by the present owner's ancestor William Clavell, the imposing Georgian front was added in 1760s. Beautiful walled garden with many special and interesting plants. Popular for wedding receptions, business and private functions.

Location: OS Ref. SY924 787. 15m SW of Poole.

Opening Times: 17 May & 13 Sept: 2 - 5pm.

Admission: Adult £3.50, Child free.

ℹ️ Groups/Corporate entertainment.   ♿ Ground floor suitable.

🚶 By arrangement only.   🐕 In grounds, on leads.   🅰 Holiday lets.

WHITE MILL 🌿

Tel: 01258 858051

Sturminster Marshall, Nr. Wimborne, Dorset

Owner: The National Trust   **Contact:** The Administrator

Rebuilt in 1776 on Domesday site, this corn mill was extensively repaired in 1994 and contains much of the original and rare timber 18th century machinery (now too fragile to be operative). Peaceful setting by River Stour. Riverside picnic area nearby.

Location: OS Ref. ST958 007. On River Stour $^1/_2$ m NE of Sturminster Marshall from the B3082 Blandford to Wareham Rd, take road to SW signposted Sturminster Marshall. Mill is 1m on right. Car park nearby.

Opening Times: 28 Mar - 1 Nov: Weekends & BHs 12 - 5pm.

Admission: Adult £2, Child £1.

♿ Ground floor suitable. Braille guide.   🚶 Compulsory.   🐕 No dogs.

West Country
England

WOLFETON HOUSE

NEAR DORCHESTER, DORSET DT2 9QN

Owner: *Capt N.T.L.L. Thimbleby*   **Contact:** *The Steward*

Tel: 01305 263500 or 268748   **Fax:** 01305 265090

A fine mediaeval and Elizabethan Manor House lying in the water-meadows near the confluence of the rivers Cerne and Frome. It was much embellished around 1580 and has splendid plaster ceilings, fireplaces and panelling of that date. To be seen are the Great Hall, Stairs and Chamber, Parlour, Dining Room, Chapel and Cyder House. The mediaeval Gatehouse has two unmatched and older towers. There are good pictures and furniture.

Location: OS Ref. SY678 921. 1¹/₂ m from Dorchester on the A37 towards Yeovil. Indicated by Historic House signs.

Opening Times: May - Sept: Sun, Tue & Thur & BHs, 2 - 6pm. Groups by appointment at other times throughout the year.

Admission: Adult £3.50, Child £1.50.

✖ By arrangement.	♿ Ground floor suitable.	☕ By arrangement.
🚶 By arrangement.	🅿 Ample.	🐕 No dogs.

Orangeries:

From the sixteenth century, attempts have been made to grow citrus fruit in England. William Cecil, Lord Burghley, ordered a lemon tree from Paris in 1562 – he already had an orange tree. At first, temporary structures were erected over the trees to protect them in winter (described by John Evelyn as 'a tabernacle of boards warmed by means of stoves'), and these structures were known as orangeries. The trees usually died. In the seventeenth century, more permanent orangeries were built. In 1611/12 Saloman de Caus laid out a garden at Somerset House in The Strand, London for James I's queen, Anne of Denmark, which included 'a house for orange trees', and in the 1640s André Mollet's layout for Charles I's queen, Henrietta Maria, at Wimbledon included a large 'Orange House' with south-facing windows where 60 trees in tubs could be stored during the winter. One survives at Chatsworth dating from the 1690s, but not in its original position; it has also, at some stage, been fitted with a glass roof. It was some time before the importance of light was generally realised but once it had been grasped and the means for providing it were to hand, the building of 'orangeries' proliferated, and they can be seen all over the country, attached to or in the grounds of large country homes – today, often used as gift shops. The fashion for having orange trees in tubs passed by the middle of the eighteenth century, and the buildings called orangeries were then effectively used as winter gardens, conservatories in the original sense of the word, or greenhouses.

Extract from; "Life in the Country House" by David N Durant (published by John Murray), PB£15.99, see page twelve at the front of the book.

Athelhampton House and Gardens, Dorset.

Deans Court, Dorset.

NO. 1 ROYAL CRESCENT
Bath

NUMBER 1 was the first house to be built in the Royal Crescent, John Wood the Younger's fine example of Palladian architecture. The Crescent was begun in 1767 and completed by 1774.

The House was given to the Bath Preservation Trust in 1968 and both the exterior and interior have been accurately restored. Visitors can see a grand town-house of the late 18th century with authentic furniture, paintings and carpets.

On the ground floor are the Study and Dining Room and on the first floor a Lady's Bedroom and Drawing Room. A series of maps of Bath are on the second floor landing. In the Basement is a Kitchen and a Museum Shop.

❖

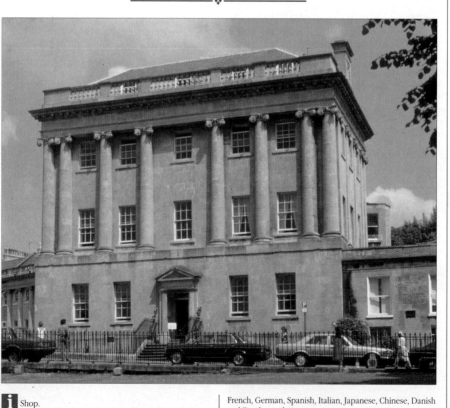

CONTACT

Mrs Hilary Bryan
Curator/Administrator
1 Royal Crescent
Bath
BA1 2LR

Tel: (01225) 428126

Fax: (01225) 481850

LOCATION

OS Ref. ST746 653

M4/J18,
then the A46 to Bath
2¹/₂ hrs from London
¹/₄ m NW of city centre.

Rail: Bath Spa
Railway Station
(1hr, 20 mins
from London).

Taxi: Streamline.

OPENING TIMES

SUMMER

10 February - 1 November
Daily except Mon
10.30am - 5pm
Closed Good Fri.
Open BHs and
Bath Festival Mon.

WINTER

3 - 29 November
Daily except Mon
10.30am - 4pm.

Last admission 30 mins
before closing.

Special tours by
arrangement with
the administrator.

ADMISSION

ALL YEAR

Adult	£3.80
Child*	£3.00
Student	£3.00
OAP	£3.00
Family	£8.00

Groups
Adult	£2.50
School*	£2.50
Student	£2.50

* Aged 5 - 16yrs.

i Shop.

Not suitable.

No restaurant or tearoom, but many facilities in Bath.

Guides in every room. Tours in French and Italian on request. Tour time 45 mins. Guide books available in French, German, Spanish, Italian, Japanese, Chinese, Danish and Dutch translations on request.

P Be aware of restrictions in The Royal Crescent and parking regulations in the centre of Bath.

The cost per child is £2. Guides can be provided.

West Country England

National Trust Photographic Library.

Andreas von Einsiedel

MUSEUM OF COSTUME & ASSEMBLY ROOMS
Bath

The Assembly Rooms in Bath are open to the public daily (no charge) and are also popular for dinners, dances, concerts and conferences.

Originally known as the Upper Rooms, they were designed by John Wood the Younger and opened in 1771. The magnificent interior consists of a splendid Ball Room, Tea Room and Card Room, connected by two fine octagonal rooms. This plan was perfect for 'assemblies', evening entertainments popular in the 18th century, which included dancing, music, card-playing and tea drinking. They are now owned by The National Trust and managed by Bath & North East Somerset Council, which runs a full conference service.

The building also houses one of the largest and most comprehensive collections of fashionable dress in the country, the Museum of Costume. Its extensive displays cover the history of fashion from the late 16th century. Hand-held audioguides allow visitors to learn about the fashions on display while keeping lighting to levels suitable for fragile garments. The 'Dress of the Year' collection traces significant moments in fashion history from 1963 to the present day. For the serious student of fashion, the reference library and study facilities of the nearby Fashion Research Centre are available by appointment.

The museum shop sells publications and gifts associated with the history of costume and is open daily to all visitors.

CONTACT

Mrs Ruth Warren
Sales Officer
Stall Street
Bath
BA1 1LZ

Tel: (01225) 477782

Fax: (01225) 477476

www: http//museumof
costume.co.uk

LOCATION

OS Ref. ST750 648

Near centre of Bath, 10m
from M4/J18.

Rail: Great Western from
London Paddington
(regular service).

Air: Bristol airport 20m.

National Trust Photographic Library.

CONFERENCE/FUNCTION		
ROOM	SIZE	MAX CAPACITY
Ballroom	104' x 40'	529
Octagon	47' x 47'	200
Tea Room	58' x 41'	250
Card Room	50' x 16'	70

OPENING TIMES

ALL YEAR
10am - 5pm

Closed 25 & 26 December

Last admission 30 mins
before closing.

ADMISSION

Assembly Rooms:
.................Free of charge

Museum of Costume:
Adult £3.80
Child* £2.70
OAP........................£3.50
Groups (min 20)
Adult £3.50
Child (summer) £1.90
Child (winter) £1.60

* Age 6 - 18.
Child under 6yrs free

- Shop. Conference facilities, corporate hospitality.
- Function facilities.
- Suitable. WC.
- Garden café in August.
- Hourly. Individual guided tours by arrangement.
- Nearby car park.
- Educational programme, teachers' pack.
- Guide dogs only.
- Civil Wedding Licence.

West Country England

THE ROMAN BATHS & PUMP ROOM
Bath

The first stop for any visitor to Bath is the Roman Baths Museum surrounding the hot springs where the city began and which are still its heart. Here you'll see one of the country's finest ancient monuments – the great Roman temple and bathing complex built almost 2000 years ago. Discover the everyday life of the Roman spa and see ancient treasures from the Temple of Sulis Minerva and many other objects recovered from the Sacred Spring where they were thrown as offerings to the goddess.

The Grand Pump Room, overlooking the Spring, is the social heart of Bath. The elegant interior of 1795 is something every visitor to Bath should see. The present Pump Room replaced an original Pump House dating from 1706. Today's visitors can enjoy a glass of spa water drawn from the fountain, perhaps as an appetiser to a traditional Pump Room tea, morning coffee or lunch. Musical accompaniment is provided by the Pump Room Trio – the longest established resident ensemble in Europe.

In the evening, the Pump Room is available for banquets, dances and concerts. Nothing could be more magical than a meal on the terrace which overlooks the Great Bath, or a pre-dinner drinks reception by torchlight around the Great Bath itself.

❖

CONTACT

For room hire:
Mrs Ruth Warren
Sales Officer
Stall Street
Bath
BA1 1LZ

Museum Enquiries:
01225 477785

Tel: (01225) 477782

Fax: (01225) 477476

e-mail:
ruth_warren@bathnes.gov.uk

www:
romanbaths.co.uk

LOCATION

OS Ref. ST750 648

Centre of Bath, 15m from M4/J18

Rail: Great Western from London Paddington, hourly service, 1 hr 17 mins duration. Good connection to other UK cities.

CONFERENCE/FUNCTION		
ROOM	SIZE	MAX CAPACITY
Great Roman Bath		400 summer 200 winter
Pump Rm.	65' x 43'	180
Terrace overlooking Great Bath	83' x 12'	70
Concert Rm	67' x 36'	110
Smoking Rm & Drawing Rm	30' x 16'	40

ℹ️ Shop. Award winning guide book in English, French and German. The Historic Buildings of Bath include the Assembly Rooms, Guildhall and Victoria Art Gallery, all available for private hire by contacting the Pump Room.

✖️ Comprehensive service for private and corporate entertainment. Telephone for details.

♿ Free access to terrace. Restricted access to the Museum, special visits for disabled groups by appointment. People with special needs welcome, teaching sessions available.

☕ Pump Room coffees, lunches and teas, no reservation needed. Music by Pump Room Trio or pianist.

🚶 Hourly visits in English in addition to personal audio tours in six languages. Private tours are available to hirers of the historic rooms.

👪 Teaching sessions available. Pre-booking necessary.

🔔 Civil Wedding Licence.

OPENING TIMES

SUMMER
April - September
9am - 6pm.

August
9am - 6pm & 8pm - 10pm.

WINTER
October - March
9.30am - 5pm
Sun: 10am - 5pm.

Last admission ¹/₂ hr before closing.

Museum Enquiries:
01225 477785

ADMISSION

Adult £6.30
Child* £3.80
Family (2+4) £16.50
OAP........................£5.65

Groups (20+)
    Adult £5.00
    Child* (summer)....£2.75
    Child* (winter).......£2.20

Combined ticket with Museum of Costume, Bath

Adult £8.40
Child* £5.00
OAP........................£7.50
Family (2 + 4).........£22.00

Groups (20+)
    Adult £6.40
    Child* (summer)....£3.80
    Child* (winter).......£3.00

* 6 - 18 yrs.

NO. 1 ROYAL CRESCENT

See page 130 for full page entry.

BARRINGTON COURT

Rick Godley

BARRINGTON, ILMINSTER, SOMERSET TA19 0NQ

Owner: *The National Trust*   **Contact:** *Visitor Reception Manager*

Tel: 01460 241938

A beautiful garden influenced by Gertrude Jekyll and laid out in a series of rooms, including the white garden, the rose and iris garden and the lily garden. The working kitchen garden has apple, pear and plum trees trained along high stone walls. The Tudor Manor house was restored in the 1920s by the Lyle family. It is let to Stuart Interiors and is also open to NT visitors.

Location: OS Ref. ST395 181. In Barrington village, 5m NE of Ilminster, on B3168.

Opening Times: Garden & Court House: 1 Apr - 31 Oct: daily except Fri, 11am - 5.30pm. Last admission 5pm. Coach parties by appointment tel: 01460 241938.

Admission: Adult £4.20, Child £2.10. Groups: Adult £3.70, Child £1.90.

ⓘ Shop.   ♿ Grounds suitable. WC.   ☕ Licensed.

THE BISHOP'S PALACE 🏛

Tel: 01749 678691   **Fax:** 01749 678691

Wells, Somerset BA5 2PD

Owner: Church Commissioners   **Contact:** Mrs K J Scarisbrick

Fortified and moated medieval palace which is today the private residence of the Bishop of Bath and Wells. Extensive grounds and arboretum. Available for functions.

Location: OS Ref. ST552 457. 20m S of Bristol and Bath on A39.

Opening Times: Easter Sat - 31 Oct: Tue - Fri & BHs and every day in Aug, 10.30am - 6pm. Sun: 2 - 6pm.

Admission: Adult £3, Child (12 - 18) £1, OAP £2, Conc. £1.50. Groups (min 10) £2. Guided tour £30 plus £2 per person.

ⓘ Corporate hospitality.   ✗ Wedding receptions.   ♿ Partially suitable.

☕ Tearoom & restaurant.   🚶 By arrangement.   🐕 In grounds on leads.

THE BUILDING OF BATH MUSEUM

Tel: 01225 333895   **Tel:** 01225 445473

The Countess of Huntingdon's Chapel, The Vineyards, The Paragon, Bath BA1 5NA

Owner: Bath Preservation Trust   **Contact:** The Administrator

The Building of Bath Museum tells the story of the creation of Georgian Bath. The exhibition depicts resort life in the time of 'Beau' Nash and explains how the splendid houses were built from the laying of the foundation stone to the last coat of paint. Exhibits include a spectacular push-button illuminated model of the entire city.

Location: OS Ref. ST751 655. 5 mins walk from city centre. Bath M4/J18.

Opening Times: 15 Feb - 30 Nov: Tue - Sun, including BHs, 10.30am - 5pm.

Admission: Adult £3, Child £1.50, Conc. £2 Groups: Adult £2. Child £1, Conc. £1.50.

♿ Suitable.   🚶 Available.   🐕 Guide dogs only.

CLAPTON COURT GARDENS

Tel/Fax: 01460 73220

Clapton, Nr Crewkerne, Somerset TA18 8PT

Owner: Mr P Giffin   **Contact:** Michael Cox

Over 10 acres of tranquil formal and informal gardens.

Location: OS Ref. SY418 068. 3m S of Crewkerne on B3165 to Lyme Regis road.

Opening Times: Apr - Sept: Tue, Wed & Thur, 2 - 5pm.

Admission: Adult £3, Child free. Groups by arrangement.

CLAVERTON MANOR

THE AMERICAN MUSEUM, BATH, SOMERSET BA2 7BD

Owner: *The Trustees of the American Museum in Britain*   **Contact:** *Miss S Carter*

Tel: 01225 460503   **Fax:** 01225 480726

The American Museum is housed in a Georgian mansion set in extensive grounds which include a replica of George Washington's garden and arboretum of North American trees and shrubs. The museum shows, in a series of period rooms, life from early New England Colonies to New Orleans on the eve of the Civil War. 1998 Special Exhibition: Shaker - The Art of Craftmanship.

Location: OS Ref. ST784 640 2m SE of Bath. Well-signed from city centre.

Opening Times: 21 Mar - 1 Nov: Tue - Sun & BH Mon. Grounds: 1 - 6pm. Museum: 2 - 5pm (except Mons). Christmas week openings, Sat & Sun 21/22 & 28/29 Nov. 5/6 & 12/13 Dec.

Admission: Adult £5, Child £3, OAP/Student £4.50. Groups of 20+: Adult £4, Child £2.50, OAP/Student £3.50.

ⓘ Shop.   ♿ Ground floor suitable. WC.   ☕ Tearoom.   🐕 In grounds, on leads.

CLEEVE ABBEY ⌗

Tel: 01984 640377

Washford, Nr. Watchet, Somerset TA23 0PS

Owner: English Heritage   **Contact:** The Custodian

There are few monastic sites where you will see such a complete set of cloister buildings, including the refectory with its magnificent timber roof. Built in the 13th century, this Cistercian abbey was saved from destruction at the Dissolution by being turned into a house and then a farm.

Location: OS181 Ref. ST047 407. In Washford, $^{1}/_{4}$ m S of A39.

Opening Times: 1 Apr - 31 Oct: daily 10am - 6pm or dusk if earlier. 1 Nov - 31 Mar: daily 10am - 4pm (closed lunch 1 - 2pm). Closed 24 - 26 December.

Admission: Adult £2.50, Child £1.30, Conc. £1.90. 15% discount for groups of 11+.

ⓘ Shop.   ♿ Ground floor & grounds suitable.   ☕ Kiosk.   Ⓟ Ample.   🐕 In grounds, on leads.

CLEVEDON COURT 🌿

Tel: 01275 872257

Tickenham Road, Clevedon, North Somerset BS21 6QU

Owner: The National Trust   **Contact:** The Administrator

Home of the Elton family, this 14th century manor house, once partly fortified, has a 12th century tower and 13th century hall. Collection of Nailsea glass and Eltonware. Beautiful terraced garden.

Location: OS Ref. ST423 716. $1^{1}/_{2}$ m E of Clevedon, on B3130, signposted from M5/J20.

Opening Times: 1 Apr - 30 Sept: Wed, Thur, Sun & BH Mon, 2 - 5pm. Last adm. 4.30pm.

Admission: Adult £4, Child £2.

♿ Ground floor suitable.   ☕ Tearoom.   Ⓟ Limited.   🐕 No dogs.

COLERIDGE COTTAGE 🌿

Tel: 01278 732662

35 Lime Street, Nether Stowey, Bridgwater, Somerset TA5 1NQ

Owner: The National Trust   **Contact:** The Custodian

Coleridge's home for three years from 1797. It was here that he wrote the *Rhyme of the Ancient Mariner*, part of *Christabel* and *Frost at Midnight*.

Location: OS Ref. ST191 399. At W end of Nether Stowey, on S side of A39, 8m W of Bridgwater.

Opening Times: Parlour & Reading room: 1 Apr - 1 Oct: Tue - Thur & Sun, 2 - 5pm. In winter by written application.

Admission: Adult £1.70, Child 80p, no reduction for groups, which must book.

🐕 No dogs.

COMBE SYDENHAM COUNTRY PARK   Tel: 01984 656284

Monksilver, Taunton, Somerset TA4 4JG
Owner: Theed Estates   **Contact:** Mr A Hudson
Built in 1580 on the site of a monastic settlement. Deer Park and woodland walks.
Location: OS Ref. ST075 366. Monksilver
Opening Times: Country Park: 1 Mar - end Sept: Sun - Fri, 9am - 5pm. Other attractions: By guided tour: May BH - end Sept: Mon, Thur & Fri, 2pm. Evening tours by arrangement.
Admission: Car park £2 per vehicle, refunded when guided tour taken. Adults £4, Child £2.

CROWE HALL   Tel: 01225 310322

Widcombe Hill, Bath, Somerset BA2 6AR
Owner: John Barratt Esq   **Contact:** John Barratt Esq
10 acres of romantic hillside gardens. Victorian grotto, classical Bath villa with good 18th century furniture and paintings.
Location: OS Ref. ST360 640. In Bath, ½ m SE of city centre.
Opening Times: Gardens only open 22 Mar, 19 Apr, 10 & 24 May, 14 Jun, 12 Jul: 2 - 6pm. House and Gardens by appointment.
Admission: House & Gardens: Adult £4. Gardens only: Adult £2, Child £1.

☕ Teas available.   🐕 Dogs are welcome.

DODINGTON HALL   Tel: 01278 741400

Nr Nether Stowey, Bridgwater, Somerset TA5 1PU
Owner: Lady Gass   **Contact:** Mr & Mrs P Quinn
Small Tudor manor house on the slopes of the Quantock Hills. Semi-formal garden with roses and clematis.
Location: OS Ref. ST173 406. ½ m from A39, 11m from Bridgwater, 7m from Williton.
Opening Times: 31 May - 1 Jun, 7 - 8, 14 - 15, 21 - 22 & 28 - 29 Jun (Sat & Sun).
Admission: Donations to Amnesty International.

♿ Unsuitable.   🅿 15 cars.   🐕 No dogs.

DUNSTER CASTLE   Tel: 01643 821314   Fax: 01643 823000

Dunster, Nr Minehead, Somerset TA24 6SL
Owner: The National Trust   **Contact:** The Property Manager
From Norman motte-and-bailey to Jacobean mansion and Victorian eccentricity there is something for everyone. 600 years of Luttrell family residence has groomed and moulded the property from coastal fortress to a secluded country seat. The house and medieval ruins are magically framed with sub-tropical plants including the famous Dunster Lemon.
Location: OS Ref. SS992 436. In Dunster, 3m SE of Minehead.
Opening Times: Castle: 30 Mar - 30 Sept: daily except Thur & Fri, 11am - 5pm. 3 Oct - 1 Nov: daily except Thur & Fri, 11am - 4pm. Garden & Park: Jan - Mar, Oct - Dec: daily, 11am - 4pm (closed 25 Dec). Apr - Sept: 10am - 5pm (open Good Fri). Last admission 30 mins before closing.
Admission: Adult £5.20, Child £2.70. Pre-arranged Groups: £4.60.

ℹ Shop.   ♿ Suitable.   👪 Educational programme.   🐕 Guide dogs only.

DUNSTER WORKING WATERMILL   Tel: 01643 821759

Mill Lane, Dunster, Minehead, Somerset TA24 6SW
Owner: The National Trust   **Contact:** The Administrator
Built on the site of a mill mentioned in the Domesday Survey of 1086, the present mill dates from the 18th century and was restored to working order in 1979.
Location: OS Ref. SS991 434. On River Avill, beneath Castle Tor, approach via Mill Lane or Castle gardens on foot.
Opening Times: 1 Apr - end Jun: daily, except Sat (open Easter) 10.30am - 5pm. Jul & Aug: daily 10.30am - 5pm. Sept & Oct: daily, except Sat 10.30am - 5pm.
Admission: £1.80. Family tickets available. Group rates by prior arrangement.

ℹ Shop.   ♿ Ground floor suitable.   ☕ Tearoom.   🅿 Ample.

Dunster Castle, Somerset.

EAST LAMBROOK MANOR GARDEN   Tel: 01460 240328   Fax: 01460 242344

South Petherton, Somerset TA13 5HL
Owner: Mr & Mrs A Norton   **Contact:** The Secretary
The garden at East Lambrook Manor is one of the best loved in Britain. It was the home of the late Margery Fish who through her eight books and many articles and lectures popularised the 'Cottage' style of gardening. The garden remains of continuing interest and is the subject of very many articles, books, television and radio programmes, films and lectures. The garden is listed Grade I and is maintained as a living memorial to its creator. Its abundant planting of rare and ordinary plants gives a feeling of timeless tranquility. The old house dating from 1470 and the 17th century malthouse, in the centre of the garden, are reminders of a bygone time. The house is no longer open to the public but the malthouse has been developed to offer the visitor shelter from any inclement weather and the modern facilities that are expected; such as toilets, giftshop and information about the garden and its plants. There is also a continually changing exhibition of local professional and amateur artists in the gallery. During pre-booked refreshments visitors are given a short welcome and introductory talk about the garden.
Location: OS177 Ref. ST431 189. 2m N of S Petherton off A303 (signed).
Opening Times: Gardens only: 1 Mar - 31 Oct: Mon - Sat, 10am - 5pm. 1 Nov - 30 Apr: Mon - Fri, 11am - 3pm. Closed Christmas - New Year.
Admission: Adult £2.50, Child/Student 50p, Conc. £2, Groups by prior arrangement £2pp.

ℹ Shop. Plant nursery. Art gallery. NCCPG National Geranium collection.

♿ Not suitable.   ☕ Tearoom.   🚶 By arrangement.   🅿 Ample.   🐕 No dogs.

ENGLISHCOMBE TITHE BARN   Tel: 01225 425073   Fax: 01225 425073

Rectory Farmhouse, Englishcombe, Bath BA2 9DU
Owner: Mrs Jennie Walker   **Contact:** Mrs Jennie Walker
An early 14th century cruck-framed Tithe Barn built by Bath Abbey. Mason marks, geometric patterns and animals are carved into the Ashlar walls. After a freak storm in 1990, the Grade II* building was restored under the auspices of English Heritage, and is now a beautiful and intimate venue.
Location: OS172 Ref. ST716 628. Adjacent to Englishcombe Village Church. 1m SW of Bath.
Opening Times: Easter - Sept: Sun & BHs, 3 - 5.30pm. Other days and times by arrangement.
Admission: Free.

ℹ No inside photography.   ✕ Wedding receptions.   ♿ Suitable. WC.
🚶 By arrangement.   👪 Welcome.   🅿 Ample.   🐕 Guide dogs.
🅰 2 single & 2 double.

SPECIAL EVENTS
MAY 30: Eden – Stell Guitar Duo.

FARLEIGH HUNGERFORD CASTLE   Tel: 01225 754026

Farleigh Hungerford, Bath, Somerset BA3 6RS
Owner: English Heritage   **Contact:** The Custodian
Extensive ruins of 14th century castle with a splendid chapel containing wall paintings, stained glass and the fine tomb of Sir Thomas Hungerford, builder of the castle.
Location: OS173 Ref. ST801 577. In Farleigh Hungerford 3½ m W of Trowbridge on A366.
Opening Times: 22 Mar - 31 Oct: daily 10am - 6pm or dusk of earlier. 1 Nov - 31 Mar: Wed - Sun, 10am - 4pm (closed for lunch 1 - 2 pm). Closed 24 - 26 Dec.
Admission: Adult £2.10, Child £1.10, Conc. £1.60. 15% discount for groups of 11+.

♿ Grounds suitable.   ☕ Kiosk.   🅿 Ample.   🐕 Guide dogs only.

GANTS MILL   Tel: 01749 812393

Bruton, Somerset BA10 0DB
Owner: Brian and Alison Shingler   **Contact:** Brian and Alison Shingler
Gants Mill is a 4-storey working water mill attractively set in the valley of the River Brue, close to the historic town of Bruton. John le Gaunt built a fulling mill here around 1290, and later it was a silk mill and and a grist mill. The present building built by Lord Berkeley around 1740 has been fully restored to make it accessible to the public. There are working demonstrations of corn grinding and historical and interpretative displays. Picnic area.
Location: OS Ref. ST674 342. Off A359 ½ m SW of Bruton.
Opening Times: Easter - end Sept: Thur & BH Mon, 2 - 5pm.
Admission: Adult £2.50, Child £1. Groups by arrangement.

♿ Grounds suitable.   🚶 Compulsory.   🅿 Ample.   🐕 In grounds, on leads.

GATCOMBE COURT   Tel: 01275 393141   Fax: 01275 394274

Flax Bourton, Bristol BS19 1PX
Owner: Mr & Mrs Charles Clarke   **Contact:** Mr Charles Clarke
A Somerset manor house, dating from early 13th century, which has evolved over the centuries since. It is on the site of a large Roman village, traces of which are apparent.
Location: OS Ref. ST525 698. 5m W of Bristol, N of the A370, between the villages of Long Ashton and Flax Bourton.
Opening Times: By written appointment only.

♿ Not suitable.   🚶 By arrangement.   🅿 Ample.   🐕 No dogs.

GAULDEN MANOR

Tel: 01984 667213

Tolland, Lydeard St. Lawrence, Nr. Taunton, Somerset TA4 3PN

Owner: James Le Gendre Starkie   **Contact:** James Le Gendre Starkie

Small historic manor of great charm. A real lived-in family home, guided tours by owner. Past seat of the Turberville family, immortalised by Thomas Hardy. Magnificent early plasterwork, fine furniture, many examples of embroidery by owner's wife. Interesting gardens include herb garden, old fashioned roses, bog garden and secret garden beyond monks fish pond.

Location: OS Ref. ST111 314. 9m NW of Taunton off A358 and B3224.

Opening Times: 24 May - 30 Aug: Sun & Thur and all summer BHs, 2 - 5pm. Groups on other days by appointment.

Admission: House & Garden: Adult £3.80, Child £1.80. Garden only: £1.80.

| ℹ️ Shop. | ♿ Ground floor & grounds suitable. | ☕ Suns & BHs only. |
| 🚶 Compulsory. | 🅿️ Ample. | 🐕 No dogs. |

GLASTONBURY TRIBUNAL ⚏

Tel: 01458 832954

Glastonbury High Street, Glastonbury, Somerset

Owner: English Heritage   **Contact:** The Manager

A well preserved medieval town house, reputedly once used as the courthouse of Glastonbury Abbey.

Location: OS182 Ref. ST499 390. In Glastonbury High Street.

Opening Times: Easter - 30 Sept: Sun - Thur 10am - 5pm (Fri & Sat to 5.30pm). 1 Oct - Easter: Sun - Thur, 10am - 4pm (Fri & Sat, 4.30pm).

Admission: Telephone for details.

| ℹ️ Shop. | ♿ Ground floor suitable. | 🅿️ No parking. | 🐕 No dogs. |

HATCH COURT 🏛️

HATCH BEAUCHAMP, TAUNTON, SOMERSET TA3 6AA

Owner: Dr & Mrs Robin Odgers   *Contact:* Dr & Mrs Robin Odgers

Tel: 01823 480120 **Fax:** 01823 480058

An attractive and unusual Palladian Bath stone mansion surrounded by beautiful parkland with a herd of fallow deer. Still very much a family home, it has a good collection of pictures and furniture, a china room and military museum. The extensively restored gardens feature a spectacular working walled kitchen garden.

Location: OS193 Ref. ST306 207. Off A358 5m SE of Taunton. M5/J25.

Opening Times: House: 11 Jun - 10 Sept: Thur, 2.30 - 5.30pm. Garden: 13 Apr - 30 Sept: daily, 10am - 5.30pm. Groups throughout year by appointment.

Admission: House & Garden: Adult £3.50, Child £1.50, Group 25+ £2.75pp. Garden only: Adult £2.50, Child £1, Group 25+ £2pp.

| ℹ️ Plant sales. Conferences. | ✖️ Available. | ♿ Grounds suitable. |
| ☕ Homemade teas. | 🅿️ Ample free parking. | 🐕 No dogs. |

SPECIAL EVENTS:
APR 25: NCCPG Rare Plant Sale.

HESTERCOMBE HOUSE GARDENS

Tel: 01823 413923 **Fax:** 01823 413747

Hestercombe Gardens, Cheddon Fitzpaine, Taunton, Somerset TA2 8LG

Owner: Somerset County Council & Hestercombe Gardens Project   **Contact:** Mr P White

Hestercombe's 50 acres of gardens and parklands include the famous Lutyens Jekyll garden and the magnificent landscape garden with its temples, waterfalls and delightful woodland walks.

Location: OS Ref. ST241 287. 4m N from Taunton, 1m NW of Cheddon Fitzpaine.

Opening Times: All year: daily, except Christmas, Boxing Day & New Year's Day, 10am - 5pm.

Admission: Adult £3.25. Child (5-15yrs) £1. Coach parties by arrangement.

| ℹ️ Shop. Plant centre. | ☕ Tearoom. | 🅿️ Ample. | 🐕 Guide dogs only. |

KENTSFORD

Washford, Watchet, Somerset TA23 0JD

Owner: Mrs Wyndham   **Contact:** Mr R Dibble

Location: OS Ref. ST058 426.

Opening Times: House by written appointment with Mr R Dibble. Gardens: Tue & BHs. 10 Mar - 31 Aug.

Admission: Donations towards renovation of fabric.

| ♿ Gardens only suitable. | 🐕 Guide dogs only. |

KING JOHN'S HUNTING LODGE 🌿

Tel: 01934 732012

The Square, Axbridge, Somerset BS26 2AP

Owner: The National Trust   **Contact:** The Administrator

An early Tudor merchant's house, extensively restored in 1971.

Location: OS Ref. ST431 545. In the Square, on corner of High Street, off A371.

Opening Times: Easter - end Sept: daily 2 - 5pm.

Admission: Free. School parties by arrangement.

| ♿ Ground floor suitable. | 🅿️ Ample. |

LEIGH COURT

Tel: 01275 373393 **Fax:** 01275 374681

Abbots Leigh, Bristol BS8 3RA

Owner: J T Group   **Contact:** Mrs Sally Barker

The style of the buildings is Greek Revival and they stand in 25 acres of parkland.

Location: OS Ref. ST543 747. 2m from M5/J19. NE of A369. 3m W of Bristol.

Opening Times: All year.

Admission: As Leigh Court is used as a Conference Centre prior booking to view is strongly advised.

| ✖️ Available. | ♿ Suitable. WC. | 🍽️ Licensed restaurant. | 🅿️ Ample. |
| 🐕 Guide dogs. | 💒 Civil Wedding Licence. | | |

LOWER SEVERALLS

Tel: 01460 73234

Owner: Mr & Mrs Howard Pring   **Contact:** Mary Cooper

2 acre garden, developed over the last 25 years including herb gardens, mixed borders and island beds with innovative features, i.e. a giant living willow basket and a wadi.

Location: OS Ref. ST457 112. 1½ m NE of Crewkerne, between A30 & A356.

Opening Times: 1 Mar - 20 Oct: daily (except Thursdays) 10am - 5pm, Sundays 2 - 5pm.

Admission: Adult £1.50, Child (under 16yrs) free.

LYTES CARY MANOR 🌿

Tel: 01985 843600

Nr Charlton Mackrell, Somerset TA11 7HU

Owner: The National Trust   **Contact:** The Administrator

A manor house with a 14th century chapel, 15th century hall and 16th century great chamber. The home of Henry Lyte, translator of Niewe Herball (1578). Hedged gardens with long herbaceous border.

Location: OS Ref. ST534 265. 1m N of Ilchester bypass A303, signposted from roundabout at junction of A303. A37 take A372.

Opening Times: 1 Apr - 31 Oct: Mon, Wed & Sat, 2 - 6pm or dusk if earlier. Last admission: 5.30pm.

Admission: £4, Child £2.

| ♿ Grounds suitable. | 🅿️ Limited. | 🐕 No dogs. |

MAUNSEL HOUSE

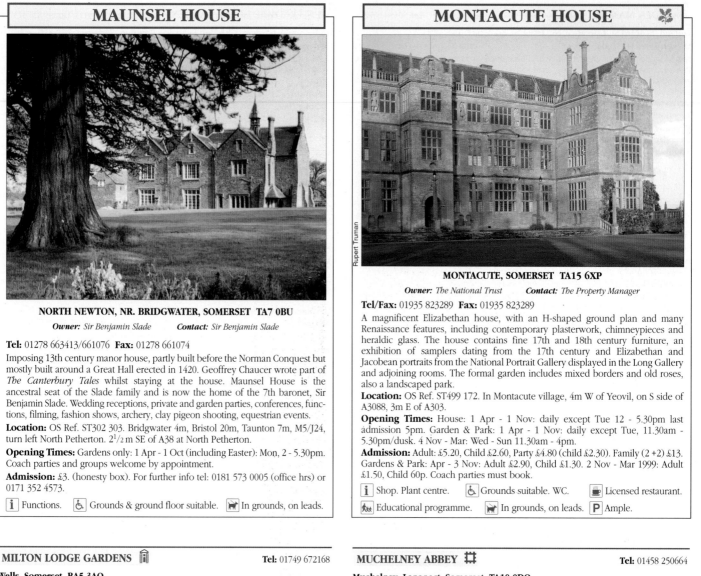

NORTH NEWTON, NR. BRIDGWATER, SOMERSET TA7 0BU

Owner: Sir Benjamin Slade   *Contact:* Sir Benjamin Slade

Tel: 01278 663413/661076   **Fax:** 01278 661074

Imposing 13th century manor house, partly built before the Norman Conquest but mostly built around a Great Hall erected in 1420. Geoffrey Chaucer wrote part of *The Canterbury Tales* whilst staying at the house. Maunsel House is the ancestral seat of the Slade family and is now the home of the 7th baronet, Sir Benjamin Slade. Wedding receptions, private and garden parties, conferences, functions, filming, fashion shows, archery, clay pigeon shooting, equestrian events.

Location: OS Ref. ST302 303. Bridgwater 4m, Bristol 20m, Taunton 7m, M5/J24, turn left North Petherton. 2^1/$_2$ m SE of A38 at North Petherton.

Opening Times: Gardens only: 1 Apr - 1 Oct (including Easter): Mon, 2 - 5.30pm. Coach parties and groups welcome by appointment.

Admission: £3. (honesty box). For further info tel: 0181 573 0005 (office hrs) or 0171 352 4573.

ⓘ Functions.   ♿ Grounds & ground floor suitable.   In grounds, on leads.

MONTACUTE HOUSE

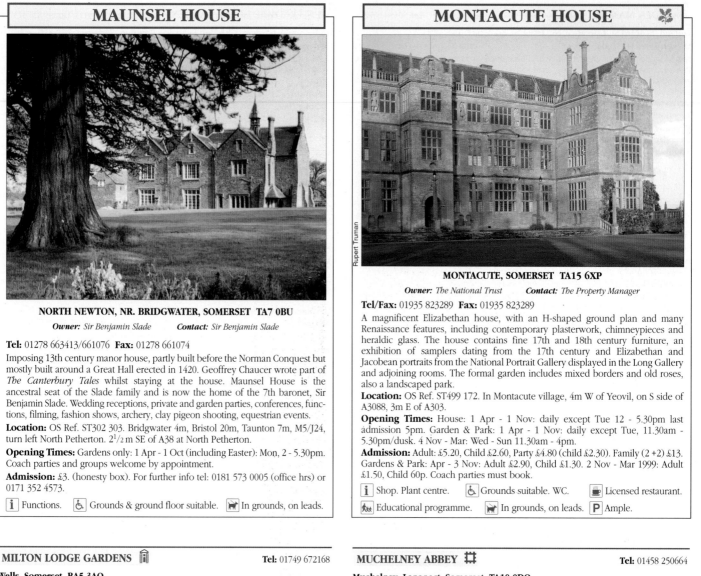

MONTACUTE, SOMERSET TA15 6XP

Owner: The National Trust   *Contact:* The Property Manager

Tel/Fax: 01935 823289   **Fax:** 01935 823289

A magnificent Elizabethan house, with an H-shaped ground plan and many Renaissance features, including contemporary plasterwork, chimneypieces and heraldic glass. The house contains fine 17th and 18th century furniture, an exhibition of samplers dating from the 17th century and Elizabethan and Jacobean portraits from the National Portrait Gallery displayed in the Long Gallery and adjoining rooms. The formal garden includes mixed borders and old roses, also a landscaped park.

Location: OS Ref. ST499 172. In Montacute village, 4m W of Yeovil, on S side of A3088, 3m E of A303.

Opening Times: House: 1 Apr - 1 Nov: daily except Tue 12 - 5.30pm last admission 5pm. Garden & Park: 1 Apr - 1 Nov: daily except Tue, 11.30am - 5.30pm/dusk. 4 Nov - Mar: Wed - Sun 11.30am - 4pm.

Admission: Adult: £5.20, Child £2.60, Party £4.80 (child £2.30). Family (2 +2) £13. Gardens & Park: Apr - 3 Nov: Adult £2.90, Child £1.30. 2 Nov - Mar 1999: Adult £1.50, Child 60p. Coach parties must book.

ⓘ Shop. Plant centre.   ♿ Grounds suitable. WC.   Licensed restaurant.

Educational programme.   In grounds, on leads.   Ⓟ Ample.

MILTON LODGE GARDENS   **Tel:** 01749 672168

Wells, Somerset BA5 3AQ

Owner: D Tudway Quilter Esq   **Contact:** D Tudway Quilter Esq

"The great glory of the gardens of Milton Lodge is their position high up on the slopes of the Mendip Hills to the north of Wells ... with broad panoramas of Wells Cathedral and the Vale of Avalon", (Lanning Roper). Charming, mature, Grade II listed terraced garden dating from 1909. Replanned 1962 with mixed shrubs, herbaceous plants, old fashioned roses and ground cover; numerous climbers; old established yew hedges. Fine trees in garden and in 7-acre arboretum.

Location: OS Ref. ST549 470. ^{1}/$_2$ m N of Wells from A39. N up Old Bristol Road. Free car park first gate on left.

Opening Times: Garden & Arboretum: Good Fri - 31 Oct: daily (except Sat) 2 - 6pm. Parties & coaches by prior arrangement.

Admission: Adult £2, Child (0-13) free. Open certain Suns in aid of National Gardens Scheme.

♿ Not suitable.   Tearoom.   Ⓟ Ample.   No dogs.

MUCHELNEY ABBEY   **Tel:** 01458 250664

Muchelney, Langport, Somerset TA10 0DQ

Owner: English Heritage   **Contact:** The Custodian

Well preserved ruins of the cloisters, with windows carved in golden stone, and abbot's lodging of the Benedictine abbey, which survived by being used as a farmhouse after the Dissolution.

Location: OS193 Ref. ST428 248. In Muchelney 2m S of Langport.

Opening Times: 1 Apr - 31 Oct: daily 10am - 6pm/dusk if earlier.

Admission: Adult £1.60, Child 80p, Conc. £1.20. 15% discount for groups of 11+.

ⓘ Shop.   ♿ Ground floor & grounds suitable.   Kiosk.   Ⓟ Ample.   No dogs.

MUSEUM OF COSTUME & ASSEMBLY ROOMS

See page 131 for full page entry.

NUNNEY CASTLE   **Tel:** 01179 750700

Nunney, Somerset

Owner: English Heritage   **Contact:** The South West Regional Office

A small 14th century moated castle with a distinctly French style. Its unusual design consists of a central block with large towers at the angles.

Location: OS183 Ref. ST737 457. In Nunney 3^1/$_2$ m SW of Frome, 1m N of the A361.

Opening Times: Any reasonable time.

ORCHARD WYNDHAM   **Tel:** 01984 632309 **Fax:** 01984 633526

Williton, Taunton, Somerset TA4 4HH

Owner: Mrs Wyndham   **Contact:** Wyndham Estate Office

English manor house. Family home for 700 years encapsulating continuous building and alteration from the 14th to the 20th century. Narrow access road suitable for light vehicles only.

Location: OS Ref. ST072 400. 1m from A39 at Williton.

Opening Times: House and Garden: 31 Jul - 31 Aug: Thur, Fri & BH, 2 - 5pm. Guided tours only, last tour begins at 4pm. Limited showing space within the house. To avoid disappointment please book places on tour by telephone or fax.

Admission: Adult £4, Child (under 12) £1.

♿ House unsuitable for wheelchairs, grounds suitable.   Compulsory & pre-booked.

In grounds, on leads.

PRIEST'S HOUSE

Tel: 01458 252621

Muchelney, Langport, Somerset TA10 0DQ

Owner: The National Trust   **Contact:** The Administrator

A late medieval hall house with large Gothic windows, originally the residence of priests serving the parish church across the road. Lived-in and recently repaired.

Location: OS Ref. ST429 250. 1m S of Langport.

Opening Times: 5 Apr - 28 Sept: Sun & Mon, 2.30 - 5.30pm. Last admission 5.15pm.

Admission: £1.60, no reductions.

No dogs.

PRIOR PARK LANDSCAPE GARDEN

Joe Cornish

RALPH ALLEN DRIVE, BATH BA2 5AH

Owner: *The National Trust*   **Contact:** *Gardener-in-Charge*

Tel: 01225 833422

Beautiful and intimate 18th century landscape garden created by Bath entrepreneur Ralph Allen (1693 - 1764) with advice from the poet Alexander Pope and Lancelot 'Capability' Brown. Sweeping valley with magnificent views of the City of Bath, Palladian bridge and lakes. Major restoration of the garden continues. Planning permission to open the property was granted until September 1998 only; renewal is likely to be conditional on the success of the 'green transport' scheme as no car park can be provided. For further details 01225 833422 or 24 hour information line 0891 335242 (45p per minute cheap rate, 50p per minute at all other times).

Location: OS Ref. ST760 632. No car parking, Frequent bus service from City Centre. Badgerline 2 & 4.

Opening Times: All year: daily except Tue, 12 - 5.30pm or dusk if earlier. Closed 25 - 26 Dec & 1 Jan.

Admission: Adult: £3.80, Child £1.90. All visitors who produce a valid bus or train ticket will receive £1 off admission. NT members will receive a £1 voucher.

Grounds suitable. WC.   No parking.   No dogs.

THE ROMAN BATHS & PUMP ROOM

See page 132 for full page entry.

STEMBRIDGE TOWER MILL

Tel: 01985 843600

High Ham, Somerset TA10 9DJ

Owner: The National Trust   **Contact:** The Administrator

The last thatched windmill in England, dating from 1822 and in use until 1910.

Location: OS Ref. ST432 305. 2m N of Langport, 1/2 m E of High Ham.

Opening Times: 1 Apr - 30 Sept: Sun, Mon & Wed, 2 - 5pm.

Admission: Adult £1.70, Child 80p, groups by prior arrangement.

Limited.   No dogs.

STOKE-SUB-HAMDON PRIORY

Tel: 01985 843600

North Street, Stoke-sub-Hamdon Somerset TA4 6QP

Owner: The National Trust   **Contact:** The Administrator

A complex of buildings, begun in the 14th century for the priests of the chantry chapel of St Nicholas, which is now destroyed.

Location: OS Ref. ST473 174. 1/2 m S of A303. 2m W of Montacute between Yeovil and Ilminster.

Opening Times: 1 Apr - 31 Oct: daily 10am - 6pm or dusk if earlier.

Admission: Free.

Limited.   No dogs.

TINTINHULL GARDEN

Tel: 01935 822545

Farm Street, Tintinhull, Somerset BA22 9PZ

Owner: The National Trust   **Contact:** The Head Gardener

A 20th century formal garden surrounding a 17th century house. The garden layout, divided into areas by walls and hedges, has border colour and plant themes, including shrub roses and clematis, there is also a kitchen garden.

Location: OS Ref. ST503 198. 5m NW of Yeovil, 1/2 m S of A303, on E outskirts of Tintinhull.

Opening Times: 1 Apr - 30 Sept: Wed - Sun & BH Mon, 12 - 6pm.

Admission: Adult £3.70, Child £1.80, no reduction for groups.

Grounds suitable.   Tearoom.   Limited.   No dogs.

TREASURER'S HOUSE

Tel: 01935 825801

Martock, Somerset TA12 6JL

Owner: The National Trust   **Contact:** The Administrator

A small medieval house, recently refurbished by The Trust. The two-storey hall was completed in 1293 and the solar block is even earlier. There is also a kitchen, added later, and an interesting wall painting.

Location: OS Ref. ST462 191. 1m NW of A303 between Ilminster and Ilchester.

Opening Times: 5 Apr - 29 Sept: Sun, Mon & Tue, 2 - 5pm.

Admission: Adult £1.60 (no reductions). Groups by prior appointment.

Unsuitable for coaches, limited for cars.

WELLS CATHEDRAL

Tel: 01749 674483 **Fax:** 01749 677360

Wells, Somerset BA5 2PA

Owner: Dean & Chapter of Wells   **Contact:** Mr John Roberts

Fine medieval Cathedral. The West front with its splendid array of statuary, the Quire with colourful tapestries and stained glass, Chapter House and astronomical clock should not be missed.

Location: OS Ref. ST552 458. In Wells, 20m S from both Bath & Bristol.

Opening Times: Daily: 7.15am - 8.30pm (summer), or 7.15am - 6pm (winter).

Admission: No entry charge. Donations welcomed. Photo permit £1.

Shop.   Available for small functions.   Ground floor suitable. WC.

Licensed restaurant.   Available.   No parking.

Full education programme.   Guide dogs only.

WESTBURY COLLEGE GATEHOUSE

Tel: 01985 843600

College Road, Westbury-on-Trym, Bristol

Owner: The National Trust   **Contact:** Rev G M Collins

The 15th century gatehouse of the College of Priests (founded in the 13th century) of which John Wyclif was a prebend.

Location: OS Ref. ST572 775. 3m N of the centre of Bristol. Just E of main street.

Opening Times: Visitors to collect the key by prior written arrangement with Rev Collins, or tel. 0117 962 1536.

Admission: Adult £1.10, Child 50p.

Limited.   No dogs.

Strapwork:

A Mannerist decoration originating in the Netherlands c.1540 and brought to England with Flemish religious refugees, popular in the later Elizabethan period. Interlaced bands of cut stone, carved wood or moulded plaster, in appearance similar to a pattern made of leather straps or ribbons, were used to decorate overmantels, balustrades, ceilings, screens and funerary monuments, and were also stamped, cast or engraved on silver, and painted on ceramics. Strapwork evolved in the mid-sixteenth century from Italian grotesque decoration, itself probably of Islamic origin.

The style was copied from book plates published in the Netherlands which used curling straps as a decorative feature.

Extract from; "Life in the Country House" by David N Durant (published by John Murray), PB£15.99, see page twelve at the front of the book.

West Country
England

BOWOOD HOUSE
Calne

CONTACT

The Administrator
Bowood House and
Gardens
Calne
Wiltshire
SN11 0LZ

Tel: (01249) 812102

LOCATION

OS Ref. ST974 700

From London M4/J17,
2 hrs S of A4 between
Chippenham and Calne.
Swindon 17m,
Bristol 26m,
Bath 16m.

Bus: to the gate,
1¹/₂ m through
park to House.

Rail: Chippenham
Station 5m.

Taxi: AA Taxis,
Chippenham 657777.

BOWOOD is the family home of the Earl and Countess of Shelburne, the Earl being the eldest son of the Marquess of Lansdowne. Begun c1720 for the Bridgeman family, the house was purchased by the 2nd Earl of Shelburne in 1754 and completed soon afterwards. Part of the house was demolished in 1955, leaving a perfectly proportioned Georgian home, over half of which is open to visitors. Robert Adam's magnificent Diocletian wing contains a splendid library, the laboratory where Joseph Priestley discovered oxygen gas in 1774, the orangery, now a picture gallery, the Chapel and a sculpture gallery in which some of the famous Lansdowne Marbles are displayed.

Among the family treasures shown in the numerous exhibition rooms are Georgian costumes, including Lord Byron's Albanian dress; Victoriana; Indiana (the 5th Marquess was Viceroy 1888-94); and superb collections of watercolours, miniatures and jewellery.

The House is set in one of the most beautiful parks in England. Over 2,000 acres of gardens and grounds were landscaped by 'Capability' Brown between 1762 and 1768, and are embellished with a Doric temple, a cascade, a pinetum and an arboretum. The Rhododendron Gardens are open for six weeks during May and June. All the walks have seats.

❖

OPENING TIMES

House & Garden

1 Apr - 1 November
Daily
11am - 6pm or
dusk if earlier.

Rhododendron Walks

May - June: for 6 weeks
11am - 6pm.

ADMISSION

House and Garden

Adult	£5.20
Child*	£3.00
OAP	£4.30

Groups (min 20)

Adult	£4.50
Child*	£2.50
OAP	£3.80

Rhododendron Walks

Adult	£3.00
Child*	Free
OAP	£3.00

The charge for Rhododendron Walks £2.00 if combined on same day with a visit to Bowood House & Gardens.

* 5 - 15yrs.

---

i Shop. Receptions, film location, 2,000 acre park, 40 acre lake, 18-hole golf course and Country Club, open to all players holding a current handicap.

X Available for functions, for 45 - 85 persons.

♿ Visitors may alight at the House before parking. WCs.

☕ The Bothy (self-service light snacks, capacity 50) and the Restaurant (waitress-service, capacity 85). Parties that require lunch or tea should book in advance.

🚶 On request, groups can be given introductory talk, or for an extra charge, a guided tour. Tour time 1¹/₄ hrs. Guide sheets in French, German, Dutch, Spanish & Japanese.

P 1,000 cars, unlimited for coaches, 400 yds from house. Allow 2-3 hrs to visit house, gardens and grounds.

👨‍👩‍👧 Welcome. Special guide books. Picnic areas. Adventure playground.

🐕 No dogs.

West Country England

CORSHAM COURT
Corsham

CONTACT

Corsham Court
Corsham
Wiltshire
SN13 0BZ

Tel/Fax: (01249) 701610

LOCATION

OS Ref. ST874 706

Corsham is signposted
from the M4.
From Edinburgh, A1, M62,
M6, M5, M4, 8 hrs.
From London, M4, 2¹/₄ hrs.
From Chester,
M6, M5, M4, 4 hrs.

Motorway: M4/J17 9m.

Rail: Chippenham
Station 6m.

Taxi: (01249) 715959.

CORSHAM COURT is an Elizabethan house of 1582 and was bought by Paul Methuen in the mid-18th century, to house a collection of 16th and 17th century Italian and Flemish master paintings and statuary. In the middle of the 19th century, the house was enlarged to receive a second collection, purchased in Florence, principally of fashionable Italian masters and stone-inlaid furniture.

Paul Methuen (1723-95) was a great-grandson of Paul Methuen of Bradford-on-Avon and cousin of John Methuen, ambassador and negotiator of the Methuen Treaty of 1703 with Portugal which permitted export of British woollens to Portugal and allowed a preferential 33¹/₃% duty discount on Portuguese wines, bringing about a major change in British drinking habits.

The architects involved in the alterations to the house and park were Lancelot 'Capability' Brown in the 1760s, John Nash in 1800 and Thomas Bellamy in 1845-9. Brown set the style by retaining the Elizabethan Stables and Riding School, but rebuilding the Gateway, retaining the gabled Elizabethan stone front and doubling the gabled wings at either end and inside, by designing the East Wing as Stateroom Picture Galleries. Nash's work has now largely disappeared, but Bellamy's stands fast, notably in the Hall and Staircase.

The State Rooms, including the Music Room and Dining Room, provide the setting for the outstanding collection of over 150 paintings, statuary, bronzes and furniture. The collection includes work by such names as Chippendale, the Adam brothers, Van Dyck, Reni, Rosa, Rubens, Lippi, Reynolds, Romney and a pianoforte by Clementi.

GARDENS

'Capability' Brown planned to include a lake, avenues and specimen trees such as the Oriental Plane now with a 200-yard perimeter. The gardens, designed not only by Brown but also by Repton, contain a ha-ha, herbaceous borders, secluded gardens, lawns, a rose garden, a lily pool, a stone bath house and the Bradford Porch.

ℹ️ Souvenir desk. No umbrellas, no photography.

♿ Visitors may alight at the entrance to the property, before parking in the allocated areas.

☕ Tearooms nearby.
Tel: Corsham (01249) 713260.

🚶 For up to 55. If requested the owner may meet the group.
Tour time 1¹/₂ hrs.

🅿️ 400 cars, 120 yards from the house. Coaches may park at the door to the house. Coach parties must book in advance.

👪 Available: rate negotiable.
A guide will be provided.

🐕 Must be kept on leads in the garden.

OPENING TIMES

SUMMER

20 March - 30 September
Daily except Mon but
including BH Mons
11am - 5.30pm
Last admission 5pm.

WINTER

1 October - 19 March
Weekends only
2 - 4.30pm
Last admission 4pm.

Closed December.

NB. Open throughout the year by appointment only for groups of 15+.

ADMISSION

ALL YEAR

House & Garden

Adult £4.50
Child* £2.50
OAP..........................£3.50

Groups**
Adult £3.50
includes guided tour
approximately 1hr.

Garden only

Adult £2.00
Child* £1.00
OAP..........................£1.50

Groups**
Per person £3.50

* Aged 5 - 16yrs.
** Includes guided tour of approximately 1hr.

West Country
England

LONGLEAT HOUSE
Warminster

LONGLEAT HOUSE lies in a sheltered valley amidst rolling parkland. The magnificent Elizabethan property, built by Sir John Thynne and completed in 1580, has been the home of the same family ever since.

The house contains many treasures, including paintings by Tintoretto, Wootton, exquisite French and Flemish tapestries and fine ceilings from the 'School of Titian'. Lovers of books will revel in the splendid collections which are to be found in Longleat's seven libraries.

The murals in the family apartments in the west Wing were painted by Alexander, the present Marquess, and are fascinating and remarkable additions to the collections.

Apart from the ancestral home, Longleat is probably best known for its Safari Park. Here, visitors have the rare opportunity to see animals in a natural setting. The East African Reserve is home to giraffe, zebra and camels and is the only place where you can walk freely amongst these exotic animals. Rhinos, rhesus monkeys, gorillas, tigers and the ever popular Longleat lions are also to be found in the park.

Other attractions include the 'World's Longest Maze', children's adventure castle, Victorian kitchens, tropical butterfly garden, needlework centre, boat, train rides, Airborne 1 Balloon Ride and new mirror maze, enough variety to keep anyone occupied, whatever their age and interest.

❖

ℹ Shop. Fashion shows, concerts, archery, garden parties, equestrian events shows, rallies, filming, product launches, promotions, grand piano, parkland, helicopter pad. Lectures on the property and its history can be arranged for up to 50. Rooms can be hired. Coach driver friendly.

☕ Cellar Café (capacity 80). Parties book in advance for tea and other meals. Cream teas as well as lunch from £5 and sandwiches and snacks from £1.20.

🚶 Groups of up to 20. Pre-book tours when required in French, Spanish or German. Tour time 1 hr.

👫 Welcome with 1 teacher given free entry per 8 children. Group and education pack available on request.

PASSPORT TICKETS
Apr - Oct: includes Safari Park, Longleat House, Dolls' Houses, Boat Ride, Lord Bath's Bygones, VIP Vehicles, Maze, Butterfly Garden, Postman Pat's Village, Railway, Pets Corner, Simulator, Adventure Castle, Memorial Exhibition, Grounds and Garden.

CONTACT

Customer Relations Dept.
The Estate Office
Longleat
Warminster
Wiltshire
BA12 7NW

Tel: (01985) 844400

Fax: (01985) 844885

LOCATION

OS Ref. ST809 430

London 2 hrs.
M3, A303, A36, A362.
Midway between
Warminster and Frome or
from NW M4/J18.

Rail: Mainline Paddington
to Westbury 12m.

Air: Bristol airport 30m.

Taxi: Beeline Taxis
(01985) 212215.

CONFERENCE/FUNCTION		
ROOM	SIZE	MAX CAPACITY
Library	42' x 22'	90
Great Hall	48' 9" x 27'	150

OPENING TIMES

SUMMER
14 March - 1 November
House, Grounds and
Safari Park
Daily, 10am - 6pm
Last admission 5.30pm
or sunset if earlier.

Other attractions:
11am - 6pm.

WINTER
November - March
(except Christmas Day)
House, grounds only
daily, 10am - 4pm
by guided tour.
Times will vary.

ADMISSION

SUMMER

House only
  Adult £5.00
  Child* £4.00
  OAP........................£4.00
Groups (min 12 people)
  Adult £4.50
  Child* £3.00
  OAP........................£3.00

Grounds only
  Adult £2.00
  Child* £1.00
  OAP........................£1.00
Groups of over 12 Free.

Passport Tickets
(see left under photo)
  Adult £12.00
  Child* £10.00
  OAP......................£10.00
Groups (min 12 people)
  Adult £9.00
  Child* £7.50
  OAP........................£7.50
*Age 4 -14.

WINTER
House only.

West Country
England

WILTON HOUSE
Nr. Salisbury

The 17th Earl of Pembroke and his family live in Wilton House which has been their ancestral home for 450 years. In 1544 Henry VIII gave the Abbey and lands of Wilton to Sir William Herbert who had married Anne Parr, sister of Catherine, sixth wife of King Henry.

The Clock Tower, in the centre of the east front, is reminiscent of this part of the Tudor building which survived a fire in 1647. Inigo Jones and John Webb were responsible for the rebuilding of the house in the Palladian style, whilst further alterations were made by James Wyatt from 1801.

The chief architectural features are the magnificent 17th century state apartments (including the famous Single and Double Cube rooms) and the 19th century cloisters.

The house contains one of the finest art collections in Europe, with over 230 original paintings on display, including works by Van Dyck, Rubens, Joshua Reynolds and Brueghel. Also on show are Greek and Italian statuary, a lock of Queen Elizabeth I's hair, Napoleon's despatch case, and Florence Nightingale's sash.

The visitor centre houses a dynamic introductory film (narrated by Anna Massey), the reconstructed Tudor kitchen and the Estate's Victorian laundry. It provides a new home for the 'Wareham Bears', an exhibition of some 200 miniature costumed teddy bears with their own house, stables and other scenes. 21 acres of landscaped parkland, water and old English rose gardens, Palladian Bridge and adventure playground.

CONTACT

Mr Alun Williams
The Estate Office
Wilton House
Wilton
Salisbury
SP2 0BJ

Tel: (01722) 746720

Fax: (01722) 744447

LOCATION

OS Ref. SU099 311

3m W of Salisbury
on the A30.

Rail: Salisbury
Station 3m.

Bus: Every 10 mins from
Salisbury, Mon - Sat.

Taxi: Sarum Taxi
(01722) 334477.

CONFERENCE/FUNCTION

ROOM	SIZE	MAX CAPACITY
Double cube	60' x 30'	150
Exhibition Centre	50' x 40'	140
Film Theatre	34" x 20"	67

OPENING TIMES

SUMMER

4 April - 25 October 1998
Daily: 11am - 6pm
Last admission 5pm.

WINTER

Closed, except for private parties by prior arrangement.

ADMISSION

SUMMER
House, Grounds & Exhibition
Adult £6.75
Child* £4.00
OAP/Student...........£5.75
Family (2+2) £17.50

Groups (min 15 people)
Adult £5.25
Child £3.50

Grounds only
Adult £3.75
Child £2.50

Season Tickets
Family £39.50
Individual.............£19.50

WINTER
Prices on application.

* 5 - 15 yrs - under 5s free.

SPECIAL EVENTS

• **MAR 6 - 8:**
21st Anniversary Antiques Fair.

• **APR 12:**
Easter Egg Treasure Hunt Quiz.

• **APR 18 - 19:**
Celebration of Shakespeare.

• **JUN 5 - 7:**
Wessex Craft & Flower Fayre.

• **JUN 27 - 28:**
Wilton Horse Trials.

• **JUL 18:**
Concert with Fireworks.

• **AUG 1 - 2:**
Have a Go at Archery.

• **AUG 23:**
Teddy Bears' Picnic.

ℹ Shop. Film location, fashion shows, product launches, equestrian events, garden parties, antiques fairs, concerts, vehicle rallies. No photography in house. French, German, Spanish, Italian, Japanese and Dutch information.

✗ Exclusive banquets.

♿ Excellent wheelchair access. Visitors may alight at the entrance. WCs.

☕ Self-service restaurant open 11am - 5.30pm. Groups must book. Hot lunches 12 noon - 2pm.

🚶 Pre-booking a necessity.

🅿 200 cars and 12 coaches. Free coach parking. Group rates (min 15), meal vouchers, drivers' lounge.

👥 Teachers' handbook for National Curriculum. EFL students welcome. Free preparatory visit for group leaders.

🐕 Guide dogs only.

West Country
England

ALEXANDER KEILLER MUSEUM

Tel: 01672 539250

Avebury, Nr. Marlborough, Wiltshire SN8 1RF

Owner: The National Trust   **Contact:** The Custodian

The investigation of Avebury Stone Circles was largely the work of Alexander Keiller in the 1930s. He put together one of the most important prehistoric archaeological collections in Britain which can be seen at the Alexander Keiller Museum.

Location: OS Ref. SU100 699. In Avebury 6m W of Marlborough.

Opening Times: 1 Apr - 31 Oct: daily 10am - 6pm/dusk if earlier. 1 Nov - 31 Mar: daily, 10am - 4pm. Closed 24-26 Dec & 1 Jan.

Admission: Adult £1.50. Child 80p. English Heritage members free.

AVEBURY MANOR GARDEN

Tel: 01672 539250

Avebury, Nr. Marlborough, Wiltshire SN8 1RF

Owner: The National Trust   **Contact:** The Custodian

A regularly altered house of monastic origin, the present buildings date from the early 16th century, with notable Queen Anne alterations and Edwardian renovation by Col Jenner. The topiary and flower gardens contain medieval walls, ancient box and numerous compartments.

Location: OS Ref. SU101 701. 6m W of Marlborough, 1m N of the A4 on A4361 and B4003.

Opening Times: House, 1 Apr - 28 Oct: Tue, Wed, Sun & BH Mon, 2 - 5.30pm. Garden: 1 Apr - 1 Nov: daily except Mon (open BH Mon) & Thur, 11am - 5.30pm, last adm: 5pm.

Admission: House & Garden: Adult £3, Child £1.50. Group: Adult £2.75, Child £1.25. Garden only: Adult £2.25, Child £1. Groups: Adult £2, Child 75p.

[i] Shop.   [&] Grounds suitable.   [☕] Restaurant.   [🐕] No dogs.

AVEBURY STONE CIRCLES

Tel: 01672 539250

Avebury, Nr. Marlborough, Wiltshire SN8 1RF

Owner: The National Trust   **Contact:** The Property Manager

One of the most important Megalithic monuments in Europe, this 28½ acre site with stone circles enclosed by a ditch and external bank, is approached by an avenue of stones. The site also includes the Alexander Keiller Museum and the Wiltshire Life Society's display of Wiltshire rural life in the Great Barn. The site is managed and owned by the National Trust.

Location: OS Ref. SU102 699. 6m W of Marlborough, 1m N of the A4 on A4361 and B4003.

Opening Times: Stone Circle: daily. Great Barn: telephone for details.

BOWOOD HOUSE

See page 138 for full page entry.

BRADFORD-ON-AVON TITHE BARN

Tel: 0117 975 0700

Bradford-on-Avon, Wiltshire

Owner: English Heritage   **Contact:** South West Regional Office

A magnificent medieval stone-built barn with a slate roof and wooden beamed interior.

Location: OS173 Ref. ST824 604. ¼ m S of town centre, off B3109.

Opening Times: Daily, 10.30am - 4pm.

Admission: Free.

BROADLEAS GARDENS

Tel: 01380 722035

Devizes, Wiltshire SN10 5JQ

Owner: Broadleas Gardens Charitable Trust   **Contact:** Lady Anne Cowdray

10 acres full of interest, notably The Dell, where the combination of greensand and sheltered site allows plantings of magnolias, camellias, rhododendrons and azaleas with underplantings of spring bulbs and other woodland plants.

Location: OS Ref. SU001 601. Signposted SW from town centre at S end of housing estate, (coaches must use this entrance) or 1m S of Devizes on W side of A360.

Opening Times: Apr - Oct: Sun, Wed & Thur, 2 - 6pm or by arrangement for groups.

Admission: Adult £2.50, Child (under 12) £1, Groups over 10 £2.20.

[i] Plant shop.   [&] Grounds partially suitable.
[☕] Tearoom.   [🐕] In grounds, on leads.

CORSHAM COURT

See page 139 for full page entry.

THE COURTS

Tel: 01225 782340

Holt, Trowbridge, Wiltshire BA14 6RR

Owner: The National Trust   **Contact:** Head Gardener

A small 3 acre garden in the Hidcote tradition, full of charm and variety and set within an arboretum containing fine specimen trees. There are many interesting plants and an imaginative use of colour.

Location: OS Ref. ST861 618. 3m SW of Melksham, 3m N of Trowbridge, 2½ m E of Bradford-on-Avon, on S side of B3107.

Opening Times: Garden: 1 Apr - 1 Nov, daily (except Sat), 1.30 - 5.30pm. Other times by appointment.

Admission: £3, Child £1.50, groups by arrangement.

[P] Limited.   [🐕] No dogs.

GREAT CHALFIELD MANOR

Tel: 01225 782239

Melksham, Wiltshire SN2 8NJ

Owner: The National Trust   **Contact:** The Tenant

A charming manor house, encircled by a moat and defensive wall and with beautiful oriel windows and a great hall. Completed in 1480, the manor and gardens were restored earlier this century by Major R Fuller, whose family still live here and manage the property.

Location: OS Ref. ST860 633. 3m SW of Melksham via Broughton Gifford Common.

Opening Times: 1 Apr - 29 Oct: Tue, Wed, Thur by guided tours only, starting 12.15pm, 2.15pm, 3pm, 3.45pm and 4.30pm. Guided tours of the manor take 45 minutes and numbers are limited to 25. It is suggested that visitors arriving when a tour is in progress visit the adjoining Parish Church and garden first. Closed public holidays. Groups by arrangement.

Admission: £3.50, no reductions.

[&] Grounds suitable.   [P] Limited.   [🐕] No dogs.

HAMPTWORTH LODGE

Tel: 01794 390215   **Fax:** 01794 390700

Hamptworth, Landford, Salisbury, Wiltshire SP5 2EA

Owner: Mr N J M Anderson   **Contact:** Mr N J M Anderson

Rebuilt Jacobean manor house standing in woodlands on the edge of the New Forest. Grade II* family house with period furniture including clocks. The Great Hall has an unusual roof construction. There is a collection of prentice pieces and the Moffatt collection of contemporary copies. Garden also open.

Location: OS Ref. SU227 195. 10m SE of Salisbury on road linking Downton on Salisbury/ Bournemouth Road (A338) to Landford on A36, Salisbury - Southampton.

Opening Times: 30 Mar - 30 Apr: 2.15 - 5pm except Sun. Coaches, by appointment only, 1 Apr - 30 Oct except Sun.

Admission: £3.50, Child under 11 free. Groups by arrangement.

[&] Ground floor & grounds suitable.

HEALE GARDEN

WOODFORD, SALISBURY, WILTSHIRE SP4 6NT

Owner: Mr Guy Rasch   *Contact:* Major David Rasch

Tel: 01722 782504

First winner of Christie's/HHA Garden of the Year award. Grade I Carolean Manor House where King Charles II hid during his escape in 1651. In January great drifts of snowdrops and aconites bring early colour and the promise of spring. The garden provides a wonderfully varied collection of plants, shrub, musk and other roses, growing in the formal setting of clipped hedges and mellow stonework. Particularly lovely in spring and autumn is the water garden surrounding an authentic Japanese Tea House and Nikko Bridge which create an exciting focus in this part of the garden.

Location: OS Ref. SU125 365. 4m N of Salisbury on Woodford Valley road between A345 and A360.

Opening Times: Garden, shop & plant centre: All year, 10am - 5pm. Teas for groups of 20+ by arrangement.

Admission: Adult £2.75, child under 14 free.

[i] Shop. Plant centre.   [&] Grounds suitable.   [🐕] In grounds, on leads.

IFORD MANOR GARDEN

BRADFORD-ON-AVON, WILTSHIRE BA15 2BA

Owner: Mrs E A J Cartwright-Hignett   *Contact:* Mrs E A J Cartwright-Hignett

Tel: 01225 863146   **Fax:** 01225 862364

An enchanted garden. Iford Manor, a Tudor house with a classical façade, was once a busy centre of the woollen industry. Set in a romantic river valley it is now surrounded by a peaceful terraced garden of unique character. Designed by the Edwardian architect Harold Peto, it has pools, statuary, a colonnade, terraces and a cloister. Featured in *Landscape and Memory 1995*, BBC.

Location: OS Ref. ST800 589. 7m SE of Bath via A36, signposted Iford. 2m SW of Bradford on Avon via Westwood.

Opening Times: Apr & Oct: Sun only & Easter Mon, 2 - 5pm. May - Sept: Tue, Wed, Thur, Sat, Sun & BH Mon, 2 - 5pm. Coaches by appointment at other times.

Admission: Adult £2.50, Child/OAP £1.90. Picnic area by river.

☕ Teas (May - Aug: Sat, Sun & BH Mon).   🅿 Free. Coaches by appointment.

THE KING'S HOUSE   Tel: 01722 332151   Tel: 01722 325611

SALISBURY & SOUTH WILTSHIRE MUSEUM

65 The Close, Salisbury, Wiltshire SP1 2EN

Owner: Salisbury & South Wiltshire Museum Trust   **Contact:** P R Saunders

Location: OS Ref. SU141 295. In Salisbury Cathedral Close, W side, facing cathedral.

Opening Times: Mon - Sat: 10am - 5pm. Sun, Jul, Aug: 2 - 5pm.

Admission: Adult £3, Child 75p, Conc. £2, Groups £2. Suitable for disabled.

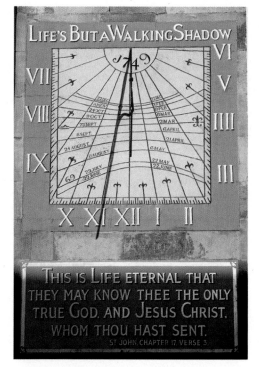

Malmesbury House, Salisbury.

LACOCK ABBEY

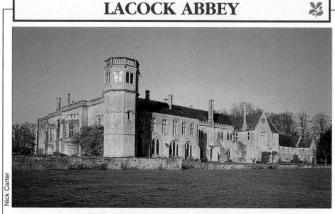

Nick Carter

LACOCK, CHIPPENHAM, WILTSHIRE SN15 2LG

Owner: The National Trust   *Contact:* The Custodian

Tel: 01249 730227 / 730459

The Abbey was founded in 1232 and converted into a Tudor country house, where the pioneer of photography, William Fox Talbot, lived with his family. Main architectural features of the Abbey are the Medieval Cloisters and Chapter House. The oriel window, subject of the first negative, is easily seen from the south lawn; it also boasts a 16th century stable court yard with half timbered gables and clockhouse. The woodland garden boasts a fine display of spring flowers and includes the recently restored Victorian rose garden. The grounds are laid out in the informal romantic style of the Victorian era with a fine collection of rare and unusual trees, and is the perfect setting for the Abbey. The museum of photography commemorates the achievements of Fox Talbot and houses a collection of cameras and associated equipment. Photographic exhibitions change through the year.

Location: OS Ref. ST919 684. In the village of Lacock, 3m N of Melksham, 3m S of Chippenham just E of A350.

Opening Times: Museums, cloisters & grounds: 1 Mar - 1 Nov, daily (closed Good Fri) 11am - 5.30pm. Abbey: 1 Apr - 1 Nov, daily except Tue, 1 - 5.30pm. Winter: Museum only, weekends, 11am - 4pm.

Admission: Abbey, grounds, cloisters & museums: Adult £5.50, Child £3, Groups: £5, (Child £2.50). Grounds, cloisters & museum: Adult £3.50, Child £2. Museum: Winter opening, Adult £2, Child £1.

ℹ Shop.   ♿ Suitable. WC.   ☕ Tearoom.   🐕 No dogs.

LITTLE CLARENDON   Tel: 01985 843600

Dinton, Salisbury, Wiltshire SP3 5OZ

Owner: The National Trust   **Contact:** The Administrator

A Tudor house, but greatly altered in the 17th century. Principal rooms on the ground floor are open.

Location: OS Ref. SU015 316. ¼ m E of Dinton Church. 9m W of Salisbury.

Opening Times: 4 Apr - 31 Oct: Sat, 9am - 1pm, Mon, 1 - 5pm.

Admission: £1.50, no reductions. Not suitable for disabled.

LONG HALL GARDENS   Tel: 01985 850424

Stockton, Warminster, Wiltshire BA12 0SE

Owner: N H Yeatman-Biggs Esq   **Contact:** N H Yeatman-Biggs

4 acres of gardens. Long Hall Nursery is adjacent.

Location: OS Ref. ST982 381. Stockton 7m SE of Warmínster, off A36, W of A303 Wylye interchange.

Opening Times: Gardens: 5 Apr - 2 Aug: first Sat in the month, 2 - 6pm. NGS 12 Apr & 21 June. Nursery: 19 Mar - 27 Sept: Wed - Sat, 9.30am - 5.30pm.

Admission: Adult £2, Child free, Groups by appointment at £5pp including cream teas.

LONGLEAT HOUSE   See page 140 for full page entry.

Underdog:

This one is curious. The underdog was the sawyer in the bottom of the sawpit, on whom the sawdust fell; the better position was that of the upper-dog (top dog, top-sawyer) on the top end of the two-handled saw. At Erddig in Clwyd a sawpit has survived with its equipment; set up as if it has just been used, it gives a very good impression of what the underdog must have endured.

Extract from; "Life in the Country House" by David N Durant (published by John Murray). PB£15.99, see page twelve at the front of the book.

West Country England

LYDIARD PARK

LYDIARD TREGOZE, SWINDON, WILTSHIRE SN5 9PA

Owner: *Swindon Borough Council*   **Contact:** *The Keeper*

Tel: 01793 770401   **Fax:** 01793 877909

Beautifully restored Georgian house set amid rolling lawns, woodland and lakes. Former ancestral home of Viscounts Bolingbroke rescued from dereliction in 1943. Fascinating 17th century painted window and Lady Diana Spencer room are just some of the delights in store in this friendly house. Adjacent church with glittering array of monuments. Exciting adventure playgrounds, enjoyment for all the family.

Location: OS Ref. SU104 848. 4m W of Swindon, $1^1/_2$ m N of M4/J16.

Opening Times: Mon - Sat, 10am - 1pm, 2 - 5pm (10am - 5pm during summer school holidays). Sun, 2 - 5pm. Winter closing Nov - Feb: early closing at 4pm.

Admission: Adult 75p, Child 30p (to be reviewed in April 1998). Group guided tours by appointment.

ℹ️ Gift shop.   ☕ Café.   🚶 Guided tours.

MALMESBURY HOUSE

THE CLOSE, SALISBURY, WILTSHIRE SP1 2EB

Owner: *John Cordle Esq.*   **Contact:** *John Cordle Esq.*

Tel: 01722 327027   **Fax:** 01722 334414

Malmesbury House was originally a 13th century canonry. It was enlarged in the 14th century and leased to the Harris family in 1660 whose descendant became the first Earl of Malmesbury. The west façade was added by Sir Christopher Wren, to accommodate rooms displaying magnificent rococo plasterwork. Among the many illustrious visitors to the house were King Charles II and the composer Handel who used the Chapel above the St Ann Gate for recitals. Francis Webb, a direct ancestor of Queen Elizabeth II, lived here in the 1770s. Family in residence. Luncheons served in the Music Room.

Location: OS Ref. SU145 296. City of Salisbury, cathedral close. E end of North Walk, by St Ann Gate. Coaches to St John's Street.

Opening Times: Easter weekend & all BHs. Groups (12+) only by appointment throughout the year.

Admission: Adult £5. Students £3. Prices include garden.

♿ Not suitable.   ☕ Group luncheons/teas.   🚶 Compulsory.   🐕 No dogs.

MOMPESSON HOUSE 🌼   **Tel:** 01722 335659

The Close, Salisbury, Wiltshire SP1 2EL

Owner: The National Trust   **Contact:** The Property Manager

Fine Queen Anne town house, furnished as the home of a Georgian gentleman, with a walled garden. Exhibition of paintings throughout the season.

Location: OS Ref. SU142 295. On N side of Choristers' Green in Cathedral Close, near High Street Gate.

Opening Times: 1 Apr - 1 Nov: daily except Thur & Fri, 12 - 5.30pm. Last admission 5pm.

Admission: Adult £3.40, Child £1.70. Groups £2.90. Garden only 80p.

ℹ️ Shop.   ♿ Ground floor & grounds suitable.   ☕ Tearoom.   🐕 No dogs.

NEWHOUSE 🏛   **Tel:** 01725 510055

Redlynch, Salisbury, Wiltshire SP5 2NX

Owner: George and June Jeffreys   **Contact:** Mrs June Jeffreys

Brick Jacobean 'Trinity House', c1619, with two Georgian wings. Contents include costume collection, documents and the 'Hare' picture.

Location: OS Ref. SU218 214. 9m S of Salisbury, 3m E of Downton, off B3080.

Opening Times: 1 - 31 Aug: except Sun, 2 - 5.30pm. Groups of 25+ are welcome by arrangement between May & Sept. Wedding receptions by arrangement.

Admission: Adult £3, Child (under 15 yrs) £2.

🐕 No dogs.   💒 Civil Wedding Licence.

OLD SARUM ⊞

CASTLE RD, SALISBURY, WILTSHIRE SP1 3SD

Owner: *English Heritage*   **Contact:** *The Head Custodian*

Tel: 01722 335398

Built around 500BC by the iron age peoples, Old Sarum is the former site of the first cathedral and ancient city of Salisbury. A prehistoric hillfort in origin, Old Sarum was occupied by the Romans, the Saxons, and eventually the Normans who made it into one of their major strongholds, with a motte-and-bailey castle built at its centre. Old Sarum eventually grew into one of the most dramatic settlements in medieval England as castle, cathedral, bishop's palace and thriving township. When the new city we know as Salisbury was founded in the early 13th century the settlement faded away. With fine views of the surrounding countryside, Old Sarum is an excellent picnic spot.

Location: OS184 Ref. SU138 327. 2m N of Salisbury off A345.

Opening Times: 1 Apr - 31 Oct: daily, 10am - 6pm or dusk if earlier.
1 Nov - 31 Mar: daily 10am - 4pm. Closed 24 - 26 Dec.

Admission: Adult £2, Child £1, Conc. £1.50. 15% discount for groups of 11+.

ℹ️ Shop.   ♿ Grounds suitable.   ☕ Kiosk.   🅿️ Ample.   🐕 In grounds, on leads.

OLD WARDOUR CASTLE ⌗

TISBURY, WILTSHIRE SP3 6RR

Owner: English Heritage   *Contact:* The Custodian

Tel: 01747 870487

In a picture book setting, the unusual hexagonal ruins of this 14th century castle stand on the edge of a beautiful lake, surrounded by landscaped grounds which include an elaborate rockwork grotto.

Location: OS184 Ref. ST939 263. Off A30 2m SW of Tisbury.

Open: 1 Apr - 31 Oct: daily, 10am - 6pm or dusk if earlier. 1 Nov - 31 Mar: Wed - Sun, 10am - 4pm. Closed for lunch 1 - 2pm. Closed 24 - 26 Dec.

Admission: Adult £1.70, Child 90p, Conc. £1.30. 15% discount for groups of 11+.

[i] Shop. [♿] Grounds suitable. [☕] Kiosk. [P] Ample. [🐕] In grounds, on leads.

PHILLIPS HOUSE   **Tel:** 01985 843600

Dinton, Salisbury, Wiltshire SP3 5HJ

Owner: The National Trust   **Contact:** The Administrator

A neo-Grecian house by Jeffry Wyattville, completed in 1816. Principal rooms on ground floor are open.

Location: OS Ref. SU004 319. 9m W of Salisbury, N side of B3089, $^1/_2$ m W of Little Clarendon. Car park off St Mary's Road next to church.

Opening Times: 4 Apr - 31 Oct: Mon 1 - 5pm, Sat 9am - 1pm. Tel. for further information.

Admission: House £2. Access to Dinton Park is free.

[♿] House suitable, park limited.

PYTHOUSE   **Tel:** 01747 870210 **Fax:** 01747 871786

Tisbury, Wiltshire SP3 6PB

Owner: Country Houses Association   **Contact:** The Administrators

Palladian style Georgian mansion.

Location: OS Ref. SJ909 285. 2$^1/_2$ m W of Tisbury; 4$^1/_2$ m N of Shaftesbury. Rail: Tisbury 2$^1/_2$ m.

Opening Times: 1 May - 30 Sept: Wed, Thur, 2 - 5pm.

Admission: Adult/OAP/Student £2.50, Child £1.

[🐕] No dogs.   [A] 1 single & 1 double with bathroom, CHA members only.

SALISBURY CATHEDRAL   **Tel:** 01722 323273 **Fax:** 01722 330699

The Close, Salisbury, Wiltshire SP1 2EJ

Owner: Dean & Chapter   **Contact:** Visitor Department

Surrounded by ancient stone walls, peaceful lawns and historic houses, stands Salisbury Cathedral. Built between 1220 and 1258 it is a supreme example of medieval architecture, and its spire, at 404ft (123 metres) is the tallest in England. Treasures include an original Magna Carta and Europe's oldest working clock. Regular tours of Cathedral and Tower. Special tours to see conservation work on West Front also available. All visitors are welcome to attend daily services.

Location: OS Ref. SU143 295. In the close, just S of city centre.

Opening Times: Cathedral: Mon - Sat, 8am - 6.30pm (8.15pm Mid May - Mid Sept) Sun: 8 - 9am, 12.30 - 2.30 & 4 - 6.30pm. Chapter House: daily, except Dec. Closed Good Fri.

Admission: Donations. Cathedral: Adult £2.50, Child 50p, Conc. £1.50, Family £5. Chapter House: Adult 30p, Child free.

[i] Shop. [♿] Ground floor & grounds suitable. WCs. [☕] Tearoom. [🎧] Available.
[👥] Schools education programme. [🐕] Dogs on leads.

SHELDON MANOR   **Tel:** 01249 653120 **Fax:** 01249 461097

Chippenham, Wiltshire SN14 0RG

Owner: Antony Gibbs Esq.   **Contact:** Mrs M Gibbs

After 21 years of opening Sheldon Manor to the public, Mrs Martin Gibbs following doctor's orders, has been obliged to close it.

Opening Times: Sheldon Manor will be closed for 1998.

STONEHENGE ⌗

AMESBURY, WILTSHIRE SP4 7DE

Owner: English Heritage   *Contact:* The Custodian

Tel: 01980 624715 (Information Line)

The mystical and awe-inspiring stone circle at Stonehenge is one of the most famous prehistoric monuments in the world, designated by UNESCO as a World Heritage Site. Stonehenge's orientation on the rising and setting sun has always been one of its most remarkable features. Whether this was simply because the builders came from a sun-worshipping culture, or because – as some scholars have believed – the circle and its banks were part of a huge astronomical calendar, remains a mystery. Visitors to Stonehenge can discover the history and legends which surround this unique stone circle, which began over 5,000 years ago, with a complimentary three part audio tour available in 9 languages.

Location: OS Ref. SU123 422. 2m W of Amesbury on junction of A303 and A344/A360.

Opening Times: 16 Mar - 31 May: 9.30am - 6pm. 1 Jun - 31 Aug: 9am - 7pm. 1 Sept - 15 Oct: 9.30am - 6pm. 16 Oct - 15 Mar: 9.30am - 4pm.

Admission: Adult £3.90, Child £2, Conc. £2.90. Family (2+3) £9.80.

STOURHEAD

National Trust Photographic Library.

NR. WARMINSTER, WILTSHIRE BA12 6QD
Owner: *The National Trust*   **Contact:** *The Estate Manager*

Tel: 01747 841152 **Fax:** 01747 841152 (office hours only)

An outstanding example of the English landscape style, this splendid garden was designed by Henry Hoare II and laid out between 1741 and 1780. Classical temples, including the Pantheon and Temple of Apollo, are skillfully located around the central lake at the end of a series of vistas, which change as the visitor moves around the paths and through the magnificent mature woodland. The house, begun in 1721 by Colen Campbell, contains furniture by the younger Chippendale and fine paintings. King Alfred's Tower, an intriguing red-brick folly built in 1772 by Henry Flitcroft, is almost 50m high and gives breathtaking views over the estate.

Location: OS183 Ref. ST778 341. At Stourton off the B3092, 3m N of A303 (Mere).

Opening Times: Garden: All year, daily, 9am - 7pm or sunset if earlier (except 23 - 25 July when garden will close at 5pm, last admission 4pm). House: 28 Mar - 1 Nov: daily, except Thur & Fri, 12 - 5.30pm or dusk if earlier, last admission 30 mins before closing. King Alfred's Tower: 28 Mar - 1 Nov: Tue - Fri, 2 - 5.30pm, Sat & Sun, 11.30am - 5.30pm or dusk if earlier. Closed Mon except BH Mon.

Admission: House & Garden: Adult £7.90, Child £3.70, Family £20.60, Groups £7.60pp. House or Garden: Mar - Oct: Adult £4.40, Child £2.40, Family £10.30, Groups (by written appointment, 15+) £3.80. Garden only: Nov - end Feb: Adult £3.40, Child £1.50, Family £8.20.

STOURTON HOUSE FLOWER GARDEN   **Tel:** 01747 840417

Zeals, Warminster, Wiltshire BA12 6QF

Owner: Mrs E Bullivant   **Contact:** Mrs E Bullivant

4 acres of peaceful, romantic garden where grass paths lead through unique daffodils, spring flowers and camelias or scented azaleas, rhododendrons and blue poppies or delphiniums, roses and many unusual plants. Sit among the spectacular hedged borders and watch butterflies and dragonflies over the pitcher plant pond or wander among the 270 different hydrangeas, then enjoy Caroline's homemade sticky cream cakes under the flowering verandah. Interesting plants and lovely bouquets of dried flowers from the garden for sale.

Location: OS Ref. ST780 340. 2m NW of Mere next to Stourhead car park, A303. Follow blue signs.

Opening Times: Apr - end Nov: Wed, Thur, Sun, and BH Mon, 11am - 6pm. Plants & dried flowers for sale during the winter on weekdays.

Admission: Adult £2.50, Child 50p. Group guided tours by appointment.

[i] Plant & dried flower sales.   Grounds suitable.   Available.   No dogs.

WESTWOOD MANOR   **Tel:** 01225 863374

Bradford-on-Avon, Wiltshire BA15 2AF

Owner: The National Trust   **Contact:** The Tenant

A 15th century stone manor house, altered in the late 16th century, with late Gothic and Jacobean windows and Jacobean plasterwork. There is a modern topiary garden.

Location: OS Ref. ST813 589. 1½m SW of Bradford-on-Avon, in Westwood village, beside the church.

Opening Times: 1 Apr - 30 Sept: Sun, Tue & Wed, 2 - 5pm.

Admission: £3.50.

Not suitable.   [P] Limited.   No dogs.

WILTON HOUSE   See page 141 for full page entry.

Malmesbury House, Salisbury.

Iford Manor Gardens, Wiltshire.

Counties in this region:

LINCOLNSHIRE

NOTTS

LEICESTERSHIRE

RUTLAND

NORFOLK

NORTHAMPTONSHIRE

CAMBRIDGESHIRE

SUFFOLK

BEDFORDSHIRE

ESSEX

HERTFORDSHIRE

LONDON

Eastern Counties
England

Eastern Counties England

ELTON HALL
Peterborough

CONTACT

The Administrator
Estate Office
Elton Hall
Nr. Peterborough
Cambridgeshire
PE8 6SH

Tel: (01832) 280468

Fax: (01832) 280584

LOCATION

OS Ref. TL 091 930

From London, A1(M),
A605 to Elton. 86m.
From Leicester, A47,
B671, A605 to Elton.

8m SW of Peterborough.

Bus: Peterborough –
Kettering bus
passes the Hall

Rail: Peterborough 8m.

Air: Private Airport 3m.

Taxi: Norwood,
Oundle 273585.

ELTON HALL, home of the Proby family for over 350 years, stands in the midst of unspoilt landscaped parkland on a site where there has been a house since the Norman Conquest. Sir Peter Proby, Lord Mayor of London and Comptroller of the Royal Household, was granted land and property at Elton by Queen Elizabeth I. His grandson, Sir Thomas Proby, completed the main House in 1666. In the 18th Century John Proby was created the first Earl of Carysfort. He and his successors enlarged it to the 18th century character that it has today.

Elton is a fascinating mixture of styles. Every room contains treasures – magnificent furniture and fine paintings from early 15th century Old Masters to the remarkable Pre-Raphaelite work of Alma Tadema and Millais. Great British artists are well represented by Gainsborough, Constable and Reynolds. The Library is one of the finest in private hands containing some 12,000 books. The collection includes the unique Henry VIII's Prayer Book in which can be seen the writing of the Tudor King and two of his wives.

GARDENS

The formal gardens have been carefully restored in recent years. They consist of a large rose garden containing some 1,000 roses including many old fashioned varieties, a parterre, sunken garden and shrubbery.

A stunning new Gothic Orangery has recently been built as a millenium project together with a new garden.

OPENING TIMES

Late Spring BH &
August BH
Sun & Mon
2 - 5pm.

June
Wed, 2 - 5pm.

July & August
Wed, Thur & Sun
2 - 5pm.

Private groups by
appointment

ADMISSION

House & Garden
Adult £4.50
Child (under 15yrs) ....Free

Garden only
Adult £2.50
Child (under 15yrs) ....Free
Groups (min 20)*
Adult £4.50
Child (under 15yrs) ....Free

Private groups by
appointment only.

Free ticket to organisers
of groups of 20+.

* Over 50 people gain
additional 10% discount.

CONFERENCE/FUNCTION

ROOM	SIZE	MAX CAPACITY
Billiard Rm	38' x 28'	60
State Dining Rm	38'6" x 23'6"	100
Conference Room	21' x 20'	20

ℹ️ No photography in Hall. Corporate entertaining, product launches, promotions, photographic and film location work. Parkland for rallies etc. Clay pigeon shoots can be arranged. Book meals in advance, menus on request.

♿ Visitors may alight at entrance. Park in allocated areas. WCs in Plant Centre, 300 yds from house. Steps at entrance and in Hall, unsuitable for wheelchairs.

🍽 Restaurant. Lunches/buffet suppers for groups on tours, book in advance.

🚶 Groups of up to 100 can be split into groups of 20, except on BHs. Tour time 3/4 hr. Special lecture tours of Hall.

🅿 For 200 cars & 10 coaches, 250 yds from house

👫 Mainly suitable for 5th/6th formers. Special question sheet with competition for younger children. Guided tours, please apply for details.

🐕 No dogs.

ANGLESEY ABBEY

LODE, CAMBRIDGE, CAMBRIDGESHIRE CB5 9EJ

Owner: The National Trust   *Contact:* The Administrator

Tel/Fax: 01223 811200

Dating from 1600, the house, built on the site of an Augustinian abbey, contains the famous Fairhaven collection of paintings and furniture. Surrounded by an outstanding 100-acre garden and arboretum, with a wonderful display of hyacinths in spring and magnificent herbaceous borders and a dahlia garden in summer. A watermill in full working order is demonstrated on the first Saturday in each month.

Location: OS Ref. TL530 622. In Lode village, 6m NE of Cambridge on B1102, signs from A14.

Opening Times: House: 21 Mar - 11 Oct: Wed - Sun & BH Mon, 1 - 5pm. Garden: 21 Mar - 1 Nov: Wed - Sun & BH Mon: 11am - 5.30pm. Garden also open 6 Jul - 13 Sept: Mon & Tues. Lode Mill: 21 Mar - 1 Nov: Wed - Sun & BH Mon. Last admission to all attractions 4.30pm.

Admission: House & garden: £5.80 (Sun & BH Mons £6.80). Discounts for families available. Groups £4.80 (no reductions Sun & BH Mons). Garden only: £3.40, Groups £2.70. Child half price. Timed tickets are issued on Suns & BH Mons to overcome problems of overcrowding.

ℹ️ Shop. Garden centre.	♿ Braille guide. Electric buggy. WCs.
☕ Restaurant.	🐕 No dogs.

ISLAND HALL

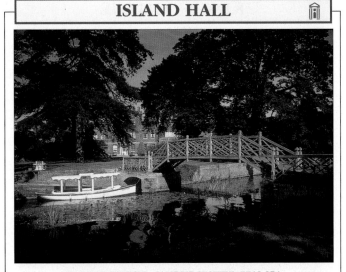

GODMANCHESTER, CAMBRIDGESHIRE PE18 8BA

Owner: Mr Christopher and the Hon. Mrs Vane Percy   *Contact:* Mr C Vane Percy

Tel: 0171 491 3724   **Fax:** 0171 355 4006

An important mid 18th century mansion of great charm, owned and restored by an award winning interior designer. This family home has lovely Georgian rooms, with fine period detail, and interesting possessions relating to the owners' ancestors since their first occupation of the house in 1800. A tranquil riverside setting with formal gardens and ornamental island forming part of the grounds in an area of Best Landscape. Octavia Hill, the Victorian reformer, and a founder of the National Trust, who stayed at Island Hall at least twice in 1859 and 1865, would instantly recognise the house and grounds, and she says in a letter to her sister "This is the loveliest, dearest old house, I never was in such a one before."

Location: OS Ref. TL244 706. 15m NW of Cambridge A14.

Opening Times: Jul: Sun: 5, 12, 19, 26 only, 2.30 - 5pm. Last admission 4.30pm. May - Sept: (except Aug) By appointment only.

Admission: Adult £3, Child (3-16) £2. Grounds only: Adult £1.50, Child (3-16) £1, Accompanied Child under 13 £1. Group rates available by arrangement for May - Sept: (except Aug) £2.50ea. (min 40). Under 15 persons, min. charge £45 per group.

♿ Not suitable.	☕ Available.	🐕 No dogs.

DENNY ABBEY

Tel: 01223 860489

Ely Road, Chittering, Waterbeach, Cambridgeshire CB5 9PQ

Owner: English Heritage   **Contact:** The Custodian

What at first appears to be an attractive stone-built farmhouse is actually the remains of a 12th century Benedictine abbey which, at different times, also housed the Knights Templar and Franciscan nuns. Founded by the Countess of Pembroke.

Location: OS Ref. TL495 684. 6m N of Cambridge on the E side of the A10.

Opening Times: 1 Apr - 31 Oct. 10am - 6pm.

Admission: Adult £3.30, Child £1.20, Conc. £2.40.

ELTON HALL

See page 150 for full page entry.

ELY CATHEDRAL

Tel: 01353 667735   **Fax:** 01353 665658

The Chapter House, The College, Ely, Cambridgeshire CB7 4DL

       Contact: Visitor Manager, Heather Kilpatrick

A wonderful example of Romanesque architecture. Octagon and Lady Chapel are of special interest. Superb medieval domestic buildings surround the Cathedral. Stained Glass Museum.

Location: OS Ref. TL541 803. Via A10, 15m N of Cambridge city centre.

Opening Times: Summer: 7am - 7pm. Winter: Mon - Sat, 7.30am - 6pm, Sun and week after Christmas, 7.30am - 5pm. Sun services: 8.15am, 10.30am and 3.45pm. Weekday services: 7.40am, 8am, and 5.30pm (Thur only also 11.30am & 12.30pm).

Admission: Adult £3, Child (up to 12yrs) £2.20, Conc. £2.20. Discounts for groups of 15+.

ℹ️ Shop.	♿ Suitable.	☕ Tearoom.	🚶 Available.
👨‍👩‍👧 Education programme available.	🐕 Guide dogs only.		

KIMBOLTON CASTLE

Tel: 01480 860505   **Fax:** 01480 861763

Kimbolton, Huntingdon, Cambridgeshire PE18 0EA

Owner: Governors of Kimbolton School   **Contact:** Mr J Mcleod

A late Stuart House, an adaptation of a 13th century fortified manor house, with evidence of Tudor modifications. The seat of the Earls and Dukes of Manchester 1615 - 1950, now a school. Katherine of Aragon died in the Queen's Room - the setting for a scene in Shakespeare's *Henry VIII.* A minor example of the work of Vanbrugh and Hawksmoor; Gatehouse by Robert Adam, the Pellegrini mural paintings on the Staircase, in the Chapel and in the Boudoir are the best examples in England of this gifted Venetian decorator.

Location: OS Ref. TL101 676. 7m NW of St. Neots on B645.

Opening Times: Easter, Spring BH: Sun & Mon, 2 - 6pm. 26 Jul & Suns in Aug, 2 - 6pm. 22/23 Jul, 29/30 Jul & 5/6 Aug (Weds & Thurs) 2 - 6pm.

Admission: Adult £2, Child £1, Conc £1. Groups by arrangement.

♿ Not suitable.	☕ Tearoom.	🚶 By arrangement only.	🅿️ Ample.
🐕 On leads in grounds only.			

Historic Scotland

SPECIAL EVENTS 1998 See the front section for full list.

KING'S COLLEGE

KING'S PARADE, CAMBRIDGE CB2 1ST

Owner: Provost and Fellows   *Contact:* Mr D Buxton

Tel: 01223 331212 **Fax:** 01223 331315

Visitors are welcome, but remember that this is a working college. Please respect the privacy of those who work, live and study here. The Chapel is often used for services, recordings, broadcasts, etc, and ideally visitors should check before arriving. Recorded message for services, concerts and visiting times: 01223 331155.

Location: OS Ref. TL447 584.

Opening Times: Out of term: Mon - Sat, 9.30am - 4.30pm. Sun, 10am - 5pm. In term: Mon: 9.30am - 4.30pm. Tue - Fri: 9.30am - 3.30pm. Sat: 9.30am - 3.15pm. Sun: 1.15 - 2.15pm, 5 - 5.30pm.

Admission: Adult £3, Child (12-17)/Student (ID required) £2, OAP £3. Child under 12 free if part of a family unit.

i Shop. Conferences.	X Available by arrangement.	& Suitable.
术 By arrangement.	P No parking.	🐕 Guide dogs only.

THE MANOR, HEMINGFORD GREY

HUNTINGDON, CAMBRIDGESHIRE PE18 9BN

Owner: Mr and Mrs P S Boston   *Contact:* Diana Boston

Tel: 01480 463134 **Fax:** 01480 465026

Built about 1130 and made famous as Green Knowe by the author Lucy Boston. The Manor is reputedly the oldest continuously inhabited house in the country and much of the Norman house remains. Visitors are offered the unique chance to walk into the books and to see the Lucy Boston patchworks. The garden features topiary, old roses and herbaceous borders.

Location: OS Ref. TL290 706. Off A14, 3m SE of Huntingdon. 12m NW of Cambridge.

Opening Times: House: all year by appointment only. Garden: all year 10am - 6pm.

Admission: Adult £4, Child £1.50. Garden only: Adult £1, Child 50p.

🐕 In garden, on leads.

LONGTHORPE TOWER ⌗   **Tel:** 01733 268482

Peterborough, Cambridgeshire

Owner: English Heritage   **Contact:** The Custodian

The finest example of 14th century domestic wall paintings in northern Europe showing a variety of secular and sacred objects. The tower, with the Great Chamber that contains the paintings, is part of a fortified manor house. Special exhibitions are held on the upper floor.

Location: OS Ref. TL163 983. 2m W of Peterborough on A47.

Opening Times: 1 Apr - 1 Nov: weekends and BHs only: 12 - 5pm.

Admission: Adult £1.30, Child 70p, Conc. £1.

🐕 No dogs.

Hangers-on:

A word of curiously macabre derivation. Before the introduction in the 1780s of the more humane trap-door, which usually broke the prisoner's neck, hanging meant death by slow strangulation. The prisoner might arrange for his friends – or pay someone – to pull heavily on his feet as the execution was carried out, in an attempt to break his neck and thus ensure a speedier death. These friends were known as hangers-on.

Extract from; "Life in the Country House" by David N Durant (published by John Murray), PB£15.99, see page twelve at the front of the book.

OLIVER CROMWELL'S HOUSE   **Tel:** 01353 662062 **Fax:** 01353 668518

29 St Mary's Street, Ely, Cambridgeshire CB7 4HF

Owner: East Cambridgeshire District Council   **Contact:** Mrs Alison Curtis-Smith

The former home of the Lord Protector. There are exhibition sets and videos on Oliver Cromwell.

Location: OS Ref. TL538 803. N of Cambridge, W of Cambridge Cathedral.

Opening Times: 1 Oct - 31 Mar: Mon - Sat, 10am - 5.15pm. 1 Apr - 30 Sept: daily 10am - 6pm.

Admission: Adult £2.30, Conc. £1.80, Family £5. Please apply for group rates.

i Shop.	术 By arrangement.	P No parking.	🐾 Teachers' pack.	🐕 Guide dogs only.

PECKOVER HOUSE & GARDENS 🍃   **Tel:** 01945 583463

North Brink, Wisbech, Cambridgeshire PE13 1JR

Owner: The National Trust   **Contact:** The Property Manager

A town house, built c1722, with fine plaster and wood rococo decoration, and a collection of the Cornwallis family portraits. The notable 2 acre Victorian garden includes an orangery and the recently restored Reed Barn.

Location: OS Ref. TF458 097. On N bank of River Nene, in Wisbech B1441.

Opening Times: House & Garden: 28 Mar - 1 Nov, Sat & Sun, Wed & BH Mon, 12.30 - 5.30pm. Garden only: Mon, Tues & Thur 12.30 - 5.30pm. Groups on house open days by appointment. Tours out of hours by arrangement.

Admission: Adult £3.20. (£2 on garden only days), Group £2.50

X Available.	& Grounds suitable. WC	☕ Tearoom.	🐕 Guide dogs only.

PETERBOROUGH CATHEDRAL   **Tel:** 01733 343342 **Fax:** 01733 552465

Peterborough, Cambridgeshire PE1 1XS   **Contact:** Miles Falla

West front unique in Christendom. Painted Nave ceiling (c1220) unique in England. Pure Romanesque interior. Exquisite fan vaulting (c1500) in retro-choir. Burial place of Katharine of Aragon. Former burial place of Mary Queen of Scots. Saxon sculptures. Monastic remains. Exhibition: 'Life of Peterborough Cathedral'.

Location: OS Ref. TL194 986. 4m E of A1, in City Centre.

Opening Times: Mon-Sat 7am - 5.15pm. Sun 7.30am - 5pm. Weekday services: 7.30am, 8am, 5.30pm (3.30pm Sats). Sun services: 8.15am, 9.30am, 10.30am, 3.30pm.

Admission: Donation suggested.

i Shop.	& Church suitable.	☕ Tearoom & café.	术 By arrangement.
P No parking.	🐾 Educational programme available.		🐕 Guide dogs only.

PRIOR CRAUDEN'S CHAPEL   Tel: 01353 662837 Fax: 01353 662187

King's School, Ely, Cambridgeshire CB7 4DB

Owner: Kings School   **Contact:** The Bursar

Early 14th century chapel recently restored to show glimpses of coloured walls and wall paintings.

Location: OS Ref. TL541 801. The College Ely Cathedral. In Cathedral Precincts, 150 yds S of Cathedral.

Opening Times: Key obtainable nearby from 9am - 5pm on weekdays.

Admission: Free.

♿ Not suitable. ✖ Available. P No parking. In grounds, on leads.

RAMSEY ABBEY GATEHOUSE   Tel: 01263 733471 (Regional office)

Abbey School, Ramsey, Cambridgeshire PE17 1DH

Owner: The National Trust   **Contact:** The Curator (in writing)

Remains of a 15th century gatehouse of the Benedictine Abbey.

Location: OS Ref. TL291 851. At SE edge of Ramsey at point where Chatteris road leaves B1096, 10m SE of Peterborough.

Opening Times: 1 Apr - end Oct: daily, 10am - 5pm, other times by written application.

Admission: Donation.

P Limited. Guide dogs only.

UNIVERSITY BOTANIC GARDEN   Tel: 01223 336265 Fax: 01223 336278

Bateman Street, Cambridge, Cambridgeshire CB2 1JF

Owner: University of Cambridge   **Contact:** Mrs B Stacey, Administrative Secretary

40 acres of outstanding gardens with lake and glasshouses, near the centre of Cambridge, incorporating nine National collections, including Geranium and Fritillaria.

Location: OS Ref. TL453 573. 1m S of Cambridge city centre, off A1309 (Trumpington Rd).

Opening Times: Daily (except Christmas Day & Boxing Day), 10am - 6pm (Summer), 10am - 5pm (Spring and Autumn) 10am - 4pm (Winter). Tours by arrangement.

Admission: Admission charged weekdays Mar to Oct inclusive and weekends and BHs throughout the year.

ⓘ Shop. ♿ Grounds suitable. WCs. Tearoom. P Street/Pay & Display.

Guide dogs only.

WIMPOLE HALL & HOME FARM

Nick Meers.

ARRINGTON, ROYSTON, CAMBRIDGESHIRE SG8 0BW

Owner: *The National Trust*   **Contact:** *Property Manager*

Tel: 01223 207257 **Fax:** 01223 207838

Largest country house in Cambridgeshire. An 18th century mansion set in landscaped parkland by 'Capability' Brown and Repton. Architects include Gibbs, Flitcroft and Soane. Farm with many thatched buildings designed by Soane. Farm houses many rare breeds of cattle, sheep and pigs. Miles of walks in parkland. Colourful parterres in the garden.

Location: OS Ref. TL336 510. Off A603 signposted 7m SW of Cambs M11/J12.

Opening Times: Hall & Garden: 14 Mar - 1 Nov: Tue, Wed. Thur, Sat & Sun 1-5pm. Also Good Fri 1-5pm, BH Suns & Mons 11-5pm and Fris in Aug 1-5pm. **Park:** All Year: daily, dawn to dusk but closes 5pm on concert nights. check with property). **Farm:** 14 Mar - 1 Nov: Tue, Wed, Thur, Sat & Sun 10.30am -5pm. Also Good Fri, BH Mons and Fris in Jul & Aug. Nov - Mar open Wed, Sat & Sun 11-4pm. Closed 25/26/27 Dec. Open New Year's Day and school half-term weeks in Feb.

Admission: Hall & Garden: Adult £5.50, Child £2.25. Garden only: Adult £2. Hall, Garden & Farm: Adult £7.50, Child £3.50. Farm: Adult £4.20, Child(over 3yrs) £2.50. Reduction for NT members. Group rates available.

ⓘ Shop. ♿ Grounds suitable. WC. Restaurant. In grounds, on leads.

Stephen Robson.

Peckover House, Cambridgeshire.

AUDLEY END HOUSE & GDNS ⌗
Saffron Walden

Audley End was a palace in all but name. Built by Thomas Howard, Earl of Suffolk, to entertain King James I. The King may have had his suspicions, for he never stayed there; in 1618 Howard was imprisoned and fined for embezzlement.

Charles II bought the property in 1668 for £50,000, but within a generation the house was gradually demolished, and by the 1750s it was about the size you see today. There are still over 30 rooms to see, each with period furnishings.

The house and its gardens, including a 19th century parterre and rose garden, are surrounded by an 18th century landscaped park laid out by 'Capability' Brown.

OPENING TIMES

1 April - 30 September
Wed - Sun and BHs
11am - 6pm.
Last admission 5pm.

1 October - 1 November
Wed - Sun
10am - 3pm

House by pre-booked guided tour only.

Guided tours only in October.

CONTACT

The General Manager
Audley End House
Audley End
Saffron Walden
Essex
CB11 4JF

Tel: (01799) 522399

Fax: (01799) 521276

LOCATION

OS Ref. TL525 382

1m W of Saffron Walden on B1383,
M11/J8 & 9 northbound
J10 southbound.

Rail: Audley End 1m

ADMISSION

House & Grounds
Adult £5.75
Child* £2.90
Conc.......................£4.30
Family (2 + 3).........£14.40

Grounds only
Adult £3.50
Child* £1.80
Concessions............£2.60
Family (2 + 3)...........£8.80

* Child 5 - 15yrs.
  Under 5 free.

Groups
15% off groups of 11+.

ℹ️ Shop. Open air concerts and other events.

♿ Ground floor and grounds suitable.

☕ Restaurant (max 50).

🚶 By arrangement for groups.

🅿 Available. Coaches to book in advance, £5 per coach. Free entry for coach drivers and tour guides. One additional place for every extra 20 people.

👥 School visits free if booked in advance. Contact Administrator or tel. 01604 730325 for bookings.

🐕 On leads only.

AUDLEY END HOUSE & PARK ⊞   See page 154 for full page entry.

BOURNE MILL ❧   Tel: 01206 572422

Colchester, Essex CO2 8RT

Owner: The National Trust   **Contact:** The Custodian
Originally a fishing lodge built in 1591. It was later converted into a mill with a 4 acre mill pond. Much of the machinery, including the waterwheel, is intact.
Location: OS Ref. TM006 238. 1m S of Colchester centre, in Bourne Road, off the Mersea Road B1025.
Opening Times: BH Mon & preceding Sun only; also Sun & Tue in Jul & Aug, 2 - 5.30pm.
Admission: Adult £1.50, Child 75p. No reduction for groups.

P Limited.   🐕 Guide dogs only.

CHELMSFORD CATHEDRAL   Tel: 01245 263660

New Street, Chelmsford, Essex CM1 1AT   **Contact:** Mrs Gillian Brandon
15th century building became a Cathedral in 1914. Extended in 1920s, major refurbishment in 1980s with contemporary works of distinction and a splendid new organ in 1994.
Location: OS Ref. TL708 070. In Chelmsford.
Opening Times: Daily: 8am - 5.30pm. Sun services: 8am, 9.30am, 11.15am and 6pm. Weekday services: 8.15am and 5.15pm.

ℹ️ Shop.   ♿ Ground floor & grounds suitable.   P No parking.   🐕 In grounds, on leads.

COGGESHALL GRANGE BARN ❧   Tel: 01376 562226

Coggeshall, Colchester, Essex CO6 1RE

Owner: The National Trust   **Contact:** The Custodian
The oldest surviving timber framed barn in Europe, dating from around 1140, and originally part of the Cistercian Monastery of Coggeshall. It was restored in the 1980s by the Coggeshall Grange Barn Trust, Braintree District Council and Essex County Council. Features a small collection of farm carts and wagons.
Location: OS Ref. TL850 223. Signposted off A120 Coggeshall bypass. West side of the road southwards to Kelvedon.
Opening Times: 29 Mar - 11 Oct: Tue, Thur, Sun & BH Mon, 1 - 5pm.
Admission: £1.50. Groups (15+) £1, by prior arrangement. Joint ticket with Paycocke's £3.

♿ Suitable. WC.   P Ample for cars.   🐕 Guide dogs only.

COLCHESTER CASTLE MUSEUM   Tel: 01206 282937   Fax: 01206 282925

14 Ryegate Road, Colchester, Essex CO1 1YG

Owner: Colchester Borough Council   **Contact:** Museum Resource Centre
The largest Norman Castle Keep in Europe with fine archaeological collections on show.
Location: OS Ref. TL999 253. In Colchester town centre, off A12.
Opening Times: All year: Mon - Sat, 10am - 5pm, also Sun 2 - 5pm during Mar - Nov.
Admission: Adult £3.50, Child/Conc. £2.20, Family £9. Groups (20+) booked in advance £3.

ℹ️ Shop.   ♿ Suitable. WC.   P No parking.   🐕 Guide dogs only.

GOSFIELD HALL   Tel: 01787 472914   Fax: 01787 479551

Gosfield, Halstead, Essex CO9 1SF

Owner: Country Houses Association   **Contact:** The Administrators
Very fine Tudor gallery.
Location: OS Ref. TL778 297. On the A1017 between Braintree & Sible Hedingham. 2¹/₂ m SW of Halstead.
Opening Times: 1 May - 30 Sept: Wed & Thur, 2 - 5pm. Tours of house 2.30 & 3.15pm.
Admission: Adult £2.50, Child under 12 £1. Group driver and organiser free.

🚶 At 2.30 & 3.15pm.   🐕 No dogs.   A 1 sgl & 1 dbl w/bathroom, CHA members only.

HARWICH MARITIME & LIFEBOAT MUSEUMS   Tel: 01255 503429

Harwich Green, Harwich

Owner: The Harwich Society   **Contact:** Mr Sheard
One housed in a disused lighthouse and the other in the nearby disused Victorian Lifeboat House, complete with full size lifeboat.
Location: OS Ref. TM262 822. On Harwich Green.
Opening Times: 1 May - 31 Aug: daily, 10am - 1pm & 2 - 5pm. Groups by appointment at any time.
Admission: Adult 50p, Child free (no unaccompanied children).

HARWICH REDOUBT FORT   Tel: 01255 503429

Main Road, Harwich, Essex

Owner: The Harwich Society   **Contact:** Mr Sheard
180ft diameter circular fort built in 1808 to defend the port against Napoleonic invasion. Being restored by Harwich Society and part is a museum. Eleven guns on battlements.
Location: OS Ref. TM262 322. Rear of 29 Main Road.
Opening Times: 1 May - 31 Aug: daily, 10am - 5pm. Sept - Apr: Sun only. Groups by appointment at any time.
Admission: Adult £1, Child free (no unaccompanied children).

HEDINGHAM CASTLE 🏛   Tel: 01787 460261

Castle Hedingham, Nr Halstead, Essex CO9 3DJ

Owner: The Hon Thomas Lindsay   **Contact:** The Manager
One of the finest Norman keeps in England and in an excellent state of preservation.
Location: OS Ref. TL787 358. On B1058, 1m off A1017 between Cambridge and Colchester.
Opening Times: Easter week - end Oct: daily, 10am - 5pm.
Admission: Adult £3, Child £2, Conc. £2.50, Family £9. Groups (20+) £2.50pp.

ℹ️ Shop.   ♿ Grounds suitable.   ☕ Tearoom.   🐕 Grounds only, on leads.

HYDE HALL RHS GARDEN

RETTENDON, NR CHELMSFORD, ESSEX

Owner: The Royal Horticultural Society

Tel: 01245 400256   **Fax:** 01245 401363
A charming hilltop garden which extends to over 24 acres. Highlights include the spring bulbs, the modern, tall and intermediate bearded irises in late May and the rope walk of climbing roses and large beds ablaze with floribunda and hybrid tea roses in midsummer. Two ornamental ponds with lilies. Delightful hot and cold meals are available in the Essex thatched barn when the garden is open.
Location: OS Ref. TQ782 995. 2m E of Rettendon, 6m SE of Chelmsford. Signed off the A130.
Opening Times: 25 Mar - 31 Oct: daily, 11am - 6pm. Sept - Oct: 11am - 5pm. Last entry 1 hour before closing.
Admission: Adult £3, Child (under 6) free, Child (6 - 16) 70p. Pre-booked groups of 10+, £2.50. Companion for disabled visitor free.

ℹ️ Plant centre.   ♿ Suitable. WC.   ☕ Available.   🐕 Guide dogs only.

HYLANDS HOUSE, PARK & GARDENS   Tel: 01245 606812   Fax: 01245 606980

Hylands Park, Writtle, Chelmsford CM2 8WF

Owner: Chelmsford Borough Council   **Contact:** Vicky Parr
Impressive Georgian mansion built in 1730 in red brick. Wings were added in the early 19th century and the house clad in white stucco under Repton's guidance. The grounds of Hylands Park (500 acres) are open all year round and include beautifully maintained woodland, open parkland and formal gardens.
During 1998 Hylands House will be closed for restoration of the East Wing. There will be events held in the adjacent Gardens and Park during this time. The House will re-open in 1999. Please telephone for further details.
Location: OS Ref. TL681 054 (gate). 2m SW of Chelmsford. Signposted from A414 between Chelmsford and Writtle.
Opening Times: Grounds: all year, 7.30am - dusk. House closed during 1998. Telephone for event details.
Admission: Grounds: Free.

♿ Suitable. WC.   P Ample.   🐕 In grounds, on leads in formal gardens.

INGATESTONE HALL

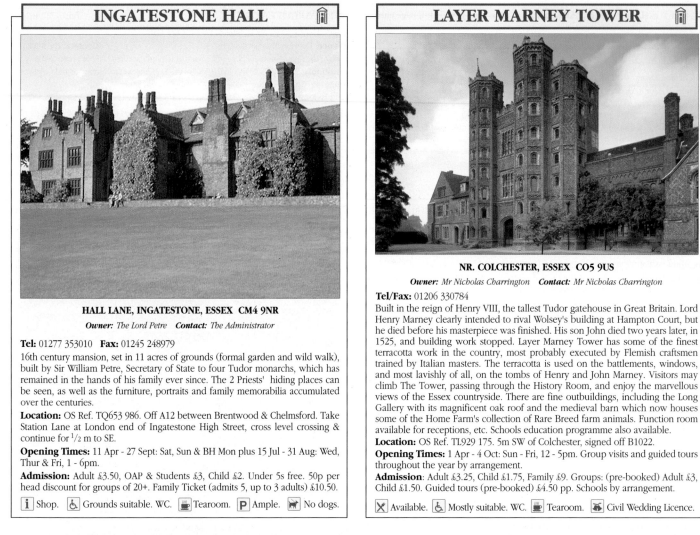

HALL LANE, INGATESTONE, ESSEX CM4 9NR

Owner: *The Lord Petre*   ***Contact:*** *The Administrator*

Tel: 01277 353010   **Fax:** 01245 248979

16th century mansion, set in 11 acres of grounds (formal garden and wild walk), built by Sir William Petre, Secretary of State to four Tudor monarchs, which has remained in the hands of his family ever since. The 2 Priests' hiding places can be seen, as well as the furniture, portraits and family memorabilia accumulated over the centuries.

Location: OS Ref. TQ653 986. Off A12 between Brentwood & Chelmsford. Take Station Lane at London end of Ingatestone High Street, cross level crossing & continue for ¹/₂ m to SE.

Opening Times: 11 Apr - 27 Sept: Sat, Sun & BH Mon plus 15 Jul - 31 Aug: Wed, Thur & Fri, 1 - 6pm.

Admission: Adult £3.50, OAP & Students £3, Child £2. Under 5s free. 50p per head discount for groups of 20+. Family Ticket (admits 5, up to 3 adults) £10.50.

ℹ️ Shop. ♿ Grounds suitable. WC. ☕ Tearoom. 🅿️ Ample. 🐕 No dogs.

LAYER MARNEY TOWER

NR. COLCHESTER, ESSEX CO5 9US

Owner: *Mr Nicholas Charrington*   ***Contact:*** *Mr Nicholas Charrington*

Tel/Fax: 01206 330784

Built in the reign of Henry VIII, the tallest Tudor gatehouse in Great Britain. Lord Henry Marney clearly intended to rival Wolsey's building at Hampton Court, but he died before his masterpiece was finished. His son John died two years later, in 1525, and building work stopped. Layer Marney Tower has some of the finest terracotta work in the country, most probably executed by Flemish craftsmen trained by Italian masters. The terracotta is used on the battlements, windows, and most lavishly of all, on the tombs of Henry and John Marney. Visitors may climb The Tower, passing through the History Room, and enjoy the marvellous views of the Essex countryside. There are fine outbuildings, including the Long Gallery with its magnificent oak roof and the medieval barn which now houses some of the Home Farm's collection of Rare Breed farm animals. Function room available for receptions, etc. Schools education programme also available.

Location: OS Ref. TL929 175. 5m SW of Colchester, signed off B1022.

Opening Times: 1 Apr - 4 Oct: Sun - Fri, 12 - 5pm. Group visits and guided tours throughout the year by arrangement.

Admission: Adult £3.25, Child £1.75, Family £9. Groups: (pre-booked) Adult £3, Child £1.50. Guided tours (pre-booked) £4.50 pp. Schools by arrangement.

✕ Available. ♿ Mostly suitable. WC. ☕ Tearoom. 💒 Civil Wedding Licence.

Hylands House, Essex.
During 1998, the house will be closed for restoration of the East Wing, although events will be held in the adjacent Gardens and Park. The House will re-open in 1999.

Patrick Lane.

LOWER DAIRY HOUSE GARDEN

Tel: 01206 262220

Water Lane, Nayland, Colchester, Essex CO6 4JS

Owner: Mr & Mrs D J Burnett   **Contact:** The Owners

Plantsman's garden, approx 1½ acres.

Location: OS Ref. TL966 330. 7m N of Colchester off A134. 1m SW of Nayland on E side of road to Little Horkesley.

Opening Times: Apr 12/13/19, 26. May 3/4/10/17/24/25. Jun 7/14/21. Jul 5/12: 2 - 6pm.

Admission: Adult £2, Child 50p. Groups welcome by appointment.

MISTLEY TOWERS ⌗

Tel: 01206 393884

Colchester, Essex

Owner: English Heritage   **Contact:** The Custodian

The remains of one of only two churches designed by the great architect Robert Adam. Built in 1776. It was unusual in having towers at both the east and west ends.

Location: OS Ref. TM116 320. On B1352, 1½ m E of A137 at Lawford, 9m E of Colchester.

Opening Times: Telephone for opening times.

Admission: Key available from Mistley Quay workshops - 01206 393884.

PAYCOCKE'S 🌿

Tel: 01376 561305

West Street, Coggeshall, Colchester, Essex C06 1NS

Owner: The National Trust   **Contact:** The Tenant

A merchant's house, dating from about 1500, with unusually rich panelling and wood carving. A display of lace for which Coggeshall was famous is on show. Delightful garden leading down to small river.

Location: OS Ref. TL848 225. Signposted off A120.

Opening Times: 29 Mar - 11 Oct: Tue, Thur, Sun & BH Mon, 2 - 5.30pm, last adm: 5pm.

Admission: £2, groups of 10+ by prior arrangement, no reduction for groups. Joint ticket with Coggeshall Grange Barn £3.

♿ Access to ground floor and garden.   P NT's at the Coggeshall Grange Barn.

PRIORS HALL BARN ⌗

Tel: 01799 522842

Widdington, Newport, Essex

Owner: English Heritage   **Contact:** Audley End House

One of the finest surviving medieval barns in south-east England and representative of the group of aisled barns centred on north-west Essex.

Location: OS Ref. TL538 319. In Widdington, on unclassified road 2m SE of Newport, off B1383.

Opening Times: 1 Apr - 30 Sept: Sat & Sun, 10am - 6pm.

Admission: Telephone for further details.

♿ Suitable.

SALING HALL GARDEN

Tel: 01371 850 243 **Fax:** 01371 850 274

Great Saling, Braintree, Essex CM7 5DT

Owner: Hugh Johnson Esq   **Contact:** Hugh Johnson Esq

12 acres including a walled garden dated 1698. Water gardens and landscaped arboretum.

Location: OS Ref. TL700 258. 6m NW of Braintree, 2m N of A120.

Opening Times: May, Jun and Jul: Wed, 2 - 5pm. Sun 28 Jun: 2 - 6pm.

Admission: Standard £2, Child free.

♿ Grounds suitable. WC.   P Limited.   🐕 Guide dogs only.

TILBURY FORT ⌗

Tel: 01375 858489

No. 2 Office Block, The Fort, Tilbury, Essex RM18 7NR

Owner: English Heritage   **Contact:** The Custodian

The best and largest example of 17th century military engineering in England, commanding the Thames. The fort shows the development of fortifications over the following 200 years. Exhibitions, the powder magazine and the bunker-like 'casemates' demonstrate how the fort protected London from seaborne attack. Elizabeth I gave a speech near here on the eve of the Spanish Armada.

Location: OS Ref. TQ651 754. ½ m E of Tilbury off A126.

Opening Times: 1 Apr - 1 Nov: daily, 10am - 6pm. 2 Nov - 31 Mar: Wed - Sun, 10am - 4pm. Closed 24 - 26 Dec.

Admission: Adult £2.30, Child £1.20, Conc. £1.70.

ℹ Shop.

WALTHAM ABBEY GATEHOUSE & BRIDGE ⌗

Tel: 01604 730320

Waltham Abbey, Essex

(Regional Office)

Owner: English Heritage   **Contact:** The Midlands Regional Office

The late 14th century abbey gatehouse, part of the north range of the cloister and the medieval 'Harold's Bridge' of one of the great monastic foundations of the Middle Ages.

Location: OS Ref. TL381 008. In Waltham Abbey off A112. Just NE of the Abbey church.

Opening Times: Any reasonable time.

Admission: Free.

Garderobe:

The medieval equivalent of the modern lavatory: no more than a seat suspended over a shaft dropping into a moat or, more usually down its own tower.

Within days of arriving in late 1568 at her first prison, Tutbury Castle in Staffordshire, Mary Queen of Scots (1542–87) was complaining of the stench of the garderobes near her apartment: Tutbury was a medieval castle, designed for about 200 occupants, but Mary's court and hangers-on, and the soldiers guarding the royal prisoner, brought the numbers above 400, and the garderobes were overloaded. Fortunate was the house where the garderobes discharged straight into a surrounding moat – as they did at Little Moreton Hall, Cheshire. Where there was no convenient moat, a hatch at the base enabled the excreta at the foot of the shaft to be cleared out once a year. Haddon Hall in Derbyshire has a two-seater garderobe, with two cleaning hatches. Provided that the drop is more than twenty feet, there is no smell in the garderobe itself. At Wollaton Hall (1580–88) near Nottingham the interior garderobes discharged into shafts flushed out by rainwater.

At Audley End in Essex, built in 1603 on the site of a Benedictine monastery, the interior garderobes discharged into culverts – the old monastic drains; the system was so efficient that they were used well into the nineteenth century. England's largest garderobe was Whittington's Longhouse in London, a public garderobe with sixty-four seats, built with money left by Sir Richard Whittington (d. 1423).

CIVIL WEDDING VENUES

See the front section for full list.

Eastern Counties England

BELVOIR CASTLE
Grantham

BELVOIR CASTLE, home of the Duke and Duchess of Rutland, commands a magnificent view over the Vale of Belvoir. The name Belvoir, meaning beautiful view, dates back to Norman times, when Robert de Todeni, Standard Bearer to William the Conqueror, built the first Castle on this superb site. Destruction caused by two Civil Wars and by a catastrophic fire in 1816 have breached the continuity of Belvoir's history. The present building owes much to the inspiration and taste of Elizabeth, 5th Duchess of Rutland and was built after the fire.

Inside the Castle are notable art treasures including works by Poussin, Holbein, Rubens, and Reynolds, Gobelin and Mortlake tapestries, Chinese silks, furniture, fine

porcelain and sculpture.

The Queen's Royal Lancers Museum at Belvoir has a fascinating exhibition of the history of the Regiment, as well as a fine collection of weapons, uniforms and medals.

GARDENS

The Statue Gardens are built into the hillside below the Castle and take their name from the collection of 17th century sculptures on view. The garden is planted so that there is nearly always something in flower.

The Duchess' private Spring Gardens are available for viewing throughout the year by pre-booked groups of 20 persons or more. Details from the Estate Office.

CONTACT

Diana Marshall
Castle Estate Office
Belvoir Castle
Grantham
Lincolnshire
NG32 1PD

Tel: (01476) 870262

Fax: (01476) 870443

LOCATION

OS Ref. SK820 337

A1 from London 110m
York 100m
Grantham 7m.
A607 Grantham-Melton Mowbray.

Air: East Midlands International.

Rail: Grantham Station 7m

Bus: Melton Mowbray - Vale of Belvoir via Castle Car Park.

Taxi: Grantham Taxis 63944 / 63988.

CONFERENCE/FUNCTION		
ROOM	SIZE	MAX CAPACITY
State Dining Room	52' x 31'	130
Regents Gallery	131' x 16'	300
Old Kitchen	45' x 22'	100

i Shop. Suitable for exhibitions, product launches, conferences, filming, photography welcomed (permit £2).

X Banquets, private room available.

Ground floor and restaurant accessible. Please telephone for advice. WCs.

Licensed restaurant. Groups catered for.

By prior arrangement £20 per group (max. 20). Tour time: 1¼ hrs.

P Ample. Coaches can take passengers to entrance by arrangement but should report to the main car park and ticket office on arrival.

Guided tours. Teacher's pack. Education room. Picnic area and adventure playground.

Guide dogs only.

SUMMER
31 March - 1 October

Tue, Wed, Thur & Sat
Sun & BHs. Suns only in Oct.
11am - 5pm.

WINTER
Groups welcome by appointment.

ADMISSION

Adult	£5.00
Child (5 - 16yrs)	£3.00
OAP	£4.00
Family (2+2)	£14.00

Groups (min 20, max 200)
Adult	£4.00
Child (5 - 16yrs)	£2.50
Student	£2.50
OAP	£3.60

SPECIAL EVENTS

- **24/25 MAY:**
Siege group.

- **28 JUNE:**
Jousting tournaments.

- **26 JULY:**
Jousting tournaments.

- **30/31 AUGUST:**
Jousting tournaments.

- **5 SEPTEMBER:**
Open air concert.

Eastern Counties
England

BURGHLEY HOUSE
Stamford

BURGHLEY HOUSE, home of the Cecil family for over 400 years, was built as a country seat during the latter part of the 16th century by Sir William Cecil, later Lord Burghley, principal adviser and Lord Treasurer to Queen Elizabeth.

The House was completed in 1587 and there have been few alterations to the architecture since that date thus making Burghley one of the finest examples of late Elizabethan design in England.

The interior was remodelled in the late 17th century by John, 5th Earl of Exeter who was a collector of fine art on a huge scale, establishing the immense collection of art treasures at Burghley.

Burghley is truly a 'Treasure House', containing one of the largest private collections of Italian art, unique examples of Chinese and Japanese porcelain and superb items of 18th century furniture. The remodelling work of the 17th century means that examples of the work of the principal artists and craftsmen of the period are to be found here at Burghley: Antonio Verrio, Grinling Gibbons and Louis Laguerre all made major contributions to the beautiful interiors.

GARDENS
The House is set in a 300-acre deer park landscaped by 'Capability' Brown under the direction of the 9th Earl. As was usual with Brown's designs, a lake was created and delightful avenues of mature trees feature largely. The park is home to a herd of fallow deer and is open to the public at all times of the year. The gardens surrounding the House are only open on certain weekends in the Spring. Please telephone for details.

CONTACT

J Culverhouse
Burghley House
Stamford
Lincolnshire
PE9 3JY

Tel: (01780) 752451

Fax: (01780) 480125

LOCATION

OS Ref. TF048 062

Burghley House
is 1m SE of Stamford.
From London, A1 2hrs.

Visitors entrance
is on B1443.

Rail: Stamford Station
$1^1/_2$ m.

Taxi: Phoenix
(01780) 482105.

CONFERENCE/FUNCTION		
ROOM	SIZE	MAX CAPACITY
Great Hall	70' x 30'	180
Orangery	100' x 20'	120

OPENING TIMES

SUMMER

1 April - 4 October
Daily
11am - 4.30pm.

NB. Closed 5 September

WINTER

5 October - 1 April
House closed to the
general public.

i   Shop. Suitable for a variety of events, large park, golf course, helicopter landing area, cricket pitch.
No photography in house.

  Visitors may alight at the entrance. WC. Chair lift to Orangery Coffee Shop, house tour involves two staircases one of which has a chairlift.

  Restaurant / tea room. Groups can book in advance.

  Tour time: $1^1/_2$ hrs at 15 min intervals. Max. 25.

P   Ample. Free refreshments for coach drivers.

  Welcome. Guide provided; £2.50 ea.

  No dogs in house.

ADMISSION

Adult*	£5.85
Child**	£2.50
OAP	£5.55
Groups (min 20)	
Adult	£4.75
Child*	£2.50

* One child (under 14) admitted FREE per paying adult.

** Aged up to 14yrs.

AUBOURN HALL

Tel: 01522 788270   **Fax:** 01522 788199

Lincoln, Lincolnshire LN5 9DZ

Owner: Sir Henry Nevile   **Contact:** Sir Henry Nevile

Late 16th century house with important staircase and panelled rooms. Garden.

Location: OS Ref. SK928 628. 6m SW of Lincoln. 2m SE of A46.

Opening Times: Weds in Jul & Aug, 2 - 6pm.

Admission: Adult £2.50, OAP £2.

♿ Grounds suitable.   No dogs.

BAYSGARTH HOUSE MUSEUM

Tel: 01652 632318

Caistor Road, Barton on Humber, Humberside DN18 6AH

Owner: North Lincolnshire Council   **Contact:** Mr D J Williams

18th century town house and park. Displays of porcelain and local history.

Location: OS Ref. TA035 215. Caistor Road, Barton on Humber.

Opening Times: Thur, Fri and BHs: 10.30am - 3.30pm. Sat and Sun, 10.30am - 4.30pm.

Admission: Free (at time of going to press).

[i] Shop.   ♿ Ground floor suitable.

BELTON HOUSE PARK & GARDENS

Tel: 01476 566116

Grantham, Lincolnshire NG32 2LS   **Fax:** 01476 579071

Owner: The National Trust   **Contact:** The Property Manager

The crowning achievement of Restoration country house architecture, built 1685 - 88 for Sir John Brownlow, and altered by James Wyatt in the 1770s. Plasterwork ceilings by Edward Goudge and fine wood carvings of the Grinling Gibbons school. The rooms contain portraits, furniture, tapestries, oriental porcelain, silver and silver gilt. Gardens with orangery, landscaped park with lakeside walk and woodland adventure playground, and Bellmount Tower. Fine church with family monuments.

Location: OS Ref. SK929 395. 3m NE of Grantham on A607. Signed off the A1.

Opening Times: House: 1 Apr - 1 Nov: Wed - Sun & BH Mon (closed Good Fri), 1 - 5.30pm. Garden & Park: 11am - 5.30pm. Last admission to house, garden and park 5pm.

Admission: House & Garden: Adult £5, Child £2.50, Family £12.50. Reduced rates for groups.

[i] Shop.   ♿ Please telephone for arrangements.   Licensed restaurant.

BELVOIR CASTLE

See page 158 for full page entry.

BURGHLEY HOUSE

See page 159 for full page entry

DODDINGTON HALL

LINCOLN LN6 4RU

Owner: *Mr & Mrs A Jarvis*   **Contact:** *Mr & Mrs A Jarvis*

Tel: 01522 694308   **Fax:** 01522 682584

Magnificent Smythson mansion was completed in 1600 and stands today with its contemporary walled gardens and gatehouse. The Hall is still very much the home of the Jarvis family and has an elegant Georgian interior with a fine collection of porcelain, furniture, paintings and textiles representing 400 years of unbroken family occupation. The beautiful gardens contain a superb layout of box-edged parterres, sumptuous borders that provide colour all seasons, and a wild garden with a marvellous succession of spring bulbs and flowering shrubs set among mature trees. Sandford Award winning schools project, and a nature trail into the nearby countryside.

Location: OS Ref. SK900 701. 5m W of Lincoln on the B1190, signposted off the A46 Lincoln Bypass.

Opening Times: Mar - Apr: Garden only: Sun, 2 - 6pm. May - Sept: House & Garden: Wed, Sun & BH Mon, 2 - 6pm.

Admission: House & Garden: Adult £4, Child £2. Garden only: Adult £2, Child £1, Family £11.

[i] Shop.   ♿ Ground floor & grounds suitable. WC.   Available.

Wife Sale:

Although divorce was difficult to impossible for any but the very wealthy until 1857, wife-sale was a cheap alternative practised by those on the bottom rungs of the social ladder. Readers of Thomas Hardy's The Mayor of Casterbridge, set in the early nineteenth century, will know that Michael Henchard, a hay-trusser, got drunk and sold his wife to a sailor for £5. The description of a real sale of 1727 tells how the husband put a halter round his wife's neck and led her to the market-place as if she had been a cow. Such sales frequently took place at Smithfield, but the sale was usually arranged beforehand, with the full agreement of the wife, for a price ranging from a few pence to a few pounds. In 1769 a Sheffield steel-burner sold his wife to a fell-monger for sixpence, and then paid half a guinea more to have her taken out of town.

Although widely accepted, the practice (medieval in origin) never had a legal basis, and indeed attempts were made to stop it in the early eighteenth century. Wife-sales were most frequent in the eighteenth century, but the last recorded case was in 1887, and the Lord Chancellor's ruling against it in 1891 effectively abolished the practice.

Extract from; "Life in the Country House" by David N Durant (published by John Murray), PB£15.99, see page twelve at the front of the book.

ELSHAM HALL COUNTRY & WILDLIFE PARK

Tel: 01652 688698

Elsham, Brigg, Lincolnshire DN20 0QZ   **Fax:** 01652 688738

Owner: Capt Jeremy Elwes / Robert Elwes   **Contact:** Robert Elwes

Winner of ten awards for tourism. Attractions include falconry, the mini zoo, Georgian courtyard, craft workshops, arboretum, theatre and conference centre, clocktower museum and beautiful lakeside gardens with carp and trout lakes.

Location: OS Ref. TA030 120. 10 mins from M180/J5, Humber Bridge turn-off.

Opening Times: Easter - mid Sept: daily including Sun & BHs, 11am - 5pm. Art Gallery: 12 - 5pm. Closed mid Sept - Easter. Theatre open separately.

Admission: Adult £3.95, Child £2.50 (3+), OAP £3.50. Group rates for groups of 20+.

[i] Shop. Plant centre.   [X] Medieval banquets.   Licensed restaurant.
♔ By arrangement.   Guide dogs only.   Civil Wedding Licence.

CIVIL WEDDING VENUES

See the front section for full list.

FULBECK HALL

GRANTHAM, LINCOLNSHIRE NG32 3JW

Owner: Mrs M Fry   **Contact:** Mrs M Fry

Tel: 01400 272205 **Fax:** 01400 272205

Home of the Fane family since 1632 with alterations and additions by nearly every generation. Mainly 18th century house. Arnhem Museum commemorates 1st Airborne Division for whom Fulbeck Hall was HQ during the War. 11 acres of garden with much interesting new planting within the Edwardian design. Conference facilities for up to 80 people, private dining and corporate hospitality. All details on request.

Location: OS Ref. SK947 505. On A607 14m S of Lincoln. 11m N of Grantham.

Opening Times: 12/13 Apr, 4 & 25 May, 28 Jun - 10 Jul, 13 Jul - 26 Jul, daily, also 24 Aug: 2 - 5pm. Museum open at any time by appointment.

Admission: House & Garden: Adult £3.50, OAP £3, Child £1.50, Family £9.50. Garden: Adult £1.50, Child £1. Arnhem Museum: Adult £1.50, Child £1.

☒ Functions/conferences. ♿ Partially suitable. WC. ♠ Groups only.

🐕 Guide dogs only.   Ⓐ Max 6, only if attending conferences/functions.

SPECIAL EVENTS

APR 12: Rare & Unusual Plant Fair   JUL 10/12: Shakespeare Weekend
For full details of events at Fulbeck Hall, see the Special Events section.

GRIMSTHORPE CASTLE, PARK & GDNS 🏛

GRIMSTHORPE, BOURNE, LINCOLNSHIRE PE10 0NB

Owner: Grimsthorpe and Drummond Castle Trust Ltd   **Contact:** Tim Clarke

Tel: 01778 591205 **Fax:** 01778 591259

Home of the Willoughby de Eresby family since 1576. Examples of 13th century architecture, Tudor period and Sir John Vanbrugh's last major work. State Rooms and picture galleries contain magnificent contents and paintings. 3,000 acre 'Capability' Brown landscaped park, with lakes, ancient woods, nature trails, woodland adventure playground, red deer herd, formal and woodland gardens, unusual ornamental vegetable gardens, family cycle trail, special events programme. The Grimsthorpe Conference Centre is available for meetings of up to 70, including catering, also private parties and wedding receptions.

Location: OS Ref. TF040 230. 4m NW of Bourne on A151, 8m E of Colsterworth roundabout off A1.

Opening Times: 12 Apr - 27 Sept: Sun, Thur & BHs from Easter Sun. Aug: daily except Fri & Sat. Park & Gardens: 11am - 6pm. Castle: 2 - 6pm. Last adm. 5pm. Guided tours for groups and schools by arrangement. Coach House/Tearoom, 11am (last orders 5.15pm).

Admission: Park & Garden: Adult £3, Conc. £2. Castle: Adult £5, Conc. £4. Combined ticket: Adult £6, Conc. £4.50. Special charges may apply for major events. Group rates on application.

ⓘ Shop. Conferences.   ☕ Licensed restaurant.   🐕 In grounds, on leads.

GAINSBOROUGH OLD HALL ⌗   **Tel:** 01427 612669

Parnell Street, Gainsborough, Lincolnshire DN21 2NB

Owner: English Heritage   **Contact:** The Custodian

A large medieval house with a magnificent Great Hall and suites of rooms. A collection of historic furniture and a re-created medieval kitchen are on display.

Location: OS Ref. SK815 895. In centre of Gainsborough, opposite library.

Opening Times: Easter Sun - 31 Oct: Mon - Sat, 10am - 5pm. Sun, 2 - 5.30pm. 1 Nov - Easter Sat: Mon - Sat, 10am - 5pm (closed Good Fri, 24 - 26 Dec & 1 Jan).

Admission: Charge made.

♿ Most of ground floor.   🐕 On leads.

SPECIAL EVENTS 1998

See the front section for full list.

Historic Scotland

GUNBY HALL 🌿   **Tel:** 01909 486411 **Fax:** 01909 486377

Gunby, Spilsby, Lincolnshire PE23 5SS

Owner: The National Trust   **Contact:** Regional Office

A red brick house with stone dressings, built in 1700 and extended in 1870s. Within the house, there is good early 18th century wainscoting and a fine oak staircase, also English furniture and portraits by Reynolds. Also of interest is the contemporary stable block, a walled kitchen and flower garden, sweeping lawns and borders and an exhibition of Field Marshall Sir Archibald Montgomery-Massingberd's memorabilia. Gunby was reputedly Tennyson's 'haunt of ancient peace'.

Location: OS Ref. TF467 668. 2m W of Burgh Le Marsh, 8m W of Skegness, from Gunby Lane off A158.

Opening Times: Ground floor of house & garden: 1 Apr - end Sept: Wed 2 - 6pm. Last admission 5.30pm. Closed public holidays. Garden also open Thur 2 - 6pm. House & garden also open Tue, Thur & Fri by written appointment to J D Wrisdale at above address.

Admission: House & Garden: Adult £3.50, Child £1.70, Family £8.70. Garden only: Adult £2.50, Child £1.20, Family £6.20. No reduction for groups. Access roads unsuitable for coaches which must park in layby at gates ¹/₂ m from Hall.

♿ Grounds suitable.   🐕 In grounds, on leads.

HARLAXTON MANOR   **Tel:** 01476 564541 **Fax:** 01476 570730

Harlaxton, Grantham, Lincolnshire NG32 1AG

Owner: University of Evansville   **Contact:** Mrs F Watkins

Neo-Elizabethan house. Grandiose and imposing exterior by Anthony Salvin. Internally an architectural tour de force with a mixture of various styles and an unparalleled Cedar Staircase. Available for conferences.

Location: OS Ref. SK895 323. 3m W of Grantham (10 mins from A1) A607. SE of the village.

Opening Times: Garden: Apr - Sept: 11am - 5pm. House: 24 May & 28 Jun: 11am - 5pm. House open at other times for group tours by appointment only.

Admission: Garden: Adult £3, Child £1.25, OAP £2. No reduction for groups. House open days: Adult £4.50, Child £2, OAP £4.

ⓘ Wedding receptions. Corporate hospitality.   ♿ House suitable. WC.

☕ Tearoom.   ♠ By appointment only.   🐕 In grounds, on leads.

LEADENHAM HOUSE

Tel: 01400 273256 **Fax:** 01400 272237

Leadenham House, Lincolnshire LN5 0PU

Owner: Mr P. Reeve **Contact:** Mr and Mrs P. Reeve

Late eighteenth century house in park setting.

Location: OS Ref. SK949 518. A17 between Newark & Sleaford.

Opening Times: 16 July - 12 Aug also Easter Mon, May, Spring & Aug BHs: daily 2 - 5pm.

Admission: Adult £3. Groups by prior arrangement only.

ℹ No photography. ♿ Suitable. 🚫🐕 Strictly no dogs.

LINCOLN CASTLE

Tel: 01522 511068

Castle Hill, Lincoln **Contact:** The Manager

Built by William the Conqueror in 1608. Informative exhibition of the 1215 Magna Carta, sealed by King John at Runnymeade. Wedding receptions. Civil Wedding Licence held.

Location: OS Ref. SK975 718. Opposite west front of Lincoln Cathedral.

Opening Times: BST: Sat 9.30am - 5.30pm, Sun 11am - 5.30pm. GMT: Mon - Sat: 9.30am - 4pm, Sun 11am - 4pm. Closed Christmas Day, Boxing Day & New Year's Day.

Admission: Adult £2.50, Child £1, Family (2+3) £6.50

ℹ Shop. ♿ Suitable. ☕ Tearoom. 🚶 By arrangement. 🚫🐕 Strictly no dogs.

LINCOLN CATHEDRAL

Tel: 01522 544544

Lincoln, Lincolnshire LN2 1PZ **Contact:** Communications Office

Medieval Gothic Cathedral of outstanding historical and architectural merit. Schools centre.

Location: OS Ref. SK978 718. At the centre of Uphill, Lincoln.

Opening Times: All year: May - Aug, 7.15am - 8pm, Sun 7.15am - 6pm. Sept - May, 7.15am - 6pm, Sun 7.15am - 5pm. Tours daily: Jan - Apr & Oct - Dec: 11am & 2pm. May - Sept: 11am, 1pm & 3pm. Roof & tower tours also available. Booked tours throughout the year.

Admission: Suggested donation of Adult £3, Child £1, Conc. £1, Annual passes £10.

ℹ Shop. ♿ Suitable. WC. ☕ Tearoom. 🚶 By arrangement. 🐕 Guide dogs only.

LINCOLN MEDIEVAL BISHOPS' PALACE ♯

Tel: 01522 527468

Minster Yard, Lincoln, Lincolnshire LN2 1PU

Owner: English Heritage **Contact:** The Custodian

In the shadow of Lincoln Cathedral are the remains of this medieval palace of the Bishop of Lincoln. Climb the stairs to the Alnwick Tower, explore the undercroft and see one of the most northerly vineyards in Europe.

Location: OS121 Ref. SK981 717. S side of Lincoln Cathedral, in Lincoln.

Opening Times: 1 Apr - 1 Nov: daily, 10am - 6pm or dusk if earlier. 2 Nov - 31 Mar: weekends only, 10am - 4pm. Closed 1 -2pm in winter. Closed 24 - 26 Dec.

Admission: Adult £1.30, Child 70p, Conc. £1. 15% discount for groups of 11+.

NORMANBY HALL

See right.

TATTERSHALL CASTLE 🌿

Tel: 01526 342543

Tattershall, Lincoln, Lincolnshire LN4 4LR

Owner: The National Trust **Contact:** The Custodian

A vast fortified tower built c1440 for Ralph Cromwell, Lord Treasurer of England. The Castle is an important example of an early brick building, with a tower containing state apartments, rescued from dereliction and restored by Lord Curzon 1911-14. Four great chambers, with ancillary rooms, contain late Gothic fireplaces and brick vaulting. There are tapestries and information displays in turret rooms.

Location: OS Ref. TF209 575. On S side of A153, 15m NE of Sleaford, 10m SW of Horncastle.

Opening Times: 1 Apr - 1 Nov: daily except Thur & Fri (closed Good Fri) 10.30am - 5.30pm. Nov - 20 Dec: Sat & Sun only, 12 - 4pm.

Admission: Adult £2.70, Child £1.30, Family £6.50. Child free Jul/Aug. Discount for groups.

♿ Ground floor. WC. 🚫🐕 Car park only.

THORNTON ABBEY ♯

Tel: 0191 261 1585

Scunthorpe, Humberside

Owner: English Heritage **Contact:** The North Regional Office

The magnificent brick gatehouse of this ruined Augustine priory stands three storeys high.

Location: OS Ref. TA115 190. 18m NE of Scunthorpe on minor road N of A180.

Opening Times: 1 Apr - 30 Sept: 1st & 3rd Sun, 12 - 6pm. 1 Oct - 31 Mar: 3rd Sun, 12 - 4pm.

Admission: Free.

WOOLSTHORPE MANOR 🌿

Tel: 01476 860338

23 Newton Way, Woolsthorpe-by-Colsterworth, Grantham NG33 5NR

Owner: The National Trust **Contact:** The Custodian

This small 17th century farmhouse was the birthplace and family home of Sir Isaac Newton. Some of his major work was formulated here, during the Plague years (1665 - 66); an early edition of his *Principia Mathematica* is on display. The orchard includes a descendant of the famous apple tree.

Location: OS Ref. SK924 224. 7m S of Grantham, 1/2 m NW of Colsterworth, 1m W of A1.

Opening Times: 1 Apr - 1 Nov: Wed - Sun & BH Mon (closed Good Fri), 1 - 5.30pm. Last adm. 5pm.

Admission: Adult £2.60, Child £1.30, Family £6.50, no reduction for groups which must book in advance.

♿ Ground floor suitable. 🅿 Limited. 🚫🐕 Car park only.

NORMANBY HALL

NORMANBY, SCUNTHORPE, NORTH LINCOLNSHIRE DN15 9HU

Owner: *North Lincolnshire Council* **Contact:** *Park Manager*

Tel: 01724 720588 **Fax:** 01724 721248

The restored working Victorian Walled Kitchen Garden is growing produce for the 'big house' as it would have done 100 years ago. Victorian varieties of fruit and vegetables are grown using organic and Victorian techniques. Set in 350 acres of Park visitors may also see the Regency Mansion, designed by Sir Robert Smirke, that the Garden was built to serve.

The ground floor rooms are displayed in Regency style while the displays on the first floor reflect the changing styles of the Victorian and Edwardian eras. Costume is also on display in the Museum Service's Costume Gallery.

Location: OS Ref. SE886 166. 4m N of Scunthorpe off B1430. Follow signs from M181 & Humber Bridge. Tours by arrangement.

Opening Times: Hall & Farm Museum: Apr, May & Sept: weekends, 1 - 5pm. Jun - Aug: daily 1-5pm. **Park:** daily, 9am - 5pm. **Walled Garden:** daily, 11am - 5pm (4pm in winter)

Admission: Prices per car admittance: Apr - Sept: Mon - Fri, £1.50, Sat £2.50. Sun £3. Oct - Mar: £1.50. Coaches £13. (1997 prices).

ℹ Shop. Conference facilities. ♿ Ground floor & grounds suitable. WC.

❌ Wedding receptions. ☕ Tearoom. 🚶 By arrangement.

🅿 Ample for coaches and cars.

👥 Educational programme available. Teacher's pack available.

🐕 In grounds, on leads.

Burghley House, Lincolnshire.

HOLKHAM HALL
Wells-next-the-Sea

HOLKHAM HALL has been the home of the Coke family and the Earls of Leicester for almost 250 years. Built between 1734 and 1762 by Thomas Coke, 1st Earl of Leicester and based on a design by William Kent, this fine example of 18th century Palladian style mansion reflects Thomas Coke's natural appreciation of classical art developed during the Grand Tour. It is constructed mainly of local yellow brick with a magnificent Entrance Hall of English alabaster.

The State Rooms occupy the first floor and contain Greek and Roman statuary, paintings by Rubens, Van Dyck, Claude, Poussin and Gainsborough and original furniture.

On leaving the House visitors pass Holkham Pottery and its adjacent shop, both under the supervision of the Countess of Leicester. Fine examples of local craftsmanship are for sale including the famous Holkham Florist Ware.

Beyond are the 19th century stables now housing the Holkham Bygones Collection; some 4,000 items range from working steam engines, vintage cars and tractors to craft tools and kitchenware. A History of Farming exhibition is in the former Porter's Lodge.

The House is set in a 3,000-acre park with 600 head of fallow deer. On the lake, 1 mile long, are many species of wildfowl. Two walks encircle either the lake or agricultural buildings.

Holkham Nursery Gardens occupy the 19th century walled Kitchen Garden and a large range of stock is on sale to the public.

❖

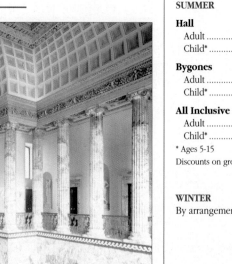

CONTACT

The Administrator
Holkham Hall
Estate Office
Wells-next-the-Sea
Norfolk
NR23 1AB

Tel: (01328) 710227

Fax: (01328) 711707

LOCATION

OS Ref. TF885 428

From London 120m
Norwich 35m
Kings Lynn 30m.

Rail: Norwich Station 35m
Kings Lynn Station 30m.

Air: Norwich Airport 32m.

ℹ️ Shop. Grounds for shows, rallies and filming. No smoking or flash photography in the Hall.

♿ Visitors may alight at entrance, stairs in the Hall. WC.

☕ Restaurant. Menus for pre-booked parties on request.

🚶 Guides are posted in each room. Audio tour £2, other times guided tours by arrangement.

🅿️ Unlimited for cars, 20+ coaches. Parking, admission, refreshments free to coach drivers, coach drivers rest room.

👪 Welcome. Areas of interest: Bygones Collection, History of Farming, 2 nature walks, deer park, lake and wildfowl.

🐕 No dogs in Hall, on leads in grounds.

OPENING TIMES

SUMMER
24 May - 30 September
Sun - Thur (inclusive)
1 - 5pm.

Easter, May, Spring & Summer BHs
Sun & Mon
11.30am - 5pm.

Last admission 4.45pm.

WINTER
October - May
Open by appointment.

ADMISSION

SUMMER

Hall
   Adult £4.00
   Child* £2.00

Bygones
   Adult £4.00
   Child* £2.00

All Inclusive
   Adult £6.00
   Child* £3.00
* Ages 5-15
Discounts on groups of 20+

WINTER
By arrangement.

SPECIAL EVENTS

• **MAY 23:**
Stately Car Boot Sale in aid of Norfolk Churches' Trust.

BERNEY ARMS WINDMILL ⬚

Tel: 01493 700605

c/o 8 Manor Road, Southtown, Gt Yarmouth NR31 0QA

Owner: English Heritage   **Contact:** The Custodian

A wonderfully situated marsh mill, one of the best and largest remaining in Norfolk, with seven floors, making it a landmark for miles around. It was in use until 1951.

Location: OS134 Ref. TG465 051. $3^1/_2$ m NE of Reedham on N bank of River Yare, 5m from Gt. Yarmouth. Accessible by boat or by footpath, from Halvergate ($3^1/_2$ m).

Opening Times: 1 Apr - 30 Sept: daily, 9am - 5pm (closed 1 - 2pm).

Admission: Adult £1.30, Child 70p, Conc. £1.

BINHAM PRIORY ⬚

Tel: 01604 730320 (Regional Office)

Binham-on-Wells, Norfolk

Owner: English Heritage   **Contact:** The Midlands Regional Office

Extensive remains of a Benedictine priory, of which the original nave of the church is still in use as the parish church.

Location: OS132 Ref. TF982 399. $^1/_4$ m NW of village of Binham-on-Wells, on road off B1388.

Opening Times: Any reasonable time.

Admission: Free.

BIRCHAM WINDMILL

Tel: 01485 578393

Snettisham Road, Great Bircham, Norfolk PE31 6SJ

Owner: Mr & Mrs G Wagg   **Contact:** Mr & Mrs G Wagg

One of the last remaining complete windmills.

Location: OS Ref. TF760 326. $^1/_2$ m W of Bircham. N of the road to Snettisham.

Opening Times: 5 Apr - 31 Sept: 10am - 5pm.

Admission: Adult £2.20, Child 75p, Retired £2.

ℹ️ Shop.   ♿ Ground floor & grounds suitable. WC.   ☕ Tearoom.

🐕 In grounds, on leads.

BURGH CASTLE ⬚

Tel: 01604 730320 (Regional Office)

Breydon Water, Great Yarmouth, Norfolk

Owner: English Heritage   **Contact:** The Midlands Regional Office

Impressive walls, with projecting bastions, of a Roman fort built in the late 3rd century as one of a chain to defend the coast against Saxon raiders.

Location: OS134 Ref. TG475 046. At far W end of Breydon Water, on unclassified road 3m W of Great Yarmouth. SW of the church.

Opening Times: Any reasonable time.

Admission: Free.

🐕 On leads.

CASTLE ACRE PRIORY ⬚

Tel: 01760 755394

Stocks Green, Castle Acre, King's Lynn, Norfolk PE32 2XD

Owner: English Heritage   **Contact:** The Custodian

The great west front of the 12th century church of this Cluniac priory still rises to its full height and is elaborately decorated. Other substantial remains include the splendid prior's lodgings and chapel and the delightful modern herb garden should not be missed.

Location: OS Ref. TF814 148. $^1/_4$ m W of village of Castle Acre, 5m N of Swaffham.

Opening Times: 1 Apr - 1 Nov: daily, 10am - 6pm or dusk if earlier. 2 Nov - 31 Mar: Wed - Sun, 10am - 4pm. Closed 24 - 26 Dec.

Admission: Adult £2.95, Child £1.50, Conc. £2.20.

ℹ️ Shop.   ♿ Ground floor & grounds.

CASTLE RISING CASTLE ⬚

Tel: 01553 631330

Castle Rising, Kings Lynn, Norfolk PE31 6AH

Owner: English Heritage   **Contact:** The Custodian

A fine mid-12th century domestic keep, set in the centre of massive defensive earthworks. Once a palace and prison to Isabella, 'She-Wolf' Dowager Queen of England. The keep walls stand to their original height and many of the fortifications are still intact.

Location: OS132 Ref. TF666 246. 4m NE of Kings Lynn off A149.

Opening Times: 1 Apr - 1 Nov: daily, 10am - 6pm or dusk if earlier. 2 Nov - 31 Mar: Wed - Sun, 10am - 4pm. Closed 24 - 26 Dec.

Admission: Adult £2.30, Child £1.20, Conc. £1.70. 15% discount for groups of 11+.

♿ Grounds suitable. WC.

DRAGON HALL

Tel: 01603 663922

115 - 123 King Street, Norwich, Norfolk NR1 1QE

Owner: Norfolk & Norwich Heritage Trust Ltd   **Contact:** Mr Neil Sigsworth

Magnificent medieval merchants' hall described as "one of the most exciting 15th century buildings in England". A wealth of outstanding features include living hall, screens passage, vaulted undercroft, superb timber-framed Great Hall, crown-post roof and intricately carved and painted dragon. Built by Robert Toppes, a wealthy and influential merchant. Dragon Hall is a unique legacy of medieval life, craftsmanship and trade.

Location: OS Ref. TG235 084. SE of Norwich city centre.

Opening Times: Apr - Oct: Mon - Sat, 10am - 4pm. Nov - Mar: Mon - Fri, 10am - 4pm. Closed 23 Dec - 2 Jan and BHs.

Admission: Adult £1.50, Child 50p, Conc. £1.

ℹ️ Shop.   ♿ House suitable.   🚶 Compulsory.   🐕 Guide dogs only.

THE FAIRHAVEN GARDENS

Tel: 01603 270449   **Fax:** 01603 270449

2 The Woodlands, Wymers Lane, South Walsham, Norwich NR13 6EA

Owner: The Trustees of Fairhaven Garden Trust   **Contact:** Mr G E Debbage

Woodland and water garden with private broad. Primroses, bluebells, primulas, rhododendrons in spring, wild flowers and much to interest naturalists and horticulturists in summer and autumn. Situated in a lovely peaceful part of the Norfolk Broads.

Location: OS Ref. TG368 134. 9m NE of Norwich just N of the B1140 at South Walsham.

Opening Times: 1 Apr - 31 Oct: Tue - Sun, 11am - 5.30pm. Closed Mon except BHs.

Admission: Adult £3, Child £1 (under 5s free), OAPs £2.70. Group reductions.

ℹ️ Shop. Plant centre.   ♿ Grounds suitable. WC.   ☕ Tearoom.   🐕 In grounds, on leads.

BLICKLING HALL 🌿

Mike Williams

BLICKLING, NORWICH, NORFOLK NR11 6NF

Owner: The National Trust   Contact: The Property Manager

Tel: 01263 733084   **Fax:** 01263 734924

A spectacular 17th century red brick house, with extensive colourful garden. Fine Jacobean plaster ceilings, furniture and collections: including the Ellys library, Peter the Great tapestry. Garden contains extensive parterre, temple, orangery and secret garden. Parkland offers good lakeside and woodland walks. Free parking.

Location: OS Ref. TG178 286. B1354 off A140 Norwich/Cromer road. $1^1/_2$ m NW of Aylsham.

Opening Times: Hall: BH Mons and Good Fri & 4 Apr - end of Jul: Wed - Sun, Aug: Tue - Sun plus Sept - 1 Nov: Wed - Sun, 1 - 4.30pm. 'Taster Tours' are available every Fri & Sun at 12.15pm. Full guided tours are available on Mons in Aug (except 31st) at intervals during the day. **Garden:** 4 Apr - end of July: Wed - Sun, Aug: daily, Sept - 1 Nov: Wed - Sun, 10.30am - 5.30pm (gates close 6pm). 2 Nov - Mar 1999: Suns only, 11am - 4pm. Restaurant, shop and plant centre open as garden. **Park:** All year: dawn - dusk. All dogs must be kept on a lead.

Admission: Hall & Garden: Adult £6, Child £3. Gardens only: Adult £3.50, Child £1.75. Family tickets available. Additional charge for 'Taster Tour' of Hall: £2 .

ℹ️ Shop.   ♿ Suitable. WC.   ☕ Restaurant.   🎫 Civil Wedding Licence.

Castle Rising, Norfolk.

Eastern Counties England

FELBRIGG HALL

National Trust Photographic Library.

ROUGHTON, NORWICH, NORFOLK NR11 8PR

Owner: The National Trust   *Contact:* The Property Manager

Tel: 01263 837444 **Fax:** 01263 837032

Felbrigg Hall is a 17th century house built on the site of a medieval Hall. It houses a superb collection of 18th century furniture, pictures and an outstanding library. There are 27 rooms to visit including the Domestic Wing, which offers the visitor a greater understanding of how a country house "worked". Close to the Hall is a beautiful Walled Garden with Dovehouse and hundreds of acres of historic parkland and mature woods may be explored via a variety of waymarked walks.

Location: OS Ref. TG193 394. 2m SW of Cromer.

Opening Times: Hall: 28 Mar - 1 Nov: Sat - Wed, 1 - 5pm also open Good Fri, BH Mon and Sun preceding, 11am - 5pm. Last admission 4.30pm. Gardens: Same days as Hall, 11am - 5.30pm. Shop: 11am - 5.30pm. Catering: 11am - 5.15pm. Groups / guided tours by arrangement.

Admission: Hall & Gardens: Adult £5.40. Family discounts available. Gardens only: Adult £2.20. Free to National Trust members.

ℹ Shop.	♿ Ground floor & grounds suitable.	✕ By arrangement.
☕ Available.	🚶 By arrangement.	🅿 Ample.	🐕 In park, on leads.

HOUGHTON HALL

HOUGHTON, KING'S LYNN, NORFOLK PE31 6UE

Owner: The Marquess of Cholmondeley   *Contact:* Susan Cleaver

Tel: 01485 528569 **Fax:** 01485 528167

Houghton Hall was built in the 18th century by Sir Robert Walpole. Original designs were by Colen Campbell and revised by Thomas Ripley with interior decoration by William Kent. It is regarded as one of the finest examples of Palladian architecture in England. Houghton was later inherited by the 1st Marquess of Cholmondeley through his grandmother, Sir Robert's daughter. Situated in beautiful parkland, the house contains magnificent furniture, pictures and china. A private collection of 20,000 model soldiers and militaria. Newly restored walled garden.

Location: OS Ref. TF792 287. 13m E of King's Lynn, 10m W of Fakenham 1¹/₂ m N of A148.

Opening Times: 12 Apr - 27 Sept: Sun, Thur & BH Mon, 2 - 5.30pm. Last adm. 5pm.

Admission: Adult £5.50, Child (5-16) £3, Groups (20+): Adult £5, Child £2.50. Excluding house: Adult £3, Child £2, Groups (20+) Adult £2.50, Child £1.50. Prices shown are for 1997, please telephone to confirm prices for 1998.

ℹ Shop.	♿ Suitable. WC.	☕ Tearoom.	🐕 No dogs.

GRIME'S GRAVES ⊞   **Tel:** 01842 810656

Lynford, Thetford, Norfolk IP26 5DE

Owner: English Heritage   **Contact:** The Custodian

These remarkable Neolithic flint mines, unique in England, comprise over 300 pits and shafts. The visitor can descend some 30 feet by ladder into one excavated shaft, and look along the radiating galleries, from where the flint used for making axes and knives was extracted.

Location: OS144 Ref. TL818 898. 7m NW of Thetford off A134.

Opening Times: 1 Apr - 1 Nov: daily, 10am - 6pm or dusk if earlier. 2 Nov - 31 Mar: Wed - Sun, 10am - 4pm (closed 1 - 2pm) Closed 24 - 26 Dec. Last visit to pit 20 mins before close.

Admission: Adult £1.75, Child 90p, Conc. £1.30.

HOLKHAM HALL 🏛   **See page 164 for full page entry.**

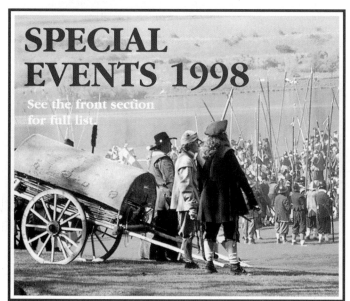

SPECIAL EVENTS 1998

See the front section for full list.

HOVETON HALL GARDENS 🏛   **Tel:** 01603 782798 **Fax:** 01603 784564

Wroxham, Norwich, Norfolk NR12 8RJ

Owner: Mr & Mrs Andrew Buxton   **Contact:** Mrs Buxton

Rhododendrons, azaleas, woodland and lakeside walks, walled herbaceous and vegetable gardens. The Hall (which is not open) was built 1809 - 1812. Designs attributed to Humphry Repton.

Location: OS Ref. TG314 202. 8m N of Norwich. 1¹/₂ m NNE of Wroxham on A1151. Follow white on brown tourist signs.

Opening Times: Easter Sun - mid Sept: Wed, Fri, Sun and BH Mons, 11am - 5.30pm.

Admission: Adult £3, Child £1, Groups £2.50 (if booked in advance).

ℹ Plant sales.	♿ Grounds suitable. WC.	☕ Tearoom.	🐕 No dogs.

MANNINGTON GARDENS & COUNTRYSIDE 🏛 **Tel:** 01263 584175

Mannington Hall, Norwich NR11 7BB   **Fax:** 01263 761214

Owner: The Lord & Lady Walpole   **Contact:** Lady Walpole

Gardens with lake, moat and woodland. Outstanding rose collection, heritage rose gardens.

Location: OS Ref. TG144 320. Signposted from Saxthorpe crossroads on the Norwich - Holt road B1149. 1¹/₂ m W of Wolterton Hall.

Opening Times: Gardens: May - Sept: Sun 12 - 5pm. Jun - Aug: Wed, Thur & Fri, 11am - 5pm. Walks: daily from 9am. Medieval Hall open by appointment.

Admission: Adult £3, Child under 16 free, Conc. £2.50, groups by application.

ℹ Shop. Plant centre. Conference facilities. No photography.	♿ Grounds suitable. WCs.
☕ Licensed tearoom.	🚶 By arrangement.	🅿 Ample.
👨‍👩‍👧 Educational programme available.	🐕 Guide dogs only.

THE MANOR HOUSE

Great Cressingham, Thetford, Norfolk IP25 6NJ

Owner: Mrs L R Chapman   **Contact:** Mrs L R Chapman

Small Tudor manor house famous for its terracotta façade.

Location: OS Ref. TF850 016. 6m S of Swaffham.

Opening Times: By written appointment only.

Admission: Prices on application.

NORWICH CASTLE MUSEUM

Tel: 01603 493648 **Fax:** 01603 765651

Norwich, Norfolk NR1 3JU

Owner: Norfolk Museums Service   **Contact:** Ms J Flannery

Norman Castle keep, housing displays of art, archaeology and natural history especially Norwich School of Art.

Location: OS Ref. TG233 085. City centre.

Opening Times: All year: Mon - Sat, 10am - 5pm, Sun, 2 - 5pm.

Admission: July - Sept: Adult £3.20, Child £1.60, Conc. £2.20, Family £8. Oct - Jun: Adult £2.40, Child £1.10, Conc. £1.60, Family £5.90.

ⓘ Shop.   🚲 Ground floor suitable. WC.   ☕ Tearoom.   🐕 No dogs.

OLD MERCHANT'S HOUSE, ROW 111 & GREYFRIARS' CLOISTERS ⌗

South Quay, Great Yarmouth, Norfolk NR30 2RQ

Tel: 01493 857900

Owner: English Heritage   **Contact:** The Custodian

Two 17th century Row Houses, rows 111 and 113, a type of building unique to Great Yarmouth, containing original fixtures and displays of local architectural fittings, salvaged from bombing in 1942 - 43. Some 100 yds N are the remains of a Franciscan friary, with a rare vaulted cloister, accidentally discovered during bomb damage repairs.

Location: OS134 Ref. TG525 072. In Great Yarmouth, make for South Quay, by riverside and dock, 1/2 m inland from beach.

Opening Times: 1 Apr - 1 Nov: daily, guided tours depart from Row 111 house at 10am, 11am, 12pm, 2pm, 3pm and 4pm.

Admission: Adult £1.75, Child 90p, Conc. £1.30. 15% discount for groups of 11+.

🐕 No dogs.

Oxburgh Hall, Norfolk.

OXBURGH HALL

OXBOROUGH, KING'S LYNN, NORFOLK PE33 9PS

Owner: The National Trust   *Contact:* The Administrator

Tel: 01366 328258 **Fax:** 01366 328066

Moated house built in 1482 by the Bedingfeld family, who still live here. The rooms show the development from Medieval austerity to Victorian comfort. Embroidery worked by Mary Queen of Scots, during her captivity, is on display. There are delightful woodland walks and a French parterre in the garden.

Location: OS Ref. TF742 012. At Oxborough, 7m SW of Swaffham on S side of Stoke Ferry Road.

Opening Times: House: 28 Mar - 1 Nov: Sat - Wed, 1 - 5pm, BH Mon, 11am - 5pm. Garden: Sat & Sun, 11am - 4pm, 28 Feb - 22 Mar: same days as house, 11am - 5.30pm. Garden open daily in Jul & Aug.

Admission: House, Garden & Estate: £4.80. Pre-arranged groups: £3.80. Garden and Estate only £2.40.

ⓘ Shop.   🚲 Ground floor & garden. WC.   ☕ Available.   🐕 Guide dogs.

RAVENINGHAM HALL GARDENS

Tel: 01508 548222 **Fax:** 01508 548958

Raveningham, Norwich, Norfolk NR14 6NS

Owner: Sir Nicholas Bacon Bt   **Contact:** Mrs J Woodard

Gardens laid out approximately 100 years ago around a red brick Georgian house which is not open to the public.

Location: OS Ref. TM399 965. Between Beccles and Loddon off B1136/B1140.

Opening Times: Easter Sun & Mon, May, Jun & Jul: Sun & BH Mon, 2 - 5pm.

Admission: Adult £2, Child free. Groups by prior arrangement.

☕ Tearoom.   🚶 By arrangement.   🐕 In grounds, on leads.

ST GEORGE'S GUILDHALL

Tel: 01553 773578

27 Kings Street, Kings Lynn, Norfolk PE30 1HA

Owner: The National Trust   **Contact:** The Administrator

The largest surviving English medieval guildhall, with adjoining medieval warehouse, now in use as an Arts Centre.

Location: OS Ref. TF616 202. On W side of King Street close to the Tuesday Market Place.

Opening Times: All year: Mon - Fri (closed Good Fri & Aug BH Mon) 10am - 4pm; Sat 10am - 1pm & 2 - 3.30pm. Closed 25, 26 Dec & 1 Jan.

Admission: Adult 50p, Child 25p.

ⓘ Shop.   🚲 Access to galleries.   ☕ Licensed tearoom/restaurant.

SANDRINGHAM

THE ESTATE OFFICE, SANDRINGHAM, NORFOLK PE35 6EN

Owner: HM The Queen   *Contact:* Mrs Gill Pattinson

Tel: 01553 772675   **Fax:** 01485 541571

Sandringham is the charming country retreat of Her Majesty The Queen hidden in the heart of 60 acres of beautiful wooded grounds. All the main ground floor rooms used by The Royal Family, full of their treasured ornaments, portraits and furniture, are open to the public. More Royal possessions dating back more than a century are displayed in the Museum housed in the old stable and coach houses. Glades, dells, lakes and lawns are surrounded by magnificent trees and bordered by colourful shrubs and flowers. A free Land Train from within the entrance will carry passengers less able to walk through the grounds to the House and back. All areas are fully accessible by wheelchair.

Location: OS Ref. TF695 287. 8m NE of King's Lynn on B1440 off A148.
Opening Times: House: 9 Apr - 21 Jul & 6 Aug - 4 Oct: daily, 11am - 4.45pm. Museum & Grounds: 9 Apr - 26 Jul & 6 Aug - 4 Oct & Oct weekends:.
Admission: Adult £4.50, Child £2.50, Conc. £3.50. Groups (min 20): 10% discount for payment in full one month in advance.

- ℹ️ Shop. Plant centre. No photography.
- ♿ Suitable. WC.
- 🍴 Tearoom, licensed restaurant.
- 🚶 By arrangement.
- 🅿️ Ample.
- 👥 Teachers' pack.
- 🐕 Guide dogs only.

WALSINGHAM ABBEY GROUNDS
Tel: 01328 820259   **Fax:** 01328 820098

Little Walsingham, Norfolk NR22 6BP
Owner: Walsingham Estate Company   **Contact:** The Agent

Set in Walsingham, a picturesque medieval village, the grounds contain the remains of an Augustinian Priory founded in 1153 on a site next to the Holy House and provide pleasant river and woodland walks. Snowdrop walks during February & March. Refreshments and accommodation in the village.

Location: OS Ref. TF934 367. B1105 N from Fakenham - 5m. Pay & Display car park 50 yds.
Opening Times: Good Fri - end Oct & snowdrop season: daily, 10am - 4pm. Entry through Museum or Estate Office when main gate closed. Access through Estate Office end Oct - Good Fri during normal office hours.
Admission: Grounds & Museum: Adult £2, Child / OAP £1. Grounds only: Adult £1.50, Child / OAP 75p.

- ♿ WCs.
- 🅿️ Pay and Display, 50 yds.
- 🐕 In grounds, under control.

WOLTERTON PARK
Tel: 01263 584175   **Fax:** 01263 761214

Norwich, Norfolk NR11 7BB
Owner: The Lord and Lady Walpole   **Contact:** The Lady Walpole

18th century Hall. Historic park with lake.
Location: OS Ref. TG164 317. Situated near Erpingham village, signposted from Norwich - Cromer Rd A140.
Opening Times: Park: daily from 9am.
Admission: £2 car park fee only. Groups by application. Hall tours: See local press, from £4 groups, £5 individuals.

- ❌ Available.
- ♿ Partially suitable. WC.
- 🚶 Compulsory for Hall.
- 🅿️ Ample.
- 👥 Educational programme.
- 🐕 In grounds, on leads.

Wet nursing:

In early modern Europe, breast-feeding of babies usually lasted for a year to eighteen months and could be a severe burden on the mother. By 1763 'the present fashion ... is to let children suck only three or four months', although others strongly advised that breast-feeding should last six to twelve months, with nine the ideal.

It had long been the custom for upper-class mothers to put their babies out to wet-nurses – that is, to mothers who were already feeding a child or who had just lost one. In 1682 the novelist and dramatist Aphra Behn (1640–89) noted that by this means 'both you and your wife are freed from tossing and tumbling with it in the night'. Breast-feeding became unfashionable, many mothers fearing that it would spoil the shape of their 'pretty breasts, firm nipples, round and smooth'. In 1748 a good wet-nurse cost £25 per year.

By the end of the eighteenth century medical opinion, always in favour of breast-feeding by the natural mother, was winning the argument. In 1789 Lady Craven reported 'that you will find in every station of life mothers of families who would shrink in horror at the thought of putting a child out from them to nurse'. The reduced likelihood of a mother conceiving during the months she was breast-feeding, although not infallible as a contraceptive measure, was also attractive. By the nineteenth century breast-feeding was firmly back in favour, to be replaced by bottle-feeding in the twentieth century. The debate continues.

Extract from; "Life in the Country House" by David N Durant (published by John Murray), PB£15.99, see page twelve at the front of the book.

Holkham Hall, Norfolk.

Eastern Counties England

KENTWELL HALL
Long Melford

CONTACT

Mrs J G Phillips
Kentwell Hall
Long Melford
Suffolk
CO10 9BA

Tel: (01787) 310207

Fax: (01787) 379318

LOCATION

OS Ref. TL864 479

Off the A134.
4m N of Sudbury, 14m S of
Bury St. Edmunds
1m NNW of Long Melford
off A134.

Rail: Sudbury Station 4m
Colchester Station 20m.

Air: Stansted 30m.
Airstrip at Kentwell
suitable for light aircraft
and microlites.

Taxi: Sudbury Town Taxis
(01787) 377366.

CONFERENCE/FUNCTION		
ROOM	SIZE	MAX CAPACITY
Great Hall	40' x 24'	120
Main Dining Room	24' x 24'	75
Drawing Rm	35' x 24'	75
Library	36' x 20'	20
Overcroft	120' x 22'	300

KENTWELL HALL is a beautiful redbrick Tudor Manor House surrounded by a broad moat.

Built by the Clopton Family, from wealth made in the wool trade, Kentwell has an air of timeless tranquillity. The exterior is little altered in 450 years. The interior was remodelled by Hopper in 1825 and his work has been embellished and enhanced in restoration by the present owners. Hopper's interiors, notably the Great Hall and Dining Room, emphasise their Tudor provenance, but the Drawing Room and Library are simply and restrainedly classical; all are eminently habitable.

Kentwell, as well as being a family home, conveys a deep feeling of the Tudor period with the service areas: great kitchen, bakery, dairy and forge always fully equipped in 16th century style. Kentwell's unique 16th century atmosphere and large collection of 16th century artefacts make it an ideal location for films and videos.

The gardens are part of Kentwell's delight. Intimate yet spacious, you are seldom far from a moat, clipped yews (some 30ft high) or mellow brick wall. There is a fine walled garden with original 17th century layout and a well established large Herb Garden and Potager.

The farm is run organically and is set around timber-framed buildings and stocked with rare breed farm animals.

Home to the award winning **'Re-creations of Tudor Domestic Life'** when visitors meet numerous 'Tudors' with dress, speech, activities and locations appropriate for the 16th century. These take place on selected weekends between April and September.

i Shop. Corporate events include conferences and 'company days', when the whole company or a division, can come for a specially devised one-day programme of fun, stimulation and challenges. A wide range of Tudor activities can be arranged for visitors, including longbow shooting, working bakery, dairy and still-room, spinning, etc. or even clay pigeon shooting in the Park. No photographs in house.

X Genuine Tudor-style banquets, wedding receptions, formal but friendly. luncheons and dinners.

Visitors may alight at house, with prior notice. WC.

Home-made food. The Undercroft comfortably seats 96. Overcroft can accommodate up to 300.

P Ample.

There is a highly developed schools programme dealing with 700 parties per year. Schools can visit a re-creation of Tudor life, re-create Tudor life themselves for the day or take one of the tours conducted by experienced guides on the House, Garden, Farm or aspects of each.

No dogs.

OPENING TIMES

House, Gardens & Farm
- 8 March - 7 June:
  Suns only also Tue 14 - Fri
  17 April and summer half
  term holiday Tue 26 - Fri 29
  May: 12 - 5pm
- 8 July - 6 September
  Daily except Sats
  12 - 5pm
- 7 Sept - 25 Oct
  Suns only
  12 - 5pm

The Great Annual Re-creation
- 14 June - 5 July:
  Sat & Sun only &
  Fri, 3 July.
  Life at Kentwell in the 16th
  century (Other w/ends during these 3 weeks: schools
  only – please phone for
  Schools' Booking Pack).
  11am - 5pm.

Tudor Life Re-created
- 10 - 13 Apr: Eastertide
- 2 - 4 May: May Day
  Celebrations
- 23 - 25 May: Whitsuntide
- 1 - 2 Aug: Lammastide and
  the Longbow shoot
- 28 - 31 Aug:
  High Summer
- 19 - 20 Sept: Michaelmas
  11am - 6pm.

ADMISSION

House, Gardens & Farm
Adult £5.10
Child (5-15)............£3.10
OAP.......................£4.30

Gardens & Farm only
Adult £3.00
Child (5-15)............£1.90
OAP.......................£2.60

Great Annual Re-creation
Adult £11.00
Child (5-15)............£7.25
OAP.......................£9.50

Other Re-creations
Adult £7.50
Child (5-15)............£5.00
OAP.......................£6.50

BELCHAMP HALL

BELCHAMP WALTER, SUDBURY, SUFFOLK CO10 7AT

Owner: Mr M M J Raymond   *Contact:* Mr & Mrs M J Raymond

Tel: 01787 372744

Superb Queen Anne house on a site belonging to the Raymond family since 1611. Historic portraits and period furniture. Suitable for receptions and an ideal film location, often seen as Lady Jane's house in *Lovejoy*. Gardens including a cherry avenue, follies, a sunken garden, walled garden and lake. Medieval church with 15th century wall paintings.

Location: OS Ref. TL827 407. 5m SW of Sudbury, opposite Belchamp Walter Church.

Opening Times: By appointment only: May - Sept: Tue, Thur & BHs, 2.30 - 6pm.

Admission: Adult £3.50, Child £1.75. Groups: Adult £3, Child £1.50.

☕ By arrangement.   ✗ Wedding receptions.   🚶 Compulsory.   P Ample.
🐕 No dogs.

FRAMLINGHAM CASTLE ⊞

FRAMLINGHAM, SUFFOLK IP8 9BT

Owner: English Heritage   *Contact:* The Custodian

Tel: 01728 724189

A superb 12th century castle which, from the outside, looks almost the same as when it was built. From the continuous curtain wall linking 13 towers, there are excellent views of Framlingham and the charming reed-fringed mere. At different times the castle has been a fortress, an Elizabethan prison, a poor house and a school. The many alterations over the years have led to a pleasing mixture of historic styles.

Location: OS Ref. TM287 637. In Framlingham on B1116. NE of town centre.

Opening Times: 1 Apr - 1 Nov: daily 10am - 6pm or dusk if earlier. 2 Nov - 31 Mar: daily 10am - 4pm. Closed 24 - 26 Dec.

Admission: Adult £2.95, Child £1.50, OAP/Student £2.20. 15% discount for groups of 11+.

♿ Ground floor & grounds suitable. WCs.   🐕 No dogs.

EAST BERGHOLT PLACE GARDEN   **Tel:** 01206 299224

East Bergholt, Suffolk

Owner: Mr & Mrs R L C Eley   **Contact:** Sara Eley

15 acres of garden and arboretum originally laid out the beginning of the century by the present owner's great grandfather. A wonderful collection of fine trees and shrubs, many of which are rarely seen growing in East Anglia and originate from the famous plant hunter George Forrest. Particularly beautiful in the spring when the rhododendrons, magnolias and camellias are in flower. There is a specialist plant centre in the Victorian Walled Garden.

Location: OS Ref. TM070 345. 2m E of A12 on B1070, Manningtree Rd, on the edge of East Bergholt.

Opening Times: Mar - Sept: Tue - Sun & BHs, 10am - 5pm.

Admission: Adult £1.50, Child free. (Proceeds to garden up-keep).

i Plant centre.   ☕ By arrangement.   🐕 No dogs.

EUSTON HALL   **Tel:** 01842 766366   **Fax:** 01842 766764

Estate Office, Euston, Thetford, Norfolk IP24 2QP

Owner: The Duke of Grafton   **Contact:** Mrs L Campbell

18th century house contains a famous collection of paintings including works by Stubbs, Van Dyck, Lely and Kneller. The Pleasure Grounds were were laid out by John Evelyn and William Kent. 17th century parish church in Wren style. River walk, watermill and picnic area.

Location: OS Ref. TL897 786. 12m N of Bury St. Edmunds, on A1088. 2m E of A134.

Opening Times: 4 Jun - 24 Sept: Thur 2.30 - 5pm. Also Sun 28 Jun & 6 Sept: 2.30 - 5pm.

Admission: Adult £3, Child 50p, OAP £2.50. Groups (min 12): Adult £2.50, Child 50p.

i Craft shop.   ♿ Grounds suitable.   ☕ Tearoom.   🐕 No dogs.

FLATFORD BRIDGE COTTAGE 🦋   **Tel:** 01206 298260   **Fax:** 01206 299193

Flatford, East Bergholt, Colchester, Essex CO7 6OL

Owner: The National Trust   **Contact:** The Property Manager

Just upstream from Flatford Mill, the restored thatched cottage houses a display about John Constable, several of whose paintings depict this property. Facilities include a tea garden, shop, boat hire, an Information Centre and countryside walks.

Location: OS Ref. TM077 332. On N bank of Stour, 1m S of East Bergholt B1070.

Opening Times: 1 Mar - end Apr & Oct: Wed - Sun 11am - 5.30pm. May - end Sept: daily 10am - 5.30pm (closed Good Fri). Nov: Wed - Sun 11am - 3.30pm.

Admission: Guided walks £1.80, accompanied child free. Car park charge (NT members included).

i Shop.   ♿ Ground floor suitable. WC.   🚶 Available.   ☕ Tearoom.   🐕 Guide dogs only.

GAINSBOROUGH'S HOUSE

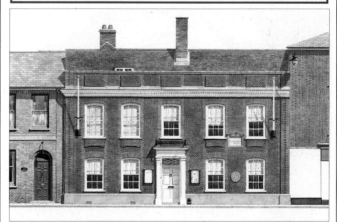

46 GAINSBOROUGH ST, SUDBURY, SUFFOLK CO10 6EU

Owner: Gainsborough's House Society

Tel: 01787 372958   **Fax:** 01787 376991

Birthplace of Thomas Gainsborough RA (1727-88). Georgian-fronted town house, with attractive walled garden, displays more of the artist's work than any other gallery. The collection is shown together with 18th century furniture and memorabilia. Varied programme of contemporary exhibitions organised throughout the year includes: fine art, craft, photography, printmaking, sculpture and highlights the work of East Anglian artists.

Location: OS Ref. TL872 413. 46 Gainsborough Street, Sudbury town centre.

Opening Times: All year: Tue - Sat, 10am - 5pm, Sun & BH Mon 2 - 5pm. Closes at 4pm Nov - Mar. Closed: Mon, Good Fri and Christmas to New Year.

Admission: Adult £2.80, OAP £2.20. Children and students £1.50.

i Shop. No photography.   ♿ Ground floor suitable. WCs.
P No parking.   👥 Educational programme available.

SPECIAL EVENTS

MAY 30 - SEPT 27: Sculpture in the Garden.

OCT 30 - NOV 22: Gainsborough Drawings on display.

Eastern Counties England

HELMINGHAM HALL

STOWMARKET, SUFFOLK IP14 6EF

Owner: The Lord & Lady Tollemache   *Contact: Ms Jane Tressider*

Tel: 01473 890363 **Fax:** 01473 890776

The Tudor Hall surrounded by its wide moat is set in a 400 acre deer park. Two superb gardens, one surrounded by its own moat and walls extends to several acres and has wide herbaceous borders and an immaculate kitchen garden. The second enclosed within yew hedges, has a special rose garden with a herb and knot garden containing plants grown in England before 1750.

Location: OS Ref. TM190 578. B1077, 9m N of Ipswich, 5m S of Debenham.

Opening Times: Gardens only: 26 Apr - 6 Sept, Sun only, 2 - 6pm. For groups of 30+ by appointment on Wed, between these dates, 2 - 5pm.

Admission: Adult £3.50, Child (5 - 15) £2, OAP £3 Groups of 30+ £3 (£3.50 Weds). Guided tour (Wed only) £6. Safari rides: Adult £2.20, Child £1.10.

i Shop. Plant centre.   & Grounds suitable. WCs.   Tearoom.
By arrangement.   P Ample.   In grounds, on leads.

ICKWORTH HOUSE & PARK

Ian Shaw.

HORRINGER, BURY ST. EDMUNDS, SUFFOLK IP33 2DH

Owner: The National Trust   *Contact: The Property Manager*

Tel: 01284 735270/735151

The eccentric Earl of Bristol (also Bishop of Derry) created this equally eccentric house, started in 1795, to display his collections. The paintings include works by Titian, Gainsborough and Velasquez and the magnificent Georgian silver collection is displayed in the oval Rotunda which is linked by curved corridors to flanking wings. The house is surrounded by an Italianate garden and is set in a 'Capability' Brown park with several waymarked woodland walks and a deer enclosure with hide.

Location: OS Ref. TL816 613. At Horringer 3m SW of Bury St. Edmunds on W side of A143.

Opening Times: House: 21 Mar - 1 Nov, Tue, Wed, Fri, Sat, Sun, BH Mon & Good Fri: 1 - 5pm. Last adm. 4.30pm. **Garden:** 21 Mar - 1 Nov, daily 10am - 5pm. 2 Nov - 20 Mar: weekdays only 10am - 4pm. **Park:** All year: daily 7am - 7pm. Garden & Park closed 25 Dec.

Admission: House, Park & Gardens: Adult £5.20, Child £2.20, Family (2+2) £10. Park & Garden: Adult £2., Child 50p. Family discount available. Pre-booked groups £4.20 (excl. Sun and BH Mon).

& Ground floor suitable.   Available.   By arrangement.   P Ample.

KENTWELL HALL

See page 170 for full page entry.

LANDGUARD FORT

Tel: 01394 286403 (evenings)

Felixstowe, Suffolk

Owner: English Heritage   **Contact:** The Custodian

Impressive 18th century fort with later additions built on a site originally fortified by Henry VIII and in use until after World War II. There is also a museum (not EH).

Location: OS Ref. TM284 318. 1m S of Felixstowe at extreme S end of dock area.

Opening Times: Museum: every Sun from 3 May - 27 Sept & BHs, 10.30am - 4.30pm. Guided tours only. Small groups by appointment.

Admission: Adult £2, Child £1, Conc. £1.50.

LAVENHAM GUILDHALL

Tel: 01787 247646

Lavenham, Suffolk

Owner: The National Trust   **Contact:** The Administrator

This early 16th century timber-framed Tudor building, originally the hall of the Guild of Corpus Christi, overlooks and dominates the market place. Within the nine rooms of the Guildhall are displays of local history, farming, industry and the development of the railway, and a unique exhibition of 700 years of the medieval woollen cloth trade. There is a delightful walled garden with a 19th century lock-up and mortuary.

Location: OS Ref. TL916 493. 6m NNE of Sudbury. Village centre. A1141 and B1071.

Opening Times: 28 Mar - 1 Nov: daily, 11am - 5pm (closed Good Fri).

Admission: Adult £2.80, accompanied child free, Groups £2.40, School groups 60p per child by prior arrangement.

i Shop.   & Grounds suitable. WC.   Tearoom.   Guide dogs only.

LEISTON ABBEY

Tel: 01604 730320 (Regional Office)

Leiston, Suffolk

Owner: English Heritage   **Contact:** The Midlands Regional Office

The remains of this abbey for Premonstratensian canons, including a restored chapel, are amongst the most extensive in Suffolk.

Location: OS Ref. TM445 642. 1m N of Leiston off B1069.

Opening Times: Any reasonable time.

Admission: Free.

LITTLE HALL

Tel: 01787 247179 **Fax:** 01787 248341

Market Place, Lavenham, Suffolk CO10 9QZ

Owner: Suffolk Preservation Society   **Contact:** R Attew

Little Hall, a Grade II Listed Building with a Crown Post roof, reveals five centuries of change. Its history mirrors the rise and fall of Lavenham's cloth trade. Restored by the Gayer-Anderson twins in the 1930s.

Location: OS Ref. TL917 494. Market Place, Lavenham. 50yds E of Guildhall.

Opening Times: Easter - Oct: Wed, Thur, Sat, Sun, 2 - 5pm. BHs: 10.30am - 5.30pm.

MANOR HOUSE MUSEUM

Tel: 01284 757076 **Fax:** 01284 757079

Honey Hill, Bury St Edmunds, Suffolk IP33 1HF

Owner: St Edmundsbury Borough Council   **Contact:** The Manager

Georgian mansion with exhibitions of horology, costumes and fine art.

Location: OS Ref. TL858 640. Bury town centre off A14. Just S of Abbey grounds.

Opening Times: Tue - Sun, 10am - 5pm. Closed Mon.

Admission: Adult £2.70, Child £1.75, Family £7.50, Conc. £1.75, Groups discount.

i Shop.   & Suitable. WC.   Licensed tearoom.   Guide dogs only.

MELFORD HALL

Tel: 01787 880286

Long Melford, Sudbury, Suffolk CO10 9AH

Owner: The National Trust   **Contact:** The Administrator

A turreted brick Tudor mansion, little changed since 1578 with the original panelled banqueting hall, an 18th century drawing room, a Regency library and a Victorian bedroom, showing fine furniture and Chinese porcelain. There is also a special Beatrix Potter display and a garden.

Location: OS Ref. TL867 462. In Long Melford on E side of A134, 14m S of Bury St Edmunds, 3m N of Sudbury.

Opening Times: Apr: Sat, Sun & BH Mon, 2 - 5.30pm. May - Sept: Wed - Sun & BH Mon, 2 - 5.30pm. Oct: Sat & Sun, 2 - 5.30pm. Last admission 5pm.

Admission: Principal rooms & garden £4, pre-arranged parties £3. Wed - Sat only.

& Suitable. Stairlift to 1st floor. WC.   Guide dogs only in Hall. In grounds, on leads.

MOYSES HALL MUSEUM

Tel: 01284 757488 **Fax:** 01284 757079

Cornhill, Bury St Edmunds, Suffolk IP33 1DX

Owner: St Edmundsbury Borough Council   **Contact:** The Gallery Supervisor

Very early 12th century flint house, now a museum of local history.

Location: OS Ref. TL853 644. Town centre off A14. 300 yds NW of Abbey grounds.

Opening Times: Daily: 10am - 5pm, except Sun: 2 - 5pm. Closed Good Fri, 25/26 Dec.

Admission: Adult £1.50, Child 95p, Conc. 95p. Free for local residents.

i Shop.   & Ground floor suitable.   By arrangement.   Guide dogs only.

ORFORD CASTLE

ORFORD, WOODBRIDGE, SUFFOLK IP12 2ND

Owner: English Heritage   *Contact: The Custodian*

Tel: 01394 450472

A royal castle built for coastal defence in the 12th century. A magnificent keep survives almost intact with three immense towers reaching to 30m (90ft). Fine views over Orford and coastline.

Location: OS169 Ref. TM419 499. In Orford on B1084, 20m NE of Ipswich.

Opening Times: 1 Apr - 1 Nov: daily 10am - 6pm or dusk if earlier. 2 Nov - 31 Mar: Wed - Sun, 10am - 4pm. Closed 1 -2pm. Closed 24 - 26 Dec.

Admission: Adult £2.30, Child £1.20, OAP/Student £1.70. 15% discount for groups of 11+.

No dogs.

OTLEY HALL

OTLEY, IPSWICH, SUFFOLK IP6 9PA

Owner: Mr. Nicholas Hagger   *Contact: Lindsey Bryce (Administrator)*

Tel: 01473 890264   **Fax:** 01473 890803

A stunning 15th century Moated Hall (Grade I), set in gardens and grounds of 10 acres, frequently described as "one of England's loveliest houses". Rich in history and architectural detail. Features of particular note are richly carved beams, superb linenfold, c1559 wall paintings, herringbone brickwork and vine-leaf pargetting. Built around 1450 it was the home of the Gosnold family for 250 years. Bartholomew Gosnold voyaged to the New World in 1602 and named Cape Cod and Martha's Vineyard. He returned in 1607 to found the Jamestown settlement, the first English-speaking settlement in the US, 13 years before the Mayflower landed. The account of the 1602 voyage is thought to have provided the geography for Shakespeare's Tempest. The Gardens are formal and informal, with canal, mount, nutteries, croquet lawn, rose garden, woodland, and new in 1998 will be a medieval knot and herb garden, herber and orchard, as well as other historically accurate Tudor features.

Location: OS Ref. TM207 563. 7m N of Ipswich, off the B1079.

Opening Times: Every BH Sun & Mon, 12.30 - 6pm. Gardens: Wed only from 15 Apr - 23 Sept, 2 - 5pm.

Admission: Adult £4, Child £2.50. Garden days: Adult £2.50, Child £1. Coach parties welcome all year by appointment for private guided tours.

Wedding receptions.   Partially suitable.   Tearoom.

By arrangement.   P Ample.   In grounds on leads.

ST EDMUNDSBURY CATHEDRAL   **Tel:** 01284 754933 **Fax:** 01284 768655

Angel Hill, Bury St Edmunds, Suffolk IP33 1LS

Owner: The Church of England   **Contact:** Charles Borthwick

Set in the renowned gardens of the ruined abbey, ancient and modern combine in harmony in Suffolk's Cathedral. Visitors commend the tranquil atmosphere of prayer and worship combined with a real sense of welcome. The 16th century nave, by the same builder as King's College, Cambridge, was enhanced with the addition of Quire and Crossing in present times by architect, Stephen Dykes Bower. The Cloisters Gallery has regular exhibitions and the treasury houses church plate from the Diocese.

Location: OS Ref. TL857 642. Bury St Edmunds town centre.

Opening Times: All year: daily 8.30am - 5.30pm. BST 8.30am - 6pm, Jun - Aug: 8.30am - 8pm.

Admission: Donation invited.

i Shop. Corporate hospitality.   X Available for groups.   Partially suitable. WC.

Licensed restaurant.   Educational programme.   Guide dogs only.

SAXTEAD GREEN POST MILL   **Tel:** 01728 685789

The Mill House, Saxtead Green, Woodbridge, Suffolk IP13 9QQ

Owner: English Heritage   **Contact:** The Custodian

The finest example of a Suffolk Post Mill. Still in working order, you can climb the wooden stairs to the various floors, full of fascinating mill machinery. Ceased production in 1947.

Location: OS Ref. TM253 645. 2^{1}/$_{2}$ m NW of Framlingham on A1120.

Opening Times: 1 Apr - 1 Nov: Mon - Sat, 10am - 6pm. Closed 1 - 2pm.

Admission: Adult £1.75, Child 90p, Conc. £1.30.

SOMERLEYTON HALL & GARDENS

SOMERLEYTON, LOWESTOFT, SUFFOLK NR32 5QQ

Owner: The Rt. Hon. Lord Somerleyton KCVO   *Contact: Lord Somerleyton KCVO*

Tel: 01502 730224 office or 01502 732950 (Entrance Gate) **Fax:** 01502 732143

Splendid early Victorian mansion built in Anglo-Italian style by Sir Morton Peto. No expense was spared in the creation or lavish interiors and magnificent carved stonework. In 1863 the entire estate was sold to carpet manufacturer Sir Francis Crossley, the present owner is his great-grandson. In the state rooms there are paintings by Landseer, Wright of Derby and Stanfield, together with fine wood carvings. Somerleyton's 12-acre gardens are justly renowned and the 1846 yew hedge maze ranks amongst the finest in the country. Special features include glasshouses by Paxton, fine statuary and ornamentation, 300ft pergola, walled garden, Vulliamy tower clock, specimen trees and the miniature railway.

Location: OS134 Ref. TM493 977. 5m NW of Lowestoft on B1074, 7m SW of Great Yarmouth off A143.

Opening Times: Easter Sun - Sept: Thur, Sun, BHs. Jul & Aug: Tue, Wed, Thur, Sun & BHs. Gardens: 12.30 - 5.30pm. Hall: 1.30 - 5pm. Closed all other dates except by appointment. Private group tours by arrangement.

Admission: Adult £4.50, Child £2.20, OAP £4.20, Family (2+2) £12.60. Groups: Adult £3.90, Child £2, Schools £2. Small extra charge for miniature railway.

i Corporate hospitality/conferences.   X Wedding receptions/functions.

Suitable. WCs.   Tearoom.   By arrangement.   P Ample.

No dogs.   Civil Wedding Licence.

Eastern Counties England

WINGFIELD OLD COLLEGE & GDNS

WINGFIELD, NR STRADBROKE, SUFFOLK IP21 5RA

Owner: Ian Chance Esq   *Contact:* Hilary Smith

Tel: 01379 384888 **Fax:** 01379 384034

Delightful family home with walled gardens. This lovely old Suffolk house with spectacular medieval great hall, contemporary art, garden sculpture, collections of ceramics and textiles, 4 acres of gardens with topiary, ponds and old roses, in unspoilt Suffolk countryside. Steeped in history, this "oasis of arts and heritage" offers an afternoon of discovery and relaxation. Children's play garden, teas in the old kitchen.

Location: OS Ref. TM230 767. Signposted off B1118, 2m N of Stradbroke and B1116 at Fressingfield.

Opening Times: 11 Apr - 27 Sept: Sat & Sun, 2 - 6pm.

Admission: Adult £2.80, Child/Student £1, OAP £2.20, Family £6.50. Pre-arranged groups (min 12 people): Adult £2.40.

i Corporate hospitality.	X Wedding receptions.	Partially suitable.
Tearoom.	By arrangement.	P Limited for coaches.	Guide dogs only.

WYKEN HALL

STANTON, BURY ST. EDMUNDS, SUFFOLK IP31 2DW

Owner: Sir Kenneth & Lady Carlisle   *Contact:* Mrs Barbara Hurn

Tel: 01359 250287 **Fax:** 01359 252256

The Elizabethan Manor House is surrounded by a romantic, plant-lover's garden with maze, knot and herb garden and rose garden featuring old roses. A walk through ancient woodlands leads to Wyken Vineyards, winner of EVA Wine of the Year. In the 16th century barn, the Vineyard Restaurant now featured in the *Good Food Guide,* serves a range of Wyken wines along with a menu of fresh fish, game and vegetables from the kitchen garden.

Location: OS Ref. TL963 717. 9m NE of Bury St. Edmunds 1m E of A143. Follow brown tourist signs to Wyken Vineyards from Ixworth.

Opening Times: 1 Feb - 24 Dec: Thur - Sun & BH Mon, 10am - 6pm. Book for meals in The Leaping Hare Cafe at Wyken Vineyards, Fri & Sat dinner from 7pm.

Admission: Gardens: Adult £2, Child under 12 free, Conc. £1.50. Groups 30+ by appointment on Wed.

i Shop.	Grounds suitable. WC.	Restaurant.	In grounds, on leads.

SPECIAL EVENTS 1998

See the front section for full list.

Historic Scotland

Meals, times of eating:

In medieval times breakfast was eaten at 6 or 7 am; dinner, the main meal of the day, at 10 am; and supper around 5 pm. The tendency was for the main meal to be eaten progressively later: in 1740 at Bulstrode Park (the now demolished home of the Dukes of Portland) in Buckinghamshire, dinner was at 2 pm. People in the country generally kept earlier hours: by 1776 the fashionable hour in London for dinner was 4.30 to 5 pm. Coming up to London from Surrey in 1776 for a rare visit, Mrs Boscowen (1719–1805), the widow of Admiral Boscowen, having dined in Surrey at 2 pm, was amazed to find that she could get another dinner at 5.

One reason for later London hours was that by the late eighteenth century, as speeches became longer, Parliament was sitting later; the Prince of Wales liked late hours, and encouraged the fashion.

In the nineteenth century, the yawning gap between breakfast and dinner was filled by the new fashion for a midday luncheon or 'nuncheon' and afternoon tea. Lord William Russell wrote to Lady Holland in 1841: 'We are 30 at table, great profusion, and admirable cuisine, besides repasts at every hour of the day. From 10 to 12 breakfast, from 2 to 3 luncheon, from 5 to 6 tea, at 7 dinner, and after balls and theatres hot suppers, otherwise cold.'. By the First World War breakfast was eaten earlier and luncheon was served at 1 pm, tea at 4 pm and dinner at 8, a timetable which is loosely maintained today.

Extract from; "Life in the Country House" by David N Durant (published by John Murray), PB£15.99, see page twelve at the front of the book.

Tudor Life Re-creation at Kentwell Hall, Suffolk.

Counties in this region:

LANCS
YORKSHIRE
CHESHIRE
DERBYSHIRE
NOTTS
LINCOLNSHIRE
STAFFS
LEICESTERSHIRE AND RUTLAND
SHROPSHIRE
WEST MIDLANDS
CAMBS
WORCS.
WARKS.
NORTHANTS
HEREFORDSHIRE
BEDS
BUCKS
GLOUCESTERSHIRE
OXON
WILTS

The Midlands
England

The Midlands England

CHATSWORTH
Bakewell

The great Treasure House of Chatsworth is everything a palace should be but still maintains the sympathetic proportions of a family home. The first house was built by Bess of Hardwick in 1552 and has been lived in by the Cavendish family, the Dukes of Devonshire, ever since. The House today owes its appearance to the 1st Duke who remodelled the building at the end of the 17th century, while the 6th Duke added a North Wing by Sir Jeffry Wyatville 130 years later. Visitors can see 26 rooms including the run of 5 virtually unaltered 17th century State Rooms and Chapel. There are painted ceilings by Verrio, Thornhill and Laguerre, furniture by William Kent and Boulle, tapestries from Mortlake and Brussels, a library of over 17,000 volumes, sculpture by Cibber and Canova, old master paintings by Rembrandt, Hals, Van Dyck, Tintoretto, Giordano, Lely as well as Landseer and Sargent; the collection of neo-classical sculpture, Oriental and European porcelain and the dazzling silver collection, including an early

English silver chandelier. The present Duke is a collector like his ancestors and the sculptures by Angela Conner and Elisabeth Frink and paintings by Lucian Freud bring the treasures up to date. In 1996, Chatsworth was voted the public's favourite house, winning the first NPI National Heritage Gold Award.

GARDEN

The 105 acre garden was created during three great eras in garden and landscape design. The 200 metre Cascade, the Willow Tree fountain and the Canal survive from the 1st Duke's formal garden. 'Capability' Brown landscaped the garden and park in the 1760s. The 6th Duke's gardener, Sir Joseph Paxton, planted rare trees and shrubs, built rockeries and designed a series of glasshouses. He also created the Emperor fountain, the tallest gravity-fed fountain in the world. More recent additions include the Rose, Cottage and Kitchen gardens, the Serpentine Hedge and the Maze.

CONTACT

Mr John Oliver
Chatsworth
Bakewell
Derbyshire
DE45 1PP

Tel: (01246) 582204
(01246) 565300

Fax: (01246) 583536

LOCATION

OS Ref. SK260 703

From London
3 hrs M1/J29,
signposted via
Chesterfield.

3m E of Bakewell,
off B6012,
10m W of Chesterfield.

Rail: Chesterfield
Station, 11m

Bus: Chesterfield -
Bakewell, 1¹/₂ m

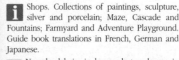

i Shops. Collections of paintings, sculpture, silver and porcelain; Maze, Cascade and Fountains; Farmyard and Adventure Playground. Guide book translations in French, German and Japanese.

No wheelchairs in house, but welcome in garden (3 electric, 2 standard available). WCs. Special leaflets.

Restaurant (max 300); home-made food. Menus on request.

Private tours of house or Greenhouses and Behind the Scenes Days, by arrangement only (extra charges apply). Tape recorded tour may be hired at entrance. Groups please pre-book.

P Cars 100 yds, Coaches 25 yds from house.

Guided tours, packs, trails and school room. Free preliminary visit recommended.

OPENING TIMES

SUMMER
18 March - 1 November
Daily: 11am - 4.30pm.

WINTER
Closed

ADMISSION

House & Garden

Adult	£6.25
Child	£3.00
OAP/Student	£5.00
Family	£16.00

Pre-booked groups

Adult	£5.75
School (no tour)	£3.00
School (w/tour)	£3.50
OAP/Student	£4.50

Garden only

Adult	£3.60
Child	£1.75
OAP/Student	£3.00
Family	£9.00

Scots Suite

Adult	£1.00
Child	£0.50

Car Park	£1.00

SPECIAL EVENTS

• **MAY 9 / 10:**
Chatsworth Angling Fair

• **SEPT 5 / 6:**
Chatsworth Country Fair

The Midlands
England

HADDON HALL
Bakewell

William the Conqueror's illegitimate son, Peverel, and his descendants held Haddon for a hundred years before it passed into the hands of the Vernons. Over the following four centuries, the existing Medieval and Tudor manor house developed from its Norman origins. In the late 16th century, the estate passed through marriage to the Manners family, later to become Dukes of Rutland, in whose possession it has remained ever since.

Little has been added since the reign of Henry VIII, whose elder brother, Arthur, was a frequent guest of the Vernons. He would have been quite familiar with the house as it stands today – the Great Hall, kitchens and Chapel all dating from the 14th century. Incredibly, despite its time-worn steps, no other Medieval house has so triumphantly withstood the passage of time. *Jane Eyre* (1996) and *The Prince and the Pauper* (1996) were filmed at Haddon.

GARDENS

The terraced Rose Gardens, stepping down to the fast-flowing River Wye, are planned for year-round colour. Over 150 varieties of rose and clematis, many over 70 years old, provide colour and scent throughout the summer. Winner of the HHA/Christie's 'Garden of the Year' Award, 1993.

CONTACT

The Comptroller
Estate Office
Haddon Hall
Bakewell
Derbyshire
DE45 1LA

Tel: (01629) 812855

Fax: (01629) 814379

LOCATION

OS Ref. SK234 663

From London 3 hrs
Sheffield 1/2 hr
Manchester 1 hr
Haddon is on the
E side of A6 1 1/2 m
S of Bakewell.
M1/J30.

Rail: Chesterfield Station, 12m

Bus: Chesterfield Bakewell.

OPENING TIMES

SUMMER
1 April - 30 September

Daily: 11am - 5.45pm
Last admission 5pm.

WINTER
October - 31 March
Closed.

ADMISSION

SUMMER
Adult £5.50
Child (5 - 15yrs)........£3.00
OAP.......................£4.75
Family (2+3) £14.75

Groups (min. 20)
Adult £4.75
Child (5 - 15yrs)........£2.50
OAP.......................£4.00

SPECIAL EVENTS

- **JUN:**
Flower Festival (tel. for dates)

Shop. Recent productions testify to Haddon's suitability as a film location: *Jane Eyre* (1996) Rochester Films; *Prince and the Pauper* (1996) BBC.

Not suitable, steep approach, varying levels of house.

Self-service restaurant (max 75). Home-made food.

Special tours of of the house. £25 extra for groups of 15, 7 days' notice.

Ample, 450 yds from house. 50p per car.

Tours of the house bring alive Haddon Hall of old. Costume room also available, very popular!

Guide dogs only.

BAKEWELL OLD HOUSE MUSEUM

Tel: 01629 813165

Cunningham Place, Bakewell DE45 1DD

Owner: Bakewell District Historical Society   **Contact:** Dr J T Brighton

A rare and curious Peakland house built by Ralf Gell in 1534. Period fireplaces, garderobe and timber interior.

Location: OS Ref. SK215 685. 100 yds W of Bakewell Parish Church.

Opening Times: 1 Apr - 31 Oct: daily, 1.30 - 4pm (Jul, Aug, 11am - 4pm). Groups by arrangement.

Admission: Adult £2, Child £1, Child under 5 free.

BOLSOVER CASTLE ⌗

NPI Award 1997:
Runner Up

CASTLE STREET, BOLSOVER DERBYSHIRE S44 6PR

Owner: English Heritage   *Contact: The Custodian*

Tel: 01246 823349 or 01246 822844

An enchanting and romantic spectacle, situated high on a wooded hilltop dominating the surrounding landscape. Built on the site of a Norman castle, this is largely an early 17th century mansion. Most delightful is the 'Little Castle', a bewitching folly with intricate carvings, panelling and wall painting. There is also an impressive 17th century indoor Riding School built by the Duke of Newcastle.

Location: OS120, Ref. SK471 707. Off M1/J29, 6m from Mansfield.

Opening Times: 1 Apr - 1 Nov: daily, 10am - 6pm or dusk if earlier. 2 Nov - 31 Mar: Wed - Sun, 10am - 4pm. Closed 24 - 26 Dec.

Admission: Adult £2.95, Child £1.50, OAP/Student £2.20. 15% discount for groups of 11+.

    Grounds suitable. WC.   No dogs.

CALKE ABBEY

Tel: 01332 863822 **Fax:** 01332 865272

Ticknall, Derbyshire DE73 1LE

Owner: The National Trust   **Contact:** The Property Manager

The house that time forgot, this baroque mansion, built 1701 - 03 for Sir John Harpur and set in a landscaped park. Little restored, Calke is preserved by a programme of conservation as a graphic illustration of the English country house in decline; it contains the family's collection of natural history, a magnificent 18th century state bed and interiors that are virtually unchanged since the 1880s. Walled garden, pleasure grounds and newly-restored orangery. Early 19th century Church. Historic parkland with Portland sheep and deer. Staunton Harold Church is nearby.

Location: OS Ref. SK356 239. 10m S of Derby, on A514 at Ticknall between Swadlincote and Melbourne.

Opening Times: House, Garden & Church: 1 Apr - 1 Nov Sat - Wed & BH Mon (closed Good Fri). House & Church: 12.45 - 5.30pm, Garden: 11am - 5.30pm. Last adm. 5pm. Park: open during daylight hours all year: Apr - Oct: closed 9pm/dusk if earlier; Nov - Mar closes at dusk.

Admission: All sites: Adult £4.90, Child £2.45, Family £12.25. Garden only: £2.20. Discount for pre-booked groups.

    Shop.   House suitable. Braille guide. Wheelchairs. WCs.

    Licensed restaurant.   In park, on leads only.

CARNFIELD HALL

SOUTH NORMANTON, NR. ALFRETON, DERBYSHIRE DE55 2BE

Owner: J B Cartland   *Contact: J B Cartland*

Tel: 01773 520084

Unspoilt Elizabethan 'Mansion House'. Panelled rooms, two 17th century staircases, great parlour. From 1502 the seat of the Revells and now of the Cartland family. Atmospheric interior with 3 centuries of family portraits, furniture, porcelain, needlework, costumes, royal relics and manorial documents. Collections of 18th century fans, snuff boxes and toys shown by appointment.

Location: OS Ref. SK425 561. 1¹⁄₂ m W of M1/J28 on B6019. Alfreton Station 5 mins walk.

Opening Times: Spring & Summer BHs including Good Fri & Mon, 11am - 6pm. Easter - Sept: Most Sat & Sun, 2 - 5.30pm. Jul & Aug: Most Tue & Thur, from 2.30pm. By appointment also throughout the year for groups (2 - 22).

Admission: Adult £3.50, Child (8 - 16) £2, OAP/Student £2.50. Groups: Adult £3, Child (8 - 16) £1.50, OAP/Student £2. Groups must book.

    Shop. Plant centre. No photography in Hall.   Grounds suitable. WCs.

    Licensed restaurant.   Compulsory.   In grounds, on leads only.

CATTON HALL

CATTON, SWADLINCOTE, DERBYSHIRE DE12 8LN

Owners: Robin & Katie Neilson   *Contact: Robin & Katie Neilson*

Tel: 01283 716311 **Fax:** 01283 712876

Catton, built in 1745 is not open to the public. It has been in the hands of the same family since 1405 and is still lived in by the Neilsons as their private home. This gives the house a unique relaxed and friendly atmosphere making guests feel at home whether they are inside for a formal occasion, or outside enjoying activities from a marquee. The 100 acres of parkland are ideal for all types of outdoor events and most types of activities from corporate multi-activity days to the more traditional country sports of shooting, fishing or falconry can be arranged. There is also a small private chapel which is ideal for special weddings.

Location: OS Ref. SK206 154. 3m E of A38 between Lichfield & Burton (8m from each). Birmingham NEC 20m.

Opening Times: By arrangement only: Corporate entertainment, management training, multi-activity days, wedding receptions, fairs, dinners, 4 x 4 course, etc.

    Conference facilities. Corporate hospitality.   Wedding receptions.

    By arrangement.   3 x four posters, 5 twin, 1 single, ideal for small groups.

SPECIAL EVENTS

JUN 20/21: National Forest Festival and Catton Park Horse Trials.

For full list of other events at Catton Hall, see the Special Events section.

CHATSWORTH

See page 178 for full page entry.

CROMFORD MILL (SIR RICHARD ARKWRIGHT'S)   Tel/Fax: 01629 823256

Cromford, Nr. Matlock, Derbyshire DE4 3RQ   **Contact:** The Visitor Services Centre
Built in 1771, Cromford Mill is the world's first successful water powered cotton spinning mill. Set in the beautiful Derwent Valley surrounded by gritstone tors and rolling hills. There is a wholefood restaurant on site with shops, free car parking and friendly staff. A tour guide will explain the story of this important historic site and describe the development plans for the future.
Location: OS Ref. SK296 569. 3m S of Matlock, 17m N of Derby just off A6.
Opening Times: All year except Christmas Day, 9am - 5pm.
Admission: Free entry. Guided tours: Adult £2, Conc. £1.50.

| i Shop. | & Partially suitable. WCs. | ☕ Restaurant. | 🚶 Compulsory. |
| P Ample for cars. | 👪 Educational programme. | 🐕 In grounds, on leads. | |

ELVASTON CASTLE COUNTRY PARK   Tel: 01332 571342 **Fax:** 01332 758751

Borrowash Road, Elvaston, Derby, Derbyshire DE72 3EP
Owner: Derbyshire County Council   **Contact:** The Park Manager
200 acre park landscaped in 19th century. Walled kitchen garden. Estate museum with exhibitions of traditional crafts.
Location: OS Ref. SK407 330. 5m SE of Derby, 2m from A6 or A52.
Opening Times: Park: All year, dawn - dusk. Shop/Exhibitions: 30 Mar - 3 Nov: daily, 11am - 4.30pm. Museum: 30 Mar - 3 Nov: Wed - Sat, 1 - 4.30pm. Sun & BHs: 10am - 5pm. Tearoom: All year, 10am - 4pm.
Admission: Museum: Adult £1.20, Child 60p, Family (2+2) £3. Park and Gardens free. Car park: Midweek 70p, weekends/BHs £1.30, Coaches £7.50.

i Shop. Conferences.	✗ Wedding receptions.	& Ground floor & grounds suitable. WCs.
☕ Licensed tearoom.	🚶 By arrangement.	P Ample.
👪 Educational programme.	🐕 In grounds, on leads.	⚭ Civil Wedding Licence.

EYAM HALL 🏛

EYAM, HOPE VALLEY, DERBYSHIRE S32 5QW

Owner: R H V Wright   *Contact:* Mrs N Wright

Tel: 01433 631976   **Fax:** 01433 631603   **e-mail:** Nicwri@globalnet.co.uk
Web Site: http://www.derbyshire.org/eyam-hall

17th century manor house situated in the famous 'plague village' of Eyam. Built and still occupied by the Wright family. A glimpse of three centuries through the eyes of one family. Contents include family portraits, tapestries, clocks, costumes and toys. Jacobean staircase and spectacular 17th century kitchen. Craft centre in converted farm buildings; with crafts people at work and authentic local products for sale.
Location: OS119, SK216 765. Approx 10m from Sheffield, Chesterfield and Buxton. Off A623 between Stockport and Chesterfield. Eyam Hall is in the centre of the village, just past the church. Coach parking is limited. Ample parking for cars.
Opening Times: 1 Apr - 1 Nov: Wed, Thur, Sun, BHs : 1st tour 11am, last tour 4.30pm. Victorian Christmas tours for booked groups: 28 Nov - 12 Dec: Tue - schools only. Concerts and Events: phone for details. Craft Centre, Buttery & Gift Shop: 28 Feb - 24 Dec: daily except Mon, 10.30am - 5.30pm.
Admission: Adult £3.50, Child £2.50, Conc. £3. Family (2+4) £10.50. (Group rates available, advance booking is essential).

| i Shop & craft centre. | & Partially suitable. WCs. | ☕ Licensed restaurant. |
| 🚶 Compulsory. | 👪 Educational programme. | 🐕 In grounds, on leads. |

HADDON HALL 🏛

See page 179 for full page entry.

HARDSTOFT HERB GARDEN   Tel: 01246 854268

Hall View Cottage, Hardstoft, Chesterfield, Derbyshire S45 8AH
Owner: Mr Stephen Raynor / L M Raynor   **Contact:** Mr Stephen Raynor
Consists of four display gardens with information boards and well labelled plants.
Location: OS Ref. SK438630. On B6039 between Holmewood & Tibshelf, 3m from J29 on M1.
Opening Times: 15 Mar - 15 Sept: 10am - 6pm.
Admission: Adult £1, Child free.

| i Shop. Plant centre. | & Not suitable. | ☕ Tearoom. |
| P Limited. | 🐕 In grounds, on leads. | |

HARDWICK ESTATE - STAINSBY MILL 🌿   Tel: 01246 850430

Stainsby, Chesterfield, Derbyshire S44 5QJ   **Fax:** 01246 854200
Owner: The National Trust   **Contact:** The Property Manager
18th century water-powered corn mill in working order.
Location: OS Ref. SK455 653. From M1/J29 take A6175, signposted to Clay Cross then first left and left again to Stainsby Mill.
Opening Times: 1 Apr - 1 Nov: Wed, Thur, Sat, Sun & BH Mon, 11am - 4.30pm. Jun - Sept: also open Fri, 11am - 4.30pm. Last admission 4pm.
Admission: Adult £1.50, Child 70p, Family £3.70. Pre-booked groups (no reduction).

| 🐕 In park, on leads. |

HARDWICK HALL 🌿   Tel: 01246 850430 Shop: 01246 854088 **Fax:** 01246 854200

Doe Lea, Chesterfield, Derbyshire S44 5QJ
Owner: The National Trust   **Contact:** The Property Manager
A late 16th century 'prodigy house' designed by Robert Smythson for Bess of Hardwick. The house contains outstanding contemporary furniture, tapestries and needlework including pieces identified in an inventory of 1601; a needlework exhibition is on permanent display. Walled courtyards enclose fine gardens, orchards and a herb garden. The country park contains Whiteface Woodland sheep and Longhorn cattle.
Location: OS Ref. SK463 638. $^{1}/_{2}$ m W of Mansfield, $9^{1}/_{2}$ m SE of Chesterfield: approach from M1/J29 via A6175.
Opening Times: Hall: 1 Apr - 1 Nov: Wed, Thur, Sat, Sun & BH Mon, 12.30 - 5pm (closed Good Fri). Last adm. to Hall 4.30pm. Garden: 1 Apr - 1 Nov: daily 12 - 5.30pm. Restaurant: open as per Hall: 12 - 2pm lunches, 2 - 4.45pm teas.
Admission: Hall & Garden: Adult £6, Child £3, Family £15. Garden only: Adult £2.70, Child £1, Family £6.50. Joint (Old & New Hall): Adult £7.70. No reduction for groups.

| i Shop. | & House limited, garden suitable. | ☕ Licensed restaurant. |
| 🐕 In park, on leads. | | |

HARDWICK OLD HALL 🎴

DOE LEA, NR CHESTERFIELD, DERBYSHIRE S44 5QJ

Owner: English Heritage   *Contact:* The Custodian

Tel: 01246 850431

This large ruined house, finished in 1591, still displays Bess of Hardwick's innovative planning and interesting decorative plasterwork. The views from the top floor over the country park and 'New' Hall are spectacular.
Location: OS120 Ref. SK463 638. $9^{1}/_{2}$ m SE of Chesterfield, off A6175, from J29/M1.
Opening Times: 1 Apr - 1 Nov: Wed - Sun, 10am - 6pm or dusk if earlier.
Admission: Adult £2.30, Child £1.20, Conc. £1.70. 15% discount for groups 11+.

| 🐕 On leads. |

KEDLESTON HALL

Oliver Benn.

DERBY, DERBYSHIRE DE22 5JH

Owner: *The National Trust*   **Contact:** *The Property Manager*

Tel: 01332 842191   **Fax:** 01332 841972

Experience the age of elegance in this neo-classical house built between 1759 and 1765 for the Curzon family and little altered since. Set in 800 acres of parkland with an 18th century pleasure ground, garden and woodland walks - a day at Kedleston is truly an experience to remember. The influence of the architect Robert Adam is everywhere, from the Park buildings to the decoration of the magnificent state rooms. Groups are welcome and an introductory talk can be arranged.

Location: OS Ref. SK312 403. 5m NW of Derby, signposted from roundabout where A38 crosses A52.

Opening Times: House: 28 Mar - 1 Nov: Sat - Wed, 1 - 5.30pm. Last adm. 5pm (from 18 Oct last adm. 4pm). Park & Gardens: 11am - 6pm. Restaurant: 11am - 5pm. Park only: Thur & Fri, 11am - 6pm vehicle charge. House opens 11am BH Sat, Sun & Mon.

Admission: Adult £4.70, Child £2.40, Family £11.50. Garden & Park: Adult £2, Child £1. Discount for groups, please telephone.

| i | Shop. | ♿ | Stairclimber & Batricar available. | | Licensed restaurant. |

| | In grounds, on leads. | | Civil Wedding Licence. |

SPECIAL EVENTS

JUL 18: Outdoor Classical Concert with Fireworks. **AUG 29 - 31:** Working Craft Show in Park.

RENISHAW HALL

SHEFFIELD, DERBYSHIRE S31 9WB

Owner: *Sir Reresby Sitwell Bt DL*   **Contact:** *William Town*

Tel: 01777 860755   **Fax:** 01777 860707

In 1625 George Sitwell built a small H-shaped manor house to which his descendant Sitwell Sitwell later 1st baronet, added vast additions, also the Georgian Stables (now containing a small museum) and various follies in and around the Park. The beautiful Italianate garden, park and lake were the creation of the eccentric Sir George Sitwell, grandfather of the present owner.

Location: OS Ref. SK435 786. 6m equidistant from Sheffield & Chesterfield, 3m M1/J30.

Opening Times: Every Fri - Sun & BH Mon. Good Fri - Sun 13 Sept: 10.30am - 4.30pm.

Admission: House: by written application only. Garden only: Adult £3, Conc. £2 Museum & Art Exhib: Adult £3, Conc. £2. Garden, Museum & Art Exhib: Adult £5, Conc £3.

| i | Shop. Plant centre. Conferences. Corporate hospitality. | ♿ | WCs. |

| | Tearoom. | | By arrangement. | P | Ample. | | In grounds, on leads. |

LEA GARDENS   **Tel:** 01629 534380 **Fax:** 01629 534260

Lea, Matlock, Derbyshire DE4 5GH

Owner: Mr & Mrs J Tye   **Contact:** Mr & Mrs J Tye

The gardens are sited on the remains of a mediaeval millstone quarry and cover 4 acres within a wooded hillside. A unique collection of rhododendrons, azaleas, kalmias.

Location: OS Ref. SK324 570. On W side of small lane 600yds SW of Lea village & $^1/_2$ m N of Holloway. $1^1/_2$ m NE of A6, $2^1/_2$ m SE of Matlock. Parking limited for coaches.

Opening Times: 20 Mar - early July: 10am - 7pm.

Admission: Adult £3, Child 50p, Season ticket £4.

| i | Plant centre. | ♿ | Partially suitable. | | Tearoom. | | In grounds, on leads. |

MELBOURNE HALL   **Tel:** 01332 862502 **Fax:** 01332 862263

Melbourne, Derbyshire DE73 1EN

Owner: Lord & Lady Ralph Kerr   **Contact:** Mrs Gill Weston

This beautiful house of history, in its picturesque poolside setting, was once the home of Victorian Prime Minister William Lamb. The fine gardens, in the French formal style, contain Robert Bakewell's intricate wrought iron arbour and a fascinating yew tunnel.

Location: OS Ref. SK389 249. 8m S of Derby. From London, exit M1/J24.

Opening Times: Hall: Aug only (not first 3 Mons) 2 - 5pm. Gardens: 1 Apr - 30 Sept: Wed, Sat, Sun, BH Mons, 2 - 6pm.

Admission: Hall: Adult £2.50, Child £1, OAP £2. Gardens: Adult £3, Child/OAP £2. Hall & Gardens: Adult £4.50, Child £2.50, OAP £3.50.

| i | Crafts & shop. | ♿ | Suitable. | | Tearoom. | P | Limited. | | Guide dogs only. |

PEVERIL CASTLE   **Tel:** 01433 620613

Market Place, Castleton, Hope Valley S33 8WQ

Owner: English Heritage   **Contact:** The Custodian

There are breathtaking views of the Peak District from this castle, perched high above the pretty village of Castleton. The great square tower stands almost to its original height. Formerly known as Peak Castle.

Location: OS110 Ref. SK150 827. S side of Castleton, 15m W of Sheffield on A625.

Open: 1 Apr - 1 Nov: daily, 10am - 6pm or dusk in October. 2 Nov - 31 Mar, Wed - Sun, 10am - 4pm. Closed 24 - 26 Dec.

Admission: Adult £1.75, Child 90p, Conc. £1.30. 15% discount for groups of 11+.

REVOLUTION HOUSE   **Tel:** 01246 453554 / 345727

High Street, Old Whittington, Chesterfield, Derbyshire S41 9LA

     Contact: Ms A M Knowles

Originally the Cock and Pynot ale house, now furnished in 17th century style.

Location: OS Ref. SK384 749. 3m N of Chesterfield on B6052 off A61.

Opening Times: Good Fri - Oct: daily, 10am - 4pm. Special opening over Christmas period.

Admission: Free.

| i | Shop. | ♿ | Ground floor suitable. | P | Limited. | | No dogs. |

SPECIAL EVENTS 1998

See the front section for full list.

Historic Scotland

RISLEY HALL GARDENS

DERBY ROAD, RISLEY, DERBYSHIRE DE72 3SS

Owner: Mrs I Crosbie   *Contact: M J Crosbie*

Tel: 0115 9399000   **Fax:** 0115 9490464

Risley Hall and Gardens, a manor house dating back to the 15th century, was built by Sir Michael Willoughby. The formal gardens extend to 12 acres and include the Grade II* listed stone terrace which extends to 200 metres above a moated stream overlooking the great lawn with its golden yews. The house has had many extensions in the 17th, 18th and 19th century, all of which have given the hall outstanding character.

Location: OS Ref. SK453 463. Midway between Nottingham and Derby on A52, 1m from M1/J25.

Opening Times: All year: daily, 2 - 5pm.

Admission: Adult £3.50, Child £1.75, Conc. £2.50. Pre-arranged groups: Adult £2.50, Child £1.50, Conc. £2.

[i] Conference facilities, corporate hospitality.   [X] Wedding receptions.

[&] Partially suitable. WC.   [☕] Tearoom, licensed restaurant.   [⟋] By arrangement.

[P] Ample.   [🐕] Guide dogs only.   [⚭] Civil Wedding Licence.

SUDBURY HALL

Tel: 01283 585305   **Fax:** 01283 585139

Ashbourne, Derbyshire DE6 5HT

Owner: The National Trust   **Contact:** The Administrator

One of the most individual of late 17th century houses, begun by George Vernon c1660. The rich decoration includes wood carvings by Gibbons and Pierce, superb plasterwork, mythological decorative paintings by Laguerre. The great staircase is one of the finest of its kind in an English house.

Location: OS Ref. SK160 323. 6m E of Uttoxeter at the junction of A50 Derby - Stoke & A515 Ashbourne.

Opening Times: 1 Apr - 1 Nov: Wed - Sun & BH Mon, 1 - 5.30pm, Sats & Suns & Jul/Aug , 12.30 - 5pm. Last adm. 30 mins before closing. Grounds: 12.30 - 6pm.

Admission: Hall: Adult £3.50, Child £1.60, Family £8.60. Groups by prior arrangement.

[i] Shop.   [&] Limited, braille guide. WC.   [☕] Licensed tearoom.   [🐕] Car park only.

Sutton Scarsdale Hall.

STAINSBY MILL - HARDWICK ESTATE

See Hardwick Estate - Stainsby Mill entry on page 181.

SUTTON SCARSDALE HALL

Tel: 01604 730320 (Regional Office)

Chesterfield, Derbyshire

Owner: English Heritage   **Contact:** Midlands Regional Office

The dramatic hilltop shell of a great early 18th century baroque mansion.

Location: OS Ref. SK441 690. Between Chesterfield & Bolsover, 1¹/₂ m S of Arkwright Town.

Opening Times: 10am - 6pm or dusk if earlier.

Admission: Free.

[&] Suitable.   [🐕] On leads.

TISSINGTON HALL

ASHBOURNE, DERBYSHIRE DE6 1RA

Owner: Sir Richard FitzHerbert Bt   *Contact: Sir Richard FitzHerbert Bt*

Tel: 01335 390246   **Fax:** 01335 390383   **e-mail:** tisshall@dircon.co.uk

Home of the FitzHerbert family for over 500 years. The hall stands in a superbly maintained estate village, and contains wonderful panelling and fine old masters. A 10 acre garden and arboretum. Schools very welcome.

Location: OS Ref. SK175 524. 4m N of Ashbourne off A515 towards Buxton.

Opening Times: Jun & Jul: Mon - Wed, 2 - 5pm. Last tour 4.30pm. Guided tour of hall by owner available out of normal opening hours.

Admission: Adult £4.50, Child (5 - 16) £2.50, OAP £4, Garden only: £2.

[i] No photography.   [&] Partially suitable. WCs at tearooms.

[☕] Tearoom tel: 01335 350501.   [⟋] Compulsory.   [P] Limited.

[👥] Educational programme, teachers' pack.   [🐕] Guide dogs only.

WINGFIELD MANOR

Tel: 01773 832060

Derbyshire

Owner: English Heritage   **Contact:** The Custodian

Huge, ruined, country mansion built in the mid-15th century. Mary Queen of Scots was imprisoned here in 1569. Though unoccupied since the 1770s, the late-Gothic Great Hall and the High Tower are fine testaments to Wingfield in its heyday. The manor has been used as a film location for *Peak Practice* and Zeffirelli's *Jane Eyre*.

Location: OS Ref. SK374 548. S side of B5035, ¹/₂ m S of South Wingfield village. Access by 600yd drive (no vehicles). From M1 J28, W on A38, A615 (Matlock road) at Alfreton and turn onto B5035 after 1¹/₂m.

Opening Times: 1 Apr - 1 Nov: Wed - Sun, 12 - 5pm. 2 Nov - 31 Mar: weekends only, 10am - 4pm. Closed 24 - 26 Dec. Closed 1 - 2pm in winter. The Manor incorporates a working farm. Visitors are requested to respect the privacy of the owners and refrain from visiting outside official opening times.

Admission: Adult £2.95, Child £1.50, Conc. £2.20.

WINSTER MARKET HOUSE

Tel: 01335 350245

Matlock, Derbyshire

Owner: The National Trust   **Contact:** The Property Manager

A market house of the late 17th or early 18th century. The ground floor is of stone with the original five open arches filled in, while the upper storey is of brick with stone dressings. The building was bought in 1906 and restored. It is now an NT Information Room.

Location: OS Ref. SK241 606. 4m W of Matlock, S side B5057 in main street of Winster.

Opening Times: 29 Mar - end Oct: daily.

Admission: Free.

BERKELEY CASTLE
Berkeley

Not many can boast of having their private house celebrated by Shakespeare nor of having held it in the possession of their family for nearly 850 years, nor having a King of England murdered within its walls, nor of having welcomed at their table the local vicar and Castle Chaplain, John Trevisa (1342-1402), reputed as one of the earliest translators of the Bible, nor of having a breach battered by Oliver Cromwell, which to this day it is forbidden by law to repair even if it was wished to do so. But such is the story of Berkeley.

This beautiful and historic Castle, begun in 1117, still remains the home of the famous family who gave their name to numerous locations all over the world, notably Berkeley Square in London, Berkeley Hundred in Virginia and Berkeley University in California. Scene of the brutal murder of Edward II in 1327 (visitors can see his cell and nearby the dungeon) and besieged by Cromwell's troops in 1645, the Castle is steeped in history but twenty-four generations of Berkeleys have gradually transformed a Norman fortress into the lovely home it is today.

The State Apartments contain magnificent collections of furniture, rare paintings by primarily English and Dutch masters, and tapestries. Part of the world-famous Berkeley silver is on display in the Dining Room. Many other rooms are equally interesting including the Great Hall upon which site the Barons of the West Country met in 1215 before going to Runnymede to force King John to put his seal to the Magna Carta.

The Castle is surrounded by lovely terraced Elizabethan Gardens with a lily pond, Elizabeth I's bowling green, and sweeping lawns.

❖

CONTACT

The Custodian
Berkeley Castle
Gloucestershire
GL13 9BQ

Tel: (01453) 810332

LOCATION

OS Ref. ST685 990

SE side of Berkeley village.
Midway between
Bristol & Gloucester,
2m W off the A38.

From motorway
M5/J14 (5m) or
J13 (9m).

Bus: No 308 from
Bristol & Gloucester

i Shop and plant centre, fashion shows and filming. Butterfly farm. No photography inside the Castle.

✗ Wedding receptions and corporate entertainment.

♿ Visitors may alight in the Outer Bailey.

▭ Licensed tearooms serving lunches & home-made teas.

🚶 Free. Max. 120 people. Tour time: 1 hr. Evening groups by arrangement. Group visits must be booked.

P Cars 150 yds from Castle and up to 15 coaches 250 yds away.

👫 Welcome. General and social history and architecture.

🐕 No dogs.

CONFERENCE/FUNCTION

ROOM	SIZE	MAX CAPACITY
Great Hall		200
Long Drawing Rm		100

OPENING TIMES

SUMMER

April - May
Tue - Sun, 1 - 5pm.

June & September
Tue - Sat, 11am - 5pm,
Sun, 1 - 5pm.

July & August
Mon - Sat, 11am - 5pm
Sun, 1 - 5pm

BH Mons, 11am - 5pm

NB. Groups must book.

WINTER

October
Sun only, 1 - 5pm.

ADMISSION

Castle and Garden
Adult £4.95
Child £2.60
OAP.........................£3.95

Groups (25+ pre-booked)
Adult £4.45
Child £2.30
OAP £3.65
Family (2+2) £13.50

Gardens only
Adult £1.75
Child 90p

Butterfly Farm
Adult £1.75
Child/OAP 85p
School Groups 50p

CHAVENAGE
Tetbury

CHAVENAGE is a wonderful Elizabethan house of mellow grey Cotswold stone and tiles which contains much of interest for the discerning visitor.

The approach aspect of Chavenage is virtually as it was left by Edward Stephens in 1576. Only two families have owned Chavenage; the present owners since 1891 and the Stephens family before them. A Colonel Nathaniel Stephens, MP for Gloucestershire during the Civil War was cursed for supporting Cromwell, giving rise to legends of weird happenings at Chavenage since that time.

Inside Chavenage there are many interesting rooms housing tapestries, fine furniture, pictures and many relics of the Cromwellian period. Of particular note are the Main Hall,

where a contemporary screen forms a minstrels' gallery and two tapestry rooms where it is said Cromwell was lodged.

Recently Chavenage has been used as a location for TV and film productions including a Hercule Poirot story *The Mysterious Affair at Styles*, many episodes of the sequel to *Are you Being Served* now called *Grace & Favour*, a *Gotcha* for *The Noel Edmonds' House Party*, episodes of *The House of Elliot*, *Casualty* and *Berkeley Square*.

Chavenage is especially suitable for those wishing an intimate, personal tour, usually conducted by the owner, or for small groups wanting a change from large establishments. It also provides a charming venue for small conferences and functions.

CONTACT

D Lowsley-Williams
Chavenage
Tetbury
Gloucestershire
GL8 8XP

Tel: (01666) 502329

Fax: (01453) 836778

LOCATION

OS Ref. ST872 952

Less than 20m from M4/J16/17 or 18. 1¾ m NW of Tetbury between the B4104 & A4135. Signed from Tetbury. Less than 15m from M5/J13 or 14. Signed from A46 (Stroud -Bath road)

Rail: Kemble Station 7m

Taxi: Tetbury Cars, Tetbury 503393

CONFERENCE/FUNCTION		
ROOM	SIZE	MAX CAPACITY
Ballroom	· 70' x 30'	120
Oak Room	25 'x 20'	30

OPENING TIMES

SUMMER
May - September
Easter Sun, Mon
& BHs, 2 - 5pm.

Thur & Sun
2 - 5pm.

NB. Will open at other times by prior arrangement for groups.

WINTER
October - March
By appointment only
for groups.

ADMISSION

Tours are inclusive in the following prices.

SUMMER
Adult £3.00
Child (5 - 16 yrs).......£1.50
Friend of HHA ....Free

CONCESSIONS
By prior arrangement, concessions may be given to groups of 20+ and also to disabled and to exceptional cases.

WINTER
Groups only:
Rates by arrangement.

ℹ️ Clay pigeon shooting, archery, cross-bows, pistol shooting, ATV driving, small fashion shows, concerts, plays, seminars, filming, product launching, photography.

✕ Corporate entertaining. In-house catering for wedding parties.

♿ Ground floor accessible. WC.

☕ Lunches, teas, dinners and picnics by arrangement.

🚶 By owner. Large groups given a talk prior to viewing. Couriers and group leaders should arrange tour format prior to visit.

🅿️ Up to 100 cars and 2 - 3 coaches. Coaches only by appointment; stop at gates for parking instructions.

👪 Chairs can be arranged for lecturing. Tour of working farm, modern dairy and corn facilities can be arranged.

SUDELEY CASTLE
Winchcombe

SUDELEY CASTLE, home of Lord and Lady Ashcombe, is one of England's great historic houses with royal connections stretching back 1000 years. Once the property of King Ethelred the Unready, Sudeley was later the magnificent palace of Queen Katherine Parr, Henry VIII's sixth wife, who is buried in the Castle church. Henry VIII, Anne Boleyn, Lady Jane Grey and Elizabeth I stayed at the Castle. Charles I resided here while Prince Rupert of the Rhine made it his headquarters during the Civil War.

During the Victorian era, a programme of reconstruction enhanced Sudeley's earlier magnificence. Among a wealth of history is an impressive collection of treasures including masterpieces by Turner, Van Dyck and Rubens. Surrounding the Castle are eight enchanting gardens which have gained international recognition and the HHA/Christie's 'Garden of the Year' award (1996) for their floral displays and topiary. Famous for its fine collection of old roses, the Queen's Garden is well worth a visit, as is the Tudor Knot Garden with intricate patterns, mosaics and water features. A now well established Victorian Kitchen Garden features vegetables grown during that era under natural organic conditions. Visitors can wander at leisure through avenues of majestic trees, wide stretches of still water, grand yew hedges and fragrant roses.

The Visitors' Centre introduces and orientates visitors to the castle, gardens and other attractions. The centre houses displays, information on the history and conservation of the castle, a shop, light refreshments and a pick-up point for the audio tour narrated by Robert Hardy.

CONTACT

Administrator
Sudeley Castle
Winchcombe
Nr Cheltenham
Gloucestershire
GL54 5JD

Tel: (01242) 603197
or (01242) 602308

Fax: (01242) 602959

LOCATION

OS Ref. SP032 277

8m NE of Cheltenham,
1/2 m SE of Winchcombe
off B4632.

From Bristol or
Birmingham M5/J9.
Take A438 towards
Stow-on-the-Wold.

Bus: Castleways to
Winchcombe.

Rail: Cheltenham
Station 8m.

Air: Birmingham or
Bristol 45m.

CONFERENCE/FUNCTION		
ROOM	SIZE	MAX CAPACITY
Chandos		70
North Hall		40
Sheldon Rm		75
Banquet Hall & Pavilion		120
The Rubens Drawing Rm		20

SPECIAL EVENTS

• **APR 17 - 19:**
  Homes & Garden Exhibition.

• **JUN 27/28:**
  'Daily Telegraph' Rose Day

• **JUL 11:**
  Philharmonic Orchestra with Fireworks.

i Shop and plant centre. Photography and filming, concerts, corporate events and conferences. Product launches, garden parties, craft fairs and activity days. No photography or video cameras. Sudeley reserves the right to close part or all of the Castle, gardens and grounds and to amend information as necessary.

✗ Private dining, banquets, and medieval dinners.

♿ Not suitable.

☕ Licensed restaurant and tea rooms. Groups must book.

🚶 Special interest tours can be arranged.

P 1,000 cars. Meal vouchers, free access for coach drivers.

👫 Worksheets. Small fee for preliminary talk, guide available on request.

🐕 No dogs.

A 14 holiday cottages for 2 - 5 occupants.

OPENING TIMES

SUMMER

Gardens, Plant Centre & Shop

1 - 31 March
Tue - Sun, 11am - 4.30pm.
1 April - 31 May, Tue - Sun,
10.30am - 5.30pm.

Castle Apartments & Church

1 April - 31 May: Tue - Sun
& BHs, 11am - 5pm.
Castle closed all day on
9 & 10 May.
1 June - 13 September:
Daily, 11am - 5pm.
14 September - 31 October
Tue - Sun, 11am - 5pm.
Last admission 4.30pm.

Gardens, Plant Centre & Church

28 Nov - 20 Dec
Thur - Sun, 11am - 3.30pm.

WINTER

By appointment
Groups (min. 30).

ADMISSION

Castle & Garden*
Adult £5.50
Child (5-15 yrs.)........£3.00
OAP........................£4.80
Family (2 +2)..........£16.00

Groups* (min. 20)
Adult £4.50
Child (5-15 yrs.)........£3.00
OAP........................£3.95

Gardens & Exhibitions*
Adult £4.00
Child (5-15 yrs.)........£1.80
OAP........................£3.20

Season Ticket
Adult £16.00
Family £32.00

Adventure Playground only £1.00

* Prices quoted are for weekdays only.

ASHLEWORTH TITHE BARN

Tel: 01684 850051

Ashleworth, Gloucestershire

Owner: The National Trust   **Contact:** The Administrator

A C15th tithe barn with two projecting porch bays and fine roof timbers with queenposts.

Location: OS Ref. SO818 252. 6m NW of Gloucester, 1¼ m E of Hartpury A417.

Opening Times: Apr - 1 Nov: daily 9am - 6pm or sunset if earlier. Closed Good Fri, other times by prior appointment only.

Admission: 60p.

P Limited.   No dogs.

BARNSLEY HOUSE GARDEN

Tel/Fax: 01285 740281

The Close, Barnsley, Cirencester GL7 5EE

Owner: Charles Verey   **Contact:** Rosemary Verey

Mature 4½ acre garden designed by Rosemary Verey. Bulbs, mixed borders, autumn colours, knot of herb garden, laburnum walk (late May, early June). Decorative vegetable garden, garden furniture by Charles Verey. Fountain and statues by Simon Verity. Two 18th century summer houses. Winner of the HHA/Christie's Garden of the Year award, 1988.

Location: OS Ref. SP076 049. In Barnsley village, 4m NE of Cirencester on B4425.

Opening Times: All year: Mon, Wed, Thur & Sat, 10am - 6pm. Nursery open Mon - Sat.

Admission: Adult £3.50, Student £2, OAP £2.50. No charge for group tour leader.

i Shop. Plant centre.   Partially suitable.   By arrangement.

P Ample for cars. Limited for coaches.   In grounds, on leads.

BATSFORD ARBORETUM

Tel: 01608 650722   **Fax:** 01608 650290

Moreton-in-Marsh, Gloucestershire GL56 9QF

Owner: The Batsford Foundation   **Contact:** Christine Dyer

50 acres of arboretum.

Location: OS Ref. SP183 324. 1½ m NW of Moreton-in-Marsh, off A44 to Broadway.

Opening Times: 1 Mar - mid Nov: daily, 10am - 5pm. House not open.

Admission: Adult £3, OAP £2.50, Child (11 - 16yrs) £2.50, under 10s free.

i Plant centre.   Grounds suitable. WC.   Tearoom.   In grounds, on leads.

BERKELEY CASTLE

See page 184 for full page entry.

BLACKFRIARS

Tel: 01179 750700

Ladybellegate Street, Gloucester

Owner: English Heritage   **Contact:** The South West Regional Office

A small Dominican priory church converted into a rich merchant's house at the Dissolution. Most of the original 13th century church remains, including a rare scissor-braced roof.

Location: OS Ref. SO830 186. In Ladybellegate St, Gloucester, off Southgate Street and Blackfriars Walk.

Opening Times: Please contact the South West Regional Office.

Admission: Free.

BOURTON HOUSE GARDEN

Tel: 01386 700121   **Fax:** 01386 701081

Bourton-on-the-Hill, Moreton-in-Marsh GL56 9AE

Owner: Mr & Mrs R Paice   **Contact:** Mrs R Paice

Imaginatively planted 3 acre garden in delightful Cotswold setting. A profusion of excitingly planted containers from lead cisterns to stone troughs and a myriad of terracotta pots. Also featured are a knot garden, herbaceous and colour borders, a potager, topiary and an exciting new shade house. A fountain and small ponds add to the tranquillity of various garden rooms. A newly planted 7 acre field will provide continuing interest in years to come. A recently established garden which is constantly evolving. Tithe Barn.

Location: OS Ref. SP180 324. 1¾ m W of Moreton-in-Marsh on A44.

Opening Times: 28 May - 23 Oct: Thur & Fri, 12 - 5pm. 24/25 May and 30/31 Aug.

Admission: Adult £3 , Child free.

i Shop. Plant sales.   Not suitable.   Tearoom.   No dogs.

CHAVENAGE

See page 185 for full page entry.

CHEDWORTH ROMAN VILLA

Ian Shaw

YANWORTH, CHELTENHAM, GLOS GL54 3LJ

Owner: The National Trust   **Contact:** The Property Manager

Tel: 01242 890256   **Fax:** 01242 890544

The remains of a Romano-British villa, excavated 1864. Set in beautiful wooded combe. Includes fine 4th century mosaics, two bath houses, spring with temple. A museum houses the smaller finds.

Location: OS163 Ref. SP053 135. 3m NW of Fossebridge on Cirencester - Northleach road A429. Coaches must avoid Withington.

Opening Times: 3 - 27 Feb: Tue - Fri, 10am - 4pm, site open for pre-booked parties. 28 Feb - 29 Nov: Tue - Sun & BH Mon, 10am - 5pm (closes 4pm from 27 Oct onwards). Open Good Fri. Also 5 - 6 Dec, 10am - 4pm.

Admission: Adult £3.20, Child £1.60, Family £8.

i Shop.   Grounds limited. WC.   By arrangement.   P Limited.   No dogs.

SPECIAL EVENTS

Chedworth has a variety of special events throughout the year. See the Special Events section at the front of the book or telephone for further details.

DYRHAM PARK

Rupert Truman

NR. CHIPPENHAM, WILTSHIRE SN14 8ER

Owner: The National Trust   **Contact:** The Property Manager

Tel: 0117 937 2501

Built for William Blathwayt, Secretary at War and Secretary of State to William III between 1691 and 1710. The rooms have changed little since they were furnished by Blathwayt and their contents are recorded in his housekeeper's inventory. Surrounding the house, the 263 acre ancient parkland with herd of fallow deer, overlooks the Severn valley.

Location: OS Ref. ST743 757. 8m N of Bath, 12m E of Bristol. Approached from Bath - Stroud road (A46), 2m S of Tormarton interchange with M4/J18.

Opening Times: Park: All year: daily 12 - 5.30pm or dusk if earlier. Open 11am on days that garden opens. Last adm. 5pm. Closed 25 Dec. Garden: 3 Apr - 1 Nov: daily except Wed & Thur, 11am - 5.30pm. House: 3 Apr - 1 Nov: daily except Wed & Thur, 12 - 5.30pm. Last adm. 5pm or dusk if earlier. Property closed 3/4 Jul for music concerts.

Admission: Adult £5.40, Child £2.70, Family (2+3) £13.30.

SPECIAL EVENTS

JUL 3: Open Air Jazz Concert.   JUL 4: 50s, 60s & 70s Open Air Concert.

FRAMPTON MANOR

Fax: 01452 740698

Frampton-on-Severn, Gloucestershire GL2 7EU

Owner: Mr & Mrs P R H Clifford   **Contact:** Mrs P R H Clifford

Mediaeval/Elizabethan timber-framed manor house with walled garden. Reputed 12th century birthplace of 'Fair Rosamund' Clifford, mistress of King Henry II. Wool barn c1500 and c1800 granary with dovecote.

Location: OS Ref. SO748 080. 3m M5/J13.

Opening Times: House & Garden: open throughout the year by written appointment. Garden: 20 Apr - 6 Jul: Mon, 2 - 5pm.

Admission: House & Garden: £3. Garden only: £2.

HAILES ABBEY

Tel: 01242 602398

Nr Winchcombe, Cheltenham, Gloucestershire GL54 5PB

Owner: English Heritage & The National Trust   **Contact:** The Custodian

Seventeen cloister arches and extensive excavated remains in lovely surroundings of an abbey founded by Richard, Earl of Cornwall, in 1246. There is a small museum and covered display area.

Location: OS150, Ref. SP050 300. 2m NE of Winchcombe off B4632. ¹/₂ m SE of B4632.

Opening Times: 1 Apr - 31 Oct: daily, 10am - 6pm or dusk if earlier. 1 Nov - 31 Mar: Sat - Sun, 10am - 4pm. Closed 24 - 26 Dec.

Admission: Adult £2.50, Child £1.30, Conc. £1.90.

ℹ️ Shop.   ♿ Ground floor & grounds suitable. WC.   ☕ Kiosk.   🐕 In grounds, on leads.

HORTON COURT

Tel: 01985 843600

Horton, Near Chipping Sodbury B17 6QR

Owner: The National Trust   **Contact:** Wessex Regional Office

A Cotswold manor house with 12th century Norman hall and early Renaissance features. Of particular interest is the late perpendicular ambulatory, detached from the house. Norman hall and ambulatory only shown.

Location: OS Ref. NT766 849. 3m NE of Chipping Sodbury, ³/₄ m N of Horton, 1m W of A46.

Opening Times: 1 Apr - 31 Oct: Wed & Sat, 2 - 6pm or dusk if earlier.

Admission: Adult £1.70, Child 80p.

KELMSCOTT MANOR

Tel: 01367 252486   **Fax:** 01367 253754

Kelmscott, Nr Lechlade, Gloucestershire GL7 3HJ

Owner: Society of Antiquaries   **Contact:** Helen Webb

The home of William Morris, poet, craftsman and socialist from 1871 until his death in 1896. The house contains an interesting collection of the possessions and works of Morris and his associates including furniture, textiles, carpets and ceramics. A centenary exhibition of 'William Morris at Kelmscott' is being held in one of the barns during normal opening times.

Location: OS Ref. SU252 988. At SE end of the village, 2m due E of Lechlade, off the Lechlade - Faringdon Road. Limited parking for coaches.

Opening Times: Apr - Sept: Wed & 3rd Sat of each month. Wed, 11am - 1pm & 2 - 5pm. Sat, 2 - 5pm. Thur & Fri by appointment. Closed Oct - Mar.

Admission: Adult £6, Child £3, Student £3.

ℹ️ Shop.   ♿ Grounds suitable. WCs.   ☕ Licensed café.   🚶 By arrangement.   🐕 No dogs.

HIDCOTE MANOR GARDEN

Stephen Robson.

CHIPPING CAMPDEN, GLOUCESTERSHIRE GL55 6LR

Owner: The National Trust   *Contact: The Property Manager*

Tel: 01386 438333   **Fax:** 01386 438817

One of the most delightful gardens in England, created this century by the great horticulturist Major Lawrence Johnston; a series of small gardens within the whole, separated by walls and hedges of different species; famous for rare shrubs, trees, herbaceous borders, 'old' roses and interesting plant species. Plants for sale.

Location: OS151 Ref. SP176 429. 4m NE of Chipping Campden, 1m E of B4632 off B4081. At Mickleton ¹/₄ m E of Kiftsgate Court.

Opening Times: 1 Apr - end Sept: daily except Tue & Fri, 11am - 7pm (closed Good Fri). June & Jul: also Tue, 11am - 7pm. Oct - 1 Nov: daily except Tue & Fri, 11am - 6pm. Last admission 1hr before closing. Coaches & groups by prior appointment only.

Admission: Adult £5.50, Child £2.75, Family £13.80.

ℹ️ Shop. Plant sales.   ♿ Grounds, but limited. WC.

☕ Licensed restaurant.   🐕 No dogs.

KIFTSGATE COURT GARDENS

CHIPPING CAMPDEN, GLOUCESTERSHIRE GL55 6LW

Owner: Mr and Mrs J G Chambers   *Contact: J G Chambers*

Tel/Fax: 01386 438777

Magnificently situated garden on the edge of the Cotswold escarpment with views towards the Malvern Hills. Many unusual shrubs and plants including trees peonies, abutilons, specie and old-fashioned roses.

Location: OS Ref. SP173 430. 4m NE of Chipping Campden. ¹/₄ m W of Hidcote Garden.

Opening Times: Apr, May, Aug, Sept: Wed, Thur & Sun, 2 - 6pm. Jun & Jul: Wed, Thur, Sat & Sun, 12 - 6pm. BH Mon, 2 - 6pm. Coaches by appointment.

Admission: Adult: £3.50, Child £1.

ℹ️ Plant centre.   ☕ Tearoom open Spring BH - Aug BH.

HODGES BARN GARDENS

Tel: 01666 880202   **Fax:** 01666 880373

Shipton Moyne, Tetbury, Gloucestershire GL8 8PR

Owner: Amanda Hornby   **Contact:** Amanda Hornby

Unusual 14th century barn surrounded by a spectacular garden of fine trees, roses in abundance. Also a water garden and woodland garden.

Location: OS Ref. ST890 895. Shipton Moyne.

Opening Times: All year: Mon, Tues, Fri: 2- 5pm.

Admission: £2.50.

♿ Suitable.   🚶 By arrangement.   🅿️ Ample.   🐕 In grounds, on leads.

LITTLEDEAN HALL

Tel: 01594 824 213

Littledean, Gloucestershire GL14 3NR

Owner: Mrs S Christopher   **Contact:** Mrs S Christopher

'Reputedly England's oldest inhabited house', Guinness Book of Records. Site of Roman temple.

Location: OS Ref. SO673 131. 2m E of Cinderford, 500 yds S of A4151.

Opening Times: 1 Apr - 31 Oct: daily, 11am - 5pm.

Admission: Adult £3, Child £1.50, OAP £2.50. Groups £2pp (by appointment).

♿ Not suitable.   🚶 By arrangement.   🐕 In grounds, on leads.

LYDNEY PARK GARDENS

Tel: 01594 842844

Lydney, Gloucestershire GL15 6BU

Owner: The Viscount Bledisloe   **Contact:** Mrs Beryl Butcher

8 acres of extensive valley gardens with trees and lakes. Roman temple site and museum.

Location: OS Ref. SO620 022. On A48 between Lydney and Aylburton.

Opening Times: Easter - 14 Jun, Sun, BHs & Wed, 11am - 6pm.

Admission: Adult £2.40 (Wed £1.40), Child free, Car park free, Groups of 25 + (min) by appointment.

MILL DENE GARDEN

Tel: 01386 700457   **Fax:** 01386 700526

Old Mill Dene, Blockley, Moreton-in-Marsh GL56 9HU

Owner: Mr and Mrs B.S Dare   **Contact:** Mrs Wendy Dare

In a naturally beautiful situation this 2^1/$_2$ acre Cotswold water-mill garden has been designed and planted by the owner. Steep lawned terraces rise from the mill-pool, stream and grotto; wander through a rose-walk to the cricket lawn, then to the potager at the top. All the garden has glimpses of the church as a back-drop and views over the Cotswold Hills. Plenty of seats encourage contemplation of tranquil water and vistas.

Location: OS Ref. SP165 345. From A44 Bourton on the Hill, take turn to Blockley. 1^1/$_3$m down hill, turn left behind 30mph sign labelled cul-de-sac.

Opening Times: 1 Apr - 30 Sept: weekdays, 2 - 5pm. For NGS: 26 Apr, 3 & 24 May, 21 & 28 Jun & 4 Jul.

Admission: Adult £2, Child 50p.

ⓘ Corporate hospitality.	✗ Lunches for groups (max 10).	☕ Tearoom.
⚐ By arrangement.	Ⓟ Limited.	🐾 No dogs.	Ⓐ 3 dble/2 ensuite bathrooms.

MISARDEN PARK GARDENS 🏛

STROUD, GLOUCESTERSHIRE GL6 7JA

Owner: Major M T N H Wills   *Contact: Major M T N H Wills*

Tel: 01285 821303   **Fax:** 01285 821530

Noted in the spring for its bulbs and flowering trees and in mid summer for the large double herbaceous borders. Fine topiary throughout and a traditional rose garden. Outstanding position, standing high overlooking the 'Golden Valley'. New water feature planned for 1998.

Location: OS Ref. SO940 089. 6m NW Cirencester. Follow signs westward from A417 from Gloucester or Cirencester or B4070 from Stroud.

Opening Times: 1 Apr - 30 Sept: Tue, Wed & Thur, 9.30am - 4.30pm.

Admission: Adult £3 (guided tours extra), Child free. 10% reduction for groups 20+ who book in advance.

ⓘ Garden nurseries: daily except Mon.	♿ Grounds suitable.	🐾 Guide dogs.

OWLPEN MANOR 🏛

ULEY, NR DURSLEY, GLOUCESTERSHIRE GL11 5BZ

Owner: Mr & Mrs Nicholas Mander   *Contact: Mrs M Keevil*

Tel: 01453 860261   **Fax:** 01453 860819   **Restaurant:** 01453 860816

Web Site: http://www.1travel.com/owlpen

Romantic Tudor manor house, 1450-1616, with Cotswold Arts & Crafts associations. Remote wooded valley setting, with 16th and 17th century formal terraced gardens and magnificent yews. Contains unique painted cloth wall hangings, family and Arts & Crafts collection. Mill (1726), Court House (1620); licensed restaurant in medieval Cyder House. Victorian church. "Owlpen - ah, what a dream is there!" - Vita Sackville-West.

Location: OS Ref. ST801 984. 3m E of Dursley, 1m E of Uley, off B4066, by Old Crown pub, or follow brown signs.

Opening Times: 1 Apr - 30 Oct: daily, Tue - Sun & BH Mon, 2 - 5pm. Restaurant 12 - 5pm.

Admission: Adult £4.20, Child (5-14) £2, Family (2+2) £11. Grounds: £2. Group rates available.

ⓘ Corporate events.	♿ Not suitable.	☕ Licensed restaurant.
🐾 In grounds, on leads.	Ⓟ Ample.	Ⓐ Holiday cottages, sleep 2 - 9.

PAINSWICK ROCOCO GARDENS 🏛

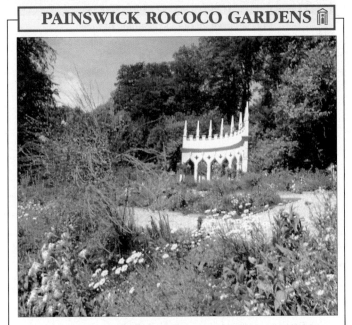

THE STABLES, PAINSWICK HOUSE, PAINSWICK, GLOS. GL6 6TH

Owner: Painswick Rococo Garden Trust   *Contact: P.R Moir*

Tel: 01452 813204

Unique 18th century garden restoration situated in a hidden 6 acre Cotswold combe. Charming contemporary buildings are juxtaposed with winding woodland walks and formal vistas. Famous for its early spring show of snowdrops.

Location: OS Ref. SO864 106. ^{1}/$_2$ m NW of village of Painswick on B4073.

Opening Times: 2nd Wed in Jan - 30 Nov: Wed - Sun & BHs. Jul - Aug: daily, 11am - 5pm.

Admission: Adult £3, OAP £2.70, Child £1.60, Family (2 + 2) £8.

ⓘ Shop. Plant centre.	☕ Licensed tearoom.	Ⓟ Ample.	🐾 In grounds, on leads.

SPECIAL EVENTS

JUN 10: Shakespeare's "A Midsummer Night's Dream" performed in the garden.
JUN 27: Evening of outdoor Summer Entertainment: music for adults & children.

THE PRIORY GARDENS

Tel: 01386 725258

The Priory, Kemerton, Nr Tewkesbury GL20 7JN

Owner: The Hon Mrs Healing **Contact:** The Hon Mrs Healing

This 4 acre garden was replanned and planted by the present owner and her husband in 1965, though tree planting had been thoughtfully planned since they came to the garden in 1939, and some 70 new specimen trees were planted. On the south facing slopes of Bredon Hill, the garden has matured and features long herbaceous borders planted in colour groups, at their best from mid-July through September and includes a stream garden, sunken garden and sweeping lawns down to a part reserved for wild flowers. There is a well stocked kitchen garden.

Location: OS Ref. SO950 378. In Kemerton. 2m E of B4030 at Bredon.

Opening Times: 24 May, 21 Jun, 12 Jul, 2 & 23 Aug & 6 Sept and every Thursday.

Admission: Adult £2. Pre-arranged groups: (min 25): Adult £2.50 except on open days.

Plant centre. Suitable. WC. Teas (Suns only). By arrangement. Limited for coaches. In grounds, on leads.

RODMARTON MANOR

CIRENCESTER, GLOUCESTERSHIRE GL7 6PF

Owner: *Mr & Mrs Simon Biddulph* **Contact:** *Simon Biddulph*

Tel: 01285 841253 **Fax:** 01285 841298

One of the last great country houses to be built in the traditional way and containing beautiful furniture, ironwork, china and needlework specially made for the house. The large garden complements the house and contains many areas of great beauty and character including the magnificent herbaceous borders, topiary, roses, rockery and kitchen garden.

Location: OS Ref. ST943 977. 1/2 m N of A433 between Cirencester & Tetbury.

Opening Times: House: by written appointment but not when the garden is open. Garden: 15 Apr - 26 Aug, 2 - 5pm, Sats 16 May - 29 Aug, 2 - 5pm. Groups welcome at other times by appointment.

Admission: Conducted tour of house with unconducted tour of Garden £5, Child (under 16) £2.50. Min. group charge £35. Garden only: £2.50, accompanied child free.

ST MARY'S CHURCH

Tel: 01179 750700

Kempley, Gloucestershire

Owner: English Heritage **Contact:** The South West Regional Office

A delightful Norman church with superb wall paintings from the 12th - 14th centuries which were only discovered beneath white wash in 1871.

Location: OS149 SO670 313. On minor road. 1 1/2 m SE of Much Marcle, A449.

Opening Times: 1 Apr - 30 Sept: 10am - 4pm, 1 - 31 Oct: 10am - 4pm.

Admission: Free.

SEZINCOTE

Moreton-in-Marsh, Gloucestershire GL56 9AW

Owner: Mr and Mrs D Peake **Contact:** Mrs D Peake

Exotic oriental water garden by Repton and Daniell. Large semi-circular orangery. House by S P Cockerell in Indian style was the inspiration for Brighton Pavilion.

Location: OS Ref. SP183 324. 2 1/2 m SW of Moreton-in-Marsh. Turn W along A44 to Broadway and left into gateway just before Bourton-on-the-Hill (opposite the gate to Batsford Park, then 1m drive.

Opening Times: Garden: Thur, Fri & BH Mon, 2 - 6pm (dusk if earlier) throughout the year except Dec. House: May, Jun, Jul & Sept, Thur & Fri, 2.30 - 6pm. Groups by appointment.

Admission: House & Garden £4.50 (no children in house), Garden: Adult £3, Child £1.

Not suitable. Guide dogs only.

SNOWSHILL MANOR

Andreas Van Einsiedel.

Andreas Van Einsiedel.

SNOWSHILL, NR. BROADWAY WR12 7JU

Owner: *The National Trust* **Contact:** *The Property Manager*

Tel: 01386 852410

A Tudor house with a c1700 façade, 21 rooms containing Charles Paget Wade's collection of craftsmanship, including musical instruments, clocks, toys, bicycles, weavers' and spinners' tools, Japanese armour, small formal garden and Charles Wade's cottage. The Manor is a 10 minute walk (500 yds) along an undulating countryside path.

Location: OS150 SP096 337. 3m SW of Broadway, turning off the A44, by Broadway Green.

Opening Times: 1 Apr - 1 Nov: daily except Tue, 1 - 5pm (closed Good Fri). Grounds & visitor facilities open at 12pm. Grounds & shop open until 5.30pm. May - Sept. Last admission to house 45mins before close. Timed tickets issued for house.

Admission: Adult £5.50, Child £2.75, Family £13.80. Grounds, shop and restaurant £2.50.

Shop. Restaurant. No dogs.

STANWAY HOUSE

STANWAY, CHELTENHAM, GLOS GL54 5PQ

Owner: *Lord Neidpath* **Contact:** *Lorna Poulton*

Tel: 01386 584469 **Fax:** 01386 584688

Stanway House was built of golden limestone in the days of Elizabeth I. The house has changed hands once in the last 1270 years. Features include the 14th century Tithe Barn, Jacobean Gatehouse, unusual furniture and the sensation of a thoroughly 'lived-in' house. Extensive landscaped grounds contain an 18th century Pyramid and Cascade (under restoration), brewery, arboretum, and dog cemetery.

Location: OS Ref. SP061 323. N of Wincombe, just off B4077.

Opening Times: Jun - Sept: Tue & Thur, 2 - 5pm. Private tours by arrangement on Wednesdays only.

Admission: Adult £3.50, Child £1, OAP £3.

No photography. Available. In village. By arrangement. Limited for coaches. In grounds on leads.

SUDELEY CASTLE 🏛   **See page 186 for full page entry.**

WESTBURY COURT GARDEN

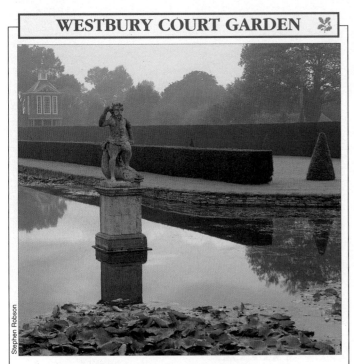

Stephen Robson

WESTBURY-ON-SEVERN, GLOUCESTERSHIRE GL14 1PD

Owner: The National Trust   *Contact:* The Head Gardener

Tel: 01452 760461

A formal water garden with canals and yew hedges, laid out between 1696 and 1705; the earliest of its kind remaining in England. Restored in 1971 and planted with species dating from pre-1700 including apple, pear and plum trees.

Location: OS162 SO718 138. 9m SW of Gloucester on A48.

Opening Times: 1 Apr - 1 Nov: Wed - Sun & BH Mon, 11am - 6pm (closed Good Fri). Other times by appointment only.

Admission: Adult £2.70, Child £1.35.

♿ Access to most parts of the garden. WC.   🐕 Guide dogs only.

WESTONBIRT ARBORETUM   **Tel:** 01666 880220   **Fax:** 01666 880559

Tetbury, Gloucestershire GL8 8QS

Owner: The Forestry Commission   **Contact:** Mr A Russell

600 acres arboretum begun in 1829, now with 18,000 catalogued trees.

Location: OS Ref. ST856 896. 3m S of Tetbury on the A433.

Opening Times: 365 days a year, 10am - 8pm (or dusk if earlier).

Admission: Adult £3.50, Child £1, OAP £2.50.

WHITTINGTON COURT 🏛   **Tel:** 01242 820556   **Fax:** 01242 820218

Whittington, Cheltenham, Gloucestershire GL54 4HF

Owner: Mr & Mrs Jack Stringer   **Contact:** Mrs J Stringer

Elizabethan manor house. Family possessions.

Location: OS Ref. SP014 206. 4m E of Cheltenham on N side of A40.

Opening Times: Sat 11 Apr - Sun 26 Apr & Sat 15 Aug - BH Mon 31 Aug: daily, 2 - 5pm.

Admission: Adult £2.50, Child £1, OAP £2.

ℹ️ Shop.   ♿ Ground floor & grounds suitable.   🅿 Limited.   🐕 No dogs.

WOODCHESTER PARK MANSION   **Tel:** 01453 750455   **Fax:** 01453 750457

High Street, Stroud, Gloucestershire GL5 1AP

Owner: Woodchester Mansion Trust   **Contact:** Mrs H Sims

Gothic style mansion in secret wooded valley, started in 1856 but abandoned before completion.

Location: OS Ref. SO795 015 (gateway on B4066). 5m S of Stroud on B4066. NW of the village of Nympsfield, then 1m path E from the gates.

Opening Times: Easter - Oct: 1st Sat & Sun each month & BH weekends (Sat/Sun/Mon) 11am - 4pm. Groups and private visits by arrangement.

Admission: Adult £3.50, Child (under 12) £1, Student £2.50. Groups and private visits by arrangement with Mrs R Westwood on 01453 860531.

ℹ️ Shop.   ♿ Not suitable.   ☕ Tearoom.   🐕 Guide dogs only.

National Trust Photographic Library.

Hidcote Manor Garden, Gloucestershire.

John Blake

CONTACT

The Property Manager
Berrington Hall
Nr. Leominster
Herefordshire
HR6 0DW

Tel: (01568) 615721

Fax: (01568) 613263

LOCATION

OS137 SP051 637

3m N of Leominster, 7m S
of Ludlow on
W side of A49.

Rail: Leominster 4m.

BERRINGTON HALL
Nr. Leominster

BERRINGTON HALL is the creation of Thomas Harley, the 3rd Earl of Oxford's remarkable son, who made a fortune from supplying pay and clothing to the British Army in America and became Lord Mayor of London in 1767 at the age of thirty-seven. The architect was the fashionable Henry Holland. The house is beautifully set above the wide valley of a tributary of the River Lugg, with views west and south to the Black Mountains and Brecon Beacons. This was the site advised by 'Capability' Brown who created the lake with its artificial island. The rather plain neo-classical exterior with a central portico gives no clue to the lavishness of the interior. Plaster ceilings now decorated in muted pastel colours adorn the principal rooms. Holland's masterpiece is the staircase hall rising to a central dome. The rooms are set off with a collection of French furniture, including pieces which belonged to the Comte de Flahault, natural son of Talleyrand, and Napoleon's step-daughter Hortense.

In the dining room, vast panoramic paintings of battles at sea, three of them by Thomas Luny, are a tribute to the distinguished Admiral Rodney.

Nadia Mackenzie

OPENING TIMES

SUMMER

House

April: Fri, Sat, Sun
& BH Mon
1.30 - 5.30pm
Closed Good Fri

May, June & September:
Wed - Sun & BH Mon
1.30 - 5.30pm

Jul & Aug: daily
1.30 - 5.30pm

Last admission 30 mins
before closing.

Gardens
Open as House:
12.30 - 6pm
(5.30pm in October)

Park Walk
July - October
days and times as house.

WINTER

October - 1 November
Fri, Sat & Sun
1.30 - 4.30pm.

ADMISSION

Adult	£4.00
Child	£2.00
Family	£10.00

Grounds only £1.80

Groups must pre-book.

The Midlands England

The Midlands
England

EASTNOR CASTLE
Ledbury

Encircled by the Malvern Hills and surrounded by a famous arboretum and lake, this fairytale castle looks as dramatic inside as it does outside.

The atmosphere Everyone is struck by it. The vitality of a young family brings the past to life and the sense of warmth and optimism is tangible. Eastnor, however grand, is a home.

'Sleeping' for the past fifty years, the Castle has undergone a triumphant renaissance – 'looking better than it probably ever has', *Country Life* 1993.

Hidden away in attics and cellars since 1939, many of the castle's treasures are now displayed for the first time – early Italian Fine Art, 17th century Venetian furniture and Flemish tapestries, mediaeval armour and paintings by Van Dyck, Romney, Wootton and Watts, photographs by Julia Margaret Cameron. Drawing Room by Pugin.

'The princely and imposing pile' as it was described in 1812 when it was being built to pitch the owner into the aristocracy, remains the home of his descendants. The Castle contains letters diaries, clothes and furnishings belonging to friends and relations who include: Horace Walpole, Elizabeth Barrett Browning, Tennyson, Watts, Julia Margaret Cameron and Virginia Woolf.

Encircled by the Malvern Hills, the mediaeval beauty of the estate remains unchanged.

GARDENS
Castellated terraces descend to a 21 acre lake with a restored lakeside walk. The arboretum holds a famous collection of mature specimen trees. There are spectacular views of the Malvern hills across a 300 acre deer park, once part of a mediaeval chase and now designated a Site of Special Scientific Interest.

CONTACT
Simon Foster
Portcullis Office
Eastnor Castle
Nr. Ledbury
Herefordshire
HR8 1RL

Tel: (01531) 633160
or (01531) 632302

Fax: (01531) 631776
or (01531) 631030

LOCATION
OS Ref. SO735 368

2m SE of Ledbury on the A438 Tewkesbury Rd. Alternatively M50/J2 & from Ledbury take the A449/A438.

Tewkesbury 20 mins, Malvern 20 mins, Gloucester 25 mins Hereford 25 mins, Worcester 30 mins, Cheltenham 35 mins Birmingham 1 hr, London 2½ hrs

Taxi: Meredith Taxis
(01531) 632852
Clive Fletcher
(0589) 299283

CONFERENCE/FUNCTION		
ROOM	SIZE	MAX CAPACITY
Library	18 x 8m	120
Great Hall	16 x 8m	150
Dining Rm	11 x 7m	80
Gothic Rm	11 x 7m	80
Octagon Rm	9 x 9m	50

OPENING TIMES
SUMMER
BH Mon,
Easter - Sept: Sun
July & August: Sun - Fri
11am - 4.30pm.

NB. Groups by appointment at other times when the Castle is closed to casual visitors.

ADMISSION
SUMMER
Castle & Grounds
Adult £4.50
Child (5-14yrs)..........£2.00
Family (2+2) £11.00
Groups* (with guide)
Adult £5.50
Child £3.00
Groups* (without guide)
Adult £4.00
Child £2.00

Grounds only
Adult £2.50
Child (5-14yrs)..........£1.00
* Min. payment for 20 people.

WINTER
By appointment.

SPECIAL EVENTS
- **MAY 3/4:**
  Spring Country Craft Festival
- **MAY 17:**
  Steam Fair & Country Show with Fred Dibnah
- **MAY 30/31:**
  Gardeners' Weekend
- **JUN 11-14:**
  Art of Living - Decorative Arts Fair
- **JUL 25/26:**
  Balloon Festival in Deer Park
- **AUG 17-21:**
  Children's Fun Week
- **AUG 30/31:**
  The White Company: Living History of the Wars of the Roses
- **OCT 3/4:**
  Christmas Craft Fair

Shop. Plant centre. Maze, off-road driving, clay-pigeon shooting, quad bikes, archery and falconry. Survival training, team-building activity days. Product launches, fashion shows, concerts, charity events, craft fairs, television and feature films. No photography. Dogs in grounds, on leads.

Corporate hospitality, wedding receptions. Superb catering within Castle for booked events.

Visitors may alight at the Castle. Priority parking nearby.

Tearoom: home-made food, menus on request, groups must book.

By appointment.

Ample 10 - 100 yds from Castle. Phone in advance to arrange parking and catering. Free meal for drivers.

Welcome. Guides available if required. Children's fun worksheets.

Luxury accommodation within castle for small groups. 3 single rooms and 8 double. Ensuite available.

Civil Wedding Licence.

ABBEYDORE COURT GARDENS
Tel: 01981 240419   **Fax:** 01981 240279

Abbey Dore, Hereford, Herefordshire HR2 0AD

Owner: Mrs C L Ward   **Contact:** Mrs C L Ward

6 acre rambling garden, intersected by the River Dore. Shrubs and herbaceous perennials, rock garden and ponds. Teddy bear loft. Home-made food.

Location: OS Ref. SO387 309. 3 m W of A465 midway Hereford - Abergavenny.

Opening Times: 1 Mar - 18 Oct: daily except Wed, 11am - 6pm.

Admission: Adult £2, Child 50p.

[i] Shop. Plant centre.   [&] Grounds suitable. WC.   [☕] Restaurant.   [🐕] No dogs.

BERRINGTON HALL
See page 192 for full page entry.

BROBURY HOUSE GARDENS
Tel: 01981 500229

Brobury, Hereford, Herefordshire HR3 6BS

Owner: E Okarma Esq   **Contact:** Mrs L Weaver

A Victorian gentleman's country house set in 8 acres of magnificent gardens with stunning views over the Wye Valley.

Location: OS Ref. SO336 446. 1½ m S of the A438 Hereford/Brecon Rd at Bredwardine Bridge.

Opening Times: All year, except Christmas and New Year: Mon to Sat, 10am - 4.30pm.

[i] Art gallery.   [&] Partially suitable.   [🐕] In grounds, on leads.   [A] Available.

CROFT CASTLE

Rupert Truman.

LEOMINSTER, HEREFORDSHIRE HR6 9PW

Owner: *The National Trust*   **Contact:** *The Administrator*

Tel: 01568 780246

Home of the Croft family since Domesday (with a break of 170 years from 1750). Walls and corner towers date from 14th and 15th centuries, interior mainly 18th century when fine Georgian-Gothic staircase and plasterwork ceilings were added; splendid avenue of 350 year old Spanish chestnuts. Iron Age Fort (Croft Ambrey) may be reached by footpath. The walk is uphill (approx. 40 mins).

Location: OS137 Ref. SO455 655. 5m NW of Leominster, 9m SW of Ludlow, approach from B4362.

Opening times: Apr & Oct - 1 Nov: Sat & Sun, 1.30 - 4.30. Closed Good Fri. May - Sept: daily except Mon & Tue (open BH Mon), 1.30 - 5.30pm. Last admission to house 30 mins before closing. Car park and Croft Ambrey open all year.

Admission: Adult £3.30, Child £1.65. Family £8.30. Grounds only car park charge £1.50 per car, £10 per coach.

[&] Suitable.   [🐕] No dogs.

CWMMAU FARMHOUSE
Tel: 01497 831251

Brilley, Whitney on Wye, Herefordshire HR3 6JP

Owner: The National Trust   **Contact:** Mr D Joyce

Early 17th century timber-framed and stone-tiled farmhouse.

Location: OS Ref. SO267 514. 4m SW of Kington between A4111 & A438, approach by a narrow lane leading S from Kington - Brilley road at Brilley Mountain.

Opening Times: May - Aug: Wed, 2 - 5.30pm.

Admission: £2.50.

[☕] Tearoom.   [🏃] Compulsory.

DINMORE MANOR

HEREFORD HR4 8EE

Owner: *R G Murray Esq*   **Contact:** *Percy Smollett*

Tel: 01432 830322   **Fax:** 01432 830503

Beautiful gardens 500 ft above sea level with outstanding views towards the Malvern Hills. These south-facing gardens are surrounded by a 12th century Chapel and modern cloisters with many stained glass windows. A most interesting music room contains an Æolian organ.

Location: OS149, Ref. SO486 504. 6½ m N of Hereford on hilltop, W of the A49. 6½ m S of Leominster off A49.

Opening times: All year, 10am - 5.30pm.

Admission: Adult £3, Child free.

[i] Plant centre.   [X] Available.   [&] Grounds suitable. WC.   [🐕] No dogs.

EASTNOR CASTLE
See page 193 for full page entry.

GOODRICH CASTLE
Tel: 01600 890538

Ross-on-Wye, HR9 6HY

Owner: English Heritage   **Contact:** The Custodian

This magnificent red sandstone castle is remarkably complete with a 12th century keep and extensive remains from 13th & 14th centuries. From the battlement there are fine views over the Wye Valley.

Location: OS162, Ref. SO579 199. 5m S of Ross-on-Wye, off A40.

Open: 1 Apr - 1 Nov: daily, 10am - 6pm or dusk if earlier. 2 Nov - 31 Mar: daily, 10am - 4pm Closed 24 - 26 Dec.

Admission: Adult £2.95, Child £1.50, Conc. £2.20. 15% discount for groups of 11+.

[🐕] No dogs.

HEREFORD CATHEDRAL
Tel: 01432 359880

Hereford HR1 2NG   **Contact:** Mr D Harding

Location: OS Ref. SO510 398. Hereford city centre on A49.

Opening Times: 7.30am - 5pm. Sun services: 8am, 10am, 11.30am & 3.30pm. Weekday services: 8am and 5.30pm. 10.30am - 5pm from May 1997.

Admission: Admission only for Mappa Mundi and Chained Library £4.

[i] Shop.   [&] Partially suitable.   [☕] Tearoom.   [🏃] By arrangement.   [🐕] Guide dogs only.

HERGEST COURT
Tel/Fax: 01544 230160

c/o Hergest Estate Office, Kington HR5 3EG

Owner: W L Banks   **Contact:** W L Banks

The ancient home of the Vaughans of Hergest, dating from the 13th century.

Location: OS Ref. SO283 554. 1m W of Kington on unclassified road to Brilley.

Opening Times: Strictly by appointment only through Estate Office.

Admission: Adult £4, Child £1.50. Group: Adult £3.50, Child £1. Discounts for groups.

[&] Not suitable.   [P] Limited.   [🐕] Guide dogs only.

HERGEST CROFT GARDENS

KINGTON, HEREFORDSHIRE HR5 3EG

Owner: W L Banks   *Contact:* Elizabeth Banks

Tel/Fax: 01544 230160

From spring bulbs to autumn colour, this is a garden for all seasons. An old-fashioned kitchen garden has spring and summer borders and roses. Over 59 champion trees and shrubs grow in one of the finest collections in the British Isles. Holds National Collection of birches, maples and zelkovas. Park Wood is a hidden valley with rhododendrons up to 30 ft tall.

Location: OS Ref. SO281 565. On W side of Kington. $^1/_2$ m off A44, left at Rhayader end of bypass. Turn right and gardens are $^1/_4$ m on left. Signposted from bypass.

Opening Times: 10 Apr - 1 Nov: 1.30 - 6pm, gardens open until 7pm. Season tickets and groups by arrangement throughout the year. Winter by appointment.

Admission: Adult £2.75, Child (under 16) free, Groups 20+ £2.25. Season ticket £10.

ℹ️ Rare plant & gift sales.   ☕ Tearoom.   🐕 In grounds, on leads.

SPECIAL EVENTS: **MAY 4:** Flower Fair. £5 entrance.

HOW CAPLE COURT GARDENS   **Tel:** 01989 740626 **Fax:** 01989 740611

How Caple, Hereford HR1 4SX

Owner: R L A Lee Esq   **Contact:** Mrs V Stevens

Exciting 11-acre garden overlooking River Wye. Combining terraced Edwardian gardens with water features and sunken Florentine garden. Mature trees and shrubs. Nursery selling old-fashioned roses and specialised herbaceous plants. Group visits and coach parties welcome by appointment.

Location: OS Ref. SO613 306. In NE end of How Caple. 1m W of the B4224 Ross-on-Wye/Fownhope Road.

Opening Times: All year: Mon - Fri, 9.30am - 5pm, Sun 10am - 5pm. Apr - Oct: Sat, 9.30am - 5pm.

Admission: Adult £2.50, Child £1.25.

ℹ️ Shop. Plant sales.   ♿ Not suitable.   ☕ Teas & light meals by arrangement.

SPECIAL EVENTS
JUN 13: Open-air opera.

LONGTOWN CASTLE   **Tel:** 01604 730320 (Regional Office)

Abbey Dore, Herefordshire

Owner: English Heritage   **Contact:** The Midlands Regional Office

An unusual cylindrical keep built c1200 with walls 15ft thick. There are magnificent views of the nearby Black Mountains.

Location: OS Ref. SO321 291. 4m WSW of Abbey Dore.

Opening Times: Any reasonable time.

Admission: Free.

LOWER BROCKHAMPTON   **Tel:** 01885 488099

Bringsty, Worcestershire WR6 5UH

Owner: The National Trust   **Contact:** The Administrator

A late 14th century moated manor house, with an attractive detached half-timbered 15th century gatehouse, a rare example of this type of structure. Also, the ruins of a 12th century chapel.

Location: OS149, Ref. SO682 546. 2m E of Bromyard N side of A44, reached by narrow road through 1$^1/_2$ m of woods and farmland.

Opening Times: Medieval Hall, parlour, minstrel gallery, gatehouse & chapel: 1 Apr - end Sept: Wed - Sun & BH Mon, 10am - 5pm. Closed Good Fri. Oct - 1 Nov: Wed - Sun, 10am - 4pm. Party bookings by written application.

Admission: Adult £2, Child £1, Family £5. Car park £1.50.

♿ Some parts of house suitable.   🐕 No dogs.

OLD SUFTON   **Tel:** 01432 870268/850328   **Fax:** 01432 850381

Mordiford, Hereford HR1 4EJ

Owner: Trustees of Sufton Heritage Trust   **Contact:** Mr & Mrs J N Hereford

A 16th century manor house which was altered and remodelled in the 18th and 19th centuries and again in this century. The orginal home of the Hereford family (see Sufton Court) who have held the manor since the 12th century.

Location: OS Ref. SO575 384. Mordiford, off B4224 Mordiford - Dormington road.

Opening Times: By appointment - letter or fax.

Admission: Adult £1.50, Child 50p.

♿ Partially suitable.   🚶 Guided tours only.   🅿️ Ample.
👨‍🏫 Educational programme.   🐕 No dogs.

ROTHERWAS CHAPEL   **Tel:** 01604 730320 (Regional Office)

Hereford, Herefordshire

Owner: English Heritage   **Contact:** Midlands Regional Office

This Roman Catholic chapel, dating from the 14th and 16th centuries is testament to the past grandeur of the Bodenham family and features an interesting mid-Victorian side chapel and High Altar.

Location: OS Ref. SO537 383. 1$^1/_2$ m SE of Hereford 500yds N of B4399.

Opening Times: Any reasonable time. Keykeeper at nearby filling station.

Admission: Free.

SUFTON COURT   **Tel:** 01432 870268/850328 **Fax:** 01432 850381

Mordiford, Hereford HR1 4LU

Owner: J N Hereford   **Contact:** Mr & Mrs J N Hereford

Sufton Court is a small paladian mansion house. Built in 1788 by James Wyatt for James Hereford. The park was laid out by Humphrey Repton whose 'red book' still survives. The house stands above the rivers Wye and Lugg giving impressive views towards the mountains of Wales.

Location: OS Ref. SO574 379. Mordiford, on B4224.

Opening Times: 12 - 25 May and 18 - 31 Aug: 2 - 5pm.

Admission: Adult £1.50, Child 50p.

♿ Partially suitable.   🚶 Guided tours only.   🅿️ Only small coaches.
👨‍🏫 Educational programme.   🐕 In grounds, on leads.

THE WEIR   **Tel:** 01684 850051

Swainshill, Hereford, Herefordshire

Owner: The National Trust   **Contact:** The Administrator

Delightful riverside garden particularly spectacular in early spring, with fine view over the River Wye and Black Mountains.

Location: OS Ref. SO435 421. 5m W of Hereford on S side of A438.

Opening Times: 14 Feb - 1 Nov: Wed - Sun (inc Good Fri) & BH Mon 11am - 6pm.

Admission: £1.80.

♿ Not suitable.   🅿️ No parking.   🐕 No dogs.

The Midlands England

STANFORD HALL
Nr Rugby

STANFORD has been the home of the Cave family, ancestors of the present owner, Lady Braye, since 1430. In the 1690s, Sir Roger Cave commissioned the Smiths of Warwick to pull down the old Manor House and build the present Hall, which is an excellent example of their work and of the William and Mary period.

As well as over 5000 books, the handsome Library contains many interesting manuscripts, the oldest dating from 1150. The splendid pink and gold Ballroom has a fine coved ceiling with four trompe l'oeil shell corners. Throughout the house are portraits of the family and examples of furniture and objects which they collected over the centuries. There is also a collection of Royal Stuart portraits, previously belonging to the Cardinal Duke of York, the last of the male Royal Stuarts. An unusual collection of family costumes is displayed in the Old Dining Room, which also houses some early Tudor portraits and a fine Empire chandelier.

The Hall and Stables are set in an attractive Park on the banks of Shakespeare's Avon. There is a walled Rose Garden behind the Stables. An early ha-ha separates the North Lawn from the mile-long North Avenue.

CONTACT

Lt Col E H L Aubrey-
Fletcher
Stanford Hall
Lutterworth
Leicestershire
LE17 6DH

Tel: (01788) 860250

Fax: (01788) 860870

LOCATION

OS Ref. SP587 793

M1/J18 6m,
M1/J19 (from / to
the N only) 2m,
M6 Exit / access at
A14 / M1(N)J 2m,
A14 2m.

Follow Historic
House signs.

Rail: Rugby Station
7¹/₂ m.

Air: Birmingham
Airport 27m.

Taxi: Fone-A-Car.
(01788) 543333

CONFERENCE/FUNCTION

ROOM	SIZE	MAX CAPACITY
Ballroom	39' x 26'	100
Old Dining Rm	30' x 20'	70
Crocodile Room	39' x 20'	60

OPENING TIMES

SUMMER

Easter - end Sept:
Sat & Sun, 2.30 - 5.30pm.

Closed Mon - Fri except
BH Mons & Tues following
2.30 - 5.30pm.

Last admission 5pm.

NB. On BHs & Events days,
open at 12pm (House at
2.30pm). Open any day or
evening for pre-booked
parties.

WINTER

October - Easter
Closed to public, except
during October for
corporate events.

ADMISSION

House & Grounds

Adult	£3.80
Child*	£1.90

Groups**

Adult	£3.50
Child*	£1.70
OAP	£3.30

Grounds only

Adult	£2.10
Child*	£1.00

Motorcycle Museum

Adult	£1.00
Child*	£0.35

School Group

Adult	FREE
Child*	£0.20

* Aged 4 - 15   ** Min 20.

SPECIAL EVENTS

- **MAY - SEPT**
  Car and motorcycle club rallies most Suns

For full details of events throughout the year, see the Special Events section at the front of the book

Photograph of interior room.

ℹ️ Shop. Craft centre (most Suns). No photography in house. Available corporate days, clay pigeon shoots, filming, photography, small conferences and fashion shows. Parkland, helicopter landing area, lecture room, Blüthner piano, fishing.

🍴 Available for lunches, dinners and wedding receptions using outside caterers.

♿ Visitors may alight at the entrance. WC.

☕ Homemade teas, lunch, and supper. Groups (70 max.) must book in advance.

🚶 Tour time: ³/₄ hr in groups of approx 25.

🅿️ 1,000 cars and 6 - 8 coaches. Free meals for coach drivers, coach parking on gravel in front of house.

👪 Welcome, price per child £1.70. Guide provided by prior arrangement, nature trail with guide book and map, motorcycle museum.

🐕 In park, on leads.

ASHBY DE LA ZOUCH CASTLE

Tel: 01530 413343

South Street, Ashby de la Zouch, Leicestershire LE65 1BR

Owner: English Heritage   **Contact:** The Custodian

The impressive ruins of this late medieval castle are dominated by a magnificent tower, over 80 feet high, which was split in two during the Civil War. Panoramic views.

Location: OS Ref. SK363 167. In Ashby de la Zouch, 12m S of Derby on A50. SE of town centre.

Opening Times: 1 Apr - 1 Nov: daily, 10am - 6pm or dusk if earlier. 2 Nov - 31 Mar: daily 10am - 4pm or dusk if earlier. Closed 24 - 26 Dec.

Admission: Adult £2.30, Child £1.20, Conc. £1.70.

Grounds suitable.   On leads.

BELGRAVE HALL

Tel: 0116 2666590

Church Road, Thurcaston Road, Leicester LE4 5PE

Owner: Leicester City Council   **Contact:** Mr Bill Garrett

Queen Anne House. Period room settings from late 17th - 19th century. Interesting gardens.

Location: OS Ref. SK593 072. Church Road, off A6. 2m N of town centre. ¹/₂ m S of A563 ring road.

Opening Times: All year: Mon - Sat; 10am - 5.30pm, Sun: 2 - 5.30pm. Closed 25/26 Dec & Good Fri.

Admission: Free.

BRADGATE PARK & SWITHLAND COUNTRY PARK

Tel: 0116 2362713

Bradgate Park, Newtown Linford, Leicestershire

Owner: Bradgate Park Trust   **Contact:** M H Harrison

Includes the ruins of the brick medieval home of the Grey family and childhood home of Lady Jane Grey, Nine Days Queen of England. Also has a medieval deer park with a herd of red and fallow deer.

Location: OS Ref. SK534 102. 7m NW of Leicester, via Anstey & Newton Linford. Country Park gates in Newton Linford. 1¹/₄ m walk to the ruins.

Opening Times: All year during daylight hours.

Admission: No charge. Car parking charges: Cars 50p up to 2 hrs, £1 over 2 hours. Minibuses: £5, Coaches £8.

Shop. Visitor Centre.   Partially suitable. WCs.   By arrangement.   Ample.

DONINGTON-LE-HEATH MANOR HOUSE

Tel: 01530 831259

Manor Road, Donington-le-Heath, Leicestershire LE67 2FW

Owner: Leicestershire County Council   **Contact:** Leicestershire County Council

Medieval Manor

Location: OS Ref. SK534 102. 7m NW of Leicester, via Anstey & Newton Linford. Country Park gates in Newton Linford, N side of Anstey road. ¹/₂m drive to the ruins.

Opening Times: 8 Apr - end Sept: Wed - Sun (closed Mon & Tue).

Admission: Free.

KIRBY MUXLOE CASTLE

Tel: 01162 386886 (Regional Office)

Kirby Muxloe, Leicestershire LE9 9MD

Owner: English Heritage   **Contact:** Midlands Regional Office

Picturesque, moated, brick built castle begun in 1480 by William Lord Hastings. It was left unfinished after Hastings was executed in 1483.

Location: OS Ref. SK524 046. 4m W of Leicester off B5380.

Opening Times: 1 Apr - 1 Nov: weekends & BHs only, 12 - 5pm.

Admission: Adult £1.75, Child 90p, Conc. £1.30.

LEICESTER GUILDHALL

Tel: 01162 532569

Guildhall Lane, Leicester LE1 5EQ

Owner: Leicester City Council   **Contact:** Nicholas Ladlow

14th century timber framed Guildhall and adjacent Mayor's parlour.

Location: OS Ref. SK584 044. W side of Leicester city centre, immediately W of the cathedral.

Opening Times: Mon - Sat, 10am - 5.30pm, Sun 2 - 5.30pm.

Admission: Free.

Shop. Corporate hospitality.   Partially suitable.   By arrangement.

Limited.   Guide dogs only.

LYDDINGTON BEDE HOUSE

Tel: 01572 822438

Blue Coat Lane, Lyddington, Uppingham, Leicestershire LE15 9LZ

Owner: English Heritage   **Contact:** The Custodian

Set among golden-stone cottages the Bede House was originally a medieval palace of the Bishops of Lincoln. It was later converted into an alms house.

Location: OS Ref. SP875 970. In Lyddington, 6m N of Corby, 1m E of A6003.

Opening Times: 1 Apr - 1 Nov: daily, 10am - 6pm (closed 1 - 2pm).

Admission: Adult £2.30, Child £1.20, Conc. £1.70.

OAKHAM CASTLE

Tel: 01572 723654

Rutland County Museum, Catmos St, Oakham, Rutland LE15 6HW

Owner: Rutland County Council   **Contact:** Mr Clough

12th century Great Hall of Norman castle, in castle grounds with earlier motte. Unique collection of horseshoes presented by visiting peers of the realm.

Location: OS Ref. SK862 088. Near town centre, E of the church.

Opening Times: Castle grounds: Apr - Oct: daily 10am - 5.30pm. Nov - Mar: daily 10am - 4pm. Great Hall: Apr - Oct: Tue - Sat & BH Mon, 10am - 1pm & 2 - 5.30pm, Sun 2 - 5.30pm. Nov - Mar: Tue - Sat, 10am - 1pm & 2 - 4pm. Sun 2 - 4pm. Closed Good Fri and 25/26 Dec.

Admission: Free.

Shop.   Great Hall suitable.   For disabled, on request.   Civil Wedding Licence.

PRESTWOLD HALL

LOUGHBOROUGH, LEICESTERSHIRE LE12 5SQ

Owner: E J Packe-Drury-Lowe   *Contact:* Mrs. Weldon

Tel: 01509 880236 **Fax:** 01636 812187

A magnificent private house, largely remodelled in 1843 by William Burn. For the past 350 years it has been the home of the Packe family and contains fine Italian plasterwork, 18th century English and European furniture and a collection of family portraits. The house is not open to the general public but offers excellent facilities as a conference and corporate entertainment venue. Up to 170 guests can be seated and the 20 acres of gardens provide a perfect setting for larger meetings using marquees. Also available are excellent chefs providing a varied menu, a fully stocked wine cellar as well as clay pigeon shooting, motor sports and archery. Activity days on request.

Location: OS Ref. SK578 215. At the heart of the Midlands, 3m E of Loughborough on B675. 5m W of A46 via B676.

Admission: Corporate entertaining venues and conference centre by arrangement only.

Conferences & corporate hospitality.   Available.

Ground floor & grounds suitable. WC.   Civil Wedding Licence.

Historic Scotland

SPECIAL EVENTS 1998 See the front section for full list.

STANFORD HALL

See page 196 for full page entry.

STAUNTON HAROLD CHURCH

Tel: 01332 863822 **Fax:** 01332 865272

Staunton Harold Church, Ashby-de-la-Zouch, Leicestershire

One of the very few churches to be built during the Commonwealth, erected by Sir Robert Shirley, an ardent Royalist. The interior retains its original 17th century cushions and hangings, and includes fine panelling and painted ceilings.

Location: OS Ref. SK379 208. 5m NE of Ashby-de-la-Zouch, W of B587.

Opening Times: 1 Apr - end Sept: Sat - Wed & BH Mon (closed Good Fri), 1 - 5pm or sunset if earlier. Oct: Sat & Sun only, 1 - 5pm.

Admission: £1 donation.

♿ Partially suitable.   ☕ Available at hall.

WARTNABY GARDENS

Tel: 01664 822296 **Fax:** 01164 822231

Melton Mowbray, Leicestershire LE14 3HY

Owner: Lord and Lady King

This garden has delightful little gardens within it, including a white garden, a sunken garden and a purple border of shrubs and roses, and there are good herbaceous borders, climbers and old-fashioned roses. A large pool has an adjacent bog garden with primulas, ferns, astilbes and several varieties of willow. There is an arboretum with a good collection of trees and shrub roses, and alongside the drive is a beech hedge in a Grecian pattern. Greenhouses, a fruit and vegetable garden with rose arches and cordon fruit.

Location: OS Ref. SK709 228. 4m NW of Melton Mowbray. From A606 turn W in Ab Kettleby for Wartnaby.

Opening Times: 28 Jun, Sun, 11am - 4pm. Groups and individuals by appointment.

Admission: Adult £2.

♿ Suitable. WC.   ☕ Tearoom.   🚶 By arrangement.   P Limited for coaches.

🐐 In grounds on leads.

WYGSTON'S HOUSE

Tel: 01162 473056 **Fax:** 01162 620964

12 Applegate, St Nicholas Circle, Leicester LE1 5LD

Owner: Leicestershire City Council   **Contact:** Nicholas Ladlow

A fine Georgian town house, backed by an older half-timbered building, now converted into a costume museum.

Location: OS Ref. SK583 044. W side of city centre, just inside the inner ring road at St. Nicholas Circle. 200yds W of Guildhall and Cathedral.

Opening Times: Mon - Sat, 10am - 5.30pm, Sun, 2 - 5.30pm.

Admission: Free.

CIVIL WEDDING VENUES

See the front section for full list.

Patrick Lane.

Staunton Harold Church, Leicestershire.

ALTHORP

ALTHORP
Northampton

Althorp has been the home of the Spencer family since 1508. The Park became the focal point for the World's attention on 6th September 1997, when Diana, Princess of Wales was laid to rest there after her tragically early death. She now lies on the island in the Round Oval, an ornamental lake, surrounded by her Family's ancestral heritage. Next to the mansion at Althorp, lies the honey-stoned Stable Block; a truly breathtaking building that is perhaps of greater external beauty than the House itself. This is the setting for the Visitor Centre, which houses an exhibition celebrating the former Lady Diana Spencer's life and honouring her memory after her death. The displays will include childhood personal effects as well as family photographs and cine film taken by her father, the 8th Earl Spencer. The freshness and modernity of the facilities will be a unique tribute to a woman who captivated the World in her all-too-brief existence.

All visitors are invited to view the House and grounds as well as the island in the Round Oval where Diana, Princess of Wales is laid to rest. There is no public access to the island itself, but for those wishing to pay their respects, the 'temple' at the edge of the lake has been dedicated to Diana's memory.

All visitors are requested to apply in advance for an invitation to visit Althorp. This is necessary in order to avoid overcrowding and thus preserve the dignity and tranquillity of every visit. Visitors arriving without an invitation will not be admitted.

———————— ❖ ————————

Coach parties will not be admitted to Althorp in 1998. The necessary facilities are under construction but will not be complete until 1999 when group visits will be welcome.

Please contact our dedicated booking line (24 hour service)
Tel: 01604 592020
Maximum 6 admissions per household.

CONTACT

Visitor Manager
Althorp
Northampton
NN7 4HQ

Tel: (01604) 770107
Fax: (01604) 770042

Dedicated booking line: (01604) 592020

LOCATION

OS Ref. SP682 652

From the M1/J15A, 6m
J16, 7m
J18, 10m.
Situated on A428
Northampton - Rugby.
London on average 85 mins away.

Rail: 5m from Northampton station.

OPENING TIMES

SUMMER

1 July - 30 August
Daily, 10am - 5pm.

Last admission 4pm.

Pre-booking essential.

WINTER

Closed.

ADMISSION

House & Garden

Adult	£9.50
Child*	£5.00
OAP	£7.00

*Children 5-17 years, under 5s free.

ℹ️ Shop. No inside photography.

✗ Not available for 1998.

♿ Partially suitable. Visitor Centre and ground floor of house accessible. WCs.

☕ Café.

🚶 Not available.

🅿️ Ample parking for cars.

🐕 Guide dogs only.

BOUGHTON HOUSE
Kettering

BOUGHTON HOUSE is the Northamptonshire home of the Duke of Buccleuch and Queensberry KT, and his Montagu ancestors since 1528. A 500 year old Tudor monastic building gradually enlarged around seven courtyards until the French style addition of 1695, which has lead to Boughton House being described as 'England's Versailles'.

The house contains an outstanding collection of 17th and 18th century French and English furniture, tapestries, 16th century carpets, porcelain, painted ceilings and notable works by El Greco, Murillo, Caracci and 40 Van Dyck sketches. There is an incomparable Armoury and Ceremonial Coach.

Beautiful parkland with historic avenues, lakes, picnic area, gift shop, adventure woodland play area, plant centre and tearoom. Boughton House is administered by The Living Landscape Trust, which was created by the present Duke of Buccleuch to show the relationship between the historic Boughton House and its surrounding, traditional, working estate.

For information on our groups visit programme and educational services, including fine arts courses run in conjunction with Sotheby's Institute, please contact The Living Landscape Trust. Our newly developed Internet website gives information on Boughton House and The Living Landscape Trust, including a 'virtual' tour, together with full details of our schools' educational facilities (Sandford Award winner 1988 and 1993).

Silver award winner of the 1st Historic House Awards, given by AA and NPI, in co-operation with the Historic Houses Association, for the privately-owned historic house open to the public which has best preserved its integrity, character of its architecture and furniture, while remaining a lived-in family home.

CONTACT

Gareth Fitzpatrick
The Living Landscape Trust
Boughton House
Kettering
Northamptonshire
NN14 1BJ

Tel: (01536) 515731

Fax: (01536) 417255

e-mail:
llt@boughtonhouse.org.uk

Website:
www.boughtonhouse.org.uk

LOCATION

OS Ref. SP900 815

3m N of Kettering on A43 - spur road from A14.

Turn E at Geddington.

OPENING TIMES

SUMMER
Grounds
1 May - 15 September
Daily: (except Fri)
1 - 5pm.
House
1 August - 1 September
Daily, 2 - 4.30pm.

Staterooms on view, strictly by prior appointment which can be made by telephone

WINTER
Daily by appointment throughout the year for educational groups - contact for details.

ADMISSION

SUMMER
House & Grounds
Adult £4.00
Child/OAP £3.00

Grounds
Adult £1.50
Child/OAP £1.00

Wheelchair visitors free.

WINTER
Group rates – contact for further details.

CONFERENCE/FUNCTION		
ROOM	SIZE	MAX CAPACITY
Lecture		120
Seminar Rm		30
Conference facilities available in stable block adjacent to House		

i Shop. Plant centre. Parkland available for film location and other events. Stable block contains 120 seats and lecture theatre. No inside photography. No unaccompanied children. Browse our web site for a 'virtual' tour of the house

Available.

Access and facilities, no charge for wheelchair visitors. WCs.

Tearoom seats 80, parties must book.

Group visits are all guided, please contact for rates.

P Ample.

Heritage Education Trust Sandford Award winner 1988 & 1993. School groups free, teachers' pack.

No dogs in house and garden, welcome in Park on leads.

DEENE PARK
Corby

A very interesting house which developed over six centuries from a typical medieval manor around a courtyard into a Tudor and Georgian mansion. Many rooms of different periods are seen by visitors who enjoy the impressive yet intimate ambience of the family home of the Brudenells, seven of whom were Earls of Cardigan. The most flamboyant of them was the 7th Earl who led the Light Brigade charge at Balaklava and of whom there are some historic relics and pictures.

The present owner is Mr Edmund Brudenell

who has carefully restored the house from its dilapidated condition at the end of the last war and also added considerably to the furniture and picture collection.

The gardens have been made over the last thirty years, with long, mixed borders of shrubs, old fashioned roses and flowers, a recent parterre designed by David Hicks and long walks under fine old trees by the water.

The car park beside the big lake is a good place for picnics.

CONTACT

The House Keeper
Deene Park
Corby
Northamptonshire
NN17 3EW

Tel: (01780) 450278
or (01780) 450223

Fax: (01780) 450282

LOCATION

OS Ref. SP950 929

6m NE of
Corby off A43.
From London via M1/J15
then A43.
or via A1, A14,
A43 - 2 hrs.

From Birmingham
via M6, A14, A43, 90 mins.

Rail: Kettering Station
20 mins.

i Shop. Suitable for indoor and outdoor events, filming, specialist lectures on house, its contents, gardens and history. No photography in house.

X Including buffets, lunches and dinners.

Visitors may alight at the entrance, access to ground floor and garden. WC.

Restaurant/tearoom, special rates for groups, bookings can be made in advance, menus on request.

Tours inclusive of admittance, tour time 90 mins. Owner will meet groups if requested.

P Unlimited, space for 3 coaches 10 yards from house.

In car park only.

A Residential conference facilities by arrangement.

CONFERENCE/FUNCTION		
ROOM	SIZE	MAX CAPACITY
Great Hall	–	150
Tapestry Rm	–	75
East Room	–	18

OPENING TIMES

SUMMER
June - August
Sun, 2 - 5pm
BH Mon only
2 - 5pm.

Open Sun & Mon for
Easter, early and late
Spring BH and August BH
2 - 5pm.

Open at all other times
by arrangement,
including pre-booked
parties.

WINTER
House and Gardens
closed to casual visitors.
Open at all other times by
arrangement for groups.

ADMISSION

SUMMER
House & Gardens
  Adult £4.50
  Child (10-14)...........£2.00
  Child (under 10) .... Free*
Gardens only
  Adult £2.50
  Child (10-14)...........£1.25
  Child (under 10) .... Free*
Groups (min 20)
  Weekdays...............£3.50
  (Min £70)
  Weekends and public
  open days £4.50
  (Min £90)

* Aged 10 and under free with
an accompanying adult.

WINTER
Groups visits only by prior
arrangement.

SPECIAL EVENTS

• **MAY 17 & SEPT 13:**
  Gardens open under
  National Garden Scheme

• **OCT 23 - 25:**
  Antiques Fair

The Midlands
England

HOLDENBY HOUSE GARDENS & FALCONRY CENTRE
Holdenby

Situated just two miles across the fields from Althorp, few places have played such a pivotal role in our history as Holdenby House. Built by Queen Elizabeth's I Chancellor as a place in which to entertain the Queen, it became by an ironic twist of fate the Palace and then the prison of her successor, Charles I, after his defeat in the Civil War.

Today, Holdenby, though no longer the largest house in England, provides a splendid backdrop to beautiful grounds, with many features designed to evoke Holdenby's historic past. There is a Falconry Centre, where you can see this traditionally royal pursuit demonstrated and even try it yourself. In the grounds, Rosemary Verey's Elizabethan Garden is a reconstruction in small scale of Sir Christopher Hatton's magnificent garden while Rupert Golby, designer of Country Life's Centenary Garden at Chelsea, has recently replanted the Fragrant Border. There is a full working Armoury, where suits of armour are still made using traditional methods, a 'bodgers' stall as well as makers of historic costumes and pine furniture. Our 17th century Farmstead powerfully evokes the sights and smells of 17th century life.

For the children there are lake-side train rides, a play area and children's farm. Our Victorian kitchen provides teas and the shop is full of crafts and Holdenby souvenirs.

CONTACT

Mrs Sarah Maughan
Holdenby House
Holdenby
Northamptonshire
NN6 8DJ

Tel: (01604) 770074

Fax: (01604) 770962

LOCATION

OS Ref. SP693 681

From London 90 mins. M1/J15, 15a or 16. Entrance 6m N/W of Northampton off the A428 or A50.

Rail: Northampton Station (London - Euston) 1 hr.

Taxi: Favell Cars (01604) 28177 / 20209.

i   Shop and plant sales. Falconry Centre, Armoury, 17th Century Farmstead, Children's Farm, Play Area, Furniture Maker, Traditional Wood-turner, Croquet, Train Rides, Piano Museum. Available for filming.

X   Large parties, wedding receptions. Video available on request.

&   Visitors can be left at house prior to parking. WC. Outside ramps.

  Home made teas, menus for light meals for pre-booked groups on request.

  Tours for groups at no additional cost, tour time 45 mins.

P   100 cars and 5 coaches.

  Winner of The Sandford Award 1985, 1990 and 1995, guide provided, school room.

OPENING TIMES

SUMMER
Easter Sun - 30 September

Gardens & Falconry Centre
Daily 2 - 6pm except Sat BH Sun & Mon 1 - 6pm.

House
BH Mon, 1 - 6pm except 4 May or by prior appointment for groups of over 25 visitors.

Shop & Tearoom
Sun & BHs only, during week by appointment.

WINTER
Groups welcome by prior arrangement.

ADMISSION

Garden & Falconry Centre
Adult £2.75
Child* £1.75
OAP.........................£2.25
Groups (min 25)
Per Person £2.25

House, Garden & Falconry Centre
Adult £3.75
Child* £2.00
OAP.........................£3.75

Bank Holidays
Adult £4.00
Child £2.00

*Aged 3 - 15yrs.

LAMPORT HALL & GARDENS
Northampton

Home of the Isham family from 1560 to 1976. The 17th and 18th century façade is by John Webb and the Smiths of Warwick and the North Wing of 1861 by William Burn.

The Hall contains a wealth of outstanding furniture, books and paintings including portraits by Van Dyck, Kneller, Lely and others. The fine rooms include the High Room of 1655 with magnificent plasterwork, the 18th century library with books from the 16th century, the early 19th century Cabinet Room containing rare Venetian cabinets with mythological paintings on glass and the Victorian Dining Room where refreshments are served.

The first floor has undergone lengthy restoration allowing further paintings and furniture to be displayed as well as a photographic record of Sir Gyles Isham, a Hollywood actor, who initiated the restoration.

The tranquil gardens were laid out in 1655 although they owe much to Sir Charles Isham the eccentric 10th Baronet who, in the mid-19th century, created the Italian Garden and the Rockery where he introduced the first garden gnomes to England. There are also box bowers, a rose garden and lily pond and extensive walks, borders and lawns all surrounded by a spacious park.

CONTACT

George Drye
Executive Director
Lamport Hall
Northampton
NN6 9HD

Tel: (01604) 686272

Fax: (01604) 686224

LOCATION

OS Ref. SP759 745

From London via M1/J15, 1¼ hours. Entrance on A508, 8m N of Northampton at junction with B576. 3½ m S of A14 (A1/M1 link).

Rail: Kettering Station 15m. Northampton 8m.

Bus: From Northampton and Market Harborough.

ℹ Shop. Conferences, corporate hospitality, garden parties, activity days, clay pigeon shoots, equestrian events, fashion shows, air displays, archery, rallies, filming, parkland, grand piano, 2 exhibition rooms. Lectures on history of property and gardens. Lecture/meeting rooms with audio-visual equipment. No unaccompanied children. No photography in house.

✗ Special functions, buffets, lunches and dinners, wedding receptions.

♿ Visitors may alight at the entrance, access to ground floor and gardens. WC.

☕ Dining/tearoom. Groups can book in advance.

🚶 At no additional cost, by prior arrangement, max 70 people, tour time 1¼ hours.

🅿 100 cars & 3 coaches, 20 yds of property. Use main entrance only (on A508).

👪 Welcome. Work room, specialist advisory teachers, study packs. Further information contact Education Officer or the Trust Office. Special guide book for children.

🐕 In grounds, on leads.

💒 Civil Wedding Licence.

OPENING TIMES

SUMMER

Easter - 4 October
Sun and BH Mon
2.15 - 5.15pm.
Last admission / tour 4pm.

August: Mon - Sat
1 tour at 4.30pm.

24 & 25 October
2.15 - 5.15pm.

Tours on other days by prior arrangement.

WINTER

Group visits only by arrangement.

ADMISSION

SUMMER
House & Garden

Adult £3.80
Child* £2.00
OAP.........................£3.30
Group**...................POA

* Aged 5 - 16yrs.

** Min. payment £125.00 including refreshments

WINTER

Group visits only by prior arrangement.

SPECIAL EVENTS

Please ring for Event leaflet.

CONFERENCE/FUNCTION		
ROOM	SIZE	MAX CAPACITY
Dining Rm	31' x 24' 6"	80

ROCKINGHAM CASTLE
Nr Corby

A Royal castle until 1530, since then home of the Watson family. Rockingham Castle was built by William the Conqueror on the site of an earlier fortification and was regularly used by the early Kings of England until the 16th century when it was granted by Henry VIII to Edward Watson whose family still live there today.

The house itself is memorable not so much as representing any particular period, but rather a procession of periods. The dominant influence in the building is Tudor within the Norman walls, but practically every century since the 11th has left its mark in the form of architecture, furniture or works of art. The Castle has a particularly fine collection of English 18th, 19th and 20th century paintings, and Charles Dickens, who was a frequent visitor, was so captivated by Rockingham that he used it as a model for Chesney Wold in *Bleak House*.

The Castle stands in 12 acres of formal and wild garden and commands a splendid view of five counties. Particular features are the 400 year old elephant hedge and the rose garden marking the foundations of the old keep. See Special Exhibition: "450 years a royal castle, 450 years a family home".

CONTACT

Miss K Barton
Rockingham Castle
Market Harborough
Leicestershire
LE16 8TH

Tel: (01536) 770240
Fax: (01536) 771692

LOCATION

OS Ref. SP867 913

2m N of Corby.
9m E of
Market Harborough.
14m SW of
Stamford on A427.
8m from
Kettering on A6003.

Vehicle entrance on A6003
just S of junction with
A6116.

OPENING TIMES

SUMMER
Easter Sun - 18 October

Thur, Sun, BH Mon & Tue
following and all Tue in
August, 1 - 5pm.

Daily by appointment
for parties and schools.

Grounds open 11.30am
on Sun & BH Mon.
Light refreshments
available from 12pm.

WINTER
Daily by appointment
for booked parties
and schools.
Closed to casual visitors.

ADMISSION

House & Garden

Adult	£4.00
Child (to 16 yrs.)	£2.60
OAP	£3.60

Groups

Adult*	£3.60
OAP	£3.60
Student	£1.70
Family (2 + 2)	£11.00

*Min. £70

Grounds only

Adult	£2.60
Child (to 16 yrs.)	£2.60
OAP	£2.60

Prices may vary for
special events in grounds.

SPECIAL EVENTS

- **MAY 24/25TH:**
  Antiques Fair

- **JUNE 20/21:**
  Rainbow Craft Fair

- **AUGUST 8/9:**
  Civil War Re-enactment

- **AUGUST 30/31:**
  The Vikings at Rockingham

- **OCTOBER 17/18:**
  Rainbow Craft Fair

CONFERENCE/FUNCTION		
ROOM	SIZE	MAX CAPACITY
Great Hall	37'6" x 22'	100
Panel Room	36' x 23'	100
Long Gallery	87' x 16'6"	100
Walkers House 1	31' x 17'6"	60
Walkers House 2	24' x 18'	50

ℹ️ Shop. Concerts, conferences, fashion shows, product launches, receptions, seminars, air displays, clay pigeon shoots, archery, equestrian events, fairs, garden parties, filming. Exhibition celebrating 900 years of life in the castle. Parkland and cricket pitch. Strip for light aircraft 4m. No photography in Castle.

✕ Buffets, meals on other days by arrangement.

♿ Visitors may alight at entrance, ramps provided.

☕ Home-made teas. Light lunches on Sun and BHs, May - Aug inclusive, waitress service.

🚶 All pre-booked parties have guided tour, except on open-days at no additional cost. Owner may meet groups by prior arrangement. Tour time 45 mins.

🅿️ Unlimited. 6 coaches.

👫 Winner of 3 Sandford Awards for Heritage Education, special pack designed with National Curriculum. Tours for schools can be arranged.

Rockingham Castle, Northamptonshire.

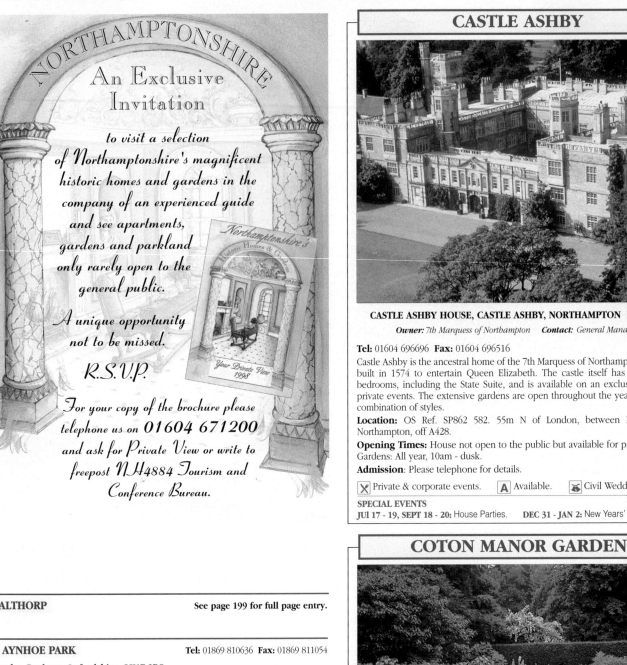

NORTHAMPTONSHIRE

An Exclusive Invitation

to visit a selection of Northamptonshire's magnificent historic homes and gardens in the company of an experienced guide and see apartments, gardens and parkland only rarely open to the general public.

A unique opportunity not to be missed.

R.S.V.P.

For your copy of the brochure please telephone us on **01604 671200** and ask for Private View or write to freepost NH4884 Tourism and Conference Bureau.

Northamptonshire's Historic Homes & Gardens — Your Private View 1998

CASTLE ASHBY

CASTLE ASHBY HOUSE, CASTLE ASHBY, NORTHAMPTON NN7 1LQ

Owner: 7th Marquess of Northampton   *Contact:* General Manager

Tel: 01604 696696 **Fax:** 01604 696516

Castle Ashby is the ancestral home of the 7th Marquess of Northampton, and was built in 1574 to entertain Queen Elizabeth. The castle itself has 26 exquisite bedrooms, including the State Suite, and is available on an exclusive basis for private events. The extensive gardens are open throughout the year and offer a combination of styles.

Location: OS Ref. SP862 582. 55m N of London, between Bedford and Northampton, off A428.

Opening Times: House not open to the public but available for private events. Gardens: All year, 10am - dusk.

Admission: Please telephone for details.

☒ Private & corporate events. Ⓐ Available. ☗ Civil Wedding Licence.

SPECIAL EVENTS
JUL 17 - 19, SEPT 18 - 20: House Parties.   **DEC 31 - JAN 2:** New Years' Eve Gala.

ALTHORP   See page 199 for full page entry.

AYNHOE PARK   **Tel:** 01869 810636 **Fax:** 01869 811054

Aynho, Banbury, Oxfordshire OX17 3BQ

Owner: Country Houses Association   *Contact:* The Administrators

Aynhoe Park was the family home of the Cartwrights from 1615 until 1954. During the Civil War, defeated Royalists destroyed it after the Battle of Naseby. It was restored and enlarged by Thomas Archer and embellished by Sir John Soane.

Location: OS Ref. SP513 331. M40/J10 then 3m W on B4100. Stations: Banbury 1½ m, Bicester 8m.

Opening Times: 1 May - 30 Sept: Wed & Thur, 2 - 5pm.

Admission: Adult £2.50, Child £1.

🚶 Available. 🐕 No dogs. Ⓐ 1 single, 1 double with bathroom. CHA members only.

BOUGHTON HOUSE 🏛   See page 200 for full page entry.

CANONS ASHBY 🌿   **Tel:** 01327 860044 **Fax:** 01327 860168

Canons Ashby, Daventry, Northamptonshire NN11 3SD

Owner: The National Trust   *Contact:* The Property Manager

Home of the Dryden family since the 16th century, this manor house was built c1550, added to in the 1590s, and altered in the 1630s and c1710; largely unaltered since. Within the house, Elizabethan wall paintings and outstanding Jacobean plasterwork are of particular interest. A formal garden includes terraces, walls and gate piers of 1710. There is also a medieval priory church and a 70 acre park.

Location: OS Ref. SP577 506. Access from M40/J11, or M1/J16. Signposted from A5 2m S of Weedon crossroads. Then 7m to SW.

Opening Times: House: 11 Apr - 1 Nov: Sat - Wed inc. BH Mons (closed Thur & Fri) 1 - 5.30pm/dusk. Last admissions 5pm. Park, Gardens & Church open as house, 12 - 5.30pm, access through garden. Shop, 12.30 - 5pm; tearoom 12 - 5pm.

Admission: Adult £3.60, Child £1.80. Discount for pre-booked parties, contact Property Manager.

ℹ Shop. ♿ Suitable, some steps. WC. ☕ Tearoom. 🐕 In grounds, on leads.

COTON MANOR GARDEN

GUILSBOROUGH, NORTHAMPTONSHIRE NN6 8RQ

Owner: Ian & Susie Pasley-Tyler *Contact:* Sarah Ball

Tel: 01604 740219 **Fax:** 01604 740838

17th century stone manor house (not open) with old English garden laid out on different levels. Water gardens, herbaceous borders, rose garden, old holly and yew hedges. Recently established herb garden and wildflower meadow, also bluebell wood in May. The Groom's Cottage Restaurant offers homemade lunches and teas at reasonable prices.

Location: OS Ref. SP675 716. 9m NW of Northampton, between A5119 and A428.

Opening Times: 1 Apr - 4 Oct: Wed - Sun & BHs, 12 - 5.30pm.

Admission: Adult £3, Child £1.50, Conc. £2.50. Groups: Adult £2.50.

ℹ Shop. Plant centre. ♿ Grounds suitable. WC. ☕ Restaurant & tearoom. 🚶 By arrangement. Ⓟ Ample. 🐕 No dogs.

COTTESBROOKE HALL & GDNS

COTTESBROOKE, NORTHAMPTONSHIRE NN6 8PF

Owner: Capt & Mrs Macdonald-Buchanan   *Contact: The Administrator*

Tel: 01604 505808 **Fax:** 01604 505619

Architecturally magnificent Queen Anne house commenced in 1702. Renowned picture collection, particularly of sporting and equestrian subjects. Fine English and Continental furniture and porcelain. Main vista aligned on celebrated 7th century Saxon church at Brixworth. House reputed to be the pattern for Jane Austen's *Mansfield Park*. Notable gardens of great variety including fine old cedars, specimen trees and herbaceous borders.

Location: OS Ref. SP711 739. 10m N of Northampton near Creaton on A5199 (formerly A50), near Brixworth on A508 or Kelmarsh on A14.

Opening Times: Easter - end Sept: House & Garden: Thur & BH Mon plus Sun in Sept, 2 - 5pm. Gardens: Tue - Fri & BH Mon plus Sun in Sept 2 - 5.30pm.

Admission: House & Gardens: Adult £4. Gardens only: Adult £2.50, Child half price. Private parties welcome (except weekends) by prior arrangement.

   Ground floor & grounds suitable. WC.   Tearoom.   Compulsory.

DEENE PARK

See page 201 for full page entry.

EDGECOTE HOUSE

Edgecote, Banbury, Oxfordshire OX17 1AG

Owner: Christopher Courage

Early Georgian house with good rococo plasterwork.

Location: OS Ref. SP505 480. 6m NE of Banbury off A361.

Opening Times: By written appointment only.

SPECIAL EVENTS 1998

See the front section for full list.

Historic Scotland

ELEANOR CROSS

Tel: 01604 730320 (Regional Office)

Geddington, Kettering, Northamptonshire

Owner: English Heritage   **Contact:** The Midlands Regional Office

One of a series of famous crosses, of elegant sculpted design, erected by Edward I to mark the resting places of the body of his wife, Eleanor, when brought for burial from Harby in Nottinghamshire to Westminster Abbey in 1290.

Location: OS Ref. SP896 830. In Geddington, off A43 between Kettering and Corby.

Opening Times: Any reasonable time.

HOLDENBY HOUSE

See page 202 for full page entry.

KELMARSH HALL

Tel: 01604 686543 **Fax:** 01604 686543

Kelmarsh, Northampton NN6 9LU

Owner: Kelmarsh Hall Estate Preservation Trust   **Contact:** Mrs C R Wright

Designed in the Palladian manner by James Gibbs and set in 3,500 acres of farm and woodland, Kelmarsh Hall was built between 1728 and 1732. In 1928 Nancy Lancaster decorated the house and created the Chinese Room. Entrance lodges by James Wyatt. Gardens, woodland walks, lake and herd of British White cattle.

Location: OS Ref. SP736 795. $^1/_2$ m N of A508 / A14 (J2). 12m N of Northampton.

Opening Times: 12 Apr - 31 Aug: Sun & BH Mon, 2.30 - 5pm.

Admission: Adult £3.50, Child £2, OAP £3. Gardens only: £2.

   No inside photography.   Wedding receptions.   Not suitable.
   Tearoom.   Available.   Ample.   In grounds, on leads.

KIRBY HALL

Tel: 01536 203230

Deene, Corby, Northamptonshire NN17 5EN

Owner: English Heritage   **Contact:** The Custodian

Outstanding example of a large, stone-built Elizabethan mansion, begun in 1570 with 17th century alterations. There are fine gardens, currently being restored.

Location: OS141 Ref. SP926 927. On unclassified road off A43, Corby to Stamford road, 4m NE of Corby. 2m W of Deene Park.

Opening Times: 1 Apr - 1 Nov: daily 10am - 6pm or dusk if earlier. 2 Nov - 31 Mar: Wed - Sun, 10am - 4pm. Closed 24 - 26 Dec.

Admission: Adult £2.30, Child £1.20, Conc. £1.70.

SPECIAL EVENTS

AUG 1/2: History in Action III: 1,500 plus re-enactments from Romans to World War II.

LAMPORT HALL & GARDENS

See page 203 for full page entry.

LYVEDEN NEW BIELD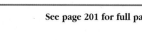

Tel: 01832 205358 **Fax:** 01832 205358

Nr Oundle, Peterborough PE8 5AT

Owner: The National Trust   **Contact:** The Custodian

An incomplete lodge or garden house, begun in 1595 by Sir Thomas Tresham and now an intriguing and roofless shell. Designed in the shape of a cross, with interesting exterior friezework.

Location: OS Ref. SP983 853. 4m SW of Oundle via A427, 3m E of Brigstock, off Harley Way. Access by foot along a $^1/_2$ m farm track.

Opening Times: All year: daily. Groups by arrangement.

Admission: £1.70.

   Limited.   On leads.

THE MENAGERIE

Tel: 01604 870957

Horton, Northampton, Northamptonshire NN7 2BX

Owner: The Executors of Gervase Jackson Stops dec.   **Contact:** Mrs A Cooley

Folly built in the 1750s by Thomas Wright of Durham. The outstanding rococo plasterwork in the main room includes signs of the zodiac. The gardens where Lord Halifax's animals were once kept, were created by Ian Kirby and include formal ponds, wetland and bog area, herbaceous borders, two thatched arbours, one circular and classical, and the other triangular and Gothic, and a grotto covered in shells and minerals featuring Orpheus playing to the animals.

Location: OS Ref. SP822 534. 5m SE of Northampton. Entry by field gate on E of A526.

Opening Times: House, Grotto and Gardens open to parties of 20 or more by prior appointment £5 pp. Gardens: Apr - Sept: Thur, 10am - 4pm. Last Sun each month, 2 - 6pm.

Admission: Adult £3, Child £1.50.

   Plant centre.   Grounds suitable.   Available.   No dogs.

NORTHAMPTON CATHEDRAL

Tel: 01604 714556 Fax: 01604 712066

Cathedral House, Kingsthorpe Road, Northampton NN2 6AG

Partly 19th century Pugin.   **Contact:** Rev K Payne

Location: OS Ref. SP753 617. $^3/_4$ m N of town centre.

Opening Times: Daily, 8am - 7.30pm. Sun Service: 7pm (Sat) 8.30am, 10.30am 5.15pm. Weekday services: 9.30am and 7pm.

Admission: Guided visit by prior application.

THE PREBENDAL MANOR HOUSE

NASSINGTON, PETERBOROUGH PE8 6QG

Owner: Mrs J Baile   *Contact:* Mrs J Baile

Tel: 01780 782575

Grade I listed and dating from the early 13th century, it is the oldest manor in Northamptonshire and one of the longest continually occupied houses in the country. The manor still retains many fine original medieval features and included in the visit are the 15th century dovecote, tithe barn museum and medieval fish ponds. Designed by Michael Brown and unique to the area and encompassing 5 acres are the 14th century re-created medieval gardens.

Location: OS Ref. TL063 962. 6m N of Oundle, 9m W of Peterborough, 7m S of Stamford.

Opening times: May, Jun & Sept: Sun, Wed and all BH Mons, 2 - 5.30pm. Jul/Aug: Sun, Wed & Thur, 2 - 6pm. Closed Christmas.

Admission: Adult £3.50, Child £1. Groups (20 - 50): Adult £3, Child £1.

- ⓘ Corporate Hospitality. No photography.
- ✗ Wedding receptions.
- ♿ Partially suitable.
- ☕ Refreshments by prior booking.
- 🅿 Limited.
- 🚶 For groups by arrangement. Free audio tours.
- 🐕 Guide dogs only.

SULGRAVE MANOR

MANOR ROAD, SULGRAVE, BANBURY, OXON OX17 2SD

Owner: Sulgrave Manor Board   *Contact:* Martin Sirot-Smith

Tel: 01295 760205

A delightful 16th century Manor House that was the home of George Washington's ancestors. Today it presents a typical wealthy man's home and gardens of Elizabethan times. Restored with scholarly care and attention to detail that makes a visit both a pleasure and an education. 'A perfect illustration of how a house should be shown to the public' - Nigel Nicholson, *Great Houses of Britain.*

Location: OS152 Ref. SP561 457. Off Banbury - Northampton road (B4525) 5m from M40/J11. 15m from M1/J15A.

Opening Times: 1 Apr - 31 Oct: daily except Wed. W/days 2 - 5.30pm. W/ends 10.30am - 1pm & 2 - 5.30pm. Nov, Dec & Mar: W/ends only, 10.30am - 1pm & 2 - 4.30pm. Also open 27 - 31 Dec. Closed 25 - 26 Dec & Jan & also Sun 14 Jun. Open by appointment for groups and school groups out of normal hours.

Admission: Adult £3.75, Child £2, Conc. £3.75. Group: Adult £3.50, Child £1.75, Conc. £3.50. Special Events: Adult £4.50, Child £2.25, Family £12. Group: Adult £4, Child £2. Gardens only: £2.

- ♿ Partially suitable.
- ☕ Tearoom.
- 🚶 Compulsory.
- 🐕 In grounds, on leads.

SPECIAL EVENTS

Sulgrave Manor has a wide range of special events, see section at front of book.

ROCKINGHAM CASTLE   **See page 204 for full page entry.**

RUSHTON TRIANGULAR LODGE ⌗   **Tel:** 01536 710761

Rushton, Kettering, Northamptonshire NN14 1RP

Owner: English Heritage   **Contact:** The Custodian

This extraordinary building completed in 1597, symbolises the Holy Trinity. It has three sides, 33 ft wide, three floors, trefoil windows and three triangular gables on each side.

Location: OS Ref. SP830 831. 1m W of Rushton, on unclassified road 3m from Desborough.

Opening Times: 1 Apr - 1 Nov: daily, 10am - 6pm.

Admission: Adult £1.30, Child 70p, Conc. £1.

SOUTHWICK HALL 🏛   **Tel:** 01832 274064

Southwick, Peterborough, Northamptonshire PE8 5BL

Owner: Christopher Capron Esq   **Contact:** Mr W J Richardson

Medieval building with Tudor rebuilding and 18th century additions.

Location: OS Ref. TL022 921. 3 m N of Oundle (A605). 4m W of Bulwick (A43).

Opening Times: Easter - Aug: BHs (Sun and Mon). May - Aug: Wed, 2 - 5pm.

Admission: Adult £3, Child £1.50, Conc. £2.50.

STOKE PARK PAVILIONS   **Tel:** 01604 862172

Stoke Bruerne, Towcester, Northamptonshire NN12 7RZ.

Owner: A S Chancellor Esq   **Contact:** Mrs C Cook

Two 17th century pavilions and colonnade by Inigo Jones.

Location: OS Ref. SP740 488. 7m S of Northampton.

Opening Times: Aug: daily, 3 - 6pm. Other times by appointment only.

Admission: Adult £3, Child £1.

- ♿ Grounds suitable.
- 🅿 Limited.
- 🐕 In grounds, on leads.

Knot Gardens:

Knot gardens – small, and usually rectangular – came to Britain from France in the sixteenth century, having originated in Italy. They consisted of low hedging of rosemary, thrift, hyssop, thyme, cotton-lavender, marjoram or, after 1600, dwarf box, laid out in a pattern, the beds the hedging enclosed filled with colour from flowers or coloured soils, stones or gravel. The pattern of the hedging was taken initially from needlework designs and, by the mid sixteenth century, from published woodcuts: Most Briefe and Pleasant Treatyse by Thomas Hill, published in 1563, shows several knot patterns; du Cerceau's Les Plus Excellent Bastiments de France, published in 1576 and 1579, shows several French gardens laid out with knot gardens. Such publications doubtless helped to popularise the fashion.

The intricate weaving patterns were best appreciated from above, from a raised walk or a mound or from the windows of long galleries. A modern recreation of a knot garden can be seen at Barnsley House, Gloucestershire.

Extract from: "Life in the Country House" by David N Durant (published by John Murray), PB£15.99, see page twelve at the front of the book.

Castle Ashby, Northamptonshire.

Tudor Life Re-enactment at Sulgrave Manor, Northamptonshire.

Coton Manor Garden, Northamptonshire.

Patrick Lane.

Wollaton Hall, Nottinghamshire.

CARLTON HALL
Tel: 01636 821421

Carlton-on-Trent, Nottinghamshire NG23 6NW
Owner: Lt Col & Mrs Vere-Laurie   **Contact:** Lt Col & Mrs Vere-Laurie
Mid 18th century house by Joseph Pocklington of Newark. Stables attributed to Carr of York.
Location: OS Ref. SK799 640. 7m N of Newark off A1. Opposite the church.
Opening Times: By appointment only.
Admission: Hall and Garden £3. Minimum charge for a group £30.

[i] Conferences.   [&] Not suitable.   [🐕] In grounds, on leads. Guide dogs in house.

CASTLE MUSEUM & ART GALLERY
Tel: 01159 9153700   **Fax:** 01159 9153653

Nottingham NG1 6EL
                               Contact: The Curator
17th century mansion with 13th century gateway, now a museum and art gallery.
Location: OS Ref. SK569 395. SW of the city centre on hilltop.
Opening Times: Daily: 10am - 5pm. Closed 25 Dec - 1 Jan).
Admission: Weekdays free. Weekends: Adult £1.50, Child 80p, Conc. for Passport to Leisure holders. Nov - Feb: Museum opens at 1pm on Fri. Closed 25 Dec - 1 Jan.

[i] Corporate hospitality. No photography.   [&] Suitable. WCs.   [☕] Licensed café.
[🚶] Compulsory.   [P] For disabled visitors only.   [👥] Educational programme.
[🐕] Guide dogs only.

CLUMBER PARK
Tel: 01909 476592   **Fax:** 01909 500721

Clumber Park, Worksop, Nottinghamshire S80 3AZ
Owner: The National Trust   **Contact:** The Estate Office
3,800 acres of parkland, farmland, lake and woodlands. The mansion was demolished in 1938, but the fine Gothic Revival Chapel, built 1886 - 89 for the 7th Duke of Newcastle, survives. Park includes the longest double lime avenue in Europe and a superb 80 acre lake. Also, classical bridge, temples, lawned Lincoln Terrace, pleasure grounds and stable block. Walled Garden including working Victorian Apiary. Vineries and Tools exhibition.
Location: OS Ref. SK626 746. 4¹/₂ m SE of Worksop, 6¹/₂ m SW of Retford, 1m S of A1/A57, 11m from M1/J30.
Opening Times: Park: All year during daylight hours. Walled Garden, Victorian Apiary, Fig House, Vineries & Garden Tools Exhibition: 4 Apr - end Sept: Sat, Sun & BH Mon, 11am - 5pm, last adm. 4.30pm. Conservation Centre: 4 Apr - 27 Sept: Sat, Sun & BH Mon 1 - 5pm. Chapel: Please call Estate Office for opening times.
Admission: Walled Garden, Victorian Apiary, Vineries & Garden Tools 70p. Vehicle Charge: Cars £3, Cars with caravans/mini coaches £4.30, Coaches £7, weekends & BHs £14.

[i] Shop. Plant centre.   [&] Grounds suitable. WC.   [☕] Licensed restaurant.

HODSOCK PRIORY GARDENS

BLYTH, NR. WORKSOP, NOTTINGHAMSHIRE S81 0TY
Owner: Sir Andrew & Lady Buchanan   *Contact: Lady Buchanan*
Tel: 01909 591204   **Fax:** 01909 591578
5 acre private garden on Domesday site. Sensational snowdrops, daffodils, bluebells, summer borders, roses, lilies, fine trees, woodland walk and ponds. Grade I listed gatehouse c1500. Italianate terrace, Victorian house (not open).
Location: OS Ref. SK612 853. W of B6045 Worksop/Blyth road, 1m SW of Blyth, less than 2m from A1.
Opening Times: Apr - Aug: Tue, Wed, Thur, 1 - 5pm. Four weeks in Feb/Mar, 10am - 4pm, telephone for further details.
Admission: Adult £2.50, Child free.

[i] Bulbs for sale.   [&] Partially suitable. WCs.   [☕] Café.   [🐕] Guide dogs only.

SPECIAL EVENTS
FEB/MAR for 4 weeks: "Snowdrop Spectacular". Unforgettable unique experience. Sheets of flowers in garden plus ¹/₂ mile walk in woods. Also aconites, etc.

HOLME PIERREPONT HALL

HOLME PIERREPONT, NOTTINGHAM NG12 2LD
Owner: Mr & Mrs Robin Brackenbury   *Contact: Robert Brackenbury*
Tel: 0115 933 2371
Visited by Henry VII in 1487, the house is peaceful and welcoming with splendid medieval rooms, a Charles II staircase and fine 17th to 20th century English country furniture and family portraits. The courtyard garden, 1875 is planted with roses, herbaceous beds and an elaborate box parterre. Filming welcome.
Location: OS Ref. SK628 392. 5m ESE of central Nottingham. Follow signs to the National Water Sports Centre and continue for 1¹/₂ m.
Opening Times: Jun: Sun. Jul: Thur & Sun. Aug: Tue, Thur, Fri & Sun. Easter, Spring & Summer holidays, Sun & Mon: 2 - 5.30pm. Groups by appointment throughout the year.
Admission: Adult £3, Child £1, Gardens only £1.50.

[&] Partially suitable. WC.   [X] Business & charity functions, wedding receptions.
[☕] Tearoom.   [🐕] In grounds, on leads.

NEWARK TOWN HALL
Tel: 01636 680353   **Fax:** 01636 680350

Market Place, Newark, Nottinghamshire NG24 1DU
Owner: Newark Town Council   **Contact:** The Town Clerk
A fine Georgian town hall. Recently refurbished to John Carr's original concept.
Location: OS Ref. SK540 639. 12m N of Nottingham 1m W of the A60 Mansfield Rd.
Opening Times: Any day by written confirmation.
Admission: Free.

NEWSTEAD ABBEY
Tel: 01623 793557   **Fax:** 01623 797136

Newstead Abbey Park, Nottinghamshire NG15 8GE   **Contact:** Mr Brian Ayers
Historic home of the poet, Lord Byron, set in grounds of over 300 acres. Mementoes of Byron and decorated rooms from medieval to Victorian times.
Location: OS Ref. SK540 639. 12m N of Nottingham 1m W of the A60 Mansfield Rd.
Opening Times: 1 Apr - 30 Sept: 12 - 6pm, last adm. 5pm. Grounds: All year except last Fri in Nov. Apr - Sept: 9am - 7.30pm. Oct - Mar: 9am - 5pm.
Admission: House & Grounds: Adult £4, Conc. £2. Grounds only: Adult £2, Conc. £1.

[i] Corporate hospitality. No photography.   [X] Wedding receptions.
[&] Partially suitable. WCs.   [☕] Café.   [🚶] By arrangement.   [P] Ample.
[👥] Educational programme.   [🐕] Guide dogs only.   [💍] Civil Wedding Licence.

NORWOOD PARK
Tel: 01636 815649   **Fax:** 01636 815649

Southwell, Nottinghamshire NG25 0PF
Owner: Sir John & Lady Starkey   **Contact:** Sarah Dodd - Events Manager
Delightful Georgian hunting lodge set in magnificent medieval oaked parkland. Suited to all manner of business or social events, ideal for filming. Extensive woodland, plus cricket field, orchards and lawns. A beautiful, adaptable setting. Combination of reception rooms and gallery complex offered for exclusive use.
Location: OS Ref. SK688 545. ³/₄ m W of Southwell off Halam Rd.
Opening Times: All year by appointment only.
Admission: Please telephone for information.

[i] Corporate hospitality. Outdoor activity days.   [X] Events/weddings.
[&] Partially suitable.   [☕] Pre-booked only.   [🚶] By arrangement.   [P] Ample.
[🐕] In grounds, on leads.   [💍] Civil Wedding Licence applied for 1998.

PAPPLEWICK HALL
Tel: 0115 963 3491 **Fax:** 0115 964 2767

Papplewick, Nottinghamshire NG15 8FE

Owner: Dr R Godwin-Austen

A beautiful stone built classical house set in a park with woodland garden laid out in the 18th century. The house is notable for its very fine plasterwork and elegant staircase. Grade I listed.

Location: OS Ref. SK548 518. 4m E of M1/J27 on B683.

Opening Times: By appointment and 1st, 3rd & 5th Wed in each month, 2 -5 pm.

Admission: Adult £3.50. Groups (min 10): Adult £2.50.

RUFFORD ABBEY
Tel: 01604 730320

Ollerton, Nottinghamshire

Owner: English Heritage   **Contact:** The Midlands Regional Office

The remains of a 17th century country house; displaying the ruins of a 12th century Cistercian Abbey. It is set in what is now Rufford Country Park.

Location: OS Ref. SK645 646. 2m S of Ollerton off A614.

Opening Times: 1 Apr - 1 Nov: Daily, 10am - 5pm. 2 Nov - 31 Mar: daily, 10am - 4pm. (Closed 24 - 26 Dec).

Admission: Free.

WINKBURN HALL
Tel: 01636 636465 **Fax:** 01636 636717

Winkburn, Newark, Nottinghamshire NG22 8PQ

Owner: Richard Craven-Smith-Milnes Esq   **Contact:** Richard Craven-Smith-Milnes Esq

A fine William and Mary house recently restored, nestles besides a charming church.

Location: OS Ref. SK711 584. 8m W of Newark 1m N of A617.

Opening Times: Throughout the year by appointment only.

Admission: Standard £4.20.

☒ Available.   ♿ Ground floor suitable.   🐕 No dogs.

WOLLATON HALL NATURAL HISTORY MUSEUM
Tel: 0115 915 3900

Wollaton Park, Nottingham NG8 2AE

Owner: Nottingham City Council   **Contact:** The Administrator

Flamboyant Elizabethan house built by Robert Smythson in a park, which despite being surrounded by Nottingham suburbs, remains attractively wild. Now used as a museum.

Location: OS Ref. SK532 392. Wollaton Park, Nottingham. 3m W of city centre.

Opening Times: Summer: 11am - 5pm. Winter: 11am - 4pm. Closed on Fridays.

Admission: Weekdays free. Weekends & BH Adult: £1, Child 50p. Joint ticket for Wollaton Hall & Industrial Museum. Grounds 50p/car (free orange badge holders).

Patrick Lane.

Wollaton Hall, Nottinghamshire.

THRUMPTON HALL

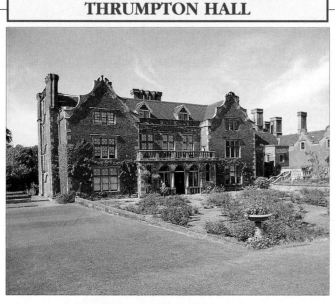

THRUMPTON, NOTTINGHAM NG11 0AX

Owner: *The Hon Mrs R Seymour*   **Contact:** *The Hon Mrs R Seymour*

Tel: 01159 830333 **Fax:** 01159 831309

Fine Jacobean house, built in 1607 incorporating an earlier manor house. Priest's hiding hole, magnificent carved Charles II staircase, carved and panelled saloon. Other fine rooms containing beautiful 17th and 18th century furniture and many fine portraits. Large lawns separated from landscaped park by ha-ha and by lake in front of the house. The house is still lived in as a home and the owner will show parties around when possible. Dining room with capacity for 52 with silver service or buffet. Free access and meal for coach drivers.

Location: OS Ref. SK508 312. 7m S of Nottingham, 3m E M1/J24, 1m from A453.

Opening Times: By appointment. Parties of 20+ 10.30am - 7.30pm.

Admission: Adult £5, Child £2.50.

ℹ️ Shop. Conferences.   ♿ Ground floor & grounds suitable. WC.

☕ Restaurant.   🐕 In grounds, on leads.

Belvederes and Prospect Towers:

Belvederes were rooms built on the roofs of houses to take advantage of a view, and might take the form of an angle turret, a cupola, a loggia, or an open gallery. The most eccentric is the Prospect Room on top of Wollaton Hall, Nottinghamshire by Robert Smythson, completed in 1588 for the erratic Sir Francis Willoughby. It has an immense panoramic view and is as big as a ballroom, but difficult to use as a space for entertaining since access is only by two very narrow and steep spiral staircases in turrets.

A prospect tower was a viewing tower standing on its own, more usually built to provide a focus to a view. Towers were a popular subject for amateur architects in the eighteenth century. Sanderson Miller (1716–80) built a sham castle and tower at Edgehill, Warwickshire on the spot where Charles I (1625–49) supposedly raised his standard before the Battle of Edgehill in 1642; Alfred's Tower, built in 1772 three miles from Stourhead at Kingsettle Hill, Wiltshire is where King Alfred is believed to have raised his standard against the Danes in 879. These are heroic towers. A more utilitarian tower is Lutterell's Tower near Eaglehurst, Southampton built in 1780 and giving a wide view of the sea. A tunnel runs from the cellar to the beach; clearly there is a connection with smuggling.

Extract from; "Life in the Country House" by David N Durant (published by John Murray), PB£15.99, see page twelve at the front of the book.

UPTON HALL
Tel: 01636 813795

Upton, Newark, Nottinghamshire NG23 5TE

Owner: British Horological Institute   **Contact:** The Director

Location: OS Ref. SK735 544. A612 between Newark and Southwell.

Opening Times: 29 Mar - 27 Oct: daily, 1.30 - 5pm.

Admission: Adult £2.50, Child (over 11 yrs) £1, OAP £2.

ℹ️ Shop. Conference facilities.   ☒ Wedding receptions.   ☕ Tearoom.

🚶 By arrangement.   🅿️ Ample.   🐕 In grounds only.

The Midlands
England

HAWKSTONE PARK
Nr. Shrewsbury

HAWKSTONE PARK, with its well hidden pathways, concealed grottos, secret tunnels and magical collection of follies is truly unique. It is a forgotten masterpiece; originally one of the most visited landscapes in Britain and now the only Grade I landscape in Shropshire.

Sir Roland Hill started it all in the 18th century with his son Richard 'The Great Hill', arranging for some 15 miles of paths and some of the best collections of follies in the world to be constructed in the grounds of their ancestral home. At the turn of the 19th century the Hills could no longer accommodate the growing number of sightseers to the Hall. As a result an Inn, which is now Hawkstone Park Hotel, was opened and guided tours were organised. Little has changed since then. The park is full of attractions, surprises and features. You can see dramatic cliffs and rocks, towers, monuments, tunnels, passageways, precipice rocks, paths, rustic 'sofas', romantic secret valleys. It takes around three hours to complete the whole tour of the Park (bring sensible shoes). From the Green House you embark upon a unique experience. Paths, steps, walls, even the Greek Urn, were put in place during the busy period at Hawkstone Park. Caves and seats, handy resting places for the weary visitor, were hewn into the rock face.

At the top of the Terrace sits a folly, the White Tower. Close by is the Monument, a 112-foot column, at the top of which stands the new statue of Sir Roland Hill, the first Protestant Lord Mayor of London. After an absence of 150 years Sika Deer have been reintroduced to the Park, these can be found close to the Monument. The seemingly endless numbers of tracks leading from the Terrace will tempt visitors off the straight and narrow perhaps to the Swiss Bridge or to St Francis' Cave or the Fox's Nob.

The tour then continues from the bottom of the Terrace to Grotto Hill via Gingerbread Hall and the magnificent Serpentine Tunnel and cleft which leads to the longest grotto passageway in Europe where you can come face to face with King Arthur.

CONTACT

Ken Darville-Smith
Hawkstone Park Hotel,
Golf Centre,
Historic Park and Follies
Weston-under-Redcastle
Nr Shrewsbury
Shropshire
SY4 5UY

Tel: (01939) 200611

Fax: (01939) 200311

LOCATION

OS Ref. SJ576 286

12m NE of Shrewsbury
off A49
3m from Hodnet
off A53/A442
M6 to M54 then either
A49 or A41, A442.

Rail: Shrewsbury
Station 12m.

Wem Station 7m.

Winner of: Europa Nostra Award, Civil Trust Award, Heart of England Award

ℹ️ Shop. Filming and TV location work, festivals, musical events and craft fairs. Golf courses (2 x 18 hole) adjacent to Park, golf tournaments, practice grounds, driving range, residential golf school, video analysis room. Clay pigeon shooting, archery. Cameras permitted.

♿ Partially suitable. WCs.

☕ Tearoom open all day. Restaurant available at Hotel (adjacent) serving snacks, grills and a full à la carte menu.

🅿️ Ample. Free refreshments for coach drivers. Bring sensible shoes.

👫 Special rates for schools, coaches and groups. Teachers' pack.

🐕 Dogs on leads permitted.

🅰️ Hotel adjacent.

CONFERENCE/FUNCTION

ROOM	SIZE (M)	MAX CAPACITY
Waterloo	15.45 x 10	200
Wellington	6.1 x 7.62	50
Redcastle	12.2 x 8.8	100
Hill	8.5 x 7	50

OPENING TIMES

SUMMER
1 April - 1 November

Park
Daily 10am - 4pm
(last admission).

WINTER
Park open Sat & Suns only
1 Nov - 28 Feb 1999
(excluding Christmas)
also Halloween Ghost
Hunt and December
weekends for Father
Christmas visits in the
caves.

Hotel: Open all year.
Tel: (01939) 200611

ADMISSION

Adult £4.50
Child £2.50
Conc........................£3.50
Family (2+3) £12.00

Groups*
Coaches (12 -15 seats)
...............................£30.00
Adult (up to 25)....£50.00
Child (up to 50) ..£100.00

* plus £3 for each
additional occupant.

Groups: Bookable and payable
in advance. Individual tickets
issued per person. Groups discounts for 15+.

BHs & Special Events

Adult £5.00
Child £2.50
Conc........................£4.00
Family (2+3) £14.00

SPECIAL EVENTS

• **EASTER:**
Egg Hunt

• **MAY 4:**
Circus Workshop

Please telephone for details
of other events.

The Midlands
England

OAKLEY HALL
Market Drayton

CONTACT

Mrs Ann E Fisher
Oakley Hall
Market Drayton
Shropshire
TF9 4AG

Tel: (01630) 653472

Fax: (01630) 653282

LOCATION

OS Ref. SJ701 367

From London 3hrs:
M1, M6/J14, then A5013 to
Eccleshall, turn right at
T-junction, 200 yards, then
left onto B5026.
Mucklestone is 1³/₄ m from
Loggerheads on B5026. 3m
NE of Market Drayton
N of the A53,
1¹/₂ m W of Mucklestone
off B5145.

OAKLEY HALL is situated in magnificent countryside on the boundary of Shropshire and Staffordshire. The present Hall is a fine example of a Queen Anne mansion house and was built on the site of an older dwelling mentioned in the Domesday Survey of 1085. Oakley Hall was the home of the Chetwode family until it was finally sold in 1919.

GARDENS

Set in 100 acres of rolling parkland, the Hall commands superb views over the surrounding countryside and the gardens include wild areas in addition to the more formal parts.

Oakley Hall is a privately owned family house and since it is not open to the general public it provides a perfect location for exclusive private or corporate functions. The main hall can accommodate 120 people comfortably and has excellent acoustics for concerts. The secluded location and unspoilt landscape make Oakley an ideal setting for filming and photography.

The surrounding countryside is rich in historical associations. St Mary's Church at Mucklestone, in which parish the Hall stands, was erected in the 13th century and it was from the tower of this Church that Queen Margaret of Anjou observed the Battle of Blore Heath in 1459. This was a brilliant victory for the Yorkist faction in the Wars of the Roses and the blacksmith at Mucklestone was reputed to have shod the Queen's horse back to front in order to disguise her escape.

❖

CONFERENCE/FUNCTION

ROOM	SIZE	MAX CAPACITY
Hall	50' x 30'	120
Dining Rm	40' x 27'	80
Ballroom	40' x 27'	80

OPENING TIMES

ALL YEAR

Not open to the public.
The house is available all
year round for private or
corporate events.

ADMISSION

Please telephone for
details.

i Concerts, conferences
(see left for rooms
available). Slide projector,
word processor, fax and
secretarial assistance are all
available by prior arrangement,
fashion shows, product
launches, seminars, clay
pigeon shooting, garden
parties and filming. Grand
piano, hard tennis court,
croquet lawn, horse riding.
No stiletto heels.

✗ Wedding receptions,
buffets, lunches and
dinners can be arranged for
large or small groups, using
high quality local caterers.

♿ Visitors may alight at
the entrance to the Hall,
before parking in allocated
areas. WCs.

🚶 By prior arrangement
groups will be met and
entertained by members of
the Fisher family.

P 100 cars, 100/200 yds
from the Hall.

🐕 No dogs.

A 3 double bedrooms
with baths.

The Midlands
England

WESTON PARK
Nr. Shifnal

CONTACT

Judy Sandy
Weston Park
Weston-under-Lizard
Nr Shifnal
Shropshire
TF11 8LE

Tel: (01952) 850207

Fax: (01952) 850430

LOCATION

OS Ref. SJ808 107

Birmingham 40 mins.
Manchester 1 hr.
Motorway access
M6/J12 or M54/J3.
House situated on A5 at
Weston under Lizard.

Rail: Nearest
Railway Stations:
Wolverhampton,
Stafford or Telford.

Air: Birmingham.

WESTON PARK is the ideal destination for a great family day out. This magnificent Stately Home set in 1,000 acres of beautiful Parkland, certainly has more to offer than history and grandeur. The house, built in 1671, was the ancestral seat of the Earls of Bradford since the 12th century and is now owned and maintained by a charity "The Weston Park Foundation".

The present house, built on the site of the original medieval manor house was designed by Lady Elizabeth Wilbraham and boasts generations of treasures including paintings by Van Dyck, Gainsborough and Stubbs. There are also superb collections of fine books, porcelain and priceless antiques including tapestries by Aubusson and Gobelin.

Step outside to appreciate the sprawling expanse

of the picturesque parkland, designed by the legendary 'Capability' Brown. Particular features are the Italian Broderie and the Rose Garden of the South Terrace. Visitors can enjoy a variety of woodland walks all with beautiful flowering trees and shrubs.

With children in mind, the parkland includes a Woodland Adventure Playground, Pets' Corner, a Deer Park and Miniature Railway that takes you on a $1^{1}/_{2}$ mile journey around the pools into the inner depths of the woodland.

There are special events throughout the year including: Festival of Transport, Horse Trials, Balloon Festival, battle re-enactments and the annual Music Festival which concludes with the 'Last Night of the Proms' open-air concert with firework spectacular.

OPENING TIMES

Easter: 11 - 14 April.

15 April - 14 June:
W/ends, BHs & everyday
Whit week (23 - 31 May).

15 June - 26 July & 19 July
Daily except Mon & Fri
and Sat 18 July.

27 July - 6 Sept:
Daily except 15/16 August.

7 - 20 September:
W/ends only.

House: 1 - 5pm
Last admission 4.30pm.

Park: 11am - 7pm
Last admission 5pm.

Closed 16/17 May.

NB. Visitors are advised to telephone first to check this information.

ADMISSION

House & Garden
Adult £5.00
Child (3 - 16yrs.)......£3.00
OAP........................£3.75

Garden only
Adult £3.50
Child (3 - 16yrs.)......£2.00
OAP........................£2.50

CONFERENCE/FUNCTION

ROOM	SIZE	MAX CAPACITY
Dining Rm	52' x 23'	120
Orangery	51' x 20'	120
Music Rm	50' x 20'	80
The Old Stables	58' x 20'	60
Conference Room	40' x 7'6"	60

ℹ️ Gift Emporium. Museum, conferences, product launches, outdoor concerts and events, filming location. Helipad and airstrip. Sporting activities organised for private groups eg. clay pigeon shooting, archery, hovercrafts, rally driving. Interior photography by prior arrangement only. Dogs on leads only.

✕ Weston Park offers a full event organisation service. Residential parties, special dinners, wedding receptions. Dine and stay arrangements in the house on selected dates.

♿ House suitable and part of the grounds. WCs.

☕ The Old Stables Restaurant and Tearoom provide meals and snacks on public open days.

🅿 Ample 100 yds away. Vehicles with private pre-booked groups may park at front door.

👪 Tue, Wed and Thur in the latter half of Jun and all Jul. Advance booking is essential. Teachers' guidance notes and National Curriculum-related workpacks available.

🅰 Weston Park offers 28 delightful bedrooms with bathrooms, 18 doubles, 7 twins, 3 singles.

🔔 Civil Wedding Licence.

ACTON BURNELL CASTLE

Tel: 01604 730320 (Regional Office)

Acton Burnell, Shrewsbury, Shropshire

Owner: English Heritage **Contact:** The Midlands Regional Office

The warm red sandstone shell of a fortified 13th century manor house.

Location: OS Ref. SJ534 019. In Acton Burnell, on unclassified road 8m S of Shrewsbury.

Opening Times: Any reasonable time.

Admission: Free.

ADCOTE SCHOOL

Tel: 01939 260202 **Fax:** 01939 261300

Little Ness, Shrewsbury, Shropshire SY4 2JY

Owner: Adcote School Educational Trust Ltd **Contact:** Mrs A Read

Adcote is a Grade I listed building designed by Norman Shaw, and built to a Tudor design in 1879. Its features include a Great Hall, Minstrels' Gallery, William De Morgan tiled fireplaces and stained glass windows. Landscaped gardens include many fine trees.

Location: OS Ref. SJ420 195. 7m NW of Shrewsbury. 2m NE of A5.

Opening Times: 30 Mar - 3 Apr & 13 Jul - 28 Aug: 2 - 5pm. Other times by appointment only.

Admission: Free, but the Governors reserve the right to make a charge.

Civil Wedding Licence.

ATTINGHAM PARK

Tel: 01743 709203

Shrewsbury SY4 4TP

Owner: The National Trust **Contact:** The Property Manager

Location: OS Ref. SJ550 099. 4m SE of Shrewsbury on N side of B4380 in Atcham village.

Opening Times: Please ring for details.

Admission: Please ring for details.

BENTHALL HALL

Tel: 01952 882159

Benthall, Nr. Broseley, Shropshire TF12 5RX

Owner: The National Trust **Contact:** The Custodian

A 16th century stone house with mullioned windows and moulded brick chimneys.

Location: OS Ref. SJ658 025. 1m NW of Broseley (B4375), 4m NE of Much Wenlock, 1m SW of Ironbridge.

Opening Times: 5 Apr - 30 Sept: Wed, Sun & BH Mon 1.30 - 5.30pm. Last adm. 5pm. Groups at other times by prior arrangement.

Admission: Adult: £3, Child: £1. Garden: £2. Reduced rates for booked parties.

Ground floor suitable. WC. By arrangement. Limited.

BOSCOBEL HOUSE

BREWOOD, BISHOPS WOOD, SHROPSHIRE ST19 9AR

Owner: *English Heritage* ***Contact:*** *The Custodian*

Tel: 01902 850244

This 17th century hunting lodge was destined to play a part in Charles II's escape from the Roundheads. A descendant of the Royal Oak, which sheltered the fugitive King from Cromwell's troops after the Battle of Worcester, still stands in the fields near Boscobel House. The timber-framed house where the King slept in a tiny 'sacred hole' has been fully restored and furnished in Victorian period and there are panelled rooms and secret hiding places. There is an exhibition in the house as well as the farmyard and smithy.

Location: OS127 Ref. SJ837 083. On unclassified road between A41 & A5. 8m NW of Wolverhampton.

Opening Times: 1 Apr - 1 Nov: daily: 10am - 6pm or dusk if earlier. 2 Nov - 31 Mar: 10am - 4pm. Closed 24 - 26 Dec and all of Jan. Last admission 1 hr before closing.

Admission: Adult £3.95, Child £2, OAP/Student/UB40 £3. 15% discount on groups of 11+.

Grounds suitable. WC. Restaurant. No dogs.

BUILDWAS ABBEY

Tel: 01952 433274

Shropshire

Owner: English Heritage **Contact:** The Custodian

Extensive remains of a Cistercian abbey built in 1135 and set beside the River Severn. The remains include the church which is almost complete except for the roof.

Location: OS Ref. SJ643 043. On S bank of River Severn on A4169, 2m W of Ironbridge.

Opening Times: 1 Apr - 1 Nov: daily, 10am - 6pm or dusk if earlier.

Admission: Adult £1.75, Child 90p, Conc. £1.30.

BURFORD HOUSE GARDENS

Tel: 01584 810777 **Fax:** 01584 810673

Burford House, Tenbury Wells, WR15 8HQ **e-mail:** treasures@burford.co.uk

Owner: Treasures of Tenbury Ltd **Contact:** Mrs Patricia Cox

Four-acre garden and early Georgian house in beautiful riverside setting. Home to the National Clematis Collection, with over 200 varieties and 2,000 varieties of other plants, in serpentine borders of harmonised colour schemes, set around sweeping lawns along the banks of the River Teme. Visitors should allow a minimum of 40 minutes in the gardens. Also on site are Treasures Plant Centre/Nursery, specialising in clematis, herbaceous, shrubs, climbers, quality selection of plants, pots, tools. Woodturning Centre; Burford Conservatories; Mulu Plants and Jungle Giants.

Location: OS Ref. SO585 680. 8m from Ludlow, 1m W of Tenbury Wells on A456.

Opening Times: All year: daily 10am - 5pm.

Admission: Adult £2.50, Child £1. Groups of 10+ £2 pp.

Shop. Plant centre. Wedding receptions. Gardens suitable. WC. Licensed Buttery. By arrangement. Ample. Guide dogs only. Civil Wedding Licence

SPECIAL EVENTS

APR - OCT: Botanical Art Show: Artist in residence, contemporary art shows

CLIVE HOUSE MUSEUM

Tel: 01743 354811 **Fax:** 01743 358411

College Hill, Shrewsbury, Shropshire SY1 1LT

Owner: Shrewsbury and Atcham Borough Council **Contact:** Mrs M White

Period room settings, natural and social history, temporary exhibitions and walled garden.

Location: OS Ref. SJ491 124. Town centre, close to TIC.

Opening Times: Tue - Sat & Summer Sun & BH Mon: 10am - 4pm. Closed mid-Dec - mid-Jan.

Admission: Adult £2, Child/Conc. £1. Groups 10% discount.

Shop. No photography. Partially suitable. Educational programme. Guide dogs only.

CLUN CASTLE

Tel: 01604 730320 (Regional Office)

Clun, Ludlow, Shropshire

Owner: English Heritage **Contact:** The Midlands Regional Office

Remains of a four storey keep and other buildings of this border castle are set in outstanding countryside. Built in the 11th century.

Location: OS Ref. SO299 809. In Clun, off A488, 18m W of Ludlow. 9m W of Craven Arms.

Opening Times: Any reasonable time.

Admission: Free.

COLEHAM PUMPING STATION

Tel: 01743 362947 **Fax:** 01743 354811

Longden Coleham, Shrewsbury, Shropshire SY3 7DN

Owner: Shrewsbury & Atcham Borough Council **Contact:** Mary White

Two Renshaw beam engines of 1901 are being restored to steam by members of Shrewsbury Steam Trust. The Trust organises open days throughout the summer months to show visitors their work. It is hoped to have "Steam up" the weekend of July 25/26.

Location: OS Ref. SJ497 122. Shrewsbury town centre, near the River Severn.

Opening Times: Apr - Sept: 4th Sun in each month, 10am - 4pm. Plus occasional other days.

Admission: Adult £1, Child 50p, Student £1.

Partially suitable. By arrangement. No parking. Educational programme. Guide dogs only.

COMBERMERE ABBEY

Tel: 01948 871637 **Fax:** 01948 871293

Whitchurch, Shropshire SY13 4AJ **e-mail:** cottages@combermereabbey.co.uk

Owner: Mrs S Callander Beckett **Contact:** Mrs S Callander Beckett

Combermere Abbey's 160 acre lake and superb natural setting first attracted the Cistercian monks in 1133. The present Gothic style house was redesigned in 1820 and still remains in private hands. The elegant Porter's Hall and splendid 17th century Library are used for weddings, concerts and lecture series.

Location: OS Ref. SJ590 440. 5m E of Whitchurch, off A530.

Opening Times: By arrangement for groups.

Admission: Groups: £5 per person inclusive of refreshments.

No photography. Wedding receptions. Not suitable. By arrangement. By arrangement. Limited. Civil Wedding Licence.

THE DOROTHY CLIVE GARDEN
Tel: 01630 647237

Willoughbridge, Market Drayton, Shropshire TF9 4EU

Owner: The Willoughbridge Garden Trust   **Contact:** Mrs M Grime

A 200 year old gravel quarry converted into a delightful woodland garden. The garden covers 8 acres and has fine views across the countryside.

Location: OS Ref. SJ753 400. On NE side of A51 between Nantwich & Stone, 2¹/₂ m SE of Woore crossroads (A525).

Opening Times: 28 Mar - 31 Oct: daily, 10am - 5.30pm.

Admission: Adult £2.80, Child (11-16yrs) £1, (up to 10 yrs free), OAP £2.40.

   Suitable. WC.   Available.

DUDMASTON

Michael Caldwell

QUATT, BRIDGNORTH, SHROPSHIRE WV15 6QN

Owner: The National Trust   *Contact:* The Administrator

Tel: 01746 780866   **Fax:** 01746 780744

Late 17th century manor house, home of Sir George Labouchere. Contains furniture and china, Dutch flower paintings, watercolours, botanical art and modern pictures and sculpture, family and natural history. 9 acres of lakeside gardens and Dingle walk. Two estate walks 5¹/₂ m and 3¹/₂ m starting from Hampton Loade car park.

Location: OS Ref. SO748 888. 4m SE of Bridgnorth on A442.

Opening Times: 1 Apr - 30 Sept: Wed & Sun, 2 - 5.30pm. Thur booked parties by arrangement. Tearoom: 1 - 2.15pm. Light lunches: 2.15 - 5.30pm. Last admission to house 5pm.

Admission: House & Garden: Adult £3.50, Child £2, Family £8. Groups £2.90. Garden only: £2.50.

   Shop.   Suitable. WC.   Tearoom.   In grounds, on leads.

HAUGHMOND ABBEY
Tel: 01743 709661

Upton Magna, Uffington, Shrewsbury, Shropshire SY4 4RW

Owner: English Heritage   **Contact:** The Custodian

Extensive remains of a 12th century Augustinian abbey, including the Chapter House which retains its late medieval timber ceiling, and including some fine medieval sculpture.

Location: OS Ref. SJ542 152. 3m NE of Shrewsbury off B5062.

Opening Times: 1 Apr - 1 Nov: daily, 10am - 6pm.

Admission: Adult £1.75, Child 90p, Conc. £1.30.

HAWKSTONE HALL & GDNS

MARCHAMLEY, SHREWSBURY SY4 5LG

Owner: The Redemptorists   *Contact:* Guest Mistress

Tel: 01630 685242 **Fax:** 01630 685565

Grade I Georgian mansion and restored gardens set in spacious parkland. A peaceful, homely atmosphere pervades the house, currently used as a pastoral centre. The principal rooms include Venetian saloon, ball room, refectory gallery, billiard room, drawing room, winter garden. The gardens comprise terraces, lawns, lily pool, rose garden and woodland.

Location: OS Ref. SJ581 299. Entrance 1m N of Hodnet on A442.

Opening Times: 5 - 31 Aug: 2 - 5pm.

Admission: Adult £2.50, Child £1.

   Partially suitable. WC.   Tearoom.   By arrangement.

   Ample.   Guide dogs only.

HAWKSTONE PARK
See page 212 for full page entry.

Hawkstone Park, Shropshire.

HODNET HALL GARDENS

HODNET, MARKET DRAYTON, SHROPSHIRE TF9 3NN

Owner: *Mr and the Hon Mrs A Heber-Percy*   **Contact:** *Mrs M A Taylor*

Tel: 01630 685202 **Fax:** 01630 685853

Beautiful woodland walks through trees and shrubs in 60 acres of flowering lakeside gardens. Tearooms now serving light lunches and afternoon teas. Free car and coach parking.

Location: OS Ref. SJ613 286. 12m NE of Shrewsbury on A53; M6/J15, M54/J3.

Opening Times: 1 Apr - 30 Sept: Tue - Sat (closed Mon), 12 - 5pm. Sun & BH Mon, 12 - 5.30pm.

Admission: Adult £3, Child £1.20, OAP £2.50. Reduced rates for groups.

⬚ Shop. Kitchen garden sales. ✖ For groups. ☕ Tearoom. 🐾 On leads.

IRONBRIDGE GORGE MUSEUMS

IRONBRIDGE, TELFORD, SHROPSHIRE TF8 7AW

Owner: *Independent Museum*   **Contact:** *Visitor Information*

Tel: 01952 433522or 432166 (w/ends) **Fax:** 01952 432204

Freephone: 0800 590258 for a **free** full colour accommodation guide.

Scene of pioneering events which led to the Industrial Revolution. The Ironbridge Gorge is host to the series of unique museums which tell the story of those momentous times. Stunning scenery, a recreated Victorian town, Coalport china and much more. You'll need 2 days here.

Location: OS Ref. SJ666 037. Telford, Shropshire via M6/M54.

Open: All year: daily from 10am (closed 24/25 Dec). Please telephone for winter details before visit.

Admission: Passport ticket which allows admission to all museums; Adult £9.50, Child/Student £5.50, OAP £8.50, Family £29. Prices valid until Easter 1999.

THE IRON BRIDGE ⬚   **Tel:** 01604 730320 (Regional Office)

Ironbridge, Shropshire

Owner: English Heritage   **Contact:** The Midlands Regional Office

The world's first iron bridge and Britain's best known industrial monument. Cast in Coalbrookdale by local ironmaster, Abraham Darby, it was erected across the River Severn in 1779.

Location: OS Ref. SJ672 034. In Ironbridge, adjacent to A4169.

Opening Times: Any reasonable time.

Admission: Free crossing.

LANGLEY CHAPEL ⬚   **Tel:** 01604 730320 (Regional Office)

Acton Burnell, Shrewsbury, Shropshire

Owner: English Heritage   **Contact:** The Midlands Regional Office

A delightful medieval chapel, standing alone in a field, with a complete set of early 17th century wooden fittings and furniture.

Location: OS Ref. SJ538 001. 1¹/₂ m S of Acton Burnell, on unclassified road 4m E of the A49, 9¹/₂ m S of Shrewsbury.

Opening Times: Open any reasonable time (closed 24- 26 Dec).

Admission: Free.

LILLESHALL ABBEY ⬚   **Tel:** 01604 730320 (Regional Office)

Oakengates, Shropshire

Owner: English Heritage   **Contact:** The Midlands Regional Office

Extensive ruins of an abbey of Augustinian canons including remains of the 12th and 13th century church and the cloister buildings. Surrounded by green lawns and ancient yew trees.

Location: OS Ref. SJ738 142. On unclassified road E of the A518, 4m N of Oakengates.

Opening Times: 1 Apr - 1 Nov: Weekends & BHs only, 10am - 6pm.

Admission: Adult £1.30, Child 70p, Conc. £1.

LUDLOW CASTLE   **Tel:** 01584 873355

Castle Square, Shropshire SY8 1AY

Owner: Trustees of Powis Castle Estate   **Contact:** Helen Duce

Dating from about 1086. Circular nave in Norman chapel. 16th century Judges' lodgings. Contemporary performances of Shakespeare in the Castle during the Ludlow Festival.

Location: OS Ref. SO509 745. 30m S of Shrewsbury. Centre of Ludlow.

Opening Times: 1 Feb - 30 Apr: 10am - 4pm. 1 May - 30 Sept: 10am - 5pm. 1 Oct - Christmas, 10am - 4pm.

Admission: Adult £2.50, Child £1.50, Conc. £2, Family £7.50. Groups 10% discount.

⬚ Shop. ♿ Ground floor & grounds suitable. WC. 🐾 In grounds, on leads.

The Ironbridge Gorge Museum, Shropshire.

MOAT HOUSE

Tel: 01743 718434

Longnor, Shrewsbury, Shropshire SY5 7PP

Owner: C P Richards   **Contact:** C P Richards

The site can be traced back to the 13th century when the occupants had, in 1290, licence to widen the "old moat" by 12 feet. The present timber-framed house is 530 years old, dating from 1467, and the house and moat together are an outstanding survival, especially as it is still occupied as a family home. The house displays unique timbers in its construction which is of considerable sophistication for the location and mid 15th century, its decoration includes two masks.

Location: OS126 Ref. SJ494 003. 8m S of Shrewsbury off A49 through village in back lane.

Opening Times: Apr - Sept: Thur and Spring and Summer BHs, 2.30 - 5pm.

Admission: Adult £3, Child £1.50, Child £1, OAP/Student £2.

🚫 Not suitable.   🚶 Compulsory.   🐕 No dogs.   **A** Available.

MORETON CORBET CASTLE

Tel: 01604 730320 (Regional Office)

Moreton Corbet, Shrewsbury, Shropshire

Owner: English Heritage   **Contact:** The Midlands Regional Office

A ruined medieval castle with the substantial remains of a splendid Elizabethan mansion, captured in 1644 from Charles I's supporters by Parliamentary forces.

Location: OS Ref. SJ562 232. In Moreton Corbet off B5063, 7m NE of Shrewsbury.

Opening Times: Any reasonable time.

Admission: Free.

MORVILLE HALL

Bridgnorth, Shropshire WV16 5BN

Owner: The National Trust   **Contact:** Dr & Mrs D Douglas

An Elizabethan house of mellow stone, converted in the 18th century. The Hall is in a fine setting, with three attractive gardens.

Location: OS Ref. SO668 940. Morville, on A458 3m W of Bridgnorth.

Opening Times: By written appointment only.

🚶 By arrangement.

OAKLEY HALL

See page 213 for full page entry.

PREEN MANOR GARDENS

Tel: 01694 771207

Church Preen, Church Stretton, Shropshire SY6 7LQ

Owner: Mr & Mrs P Trevor-Jones   **Contact:** Mrs P Trevor-Jones

6 acre garden on site of Cluniac monastery, with walled, terraced, wild, water, kitchen and chess gardens. 12th century monastic church with a yew tree reputedly the oldest in Europe.

Location: OS Ref. SO544 981. 10m SSE of Shrewsbury. 7m NE of Church Stretton, 6m SW of Much Wenlock.

Opening Times: Refer National Gardens Scheme Yellow Book. Coach parties Jun & Jul by appointment only.

🚫 Not suitable.   ☕ Tearoom.   🚶 By arrangement.   🐕 No dogs.

ROWLEY'S HOUSE MUSEUM

Tel: 01743 361196 **Fax:** 01743 358411

Barker Street, Shrewsbury, Shropshire SY1 1QH

Owner: Shrewsbury and Atcham Borough Council   **Contact:** Mrs M White

Impressive timber-framed building and attached 17th century brick mansion with costume, archaeology and natural history, geology, local history and temporary exhibitions.

Location: OS Ref. SJ490 126. Barker Street.

Opening Times: Tue - Sat: 10am - 5pm. Summer Suns and BH Mon: 10am - 4pm. Closed Christmas - 2nd week in Jan.

Admission: Adult £3, Child/Conc. £1. Groups 10% discount.

ℹ️ Shop. No photography.   🚫 Not suitable.   **P** No parking.
👥 Educational programme.   🐕 Guide dogs only.

SHIPTON HALL

Tel: 01746 785225 **Fax:** 01746 785125

Much Wenlock, Shropshire TF13 6JZ

Owner: Mr J N R Bishop   **Contact:** Mrs M J Bishop

Built around 1587 by Richard Lutwyche who gave the house to his daughter Elizabeth on her marriage to Thomas Mytton. Shipton remained in the Mytton family for the next 300 years. The house has been described as 'an exquisite specimen of Elizabethan architecture set in a quaint old fashioned garden, the whole forming a picture which as regards both form and colour, satisfies the artistic sense of even the most fastidious'. The Georgian additions by Thomas F Pritchard include some elegant rococo interior decorations and some noteworthy Tudor and Jacobean panelling. Family home. In addition to the house visitors are welcome to explore the gardens, the dovecote and the Parish Church which dates back to Saxon times.

Location: OS Ref. SO563 918. 7m SW of Much Wenlock on B4378. 10m W of Bridgnorth.

Opening Times: Easter - end Sept: Thur, 2.30 - 5.30pm. Also Sun and Mon of BH, 2.30 - 5.30pm. Groups of 20+ at any time of day or year by prior arrangement.

Admission: Adult £3, Child £1.50. Discount of 10% for groups 20+.

🚫 Not suitable.   🍴 Buffets / refreshments for pre-booked groups of 20+.
🚶 Compulsory.   🐕 Guide dogs only.

SHREWSBURY ABBEY

Tel/Fax: 01743 232723

Shrewsbury, Shropshire SY2 6BS   **Contact:** Mrs W Ford

Benedictine Abbey founded in 1083, tomb of Roger de Montgomerie and remains of tomb of St Winefride, 7th century Welsh saint. The Abbey was part of the monastery and has also been a parish church since the 12th century. Now made popular by Ellis Peters author of Brother Cadfael novels. Historical exhibition from Saxon times to present.

Location: OS Ref. SJ499 125. Signposted from Shrewsbury bypass (A5 and A49). 500yds E of town centre, across English Bridge.

Opening Times: Easter - 31 Oct: 9.30am - 5.30pm. Nov - Easter: 10.30am - 3pm.

Admission: Donation. Guided tours £10 per pre-arranged group.

ℹ️ Shop.   ♿ Suitable.   ☕ By arrangement.
🚶 By arrangement.   **P** Ample.   👥 Schools welcome.   🐕 Welcome.

SPECIAL EVENTS
JUNE 27: The Abbey Fair.

SHREWSBURY CASTLE & SHROPSHIRE REGIMENTAL MUSEUM

Castle Street, Shrewsbury, Shropshire SY1 2AT   **Tel:** 01743 358516

Owner: Shrewsbury & Atcham Borough Council   **Contact:** Steve Martin

Norman Castle with 18th century work by Thomas Telford. Free admission to attractive floral grounds. The main hall houses the Shropshire Regimental Museum and displays on the history of the castle.

Location: OS Ref. SJ495 128. Town centre, adjacent BR and Bus stations.

Opening Times: Tue - Sat & Summer Suns & BH Mon: 10am - 4.30pm. Dec/Jan opening please telephone for details. Grounds: Mon, free.

Admission: Adult £3, Child/OAP/Student £1. Groups 10% discount. Grounds free.

ℹ️ Shop. No photography.   ♿ Suitable. WC.   👥 Educational programme.
🐕 Guide dogs only.   💒 Civil Wedding Licence.

STOKESAY CASTLE

NEAR CRAVEN ARMS, SHROPSHIRE SY7 9AH

Owner: English Heritage   *Contact:* The Custodian

Tel: 01588 672544

This perfectly preserved example of a 13th century fortified manor house gives us a glimpse of the life and ambitions of a rich medieval merchant. Lawrence of Ludlow built this country house to impress the landed gentry. Lawrence built a magnificent Great Hall where servants and guests gathered on feast days, but the family's private quarters were in the bright, comfortable solar on the first floor. From the outside the castle forms a picturesque grouping of castle, parish church and timber-framed Jacobean gatehouse set in the rolling Shropshire countryside.

Location: OS137 Ref. SO436 817. 7m NW of Ludlow off A49. 1m S of Craven Arms off A49.

Opening Times: 1 Apr - 1 Nov: daily, 10am - 6pm or dusk if earlier. 2 Nov - 31 Mar (except 24 - 26 Dec): Wed - Sun, 10am - 4pm. Closed 1 - 2pm in Winter.

Admission: Adult £2.95, Child £1.50, Conc. £2.20. Groups of 11+ 15% discount.

♿ Great Hall & gardens only. WC.   🍴 Restaurant.

UPTON CRESSETT HALL

Tel: 01746 714307 **Fax:** 01746 714506

Bridgnorth, Shropshire WV16 6UH

Owner: William Cash Esq   **Contact:** William Cash

Medieval manor house in red brick, 14th century great hall. Wonderful chimneys, panelling. Magnificent turreted gatehouse with fine plasterwork. Available for letting, spacious accommodation with all modern comforts, fine antique furnishings, two very large double beds with silk hangings. Beautiful countryside. Ideal film location. 12th century church nearby.

Location: OS Ref. SO655 924. 4m W of Bridgnorth SW from A458.

Opening Times: Parties welcome throughout the year by appointment only. Closed Thur afternoons.

Admission: Adult £2.50, Child £1.

🚶 Compulsory.   🐕 In grounds, on leads.   Ⓐ Available.

WALCOT HALL

LYDBURY NORTH, NR BISHOP'S CASTLE, SHROPSHIRE SY7 8AZ

Owner: C R W Parish   *Contact:* C R W Parish

Tel: 0171 581 2782 **Fax:** 0171 589 0195

Georgian home of Lord Clive of India who commissioned Sir William Chambers to re-design it and the stable block, in 1763. His son added the free-standing Ballroom and developed 30 acres of arboretum and pools to the rear, with mile-long lakes in the front. Suitable for film locations, balls, corporate events, receptions, parties and shows.

Location: OS Ref. SO348 850. On the edge of the Clun Forest. 3m SE of Bishop's Castle on B4385; 1/2 m outside Lydbury North. The drive is adjacent to the Powis Arms Pub.

Opening Times: House & Garden: BHs, Sun & Mon (except Christmas and New Year), 2.15 - 4.30pm. All other times by appointment.

Admission: Adult £2.50, Child under 15 free. Teas by arrangement.

♿ House suitable. WC.   🐕 On leads.   Ⓐ Holiday Accommodation

WENLOCK GUILDHALL

Tel: 01952 727509

Much Wenlock, Shropshire

Owner: Much Wenlock Town Council   **Contact:** Much Wenlock Town Council

16th century half-timbered building has an open-arcade market area.

Location: OS127 Ref. SJ624 000. In centre of Much Wenlock, next to the church.

Opening Times: 1 Apr - 30 Sept: Mon - Sat, 10.30am - 12.30pm & 2 - 4pm. Suns: 2 - 4pm.

Admission: Adult 50p, Child 25p.

♿ Not suitable.   Ⓟ No parking.   🐕 Guide dogs only.

WENLOCK PRIORY

Tel: 01952 727466

Much Wenlock, Shropshire TA3 6HS

Owner: English Heritage   **Contact:** The Custodian

A prosperous, powerful priory at its peak in the Middle Ages. A great deal of the structure still survives in the form of high, romantic ruined walls and there is still an atmosphere of strength and serenity. A monastery was first founded at Wenlock in the 7th century, and little more is known of the site until the time of the Norman Conquest when it became a Cluniac monastery. These majestic ruins of the priory church are set in green lawns and there are substantial remains of the early 13th century church and Norman Chapter House,

Location: OS127 Ref. SJ625 001. In Much Wenlock.

Opening Times: 1 Apr - 1 Nov: daily: 10am - 6pm or dusk if earlier. 2 Nov - 31 Mar (except 24 - 26 Dec): Wed - Sun, 10am - 4pm (closed lunch 1 - 2pm in winter).

Admission: Adult £2.30, Child £1.20, Conc. £1.70 . 15% discount for groups of 11+.

WESTON PARK

See page 214 for full page entry.

WILDERHOPE MANOR

Tel: 01694 771363

Longville, Much Wenlock, Shropshire TF13 6EG

Owner: The National Trust   **Contact:** The Warden

This limestone house stands on southern slope of Wenlock Edge in remote country with views down to Corvedale. Dating from 1586, it is unaltered but unfurnished. Features include remarkable wooden spiral stairs, unique bow rack and fine plaster ceilings.

Location: OS Ref. SO545 929. 7m SW of Much Wenlock. 7m E of Church Stretton, 1/2 m S of B4371.

Opening Times: Apr - Sept: Wed & Sat 2 - 4.30pm. Oct - Mar: Sat only 2 - 4.30pm.

Admission: £1, no reduction for groups. Steep access to house.

WOLLERTON OLD HALL GARDEN

WOLLERTON, MARKET DRAYTON, SHROPSHIRE TF9 3NA

Owner: Mr & Mrs J D Jenkins   *Contact:* Mrs Di Oakes

Tel: 01630 685760 **Fax:** 01630 685583

3 acre plantsman's garden created around a 16th century house (not open). A series of walled gardens combine formal design and intense cultivation of perennials, roses and clematis. Peace and tranquillity in this gem of a garden in Shropshire

Location: OS Ref. SJ623 296. 14m NE of Shrewsbury off A53 between Hodnet and Market Drayton.

Opening Times: 1 May - 30 Aug: Fri, Sun & BHs, 12 - 5pm. Groups (min 25) by appointment at other times.

Admission: Adult £2.50, Child 50p.

ⓘ Plant centre.   ♿ Partially suitable.   🍵 Tearoom.

🚶 By arrangement.   Ⓟ Limited for coaches. Ample for cars..   🐕 No dogs.

WROXETER ROMAN CITY

Tel: 01743 761330

Wroxeter, Shrewsbury, Shropshire SY5 6PH

Owner: English Heritage   **Contact:** The Custodian

The part excavated centre of the fourth largest city in Roman Britain. Impressive remains of the 2nd century municipal baths. The museum has finds from the town and earlier legionary fortress.

Location: OS Ref. SJ568 088. At Wroxeter, 5m E of Shrewsbury, on B4380.

Opening Times: 1 Apr - 1 Nov: daily 10am - 6pm or dusk if earlier. 2 Nov - 31 Mar (except 24 - 26 Dec): Wed - Sun, 10am - 4pm (closed for lunch 1 - 2pm in winter).

Admission: Adult £2.95, Child £1.50, Conc. £2.20.

SHUGBOROUGH
Stafford

SHUGBOROUGH is the ancestral home of the fifth Earl of Lichfield, who as Patrick Lichfield is known worldwide as a leading photographer.

The 18th century mansion house contains a fine collection of ceramics, silver, paintings and French furniture. Part of the house continues to be lived in by the Earl and his family. Nothing could be more English!

Visitors can enjoy the 18-acre Grade I Historic Garden and a unique collection of neo-classical monuments by James Stuart. Other attractions include the County Museum and the original servants' quarters. The working laundry, kitchens, brewhouse and coach houses have all been lovingly restored. Costumed guides show how the servants lived and worked over 100 years ago.

Shugborough Park Farm is a Georgian farmstead that features an agricultural museum, working corn mill and rare breeds centre. The livestock are all historic breeds and in the farmhouse visitors can see brick bread ovens in operation and butter and cheese making in the dairy.

The estate is set in 900 acres of park and woodland with many walks and trails. A wide programme of events is conducted.

Many packages are available incorporating a lively menu of themed tours for the coach market, a 'Living History' educational programme for schools and a colourful events programme operating from April to December. Shugborough also provides a superb location for weddings, conferences, seminars, corporate activity days and product launches.

CONTACT

Anne Wood
Promotions and
Events Manager
Shugborough
Milford
Stafford
ST17 0XB

Tel: (01889) 881388

Fax: (01889) 881323

LOCATION

OS Ref. SJ992 225

From London
M1/J19, M6/J13
follow signs. 6m E of
Stafford N of A513.

Rail: BR Intercity
trains at Stafford.

Taxi: Anthony's Stafford
(01785) 252255

CONFERENCE/FUNCTION

ROOM	SIZE	MAX CAPACITY
Banqueting Hall	51' x 21'	65
Saloon	51' x 20'	80
Conference	20' x 20'	35
Granary	19' x 32'	60
Blue Drawing Rm	21' x 26'	20
Tower of the Winds	21' x 21'	20

OPENING TIMES

28 March - 27 September
Daily: 11am - 5pm.

October
Sun only.

Pre-booked parties
throughout the year.

ADMISSION

All attractions
Adults......................£8.00
Concessions*...........£6.00
Family (3 Sites)......£18.00

Gardens and Park
Cars.........................£1.50
Coaches...................Free

Single Sites
(House, Museum or Farm)
Per site
Adult.......................£3.50
Concessions*...........£2.50

* Concessions for children
(under 5s FREE), OAPs,
Students, unemployed &
groups.

** NT Members free
to mansion house,
reduced rate to
museum and farm.

ℹ️ Shop. Private and corporate entertainment, conferences, product launches and dinner parties. Filming and event location. Over 900 acres of parkland and gardens available for hire. Themed activities. No photography.

🍴 Catering for special functions/ conferences.

♿ Visitors may alight at entrance before parking. WCs. Stairclimber to house. Batricars available. Disabled friendly picnic tables available. Taped tours.

☕ Licensed tearoom/cafe seating 95 also tearoom at Farm seats 30. Prior notice for large groups.

🚶 Tour time 1hr. Themed tours as required. Groups of 15+. Please telephone for details.

🅿 Ample car and coach parking. Discounted vouchers for coach drivers' meals available.

👪 Award-winning educational packages. Curriculum-related. Contact Sales & Development Officer.

🐕 In grounds, on leads.

💒 Civil Wedding Licence.

SHUGBOROUGH continued ...

SPECIAL EVENTS

- **APR 18 & 19:**
  Gamekeepers' Fair

- **APR 25 & 26:**
  Staffordshire Spring Flower Show

- **MAY 3 & 4:**
  Classic Car Event

- **MAY 17:**
  Dressage Festival

- **MAY 23 - 25:**
  Spring Craft Show

- **JUN 6:**
  Music from the Movies with Fireworks

- **JUN 7:**
  Donkey Day

- **JUN 13:**
  Afternoon of Scottish Country Dancing

- **JUN 21:**
  All About Pigs (Park Farm). Children's Literary Day - Country Museum

- **JUL 4 - 5:**
  Gardeners' Weekend

- **JUL 18:**
  Fireworks & Laser Symphony Concert

- **JULY 19:**
  Goose Fair

- **AUG 2:**
  Victorian Street Market

- **AUG 22:**
  Last Night of the Proms

- **AUG 29 - 31:**
  Shugborough Summer Craft Festival

- **SEPT 13:**
  Wedding Fair

- **OCT 10 - 11:**
  Christmas Craft Show

- **OCT 30 - 31:**
  Halloween

- **NOV 7:**
  Bonfire Night

- **DEC 8 - 11:**
  Christmas at Shugborough

Telephone for a full list of events for 1998.

THE ANCIENT HIGH HOUSE

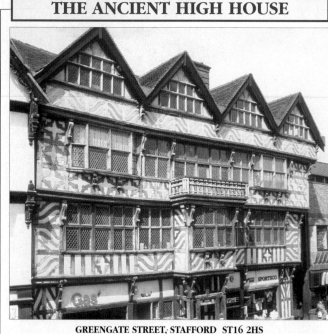

GREENGATE STREET, STAFFORD ST16 2HS

Owner: Stafford Borough Council   *Contact:* R Halliwell

Tel/Fax: 01785 240204

This building is the largest timber-framed town house in England. Built in 1595 by the Dorrington family, this house is still very impressive on Stafford's skyline. It was lived in by Richard Sneyd, a member of one of Staffordshire's greatest families, when King Charles I stayed here in 1642. It is now a registered museum with displays set out as period room settings which present aspects of the house's history. The Staffordshire Yeomanry museum is on the top floor.

Location: OS Ref. SJ922 232. Town centre.

Opening Times: Mon - Fri, 9am - 5pm. Sat (Apr - Oct) 10am - 4pm. Sat (Nov - Mar) 10am - 3pm. Check BHs.

Admission: Adult £1.75, Child/Conc. £1.10. Family (2+2) £4.

ℹ️ Shop & Tourist Information Centre.   ♿ Not suitable.   🐕 Guide dogs only.

BIDDULPH GRANGE GARDEN

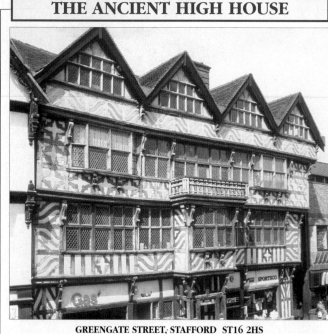
Ian Shaw

GRANGE ROAD, BIDDULPH, STOKE-ON-TRENT ST8 7SD

Owner: The National Trust   *Contact:* The Garden Office

Tel: 01782 517999

A rare and exciting survival of a high Victorian garden, restored by the National Trust. The garden is divided into a series of themed gardens within a garden, with a Chinese temple, Egyptian court, pinetum, dahlia walk, glen and many other settings.

Location: OS Ref. SJ891 592. E of A527, 3^1/$_2$ m SE of Congleton, 8m N of Stoke-on-Trent.

Opening Times: 1 Apr - 1 Nov: Wed - Fri, 12 - 6pm. Sat, Sun & BH Mon, 11am - 6pm. Also open 7 Nov - 20 Dec: Sat, Sun, 12 - 4pm or dusk if earlier.

Admission: Adult £4, Child £2, Family (2 +2)) £10. Half price Nov & Dec. Joint ticket with Little Moreton Hall available during main season. Adult £6, Child £3, Family £15.

ℹ️ Shop.   ☕ Tearoom.   🐕 In car park, on leads.

BARLASTON HALL   **Fax:** 01782 372391

Barlaston, Staffordshire ST12 9AT

Owner: Mr & Mrs James Hall   **Contact:** Mr & Mrs James Hall

Barlaston Hall is a mid-18th century palladian villa, attributed to Sir Robert Taylor. Extensively restored during the 1990s with the help of English Heritage. The four public rooms open to visitors contain some fine examples of 18th century plasterwork.

Location: OS Ref. SJ895 391. ^{1}/$_2$ m E of A34 between Stoke and Stafford.

Opening Times: By appointment to groups of 10 - 30. Admission includes refreshments. Please write to the above address or fax on 01782 372391 giving details of numbers, possible dates and a contact telephone number.

Admission: Pre-arranged groups: £3.50pp.

ℹ️ No photography.   ♿ Not suitable.   🚶 Guided tours only.   🅿️ Limited.

Biddulph Grange Garden, Staffordshire.

Patrick Lane.

CHILLINGTON HALL   **Tel:** 01902 850236

Codsall Wood, Wolverhampton, Staffordshire WV8 1RE

Owner: Mr & Mrs P Giffard   **Contact:** Mr & Mrs P Giffard

Georgian red brick house with fine saloon by Soane set in 'Capability' Brown park having one of the largest lakes created by Brown.

Location: OS Ref. SJ864 067. 2m S of Brewood off A449. 4m NW of M54/J2.

Opening Times: Jun - 14 Sept: Thur, Easter Sun, Sun prior to May BH & Sun in Aug: 2.30 -5.30pm. Other times by prior appointment for groups of 15.

Admission: Adult £3, Child £1.50. Grounds only: half price.

🚶 Compulsory.   🐕 In grounds, on leads.

FORD GREEN HALL   **Tel:** 01782 233195   **Fax:** 01782 233194

Ford Green Road, Smallthorne, Stoke-on-Trent ST6 1NG

Owner: Stoke-on-Trent City Council   **Contact:** Judith Franklin

Ford Green Hall is a timber-framed yeoman farmer's house built for the Ford family in 1624, with brick wings added in the 18th century. A rare survival from the pre-industrial Potteries, the rooms are furnished with original and reproduction pieces according to inventories of the 17th and 18th century. A period garden is being developed around the Hall.

Location: OS Ref. SJ887 508. On B5051 Burslem – Endon road in Stoke-on-Trent (the route to Leek in the Staffordshire Moorlands).

Opening Times: All year except 25 Dec - 1 Jan: Sun - Thur 1- 5pm.

Admission: Adult £1.50, Conc. £1.

ℹ️ Shop.   ♿ Partially suitable.   ☕ Tearoom.   🚶 By arrangement.

🅿️ Limited for coaches.   👪 Educational programme.   🐕 Guide dogs only.

💍 Civil Wedding Licence.

SPECIAL EVENTS

DEC: Hall dressed in traditional seasonal decorations.

IZAAK WALTON'S COTTAGE

WORSTON LANE, SHALLOWFORD, NR. STAFFORD

Owner: Stafford Borough Council   *Contact:* R Halliwell

Tel: 01785 760278

Thatched, timber-framed cottage in the heart of the Staffordshire countryside. Bequeathed by Izaak Walton, author of the *Compleat Angler*, it has displays on the history of angling. Ground floor rooms are set out in 17th century style.

Location: OS Ref. SJ876 293. Shallowford, nr Great Bridgeford, 6m N of Stafford.

Opening Times: Apr - Oct: Tue - Sun, 11am - 4.30pm.

Admission: Adult £1.75, Child/Conc. £1.10. Family (2+2) £4.

| i | Shop. | & | Suitable. WC. | 大 | By arrangement. |
| P | Ample. | | Guide dogs only. | | |

SPECIAL EVENTS:

Events programme during the summer. Please telephone for details.

MOSELEY OLD HALL

Andreas Von Einsiedel

FORDHOUSES, WOLVERHAMPTON WV10 7HY

Owner: The National Trust   *Contact:* The Property Manager

Tel: 01902 782808 **Fax:** 01902 782808

An Elizabethan House with later alterations. Charles II hid here after the Battle of Worcester and the bed in which he slept is on view, as well as the hiding place he used. The small garden has been reconstructed in 17th century style with formal box parterre; 17th century plants only are grown. The property is a Sandford Education Award Winner. Tearoom in 18th century Barn, light lunches available in high season. Charles II exhibition in the Barn.

Location: OS Ref. SJ932 044. 4m N of Wolverhampton between A449 and A460.

Opening Times: 28 Mar - 13 Dec: Mar - May: Sat, Sun, BH Mon & following Tue (except Tue 5 May), 1.30 - 5.30pm (BH Mon. 11am - 5pm). Jun - Oct: Wed, Sat, Sun, BH Mon & following Tue (also Tue in Jul & Aug): 1.30 - 5.30pm (BH Mon 11am - 5pm). Nov & Dec: Sun, 1.30 - 4.30pm (guided tours only, last tour 4pm). Pre-booked groups at other times including evening tours.

Admission: Adult £3.60, Child £1.80, Family £9.

| i | Shop. | & | Ground floor & grounds suitable. WC. | | Guide dogs only. |

| **LICHFIELD CATHEDRAL** | **Tel:** 01543 306240 **Fax:** 01543 306109 |

Lichfield, Staffordshire WS13 7LD

e-mail: lich.cath@virgin.net

Contact: Canon A Barnard

800-year old Gothic Cathedral with three spires on a 1300-year old Christian site. 8th century gospel manuscript, 16th century Flemish glass, silver collection - a worshipping community.

Location: OS Ref. SK115 097. Approach from A38 and A51, N from M42 and M6. N of city centre.

Opening Times: All year: daily. Educational programme available.

Admission: Donation.

| i | Shop. | & | Suitable. WC. | | Licensed restaurant. | P | No parking. | | Guide dogs. |

| **MIDDLETON HALL** | **Tel:** 01827 283095 |

Tamworth, Staffordshire B78 2AE

Owner: Middleton Hall Trust

Contact: Mrs Joan Dean

A Grade II listed building and the birthplace of Francis Willoughby, the naturalist.

Location: OS Ref. SP193 982. A4091, S of Tamworth.

Opening Times: Easter - end Sept: Sun & BH Mons, 2 - 5.30pm.

Admission: £1.50, Conc. 70p.

| i | Shop. Craft centre. Conferences. | X | Wedding receptions. | & | Partially suitable. WC. |
| | Tearoom. | | On leads. | | Civil Wedding Licence. |

| **SAMUEL JOHNSON BIRTHPLACE MUSEUM** | **Tel:** 01543 264972 |

Breadmarket Street, Lichfield, Staffordshire WS13 6LG

Fax: 01543 258441

Owner: Lichfield City Council

Contact: Dr G Nicholls

The house where Samuel's father had a bookshop is now a museum with many of Johnson's personal relics.

Location: OS Ref. SK115 094. Breadmarket Street, Lichfield.

Opening Times: Daily: 10.30am - 4.30pm. Closed Sundays, Nov - Jan.

Admission: Adult £1.40, Child 80p, Conc. 80p, Family £3.80. Groups 80p.

| i | Shop. | & | Not suitable. | P | No parking. | | No dogs. |

The Midlands
England

SANDON HALL

SANDON, STAFFORDSHIRE ST18 0BZ

Owner: *The Earl of Harrowby*   **Contact:** *Michael Bosson*

Tel: 01889 508004 **Fax:** 01889 508586

Ancestral seat of the Earls of Harrowby, conveniently located in the heart of Staffordshire. The imposing neo-Jacobean house was rebuilt by William Burn in 1854. Set amidst 400 acres of glorious parkland, Sandon, for all its grandeur and elegance, is first and foremost a home. The family museum which opened in 1994 has received considerable acclaim, and incorporates several of the State Rooms. The 50-acre landscaped gardens feature magnificent trees and are especially beautiful in May and autumn.

Location: OS Ref. SJ957 287. 5m NE of Stafford on the A51, between Stone and Lichfield, easy access from M6/J14.

Opening Times: All year: for events, functions and for pre-booked visits to the museum and gardens. Evening tours by special arrangement. Closed Christmas Day, Boxing Day and New Year's Day.

Admission: Museum: Adult £3.50, Child £2.50, OAP £3. Gardens: Adult £1.50, Child £1, OAP £1. NB. Max group size 22 or 45 if combined Museum and Gardens.

   Grounds suitable.　　　 Tea, if pre-booked.　　　 In grounds, on leads.

STAFFORD CASTLE & VISITOR CENTRE

NEWPORT ROAD, STAFFORD ST16 1DJ

Owner: *Stafford Borough Council*   **Contact:** *R Halliwell*

Tel: 01785 257698

This impressive site was once a Norman motte and bailey castle. Earl Ralph, a founder member of the Order of the Garter, spent part of his fortune building a stone keep in 1348. During the Civil War, the Castle was successfully defended, but eventually demolished. The current building was erected in the early 19th century and fell into ruin through this century. The Visitor Centre displays artefacts found during recent excavations. An imaginative audio-visual presentation describes the castle's mixed fortunes.

Location: OS Ref. SJ904 220. Off A518, On N side of A518, $1^1/_2$ m WSW of town centre.

Opening Times: Apr - Oct: Tue - Sun, 10am - 5pm. Nov - Mar: Tue - Sun, 10am - 4pm.

Admission: Adult £1.75, Child/Conc. £1.10. Family (2+2) £4.

   Shop.　　　 Grounds suitable. WC.　　　 Kiosk.　　　 In grounds, on leads.

SHUGBOROUGH

See pages 220/221 for full page entry.

Patrick Lane.

Stafford Castle, Staffordshire.

TAMWORTH CASTLE   **Tel:** 01827 63563 **Fax:** 01827 56567

The Holloway, Tamworth, Staffordshire B79 7LR

Owner: Tamworth Borough Council   **Contact:** Mrs Esme Ballard

Norman motte and bailey castle with fifteen period rooms spanning 800 years of history. Interactive Tamworth Story exhibition opened in 1996.

Location: OS Ref. SK206 038. Town centre off A51.

Opening Times: All year: Mon - Sat, 10am - 5.30pm. Sun 2 - 5.30pm. Last adm. 4.30pm.

Admission: Adult £3.40, Child £1.75, Conc. £1.75, Family £8.55. Groups 10+: Adult Conc. £1.25, School children 60p.

   Shop.　　　 Ground floor suitable.　　　 By arrangement.
   Educational programme.　　　 Guide dogs only.

WALL ROMAN SITE (Letocetum)   **Tel:** 01543 480768

Watling Street, Nr. Lichfield, Staffordshire WS14 0AW

Owner: English Heritage   **Contact:** The Custodian

The remains of a staging post alongside Watling Street. Foundations of an Inn and a Bath House can be seen and there is a display of finds in the site museum.

Location: OS139 Ref. SK099 067. Off A5 at Wall, nr Lichfield.

Opening Times: 1 Apr - 1 Nov: daily, 10am - 6pm or dusk if earlier.

Admission: Adult £1.75, Child 90p, OAP/Student £1.30. 15% discount for groups of 11+.

WHITMORE HALL

WHITMORE, NEWCASTLE-UNDER-LYME ST5 5HW

Owner: *Mr Guy Cavenagh-Mainwaring*   **Contact:** *Mr Michael Cavenagh-Thornhill*

Tel: 01782 680478   **Fax:** 01782 680906

Whitmore Hall is a Grade I listed building, designated as a house of outstanding architectural and historical interest, and is a fine example of a small Carolinian manor house, although parts of the hall date back to a much earlier period. The hall has beautifully proportioned light rooms, curving staircase and landing. There are some good family portraits to be seen with a continuous line, from 1624 to the present day. It has been the family seat, for over 900 years, of the Cavenagh-Mainwarings who are direct descendants of the original Norman owners. The interior of the hall has recently been refurbished and is in fine condition. The grounds include a beautiful home park with a lime avenue leading to the house, as well as landscaped gardens encompassing an early Victorian summer house. One of the outstanding features of Whitmore is the extremely rare example of a late Elizabethan stable block, the ground floor is part cobbled and has nine oak-carved stalls, while the upstairs floor houses the remains of the stable boys' rooms and a ghost !

Location: OS Ref. SP115 362. On A53 Newcastle - Market Drayton Road, 3m from M6/J15.

Opening Times: 1 May - 31 Aug: Tue, Wed & BHs, 2 - 5.30pm.

Admission: Adult £3, Child 50p.

♿ Ground floor & grounds suitable.   Ⓟ Ample.   🐕 No dogs.

Spices:

Pepper with everything was the rule in Roman cooking, and other spices such as cinnamon, sugar (then considered a spice), mustard, ginger, saffron and coriander were popular. With the withdrawal of the Romans from Britain in the fifth century AD and the virtual closure of the Mediterranean to Christian trade in the centuries of Moorish domination, imported spices became all but unavailable, until the Crusades reopened the Levant trade. Most spices followed the expensive silk route from the Far East, and so the use of the rarest was restricted to the wealthy. The price of spices fluctuated according to supply but cinnamon, pepper and ginger were usually the cheapest, mace and cloves more expensive, and saffron most costly of all.

Returning Crusaders certainly brought with them a taste for spicy dishes but it is hard to judge how heavily spiced medieval and later food was, because few contemporary recipes give quantities; however, the combination of spices and the foods in which they were used often seem very adventurous. Undoubtedly they disguised the taste of tainted flavours, unspiced foods tasted dull. Until the end of the fifteenth century Venice controlled the European end of the silk route, setting her own (high) prices. The Portuguese broke the monopoly, rounding the Cape of Good Hope in 1488, but though Portuguese spice ships were in Falmouth by 1504, their prices were little different from the Venetians'. By mid-century the Dutch were also bringing spices from the Far East. The East India Company was set up in 1600 to fill the trade vacuum left by the decline of Portuguese power, and with so much competition the cost of spices fell and they became more widely available.

Kitchen fireplaces of the seventeenth century often have a small spice cupboard set in the wall near the chimney; round wooden boxes with radiating compartments inside served the same purpose and were closed with lock and key.

Extract from; "Life in the Country House" by David N Durant (published by John Murray), PB£15.99, see page twelve at the front of the book.

Shugborough, Stafford.

SPECIAL EVENTS 1998

See the front section for full list.

Historic Scotland

The Midlands
England

ARBURY HALL
Nuneaton

CONTACT

Major W D Morris-Barker
Arbury Hall
Nuneaton
Warwickshire
CV10 7PT

Tel: (01203) 382804

Fax: (01203) 641147

LOCATION

OS Ref. SP335 893

London, M1, M6/J3
(A444 - Nuneaton),
1³/₄ hrs.
2m SW of Nuneaton.
1m W of A444.

Chester A51, A34, M6
(from J14 to J3), 2¹/₂ hrs.
Nuneaton 10 mins.

Bus: Nuneaton 3m.

Rail: Nuneaton Station 3m.

Air: Birmingham
International 17m.

Built on the site of the Augustinian Priory of Erdbury, Arbury Hall has been the seat of the Newdigate family for over 400 years. This Tudor/Elizabethan house was 'gothicised' by Sir Roger Newdigate, the 5th Baronet, in the 18th century to become "The Gothick Gem of the Midlands". The Stables portico was designed by Wren.

The saloon and dining room ceilings are especially spectacular, the former modelled on the Henry VII Chapel in Westminster Abbey. Portraits include works by Lely, Romney, Reynolds and Devis, and furniture includes Hepplewhite and Gothick Chippendale. A collection of porcelain consists of Oriental and Chelsea pieces amongst others, and there is a particularly splendid display of Jacobite toasting glasses.

The Hall stands in secluded parkland and the delightful landscaped garden of rolling lawns, winding paths and beautiful trees and lakes is mainly the result of the 2nd Baronet's influence. Spring flowers, especially daffodils and bluebells, are profuse. Seen at their glorious best in June is the vista of rhododendrons, azaleas and the giant wisteria. North of the house lies the haven of the rose garden.

George Eliot, the novelist, was born on the estate and Arbury and Sir Roger were immortalised by her in her book, *Scenes of Clerical Life.*

ℹ️ Shop. Corporate hospitality, film location, small conferences, product launches and promotion, marquee functions, clay pigeon shooting, archery and other sporting activities, grand piano in Saloon, helicopter landing site. No cameras or video recorders.

✕ Exclusive lunches and dinners for corporate parties in dining room, max. 50, buffets 120.

♿ Visitors may alight at the Hall's main entrance. Parking in allocated areas. Ramp access to main hall.

☕ Available. Menus available for pre-booked groups.

🚶 Tour time: 1¹/₂ hrs.

🅿️ 200 cars and 3 coaches 250 yards from house. Follow tourist signs. Approach map available for coach drivers.

👪 Welcome, must pre book. School room available.

🐕 On leads only, in gardens. Guide dogs only in house.

OPENING TIMES

SUMMER
12 April - 27 September

Hall
Sun and BH Mon
2 - 5.30pm.

Gardens
As Hall: 2 - 6pm.

Last admission to Hall and Gardens 5pm.

Open for pre-booked parties of 25+ on most dates.

WINTER
October - Easter
Corporate functions only.

ADMISSION

SUMMER

Hall, Park & Gardens
Adult £4.50
Child (up to 14 yrs.)...£2.50

Gardens Only
Adult £3.00
Child (up to 14 yrs.)...£2.00

Groups (25+)
Adult £4.00
Child £2.50

Evening visits...........£4.50

Special rates for pre-booked groups of 25+.

SPECIAL EVENTS

• **JUN 7:**
Motor Transport Spectacular

• **JUN 13 - 14:**
Rainbow Craft Fair

• **AUG 22 - 23:**
Rainbow Craft Fair.

CONFERENCE/FUNCTION

ROOM	SIZE	MAX CAPACITY
Dining Rm	35' x 28'	120
Saloon	35' x 30'	70
Drawing Rm	38' x 21'	40
Long Gallery	48' x 11'	40
Stables Tea Rooms	31' x 18'	80

Matthew Antrobus

CHARLECOTE PARK
Wellesbourne

CHARLECOTE has been the home of the Lucy family for some 700 years. The present house, begun by Sir Thomas Lucy in the mid-16th century, lies at the centre of an extensive wooded deer park grazed by fallow and red deer and by a herd of rare Jacob sheep introduced by George Lucy in the 18th century.

The house is built of red brick to a pleasingly irregular E-shape with great chimneys marching across the roofline and octagonal corner turrets crowned with gilded weathervanes. Charlecote seems to sum up the very essence of Elizabethan England, especially when the rose-coloured brickwork is turned to gold by the sun.

Queen Elizabeth I spent two nights here in 1572, celebrated in the proud display of her coat of arms over the two-storeyed porch. George Lucy, a cultivated and much travelled bachelor,

employed 'Capability' Brown to redesign the park, sweeping away the 17th century water gardens and altering the course of the River Hele so that it cascaded into the Avon within sight of the house. The balustraded formal garden, adorned with clipped yew is a 19th century addition. Steps lead to the cedar lawn with a Victorian orangery, now a charming tearoom.

Some of the earliest parts of the house are in the extensive outbuildings, where the stable block includes a brew-house which was in operation until the 1890s, a wash house and a coach house displaying a collection of vehicles used at Charlecote in the 19th century. But only the charming domestic gatehouse with its fretwork stone balustrade survives unaltered from the 16th century, a tantalising taste of what must have been lost.

S. Hobhouse

CONTACT

The Property Manager
Charlecote Park
Wellesbourne
Warwick
CV35 9ER

Tel: (01789) 470277

Fax: (01789) 470544

LOCATION

OS151 Ref. SP263 564

1m W of Wellesbourne, 5m E of Stratford-upon-Avon, 6m S of Warwick on N side of B4086.

OPENING TIMES

3 April - 1 November
Daily except Wed & Thur
12am - 5pm.

Closed Good Friday.

Last admission 5.15pm.

Grounds open 12 - 6pm.

ADMISSION

Adult £4.80
Child £2.40
Family £12.00

SPECIAL EVENTS

Details available from the Property Manager.

i Shop. For conservation reasons indoor photography is not permitted. Baby changing and feeding room.

♿ Pre-arrange to drop-off visitors or to park near to the house. Access to all rooms except Gatehouse Museum.

☕ Morning coffees, lunches, afternoon teas in the Orangery licensed restaurant; open as property 11am - 5.30pm.

🚶 Evening tours for pre-booked groups May - Sept: Tue 7.30 - 9.30pm, £5.50 including NT members (min charge £137.50).

👫 By prior arrangement with Administrator, schools base and resource book available.

COUGHTON COURT
Alcester

COUGHTON COURT has been the home of the Thockmortons since the 15th century and the family still live here today. The magnificent Tudor gatehouse was built around 1530 with the north and south wings completed 10 or 20 years later. The gables and the first storey of these wings are of typical mid-16th century half-timbered work.

Of particular interest to visitors is the Thockmorton family history from Tudor times to the present generation. On view are family portraits through the centuries with other family memorabilia and recent photographs. Also furniture, tapestries and porcelain.

A long-standing Roman Catholic theme runs through the family history as the Thockmortons have maintained their Catholic religion until the present day. The house has a strong connection with the Gunpowder Plot and also suffered damage during the Civil War. Exhibitions on the Gunpowder Plot as well as Children's Clothes (included in price).

Gardens

The house stands in 25 acres of gardens and grounds along with two churches and a lake. A formal garden was constructed in 1992 with designs based on an Elizabethan knot garden in the courtyard. A new $1^1/2$ acre garden in the old walled garden opened in 1996. Visitors can also enjoy a specially created walk beside the River Arrow and a new bog garden opened in 1997.

CONTACT

Mr A McLaren
Coughton Court
Alcester
Warwickshire
B49 5JA

Tel: (01789) 400777

Fax: (01789) 765544

Visitor Information:
(01789) 762435

LOCATION

OS Ref. SP080 604

Located on A435,
2m N of Alcester,
10m NW of
Stratford-on-Avon.
18m from Birmingham
City Centre.

CONFERENCE/FUNCTION

ROOM	SIZE	MAX CAPACITY
Dining Rm	45' x 27'	60
Saloon	60' x 36'	100

The Saloon, which has particularly good acoustics, is often used for music recording.

i Shop and Plant Centre. Receptions, special dinners, filming, buffets, business meetings, fairs and garden parties. The excellent acoustics of the Saloon make it ideal for concerts, especially chamber music. Marquees can be erected on the large lawn area, grand piano. No photography or stiletto heels in house.

Buffet or sit-down meals can be provided by arrangement, in the Dining Room and Saloon. Also in-house catering can be arranged for other events. Wedding receptions welcome.

Ground floor of house suitable. WC.

Licensed restaurant, 11am - 5.30pm. Capacity 100 inside and 60 outside.

By arrangement.

Unlimited for cars plus 4 coaches.

Allowed in car park only.

Civil Wedding Licence.

OPENING TIMES

SUMMER

House

14 March - end April
Sat & Sun.
Easter Mon - Wed
(closed Good Fri)
11.30am - 5pm.
BH Mons open 11am.

Easter Sat - Wed (inclusive)
11.30am - 5pm.

May - September
Daily except Thur & Fri
Jul - Aug also Fris
11.30am - 5pm.

3 - 18 October:
Sat & Sun: 11.30am - 5pm

Last admission $^1/_2$ hr before closing.

Grounds
11am - 5.30pm.

WINTER
Closed.

ADMISSION

House & Grounds
Adult £5.90
Child* (5-15yrs) £2.95
Family (2 + 4).........£18.50
Groups (min 15)
  per person £4.70

Grounds only
Adult £3.90
Child* (5-15yrs) £1.95
Family (2 + 4).........£11.00
Groups (min 15)
  per person £3.10

*under 5s free.

CONTACT

Michael Barbour
Ragley Hall
Alcester
Warwickshire
B49 5NJ

Tel: (01789) 762090

Fax: (01789) 764791

LOCATION

OS Ref. SP073 555

Off A46/A435 1m SW of
Alcester.
From London 100m, M40
via Oxford and
Stratford-on-Avon.

Bus: Birmingham -
Evesham, from
Lodge gates.

Rail: Evesham
Station 9m.

Air: Birmingham
International 20m.

Taxi: 007 Taxi
(01789) 414007

CONFERENCE/FUNCTION

ROOM	SIZE	MAX CAPACITY
Great Hall	70' x 40'	150
Red Saloon	30' x 40'	150
Green Drawing Rm	20' x 30'	150
Supper	45' x 22'	100
Seymour	25' x 23'	30

RAGLEY HALL
Alcester

RAGLEY HALL, home of the Earl and Countess of Yarmouth, was designed by Robert Hooke in 1680 and is one of the earliest and loveliest of England's great Palladian country houses. The perfect symmetry of its architecture remains unchanged except for the massive portico added by Wyatt in 1780.

The present interior is almost entirely due to two widely separated generations, in 1750, when Francis Seymour owned Ragley, James Gibbs designed the magnificent Baroque plasterwork of the Great Hall. On completion, Francis filled the Hall with French and English furniture and porcelain and had portraits of himself and his sons painted by Sir Joshua Reynolds.

The present owners are the Earl and Countess of Yarmouth who are continuing the ongoing task of restoration and renovation to maintain Ragley in its present glory. Notable also is the mural, by Graham Rust, in the South Staircase Hall which was completed in 1983.

GARDENS

The main formal garden descends in a series of wide rose-covered terraces. The rest of the 27 acre garden consists of shrubs and trees interspersed with spacious lawns providing vistas across the 400-acre park.

Other features are the lake, created in 1625, the cricket pitch, still in regular use, the adventure playground and maze.

❖

i Shop. Private and corporate entertainment. Wedding receptions, conferences, seminars, product launches, dinners and activity days, film and photographic location, park, lake and picnic area, marquee. No photography in house. Guide book translated in French and German.

Available up to 800. Telephone for details.

Visitors may alight at entrance. Parking in allocated areas. WCs. Lifts.

Licensed tea rooms 11am - 5pm. Groups must pre-book.

Private tours by Lord Yarmouth available outside opening hours. Guided tours cost of £9pp, plus VAT. Tour time 1 hour.

P Coach drivers admitted free and receive info pack and luncheon voucher. Please advise of group visits.

Welcome, £2.50 per head. Teachers' packs and work modules on request. Adventure Wood and Woodland Walk.

No dogs.

Civil Wedding Licence.

OPENING TIMES

SUMMER
2 April - 4 October

House
Thur - Sun & BH Mons
11am - 5pm

Garden & Park
Thur, Fri, Sat, & Sun
10am - 6pm.

Open BH Mon &
July - August: Daily

WINTER
7 October - 30 March
Open any time by prior
arrangement.

ADMISSION

SUMMER
House & Garden
Adult £5.00
Child (5 - 16)...........£3.50
OAP........................£4.50
Groups* (min 20, max 100)
Adult £4.50
Schoolchild (5 - 16) .£2.50
Student...................£2.50
OAP........................£4.50

*   Min. payment £80 for
groups of 20+.

WINTER
House & Garden
Private conducted tour by
arrangement.

SPECIAL EVENTS

• **APR 18 - 19:**
Gardeners' Weekend.

• **MAY 24/25:**
Transport Show.

• **JUN 21:**
Outdoor Concert.

• **AUG 1 & 8 & SEPT 4:**
Outdoor Concert.

• **AUG 22 - 23:**
Game Fair.

• **SEPT 12 - 13:**
Garden Weekend.

Mary Arden's House.

Anne Hathaway's Cottage.

THE SHAKESPEARE HOUSES
Stratford-upon-Avon

Step back in time to enjoy these beautifully preserved Tudor homes connected with William Shakespeare and his family; the architectural character, period furniture, special collections, attractive gardens, grounds and walks and craft displays.

In Town: Shakespeare's Birthplace: This half timbered house where the dramatist was born was purchased as a national memorial in 1847. It has been a place of pilgrimage for nearly 300 years. Today it is approached through a Visitors' Centre, with a fine exhibition, *William Shakespeare: His Life and Background*, and the garden.

New Place/Nash's House: The site and grounds of Shakespeare's home from 1597 until his death, with its Elizabethan-style garden, is approached through Nash's House adjoining, which contains exceptional furnishings and displays of the history of Stratford.

Hall's Croft: A delightful Elizabethan town house, once the home of Dr Hall, Shakespeare's physician son-in-law. Exceptional furniture and paintings and exhibition on Tudor medicine. Fine walled garden. Meals and refreshments available which can also be served in the beautiful garden.

Out of Town: Anne Hathaway's Cottage: This famous, picturesque thatched cottage was Anne's home before her marriage to Shakespeare. Cottage garden and Shakespeare Tree Garden as well as a garden shop and attractive Shottery Brook and Jubilee Walks. Summer tea garden.

Mary Arden's House and The Shakespeare Countryside Museum: Tudor farmstead (home of Shakespeare's mother) with outbuildings and nearby Glebe Farm containing exhibits illustrating country life over 400 years. Gypsy caravans, dovecote, duck pond, rare breeds, field walk, and all-day displays of falconry. Refreshments and picnic area.

CONTACT

Nicolas Walsh
Estate & Tourism Manager
The Shakespeare
Birthplace Trust
Henley Street
Stratford-upon-Avon
CV37 6QW

Tel: (01789) 204016

Fax: (01789) 296083

LOCATION

OS Refs:

Birthplace - **SP201 552**
New Place - **SP201 548**
Hall's Croft - **SP200 546**
Hathaway's - **SP185 547**
Arden's - **SP166 582**

Direct rail services from London (Paddington)

2 hrs from London
45 mins from
Birmingham by car.

4m from M40/J15
and well signed from
all approaches.

Shakespeare's Birthplace.

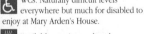

i Shops at Shakespeare's Birthplace, Hall's Croft, Anne Hathaway's Cottage and Mary Arden's House. Regular guided bus tour service connecting the town house with Anne Hathaway's Cottage and Mary Arden's House. No photography inside properties.

X Available, details upon request.

WCs. Naturally difficult levels everywhere but much for disabled to enjoy at Mary Arden's House.

Available on site or close by.

By special arrangement.

P The Trust provides a free coach terminal for delivery and pick-up of groups, max. stay 30 mins at Shakespeare's Birthplace. Parking available at Anne Hathaway's Cottage and Mary Arden's House.

Available for all properties. For information 01789 201804.

Guide dogs only.

OPENING TIMES

SUMMER
20 March - 19 October
Mon - Sat: 9.30am - 5pm

Birthplace & Anne
Hathaway's 9am - 5pm.

Sun: 10am - 5pm
Birthplace & Anne
Hathaway's 9.30am - 5pm.

WINTER
1 January - 19 March
20 October - 31 December
Mon - Sat: 10am - 4pm
Birthplace & Anne
Hathaway's 9.30am - 4pm.

Sun: 10.30am - 4pm
Birthplace & Anne
Hathaway's 10am - 4pm.

Closed 23 - 26 December.

ADMISSION

Shakespeare's Birthplace
Adult £4.50
Child £2.00
Family (2 + 3) £12.00

New Place/Nash's
House or Hall's Croft
Adult £3.00
Child £1.50

Anne Hathaway's Cottage
Adult £3.50
Child £1.50
Family (2 + 3) £9.00

Mary Arden's House
Adult £4.00
Child £2.00
Family (2 + 3) £11.00

All 3 in-town properties
Adult £7.00
Child £3.50
OAP/Student..............£6.00
Family (2+3) £18.00

All five properties
Adult £10.00
Child £5.00
OAP/Student..............£26.00

Accompanied groups 20+,
10% discount.

© N.T Severn, R. Charlton.

The Midlands
England

CONTACT

The Property Manger
Upton House
Banbury
Oxfordshire
OX15 6HT

Tel: (01295) 670266

LOCATION

OS151 Ref. SP371 461

On A422, 7m NW
of Banbury. 12m SE of
Stratford-upon-Avon

Rail: Banbury
Station , 7m.

UPTON HOUSE
Banbury

UPTON HOUSE stands less than a mile to the south of the battlefield of Edgehill and there has been a house on this site since the Middle Ages. The present house was built at the end of the 17th century and remodelled 1927 - 29 for the 2nd Viscount Bearsted.

He was a great collector of paintings, china and many other valuable works of art, and adapted the building to display them. The paintings include works by El Greco, Bruegel, Bosch, Memling, Guardi, Hogarth and Stubbs. The rooms provide an admirable setting for the china collection which includes Chelsea figures and superb examples of beautifully decorated Sèvres porcelain. The set of 17th century Brussels tapestries depict the Holy Roman Emperor Maximilian I's boar and stag hunts.

Recent extensive renovation work has resulted in the reinstatement of the 30ft high Sports Room which was originally created for the 2nd Viscount and allows the magnificent full length portraits to be hung and viewed at their best.

GARDEN

The outstanding garden is of interest throughout the season with terraces descending into a deep valley from the main lawn. There are herbaceous borders, the national collection of asters, over an acre of kitchen garden, a water garden laid out in the 1930s and pools stocked with ornamental fish.

Over a mile from the house, but just visible from the west end of the terrace on the garden front, is the lower lake which was formed in the mid-18th century after the fashion of 'Capability' Brown. A small temple with Doric columns and pediment sits in the centre of the one straight edge.

© N.T Severn, R. Charlton.

OPENING TIMES

SUMMER

4 April - 1 November
Sat - Wed including
BH Mon
2 - 6pm.

Closed Thur & Fri
including Good Fri.
Last admission 5.30pm,
5pm after 25 October.

Timed tickets at peak
times on Sun & BH Mon
when delays possible.

ADMISSION

Adult £5.00
Child £2.50
Family £12.50

Garden

Adult £2.50

SPECIAL EVENTS

• **ALL YEAR:**
Fine arts study tours, jazz
concerts and other events,
please send SAE or
telephone for details.

ℹ️ Shop. Parent and baby room. No indoor photography.

♿ Wheelchair available. Access to all ground floor rooms. WC. Motorised buggy to /from lower garden.

☕ Tearoom.

🚶 Tour time 1 hr. Groups (15+) must pre-book. Evening tours by written appointment (no reduction).

🅿️ Coaches park in the main car park.

WARWICK CASTLE
Warwick

This dramatic fortress rises majestically above the banks of the River Avon only 8 miles from Shakespeare's Stratford on a site first fortified by William the Conqueror in 1068. For centuries it was home to the mighty Earls of Warwick, the most powerful noblemen in England. The Castle is now widely regarded as the finest mediaeval castle in England, a magnificent blend of history, mystery and splendour.

Today at Warwick Castle you can experience some of that history in person. Marvel at the regal presence of Richard Neville, Earl of Warwick in 'Kingmaker - a preparation for battle' which recreates the sights, smells and sounds of a mediaeval household making ready for the battle. The 14th century Great Hall lies at the heart of the Castle, here you can see the death mask of Oliver Cromwell and Bonnie Prince Charlie's shield.

Then, skipping the centuries, you will find yourself in the midst of an aristocratic Victorian house party, in a 'Royal Weekend Party 1898', at which His Royal Highness the Prince of Wales reigns as guest of honour.

Yet the Dungeon, chilling Torture Chamber and Ghost Tower will not let us forget the once grim reality of life behind the towering Castle walls. Throughout the year there is an exciting series of special events that bring this mediaeval fortress even more to life from the soothing sounds of the minstrels to the clash of mounted kings.

In its peacetime role today the Castle is surrounded by 60 acres of grounds and gardens landscaped by Lancelot 'Capability' Brown. This is the magic of Warwick Castle where scenes, settings, sounds and smells recapture key moments in Britain's history in breathtaking surroundings.

CONTACT

Sales Office
Warwick Castle
Warwick
CV34 4QU

Tel: (01926) 495421
(Admin)
(01926) 406600
(Info Line)

Fax: (01926) 401692

LOCATION

OS Ref. SP284 648

2m from M40/J15.
Birmingham 35 mins
Leeds 2 hrs 5 mins
London, 1 hr 30 mins
Vehicle entrance from A429
1/2 m SW of town centre.

Rail: Intercity from London Euston to Coventry. Direct service Chiltern Line from Marylebone & Paddington to Warwick.

CONFERENCE/FUNCTION		
ROOM	SIZE	MAX CAPACITY
Great Hall	61' x 34'	120
State Dining Room	40' x 25'	30
Undercroft	46' x 26'	120
Stables Hayloft	44' x 19'	100
Marquees		2000

i Three shops. Corporate events, receptions and Kingmaker's Feasts. Guide books available in French, German, Japanese, Spanish and Italian.

Parking spaces in Stables Car Park, free admission for registered blind and visitors in wheelchairs.

Available, ranging from cream teas to three-course hot meals. During the summer there is an open air barbecue and refreshment pavilion in the grounds.

Available for groups (must be pre-booked). Guides in every room.

P Limited free car parking in main car park. Free coach parking, free admission and luncheon voucher for coach driver.

Ideal location, being a superb example of military architecture dating back to the Norman Conquest and with elegant interiors up to Victorian times. Group rates apply. Education packs available.

Registered Assistance Dogs only.

OPENING TIMES

SUMMER
April - October
10am - 6pm
Last admission 5.30pm.

WINTER
November - March
10am - 5pm
Last admission 4.30pm.

ADMISSION

1 Mar (1998) - 31 May & 1 Sept - 28 Feb 1999

Adult £9.25
Child* £5.60
OAP.........................£6.65
Family**................£26.00

Groups (20+)
Adult £7.50
Child £4.80
OAP.........................£5.95

1 Jun - 31 Aug 1998

Adult £9.95
Child* £5.95
OAP.........................£7.10
Family**................£27.00

Groups (20+)
Adult £7.95
Child £5.00
OAP.........................£6.40

* 4 - 16 inclusive
** 2 adults & 2 children

ARBURY HALL   See page 226 for full page entry.

BADDESLEY CLINTON

Oliver Benn.

RISING LANE, BADDESLEY CLINTON, KNOWLE, SOLIHULL B93 0DQ

Owner: The National Trust   **Contact:** The Property Manager

Tel: 01564 783294 **Fax:** 01564 782706

A romantically sited medieval moated manor house, dating from 14th century; little changed since 1634; family portraits, priest holes; garden; ponds and lake walk.

Location: OS139, Ref. SP199 715. 3/4 m W of A4141 Warwick/Birmingham road at Chadwick End.

Opening Times: 4 Mar - 1 Nov: Wed - Sun & BH Mon (Closed Good Fri). Mar, Apr & Oct: 1.30 - 5pm. May - Sept: 1.30 - 5.30pm (Grounds open from 12pm). Mar 1999: Wed - Sun, 1.30 - 5pm. Last adm: to house 30 mins before closing.

Admission: Adult £4.80, Child £2.40, Family £12. Grounds, restaurant & shop only: £2.40.

ⓘ Shop. ♿ Ground floor only & grounds. WC. ☕ Restaurant. 🐕 No dogs.

CHARLECOTE PARK   See page 227 for full page entry.

COUGHTON COURT   See page 228 for full page entry.

Gazebo:

An eighteenth century word for a small viewing tower or summer-house with a view, in a garden or park. When placed on the roof of a house it is called a Belvedere. It is difficult to distinguish Tudor Banqueting Houses from what are effectively gazebos. One at Long Melford Hall, Suffolk (c.1560) for example, has a fine view and could have served both purposes, while the seventeenth century gazebo at Packwood House in Warwickshire was built for the view and nothing else, banqueting houses being by then out of fashion. A vogue for gazebos returned in the nineteenth and early twentieth centuries, when formal garden layouts (often best viewed from an elevated position) became fashionable again.

Extract from; "Life in the Country House" by David N Durant (published by John Murray), PB£15.99, see page twelve at the front of the book.

FARNBOROUGH HALL

Matthew Antrobus.

BANBURY, OXFORDSHIRE OX17 1DU

Owner: The National Trust   **Contact:** Mr G Holbech

Tel: 01295 690002

A classical mid-18th century stone house, home of the Holbech family for 300 years; notable plasterwork, the entrance hall, staircase and 2 principal rooms are shown; the grounds contain charming 18th century temples, a 2/3 mile terrace walk and an obelisk.

Location: OS151, Ref. SP430 490. 6m N of Banbury, 1/2 m W of A423.

Opening Times: House, grounds and terrace walk: Apr - Sept: Wed & Sat also 3 & 4 May, 2 - 6pm. Terrace walk only, Thur & Fri , 2 - 6pm. Last admission to house 5.30pm.

Admission: House, grounds & terrace walk: Adult £2.90. Garden & terrace walk: £1.50. Terrace walk only (Thur & Fri) £1.

♿ House & grounds, but steep terrace walk.   🐕 In grounds, on leads.

THE HILLER GARDEN   **Tel:** 01789 490991 Fax: 01789 490439

Dunnington Heath Farm, Alcester, Warwickshire B49 5PD

Owner: Mr & Mrs R Beach   **Contact.** Mr David Carvill

2 acre garden of unusual herbaceous plants and over 200 rose varieties.

Location: OS Ref. SP066 539. 1 1/2 m S of Ragley Hall on B4088 (formerly A435).

Opening Times: All year: daily 10am - 5pm.

Admission: Free.

ⓘ Shop. Plant centre.   ☕ Licensed tearoom.   Ⓟ Ample.   🐕 In grounds, on leads.

SPECIAL EVENTS 1998

See the front section for full list.

The Midlands England

HONINGTON HALL

SHIPSTON-ON-STOUR, WARWICKSHIRE CV36 5AA

Owner: Benjamin Wiggin Esq   *Contact:* Benjamin Wiggin Esq

Tel: 01608 661434 **Fax:** 01608 663717

This fine Caroline manor house was built in the early 1680s for Henry Parker in mellow brickwork, stone quoins and window dressings. Modified in 1751 when an octagonal saloon was inserted. The interior was also lavishly restored around this time and contains exceptional mid-Georgian plasterwork. Set in 15 acres of grounds.

Location: OS Ref. SP261 427. 10m S of Stratford-upon-Avon. 1¹/₂m N of Shipston-on-Stour. Take A3400 towards Stratford, then signed right to Honington.

Opening Times: Jun - Aug: Wed only. BH Mon, 2.30 - 5pm. Groups at other times by appointment.

Admission: Adult £2.75, Child £1.

Not suitable.   Compulsory.   No dogs.

KENILWORTH CASTLE

KENILWORTH, WARWICKSHIRE CV8 1NE

Owner: English Heritage   *Contact:* The Custodian

Tel: 01926 852078

Kenilworth is the largest castle ruin in England, the former stronghold of great Lords and Kings. Its massive walls of warm red stone tower over the peaceful Warwickshire landscape. The Earl of Leicester entertained Queen Elizabeth I with 'Princely Pleasures' during her 19-day visit. He built a new wing for the Queen to lodge in and organised all manner of lavish and costly festivities. The Great Hall, where Gloriana dined with her courtiers, still stands and John of Gaunt's Hall is second only in width and grandeur to Westminster Hall. Climb to the top of the tower beside the hall and you will be rewarded by fine views over the rolling wooded countryside.

Location: OS140 Ref. SP278 723. In Kenilworth, off A452, W end of town.

Opening Times: 1 Apr - 1 Nov: daily, 10am - 6pm or dusk if earlier. 2 Nov - 31 Mar: daily 10am - 4pm. Closed 24 - 26 Dec.

Admission: Adult £3.10, Child £1.60, OAP/Student £2.30. 15% discount for groups of 11+.

Suitable. WCs.   Available.

LORD LEYCESTER HOSPITAL   **Tel:** 01926 491422

High Street, Warwick, Warwickshire CV34 4BH

Owner: The Governors of Lord Leycester Hospital   **Contact:** Capt D I Rhodes

Location: OS Ref. SP280 648. 1m N of M40/J15 on A429. SW side of town centre.

Opening Times: Tue - Sun: 10am - 5pm (Oct - Mar: 10am - 4pm). Closed Good Fri and Christmas Day.

Admission: Adult £2.75, Child £1.50, Conc. £2. Groups of 20+, 5% discount.

PACKWOOD HOUSE

LAPWORTH, SOLIHULL B94 6AT

Owner: The National Trust   *Contact:* The Administrator

Tel: 01564 782024

Originally a 16th century house, Packwood has been much altered over the years and today is the vision of Graham Baron Ash who recreated a Jacobean house in the 1920s and '30s. A fine collection of 16th century textiles and furniture. Important gardens with renowned herbaceous border and famous yew garden based on the Sermon on the Mount.

Location: OS139, Ref. 174 722. 2m E of Hockley Heath (on A3400), 11m SE of Central Birmingham.

Opening Times: 25 Mar - end Sept: Wed - Sun & BH Mon (closed Good Fri), House, 2 - 6pm; Garden, 1.30 - 6pm. Oct - 1 Nov: Wed - Sun, 12.30 - 4.30pm. Car park open 12pm.

Admission: Adult £4.20, Child £2.10, Family £10.30, Garden only: £2.10, Car Park £2 refunded on entry to house. Timed tickets may be used at busy times.

House & parts of grounds suitable. WC.   No dogs.

RAGLEY HALL   See page 229 for full page entry.

THE SHAKESPEARE HOUSES   See page 230 for full page entry.

UPTON HOUSE   See page 231 for full page entry.

WARWICK CASTLE   See page 232 for full page entry.

The Midlands
England

HAGLEY HALL
Stourbridge

Hagley Hall is set in a 350-acre landscaped park yet is only 25 minutes from Birmingham city centre, the NEC and ICC and close to the motorway network of M5, M6, M40 and M42.

The house is available throughout the year on an exclusive basis for conferences, product launches, presentations, lunches, dinners, country sporting days, team building activities, themed evenings, murder mysteries, concerts, filming and wedding receptions.

Hagley's high standards of catering are now available at other venues as well as at Hagley Hall.

The elegant Palladian house, completed in 1760, contains some of the finest examples of Italian plasterwork. Hagley's rich rococo decoration is a remarkable tribute to the artistic achievement of great 18th century amateurs and is the much loved home of the 11th Viscount Cobham.

CONTACT

Mrs Lesley Haynes
Hagley Hall
Stourbridge
West Midlands
DY9 9LG

Tel: (01562) 882408

Fax: (01562) 882632

LOCATION

OS Ref. SO920 807

Easily accessible from all areas of the country. $^1/_4$ m S of A456 at Hagley.

Close to the M42, M40, M6 and only 5m from M5/J3/J4.

Birmingham City Centre 12m.

Rail: Railway Station and the NEC 25 mins.

Air: Birmingham International Airport 25 mins.

CONFERENCE/FUNCTION

ROOM	SIZE	MAX CAPACITY
Gallery	85' x 17'	140
Crimson Rm	23' x 31'	60
State Dining Room	34' x 27'	80
Westcote	31' x 20'	60

OPENING TIMES

House

2 - 24 January
1 - 13 February
16 - 1 March
9 - 14 April
24 - 26 May
30 August - 1 September

2 - 5pm.

ADMISSION

House

Adult £3.50
Child (under 16 yrs).....£1.50
OAP.......................£2.50

i Available on an exclusive basis for conferences, presentations, lunches, dinners, product launches, themed evenings, murder mysteries, concerts, wedding receptions. Extensive parkland for country sporting days, team building activities, off road driving and filming.

✗ As well as in-house catering, Hagley also offers a unique catering service at the venue of your choice.

♿ Visitors may alight at the entrance. No WC.

☕ Teas available during opening times.

🚶 Please book parties in advance, guided tour time of house 1 hr. Colour guide book.

P Unlimited for coaches and cars.

👫 By arrangement.

⚭ Civil Wedding Licence.

The Midlands
England

ASTON HALL

TRINITY ROAD, BIRMINGHAM, WEST MIDLANDS B6 6JD

Owner: *Birmingham City Council*   **Contact:** *Curator/Manager*

Tel: 0121 327 0062   **Fax:** 0121 327 7162

A large Jacobean mansion built 1618 - 1635 from plans by John Thorpe. The hall is brick-built with a fairytale skyline of gables and turrets. The interior has period rooms from the 17th, 18th and 19th centuries and a splendid long gallery measuring 136ft. A large kitchen and servants' rooms are also on display.

Location: OS139, Ref. SP080 899. 3m NE of Birmingham, 1/4 m from A38(M).

Opening times: 4 Apr - 1 Nov: daily 2 - 5pm. Parkland open all year round.

Admission: Free.

  Ground floor & grounds suitable.   Tearoom.   Guide dogs only.

THE BIRMINGHAM BOTANICAL GARDENS AND GLASSHOUSES

WESTBOURNE ROAD, EDGBASTON, BIRMINGHAM B15 3TR

Owner: *Birmingham Botanical & Horticultural Society*   **Contact:** *Mrs W Price*

Tel: 0121 454 1860

Tropical, Mediterranean and Desert Glasshouses contain a wide range of exotic and economic flora. 15 acres of beautiful gardens with the finest collection of plants in the Midlands. Home of the National Bonsai Collection. Children's adventure playground, aviaries and gallery.

Location: OS Ref. SP048 855. 2m W of city centre. Follow signs to Edgbaston then brown tourist signs.

Opening times: Daily: 9am - Dusk (7pm latest except pre-booked groups). Sun opening time 10am.

Admission: Adult £4 (£4.30 on Sun & BHs), Child under 5 free, Conc. £2.20. Reduced rates for groups of 11+.

  Shop. Plants for sale.   Suitable. WC.   Licensed restaurant.   Ample.   Guide dogs only.   Civil Wedding Licence.

SPECIAL EVENTS

APR 26: Orchids Show   **MAY 10:** Plant Market   **JUN 14:** Bonsai Show.
OCT 25: Christmas Markets.   **NOV 29:** Craft Fair.

BLAKESLEY HALL

BLAKESLEY ROAD, YARDLEY, BIRMINGHAM B13 8RL

Owner: *Birmingham City Council*   **Contact:** *Curator/Manager*

Tel: 0121 783 2193

An Elizabethan yeoman farmhouse dating from 1590, located on the edge of Birmingham. The interior has period rooms, displays on 17th century life and timber-framed buildings, a fine long gallery and great parlour. Important surviving 16th century wall-paintings are also on display in the painted chamber.

Location: OS139, Ref. SP130 862. 4m E of Birmingham city centre off A4040 from A45.

Opening times: 4 Apr - 1 Nov: daily 2 - 5pm.

Admission: Free.

  Ground floor & grounds suitable.   Limited.   No dogs.

CASTLE BROMWICH HALL GARDENS   **Tel:** 0121 749 4100

Chester Road, Castle Bromwich, Birmingham B36 9BT

Owner: Castle Bromwich Hall Gardens Trust   **Contact:** The Administrator

A unique example of 17th and 18th century garden design. Major restoration of the Orangery and Music Room, at either end of the long Holly Walk, together with classic surrounding walls enhances the beauty of the garden.

Location: OS Ref. SP142 898. Chester Road, Castle Bromwich.

Opening Times: All year: Mon - Thur, 1.30 - 4.30pm. Sat/Sun/BHs 2 - 6pm.

Admission: Adult £2, Child 50p, Conc. £1.50.

  Shop. Plant sales.   Suitable.   Tearoom.   Ample.   In grounds, on leads.

COVENTRY CATHEDRAL   **Tel:** 01203 227597   **Fax:** 01203 631448

Coventry, West Midlands

Owner: Provost & Canons of Coventry Cathedral   **Contact:** The Visits Secretary

The remains of the medieval Cathedral, bombed in 1940, stand beside the new Cathedral by Basil Spence, consecrated in 1962. Modern works of art include huge tapestry by Graham Sutherland, stained glass window by John Piper and bronze sculpture by Epstein. 'Reconciliation' statue by Josefina de Vasconcellos.

Location: OS Ref. SP336 790. City centre.

Opening Times: Easter - Oct: from 9.30am - 6pm. Nov - Easter: 9.30am - 5pm.

Admission: Donation £2 for Cathedral.

  Shop.   Suitable.   Tearoom.   No parking.   Guide dogs only.

HAGLEY HALL   See page 235 for full page entry.

HALESOWEN ABBEY   **Tel:** 01604 730320 (Regional Office)

Halesowen, Birmingham, West Midlands

Owner: English Heritage   **Contact:** The Custodian

Remains of an abbey founded by King John in the 13th century, now incorporated into a 19th century farm. Parts of the church and the monks' infirmary can still be made out.

Location: OS Ref. SO975 828. Off A456 Kidderminster road, 6m W of Birmingham city centre.

Opening Times: Jul - Aug: Weekends only 10am - 6pm.

Admission: Adult £1.30, Child 70p, Conc £1.

RYTON ORGANIC GARDENS

Tel: 01203 303517 **Fax:** 01203 639229

Ryton-on-Dunsmore, Coventry, West Midlands CV8 3LG

Owner: Henry Doubleday Research Association   **Contact:** S Furness

The Midlands' most talked about gardens. 10 acres of beautiful and informative gardens including herbs, shrubs, flowers, rare and unusual vegetables, all organically grown.

Location: OS Ref. SP400 745. 5m SE of Coventry off A45 on the road to Wolston.

Opening Times: Daily except during Christmas week: 10am - 5pm.

Admission: Adult £2.50, Child (5 - 16) £1.25, OAP £2.

- i Shop. Conference centre. Corporate hospitality.
- ♿ Grounds suitable. WC.
- ☕ Award-winning licensed restaurant.
- 🚶 By arrangement.
- P Ample.
- 👫 Educational programme.
- 🐕 Guide dogs only (shade & water available).

SELLY MANOR

Tel: 0121 472 0199

Maple Road, Bournville, West Midlands B30 1UB

Owner: Bournville Village Trust   **Contact:** Gillian Ellis

Two half timber buildings rescued and reassembled by George Cadbury. Now a local museum.

Location: OS Ref. SP045 814. N side of Sycamore Road, just E of Linden Road (A4040). 4m SSW of City Centre.

Opening Times: Tue - Fri & BH, 10am - 5pm. Sat & Sun 2 - 5pm. Closed Mons.

Admission: Adult £1.50, Child 50p.

- i Shop.
- ♿ Partially suitable. WC.
- 🚶 By arrangement.
- P Limited for cars.
- 👫 Educational programme.
- 🐕 Guide dogs only.

SOHO HOUSE

Tel: 0121 554 9122 **Fax:** 0121 554 5929

Soho Avenue, Handsworth, Birmingham B18 5LB

Owner: Birmingham City Council   **Contact:** Curator/Manager

The elegant home of the industrial pioneer Matthew Boulton from 1766 to 1809, Soho House has been carefully restored. Special features include an early 19th century hot air heating system.

Location: OS Ref. SP054 893. S side of Soho Avenue, just SW of Soho Hill/Soho Road (A41). 2m NW of city centre.

Opening Times: Tue - Sat, 10am - 5pm. Sun 12 - 5pm. Closed Mons except BHs.

Admission: Adult £2, Conc. £1.50. 10% discount for pre-booked groups.

- i Shop. Meeting room.
- ♿ Suitable. WCs.
- ☕ Tearoom.
- 🚶 By arrangement.
- P Limited for cars.
- 👫 Teachers' pack available.
- 🐕 Guide dogs only.

WIGHTWICK MANOR

National Trust Phtographic Library.

WIGHTWICK BANK, WOLVERHAMPTON, WEST MIDLANDS WV6 8EE

Owner: *The National Trust*   **Contact:** *The Property Manager*

Tel: 01902 761108 **Fax:** 01902 764663

Begun in 1887, the house is a notable example of the influence of William Morris, with many original Morris wallpapers and fabrics. Also of interest are pre-Raphaelite pictures, Kempe glass and de Morgan ware. The 17-acre Victorian/Edwardian garden designed by Thomas Mawson has formal beds, pergola, yew hedges, topiary and terraces, woodland and two pools.

Location: OS Ref. SO869 985. 3m W of Wolverhampton, up Wightwick Bank (A454), beside the Mermaid Inn.

Opening Times: 1 Mar - 31 Dec: Thur & Sat, 2.30 - 5.30pm (last entry 5pm). Admission by timed ticket. Guided groups through ground floor, freeflow upstairs. Minimum tour time approx. 1 hr 30 mins. Also open BH Sat, Sun and Mon, 2.30 - 5.30pm (last entry 5pm) - ground floor only, no guided tours. pre-booked groups Wed and Thur. Garden: Wed & Thur, 11am - 6pm; Sat, BH Sun & Mon, 1 - 6pm.

Admission: Adult £5.40, Child £2.60. Garden only: £2.40.

- i Shop.
- ♿ Ground floor & grounds suitable.
- ☕ Tearoom.
- 👫 In grounds, on leads.

SPECIAL EVENTS 1998

See the front section for full list.

Historic England

Shutters:

Before glass became readily available (oiled cloth or thin sheets of horn were other and earlier alternatives), windows were covered by interior shutters, which served to reduce draughts slightly. A set of shutters in the medieval hall at Stokesay Castle, Shropshire gives an impression of their effectiveness. Shutters were not generally a feature of Tudor houses, which is surprising in view of the amount of draught filtering through in spite of the small diamond-shaped glass quarries. By the latter half of the seventeenth century they were fitted to many new houses; when closed with a cross-bar they provided a certain security, and also insulation – an early form of double glazing. Cottages have traditionally had shutters fixed to the outsides of their windows, for these very reasons. Window curtains were not at all commonplace until well into the eighteenth century, so shutters were highly visible decorative features. The festoon curtains fashionable in the 1720s were often left drawn up to reveal richly decorated shutter-panels, clearly intended to be seen, but by the 1770s paired curtains which concealed the shutters had come into vogue, so undecorated shutters in plain panelling were fitted. The popular unrest and rioting of the first three decades of the nineteenth century brought shutters back into use once more as a security measure, but by the end of the nineteenth century, when the majority of the population of the British Isles lived in small houses with better glazing, and large-scale rioting belonged to the past, shutters went out of fashion again.

Extract from; "Life in the Country House" by David N Durant (published by John Murray), PB£15.99, see page twelve at the front of the book.

The Midlands England

AVONCROFT MUSEUM

Tel: 01527 831886 **Fax:** 01527 876934

Stoke Heath, Bromsgrove, Worcestershire B60 4JR

Owner: Council of Management   **Contact:** Dr Simon Penn

Historic buildings rescued and restored in 15 acres of Worcestershire countryside. Exhibits include the magnificent 14th century roof of the Guesten Hall of Worcester Cathedral, 1946 prefab. Timber-framed buildings, chainshop, nailshop, toll house and a working windmill. National Telephone Kiosk Collection with examples from 1922 to today. Picnic site.

Location: OS Ref. SO954 684. 2m S of Bromsgrove just SE of A38 by-pass.

Opening Times: Mar - Nov: Most days. Please ring for details.

Admission: Adult £4.25, Child £2.15, OAP £3.50, Family (2+3) £12. Booked groups at reduced rates.

i Shop. Conference facilities.	**X** Wedding receptions.	☕ Tearoom.
♿ Ground floor & grounds suitable. WC.	🚶 By arrangement.	**P** Ample.
Educational programme.	In grounds, on leads.	Civil Wedding Licence.

BROADWAY TOWER COUNTRY PARK

BROADWAY, WORCESTERSHIRE WR12 7LB

Owner: Broadway Tower Country Park Ltd   *Contact: Annette Gorton*

Tel: 01386 852390 **Fax:** 01386 858829

Broadway Tower is probably the most unique historic building on top of the Cotswold ridge, having been built by the 6th Earl of Coventry in the late 1790s. Its architecture, the fascinating views as well as its exhibitions on famous owners and occupants (including William Morris) make the Tower a "must" for all visitors to the Cotswolds. The Tower is surrounded by 35 acres of parkland with animal enclosures, picnic/BBQ facilities and adventure playground. A complete family day out.

Location: OS Ref. SP115 362. 1/2 m SW of the A44 Evesham to Oxford Rd. 1 1/2 m E of Broadway.

Open: 28 Mar – 31 Oct: daily, 10am - 6pm or dusk if earlier. Nov - Mar: Sat & Sun (weather permitting) 11am - 3pm.

Admission: Adult £3, Child £2.20, OAP/ Student £2.50, Family (2+4) £9. Groups: Adult £2.25, Child £1.65, OAP/Student £1.90. Passport Ticket: (free adm. for 1 yr) Adult £9, OAP/Child/Student £7, Family £27.

i Shop.	**X** Wedding receptions.	♿ WC.
P Ample.	☕ Café, licensed restaurant.	Teachers' pack.
In grounds, on leads.		

THE COMMANDERY

Tel: 01905 355071 **Fax:** 01905 764586

Sidbury, Worcester WR1 2HU

Owner: Worcester City Council   **Contact:** Amanda Lunt

A complex of timber-framed buildings, the Commandery was originally founded as a monastic institution in 1085 serving as the headquarters of Charles II at the Battle of Worcester. It now contains a museum devoted to England's Civil War plus historic Tudor and Stuart interiors and a range of temporary exhibitions.

Location: OS Ref. SO853 544. Worcester city centre. 350 yds SE of cathedral.

Opening Times: All year: Mon - Sat, 10am - 5pm; Sun, 1.30 - 5.30pm. Closed Christmas Day, Boxing Day and New Year's Day.

Admission: Adult £3.40, Child/Conc. £2.30. Groups: Adult £2.40, Child/Conc. £1.90. Schools' package available. Also room hire. Prices only valid until Apr 1998.

♿ Ground floor & grounds suitable.	☕ Tearoom.	Guide dogs only.

SPECIAL EVENTS

APR 10-13, 18/19, MAY 9, 23 - 25, JUN 13/14, AUG 9-31, SEPT 4 - 6, 12/13 Commandery Time Travellers.

DEC 4 - 18: Christmas Festival.
For full details of events see the Special Events section at the front of the book.

THE ELGAR BIRTHPLACE MUSEUM

Tel/Fax: 01905 333224

Crown Lane East, Upper Broadheath, Worcester WR2 6RH

Owner: Elgar's Birthplace Trust   **Contact:** The Curator

The cottage, where the composer Sir Edward Elgar was born in 1857, now houses a unique collection of priceless manuscripts and press cuttings.

Location: OS Ref. SO805 558. 3m W of Worcester 1m NW of A44.

Opening Times: 1 May - 30 Sept: 10.30am - 6pm. 1 Oct - 15 Jan: 1.30 - 4.30pm. Closed 16 Jan - 15 Feb. 16 Feb - 30 Apr: 1.30 - 4.30pm. Closed on Wed throughout the year.

Admission: Adult £3, Child 50p, OAPs £2, Conc. £1. Groups on application.

i Shop.	♿ Ground floor suitable.	**P** Ample.
Educational programme.	Guide dogs only.	

THE GREYFRIARS

Tel: 01905 23571

Worcester WR1 2LZ

Owner: The National Trust   **Contact:** The Custodian

Built in 1480, with early 17th and late 18th century additions, this timber-framed house was rescued from demolition at the time of the Second World War and has been restored and refurbished; interesting textiles and furnishings add character to the panelled rooms; an archway leads through to a delightful garden.

Location: OS150, Ref. SO852 546. Friar Street in centre of Worcester.

Opening Times: 13 Apr - end Oct: Wed, Thur & BH Mon, 2 - 5pm.

Admission: Adult £2.40, Child £1.20, Family £6.

SPECIAL EVENTS
DEC 3/4/5: Street Fayre.

HANBURY HALL

DROITWICH, WORCESTERSHIRE WR9 7EA

Owner: The National Trust   *Contact: The Property Manager*

Tel: 01527 821214 **Fax:** 01527 821251

Set in 400 acres of parkland and gardens, this delightful William and Mary house was home to the Vernon family for three centuries. The permanent home of the Watney collection of fine porcelain and Dutch flower paintings, Hanbury Hall also boasts magnificent staircase and ceiling paintings by Sir James Thornhill. Restored 18th century garden, orangery and ice house.

Location: OS150, Ref. SO943 637. 4 1/2 m E of Droitwich, 4m SE M5/J5.

Opening Times: 29 Mar - 28 Oct: Sun - Wed, 2 - 6pm. Last adm. 5.30pm or dusk if earlier. 30 Oct - Mar: available for private use only.

Admission: House & Garden: Adult £4.30, Child £2.15, Family £10.50. Garden only: Adult £2.50, Child £1. Special rates for groups by prior arrangement.

X Available.	♿ Ground floor & grounds suitable. WC.	☕ Tearoom.
🚶 For pre-booked groups.	Guide dogs.	Civil Wedding Licence.

HARTLEBURY CASTLE

Tel: 01299 250410 **Museum:** 01299 250416

Hartlebury, Kidderminster DT11 7XX

Owner: The Church Commissioners   **Contact:** Bishop of Worcester

Home of the Bishops of Worcester for over 1,000 years. The state rooms include a medieval great hall, Hurd library and saloon. Fine plasterwork and a collection of episcopal portraits.

Location: OS Ref. SO839 710. N side of B4193, 2m E of Stourport, 4m S of Kidderminster.

Opening Times: 23 Feb - 30 Nov. County Museum: Mon - Thur, 10am - 5pm. Fri & Sun, 2 - 5pm, BHs, 11am - 5pm. Staterooms: Tues - Thurs, 10am - 5pm.

Admission: Combined ticket (museum & staterooms): Adult £2.20, Child/OAP £1.10. Family (2+3) £6.

HARVINGTON HALL
Tel: 01562 777846

Harvington, Kidderminster, Worcestershire DY10 4LR

Owner: Roman Catholic Archdiocese of Birmingham   **Contact:** The Administrator

Moated Medieval and Elizabethan manor, with secret hiding places and rare wall paintings.

Location: OS Ref. SO839 710. On minor road, 1/2 m NE of A450/A448 crossroads at Mustow Green. 3m SE of Kidderminster.

Opening Times: 2 Mar - 31 Oct: Sun, Tue, Wed & Thur, 11.30am - 5.30pm. Open at other times by appointment.

Admission: Adult £3.50, Child £2, OAP £2.50. Gardens: £1

ℹ️ Shop.   ✗ Wedding receptions.   ☕ Licensed restaurant.

HAWFORD DOVECOTE
Tel: 01684 850051

Hawford, Worcestershire

Owner: The National Trust   **Contact:** Regional Office

A 16th century half-timbered dovecote.

Location: OS Ref. SO846 607. 3m N of Worcester, 1/2 m E of A449.

Opening Times: Apr - 1 Nov: daily 9am - 6pm or sunset if earlier. Closed Good Fri, other times by prior appointment.

Admission: 60p.

LEIGH COURT BARN
Tel: 01604 730320 - Regional Office

Worcester

Owner: English Heritage   **Contact:** The Midlands Regional Office

Magnificent 14th century timber-framed barn built for the monks of Pershore Abbey. It is the largest of its kind in Britain.

Location: OS Ref. SO784 534. 5m W of Worcester on unclassified road off A4103.

Opening Times: 1 Apr - 30 Sept: Thur - Sun, 10am - 6pm.

Admission: Telephone for details.

LITTLE MALVERN COURT
Tel: 01684 892988   **Fax:** 01684 893057

Nr. Malvern, Worcestershire WR14 4JN

Owner: Trustees of the late T M Berington   **Contact:** Mrs T M Berington

Prior's Hall, associated rooms and cells, c1480, of former Benedictine Monastery. Formerly attached to, and forming part of the Little Malvern Priory Church which may also be visited. It has an oak-framed roof, 5-bay double-collared roof, with two tiers of cusped windbraces. Library. Collections of religious vestments, embroideries and paintings. Gardens: 10 acres of former monastic grounds with spring bulbs, blossom, old fashioned roses and shrubs.

Location: OS130, Ref. SO769 403. 3m S of Great Malvern on Upton-on-Severn Rd (A4104).

Opening Times: 15 Apr - 16 Jul: Wed & Thur, 2.15 - 4.30pm.

Admission: House & Garden: Adult £4, Child £2, Garden only: Adult £3, Child £1.

♿ Not suitable.   🐕 No dogs.

MADRESFIELD COURT
Tel: 01684 573614   **Fax:** 01684 569197

Madresfield, Malvern WR13 5AH

Owner: The Trustees of Madresfield Estate   **Contact:** Mr Peter Hughes

Elizabethan and Victorian house with medieval origins. Fine contents. Extensive gardens and arboretum.

Location: OS Ref. SO809 474. 6m SW of Worcester. 1 1/2 m SE of A449. 2m NE of Malvern.

Opening Times: Limited, by appointment. Apr - Jul.

Admission: £6.

♿ Not suitable.   🚶 Available.   🐕 No dogs.

SPETCHLEY PARK GARDEN

SPETCHLEY, NR. WORCESTER WR5 1RS

Owner: Spetchley Garden Charitable Trust   *Contact:* Mr R J Berkeley

Tel: 01905 345213 or 01905 345224

30 acre private garden containing large collection of trees, shrubs and plants, many rare or unusual. A new garden part formal, part sunk in the old walled kitchen garden is now completed. Close by is the Deer Park with red and fallow deer.

Location: OS Ref. SO895 540. 2m E of Worcester on A422. Leave M5/J6 or J7.

Opening Times: 1 Apr - 30 Sept: Tue - Fri and BH Mon, 11am - 5pm. Sun 2 - 5pm.

Admission: Adult £2.90, Child £1.40. Groups: Adult £2.70, Child £1.30.

♿ Grounds suitable.   ☕ Tearoom.   🅿 Ample.   🐕 No dogs.

WITLEY COURT

GREAT WITLEY, WORCESTER WR6 6JT

Owner: English Heritage   *Contact:* The Custodian

Tel: 01299 896636

The spectacular ruins of a once great house. An earlier Jacobean manor house, converted in the 19th century into an Italianate mansion, with porticos by John Nash. The adjoining church, by James Gibbs, has a remarkable 18th century baroque interior. The gardens, William Nesfield's 'Monster Work' were equally elaborate and contained immense fountains, which survive today. The largest, the Poseidon Fountain, is being restored to working order.

Location: OS150, Ref. SO769 649. 10m NW of Worcester on A443.

Opening Times: 1 Apr - 1 Nov: daily, 10am - 6pm or dusk if earlier. 2 Nov - 31 Mar: Wed - Sun, 10am - 4pm. Closed 24 - 26 Dec.

Admission: Adult £3.10, Child £1.60, Conc. £2.30. 15% discount for groups of 11+.

♿ In grounds. WC.   ☕ Restaurant.

Counties in this region:

Northern Counties
England

Crag Lough, Northumberland. *Northumbria Tourist Board.*

Northern Counties
England

ADLINGTON HALL
Macclesfield

ADLINGTON HALL, the home of the Leghs of Adlington from 1315 to the present day, was built on the site of a Hunting Lodge which stood in the Forest of Macclesfield in 1040. Two oaks, part of the original building, remain with their roots in the ground and support the east end of the Great Hall, which was built between 1480 and 1505.

The Hall is a Manor House, quadrangular in shape, and was once surrounded by a moat. Two sides of the Courtyard and the east wing were built in the typical 'Black and White' Cheshire style in 1581. The south front and west wing (containing the Drawing Room and Dining Room) were added between 1749 and 1757 and are built of red brick with a handsome stone portico with four Ionic columns on octagonal pedestals. Between the trees in the Great Hall stands an organ built by 'Father' Bernard Smith (c1670-80). Handel subsequently played on this instrument, and now fully restored, it is the largest 17th century organ in the country.

GARDENS
The Wilderness was landscaped in the style of 'Capability' Brown in the mid 18th century and incorporates both earlier 17th century plantings and sympathetic Victorian additions. The formal French style has given way to an apparently wild, but very carefully cultivated informality. Dotted about the circuitous paths are a number of decorative buildings. Old fashioned rose garden and yew maze recently planted.

CONTACT

The Guide
Adlington Hall
Macclesfield
Cheshire
SK10 4LF

Tel: (01625) 829206
Corporate
(01625) 820875
Hall Tours

Fax: (01625) 828756

LOCATION

OS Ref. SJ905 804

5m N of Macclesfield, A523, 13m S of Manchester. London 178m.

Rail: Macclesfield and Wilmslow stations 5m.

Air: Manchester Airport 8m.

CONFERENCE/FUNCTION		
ROOM	SIZE	MAX CAPACITY
Great Hall	37' x 26'	125
Dining Rm	35' x 23'	50
Hunting Lodge	60' x 30'	150

 Suitable for corporate events, product launches, business meetings, conferences, concerts, fashion shows, garden parties, rallies, clay-pigeon shooting and filming.

The Great Hall and Dining Room available when Hall is closed to the public. Catering can be arranged.

Visitors may alight at entrance to Hall. WCs.

Tearoom.

Available.

For 100 cars and 4 coaches, 100 yds from Hall.

Schools welcome. Guide can be provided.

OPENING TIMES

Open throughout the year to groups by prior arrangement only.

ADMISSION

Hall & Gardens

Adult £4.00
Child £1.50
Groups (Min. 25 people)
Adult £3.50
Child £1.00

School groups.........£1.50
(per child)

ARLEY HALL & GARDENS
Northwich

ARLEY HALL, home of Viscount and Viscountess Ashbrook, was built c1840 by the owner's great-great-grandfather, Rowland Egerton - Warburton, to the design of the Nantwich architect, George Latham. An important example of the Victorian Jacobean style, it has fine plasterwork and wood panelling as well as interesting furniture, pictures and other contents. Adjoining Arley Hall is a large private Chapel designed by Anthony Salvin.

An impressive range of activities can be held both in the Hall and in the grounds, from corporate conferences of any size to cocktail parties and ambassadorial receptions. Arley Hall offers all its visitors an elegant setting combined with the professional approach to top class management. Catering to the highest standards.

GARDENS
Overlooking beautiful parkland, and providing great variety of style and design, the Gardens extending over 12 acres, rank among the finest in the country. Winner of the Christie's/HHA 'Garden of the Year' award in 1987. The features include the Double Herbaceous Border, one of the earliest to be established in England (1846), unique avenue of clipped Quercus Ilex, collection of shrub roses, fine yew hedges, Herb Garden, Walled Garden, Woodland Garden with exotic trees, shrubs, azaleas and a collection of over 200 varieties of rhododendrons.

CONTACT

Eric Ransome
Arley Hall & Gardens
Nr Northwich
Cheshire
CW9 6NA

Tel: (01565) 777353

Fax: (01565) 777465

LOCATION

OS Ref. SJ675 809

Car: Knutsford, 5m NW
Northwich, 5m N
M6/J19 & 20, 5m
M56 /J9 & 10, 5m

Rail: Knutsford, 5m
Northwich, 5m

Air: Manchester Airport 16m.

ℹ️ Shop and specialist plant nursery, check opening times. Photography in gardens only. Business meetings and conferences, corporate events, concerts, filming. 100 acres of parkland, grass, cricket pitch. Grand piano in Gallery.

🍴 Receptions and dinner parties. Catering can be arranged.

♿ Visitors may alight at entrance to Hall then park in allocated areas. WCs and access to restaurant, shop and Chapel.

☕ Licensed restaurant, café & tearoom for up to 100.

🚶 25 people per guide around Hall. Garden tours arranged for £40. Tour times: Hall 1hr, Gardens 1½ hrs.

🅿️ Ample. Free entry and refreshments for courier and coach drivers. Function parking 50 yds from Hall.

👪 Hall & Garden tours: Mon & Fri only. Environmental and Heritage Trails. Picnic area. Wet weather cover.

🐕 Dogs on leads welcome.

🔔 Civil Wedding Licence.

OPENING TIMES

SUMMER
10 April - 27 September

Grounds, Gardens & Chapel
Tue - Sun & BH Mon.
11am - 5pm

Hall open Tuesdays and Sundays. During April & September Sundays only.

WINTER
Open by arrangement only for groups and on special advertised occasions.

SPECIAL EVENTS

- **MAR 13/14/15**
  Arley Spring Antiques Fair

- **APR 5**
  Plant Hunters' Fair

- **APR 12/13**
  Crafts Fair

- **APR 24/25/26**
  CAMPEX '98 Show

- **JUN 12/13/14**
  Summer Antiques Fair

- **JUN 27/28**
  The Arley Garden Festival

- **JUL 4**
  Firework & Orchestral Concert in Park

- **OCT 9/10/11**
  Autumn Antiques Fair

- **OCT 31 - NOV 1**
  Christmas Craft Fair

- **DEC 5 & 12**
  The Arley Christmas Evenings

- **DEC 6 & 13**
  Christmas Days at Arley

For a full listing see the Special Events section.

ADMISSION

Gardens, Grounds & Chapel
Adult £3.60
Child (5 -16).............£1.80
Child (under 5).........FREE*
OAP.........................£3.00
Groups (min. 15 people)
Adult £3.20
Child £1.60
OAP.........................£2.80

HALL (extra)
Adult £2.50
Child (5-16).............£1.25
Child (under 5)......FREE*
OAP.........................£2.20
Groups (min. 15 people)
Adult £2.30
Child £1.20
OAP.........................£2.10

*When part of a family group only

Family (2+2)
Gardens £9.00
Season ....£16.00 ea.

Friends of Arley Assoc.
contact 01606 891754
Membership secretary.

CONFERENCE/FUNCTION

ROOM	SIZE	MAX CAPACITY
Drawing Room	38' x 22'	110
Gallery	41' x 25'	100
Front Hall	35' x 22'	22
Tudor Barn	56' x 22'	200

CAPESTHORNE HALL
Macclesfield

CAPESTHORNE HALL has been the home of the Bromley-Davenport family and their ancestors since Domesday times when the appointment of Chief Forester carrying the responsibility of law and order in the Forests of Macclesfield and Leek was granted to them. Since then many generations have served in Parliament, the Bromley side providing both a Chancellor and Speaker. The present owner is H.M. Lord Lieutenant for Cheshire.

The existing Hall dating from 1719 was originally designed by the Smiths of Warwick, then altered by both Blore in 1837 and Salvin in 1861, the latter rebuilding the centre section following a disastrous fire.

The Hall contains a great variety of paintings, sculptures, furniture and tapestry including a collection of Colonial furnishings brought over by the late Lady Bromley-Davenport from her former American home in Philadelphia.

The park and gardens extend to some 60 acres and feature a beautiful Georgian Chapel dating from 1720 where services are still held, a chain of man-made lakes, the central one being spanned by a multi-arch brick bridge, a pair of 18th century Milanese gates, and a nature trail and woodland walk where an old Ice House and Water Cascade can be seen.

❖

CONTACT

Jacquie Caldwell
Capesthorne Hall
Siddington
Macclesfield
Cheshire
SK11 9JY

Tel: (01625) 861221

Fax: (01625) 861619

LOCATION

OS Ref. SJ840 727

5m W of Macclesfield.

30 mins S of Manchester on A34.

Near M6, M63 and M62.

Airport: Manchester International 20 mins.

Helicopter: (0151) 427 1609.

Rail: Macclesfield 5m (2 hrs from London).

Taxi: (01625) 533464.

Air Taxi: (0161) 499 1447

CONFERENCE/FUNCTION

ROOM	SIZE	MAX CAPACITY
Theatre	120' x 25'	155
Garden Restaurant	100' x 20'	100
Saloon	40' x 25'	100
Queen Anne Rm	38' x 26'	100

SPECIAL EVENTS

- **APR 4/5:** Rainbow Craft Fair
- **MAY 17:** Cheshire Kit Car show
- **JUL 26:** Classic Car show
- **AUG 9:** Fireworks and laser symphony concert by Performing Arts Management
- **SEPT 19/20:** Rainbow Craft Fair

i No photography in Hall. Product launches, filming, still photography, fishing, caravanning, equestrian events (own cross-country course), clay pigeon shooting, garden parties, rallies, barbecues, survival games, murder mystery evenings, firework displays, son et lumière etc. Theatre used as Lecture Room, seats up to 150.

X Catering can be provided for groups (full menus on request). Function rooms available for wedding receptions, corporate hospitality, meetings and other special events. 'The Butler's Pantry' serves tea, coffee and ices.

Compacted paths, ramps and WCs.

For up to 50. Also available in Italian. The owner can meet tours visiting house. Tour time 1 hr.

P 100 cars/20 coaches on hard-standing and unlimited in park, 50 yds from house. Rest room and free refreshment for coach drivers.

In park only.

OPENING TIMES

SUMMER
March - October
Bank Hols, Wed & Sun.

House, Gardens & Chapel
Open at 1.30pm
Last admission 3.30pm

Gardens & Chapel
12 - 6pm.

Groups welcome by appointment.

Caravan Park also open Easter - end September.

Corporate enquiries welcome all year.

ADMISSION

SUMMER

House & Garden
Adult £4.50
Child* £2.00
OAP.........................£4.00

Garden only
Adult £2.50
Child* £1.00
OAP.........................£2.00
Family £9.50

Groups**
Please telephone for details.

* Aged 5 - 16yrs.
**Min 25 people

The National Trust Photographic Library.

TATTON PARK
Knutsford

TATTON is one of the most complete historic estates in Britain. Five separate features, special events and private functions attract over 700,000 visits each year.

Man's occupation of Tatton began 10,000 years ago. The Landscape History Trail guides walkers through time. The Palladian Mansion by Wyatt is the jewel in Tatton's crown. The Egerton family collection of fine paintings, porcelain and furniture is found in the splendid setting of the magnificent staterooms. In stark contrast, the Victorian kitchens and cellars give a fascinating insight into life 'downstairs'. The Home Farm is still working with traditional breeds of animal and estate workshops.

Extending to 50 acres, the gardens are amongst the most important in England. Attractions include the famous Japanese garden, newly restored orangery, New Zealand tree fernery, Italian terraced garden and maze.

Across the Park at Old Hall, visitors are guided through the smoky shadows of the 15th century great hall, lit by flickering candles and through time to the home of a 1950s estate employee. The Old Hall was leased to his cousin by Thomas Egerton, Lord Chancellor of England during the reign of Queen Elizabeth I and James I.

800 red and fallow deer can be seen when walking or driving in the parkland and around the two meres. Tatton Park is maintained, managed and financed by Cheshire County Council on lease from the National Trust to whom the Mansion and Gardens were bequeathed in 1958 by the late Right Honourable Maurice, Baron Egerton of Tatton, 'for the benefit of the Nation'.

CONTACT

Conferences, exhibitions, social occasions
Karen Hay
Functions/Events Manager

Party Visits
Kevin Baxter
Tatton Park
Knutsford
Cheshire WA16 6QN

Tel: (01565) 654822
or (01565) 750260

Fax: (01565) 650179

LOCATION

OS Ref. SJ745 815

From M56/J7 follow signs.

From M6/J19, signed on A56 & A50.

Rail: Knutsford or Altrincham Station, then taxi.

CONFERENCE/FUNCTION

ROOM	SIZE	MAX CAPACITY
Tenants Hall	125' x 45'	330 - 400
Foyer	23' x 20'	50 - 100

Tenants Hall Event Wing – total of 8,000 sq.ft. available

Lord Egerton's Apartment	20' x 16'	16 - 40
	24' x 18'	19 - 40
Stable Block	31' x 20'	80

i Shop and Housekeeper's Store offering estate produce. Home grown plants. Gifts. Conferences, trade exhibitions, presentations, product launches, concerts and fashion shows. Special family days. Spotlights, stages, dance floor, PA system. The Tenants Hall seats up to 400 for presentations.

X Available telephone for details. Dinners, dances, receptions, wedding and champagne receptions

♿ Upstairs in Mansion, Old Hall & areas of farm not accessible. Wheelchairs & electric vehicles available. WCs.

☕ Self-service restaurant and tuck shop for snacks.

🚶 Mansion tours: weekdays, except Jul/Aug. Tours of Old Hall. Tour time 1¹/₂hrs.

P Ample, 200-300 yds away. Meal vouchers for coach drivers.

👫 Award-winning educational programmes, please book. Environmental days, windsurfing & sailing instruction, orienteering, adventure playground.

🐕 In park only.

💒 Civil Wedding Licence.

OPENING TIMES

SUMMER
3 April - 1 November

Park: Daily 10.30am - 6pm
Gardens: Tue - Sun 10.30am - 5pm
Mansion: Tue - Sun 12 - 4pm. (1 - 26 Oct: Sat & Sun only.)
Old Hall: Guided tours, 3pm & 4pm.
Restaurant: Daily
Shops: Tue - Sun

WINTER
2 Nov - 31 Mar 1999

Park: Tue - Sun 11am - 4pm
Gardens: Tue - Sun 11am - 4pm
Opening times for Farm and Old Hall on request.

Restaurant, Garden Shop & Housekeeper's Store:
Tue - Sun

Gift Shop: W/ends only.

All attractions open w/ends in Oct. Mansion, Farm open w/ends in Dec. before Xmas.

ADMISSION

Any two attractions
	Single	Group*
Adult	£4.50	£3.20
Child**	£2.50	£2.00

Mansion or Garden
Adult	£2.80	£2.30
Child**	£1.80	£1.50
Family	£8.00	

Farm or Old Hall
Adult	£2.50	£2.00
Child**	£1.50	£1.20
Family	£8.00 (NT Free)	

Parking
Per car		£3.00
Coaches		Free

*Min. 12 ** Aged 4 - 15yrs.
OAP rate as Adult
Tours available outside normal opening times £6.

SPECIAL EVENTS

Over 60 public special events are held in the Park, from the Hallé Orchestra with Fireworks to large gatherings of vintage cars.

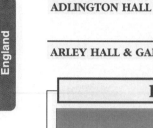

Northern Counties England

ADLINGTON HALL　　　　　　See page 242 for full page entry.

ARLEY HALL & GARDENS 　　See page 243 for full page entry.

BEESTON CASTLE

BEESTON, TARPORLEY, CHESHIRE CW6 9TX

Owner: English Heritage　　　*Contact:* The Custodian

Tel: 01829 260464

Standing majestically on sheer, rocky crags which fall sharply away from the castle walls, Beeston has possibly the best views of the surrounding countryside of any castle in England and the rock has a history stretching back over 2,500 years. New for 1998: extended shop and exciting new exhibition.

Location: OS117, Ref. SJ537 593. 11m SE of Chester on minor road off A49, or A41. 2m SW of Tarporley.

Opening Times: 1 Apr - 1 Nov: daily, 10am - 6pm (or dusk if earlier in Oct). 2 Nov - 31 Mar: daily, 10am - 4pm. Closed 24 - 26 Dec.

Admission: Adult £2.70, Child £1.40, Conc. £2. 15% discount for groups of 11+.

[i] Shop.　[&] Not suitable.　[🐕] In grounds on leads only.

BRAMALL HALL　　　　　　　**Tel:** 0161 485 3708

Bramhall Park, Bramhall, Stockport, Cheshire SK7 3NX

Owner: Stockport Metropolitan Borough Council　　**Contact:** Ruth Edwards

Tudor manor house set in 70 acres of parkland.

Location: OS Ref. SJ886 863. 4m S of Stockport, off A5102.

Opening Times: Good Fri - 30 Sept: Mon - Sat, 1 - 5pm. Sun & BH, 11am - 5pm. 1 Oct - 1 Jan: Tue - Sat, 1 - 4pm. Sun & BHs, 11am - 4pm. Closed 25 & 26 Dec. 2 Jan - 4 Apr: Sat & Sun, 12 - 4pm. Groups by arrangement including out of hours.

Admission: Adult £3.50, Child/OAP £2.

CAPESTHORNE HALL 　　　See page 244 for full page entry.

CHESTER CATHEDRAL　　**Tel:** 01244 324756　**Fax:** 01244 341110

12 Abbey Square, Chester, Cheshire CH1 2HU　　**Contact:** Mr N Fry

Founded in 1092 as a Benedictine monastery, it became an Anglican cathedral in 1541. All styles of architecture are represented as well as spectacular medieval woodwork.

Location: OS Ref. SJ406 665. Chester city centre.

Opening Times: 7.30am - 6.30pm, daily.

Admission: Donation.

CHESTER ROMAN AMPHITHEATRE ⊞　　**Tel:** 0191 2611585

Vicars Lane, Chester, Cheshire

Owner: English Heritage　　**Contact:** The North Regional Office

The largest Roman amphitheatre in Britain, partially excavated. Used for entertainment and military training by the 20th Legion, based at the fortress of Deva.

Location: OS Ref. SJ404 660. On Vicars Lane beyond Newgate, Chester.

Opening Times: Any reasonable time.

Admission: Free.

[&] Not suitable.　[P] No parking.　[🐕] On leads.

CHOLMONDELEY CASTLE GARDEN

MALPAS, CHESHIRE SY14 8AH

Owner: The Marchioness of Cholmondeley　　*Contact:* The Secretary

Tel/Fax: 01829 720383

Extensive pleasure gardens dominated by romantic Gothic Castle built in 1801 of local sandstone. Imaginatively laid out with fine trees, water gardens and extensively replanted since the 1960s with rhododendrons, azaleas, magnolias, cornus, acer and many other acid loving plants. As well as the beautiful water garden, there is a rose garden and many mixed borders. Lakeside picnic area, rare breeds of farm animals, including llamas. Ancient private chapel in park.

Location: OS Ref. SJ540 515. Off A41 Chester/Whitchurch Rd. & A49 Whitchurch / Tarporley Road. 7m N of Whitchurch.

Opening Times: 1 Apr, Good Fri (10 Apr) & every following Sun, Wed, Thur & BH Mon until 30 Sept. Good Fri, Sun & BH Mon, 11.30am - 5.30pm. Weds & Thurs, 12 - 5pm. Other days for coach groups 25+ by prior arrangement at reduced rates.

Admission: Adult £2.50, OAP £2, Child 75p.

[i] Shop. Plant centre.　[X] Available.　[&] Limited suitability. WCs.

[☕] Tearoom.　[🐎] In grounds on leads only.

DORFOLD HALL

ACTON, NR NANTWICH, CHESHIRE CW5 8LD

Owner: Richard Roundell　　*Contact:* Richard Roundell

Tel: 01270 625245　**Fax:** 01270 628723

Jacobean country house built in 1616 for Ralph Wilbraham. Family home of Mr & Mrs Richard Roundell. Beautiful plaster ceilings and oak panelling. Attractive woodland gardens and replanted herbaceous borders.

Location: OS Ref. SJ634 525. 1m W of Nantwich on the A534 Nantwich - Wrexham road.

Opening Times: Apr - Oct: Tue only and BH Mons, 2 - 5pm.

Admission: Adult £3, Child £2. Groups: min 10, max 35.

[🚶] Guided tours only.　[P] Limited. Narrow gates with low arch prevent coaches.

[🐕] In grounds, on leads.

DUNHAM MASSEY

Patrick Lane

ALTRINCHAM, CHESHIRE WA14 4SJ

Owner: The National Trust   *Contact:* The Property Manager

Tel: 0161 941 1025   **Fax:** 0161 929 7508

Originally an early Georgian house, Dunham Massey has sumptuous interiors, with collections of walnut furniture, paintings and magnificent Huguenot silver. The richly planted garden contains waterside plantings, late flowering azaleas, an orangery and Elizabethan mount. The surrounding deer park escaped the attentions of 18th century landscape gardeners and contains some notable specimen trees. No photography in house.

Location: OS Ref. SJ735 874. 3m SW of Altrincham off A56. M56/J7.

Opening Times: House: 4 Apr - 1 Nov: Sat - Wed, 12 - 5pm (11am - 5pm BH Sun & Mon), last admission 4.30pm. Garden: 4 Apr - 1 Nov: daily, 11am - 5.30pm, last admission 5pm. Mill machinery will normally operate Wed & Sun afternoon. Park open daily throughout the year.

Admission: House & Garden: Adult £5, Child £2.50, Family £12.50 (2 adults + children). House or Garden only: Adult £3, Child £1.50. Car entry: £2.80 per car. Coach / minibus entry: £5 (free to booked parties). Motorcycle: £1. Booked Groups: £4 for 15 or more paying adults, not available Sun & BHs.

ⓘ Shop. Plant centre.   ♿ Partially suitable. WC. Batricars available.

🍴 Licensed restaurant   🚶 By arrangement.   Ⓟ Ample.

👪 Teachers' pack, educational programme.   🐕 In grounds, on leads.

GAWSWORTH HALL

MACCLESFIELD, CHESHIRE SK11 9RN

Owner: Mr and Mrs T Richards   *Contact:* Mr T Richards

Tel: 01260 223456   **Fax:** 01260 223469

Fully lived-in Tudor half-timbered manor house with Tilting Ground. Former home of Mary Fitton, Maid of Honour at the Court of Queen Elizabeth I, and the supposed 'Dark Lady' of Shakespeare's sonnets. Pictures, sculpture and furniture. Open air theatre with covered grandstand - June, July and August, please telephone for details. Situated halfway between Macclesfield and Congleton in an idyllic setting close to the lovely medieval church.

Location: OS Ref. SJ892 697. 3m S of Macclesfield on the A536 Congleton to Macclesfield road.

Opening Times: 9 Apr - 4 Oct: daily, 2 - 5.30pm. Evening parties by arrangement.

Admission: Adult £3.80, Child £1.90. Groups of 20+ £2.80pp.

ⓘ Shop.   Ⓟ Ample.   🐕 Guide dogs in garden only.

HARE HILL

Over Alderley, Macclesfield, Cheshire SK10 4QB

Owner: The National Trust   **Contact:** The Head Gardener

A woodland garden surrounding a walled garden with pergola, rhododendrons and azaleas; parkland: link path to Alderley Edge (2m).

Location: OS Ref. SJ875 768. Between Alderley Edge and Prestbury, turn N at B5087, Greyhound Road.

Opening Times: 3 Apr - 30 Oct: Wed, Thur, Sat, Sun & BH Mon, 10am - 5.30pm. Special opening to see rhododendrons & azaleas: 12 May - 1 Jun: daily, 10am - 5.30pm. Closed Nov - Mar.

Admission: £2.50pp. Entrance per car £1.50 refundable on entry to garden. Groups by written appointment c/o Garden Lodge at address above. Not suitable for school groups.

♿ Gravel paths - strong companion advisable.   🐕 No dogs.

LITTLE MORETON HALL

Robert Aukland

CONGLETON, CHESHIRE CW12 4SD

Owner: The National Trust   *Contact:* The Property Manager

Tel: 01260 272018

Begun in 1450 and completed 130 years later, Little Moreton Hall is regarded as the finest example of a timber-framed moated manor house in the country. The drunkenly reeling South Front topped by its Elizabethan Long Gallery opens onto a cobbled courtyard and the main body of the Hall. The Chapel, Great Hall, wall paintings and Knot Garden are of particular interest. Location for *Granada TV's* recent (1996) adaption of Daniel Defoe's novel *Moll Flanders*.

Location: OS Ref. SJ833 589. 4m SW of Congleton on E side of A34.

Opening Times: 21 Mar - 1 Nov: Wed - Sun, 12 - 5.30pm. Property opens 11am on BH Mons, and from 25 Jul - 6 Sept. Last adm. 5pm. 7 Nov - 20 Dec: Sat & Sun, 12 - 4pm, access to Great Hall, Parlour, shop & restaurant only. Christmas festivities & decorations Dec weekends, 12 - 4pm. Open at other times for pre-booked groups.

Admission: Adult £4, Child £2, Family £10, pre-booked groups £3. Joint ticket available with Biddulph Grange Garden £6, Family £15. 7 Nov - 20 Dec: free admission.

ⓘ Shop.   ♿ Suitable. Braille guide, wheelchair & electric vehicle. WCs.

🍵 Tearoom.   🐕 Dogs in car park only.

Patrick Lane.

Bramall Hall, Cheshire.

LYME PARK

DISLEY, STOCKPORT, CHESHIRE SK12 2NX

Owner: The National Trust   *Contact:* The Property Manager

Tel: 01663 762023 **Infoline:** 01663 766492 **Fax:** 01663 765035

Legh family home for 600 years. Part of the original Elizabethan house survives with 18th and 19th century additions by Giacomo Leoni and Lewis Wyatt. Four centuries of period interiors - Mortlake tapestries, Grinling Gibbons carvings, unique collection of English clocks. Historic gardens with conservatory by Wyatt, a lake and a 'Dutch' garden. A 1,400 acre park, home to red and fallow deer. Exterior featured as 'Pemberley' in BBC's *Pride and Prejudice*.

Location: OS Ref. SJ966 843. Off the A6. $6^{1}/_{2}$ m SE of Stockport.

Opening Times: Park: Apr - Oct: daily, 8am - 8.30pm & Nov - Mar 8am - 6pm. Gardens: 3 Apr - 31 Oct: Fri - Tue, 11am - 5pm, Wed/ Thur 1 - 5pm. House: 3 Apr - 31 Oct: Fri - Tue, 1 - 5pm, last entry 4.30pm. BHs 11am - 5pm. Park Shop & Coffee Shop: Apr - Oct: daily 11am - 5pm. Hall, Tea Room & Gift Shop: 3 Apr - 31 Oct: Fri - Tue 11am - 5pm. For Nov - Mar opening times please telephone for details.

Admission: Park only £3.30/car. Garden only: Adult £2. House only: Adult £3, Combined House & Garden: £4. Family £10.

ℹ️ Shop.   ♿ By arrangement. WCs.   🚶 By arrangement.

🐕 In park, close control. In house and garden, guide dogs only.

NESS BOTANIC GARDENS   Tel: 01513 530123 **Fax:** 01513 531004

Ness, Neston, Cheshire L64 4AY

Owner: University of Liverpool   **Contact:** Dr E J Sharples

Location: OS Ref. SJ302 760 (village centre). Off A540. 10m NW of Chester. $1^{1}/_{2}$ m S of Neston.

Opening Times: 1 Mar - 31 Oct: 9.30am - dusk. Nov - Feb: 9.30am - 4pm.

Admission: Adult £4, Conc. £3.50, Groups £3.50pp. Accompanied child (under 18yrs) free.

ℹ️ Shop. Plant centre. Conferences.   🚶 By arrangement.   ♿ Grounds suitable. WCs.

☕ Licensed café.   🚶 By arrangement.   🐕 Guide dogs only.   💒 Civil Wedding Licence.

NETHER ALDERLEY MILL   Tel: 01625 523012

Congleton Road, Nether Alderley, Macclesfield, Cheshire SK10 4TW

Owner: The National Trust   **Contact:** The National Trust

A fascinating overshot tandem wheel watermill, dating from the 15th century, with a stone-tiled low pitched roof. The machinery was derelict for 30 years, but has now been restored to full working order, and grinds flour occasionally for demonstrations.

Location: OS Ref. SJ844 763. $1^{1}/_{2}$ m S of Alderley Edge, on E side of A34.

Opening Times: 1 Apr - end May, Oct & 1 Nov: Wed, Sun & BH Mon, 1 - 4.30pm. Jun - Sept: Tue - Sun & BH Mon, 1 - 5pm.

Admission: Adult £2, Child £1. Groups by prior arrangement (max. 20).

♿ Not suitable.   🚶 By arrangement.   🐕 No dogs.

NORTON PRIORY WALLED GARDEN & MUSEUM   Tel: 01928 569895

Tudor Road, Manor Park, Runcorn, Cheshire WA7 1SX

Owner: The Norton Priory Museum Trust   **Contact:** Norton Priory Museum

Site of Medieval priory set in beautiful woodland gardens.

Location: OS Ref. SJ545 835. 3m from M56/J11. 2m E of Runcorn.

Opening Times: Every afternoon from 1 Mar - 31 Oct (museum open all year).

Admission: Adult £3, Child £1.70, Conc. £1.70, Family £7.90, Group £1.60.

ℹ️ Shop. Plant centre. Conferences.   ♿ W/chairs, braille guide, audio tapes & WC.

☕ Tearoom.   🚶 By arrangement.   🅿️ Ample.

👨‍👩‍👧 Educational programme.   🐕 In grounds on leads.

PECKFORTON CASTLE   Tel: 01829 260930 **Fax:** 01829 261230

Stonehouse Lane, Nr Tarporley CW6 9TN

Owner: Mrs Graybill   **Contact:** Mrs Graybill

19th century built by Lord Tollemache in local red sandstone on a hilltop.

Location: OS Ref. SJ533 581. Access by gateway on W side of minor road $^{3}/_{4}$ m S of Beeston village, $^{3}/_{4}$ m N of Peckforton village.

Opening Times: Easter - 13 Sept: daily, 10am - 6pm.

Admission: Adult £2.50, Conc. £1.50. Groups over 20 £1.

ℹ️ Shop. Conferences. Corporate hospitality.   ✖️ Wedding receptions.

♿ Partially suitable. WCs.   ☕ Licensed tearoom.   🅿️ Ample.

👨‍👩‍👧 Teachers' pack available.   🐕 Strictly no dogs.   💒 Civil Wedding Licence.

PEOVER HALL

OVER PEOVER, KNUTSFORD

Owner: Randle Brooks   *Contact:* I Shepherd

Tel: 01565 632358

An Elizabethan House dating from 1585. Fine Carolean stables. Mainwaring Chapel, 18th century landscaped park. Large garden with topiary work, also walled and herb gardens.

Location: OS Ref. SJ772 734. 4m S of Knutsford off A50 at Whipping Stocks Inn.

Opening Times: House, Stables & Gardens: May - Sept: Mon except BHs, 2.30 - 4.30pm. Stables & Gardens only: Thur, 2 - 5pm.

Admission: House, Stables & Gardens: Adult £3, Child £2. Stables & Gardens only: Adult £2, Child £2.

☕ Available Mondays only.   🚶 Compulsory.   🐕 No dogs.

Peover Hall, Cheshire.

QUARRY BANK MILL & STYAL COUNTRY PARK

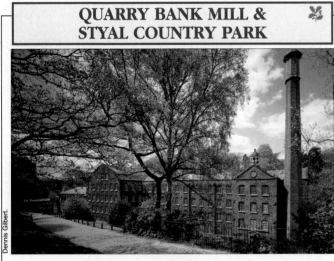

Dennis Gilbert.

STYAL, WILMSLOW, CHESHIRE SK9 4LA

Owner: *The National Trust*   **Contact:** *Quarry Bank Mill Trust Ltd.*

Tel: 01625 527468   **Fax:** 01625 539267

Georgian cotton mill, built in 1784 by Samuel Greg, an early pioneer of the factory system, surrounded by 300 acres of wooded river valley. Working Mill gives fascinating insight into the evolution of the cotton textile industry and the early industrial revolution. The restored Apprentice House provides a glimpse into the life of the pauper apprentice child workers. The Mill is powered by a magnificent 50 ton water wheel. New for 1998: 3 galleries dedicated to water and steam power and technology, hands-on displays and exhibits, an 1840 Beam engine, steaming daily and an AV theatre.

Location: OS Ref. SJ835 830. 1^1/$_2$ m N of Wilmslow off B5166. 2^1/$_2$ m from M56/J5.

Opening Times: Apr - Sept: Mill daily, 11am - 6pm, last entry 4.30pm. Oct - Mar (closed Mons): 11am - 5pm, last entry 3.30pm. Apprentice House & Garden: Apr - Sept (closed Mon except BH Mon) Tue - Fri, 2 - 4.30pm. Weekends and during Aug: as Mill. Oct - Mar: Tue - Fri, 2 - 4.30; weekends as Mill.

Admission: Mill & Apprentice House: Adult £5.50, Child/Conc. £3.50, Family £15. Mill only: Adult £4.20, Child/Conc. £3, Family £12. Apprentice House & Garden: Adult £3.50, Child/Conc. £2.50. Groups by arrangement.

ⓘ Shop. Conferences.   ♿ WCs.   ☕ Restaurant.   🐂 In grounds on leads.

TABLEY HOUSE

KNUTSFORD, CHESHIRE WA16 0HB

Owner: *Victoria University of Manchester*   **Contact:** *The Administrator*

Tel: 01565 750151

Magnificent Palladian Mansion, Grade I, by John Carr of York completed 1769 for the Leicester family who lived at Tabley for over 700 years. Their fine collection of English works of art, furniture, memorabilia can be seen in the State Rooms. Private chapel 1678.

Location: OS Ref. SJ725 777. M6/J19, A556 S on to A5033. 2m W of Knutsford.

Opening Times: Apr - end Oct inclusive: Thur, Fri, Sat, Sun & BHs, 2 - 5pm.

Admission: Adult £3.50. Child £1. Group bookings on application.

ⓘ Shop.   ♿ Suitable.   ☕ Tearoom.   Ⓟ Ample.   🎎 Civil Wedding Licence.

RODE HALL 🏛   **Tel:** 01270 873237   **Fax:** 01270 882962

Church Lane, Scholar Green, Stoke-on-Trent ST7 3QP

Owner: Sir Richard Baker Wilbraham   **Contact:** The Owner

18th century country house with Georgian stable block. Later alterations by L. Wyatt and Darcy Braddell.

Location: OS Ref. SJ819 573. 5m SW of Congleton between A34 and A50. Rail: Kidsgrove. 2m NW of Kidsgrove.

Opening Times: 8 Apr - 30 Sept: Wed & BHs (not Good Fri), 2 - 5pm. Garden only: Tue & Thur.

Admission: House, Garden & Kitchen Garden: £3.50. Garden & Kitchen Garden: £2.

☕ Home-made teas by appointment only.   🐕 No dogs.

STAPELEY WATER GARDENS   **Tel:** 01270 628628   **Fax:** 01270 624188

London Road, Stapeley, Nantwich, Cheshire CW5 7LH

Owner: Stapeley Water Gardens Ltd.   **Contact:** Reception

Home of the National Collection of Nymphaea (Water Lilies) with over 350 varieties at their best from June to September. The world's largest water garden centre with three acres of display gardens, aquatic plants, pools and fountains. Expert advice and ideas.

The Palms Tropical Oasis – a 1.3 acre pavilion housing piranhas, parrots, monkeys and aquariums in tropical and Mediterranean garden settings. The Stapeley Angling Centre - premier angling, superstore covering every facet of fishing.

Location: OS Ref. SJ675 503. 1m SE of Nantwich on A51 to Stone. Follow brown tourist signs from M6/J16.

Opening Times: All year (except 25 Dec) Garden Centre: from 9am, The Palms: from 10am. Please telephone for details.

Admission: Palms Tropical Oasis only: Adult £3.35, Child £1.75, OAP £2.65. Groups (min 15): Adult £2.85, Child £1.50, OAP £2. Garden Centre free entry.

ⓘ Shop. Garden centre. Conferences. Corporate hospitality.   ☒ Wedding receptions.

♿ Suitable. Free wheelchair loan. WCs.   ☕ Restaurant.   🏃 By arrangement.

Ⓟ Ample.   👥 Educational programme.   🐕 Guide dogs.   Ⓐ 3 dble. Ensuite.

TATTON PARK 🌿   See page 245 for full page entry.

WOODHEY CHAPEL   **Tel:** 01270 524215

Faddiley, Nr Nantwich, Cheshire

Owner: The Trustees of Woodhey Chapel

Small private chapel that has been recently restored.

Location: OS Ref. SJ573 528. Proceeding W from Nantwich on A534, turn left 1m W of the Faddiley - Bridley villages onto narrow lane, keep ahead at next turn, at road end obtain key from farmhouse.

Opening Times: Apr - Oct: Sat & BHs, 2 - 5pm, or apply for key at Woodhey Hall.

Admission: £1.

Arley Hall, Cheshire.

APPLEBY CASTLE
Appleby-in-Westmorland

Situated in the beautiful Eden Valley at the edge of the ancient county town of Westmorland Appleby Castle has stood for over 800 years. Dominated by its impressive Norman Keep, the castle was a major stronghold of the powerful Clifford family, who helped to hold the northern marches during medieval times and fought (and sometimes died) in most of the famous medieval battles, Bannockburn, Crécy, the Wars of the Roses and Flodden.

Later the castle was a favourite home of Lady Anne Clifford, the last of her line, who stubbornly held out for her heritage in the troubled years of the civil war and left an enduring legacy at the castle, which was further enhanced by her descendants, the Tufton family.

Today visitors may enjoy a castle which has something to offer from each period of history. The Norman Keep has five floors and a dramatic view from the top. The curtain wall and defensive earthworks are amongst the most impressive in northern England. The Great Hall of the castle contains the famous Great Painting of Lady Anne and her family, together with other period pieces.

In the grounds, the castle has a variety of birds and animals, both domestic and foreign, including rare breeds, with special gentle areas for children. The castle's stable block, built in the outer bailey is also of interest as is Lady Anne's 'Beehouse', actually a small oratory.

CONTACT

Administrator
Appleby Castle
Appleby
Cumbria
CA16 6XH

Tel: (01768) 351402

Fax: (01768) 351082

LOCATION

From M6/J38 northbound,
J40 southbound.
Penrith - Scotch Corner
A66 Trunk Road to A1(M).

Rail: Appleby ¹/₂ m on
scenic
Settle - Carlisle line.
Penrith 11m.

Air: Teesside 45m.

CONFERENCE/FUNCTION

ROOM	SIZE	MAX CAPACITY
Great Hall		70
Training Rm		100
Dining Rm		12
Syndicate Rooms (4)		20

OPENING TIMES

4 April - 31 October

Daily
10am - 5pm (4pm in Oct)

ADMISSION

Adult	£4.00
Child*	£2.00
Student	£3.00
OAP	£2.00
Under 5s	Free

Groups (min 20, max 120)

Adult	£3.00
Child*	£1.50
Student	£1.50
OAP	£1.50

* 5 - 15 years inclusive.

SPECIAL EVENTS

- **MAY 3 - 4:**
Historical Re-enactment.

- **MAY 10:**
Devil's Own Classic Car Rally.

- **MAY 17:**
Rolls Royce Car Owners Club Rally.

- **MAY 24:**
Teesside Yesteryear Car Club Rally and Display.

- **JUN 27 - 28:**
Historical Re-enactment.

- **AUG 29 - 31:**
Historical Re-enactment.

Visitors specifically wishing to attend any event are advised to telephone the Castle for further information beforehand on 01768 351402 to check details and timings.

i Shop. Plant centre. Conference facilities, corporate hospitality. Suitable for garden parties, fund raising events, meetings, and filming. No photography in house.

X Wedding receptions.

& Partially suitable. WC.

Tearoom, café. Licensed for conference.

By arrangement.

P Ample. Additional parking in town.

Teacher's pack.

In grounds, on leads.

A 4 single, 13 twin or double, some with ensuite.

Civil Wedding Licence.

DALEMAIN
Penrith

DALEMAIN is a fine mixture of Medieval, Tudor and Early Georgian architecture. The imposing Georgian façade strikes the visitor immediately but in the cobbled courtyard the atmosphere of the North Country Tudor Manor is secure. The present owner's family have lived at Dalemain since 1679 and have collected china, furniture and family portraits. Visitors can see the grand Drawing Rooms with 18th century Chinese wallpaper and fine oak panelling, also the Nursery and Housekeeper's Room. The Norman Pele Tower contains the regimental collection of the Westmorland and Cumberland Yeomanry. The House is full of the paraphernalia of a well established family House which is still very much lived in by the family.

The 16th century Great Barn holds a collection of agricultural bygones and a Fell Pony Museum. Nursery with toys from all ages. Do not miss Mrs Mouse's house on the back stairs. Interest for all the family. Location for LWT's production of *Jane Eyre*.

GARDENS

The Gardens have a long history stretching back to a medieval Herb Garden. Today a Knot Garden remains, with a fine early Roman fountain and box hedges enclosing herb beds. The imposing terrace wall supports a full and colourful herbaceous border during the summer months. Visitors can enjoy the fine views of the park and the woodland and riverside walks. The gardens have been featured on television's *Gardener's World* and also in *Country Life*. Deer Park.

CONTACT

Bryan McDonald
Administrator
Dalemain Estate Office
Dalemain
Penrith
Cumbria
CA11 0HB

Tel: (017684) 86450

Fax: (017684) 86223

LOCATION

OS Ref. NY477 269

On A592 1m S of A66.
4m SW of Penrith.
From London, M1,
M6/J40: 4 hrs.

From Edinburgh,
A73, M74,
M6/J40: 2½ hrs

Rail: Penrith 4m

Taxi: Walkers Taxis,
Penrith (01768) 862349

CONFERENCE/FUNCTION		
ROOM	SIZE	MAX CAPACITY
Dining Room		40
Old Hall		50

ℹ️ Shop. Fashion shows, archery, clay pigeon shooting, garden parties, rallies, filming, caravan rallies, antique fairs and children's camps. Business meetings and conferences with limited numbers during closed season. Grand piano. Parkland and Lake District National Park available and Deer Park. Lectures on the house, gardens and history by arrangement (max 60). No photography in house. Surplus plants on sale in the courtyard and also old fashioned roses in conjunction with Stydd Nurseries. Moorings on Ullswater.

❌ Telephone for details.

♿ Visitors may alight at entrance. Adm. free for visitors in wheelchairs. WCs.

☕ Licensed restaurant / tearoom seats 60. Groups pre-book for lunches / high teas.

🚶 1 hr tours. German and French translations in every room. Garden tour for groups extra.

🅿️ Ample for cars & coaches, 50 yds from house.

👫 Welcome. Guides can be arranged. Interest includes Military, Country Life, Agricultural and Fell Pony Museums, also country walk past Dacre Castle to St Andrew's Church, Dacre where there is a fine Laurence Whistler window.

🐕 Guide dogs in house only. Strictly no dogs in garden but allowed in grounds.

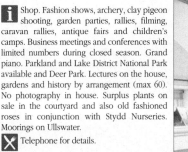

OPENING TIMES

SUMMER

5 April - 4 October
Sunday - Thursday

Gardens, restaurant, shop
& museums:
10.30am - 5pm.

House: 11.15am - 5pm.

NB. Groups of 15+
should pre-book.

WINTER

Mid October - Easter
open by special
arrangement.

ADMISSION

House & Garden

Adult	£5.00
Child (under 16yrs)	£3.00
Family	£13.00
Disabled*	Free

Gardens only

Adult	£3.00
Child (under 16yrs)	Free
Groups (min. 12)	
Adult	£4.00
Child (under 16yrs)	£3.00

* Disabled in wheelchair.

All prices include VAT.

SPECIAL EVENTS

• **MAY 22:**
Phillips International
Auctioneers & Valuers Lecture
& Afternoon Tea

• **MAY 24:**
Ford RS Owners Club Rally.

• **JUN 21:**
Cumbrian Classic Car Caper

• **JUL 18 & 19:**
Dalemain Craft Fair

• **AUG 30:**
Cumbrian Classic Car Show

Please telephone for further
details.

Northern Counties England

Jarrold Publishing

HOLKER HALL
Grange-over-Sands

HOLKER HALL, home of Lord and Lady Cavendish, shows the confidence, spaciousness and prosperity of Victorian style on its grandest scale. The New Wing, built by the 7th Duke of Devonshire (1871-4), replaced a previous wing totally destroyed by fire. Workmanship throughout is of the highest quality, particularly the detailed interior carving and linenfold panelling.

Despite this grand scale, Holker is very much a family home. Visitors can wander freely throughout the New Wing. Photographs, beautiful floral displays and bowls of scented pot pourri create the warm and friendly atmosphere so often remarked upon by visitors. Varying in period and style, Louis XV pieces happily mix with the Victorian. Pictures range from an early copy of the famous triple portrait of Charles I by Van Dyck to a modern painting by Douglas Anderson.

GARDENS

Christie's/HHA Garden of the Year (1991), includes formal and woodland areas covering 24 acres. Designated "amongst the best in the world in terms of design and content" by the *Good Gardens Guide*. This wonderful Italianate-cum-English Garden includes a lime-stone cascade, a fountain, a rose garden and many rare and beautiful plants and shrubs. Holker is also home to the Holker Garden Festival held from 29 - 31 May.

CONTACT

Mrs Carolyn Johnson
Holker Hall & Gardens
Cark-in-Cartmel
Grange-over-Sands
Cumbria
LA11 7PL

Tel: (015395) 58328

Fax: (015395) 58776

LOCATION

OS Ref. SD359 773

Close to Morecambe Bay,
5m W of Grange-over-
Sands by B5277.
From Kendal, A6, A590,
B5277, B5278: 16m.

Motorway: M6/J36.

Bus: From Grange-
over-Sands.

Rail: To Cark Station.

Taxi: Parkers Motors,
Grange-over-Sands.

OPENING TIMES

SUMMER
1 April - 30 October
Daily except Sat
10am - 6pm.

NB. Last admission
4.30pm.

WINTER
1 November - 31 March
Closed.

ADMISSION

SUMMER
(1997 prices)

House & Garden

Adult	£5.50
Child	£3.00

Groups
Adult	£3.55
OAP	£3.35
Child	£2.55

SPECIAL EVENTS

• **MAY 29, 30 & 31:**
Holker Garden Festival. Magnificent horticultural displays & floral art combines with countryside displays, gardens. Champagne & wine bar, and much more.
Show office -
Tel: 015395 58838
Fax: 015395 58776

• **AUG 30:**
MG Rally. Post and Pre 1955 MGs in concours and driving trials. Discounted admission to MG drivers. Competition entries on the day.

ℹ️ Shop. Suitable for filming and photography. Deer Park. Lakeland Motor Museum, adventure playground and exhibitions. No photography in house. Guide Book translations in French, Spanish and German.

✕ Wedding receptions.

♿ Visitors alight at entrance. Ramps and unisex WCs.

☕ The Coach House licensed café (max 120).

🚶 Pre-booked tours at additional cost of 50p each.

🅿️ Ample, 150 yds from Hall. Plus grass car parking.

👪 Environmental study day for primary school children £2pp. Holker holds 2 Sandford Awards for Heritage Education and provides a wide range of educational opportunities for primary aged children to fit in with curriculum requirements, ie. Houses and Home, Technology and Design; Structures, Victorians.

Northern Counties
England

LEVENS HALL
Kendal

Levens Hall is an Elizabethan mansion built around a 13th century pele tower. The much loved home of the Bagot family, visitors comment on the warm and friendly atmosphere. Fine panelling and plasterwork, period furniture, Cordova leather wall coverings, paintings by Rubens, Lely and Cuyp, the earliest English patchwork and Wellingtoniana combine with other beautiful objects to form a fascinating collection.

The world famous Topiary Gardens were laid out by Monsieur Beaumont from 1694 and his design has remained largely unchanged to this day. Over ninety individual pieces of topiary, some over nine metres high, massive beech hedges create a magnificent visual impact. Spring and summer bedding provides a mass of colour, and herbaceous borders contain many unusual plants. A new Fountain Garden was created in 1994 and in the same year Levens Gardens were awarded the prestigious HHA/Christie's Garden of the Year Award.

On Sundays and Bank Holidays 'Bertha', a full size Showman's Engine, is in steam together with a scale model 'Little Gem'. The fine collection of working model steam engines runs on House Open Days from 2 - 5pm. Delicious home-made lunches and teas are available together with the Levens Beer 'Morocco Ale'.

CONTACT

Peter Milner
Levens Hall
Kendal
Cumbria
LA8 0PD

Tel: (01539) 560321
Fax: (01539) 560669

LOCATION

OS Ref. SD495 851

5m S of Kendal on the A6.
Exit M6/J36.

Rail: Oxenholme 5m.

NPI Award 1997:
Runner Up

i   Shop. Plant centre. No internal photography.

  Partially suitable. WC. Wheelchair loan - gardens only suitable.

  Licensed tearoom.

  By arrangement.

P   Ample.

  Educational Programme.

  No dogs.

OPENING TIMES

SUMMER

1 April - 15 October
Sun - Thur

Gardens & Tearoom:
10am - 5pm.

House: 12 - 5pm
Last admission 4.30pm.

Closed Friday & Saturday

WINTER

Closed

ADMISSION

House & Gardens

Adult £5.20
Child* £2.80
Groups (min 20)
   Adult £4.30
   School* £2.40
   Family (2+3) £15.00

Gardens

Adult £3.80
Child* £2.10
Groups (min 20)
   Adult £3.30
   School* £1.80
   Family (2+3) £11.00

Evening tours

House & Garden for groups (min 20) by prior arrangement.......£6.20pp

Gardens only groups (min 20) by prior arrangement.......£4.20pp

Season Tickets

Garden (single) £11.00

MUNCASTER CASTLE
Ravenglass

MUNCASTER CASTLE has been owned by the Pennington family since 1208. It has grown from the original pele tower built on Roman foundations to the impressive structure visible today. Outstanding features are the Great Hall and Salvin's octagonal library and the Drawing Room with its barrel ceiling.

The Castle contains many treasures including beautiful furniture, exquisite needlework panels, tapestries and oriental rugs. The family silver is very fine and is accompanied in the Dining Room by the Ongley Service, the most ornamental set of porcelain ever created by the Derby factory, Florentine 16th century bronzes and an alabaster lady by Giambologna can be seen. The Castle is allegedly haunted. All the rooms open to the public are lived in by the family who are actively involved in entertaining their many visitors.

The woodland gardens cover 77 acres and command spectacular views of the Lakeland Fells, with many delightful walks. From mid-March to June the rhododendrons, azaleas, camellias and magnolias are at their best.

The Owl Centre boasts a fine collection of owls from all over the world. 'Meet the Birds' occurs daily at 2.30pm (29 Mar to 1 Nov), when a talk is given on the work of the centre. Weather permitting, the birds fly.

CONTACT

Peter Frost-Pennington
Muncaster Castle
Ravenglass
Cumbria
CA18 1RQ

Tel: (01229) 717614

Fax: (01229) 717010

LOCATION

OS Ref. SD103 965

On the A595 1m E of Ravenglass, 19m S of Whitehaven.

From London 6 hrs, Chester 2^1/$_2$ hrs Edinburgh 3^1/$_2$ hrs M6/J36, A590, A595 (from S). M6/J40, A66, A595 (from E). Carlisle, A595 (from N).

Rail: Ravenglass (on Barrow-in-Furness-Carlisle Line) 1^1/$_2$ m.

CONFERENCE/FUNCTION		
ROOM	SIZE	MAX CAPACITY
Drawing Rm	–	120
Dining Rm	–	50
Family Dining Rm	–	60
Great Hall	–	110

i Shops. Plant centre. Church. Suitable for fashion shoots, garden parties, film location, clay pigeon shooting. No photography inside the Castle. Home of the World Owl Trust, run by TV naturalist Tony Warburton.

X Wedding receptions. For catering, functions in the Castle Tel: 01229 717614.

& By prior arrangement visitors alight near Castle. Wheelchairs for loan. WCs. Special audio tour tapes for the partially sighted/those with learning difficulties. Allocated parking.

▭ The Stables Buttery (licensed) (max 80) - full menu. Groups can pre-book on 01229 717432 to qualify for discounts. Café & tearoom.

▸ Individual audio tour (40mins) included in price. Private tours with a personal guide (family member possible) can be arranged at additional fee. Lectures by arrangement.

P Free for 500 cars 800 yds from House; coaches may park closer.

▵ Welcome – guides available. Historical subjects, horticulture, owl tours.

▯ In grounds, on leads.

▯ Civil Wedding Licence.

OPENING TIMES

SUMMER
29 March - 1 November

Castle
Daily except Sat
12.30 - 4pm (last entry).

Gardens & Owl Centre
Daily: 11am - 5pm.

WINTER
Castle
Closed.
Open by appointment for groups.

Gardens & Owl Centre
Daily: 11am - 5pm

ADMISSION

Castle, Gardens & Owl Centre
Adult £5.20
Child* (5 - 15yrs) £3.10
Family (2+2) £14.50
Groups
Adult £4.20
Child* (5 - 15yrs) £2.50

Season Tickets
Adult £12.50
Family(2+3)...........£28.00

Gardens & Owl Centre
Adult £3.50
Child* (5 - 15yrs) £2.00
Family (2+2) £9.50
Groups
Adult £3.10
Child* (5 - 15yrs) £1.50

* Under 5s free.

ABBOT HALL ART GALLERY
Tel: 01539 722464 **Fax:** 01539 722494

Kendal, Cumbria LA9 5AL
Owner: Lake District Art Gallery & Museum Trust   **Contact:** Mr E King

Elegant Georgian house with portraits and furniture displayed in restored rooms. Contemporary upstairs galleries showing temporary and touring exhibitions.

Location: OS Ref. SD516 923. Kirkland, Kendal.

Opening Times: 1 Apr - 31 Oct: daily 10.30am - 5pm. 1 Nov - 31 Mar: daily 10.30am - 4pm. Closed mid Dec to mid Feb.

Admission: Adult £2.80, Child/Student £1.25, OAP £2.50, Family £6.90.

ⓘ Shop.   ♿ Chairlifts in split level galleries. WCs.   ☕ Licensed tearoom.
🚶 By arrangement.   Ⓟ Ample.   👥 Educational programme.   🐕 Guide dogs only.

ACORN BANK GARDEN & WATERMILL 🍂
Tel: 017683 61893

Temple Sowerby, Penrith, Cumbria CA10 1SP
Owner: The National Trust   **Contact:** The Administrator

A 1 hectare garden protected by fine oaks under which grow a vast display of daffodils. Inside the walls there are orchards containing a variety of fruit trees surrounded by mixed borders with shrubs, herbaceous plants and roses, while the impressive herb garden has the largest collection of culinary and medicinal plants in the north. A circular woodland walk runs beside the Crowdundle Beck to Acorn Bank watermill. Although work to restore the mill continues, it will be open to visitors at the same time as the garden during 1998.

Location: Gate: OS Ref. NY612 281. Just N of Temple Sowerby, 6m E of Penrith on A66.

Opening Times: 28 Mar - 1 Nov: daily 10am - 5.30pm. Last admission 5pm.

Admission: Adult £2.20, Child £1.10, Family £5.80. Pre-arranged groups £1.60pp.

ⓘ Shop.   ♿ Grounds only. WCs.   🐕 No dogs.

APPLEBY CASTLE
See page 250 for full page entry.

BEATRIX POTTER GALLERY 🍂
Tel: 01539 436355

Main Street, Hawkshead, Cumbria LA22 0NS
Owner: The National Trust   **Contact:** The Custodian

An annually changing exhibition of original illustrations from the children's stories. One of many historic buildings in this picturesque village. This was once the office of the author's husband, the solicitor William Heelis, and the interior remains largely unaltered.

Location: OS Ref. SD352 982. 5m SSW of Ambleside. In the square.

Opening Times: 1 Apr - 1 Nov: Sun - Thur (closed Fri & Sat except Good Fri) 10.30am - 4.30pm. Last admission 4pm. Admission is by timed ticket (incl. NT members).

Admission: Adult £2.80, Child £1.40. No reduction for groups.

ⓘ Shop.   🐕 Guide dogs only.

BROUGH CASTLE ⌗
Tel: 01912 611585

Brough, Cumbria
Owner: English Heritage   **Contact:** The North Regional Office

Perched on a superb vantage point overlooking an old trade route, now the A66, this ancient site dates back to Roman times. The 12th century keep replaced an earlier stronghold destroyed by the Scots in 1174. The castle was restored by Lady Anne Clifford in the 17th century.

Location: OS Ref. NY791 141. 8m SE of Appleby S of A66. South part of the village.

Opening Times: Any reasonable time.
Admission: Free.

♿ Not suitable.   🐕 In grounds, on leads.

BROUGHAM CASTLE ⌗
Tel: 01768 862488

Penrith, Cumbria CA10 2AA
Owner: English Heritage   **Contact:** The Custodian

These impressive ruins on the banks of the River Eamont include an early 13th century keep and later buildings. You can climb to the top of the keep and survey the domain of its eccentric one time owner Lady Anne Clifford, who restored the castle in the 17th century. There is a small exhibition of Roman tombstones from the nearby fort.

Location: OS Ref. NY537 290. 1½m SE of Penrith.

Opening Times: 1 Apr - 1 Nov: daily, 10am - 6pm (dusk if earlier in Oct).

Admission: Adult £1.90, Child £1, Conc. £1.40. Groups: Adult £1.20, Child 65p, Conc £1. 15% discount for groups of 11+.

ⓘ Shop.   ♿ Grounds suitable.   🐕 In grounds, on leads.

CARLISLE CASTLE ⌗

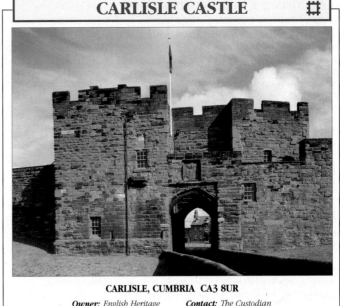

CARLISLE, CUMBRIA CA3 8UR
Owner: *English Heritage*   **Contact:** *The Custodian*

Tel: 01228 591922

This impressive medieval castle, where Mary Queen of Scots was once imprisoned, has a long and tortuous history of warfare and family feuds. A portcullis hangs menacingly over the gatehouse passage, there is a maze of passages and chambers, endless staircases to lofty towers and you can walk the high ramparts for stunning views. There is also a medieval manor house in miniature: a suite of medieval rooms furnished as they might have been when used by the castle's former constable. The castle is also the home of the Museum of the King's Own Border Regiment (included in the admission price).

Location: OS85 Ref. NY397 563. In Carlisle town.

Open: 1 Apr - 1 Nov: daily 9.30am - 6pm (or dusk if earlier in Oct). 2 Nov - 31 Mar: daily 10am - 4pm.

Admission: Adult £2.90, Child £1.50, Conc £2.20. 15% discount for groups of 11+.

ⓘ Shop.   ♿ Partially suitable, wheelchairs available.   🚶 By arrangement.
Ⓟ No parking.   🐕 Dogs on leads.

CARLISLE CATHEDRAL
Tel: 01228 48151

Carlisle, Cumbria CA3 8TZ   **Contact:** Ms C Baines

Fine sandstone Cathedral, founded in 1122. Medieval stained glass. Carvings and painted wall panels. Treasury with displays of silver, diocesan and cathedral treasures.

Location: OS Ref. NY399 559. Carlisle city centre, 2m from M6/J43.

Opening Times: Mon - Sat: 7.45am - 6.15pm, Suns 7.45 - 5pm. Closes 4pm between Christmas Day & New Year. Sun services: 8am, 10.30am & 3pm. Weekday services: 8am, 12.30pm, 5.30pm & a 12.30 service on Wed, Fri and Saints Days.

Admission: Donation.

ⓘ Shop.   ♿ Access except treasury & restaurant. WC.   ☕ Restaurant.
🐕 Guide dogs only.

CONISHEAD PRIORY & MAJUSHRI BUDDHIST TEMPLE

Ulverston, Cumbria LA12 9QQ   **Tel:** 01229 584029 **Fax:** 01229 580080
Owner: Majushri Mahayana Buddhist Centre   **Contact:** Mr R Tyson

A Georgian Gothic mansion on site of a medieval Augustinian Priory. Now a major Buddhist Centre and under restoration. It has fine plaster ceilings, stained glass windows, a cantilever staircase, an Oak Room, vaulted hall and cloister. Private woodland walk to Morecambe Bay.

Location: OS Ref. SD300 750. 2m S of Ulverston on Bardsea Coast Rd A5087.

Opening Times: Easter - Oct, w/e & BHs, 2 - 5pm. Closed 20/21 June, 1 - 31 Aug.

Admission: Free. House tours and audio visual: Adult £2, Child 75p, OAP £1.

ⓘ Shop.   ♿ Partially suitable.   ☕ Tearoom.   Ⓟ Ample.
👥 Educational programme.   🐕 In grounds, on leads.

DALEMAIN 🏛
See page 251 for full page entry.

DOVE COTTAGE & WORDSWORTH MUSEUM

Tel: 01539 435544/435547

Grasmere, Cumbria LA22 9SH   **Fax:** 01539 435748

See full page advertisement on page twenty five.

Owner: Wordsworth Trust   **Contact:** Sylvia Wordsworth

Wordsworth's home 1799 - 1808, Dove Cottage is beautifully preserved. Visitors are offered guided tours. The garden is open, weather permitting. The award-winning Wordsworth Museum displays a permanent exhibition and a programme of special exhibitions and events. Reciprocal discount ticket with Rydal Mount and Wordsworth House, Cockermouth.

Location: OS Ref. NY340 070. Immediately S of Grasmere village on A591. Main car/coach park next to Dove Cottage Tea Rooms.

Opening Times: All year: daily 9.30am - 5.30pm. Closed 12 Jan - 8 Feb (inc) & 24 - 26 Dec.

Admission: Adult £4.40, Child £2.20, OAP/Student £4.20. Pre-arranged groups (min 15, max 60): Adult £3.75, Child £2.20.

[i] Shop. No photography. [&] Partially suitable. WC. [tearoom] Tearoom. [person] Compulsory.
[P] Limited. [dog] Guide dogs only. [education] Educational programme. Teachers' pack.

FURNESS ABBEY [symbol]

Tel: 01229 823420

Barrow-in-Furness, Cumbria LH13 0TJ

Owner: English Heritage   **Contact:** The Custodian

Hidden in a peaceful green valley are the beautiful red sandstone remains of the wealthy abbey founded in 1123 by Stephen, later King of England. This abbey first belonged to the Order of Savigny and later to the Cistercians. There is a museum and exhibition.

Location: OS96, Ref. SD218 717. $1^1/_2$ m N of Barrow-in-Furness.

Opening Times: 1 Apr - 1 Nov: daily, 10am - 6pm or dusk if earlier in Oct. 2 Nov - 31 Mar: Wed - Sun, 10am - 4pm. Closed 24 - 26 Dec.

Admission: Adult £2.50, Child £1.30, Conc. £1.90. 15% discount for groups of 11+.

[i] Shop. [&] Grounds suitable. [person] Inclusive audio tour. [dog] In grounds, on leads.

HARDKNOTT ROMAN FORT [symbol]

Tel: 01912 611585

Ravenglass, Cumbria

Owner: English Heritage   **Contact:** The North Regional Office

One of the most dramatic sites in Britain, with stunning views across the Lakeland fells. This fort, built between AD120 and 138, controlled the road from Ravenglass to Ambleside. There are visible remains of granaries, the headquarters buildings and the commandant's house, with a bath house and parade ground outside the fort.

Location: OS Ref. NY218 015. At the head of Eskdale, 9m NE. 9m NE of Ravenglass, at W end of Hardknott Pass.

Opening Times: Any reasonable time. Access may be hazardous in winter.

Admission: Free.

[&] Not suitable. [P] Limited. [dog] In grounds, on leads.

HERON CORN MILL & MUSEUM OF PAPERMAKING

Tel: 015395 65027

c/o Henry Cooke, Waterhouse Mills, Beetham, Milnthorpe, Cumbria LA7 7AR

Owner: Heron Corn Mill Beetham Trust   **Contact:** Mr Neil Stobbs

Location: OS Ref. SD497 800. At Beetham. 1m S of Milnthorpe on the A6.

Opening Times: Easter: 1 Apr - 30 Sept: Tue - Sun & BH Mon, 11am - 5pm.

Admission: Adult £1.50, Child/OAP £1, Family (2+2) £4.50, Coach parties/groups 10% discount if pre-booked.

[i] Shop. [&] Ground floor suitable with help. [dog] In grounds, on leads.

HILL TOP [symbol]

Tel: 01539 436269

Near Sawrey, Ambleside, Cumbria LA22 0LF

Owner: The National Trust   **Contact:** The Administrator

Beatrix Potter wrote many Peter Rabbit books in this little 17th century house, which contains her furniture and china.

Location: OS Ref. SD370 955. 2m S of Hawkshead, in hamlet of Near Sawrey, behind the Tower Bank Arms.

Opening Times: 1 Apr - 1 Nov: Sat - Wed & Good Fri, 11am - 5pm. Last adm: 4.30pm.

Admission: Adult £3.80, Child £1.70, no reduction for groups.

[i] Shop. [&] By prior arrangement. [dog] No dogs.

HOLEHIRD

Tel: 01539 446008

Patterdale Road, Windermere, Cumbria LA23 1NP

Owner: Lakeland Horticultural Society   **Contact:** The Hon. Secretary

Over 4 acres of hillside gardens overlooking Troutbeck Valley, with magnificent views of Windermere lake and fells, including a walled garden and national collection of astilbes, hydrangeas and polystichum ferns. All of the work in the gardens is done by volunteers.

Location: OS Ref. NY410 008. On A592, $^3/_4$ m N of junction with A591. $^1/_2$ m N of Windermere. 1m from Townend.

Opening Times: All year, dawn to dusk.

Admission: By donation, suggestion of £1 per adult.

HOLKER HALL [symbol]

See page 252 for full page entry.

HUTTON-IN-THE-FOREST [symbol]

PENRITH, CUMBRIA CA11 9TH

Owner: Lord Inglewood   *Contact: Edward Thompson*

Tel: 01768 484449 **Fax:** 01768 484571

The home of Lord Inglewood's family since 1605. Built around a medieval pele tower with 17th, 18th and 19th century additions. Fine collections of furniture and paintings, ceramics and tapestries. Outstanding gardens and grounds with terraces, walled garden, dovecote and woodland walk through magnificent specimen trees. Picnic area.

Location: OS Ref. NY460 358. 7m NW of Penrith & $2^1/_2$ m from M6/J41 on B5305.

Opening Times: House: Easter: Good Fri, Sun & Mon. 1 May - 4 Oct: Thur, Fri, Sun & BH Mons. 1 - 4pm (last entry). Tearoom: As house: 12 - 4.30pm. Grounds: daily except Sat, 11am - 5pm.

Admission: House, Gardens & Grounds: Adult £4, Child £2, Family £10. Gardens & Grounds: Adult £2.50, Child free.

[i] Gift stall. [X] By arrangement. [&] Ground floor and grounds suitable.
[tearoom] Tearoom. [person] Compulsory (except Jul/Aug & BHs). [education] Educational prog.

LANERCOST PRIORY [symbol]

Tel: 01697 73030

Brampton, Cumbria CA8 2HQ

Owner: English Heritage   **Contact:** The Custodian

This Augustinian priory was founded c1166. The nave of the church, which is intact and in use as the local parish church, contrasts with the ruined chancel, transepts and priory buildings.

Location: OS86, Ref. NY556 637. 2m NE of Brampton. 1m N of Naworth Castle.

Opening Times: 1 Apr - 1 Nov: daily, 10am - 6pm (or dusk if earlier in Oct).

Admission: Adult £1.90, Child £1, Conc. £1.40. Groups: 15% discount for groups of 11+.

[i] Shop. [&] Ground floor suitable. [person] Inclusive audio tour. [P] Limited. [dog] No dogs.

LEVENS HALL [symbol]

See page 253 for full page entry.

MIREHOUSE [symbol]

Tel/Fax: 01768 772287

Keswick, Cumbria CA12 4QE

Owner: John Spedding Esq   **Contact:** Clare Spedding

In a spectacular setting between mountains and lake this family home has passed by descent since 1688. Unusually wide ranging literary and artistic associations, illustrated by paintings, manuscripts and photographs. Live piano music. Relaxed welcome for children. Sheltered gardens include newly restored walled Bee Garden, Rose Garden and Colonade, Lovers' Lane and Lakeside Walk. Tearoom in interesting old sawmill offers generous Cumbrian home-cooking.

Location: OS Ref. NY235 284. Beside A591, $3^1/_2$ m N of Keswick. Regular bus service.

Opening Times: Gardens & Tearoom. Easter - Oct, daily 10.30am - 5.30pm. Weekends only in Nov: House: Easter - Oct, Sun & Wed (also Fri in Aug), 2 - 4.30pm (last admission). Other times throughout the year by appointment.

Admission: House & Garden: Adult £3.50, Child £1.75. Gardens & lakeside walk: Adult £1.50, Child 80p.

[X] Available. [&] Full facilities. [tearoom] Tearoom. [person] By arrangement.
[education] Seasonal nature notes, history trail notes. [dog] In grounds, on leads.

SPECIAL EVENTS

WEDS IN JUN, JULY & SEPT: Lace-making demonstrations.

Live piano music in house on open days.

MUNCASTER CASTLE

See page 254 for full page entry.

MUNCASTER WATER MILL

Tel: 01229 717232

Ravenglass, Cumbria CA18 1ST

Owner: Lake District Estates   **Contact:** E & P Priestly

Working old Manorial Mill with 13ft overshot wheel and all milling equipment.

Location: OS Ref. SD094 977. 1m N of Ravenglass on A595.

Opening Times: Easter - Oct: daily 10am - 5pm. Nov - Mar: weekends only, 11am - 4pm.

Admission: Adult £1.60, Child 80p, Family £4.

ℹ️ Shop.   ♿ Suitable. WCs.   ☕ Tearoom.   🚶 By arrangement.

🅿️ Ample for cars, limited for coaches.   🐕 In grounds, on leads.

NAWORTH CASTLE

See opposite.

PENRITH CASTLE

Tel: 0191 261 1585

Penrith, Cumbria

Owner: English Heritage   **Contact:** The North Regional Office

This 14th century castle, set in a park on the edge of the town, was built to defend Penrith against repeated attacks by Scottish raiders.

Location: OS Ref. NY513 299. Opposite Penrith railway station. W of the town centre. Fully visible from the street.

Opening Times: Park opening hours.

Admission: Free.

♿ Ground floor suitable.   🅿️ No parking.   🐕 In grounds, on leads.

RYDAL MOUNT & GARDENS

Tel: 01539 433002 **Fax:** 01539 431738

Ambleside, Cumbria LA22 9LU

Owner: Rydal Mount Trustees   **Contact:** Peter & Marian Elkington

See full page advertisement on page twenty five.

The historic house of William Wordsworth from 1813 until his death in 1850, now the family home of his descendants. It contains family portraits and his personal possessions. The extensive garden, landscaped by the poet, includes terraces, rare shrubs, trees and the poet's summerhouse which overlooks beautiful Rydal Water.

Location: OS Ref. NY364 063. 1 1/2 m N of Ambleside on A591 Grasmere Road.

Opening Times: Mar - Oct: Daily, 9.30am - 5pm. Nov - Feb: Daily except Tues, 10am - 4pm.

Admission: Adult £3.50, Child £1, OAP/Student £3. Groups (min 10+): £2.50pp. Garden only: £1.50. Free parking. Reciprocal discount ticket with Dove Cottage and Wordsworth House.

ℹ️ Shop. No inside photography.   ♿ Partially suitable.   🚶 By arrangement.

🅿️ Limited.   👥 Teachers' pack.   🐕 In grounds, on leads. Guide dogs only in house.

SIZERGH CASTLE

Tel: 01539 560070

Nr. Kendal, Cumbria LA8 8AE

Owner: The National Trust   **Contact:** The Administrator

The Strickland family have lived here for more than 750 years. The impressive 14th century pele tower was extended in Tudor times, with some of the finest Elizabethan carved overmantels in the country. Contents include good English and French furniture and family portraits. The castle is surrounded by gardens of beauty and interest, including the Trust's largest limestone rock garden; good autumn colour. Large estate; walks leaflet available in shop.

Location: OS Ref. SD498 878. 3 1/2 m S of Kendal, NW of the A590/A591 interchange.

Opening Times: Castle 1 Apr - 29 Oct: Sun - Thur, 1.30 - 5.30pm. Garden: as Castle from 12.30pm. Last admission 5pm.

Admission: Adult £4, Child £2, Family £11. Garden only: £2. Groups of 15+, £3.20, by arrangement (not BHs).

ℹ️ Shop.   ♿ Suitable. WCs.   ☕ Tearoom.   🐕 No dogs.

STAGSHAW GARDEN

Tel: 015394 35599 **Fax:** 015394 35353

Ambleside, Cumbria LA22 0HE

Owner: The National Trust   **Contact:** The Administrator

This woodland garden was created by the late Cubby Acland, Regional Agent for the National Trust. It contains a fine collection of azaleas and rhododendrons, planted to give good blends of colour under the thinned oaks on the hillside; also many trees and shrubs, including magnolias, camellias and embothriums.

Location: OS Ref. NY380 030. 1/2 m S of Ambleside on A591.

Opening Times: 1 Apr - end Jun: daily 10am - 6.30pm. Jul - end Oct: by appointment.

Admission: £1.30, no reduction for groups.

♿ Not suitable.   🅿️ No parking.   🐕 No dogs.

NAWORTH CASTLE

BRAMPTON, CUMBRIA CA8 2HF

Owner: Philip Howard   *Contact: Colleen Hall*

Tel: 01697 73229   **Fax:** 01697 73679   **e-mail:** naworth.co.uk

Naworth Castle is a romantic Border Castle dating back to 1335. Owned by Philip Howard it is now Cumbria's premier historic function venue and offers exclusive use and outstanding personal service. In 1997 over 40 weddings took place. Corporate clients include British Telecom, Thorn Security, Ford UK, Iveco, Kleinwort Benson and Jaguar Cars. 1997 filming included Border Television, Granada TV's '*Love Me Do*'. We were Thornfield in LWT's '*Jane Eyre*' and used in Catherine Cookson's '*Black Candle*'. 17th century walled garden, 400 acres of woodland.

Location: OS Ref. NY560 626. 1/2 m off main A69 Carlisle - Newcastle road. 3m E of Brampton. Carlisle 12m, Newcastle 46m, M6 9m.

Opening Times: All year by appointment only. All tours must be pre-booked: minimum 15 people, maximum 100. Lunches, teas and dinners available. Most guided tours by owner. Tours can be conducted throughout the year depending upon availability. We also can accommodate small specialist parties during the week and the owner can arrange to accompany them on tours of the region.

ℹ️ Riding stables, clay pigeon shooting, river & lake fishing, game shooting, conference & corporate breaks, team building days, product launches, fashion shows, concerts, charity events, exhibitions.

✖️ High quality retained caterers available for all events and overnight parties. Own wine list and wine company 'Naworth Castle Wines'.

🅰️ Accommodation available with special functions. 13 double bedrooms all with en-suite shower/bathrooms. Separate 2 bedroomed apartment.

💍 Civil Wedding Licence.

SPECIAL EVENTS

MAR 27 - 29: Galloway Antiques Fair.   **APR 19:** Open Day.
JUN 25: Thomson Roddick & Laurie Fine Pictures & Furniture Auction (viewing Jun 24).
AUG 28 - 31: August Galloway Antiques Fair.   **OCT 22:** Fine Art & Furniture Sale (view Oct 21).

STEAM YACHT GONDOLA 🌿
Tel: 01539 463849 (NT Gondola Bookings)

National Trust Office, The Hollens, Grasmere, Cumbria LA22 9QZ

Owner: The National Trust   **Contact:** The Manager

The Steam Yacht Gondola, first launched in 1859 and now completely renovated by the Trust, provides a steam-powered passenger service, carrying 86 passengers in opulently upholstered saloons. A superb way to see Coniston's scenery.

Location: OS Ref. SD305 975. Coniston (¹/₂ m to Coniston Pier).

Opening Times: Sails to scheduled daily timetable during the season, weather permitting, starting at 11am, except Sat, when sailings start at 12.05pm. 1998 sailings begin on 1 Apr and continue to 1 Nov. The Trust reserves the right to cancel sailings in the event of high winds or lack of demand. Piers at Coniston, Park-a-Moor and Brantwood (not NT).

Admission: Ticket prices & timetable on application and published locally. Family ticket available. No reduction for NT members as Gondola is an enterprise and not held solely for preservation. Groups & private charters by prior arrangement.

  🦽 Not suitable.   🐕 Dogs on leads, outside saloons, 50p any journey.

STOTT PARK BOBBIN MILL ⌗
Tel: 01539 531087

Low Stott Park, Ulverston, Cumbria LA12 8AX

Owner: English Heritage   **Contact:** The Custodian

When this working mill was built in 1835 it was typical of the many mills in the Lake District which grew up to supply the spinning and weaving industry in Lancashire but have since disappeared. A remarkable opportunity to see a demonstration of the machinery and techniques of the Industrial Revolution. There is a working Static Steam Engine on Tuesdays to Thursdays.

Location: OS96 Ref. SD373 883. Near Newby Bridge on A590.

Opening Times: 1 Apr - 1 Nov: daily, 10am - 6pm (dusk if earlier in Oct). Last admission 1hr before closing.

Admission: Adult £2.90, Child £1.50, Conc. £2.20. Groups: discount for groups of 11+.

  ℹ️ Shop. 🦽 Ground floor suitable. WC. 🚶 Inclusive. 🅿️ Ample. 🐕 No dogs.

TOWNEND 🌿
Tel: 01539 432628

Troutbeck, Windermere, Cumbria LA23 1LB

Owner: The National Trust   **Contact:** The Administrator

An exceptional relic of Lake District life during past centuries. Originally a 'statesman' (wealthy yeoman) farmer's house, built about 1626. Townend contains carved woodwork, books, papers, furniture and fascinating implements of the past which were accumulated by the Browne family who lived here from 1626 until 1943.

Location: OS Ref. NY407 020. 3m SE of Ambleside at S end of Troutbeck village. 1m from Holehird, 3m N of Windermere.

Opening Times: 1 Apr - 1 Nov: Tue - Fri, Sun & BH Mon, 1 - 5pm or dusk if earlier. Last admission 4.30pm.

Admission: Adult £2.80, Child £1.40, Family £7.50. No reduction for groups which must be pre-booked. Townend and village unsuitable for coaches; 12 - 15 seater mini-buses are acceptable; permission to take coaches to Townend must be obtained from the Transportation and Highways Dept, Cumbria CC, Carlisle, Cumbria (tel: 01228 23456).

  🦽 Unsuitable for wheelchairs. Braille guide. 🐕 No dogs.

WORDSWORTH HOUSE 🌿
Tel: 01900 824805

Main Street, Cockermouth, Cumbria CA13 9RX

Owner: The National Trust   **Contact:** Mrs Jill Durey

See full page advertisement on page twenty five.

The house where William Wordsworth was born in 1770. This north-country Georgian town house was built in 1745. Seven rooms are furnished in 18th century style, with some personal effects of the poet; his childhood garden, with terraced walk, leads down to the Derwent. Video display, last showing 4pm.

Location: OS Ref. NY118 307. Main Street, Cockermouth.

Opening Times: 1 Apr - 30 Oct: weekdays, 11am - 5pm. Also the following Sats: 11 Apr, 2 & 23 May, all Sats from 27 Jun - 5 Sept and Oct 24. Last admission 4.30pm.

Admission: Adult £2.80, Child £1.40, Family £7.50. Pre-booked groups £2pp. Reciprocal discount ticket with Dove Cottage and Rydal Mount.

  ℹ️ Shop. 🦽 By arrangement only. ☕ Tearoom. 🅿️ No parking. 🐕 No dogs.

Fishing:

Rights over river and lake fishing belong to the owner over whose land the water flows or on whose land it sits (in the case of a lake); the owner is not restricted in the use of machinery, so long as that machinery does not impede navigation. The principal fresh-water fish are barbel, bream, carp, chub, roach, salmon, tench and trout.

Although rod and line have been used immemorially for fresh-water fishing, other methods have had their fashion. In medieval times, monasteries and sometimes large estates maintained stew ponds to breed fish for meatless days, catching them in large quantities with nets, a practice which continued until the Reformation, when meatless days were abandoned and the ponds fell into disuse, and often into decay in the case of those belonging to monasteries. In Anglo-Saxon and medieval times, those without stew ponds caught fish by putting a wicker fish weir across a river to trap fish running downstream.

The first work on fishing published in England was in 1496, by Wynkyn de Worde, but the most famous is undoubtedly The Compleat Angler by Isaac Walton, first published in 1653. Walton recognised that the finest fresh-water fishing and sport was fly-fishing for brown trout, closely run by salmon fishing. Trout spawn in October and November and salmon from the end of autumn until the beginning of spring.

Fishing houses:

Sometimes called fishing pavilions. The earliest reference to these charming retreats dates to c.1570 at Anthony House in Cornwall, where Richard Carew proposed (but never built) a combined banqueting and fishing house on an island; Bourne Mill in Essex is a converted banqueting-cum-fishing-house of 1591. However, fishing houses only really came into fashion in the mid-eighteenth century: in the 1760s Robert Adam built one on the edge of a lake at Kedleston Hall, Derbyshire for the first Lord Scarsdale. This comprises a fine reception room with windows opening onto the lake, for the ladies to fish from; below, at water level, is a cold plunge bath and a boat-house. Another example is to be seen at Exton Hall in Leicestershire, built in the early nineteenth century.

Extract from; "Life in the Country House" by David N Durant (published by John Murray), PB£15.99, see page twelve at the front of the book.

Loweswater, Cumbria. Cumbria Tourist Board.

Northern Counties England

Lord Barnard

CONTACT

Mr D R Hall
Administrator
Raby Castle
PO Box 50
Staindrop
Darlington
Co Durham
DL2 3AY

Tel: (01833) 660202

Fax: (01833) 660169

E-mail: D.Hall@Raby
Castle.onyxnet.co.uk

LOCATION

OS Ref. NZ129 218

On A688, 1m N of
Staindrop. 8m NE of
Barnard Castle, 12m WNW
of Darlington.

Rail: Darlington Station,
12m.

Air: Teesside Airport,
20m.

RABY CASTLE
Darlington

RABY CASTLE, home of Lord Barnard's family for over 370 years, is set in a 200 acre Deer Park. The Castle was mainly built in the 14th century, on the site of an earlier Manor House, by the powerful Neville family, who owned it until the Rising of the North in 1569, when Raby was seized by the Crown. It remained Crown property until 1626, when it was bought from Charles I by the eminent statesman and politician Sir Henry Vane, Lord Barnard's ancestor.

Despite its appearance, Raby was intended to be a fortified home rather than a fortress, although it played an important part in the Wars of the Roses and the English Civil War.

In the 18th century, the Castle was transformed from a rugged stronghold to an elegant country residence, with further alterations in the mid 19th century. Despite this, much of the original exterior remains, with important medieval rooms, notably the Great Kitchen (used for over 600 years until 1952), with its vast ranges and collection of Victorian copper utensils, and the original Garrison of the Castle, now the Servants' Hall.

Today, serene in its tranquil setting, Raby still conveys the sense of its historic past, enhanced by its elegant furnishings and renowned collection of Meissen porcelain. Raby is living history, not a dead museum.

❖

ℹ️ Shops. Game and soft fruits available in season. Lectures on Castle, its contents, gardens and history. No photography or video filming is permitted, slides are on sale.

♿ Suitable. WC.

☕ Tearooms.

🚶 Available. Tour time: 1½ hrs.

🅿️ Ample.

👫 Suitable for up to 60 children.

🐕 Guide dogs only in Castle. On leads in park.

OPENING TIMES

SUMMER

Castle
Easter & all BH weekends
Sat - Wed.

May - June
Wed & Sun only
1 - 5pm.

July - September
Daily except Sat
1 - 5pm.

Garden and Park
11am - 5.30pm on days
shown above.

Groups by arrangement
Easter - end June
Mon - Fri
10am - 4.30pm.

July - end September
Mon - Fri
Mornings only.

WINTER

October -Easter
Closed.

ADMISSION

Castle, Park & Gardens
Adult £4.00
Child £1.50
OAP........................£3.00
Bulmer's Tower £0.50
(when open)
Family (2 + 2/3)......£10.00

Park & Gardens
Adult £1.50
Child (5-15yrs) £1.00
OAP...................£1.00

Groups (min 25)
By arrangement.

AUCKLAND CASTLE

BISHOP AUCKLAND, CO. DURHAM DL14 7NR

Owner: Church Commissioners   Contact: The Manager

Tel: 01388 601627 **Fax:** 01388 609323

Principal country residence of the Bishops of Durham since Norman times and now the official residence of the present day Bishops. The Chapel, reputedly the largest private chapel in Europe, was originally the 12th century banquet hall. Chapel and State Rooms including the Throne Room, Long Dining Room and King Charles Dining Room are open to the public. Exhibition in the medieval kitchens dedicated to the life of St Cuthbert and the history of the Durham diocese. Access to the adjacent Bishop's Park with its 18th century Deer House.

Location: OS Ref. NZ213 301. Bishop Auckland, N end of town centre.

Opening Times: May & Jun: Fri & Sun, 2 - 5pm. Jul: Thur, Fri & Sun, 2 - 5pm. Aug: Thur, Fri, Sat & Sun, 2 - 5pm. Sept: Fri & Sun, 2 - 5pm. BH Mon: 2 - 5pm. Bishop's Park: daily, 7am - sunset. Last admission 1/2 hr before close.

Admission: Adult £3, Child/Conc. £2. Child under 12 free. Discounts available for group bookings. Bishop's Park: free

[i] Shop. Conferences, exhibitions, concerts. [X] Wedding receptions. Functions.
[k] Available.   [P] Ample.   [people] Welcome.   [dog] Guide dogs only.

AUCKLAND CASTLE DEER HOUSE   ⌘   **Tel:** 0191 2611585

Bishop Auckland, Durham

Owner: English Heritage   **Contact:** The North Regional Office

A charming building erected in 1760 in the Park of the Bishops of Durham so that the deer could shelter and find food.

Location: OS Ref. NZ216 305. In Bishop Auckland Park, just N of town centre on A689. About 500 yds N of the castle.

Opening Times: May - Sept: daily, 7am - sunset.

Admission: Free.

[dog] On leads.

BARNARD CASTLE   ⌘   **Tel:** 01833 638212

Barnard Castle, Castle House, Durham DL12 9AT

Owner: English Heritage   **Contact:** The Custodian

The substantial remains of this large Castle stand on a rugged escarpment overlooking the River Tees. Parts of the 14th century Great Hall and the cylindrical 12th century tower, built by the Baliol family can still be seen.

Location: OS92 Ref. NZ049 165. In Barnard Castle.

Opening Times: 1 Apr - 1 Nov: daily, 10am - 6pm. 2 Nov - 31 Mar: Wed - Sun, 10am - 4pm (closed 1   2pm). Closed 24 - 26 Dec.

Admission: Adult £2.20, Child £1.10, Conc. £1.70. 15% discount for groups of 11+.

[i] Shop. [wheelchair] Grounds suitable. [k] Inclusive. [P] No parking. [dog] In grounds, on leads.

DERWENTCOTE STEEL FURNACE   ⌘   **Tel:** 0191 2611585

Newcastle, Durham

Owner: English Heritage   **Contact:** The Custodian

Built in the 18th century it is the earliest and most complete authentic steel making furnace to have survived.

Location: OS Ref. NZ131 566. 10m SW of Newcastle N of the A694 between Rowland's Gill and Hamsterley.

Opening Times: 1 Apr - 30 Sept: 1 - 5pm, 1st & 3rd Sun of every month.

Admission: Free.

[P] Ample.   [dog] In grounds, on leads.

DURHAM CATHEDRAL   **Tel:** 01913 864266 **Fax:** 0191 3864267

Durham DH1 3EH   **Contact:** Miss A Heywood

A world heritage site. Norman architecture. Burial place of St Cuthbert and the Venerable Bede. Claustral buildings including Monk's Dormitory and medieval kitchen.

Location: OS Ref. NZ274 422. Durham city centre.

Opening Times: Summer: 7.15am - 8pm (2 May - 5 Sept), Winter: 7.15am - 6pm (6 Sept - 1 May). Sun services: 8am, 10am, 11.15am and 3.30pm. Weekday services: 7.30am, 9am and 5.15pm. Treasury will be closed for refurbishment from 9 Jan - end June.

Admission: Tower: Adult £2, Child £1, Monk's Dormitory: Adult 80p, Child 20p, Family £1.50. AV: Adult 80p, Child 20p, Family £1.50. Treasury: Adult £1, Child 20p.

[i] Shop.   [wheelchair] Ground floor & grounds suitable. WC.   [cup] Licensed restaurant.
[P] No parking.   [dog] Guide dogs only.

EGGLESTONE ABBEY   ⌘   **Tel:** 0191 2611585

Durham

Owner: English Heritage   **Contact:** The North Regional Office

Picturesque remains of a 12th century abbey, located in a bend of the River Tees. Substantial parts of the church and abbey buildings remain.

Location: OS Ref. NZ062 151. 1 1/2 m SE of Barnard Castle on minor road off B6277.

Opening Times: Any reasonable time.

Admission: Free.

[wheelchair] Grounds suitable.   [P] Limited.   [dog] In grounds, on leads.

FINCHALE PRIORY   ⌘   **Tel:** 0191 3863828

Finchdale Priory, Brasside, Newton Hall DH1 5SH

Owner: English Heritage   **Contact:** The Custodian

These beautiful 13th century priory remains are located beside the curving River Wear.

Location: OS85 Ref. NZ297 471. 4 1/2 m NE of Durham.

Opening Times: 1 Apr - 30 Sept: daily, 12 - 5pm.

Admission: Adult £1.20, Child 60p, Conc. 90p. 15% discount for groups of 11+.

[P] South side of river, charge payable.   [dog] On leads.

RABY CASTLE   🏛   See page 260 for full page entry.

ROKEBY PARK   🏛

ROKEBY PARK, NR BARNARD CASTLE, CO DURHAM DL12 9RZ

Owner: Trustees of Mortham Estate   Contact: Mrs P I Yeats (Curator)

Tel: 01833 637334

Rokeby, a fine example of a 18th century Palladian-style country house, was built by its owner Sir Thomas Robinson, a leading amateur architect of the day. The house was completed by 1735 and continued to be owned by Sir Thomas until 1769 when it was sold to J S Morritt, an ancestor of the present owner. A special feature of the house is a unique collection of needlework pictures worked in the 18th century by Anne Morritt with enormous skill. The house also has a very early 'print room'. For many years Velasquez's painting 'Toilet of Venus', now in the National Gallery, hung in the house and a very good copy can still be seen in the original room. Sir Walter Scott was a frequent guest at Rokeby and he dedicated his epic poem 'Rokeby' to his host.

Location: OS Ref. NZ082 142. Between A66 & Barnard Castle.

Opening Times: May BH (Mon), Spring BH (Mon & Tue) then Mon & Tue until 2nd Tue in Sept: 2 - 5pm. Last admission 4.30pm. Groups of 25+ on other days by appointment.

Admission: Adult £3.50, Child £1.50, OAP £3. Group prices on request.

[wheelchair] Ground floor suitable. WC.   [k] By arrangement.   [dog] No dogs.

Northern Counties England

LEIGHTON HALL
Carnforth

Mrs C S Reynolds
Leighton Hall
Carnforth
Lancashire
LA5 9ST

Tel: (01524) 734474

Fax: (01524) 720357

LOCATION

OS Ref. SD494 744

9m N of Lancaster,
10m S of Kendal,
3m N of Carnforth.
1 1/2 m W of A6.
3m from M6/A6/J35,
signed from J35A.

Rail: Lancaster
Station 9m.

Air: Manchester
Airport 65m.

Taxi: Carnforth Radio
Taxis, Carnforth 732763.

LEIGHTON HALL is one of the most beautifully sited houses in the British Isles, situated in a bowl of parkland, with the whole panorama of the Lakeland Fells rising behind. The Hall's neo-Gothic façade was superimposed on an 18th century house, which, in turn, had been built on the ruins of the original mediaeval house. The present owner is descended from Adam d'Avranches who built the first house in 1246.

The whole house is lived in by the Reynolds family and emphasis is put on making visitors feel welcome in a family home.

Connoisseurs of furniture will be particularly interested in the 18th century pieces by Gillow of Lancaster. Mr Reynolds is directly descended from the founder of Gillow and Company, hence the strong Gillow connection with the house. Also on show are some fine pictures, clocks, silver and objets d'art.

GARDENS

The main garden has a continuous herbaceous border and rose covered walls, while the Walled Garden contains flowering shrubs, a herb garden, an ornamental vegetable garden and a maze. Beyond is the Woodland Walk, where wild flowers abound from early Spring.

A varied collection of Birds of Prey is on display in the Bird Garden, and flown each afternoon that the Hall is open, weather permitting.

❖

Where Eagles Fly

ℹ Shop. Product launches, seminars, filming, garden parties, conferences, rallies, overland driving, archery and clay pigeon shoots, grand piano. No photography in house. Large collection of birds of prey on display in the afternoon, some of which fly at 3.30pm, weather permitting.

✗ Available for buffets, lunches, dinners and wedding receptions.

♿ Visitors may alight at the entrance.

☕ Restaurant. Groups must book, menus on request.

🏃 Available. By prior arrangement owner may meet groups, tour time: 45 mins. House and flying display tour time: 2 hrs. Lectures on property, its contents, gardens and history.

🅿 Ample.

👥 School programme 10am-2pm daily May-Sept except Mon & Sat. Birds of prey flown for schools at 12pm. Schools Visit Programme won the Sandford Award for Heritage Education in 1983 and in 1989.

🐕 Guide dogs only in the house & gardens.

OPENING TIMES

SUMMER

1 May - 30 September
Daily except Mon & Sat
2 - 5pm.
Open BH Mons.

August only:
11.30am - 5pm.

NB. Pre-booked parties of 25+ at any time by appointment.

WINTER

1 October - 30 April
Open to pre-booked groups of 25+.

ADMISSION

SUMMER

House, Garden & Birds

Adult £3.60
Child (up to 16yrs).......£2.40
OAP.........................£3.10
Groups (Min. payment £70)
Adult £3.00
Child (up to 16yrs).......£2.00
OAP.........................£3.00
Family (2 + 3) £11.00

Grounds only

Per person £1.50

WINTER

As above but groups by appointment only.

SPECIAL EVENTS

• **JUN 5/6/7:**
Antiques Fair

• **JUL 3:**
Open air concert with fireworks

• **AUG 7/8:**
Shakespeare in the Garden:
'A Midsummer Night's Dream'

• **SEPT: 12/13:**
Rainbow Craft Fair

• **OCT 3/4:**
Wedding Fair

• **OCT 18:**
Dolls House & Miniaturist Fair

CONFERENCE/FUNCTION		
ROOM	SIZE	MAX CAPACITY
Music Room	24' x 21' 6"	80

ASTLEY HALL

Tel: 01257 515555　**Fax:** 01257 515556

Astley Park, Off Hall Gate, Chorley, Lancashire PR7 1NP

Owner: Chorley Borough Council　　　　　**Contact:** Mrs Janet Ingham

A charming house, dating back to 1580, with additions in the 1660s & 1820s. Interiors include sumptuous plaster ceilings, fine 17th century oak furniture and tapestries, plus displays of fine and decorative art. Set in parkland.

Location: OS Ref. SD574 183. 2m W of Chorley, off A581 Chorley - Southport road. 5 mins from M61/J8.

Opening Times: Easter - end Oct: Tue - Sun, 12 - 5pm. Plus BH Mons. Nov - Easter: Fri - Sun, 12 - 4pm. Closed between Christmas and New Year.

Admission: Adult £2.80, Child/OAP/Student £1.80. Groups: Adult £2.20, Conc £1.20.

ⓘ Shop. Corporate hospitality. No photography. ♿ Partially suitable. Braille guide.

☕ Tearoom. Available. Guide dogs only. Civil Wedding Licence.

BLACKBURN CATHEDRAL

Tel: 01254 51491　**Fax:** 01254 699963

Blackburn, Lancashire BB1 5AA

　　　　　　　　　　　　　　　　　　　　Contact: Mrs Janet Ingham

On a historic Saxon site in town centre. Built as the Parish Church in 1826, subsequent extensions give a uniqueness to both interior and exterior. Features include the lantern tower, central altar with corona above, fine Walker organ, stained glass from medieval period onwards. Recent restoration work gives a new magnificence.

Location: OS Ref. SD684 280. 9m E of M6/J31, via A59 and A677. City centre.

Opening Times: Mon - Fri: 9am - 5.30pm, Sat: 9.30am - 4pm, Sun: 8am - 5pm.

Admission: Donation.

Available by prior arrangement.

BROWSHOLME HALL

Tel: 01254 826719　**Fax:** 01254 826739

Clitheroe, Lancashire BB7 3DE

Owner: Mr R R Parker　　　　　　　**Contact:** Mr R R Parker

Built in 1507 and set in a landscaped park, the ancestral home of the Parker family, with an Elizabethan facade and regency west wing re-cast by Sir Jeffrey Wyatville. Portraits including Devis and Romney, a major collection of furniture, arms, stained glass and other strange antiquities from Stone Age axes to fragment of a Zeppelin.

Location: OS Ref. SD683 452. 5m NW of Clitheroe off B6243.

Opening Times: Between 2 - 4pm, Good Fri, Easter weekend and Spring BH weekend. Aug: Fri, Sat & Sun and BH Mon. Groups at other times by appointment.

Admission: Adult £3, Child £1. Pre-arranged groups: Adult £2.80, Child £1.

ⓘ Shop. ♿ Partially suitable. ☕ Daytime booked groups only. Compulsory.

Ⓟ Ample. Teachers' pack. In grounds, on leads.

GAWTHORPE HALL

Tel: 01282 771004　**Fax:** 01282 770178

Padiham, Nr Burnley, Lancashire BB12 8UA

Owner: The National Trust　　　　　**Contact:** The Principal Keeper

The house was built in 1600-05, and restored by Sir Charles Barry in the 1850s. Barry's designs have been re-created in the principal rooms. Gawthorpe was the home of the Shuttleworth family, and the Rachel Kay-Shuttleworth textile collections are on display in the house, private study by arrangement. Collection of portraits on loan from the National Portrait Gallery.

Location: OS Ref. SD806 340. On E outskirts of Padiham, ³/₄ m to house on N of A671.

Opening Times: Hall: 1 Apr - 31 Oct: daily except Mon & Fri, open Good Fri & BH Mon, 1 - 5pm. Last adm. 4.15pm. Garden: All year, daily, 10am - 6pm.

Admission: Hall: Adult £2.90, Child £1.30, Family £8. Garden: free. Parties must book.

♿ Prior warning of visit essential. ☕ Tearoom. No dogs.

HALL I'TH'WOOD

Tel: 01204 301150

Greenway, Tonge Moor, Bolton BL1 8UA

Owner: Manchester City Council　　　　**Contact:** W H Farrell

Late mediaeval manor house with 17/18th century furniture, paintings and decorative art.

Location: OS Ref. SD724 116. 2m NNE of central Bolton. ¹/₄ m N of A58 ring road between A666 and A676 crossroads.

Opening Times: Apr - Sept: Tue - Sat, 11am - 4.30pm. Sun 2pm - 4.30pm. Closed Mon except BHs.

Admission: Adult £2, Conc. £1.

HOGHTON TOWER

HOGHTON, PRESTON, LANCASHIRE PR5 0SH

Owner: Sir Bernard de Hoghton　　Contact: C Daniels

Tel: 01254 852986　**Fax:** 01254 852109

Hoghton Tower, home of 14th Baronet, is one of the most dramatic looking houses in northern England. Three houses have occupied the hill site since 1100 with the present house re-built by Thomas Hoghton between 1560 - 1565. Rich and varied historical events including the Knighting of the Loin 'Sirloin' by James I in 1617.

Location: OS Ref. SD622 264. Midway between Preston & Blackburn on A675.

Opening Times: Jul, Aug & Sept: Mon - Thur, 11am - 4pm. Sun, 1 - 5pm. BH Sun & Mon excluding Christmas & New Year. Group visits by appointment all year.

Admission: House only: Adult £2.50, Child £1.25, Conc £2. Pre-arranged groups: Adult £3.50. Gardens, Shop & Tearoom only £1.

ⓘ Shop. Conferences, corporate hospitality. ✕ Wedding receptions.

♿ Not suitable. ☕ Tearoom. Compulsory. Ⓟ Ample.

Educational programme. No dogs.

LEIGHTON HALL

See page 262 for full page entry.

MANCHESTER CATHEDRAL

Tel: 0161 833 2220　**Fax:** 0161 839 6226

Manchester M3 1SX

In addition to regular worship and daily offices, there are frequent professional concerts, day schools, organ recitals, guided tours and brassrubbing. The Cathedral contains a wealth of beautiful carvings and has the widest medieval nave in Britain.

Location: OS Ref. SJ838 988. Manchester.

Opening Times: Daily.

Admission: Donations welcome.

ⓘ Shop. ♿ Partially suitable. WCs. By arrangement. Guide dogs only.

MARTHOLME

Great Harwood, Blackburn, Lancashire BB6 7UJ

Owner: Mr & Mrs T H Codling　　　　　**Contact:** Miss P M Codling

Part of medieval manor house with 17th century additions and Elizabethan gatehouse.

Location: OS Ref. SD753 338. 2m NE of Great Harwood off A680 to Whalley.

Opening Times: By written appointment only.

Admission: £3.50.

♿ Not suitable. Compulsory. Ⓟ Limited. Guide dogs only.

ROSSENDALE MUSEUM

Tel: 01706 217777 or 01706 226509

Whitaker Park, Rawtenstall, Rossendale, Lancashire BB4 6RE

Owner: Rossendale Borough Council　　　　**Contact:** Mrs S Cruise

Former 19th century mill owner's house set in Whitaker Park. Displays include fine and decorative arts, furniture, a Victorian drawing room, plus local/social history, natural history and costume.

Location: OS Ref. SD805 226. Off A681, ¹/₄ m from Rawtenstall Centre.

Opening Times: Apr - Oct: Mon - Fri, 1 - 5pm, Sat 10am - 5pm, Sun 12 - 5pm. Nov - Mar: Mon - Fri, 1 - 5pm, Sat, 10am - 4pm, Sun, 12 - 4pm. BH, 1 - 5pm. Closed Christmas Day, Boxing Day and New Year's Day.

Admission: Free.

♿ Ground floor & grounds suitable. WC. In grounds, on leads. Guide dogs.

Northern Counties England

RUFFORD OLD HALL

Tel/Fax: 01704 821254

Rufford, Nr Ormskirk, Lancashire L40 1SG

Owner: The National Trust   **Contact:** Mrs Maureen Dodsworth

There is a legend that William Shakespeare performed here for the owner Sir Thomas Hesketh in the Great Hall of this, one of the finest 16th century buildings in Lancashire. The playwright would have delighted in the magnificent hall with its intricately carved movable wooden screen. Built in 1530, it established the Hesketh family seat for the next 250 years. In the Carolean Wing, altered in 1821, there are fine collections of 16th and 17th century oak furniture, arms, armour and tapestries.

Location: OS Ref. SD463 160. 7m N of Ormskirk, in village of Rufford on E side of A59.

Opening Times: 1 Apr - 1 Nov: Sat - Wed, 1 - 5pm. Last admission 4.30pm. Also open selected Thurs: 16 Apr, 28 May, 23 Jul - 27 Aug & 29 Oct. Garden: same days as house, 12 - 5.30pm.

Admission: House & Garden: Adult £3.50, Child £1.70, Family £9.50. Garden only: £1.80. Children free during school holidays. Reduction for pre-booked groups (no groups on Sun & BH Mon).

Shop.   Limited suitability.   Tearoom.   In grounds, on leads.

SAMLESBURY HALL

Tel: 01254 812010   **Fax:** 01254 812174

Preston New Road, Preston PR5 0UP

Owner: Samlesbury Hall Trust   **Contact:** Mr David Hornby

Built in 1325, the hall is an attractive black and white timbered manor house set in extensive grounds. Relax in pleasant surroundings and enjoy a superb selection of antiques, collectors items, crafts and exhibitions.

Location: OS Ref. SD623 305. N side of A677, 4m WNW of Blackburn.

Opening Times: All year everyday except Mon: 11am - 4.30pm. Closed over Christmas and New Year.

Admission: Adult £2.50, Child £1. Parking for 70 cars.

Ground floor & grounds suitable. WC.   Licensed tearoom.   Guide dogs only.

SMITHILLS HALL MUSEUM

Tel: 01204 841265

Smithills Dean Road, Bolton BL1 7NP

Owner: Bolton Metropolitan Borough Council   **Contact:** W H Farrell

14th century fortified Manor House with Tudor panelling. Stuart furniture. Stained glass.

Location: OS Ref. SD699 119. 2m NW of central Bolton, ½ m N of A58 ringroad.

Opening Times: Apr - Sept: Tue - Sat, 11am - 4.30pm. Sun 2 - 4.30pm. Closed Mon except BHs.

Admission: Adult £2, Conc. £1.

STONYHURST COLLEGE

Tel: 01254 826345   **Fax:** 01254 826732

Stonyhurst, Clitheroe, Lancashire BB7 9PZ

Contact: Mrs F Aherne

The original house dates from the late 16th century. Set in extensive grounds with ornamental gardens.

Location: OS Ref. SD690 391. 4m SW of Clitheroe off B6243.

Opening Times: House: 20 Jul - 24 Aug: Sat - Thur (including Aug BH Mon), 1 - 5pm. Grounds & Gardens: 1 Jul - 24 Aug: Sat - Thur (including Aug BH Mon), 1 - 5pm.

Admission: House & Grounds: Adult £4, Child (4 - 14) £3, OAP £3. Grounds only £1.

Shop.   Refreshments.   Available.

TOWNELEY HALL ART GALLERY & MUSEUMS

Burnley BB11 3RQ   **Tel:** 01282 424213   **Fax:** 01282 436138

Owner: Burnley Borough Council   **Contact:** Miss Susan Bourne

House dates from the 14th century with 17th and 19th century modifications. Collections include oak furniture, 18th and 19th century paintings. There is a Museum of Local Crafts and Industries and a Natural History Centre with an aquarium in the grounds.

Location: OS Ref. SD854 309. ½ m SE of Burnley on E side of Todmorden Road (A671).

Opening Times: All year: Mon - Fri, 10am - 5pm. Sun 12 - 5pm. Closed Sat throughout the year. Closed Christmas - New Year.

Admission: Free. Guided tours: Tue, Wed & Thur afternoons.

Shop. Plant centre.   Grounds floor & grounds suitable. WC.   Tearoom.

TURTON TOWER

Tel: 01204 852203   **Fax:** 01204 853754

Chapeltown Road, Turton BL7 0HG

Owner: Lancashire County Council   **Contact:** Martin Dowland

Medieval Tower extended by Tudors, Stuarts and Victorians.

Location: OS Ref. SD733 153. On B6391, 4m N of Bolton.

Opening Times: Feb & Nov: Sun 1 - 4pm. Mar, Apr & Oct: Sat - Wed: 1 - 4pm. May - Sept: Mon - Thur, 10am - 12pm, 1 - 5pm. Sat & Sun 1 - 5pm.

Admission: Adult £2, Child/OAP £1, Family £5.

Shop.   Partially suitable. WCs.   Tearoom.   By arrangement.   Ample.   Educational programme.   In grounds, on leads.

WARTON OLD RECTORY

Tel: 0191 261 1585

Warton, Carnforth, Lancashire

Owner: English Heritage   **Contact:** The North Regional Office

A rare medieval stone house with remains of the hall, chambers and domestic offices.

Location: OS Ref. SD499 723. At Warton, 1m N of Carnforth on minor road off A6.

Opening Times: Any reasonable time.

Admission: Free.

Ground floor suitable.   No parking.   In grounds, on leads.

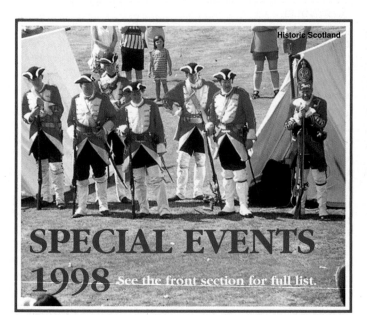

Historic Scotland

SPECIAL EVENTS 1998 See the front section for full list.

Chimney-glass or overmantel mirror:

A French architect, Robert de Cotte (1656–1735), is credited with the introduction of mirrors placed over fireplaces, and the fashion came to Britain in the early eighteenth century. From the beginning it posed problems. British glass-makers could not produce large pieces of flat glass, so mirrors were therefore made up of smaller pieces, the joins covered by fillets of decorated gold-work. In France the secret of making large pieces of glass was discovered at the St Gobain glass works in Picardy at the end of the seventeenth century, and larger and larger pieces were produced as the eighteenth century progressed. However, French glass was expensive even in France, and in Britain the cost was even greater, so it was rarely used. Overmantel-mirrors of French glass may be seen at Osterley Park, Greater London, fitted by Robert Adam in the 1760s and at Newby Hall in North Yorkshire, again by Adam (1770s). It was only in the 1790s that the Ravenhead Glass Works in Lancashire was able to manufacture glass of comparable size to the French.

Extract from: "Life in the Country House" by David N Durant (published by John Murray), PB£15.99, see page twelve at the front of the book.

CROXTETH HALL & COUNTRY PARK Tel: 0151 228 5311 Fax: 0151 228 2817

Liverpool, Merseyside L12 0HB

Owner: Liverpool City Council   **Contact:** Mrs Irene Vickers

Ancestral home of the Molyneux family. 500 acres country park. Special events and attractions most weekends.

Location: OS Ref. SJ408 943. 5m NE of Liverpool city centre.

Opening Times: Parkland: daily throughout the year. Hall, Farm & Garden: daily, 11am - 5pm during main season. Telephone for exact dates.

Admission: Parkland: Free.

♿ Suitable.   ☕ Café.

LIVERPOOL CATHEDRAL   Tel: 0151 709 6271 Fax: 0151 709 1112

Liverpool, Merseyside L1 7AZ

Owner: The Dean and Chapter   **Contact:** Canon Noel Vincent

Sir Giles Gilbert Scott's greatest creation. Built this century from local sandstone with superb glass, stonework and major works of art, it is the largest Cathedral in Britain and has a fine musical tradition, a tower offering panoramic views, and an award-winning refectory. There is a unique collection of church embroidery, a full range of souvenirs, cards and religious books.

Location: OS Ref. SJ354 893. Central Liverpool, 1/2 m S of Lime Street Station.

Opening Times: 8am - 6pm. Sun services: 8am, 10.30am, 3pm, 4pm. Weekdays: 8am & 5.30pm. Sat: 8am & 3pm.

Admission: Donation.

ℹ Shop. Conference facilities.   ♿ Grounds suitable. WC.   ☕ Refectory.

P Ample.   Educational programme.   Guide dogs only.

LIVERPOOL CATHEDRAL CHURCH OF CHRIST THE KING

Liverpool, Merseyside L3 5TQ   **Tel:** 0151 709 9222 **Fax:** 0151 708 7274

Owner: Roman Catholic Archdiocese of Liverpool   **Contact:** Rt Rev P Cookson

Modern circular cathedral with spectacular glass by John Piper and numerous modern works of art. Extensive earlier crypt by Lutyens. Grade II* listed.

Location: OS Ref. SJ356 903. Central Liverpool, 1/2 m E of Lime Street Station.

Opening Times: 8am - 6pm (closes 5pm Sun in Winter). Sun services: 8.30am, 10am, 11am, 3pm & 7pm. Weekday services: 8am, 12.15pm, 5.15pm & 5.45pm. Sat 9am & 6.30pm.

Admission: Donation.

ℹ Shop.   X Wedding receptions.   ♿ Grounds suitable. WCs.

☕ Licensed tearoom.   By arrangement.   P Ample for cars.

Educational programme.   Guide dogs only.

MEOLS HALL   Tel: 01704 228326 Fax: 01704 507185

Churchtown, Southport, Merseyside PR9 7LZ

Owner: Robert Hesketh Esq   **Contact:** Pamela Whelan

17th century house with subsequent additions. Interesting collection of pictures and furniture. Newly refurbished Tithe Barn may be hired for corporate and private events. Accommodates 120 people. Clay shooting and other activities in the grounds.

Location: OS Ref. SD365 184. 3m NE of Southport town centre in Churchtown. SE of A565.

Opening Times: 14 Aug - 14 Sept: daily, 2 - 5pm. Open at other times throughout the year by prior arrangement for coach parties. Afternoon tea included for groups.

Admission: Adult £3, Child £1. Groups £8 inclusive of afternoon tea.

ℹ Conference facilities. Corporate hospitality. 4 x 4 course.   X Wedding receptions.

♿ Suitable. WCs.   Compulsory, and by arrangement for coach parties.

P Ample.   In grounds, on leads. Guide dogs only in house.

SPECIAL EVENTS

JUN 27/28: Southport Vintage/Yesteryear show

JUL 25: The Great Northern Western Line Dancing Competition

JUL 26: Summer Proms in the Park   **SEPT 27:** Churchtown Country Show

NOV 7: Grand Bonfire & Firework Display

PORT SUNLIGHT HERITAGE CENTRE   Tel: 0151 6446466 Fax: 0151 6458973

95 Greendale Road, Port Sunlight L62 4XE   **Contact:** Information Officer

Port Sunlight is a picturesque 19th century garden village on the Wirral, built by William Hesketh Lever for the workers in his soap factory.

Location: OS Ref. SJ340 845. Follow signs from M53/J4 or 5 or follow signs on A41.

Opening Times: 1 Apr - 30 Oct: daily, 10am - 4pm. Nov - Mar: Mon - Fri, 10am - 4pm.

Admission: Adult/Conc. 40p, Child 20p. Groups 12+ £5.

ℹ Shop.   ♿ Ground floor suitable.   Available for pre-booked coach parties.

SPEKE HALL   Tel: 0151 427 7231 Fax: 0151 427 9860

The Walk, Liverpool L24 1XD   **Info Line:** 0345 585702 (local rate)

Owner: The National Trust   **Contact:** The Property Manager

One of the most famous half-timbered houses in the country, set in varied gardens and attractive wooded estate. Tudor Great Hall, Victorian interiors, William Morris wallpapers. Rose and Stream Gardens. Woodland walks and stunning views of the Mersey estuary.

Location: OS Ref. SJ419 825. North bank of the Mersey, 6m SE of city centre. Follow signs for Liverpool airport.

Opening Times: House: 4 Apr - 31 Oct: daily except Mon (but open BH Mon), 1 - 5.30pm. 25 Oct - 31 Oct: closes 4.30pm. 1 Nov - 13 Dec: Sat & Sun, 1 - 4.30pm. Garden: 4 Apr - 31 Oct: open as house from 12 noon. Nov - Mar 1998: daily except Mon, 12 - 4pm. Closed 24/25/26/31 Dec & 1 Jan. Last admission 30 mins before close.

Admission: House & Garden: £4. Garden only: £1.40, half price for children. Family £10.

ℹ Shop.   ♿ Ground floor & grounds suitable.   ☕ Tearoom.   In grounds, on leads.

KINGS AND QUEENS FROM 1485 TO 1998

DYNASTIES / Periods / Reigns	DATES	DYNASTIES / Periods / Reigns	DATES
TUDOR		HANOVER	
Tudor	1485 - 1558	Georgian	1714 - 1811
	Henry VII 1485 -	George I	1714 - 1727
1509		George II	1727 - 1760
Henry VIII	1509 - 1547	George III	1760 - 1820
Edward VI	1547 - 1553	Regency	1811 - 1837
Mary I (Bloody Mary)	1553 - 1558	George IV	1820 - 1830
Elizabethan	1558 - 1603	William IV	1830 - 1837
Elizabeth I	1558 - 1603	Victorian	1837 - 1901
STUART		Victoria	1837 - 1901
Jacobean	1603 - 1625	Edwardian	1901 - 1910
James I	1603 - 1625	Edward VII	1901 - 1910
(James VI of Scotland)		WINDSOR	
Carolean	1625 - 1702	George V	1910 - 1936
Charles I	1625 - 1649	Edward VIII	1936
The Commonwealth	1649 - 1660	George VI	1936 - 1952
Charles II	1660 - 1685	Elizabeth II	1952 - Present
James II	1685 - 1688		
William and Mary	1688 - 1702		
William III (of Orange)	1688 - 1702		
and Mary II (died 1694)			
Queen Anne	1702 - 1714		
Anne	1702 - 1714		

Northern Counties
England

ALNWICK CASTLE
Alnwick

ALNWICK CASTLE, home of the Duke of Northumberland, is the second largest inhabited Castle in England after Windsor and has been in the possession of the Percys, Earls and Dukes of Northumberland, since 1309. The earliest parts of the present Castle were erected by Yvo de Vescy, the first Norman Baron of Alnwick who became the owner of the town soon after 1096.

The rugged medieval exterior belies the richness of the interior, refurbished in the classical style of the Italian Renaissance. This replaces the Gothic decoration carried out by Robert Adam in the 18th century.

The Castle houses an exquisite collection of art treasures, including the finest examples of Italian paintings in the north of England with works by other great artists including Van Dyck and Turner. In addition to fine English and French furniture and ornately carved wooden ceilings, the Castle also houses one of the country's most important collections of early Meissen porcelain.

Other attractions include the Percy State Coach, the dungeon, the gun terrace and the gardens, which offer peaceful walks and superb views over the surrounding countryside.

The Duchess of Northumberland's millennium project is the restoration of the formal Italian Gardens created during the 19th century by the 4th Duke.

CONTACT

A Fricker
Alnwick Castle
Estate Office
Alnwick
Northumberland
NE66 1NQ

Tel: (01665) 510777
or (01665) 603942
weekends only

Fax: (01665) 510876

LOCATION

OS Ref. NU187 135

In Alnwick 1½ m W of A1

From London 6 hrs,
Edinburgh 2 hrs,
Chester 4 hrs,
Newcastle under 1 hr.

Bus: From bus station in Alnwick.

Rail: Alnmouth Station 5m.

OPENING TIMES

SUMMER
Easter - end September
Daily except Fri
11am - 5pm
Last admission 4.15pm.

Open all BHs including
Good Fri.

WINTER
October - Easter
Pre-booked parties only.

ADMISSION

SUMMER
House & Garden
Adult......................£5.95
Child*.....................£3.50
OAP/Student..........£5.45
Family (2+2)....... £15.00

Pre-booked Groups
(min 12)
Adult......................£5.45
Child*.....................£3.20
OAP/Student..........£5.25

Grounds
Per person.................£4.00

WINTER
By arrangement only.

* Age 5 - 16

CONFERENCE/FUNCTION		
ROOM	SIZE	MAX CAPACITY
The Great Guest Hall	100' x 30'	300

ℹ Shop. Conference facilities, corporate hospitality. Fashion Shows, fairs, filming, parkland for hire. No photography inside the castle. No unaccompanied children.

✕ Wedding receptions.

♿ Please telephone for details. Partially suitable. WC.

☕ Tearoom, coffee, light lunches and teas, seats 80.

🅿 70 cars and 4 coaches.

👥 Guidebook and worksheet, special rates for children and teachers.

🐕 Guide dogs only.

CONTACT

P Bolam
R G Bolam & Son
Townfoot
Rothbury
Northumberland
NE65 7SP

Tel: (01669) 620314

Fax: (01669) 621236

LOCATION

OS Ref. NU184 351

42m N of
Newcastle-upon-Tyne.
20m S of Berwick upon
Tweed. 6m E of Belford by
B1342 from A1 at Belford.

Bus: Bus service
200 yards.

Rail: Berwick-upon-
Tweed 20m.

Taxi: J Swanston
(01289) 306124.

Air: Newcastle-upon-
Tyne 45m.

BAMBURGH CASTLE
Bamburgh

BAMBURGH CASTLE is the home of Lady Armstrong and her family. The earliest reference to Bamburgh shows the craggy citadel to have been a royal centre by AD 547. Recent archaeological excavation has revealed that the site has been occupied since prehistoric times.

The Norman Keep has been the stronghold for nearly nine centuries, but the remainder has twice been extensively restored, initially by Lord Crewe in the 1750s and subsequently by the first Lord Armstrong at the end of the 19th century. This Castle was the first to succumb to artillery fire - that of Edward IV.

The public rooms contain many exhibits, including the loan collections of armour from HM Tower of London, the John George Joicey Museum, Newcastle-upon-Tyne and other private sources, which complement the Castle's armour. Porcelain, china, jade, furniture from many periods, oils, water-colours and a host of interesting items are all contained within one of the most important buildings of Britain's national heritage.

VIEWS

The views from the ramparts are unsurpassed and take in Holy Island, the Farne Islands, one of Northumberland's finest beaches and, landwards, the Cheviot Hills.

OPENING TIMES

April - October
Daily, 11am - 5pm.
Last entry 4.30pm.

Tours by arrangement
at any time.

ADMISSION

SUMMER

Adult £3.50
Child* £1.50
OAP.........................£2.50
Groups**
Adult £2.50
Child* £1.00
OAP.........................£1.50

* 6 to 16
** Min payment £30

WINTER

Group rates only quoted.

i Shop. Filming. No photography in house.

Limited access. WC.

Tearooms for light refreshments. Groups can book.

By arrangement at any time, min charge out of hours £30.

P 100 cars, coaches park on tarmac drive at entrance.

Welcome. Guide provided if requested, educational pack.

Guide dogs only.

CHILLINGHAM CASTLE
Nr Alnwick

This remarkable Castle, the home of Sir Humphry Wakefield Bt, with its alarming dungeons has, since the 1200s, been continuously owned by the family of the Earls Grey and their relations. You will see active restoration of complex masonry, metalwork and ornamental plaster as the great halls and state rooms are gradually brought back to life with antique furniture, tapestries, arms and armour as of old and even a torture chamber.

At first a 12th century stronghold, Chillingham became a fully fortified Castle in the 14th century. Wrapped in the nation's history it occupied a strategic position as a fortress during Northumberland's bloody border feuds, often besieged and at many times enjoying the patronage of royal visitors. In Tudor days there were additions but the underlying medieval character has always been retained. The 18th and 19th centuries saw decorative refinements and extravagances including the lake, garden and grounds laid out by Sir Jeffrey Wyatville, fresh from his triumphs at Windsor Castle.

GARDENS

With romantic grounds the Castle commands breathtaking views of the surrounding countryside. As you walk to the lake you will see, according to the season, drifts of snowdrops, daffodils or bluebells and an astonishing display of rhododendrons. This emphasises the restrained formality of the Elizabethan topiary garden, with its intricately clipped hedges of box and yew. Lawns, the formal gardens and woodland walks are all fully open to the public.

❖

CONTACT

The Administrator
Chillingham Castle
Near Alnwick
Northumberland
NE66 5NJ

Tel: (01668) 215359

Fax: (01668) 215463

LOCATION

OS Ref. NU062 258

45m N of Newcastle
between A697 & A1.
2m S of B6348 at Chatton.
6m SE of Wooler.

Rail: Alnmouth or Berwick

CONFERENCE/FUNCTION		
ROOM	SIZE	MAX CAPACITY
King James I Room		120
Great Hall		150
Minstrels' Hall		75
2 x Drawing Room		60 each
Museum		150
Tea Room		100
Lower Gallery		30
Upper Gallery		40

OPENING TIMES

SUMMER
1 May - 30 September
12 - 5pm
closed Tue.

July - August and BHs,
Daily
12 - 5pm.

WINTER
January - December
any time by
appointment only.

ADMISSION

SUMMER
Adult £3.90
OAP..........................£3.75
Child*........................Free

Groups (min 10)
Per person £3.30
Pre-booking is essential.
Guided tours available

* up to 5 accompanied
children

i Shop.
Corporate hospitality.

X Corporate entertainment, lunches, drinks, dinners, wedding ceremonies and receptions.

Tearoom, booked meals for up to 100.

Guided group tours by arrangement.

P Avoid Lilburn route, coach parties especially welcome by prior arrangement.

No dogs.

A 8 self-contained 2 bedroom apartments. For up to 30 guests.

Civil Wedding Licence.

ALNWICK CASTLE

See page 266 for full page entry.

AYDON CASTLE   Tel: 01434 632450

Corbridge, Northumberland NE45 5PJ
Owner: English Heritage   **Contact:** The Custodian
One of the finest fortified manor houses in England, dating from the late 13th century. Its survival, intact, can be attributed to its conversion to a farmhouse in the 17th century.
Location: OS87 Ref. NZ002 663. 2m NE of Corbridge, on minor road off B6321 or A68.
Opening Times: 1 Apr - 1 Nov: daily, 10am - 6pm or dusk if earlier in Oct.
Admission: Adult £1.90, Child £1, Conc. £1.40. 15% discount for groups of 11+.

[i] Shop.   [&] Ground floor & grounds suitable.   [☕] Kiosk.   [P] Limited.
[🐕] In grounds, on leads.

BAMBURGH CASTLE

See page 267 for full page entry.

BELSAY HALL, CASTLE & GARDENS

See opposite.

BERWICK BARRACKS   Tel: 01289 304493

The Parade, Berwick-upon-Tweed, Northumberland TD15 1DF
Owner: English Heritage   **Contact:** The Custodian
Among the earliest purpose built barracks, these have changed very little since 1717. They house an exhibition 'By Beat of Drum', which recreates scenes such as the barrack room from the life of the British infantryman, the Museum of the King's Own Scottish Borderers and the Borough Museum with fine art, local history exhibition and other collections. Guided tours available.
Location: OS75 Ref. NT994 535. On the Parade, off Church Street, Berwick town centre.
Opening Times: 1 Apr - 1 Nov: daily, 10am - 6pm (dusk if earlier in Oct). 2 Nov - 31 Mar: Wed - Sun, 10am - 4pm. Closed 1 - 2pm and 24 - 26 Dec.
Admission: Adult £2.50, Child £1.30, Conc. £1.90. 15% discount for groups of 11+.

[i] Shop.   [&] Ground floor & grounds suitable.   [P] Limited.   [🐕] In grounds, on leads.

BERWICK RAMPARTS   Tel: 0191 261 1585

Berwick-upon-Tweed, Northumberland
Owner: English Heritage   **Contact:** The North Regional Office
A remarkably complete system of town fortifications consisting of gateways, ramparts and projecting bastions built in the 16th century.
Location: OS Ref. NT994 535. Surrounding Berwick town centre on N bank of River Tweed.
Opening Times: Any reasonable time.
Admission: Free.

[&] Grounds suitable.   [🐕] In grounds, on leads.

BRINKBURN PRIORY   Tel: 01665 570628

Long Framlington, Morpeth, Northumberland NE65 8AF
Owner: English Heritage   **Contact:** The Custodian
This late 12th century church is a fine example of early Gothic architecture, almost perfectly preserved, and is set in a lovely spot beside the River Coquet.
Location: OS81, Ref. NZ116 984. 4$\frac{1}{2}$m SE of Rothbury off B6344 5m W of A1.
Opening Times: 1 Apr - 1 Nov: daily, 10am - 6pm (or dusk in Oct).
Admission: Adult £1.50, Child 80p, Conc. £1.10. 15% discount for groups of 11+.

[&] Not suitable.   [P] Limited.

View from Bamburgh Castle, Northumberland.

Northumbria Tourist Board.

BELSAY HALL, CASTLE & GARDENS

BELSAY, NR PONTELAND, NORTHUMBERLAND NE20 0DX
Owner: English Heritage   Contact: The Custodian

Tel: 01661 881636 **Fax:** 01661 881043
Belsay is one of the most remarkable estates in Northumberland's border country. The buildings, set amidst 30 acres of magnificent landscaped gardens, have been occupied by the same family for nearly 600 years. The gardens, created largely in the 19th century, are a fascinating mix of the formal and the informal with terraced gardens, a rhododendron garden, magnolia garden, mature woodland and even a winter garden. The buildings comprise a 14th century castle, a manor house and Belsay Hall, an internationally famous mansion designed by Sir Charles Monck in the 19th century in the style of classical buildings he had encountered during a tour of Greece.

Location: OS87, Ref. NZ088 785. In Belsay 14m (22.4 km) NW of Newcastle on SW of A696. 7m NW of Ponteland. Nearest airport and station is Newcastle.
Opening Times: 1 Apr - 1 Nov: daily, 10am - 6pm or dusk in Oct. 2 Nov - 31 Mar: 10am - 4pm.
Admission: Adult £3.60, Child £2.70, Conc. £1.80. Groups: Adult £2.97, Child £2.20, Conc. £1.53.

[i] Shop.   [&] Partially suitable. WC.
[☕] During summer & weekends in Mar & Oct.
[🚶] Introductory talk on request.   [P] Ample.
[👥] Free if booked in advance.   [🐕] In grounds on leads.

CAPHEATON HALL
Tel: 01830 530253

Newcastle-upon-Tyne NE19 2AB

Owner: J Browne-Swinburne   **Contact:** J Browne-Swinburne

Built for Sir John Swinburne in 1668 by Robert Trollope, an architect of great and original talent.

Location: OS Ref. NZ038 805. 17m NW of Newcastle off A696.

Opening Times: By written appointment only.

Admission: Adult £3.

CHERRYBURN
Tel: 01661 843276

Station Bank, Mickley, Stocksfield, Northumberland NE43 7DB

Owner: The National Trust   **Contact:** The Administrator

Birthplace of Northumbria's greatest artist, wood engraver and naturalist, Thomas Bewick, b.1753. The Museum explores his famous works and life with occasional demonstrations of wood block printing in the printing house. Farmyard animals, picnic area, garden.

Location: OS Ref. NZ075 627. 11m W of Newcastle on A695 (200yds signed from Mickley Square). 1¹/₂ m W of Prudhoe.

Opening Times: 2 Apr - 1 Nov: daily except Tue & Wed, 1 - 5.30pm. Last admission 5pm.

Admission: Adult £2.80. No group rate.

ℹ️ Shop.   ♿ Some steps. WC.   ☕ Morning coffee for pre-booked parties.

CHESTERS ROMAN FORT & MUSEUM

CHOLLERFORD, NR HEXHAM, NORTHUMBERLAND NE46 4EP
Owner: English Heritage   *Contact:* The Custodian

Tel: 01434 681379

The best preserved example of a Roman cavalry fort in Britain, including remains of the bath house on the banks of the River North Tyne. The museum houses a fascinating collection of Roman sculpture and inscriptions.

Location: OS87, Ref. NY913 701. 1¹/₂ m from Chollerford on B6318.

Opening Times: 1 Apr - 1 Nov: daily, 9.30am - 6pm or dusk if earlier in Oct. 2 Nov - 31 Mar: daily, 10am - 4pm. Closed 24 - 26 Dec.

Admission: Adult £2.70, Child £1.40, Conc. £2. 15% discount for groups of 11+. Free coach parking.

ℹ️ Shop.   ♿ Grounds suitable. WC.   ☕ Summer only.   🅿️ Ample.

🐕 In grounds, on leads.

CHILLINGHAM CASTLE
See page 268 for full page entry.

CHIPCHASE CASTLE
Tel: 01434 230203 **Fax:** 01434 230740

Wark, Hexham, Northumberland NE48 3NT

Owner: Mrs P J Torday   **Contact:** Mrs P J Torday

The Castle overlooks the River North Tyne and is set in formal and informal gardens. One walled garden is used as a nursery specialising in unusual perennial plants.

Location: OS Ref. NY882 758. 10m NW of Hexham via A6079 to Chollerton. 2m SE of Wark.

Opening Times: Castle: 1 - 28 Jun: daily 2 - 5pm. Tours by arrangement at other times. Castle Gardens & Nursery: Easter - 31 Jul, Thur - Sun and BH Mon, 10am - 5pm.

Admission: Castle £3, Garden £1.50, concessions available, Nursery free.

♿ Not suitable.   🏃 Compulsory.   🐕 No dogs.

CORBRIDGE ROMAN SITE
Tel: 01434 632349

Corbridge, Northumberland NE45 5NT

Owner: English Heritage   **Contact:** The Custodian

A fascinating series of excavated remains, including foundations of granaries with a grain ventilation system. From artefacts found, which can be seen in the site museum, we know a large settlement developed around this supply depot.

Location: OS87 Ref. NY983 649. ¹/₂ m NW of Corbridge on minor road, signposted for Corbridge Roman Site.

Opening Times: 1 Apr - 1 Nov: daily, 10am - 6pm or dusk if earlier in Oct. 2 Nov - 31 Mar: Wed - Sun, 10am - 4pm. Closed 1 - 2pm and 24 - 26 Dec.

Admission: Adult £2.70, Child £1.40, Conc. £2. 15% discount for groups of 11+.

ℹ️ Shop.   ♿ Partially suitable.   🏃 Inclusive audio tour.

🅿️ Limited for coaches.   🐕 In grounds, on leads.

CRAGSIDE
Tel/Fax: 01669 620150

Rothbury, Morpeth, Northumberland NE65 7PX

Owner: The National Trust   **Contact:** Property Manager

Set in 1,000 acres of pine covered hillside, lakes and rumbling streams, the Victorian mansion built for the first Lord Armstrong is a showcase of Victorian art, architecture and technology. Explore over 40 miles of footpaths through the woods, admire the rotating pots in the Orchard House or simply relax with friends in the Visitor Centre.

Location: OS Ref. NU073 022. 13m SW of Alnwick B6341. 1m NE of Morpeth on Wooler Road A697.

Opening Times: House: 1 Apr - 1 Nov: daily except Mon (open BH Mon), 1 - 5.30pm. Last admission 4.45pm. Grounds: as house, 10.30am - 7pm, last admission 5pm, also Nov - Dec: weekends and selected weekdays. Garden: As grounds: 10.30am - 6.30pm.

Admission: House, Garden & Grounds: £6, Pre-booked groups £5.70, Family (2 + 2) £15. Garden & Grounds: £3.80, Pre-booked groups £3.50. Accompanied children under 12 free during school holidays.

ℹ️ Shop.   ♿ Suitable. WC.   ☕ Restaurant.   💐 Civil Wedding Licence.

DUNSTANBURGH CASTLE
Tel: 01665 576231

c/o 14 Queen Street, Alnwick, Northumberland NE66 1RD

Owner: The National Trust   **Guardian:** English Heritage   **Contact:** The Custodian

An easy, but bracing, coastal walk leads to the eerie skeleton of this wonderful 14th century castle sited on a basalt crag, rearing up more than 100 feet from the waves crashing on the rocks below. The surviving ruins include the large gatehouse, which later became the keep, and curtain walls.

Location: OS75 Ref. NU258 220. 8m NE of Alnwick.

Opening Times: 1 Apr - 1 Nov: daily, 10am - 6pm or dusk if earlier in Oct. 2 Nov - 31 Mar: Wed - Sun, 10am - 4pm. Closed 24 - 26 Dec.

Admission: Adult £1.70, Child 90p, Conc. £1.30. 15% discount for groups of 11+.

♿ Not suitable.   🅿️ No parking.   🐕 In grounds, on leads.

EDLINGHAM CASTLE
Tel: 0191 2611585

Edlingham, Alnwick, Northumberland

Owner: English Heritage   **Contact:** The North Regional Office

Set beside a splendid railway viaduct this complex ruin has defensive features spanning the 13th and 15th centuries.

Location: OS Ref. NU115 092. At E end of Edlingham village, on minor road off B6341 6m SW of Alnwick.

Opening Times: Any reasonable time.

Admission: Free.

♿ Grounds suitable.   🅿️ No parking.   🐕 In grounds, on leads.

Dunstanburgh Castle, Northumberland.

ESHOTT HALL

MORPETH, NORTHUMBERLAND NE65 9EP

Contact: *Margaret Sanderson*

Tel: 01670 787777   **Fax:** 01670 787020

Eshott Hall is a unique location. Set in 450 acres of Northumbrian countryside, this privately owned listed building surrounded by its own sporting and leisure estate offers its guests the perfect alternative to a first class hotel. The estate dates back to 1205, and the Hall itself was built by Robert Trollope in 1660 and then extended in 1877. The present owners are restoring the Hall and grounds in meticulous detail to their former glory. Since the Hall is a private house, your event has exclusive use of the premises, which has been developed into a venue that offers superb facilities for both business and pleasure. The complete privacy, atmosphere of calm and relaxation together with the outstanding surroundings make Eshott the finest choice of the discerning event or conference organiser.

Location: OS87 Ref. NY203 978. Between Morpeth & Alnwick, 1m E of the A1. 20m N of Newcastle-upon-Tyne.

Opening Times: All year.

Admission: Exclusive use of house and grounds for events and activity days without accommodation: £465. Accommodation rates: Single with bath: £45. Double with bath: £70. Dinner: £20.

i Conferences, corporate hospitality.   X Exclusive dinners, wedding receptions.   Suitable.   P Ample.   A Available.   Civil Wedding Licence.

HOUSESTEADS ROMAN FORT & MUSEUM

NR HAYDON BRIDGE, NORTHUMBERLAND NE47 6NN

Owner: *National Trust*   ***Guardian:*** *English Heritage*   ***Contact:*** *The Custodian*

Tel: 01434 344363

Perched high on a ridge overlooking open moorland, this is the best known part of the Wall. The fort covers five acres and there are remains of many buildings, such as granaries, barrack blocks and gateways. A small exhibition displays altars, inscriptions and models.

Location: OS87 Ref. NY790 687. 2m NE of Bardon Mill.

Opening Times: 1 Apr - 1 Nov: daily, 10am - 6pm or dusk if earlier in Oct. 2 Nov - 31 Mar: daily, 10am - 4pm. Closed 24 - 26 Dec.

Admission: Adult £2.70, Child £1.40, Conc. £2. 15% discount for groups of 11+.

i Shop.   Not suitable.   Tearoom.   P Ample but charged.   Educational programme.   In grounds, on leads.

ETAL CASTLE   **Tel:** 01890 820332

Cornhill-on-Tweed, Northumberland

Owner: English Heritage   **Contact:** The Custodian

A 14th century castle located in the picturesque village of Etal. Award winning exhibition about the Castle, Border warfare and the Battle of Flodden.

Location: OS75 Ref. NT925 394. In Etal village, 10m SW of Berwick.

Opening Times: 1 Apr - 1 Nov: daily, 10am - 6pm or dusk if earlier in Oct.

Admission: Adult £2.50, Child £1.30, Conc. £1.90. 15% discount for groups of 11+.

i Shop.   Partially suitable. WC.   Inclusive audio tour.   P Limited.   In grounds, on leads.

HERTERTON HOUSE GARDENS   **Tel:** 01670 774278

Hartington, Cambo, Morpeth, Northumberland NE61 4BN

Owner: Frank Lawley   **Contact:** Frank or Marjorie Lawley

1 acre of formal garden in stone walls around a 16th century farmhouse, including a small topiary garden, physic garden and flower garden.

Location: OS Ref. NZ022 881. 2m N of Cambo, just off B6342.

Opening Times: 1 Apr - 30 Sept: Mon, Wed, Fri, Sat & Sun, 1.30 - 5.30pm.

Admission: £2.

i Plant centre.   Not suitable.   By arrangement.   P Limited.   Educational programme. Guided tours for adult students only.   Strictly no dogs.

HOWICK HALL GARDENS   **Tel:** 01665 577285 **Fax:** 01665 577285

Howick, Alnwick, Northumberland NE66 3LB

Owner: Howick Trustees Ltd   **Contact:** Lord Howick

Romantically landscaped grounds surrounding the house in a little valley, with rare rhododendrons and flowering shrubs and trees.

Location: OS Ref. NU249 175. 6m NE of Alnwick. 1m E of B1339.

Opening Times: Apr - Oct: daily 1 - 6pm.

Admission: Adult £2, Child £1, OAP £1, Student (up to 16yrs) £1. Season tickets available.

Grounds partly suitable. WC.   P Limited.   No dogs.

KIRKLEY HALL GARDENS   **Tel:** 01661 860808 **Fax:** 01661 860047

Ponteland, Northumberland NE20 0AQ   **Contact:** Mike Swinton

Over 9 acres of beautiful gardens, set in spectacular countryside and incorporating a Victorian walled garden, woodland walks, sunken garden and wildlife areas and ponds.

Location: OS Ref. NZ150 772. 10m from the centre of Newcastle upon Tyne. 2 1/2 m N of Ponteland on byroad to Morpeth.

Opening Times: Throughout the year: daily 10am - 5pm.

Admission: Adult £1.50, Child 70p, Child under 8 free, Family £3, Conc. 70p. Group £1.20 per person. Guided group £2.50 per person.

i Plant sales.   Kiosk.   By arrangement.

HWTP

Hadrian's Wall.

Northern Counties England

THE LADY WATERFORD HALL & MURALS

Ford, Berwick-upon-Tweed TD15 2QA   **Tel:** 01890 820524 **Fax:** 01890 820384

Owner: Ford & Etal Estates   **Contact:** The Caretaker

Built in 1860 as a village school, Louisa Anne, Marchioness of Waterford decorated the walls of this beautiful building over a period of 21 years, with delightful murals. The school children and their families were used as models for the characters from well known Bible stories, making the hall a portrait gallery of the residents of Ford during the 1860s and 1870s. John Ruskin, a friend of Louisa's visited the hall, along with many other dignitaries of the day.

Location: OS Ref. NT945 374. 9m from Berwick-upon-Tweed on the B6354, 8m N of Wooler off the A697.

Opening Times: 1 Apr - 1 Nov: daily, 10.30am - 12.30pm and 1.30 - 5.30pm. Open by arrangement with caretaker during winter.

Admission: Adult £1.25, Child free, Conc. 75p. Groups can be catered for by prior arrangement.

♿ Suitable. P Parking at door. 🐕 Guide dogs only.

LINDISFARNE CASTLE ✿

                                     Tel: 01289 389244

Holy Island, Berwick-upon-Tweed, Northumberland TD15 2SH

Owner: The National Trust   **Contact:** The Administrator

Built in 1550 to protect Holy Island harbour from attack, the castle was restored and converted into a private house for Edward Hudson by Sir Edwin Lutyens in 1903. Small walled garden was designed by Gertrude Jekyll. 19th century lime kilns in field by the castle.

Location: OS Ref. NU136 417. On Holy Island, ³/₄ m E of village, 6m E of A1 across causeway. Usable at low tide.

Opening Times: 1 Apr - 29 Oct: daily except Fri (but open Good Fri) 1 - 5.30pm. Last admission 5pm. Admission to garden only when gardener in attendance.

Admission: £4, Family £10. No group rate. Groups of 15+ must pre-book.

ℹ NT Shop (in Main St.) ♿ Not suitable. P No parking. 🐕 In grounds, on leads.

MORPETH, NORTHUMBERLAND NE61 3SW

Owner: M Cookson   *Contact:* M Cookson

Tel: 01670 772661

Isaac Cookson III purchased the Meldon land in 1832. John Dobson, the famous architect, was commissioned to build a house by Isaac Cookson and he recommended the present site. The entrance is through an Ionic porch having two rows of columns to the front door. Once inside you are in the main hall which has an enormous staircase lit by a large window to the north. Between the two World Wars Edwin Lutyens was employed to enrich the Hall, which included mahogany balustrades and 18th century decorations. The garden has a wonderful collection of rhododendrons best seen in early June, an old-fashioned kitchen garden and greenhouses.

Location: OS Ref. NZ105 856. 7m W of Morpeth on B6343. 5m N of Belsay.

Opening Times: Last week in May to end of 3rd week in Jun and Aug BH weekend, 2 - 5pm.

Admission: Adult £3, Child £1.50, OAP £2.

ℹ No photography. ♿ Suitable. WC. ☕ Sun only. 🚶 By arrangement. P Ample. 🐕 Guide dogs only.

NORHAM CASTLE ⎣

                                       Tel: 01289 382329

Norham, Northumberland

Owner: English Heritage   **Contact:** The Custodian

Set on a promontory in a curve of the River Tweed, this was one of the strongest of the border castles, built c1160.

Location: OS75 Ref. NT907 476. 6m SW of Berwick.

Opening Times: 1 Apr - 1 Nov: daily, 10am - 6pm or dusk if earlier in Oct.

Admission: Adult £1.70, Child 90p, Conc. £1.30. 15% discount for groups of 11+.

ℹ Shop. ♿ Suitable excluding Keep. 🚶 Inclusive audio tour. P Limited.

PRESTON TOWER 🏛

                                       Tel: 01665 589227

Chathill, Northumberland NE67 5DH

Owner: Major T Baker Cresswell   **Contact:** Major T Baker Cresswell

The Tower was built by Sir Robert Harbottle in 1392 and is one of the few survivors of 78 Pele Towers listed in 1415. The tunnel vaulted rooms remain unaltered and provide a realistic picture of the grim way of life under the constant threat of "Border Reivers". Two rooms are furnished in contemporary style and there are displays of historic and local information. Visitors are welcome to walk in the grounds which contain a number of interesting trees and shrubs. A woodland walk to the natural spring from which water is now pumped up to the Tower for the house and cottages.

Location: OS Ref. NU185 253. Follow Historic Property signs on A1 7m N of Alnwick.

Opening Times: Daylight hours all year.

Admission: Adult £1, Child/Conc./Groups 50p.

♿ Grounds suitable. 🐕 No dogs.

HOLY ISLAND, BERWICK-UPON-TWEED TD15 2RX

Owner: English Heritage   *Contact:* The Custodian

Tel: 01289 389200

The site of one of the most important early centres of Christianity in Anglo-Saxon England. St Cuthbert converted pagan Northumbria, and miracles occurring at his shrine established this 11th century priory as a major pilgrimage centre. The evocative ruins, with the decorated 'rainbow' arch curving dramatically across the nave of the church, are still the destination of pilgrims today. The story of Lindisfarne is told in an exhibition which gives an impression of life for the monks, including a reconstruction of a monk's cell.

Location: OS75 Ref. NU126 418. On Holy Island, check tide times.

Opening Times: 1 Apr - 1 Nov: daily, 10am - 6pm or dusk if earlier in Oct. 2 Nov - 31 Mar: daily, 10am - 4pm. Closed 24 - 26 Dec.

Admission: Adult £2.70, Child £1.40, Conc. £2. 15% discount for groups of 11+.

ℹ Shop. ♿ Not suitable.

PRUDHOE CASTLE ⎣

                                       Tel: 01661 833459

Prudhoe, Northumberland NE42 6NA

Owner: English Heritage   **Contact:** The Custodian

Set on a wooded hillside overlooking the River Tyne are the extensive remains of this 12th century castle including a gatehouse, curtain wall and keep. Small exhibition and video presentation.

Location: OS88 Ref. NZ092 634. In Prudhoe, on minor road N from A695.

Opening Times: 1 Apr - 31 Oct: daily, 10am - 6pm (dusk in Oct).

Admission: Adult £1.70, Child 90p, Conc. £1.30. 15% discount for groups of 11+.

ℹ Shop. ♿ Ground floor & grounds suitable. ☕ Kiosk. P Limited. 🐕 In grounds, on leads.

SEATON DELAVAL HALL

SEATON SLUICE, WHITLEY BAY, NORTHUMBERLAND NE26 4QR

Owner: The Lord Hastings   *Contact:* F Hetherington

Tel: 0191 2373040 / 0191 2371493

A splendid English baroque house, regarded by many as Sir John Vanbrugh's masterpiece. The playwright who turned so successfully to architecture began the great house in 1718 for Admiral George Delaval. Building on the central block (Vanbrugh's Palladian Villa) ceased about 1728. The wings, which are arcaded and pedimented, include the East Wing containing the magnificent stables. In the grounds are extensive and beautiful gardens. There is also a coach house, ice house and a unique Norman church.

Location: OS Ref. NZ322 766. $^{1}/_{2}$ m from Seaton Sluice on A190, 3m from Whitley Bay.

Opening Times: May BH Suns & Mons. Jun: Wed & Sun. Jul & Aug: Wed, Thur, Sun & BH Mon, 2 - 6pm.

Admission: Adult £3, Child £1, OAP £2.50.

i Shop.   Grounds suitable. WC.   Tearoom.   In grounds, on leads.

WARKWORTH CASTLE

WARKWORTH, MORPETH, NORTHUMBERLAND NE66 0UJ

Owner: English Heritage   *Contact:* The Custodian

Tel: 01665 711423

The great towering keep of this 15th century castle, once the home of the mighty Percy family, dominates the town and River Coquet.

Location: OS81 Ref. NU247 057. 7m S of Alnwick on A1068.

Opening Times: 1 Apr - 1 Nov: daily, 10am - 6pm or dusk if earlier in Oct. 2 Nov - 31 Mar: daily, 10am - 4pm. Closed 1 - 2pm and 24 - 26 Dec.

Admission: Adult £2.70, Child £1.40, Conc. £2. 15% discount for groups of 11+.

i Shop.   Grounds suitable.   Audio tours available.

P Ample.   On leads.

VINDOLANDA

Tel: 01434 344277   **Fax:** 01434 344060

Bardon Mill, Hadrian's Wall, Hexham, Northumberland NE47 7JN

Contact: Mrs P Birley

Recent excavations have uncovered some of the most unusual and well preserved objects to come from the Roman world.

Location: OS Ref. NY771 664. 8m W of Hexham, $1^{1}/_{2}$ m N of A69 at Bardon Mill.

Opening Times: mid Feb - mid Nov: daily from 10am. Closes: 4pm in winter & 6.30pm in summer.

Admission: Adult £3.50, Child £2.50, Conc. £2.90, 10% discount for groups of 15+. 20% if also visiting our sister site at the Roman Army Museum.

i Shop.   Partially suitable.   Tearoom.   P Ample.

Educational programme.   No dogs.

WALLINGTON

Tel: 01670 774283

Cambo, Morpeth, Northumberland NE61 4AR

Owner: The National Trust   **Contact:** The Property Manager

The much loved country home of the Trevelyan family, built in 1688, sits in 100 acres of lawns, lakes and woodland. The Central Hall, decorated with William Bell Scott's paintings from Northumberland history, is a room you must visit! Other rooms give a taste of the pleasures and pastimes of a lifestyle long gone. Children will enjoy the doll's house collection, nursery and Museum of Curiosities.

Location: OS Ref. NZ030 843. 12m W of Morpeth on B6343, 6m NW of Belsay A696, B6342 to Cambo.

Opening Times: House: 1 Apr - 30 Sept: daily, except Tue, 1 - 5.30pm, last adm. 5pm. 1 Oct - 1 Nov: daily except Tue 1 - 4.30pm last adm. 4pm. Walled Garden: 1 Apr - end Sept: daily 10am - 7pm. 1 Oct - 1 Nov: 10am - 6pm. Nov - Mar: '99 10am - 4pm (or dusk if earlier) Shop/Plant centre & Tearoom: 4 Nov - 20 Dec: Wed - Sun, 12 - 4pm. Grounds: all year, daily during daylight hours.

Admission: House, Walled Garden & Grounds: £4.80. Pre-booked groups £4.30. Walled Garden & Grounds: £2.80. Pre-booked groups £2.30. Family (2+2) £12. Accompanied children 12 and under free during school summer holidays.

i Shop.   Suitable. WC.   Restaurant.   Civil Wedding Licence.

WARKWORTH HERMITAGE

Tel: 01665 711423

Warkworth, Northumberland

Owner: English Heritage   **Contact:** The Custodian

Upstream by boat from the castle this curious hermitage cuts into the rock of the river cliff.

Location: OS Ref. NU247 057. $7^{1}/_{2}$ m SE of Alnwick on A1068.

Opening Times: 1 Apr - 30 Sept: Sun & BH, 11am - 5pm.

Admission: Adult £1.20, Child 60p, Conc. 90p.

Not suitable.   P No parking.   No dogs.

Hippocras:

An old medicinal drink or cordial made from spiced, sweetened wine, so-called because the bag through which it was strained was thought to resemble Hippocrates' sleeve in shape. The wine, coloured with turnsole (sunflower) or cochineal, and sweetened with honey, was spiced with ginger, cinnamon, and grains of paradise (a type of ginger). Originally a medieval recipe, its popularity continued into the seventeenth century, by which time milk or cream was also strained into the mixture. When the banquet course went out of fashion in Stuart times, so did the recipe.

Extract from; "Life in the Country House" by David N Durant (published by John Murray), PB£15.99, see page twelve at the front of the book.

ARBEIA ROMAN FORT
Tel: 0191 456 1369   **Fax:** 0191 427 6862

Baring Street, South Shields, Tyne & Wear   NE33 2BB

Owner: Tyne & Wear Museums   **Contact:** The Curator

Extensive remains of 2nd century Roman fort, including fort defences, stone granaries, gateways and latrines. Full scale simulation of Roman gateway and museum. Watch excavations in the summer.

Location: OS Ref. NZ365 679. Near town centre and Metro Station.

Opening Times: Easter - Oct: Mon - Sat: 10am - 5.30pm, Sun 2 - 5pm. Open BH Mon. Winter: Mon - Sat, 10am - 4pm.

Admission: Free, except for guided tours and Timequest Gallery: Adult £1, Conc. 50p.

ℹ️ Shop. Plant centre. Picnic area.   ♿ Partially suitable. WCs.   🚶 By arrangement.
🅿️ Ample.   👫 Teachers' pack available.   🐕 In grounds, on leads.

BEDE'S WORLD MUSEUM
Tel: 0191 489 2106   **Fax:** 0191 428 2361

Church Bank, Jarrow, Tyne & Wear   NE32 3DY

Owner: Jarrow 700AD Ltd   **Contact:** Miss Susan Mills

7th century church and monastery remains where the Venerable Bede lived, plus late Georgian Jarrow Hall, now a museum.

Location: OS Ref. NZ339 652. Just off A19, S end of Tyne Tunnel.

Opening Times: Apr - Oct: Tue - Sat, 10am - 5.30pm, Sun 2.30 - 5.30pm. Nov - Mar: Tue - Sat, 10am - 4.30pm, Sun 1.30 - 4.30pm. May - Sept: Sun 12 - 5.30pm.

Admission: Adult £3, Conc. £1.50. Groups by arrangement.

ℹ️ Shop. No photography.   ✖️ Wedding receptions.   ♿ WCs.   🚶 By arrangement.
🅿️ Ample.   👫 Educational programme.   🐕 Guide dogs only.

BESSIE SURTEES HOUSE ⌗
Tel: 0191 261 1585

41 - 44 Sandhill, Newcastle, Tyne & Wear

Owner: English Heritage   **Contact:** The Custodian

Two 16th and 17th century merchants' houses stand on the quayside near the Tyne Bridge. One is a rare example of Jacobean domestic architecture. 3 rooms open.

Location: OS Ref. NZ252 639. 41- 44 Sandhill, Newcastle.

Opening Times: Weekdays only: 10am - 4pm. Closed BHs, 24 - 26 Dec and 1 Jan.

Admission: Free.

♿ Not suitable.   🚶 By arrangement.   🅿️ No parking.   🐕 No dogs.

CATHEDRAL CHURCH OF ST NICHOLAS

Newcastle upon Tyne, Tyne & Wear   NE1 1PF   **Tel:** 0191 232 1939   **Fax:** 0191 230 0735

Contact: Rev Canon Peter Strange

Mostly 14th century surmounted by 15th century lantern spire, one medieval window, two renaissance memorials, one large 15th century Flemish brass.

Location: OS Ref. NZ250 640. City centre, 1/2 m from A167 signposted from Swan House roundabout.

Opening Times: Sun: 7am - 12 noon, 4 - 7pm. Mon - Fri: 7am - 6pm. Sat: 8.30am - 4pm.

ℹ️ Shop.   ♿ Suitable. WC.   ☕ Café.   🚶 By arrangement.   🅿️ No parking.
👫 Educational programme, teachers' pack.   🐕 Guide dogs only.

GIBSIDE 🍃
Tel: 01207 542255

Nr Rowlands Gill, Burnopfield, Newcastle upon Tyne   NE16 6BG

Owner: The National Trust   **Contact:** The Administrator

Gibside is one of the finest 18th century designed landscapes in the north of England. The Chapel was built to James Paine's design soon after 1760. Outstanding example of Georgian architecture approached along a terrace with an oak avenue. Walk along the River Derwent through woodland.

Location: OS Ref. NZ172 583. 6m SW of Gateshead, 20m NW of Durham. Entrance on B6314 between Burnopfield and Rowlands Gill.

Opening Times: 1 Apr - 1 Nov: daily except Mon (open BH Mon) 11am - 5pm. Last adm. 4.30pm. Winter: 8 Nov - end Mar 1999. Grounds only: Suns 10am - 4pm.

Admission: Chapel and Grounds: Adult £3, Child half price. Pre-booked groups £2.60.

ST PAUL'S MONASTERY ⌗
Tel: 0191 489 2106

Jarrow, Tyne & Wear

Owner: English Heritage   **Contact:** The Custodian

The home of the Venerable Bede in the 7th and 8th centuries, partly surviving as the chancel of the parish church. It has become one of the best understood Anglo-Saxon monastic sites.

Location: OS Ref. NZ339 652. In Jarrow, on minor road N of A185.

Opening Times: Monastery ruins any reasonable time. Nearby museum open 1 Apr - 31 Oct, Tue - Sat & BHs, 10am - 5.30pm. 1 Nov - 31 Mar: Tue - Sat, 11am - 4.30pm, Sun 2.30 - 5.30pm. Closed Christmas, New Year.

Admission: Museum: Adult £2.50, Child/Conc. £1.25. Family £6, UB40 Family £4.

♿ Ground floor suitable.   ☕ Tearoom.   🅿️ No parking.   🐕 In grounds, on leads.

SOUTER LIGHTHOUSE 🍃
Tel: 0191 529 3161

Coast Road, Whitburn, Tyne & Wear   SR6 7NR

Owner: The National Trust   **Contact:** The Property Manager

Shore-based lighthouse and associated buildings, built in 1871, the first to be powered by an alternative electric current.

Location: OS Ref. NZ408 641. 2 1/2 m S of Southshields on A183. 5m N of Sunderland.

Opening Times: 1 Apr - 1 Nov: daily except Fri (open Good Fri), 11am - 5pm. Last admission 4.30pm.

Admission: Adult £2.50, Child half price. Pre-booked parties £2.

ℹ️ Shop.   ♿ Ground floor & grounds suitable. WC.   ☕ Tearoom.
🚶 By arrangement.   🐕 In grounds, on leads.

TYNEMOUTH PRIORY & CASTLE ⌗

NORTH PIER, TYNEMOUTH, TYNE & WEAR   NE30 4BZ

Owner: English Heritage   *Contact:* The Custodian

Tel: 0191 2571090

The castle walls and gatehouse enclose the substantial remains of a Benedictine priory founded c1090 on a Saxon monastic site. Their strategic importance has made the castle and priory the target for attack for many centuries. In World War I, coastal batteries in the castle defended the mouth of the Tyne.

Location: OS88 Ref. NZ374 695. In Tynemouth.

Opening times: 1 Apr - 1 Nov: daily, 10am - 6pm/dusk in Oct. 2 Nov - 31 Mar: Wed - Sun, 10am - 4pm. Closed 1 - 2 pm.

Admission: Adult £1.70, Child 90p, Conc. £1.30. 15% discount for groups of 11+.

ℹ️ Shop.   ♿ Grounds suitable.   🚶 By arrangement.   🐕 In grounds, on leads.

WASHINGTON OLD HALL 🍃
Tel: 0191 416 6879

The Avenue, Washington Village, Tyne & Wear   NE38 7LE

Owner: The National Trust   **Contact:** The Property Manager

Jacobean manor house incorporating portions of 12th century house of the Washington family.

Location: OS Ref. NZ312 566. In Washington on E side of Avenue. 5m W of Sunderland (2m from A1), S of Tyne Tunnel, follow signs for Washington New Town District 4 and then village.

Opening Times: 1 Apr - 1 Nov: daily except Thur, Fri & Sat (open Good Fri), 11am - 5pm. Last admission 4.30pm.

Admission: Adult £2.50, Child half-price, Groups (15+) by prior arrangement only, £2,

ℹ️ Shop. Conferences.   ♿ Ground floor & grounds suitable.   ☕ Tearoom.
🚶 By arrangement.   🅿️ Limited.   🐕 In grounds, on leads.

ALLERTON PARK
Nr. Knaresborough

Allerton Park, the ancestral home of Lord Mowbray, Segrave and Stourton, the premier Baron in England, is the finest surviving Gothic Revival stately home. Steeped in history, in the 18th century the property was owned by Prince Frederick, the Duke of York, brother to King George IV. Legend has it that The Temple of Victory and its hill are referred to in the nursery rhyme *The Grand Old Duke of York.*

The house was purchased in 1982 by Dr Gerald Arthur Rolph and extensive renovations to both the house and grounds have been undertaken. Recently awarded the coveted Grade I status, Allerton Park is now maintained and operated by the Gerald Arthur Rolph Foundation for Historic Preservation and Education to ensure its continued conservation.

The Great Hall provides a stunning entrance. One of the highest Baronial Halls in England, almost 80 feet high, is adorned by intricately carved oak panelling lit by stained glass windows and with galleried landings whose walls are hung with portraits. Access from this to the Library with original rosewood bookcases, the Dining Room with oak panelled walls and ceiling, the Conservatory and access to the terraces, the Billiard Room and Drawing Room. Clients have exclusive use of the public rooms for the duration of their occasion.

CONTACT

Jeannette Sinfield
The Courtyard
Allerton Park
Nr. Knaresborough
HG5 0SE
or
Mike Farr
Administrator

Tel: (01423) 331123
or (01423) 330927

Fax: (01423) 331125

LOCATION

OS Ref. SE416 580

A1M junction with A59.
1/2 m towards
York off A59.

Rail: York 14m
Harrogate 10m
Leeds 20m.

Air: Leeds/Bradford 18m.

OPENING TIMES

SUMMER

Easter Sun - 27 September
Sun and BH Mon
1 - 5pm.

Groups by appointment.

ADMISSION

House and Garden

Adult	£4.00
Child	£3.50
OAP	£3.50
Groups of 25+	
Adult	£3.50

CONFERENCE/FUNCTION		
ROOM	SIZE	MAX CAPACITY
Great Hall	2087 sq. ft.	225
Dining Rm.	1037 sq. ft.	140
Ballroom	1297 sq. ft.	200
Drawing Rm	735 sq. ft.	80
Library	721 sq. ft.	40
Morning Rm.	598 sq. ft.	30

i Suitable for wedding receptions, filming, balls, dinners, banquets, marquee events, concerts, outdoor activities, conferences and field events. Also features a Mechanical Musical Instrument Collection.

& Assistance with access at rear of building with advance notice, Lift to public rooms. WCs.

Tearoom. Group bookings by arrangement.

Easter to Sept: Sun afternoon. Group bookings by appointment only, at any reasonable time.

P Ample.

Welcome. Pre-booking essential.

Civil Wedding Licence.

BROUGHTON HALL
Skipton

CONTACT

The Estate Office
Broughton Hall
Skipton
Yorkshire
BD23 3AE

Tel: (01756) 799608

Fax: (01756) 700357

e-mail: tempest@
broughtonhall.co.uk

LOCATION

OS Ref. SD943 507

Skipton A59, 3m.
From London M1
to Leeds and Skipton,
A59 to Broughton.
S side of A59,
3m SW of Skipton.

Air: Bradford/Leeds
Airport 40 mins,
Manchester 1 hr.

Rail: Skipton Station 3m.

Bus: Regular service.

CONFERENCE/FUNCTION

SUBJECT TO PRIOR ARRANGEMENT ALL
ROOMS CAN BE MADE AVAILABLE
FOR FUNCTIONS.

BROUGHTON HALL was built in 1597 by Henry Tempest and continues to be the home of the Tempest family, whose ancestry can be traced back 29 generations to Roger Tempest who was established in the area by 1120. This Grade I listed historic building has Elizabethan origins but was extensively added to during the 18th and 19th centuries, hence its Palladian appearance.

Set in 3,000 acres of beautiful Yorkshire parkland and countryside, the Broughton Hall family home and Estate, is open to the public by prior arrangement and is also available as an exclusive venue for both business and pleasure.

The present design of the grounds owes much to the landscape architecture of Nesfield around 1855. To the east of the Hall is a fine Italianate garden with balustrades and a gazebo. To the rear there are sweeping lawns (ideal for marquee events) enhanced by extensive wooded views and fountains.

The owners like to make every event unique and highly successful so are always ready to discuss with clients how they can help them to achieve their objectives by placing their facilities and experience at their disposal. To arrange such a consultation it is only necessary to telephone the Estate Office on 01756 799608.

❖

i Ideal for dinners, seminars, corporate entertainment, product launches, clay shoots, archery, fashion shows, equestrian events, firework and laser shows, filming and still photography. Events will have exclusive use of hall and grounds. Musical evenings are very successful. Grand piano. Full size billiard table.

X By prior arrangement. Wide range of options. Buffets and full sit down meals with accent on quality and value. Up to 150 people can be catered for.

♿ Visitors may alight at entrance, then park vehicles in allocated area.

🚶 At no additional cost, conducted for up to 200 people. Large groups are split into smaller parties. If requested, the owner will meet group. Lectures on property, contents, garden and history can be held in a lecture room seating 80.

P Ample parking and an area for light aircraft/ helicopters. When travelling from Skipton on the A59 towards Clitheroe, watch for the Bull Inn on left hand side, 3m from Skipton. Take turning to left approx. 200 yds past Bull Inn. The hall and entrance gates can then be seen.

A Broughton is 3m from the historic market town of Skipton. The Yorkshire Dales National Park with some of the finest countryside in England is on the doorstep. Excellent local hotels provide overnight accommodation.

OPENING TIMES

SUMMER
BH Mon
11am - 4pm.

Guided tours can be arranged by prior appointment.
The duration of a tour is approx. 1½ hours.

ADMISSION

House & Garden

Per person £5.00

Guided Tours
Groups*
Per person £5.00

* Minimum payment if by prior appointment, £60.

CASTLE HOWARD
York

CONTACT

Mrs M E Carmichael
Castle Howard
York
North Yorkshire
YO6 7DA

Tel: (01653) 648444

Fax: (01653) 648462

LOCATION

OS Ref. SE716 701

York 15m (20 mins), A64.
From London: M1/J32,
M18 to A1(M) to A64,
York/Scarborough Road,
3¹/₂ hrs.

Train: London Kings Cross
to York 1hr. 50 mins. York
to Malton Station 30 mins.

Bus: Service and tour
buses from York Station
to Castle Howard.

In a dramatic setting between two lakes with extensive gardens and impressive fountains, this 18th century Palace was designed by Sir John Vanbrugh in 1699. Undoubtedly the finest private residence in Yorkshire it was built for Charles Howard, 3rd Earl of Carlisle, whose descendants still live here.

With its painted and gilded dome reaching 80ft into the Yorkshire sky, this impressive house has collections of antique furniture, porcelain and sculpture, while its fabulous collection of paintings is dominated by the famous Holbein portraits of Henry VIII and the Duke of Norfolk.

GARDENS

Designed on a heroic scale covering 1,000 acres. The gardens include memorable sights like The Temple of the Four Winds and the Mausoleum, New River Bridge and the recently restored waterworks of the South Lake, Cascade, Waterfall and Prince of Wales Fountain. The walled garden has collections of old and modern roses.

Ray Wood, acknowledged by the Royal Botanic Collection, Kew, as a 'rare botanical jewel' has a unique collection of rare trees, shrubs, rhododendrons, magnolias and azaleas.

OPENING TIMES

SUMMER

13 March - 1 November
Daily, 11am - 4.30pm.

Last admission 4.30pm.

NB. Grounds, Rose Gardens and Plant Centre open 10am.

WINTER

November - mid March

Open by pre-booked appointment and availability for groups.

Grounds open most days November, December and January - telephone for confirmation.

ADMISSION

SUMMER

House & Garden

Adult	£7.00
Child*	£4.00
OAP	£6.00

Groups (min 12 people)

Adult	£6.00
Child*	£3.50
OAP	£5.50

Garden only

Adult	£4.50
Child*	£2.50

*Age 4-16

WINTER
By arrangement.

CONFERENCE/FUNCTION

ROOM	SIZE	MAX CAPACITY
Long Gallery	197' x 24'	280
Grecian Hall	40' x 40'	160

i Shop and Plant Centre. Suitable for concerts, craft fairs, fashion shows, clay pigeon shooting, equestrian events, garden parties, filming, product launches. Helicopter landing. Firework displays.

X Grecian Hall available for pre-booked private parties and receptions, min. 25.

♿ Transport equipped for wheelchairs. Chairlift in house to main floor. WCs.

☕ Two cafeterias.

🚶 Guides posted throughout house. Private garden tours and lectures by arrangement covering house, history, contents and garden.

P 400 cars, 20 coaches. Approaching from S, A64 to Malton, on entering Malton, take Castle Howard road via Coneysthorpe village. Or from A64 following signs to Castle Howard via the Carrmire Gate 9' wide by 10' high.

👥 Welcome. 1:10 teacher/pupil ratio required. Special interest: 18th century architecture, art, history, wildlife, horticulture.

CONTACT

Estate Office
Duncombe Park
Helmsley
York YO6 5EB

Tel: (01439) 770213

Fax: (01439) 771114

LOCATION

OS Ref. SE604 830

Entrance just off Helmsley Market Square, signed off A170 Thirsk - Scarborough road.

Taxi: (01439) 770817 / 771384 / 770512.

DUNCOMBE PARK
Helmsley

The house dates from 1713 and was built for Thomas Duncombe by William Wakefield, a friend of Vanbrugh. A fine forecourt and two pavilions were added by Sir Charles Barry in 1843. Its interiors were remodelled by the First Earl of Feversham after a fire in 1879. The main showrooms are now a fine example of the type of grand interior popular at the turn of the century.

Following the death of the second Earl of Feversham at the Battle of the Somme in 1916, Duncombe Park was leased as a girls' school. In 1985 the present Lord and Lady Feversham decided to restore the house to a family home. After the closure of the school, there was little more than an empty, echoing shell. Today the visitor will see a superb example of the best of British craftsmanship. The restoration is very

much a family project and the interior finishes have been deliberately chosen to show visitors a selection of the styles of decoration typical in the 18th and 19th centuries. There are fine family pictures and Lord Feversham's collection of English and Continental furniture.

The unique 30 acre early 18th century landscape garden, set in 300 acres of dramatic parkland, has been described as 'the supreme masterpiece of the art of the landscape gardener'. Its vast expanses of lawn, terraces, temples, woodland walks and fine views across the surrounding North York Moors are something to be explored at leisure.

Winner, British Tourist Authority *'Come to Britain'* Special Award and Yorkshire and Humberside *'White Rose'* Awards. Duncombe Park is now a National Nature Reserve.

OPENING TIMES

House & Garden
29 March - 3 November
April/October: Sun - Thur
(closed Fri & Sat, except Easter weekend)
May - September: Sun - Fri
(closed Sat).
11am - 5.30pm
last admission 4.30pm.

The Parkland Centre Tearoom/Shop, & National Nature Reserve
29 March - 3 November
Daily, 10.30am - 5.30pm
(Open to non-visitors to the house)

ADMISSION

House, Garden & Park
Adult £5.50
Child (10 - 16) £2.50
OAP.........................£4.50
Student.....................£4.50
Family (2 + 2).........£12.50
Group £4.00
Garden only
Adult £3.50
Child (10 - 16) £1.50

National Nature Reserve
.................................£1.50

Family Season Ticket.........£30.00
Includes events in any 12 months.

NOTE: Joint visiting arrangements for groups in conjunction with Hovingham Hall, Helmsley Walled Garden and Cropton Brewery.

SPECIAL EVENTS

• Country Fair, Antiques Fairs, Steam Fair, Craft Festivals, Point to Point

Please contact the Estate Office for details

CONFERENCE/FUNCTION		
ROOM	SIZE (m)	MAX CAPACITY
Saloon	29 x 7	200
Stone Hall	12 x 12	100
Butler's Pantry	5 x 6	30

i Shop. Plant Centre. Picnic area, playground, way-marked country walks and orienteering course, concerts, fashion shows, conferences, product launches, filming and a range of outdoor events. Grand piano, tennis court, croquet lawn. Details from Visitor Co-ordinator. No flash photography in house. Video permits available. Allow 3 hrs for group visits.

X Dinners, receptions and weddings.

& Portable ramps. Parking allowed in forecourt. Not particularly suited to those with walking difficulties. WC.

Licensed tearoom. Home made food, max. 60. Groups should pre-book.

P Free 400 yds from house. Coach park.

Every day except Sun and BH Mon. Allow 3 hrs to see estate.

Welcome. Info pack. Teacher/pupil ratio required is 1:10.

In grounds, on leads.

Civil Wedding Licence.

FAIRFAX HOUSE
York

FAIRFAX HOUSE was acquired and fully restored by the York Civic Trust in 1983/84. The house, described as a classic architectural masterpiece of its age and certainly one of the finest townhouses in England, was saved from near collapse after considerable abuse and misuse this century, having been converted into a cinema and dance hall.

The richly decorated interior with its plasterwork, wood and wrought-iron, is now the home for a unique collection of Georgian furniture, clocks, paintings and porcelain.

The Noel Terry Collection, gift of a former treasurer of the York Civic Trust has been described by Christie's as one of the finest private collections formed this century. It enhances and complements the House and helps to create that special 'lived-in' feeling, providing the basis for what can be considered a fully furnished Georgian townhouse.

❖

CONTACT

Mr Peter Brown
Fairfax House
Castlegate
York
YO1 1RN

Tel: (01904) 655543

Fax: (01904) 652262

LOCATION

OS Ref. SE605 515

London 4 hrs by car,
2 hrs by train.

Fairfax House situated in centre of York between Castle Museum and Jorvik Centre.

Rail: York Station,
10 mins walk.

Taxi: Station Taxis
(01904) 623332

OPENING TIMES

SUMMER

20 February - 6 January

Mon - Thur
11am - 5pm.

Closed Fri except in August.

Sat, 11am - 5pm.

Sun, 1.30 - 5pm.

Last admission 4.30pm.

WINTER

7 January - 19 February Closed.

ADMISSION

Adult	£3.75
Child (5 - 16yrs)	£1.50
OAP	£3.00
Student	£3.00
Groups*	
Adult	£3.00
Child (5 - 16yrs)	£1.00
OAP	£2.50
Student	£2.50

* Min payment 15 persons.

SPECIAL EVENTS

- **OCT 10 - DEC 28:**
Heritage Regained: silver from the Gilbert Collection.

- **DEC 3 - JAN 6:**
Exhibition on the 'Keeping of Christmas'. Information extracted from the family papers helps re-create in a very tangible way the ritual and decoration of Christmas celebrations in Fairfax House from 1760-1840. Booked parties can be given mulled wine and mince pies at end of the tour.
Closed 24 - 26 Dec.

Shop. Suitable for filming. No photography inside the house. Liveried footmen, musical and dancing performances also arranged.

In the dining room, max. 28 seated. For groups up to 50 a buffet can be provided.

Visitors may alight at entrance prior to parking. No WCs except for functions.

A guided tour can be arranged at a cost of £4.50pp. Evening and daytime guided tours, telephone for details. Available in French and German. Tour time: 1¹/₂ hrs.

300 cars, 50 yds from house. Coach park is ¹/₂ m away, parties are dropped off; drivers please telephone for details showing the nearest coach park and approach to the house.

Mike Williams

FOUNTAINS ABBEY & STUDLEY ROYAL
Ripon

One of the most remarkable sites in Europe, sheltered in a secluded valley, Fountains Abbey and Studley Royal, a World Heritage Site, encompasses the spectacular remains of a 12th century Cistercian abbey, an Elizabethan mansion, and one of the best surviving examples of a Georgian green water garden. Elegant ornamental lakes, avenues, temples and cascades provide a succession of unforgettable eye-catching vistas in an atmosphere of peace and tranquillity. St Mary's

Church, built by William Burges in the 19th century, provides a dramatic focal point to the medieval deer park with over 600 deer.

Audio visual programme and exhibition at the Visitor Centre. Small museum near to the Abbey. Exhibitions in Fountains Hall and Swanley Grange.

The Abbey is maintained by English Heritage. St Mary's Church is owned by English Heritage and managed by the National Trust.

❖

CONTACT

The National Trust
Fountains Abbey
and Studley Royal
Ripon
North Yorkshire
HG4 3DY

Tel: Weekdays
(01765) 608888

Fax: (01765) 608889

LOCATION

OS Ref. SE271 683

Abbey entrance;
4m W of Ripon off B6265.

8m W of A1.

OPENING TIMES

ALL YEAR
except 24/25 December
and Fri November -
January.

April - September
10am - 7pm.

January - March &
October - December
10am - 5pm.

Last admission 1 hr
before closing.

Closes at 4pm on
10/11 July &
1 August, 1998.

ADMISSION

Adult	£4.20
Child	£2.00
Family	£10.00

Groups of 15+
Adult	£3.70
Child	£1.90

Groups of 40+
Adult	£3.20
Child	£1.70

Group discount
applicable only with
prior booking.

Group visits and disabled
visitors, please telephone
in advance, 01765 601005.

ℹ️ Two shops. Events held throughout the year. Exhibitions. Corporate hospitality, seminar facilities. Outdoor concerts, meetings, activity days, walks.

✕ Dinners and dances.

♿ Batricars and wheelchairs, please pre-book. 3-wheel batricars not permitted due to terrain. Tours for visually impaired, please book. WC.

☕ Available. Groups please pre-book, discounted rates.

🚶 Free, but seasonal. Groups, please use Visitor Centre entrance.

🅿️ Drivers must pre-book groups.

👪 Welcome by prior arrangement.

🐕 On leads only.

HAREWOOD HOUSE
Leeds

Designed by John Carr in 1759 for Edwin Lascelles, Harewood House has been lived in by his family ever since. The magnificent interior, created by Robert Adam, has superb ceilings and plasterwork and contains what experts describe as 'the richest collection of Chippendale in the world'. A surprising variety of paintings are displayed, including Italian Renaissance, Turner, 18th century portraits and even 20th century masterpieces. Dedicated watercolour rooms showcase key historic works and below stairs, the Terrace Gallery is a venue for the work of leading contemporary artists.

The Earl of Harewood is the son of the late Princess Mary, daughter of King George V, and is a cousin of HM Queen Elizabeth II.

Princess Mary lived at Harewood for 35 years and much of her fascinating royal memorabilia is displayed in her former rooms.

In the grounds, landscaped by 'Capability' Brown, are lakeside and woodland walks, a magnificent collection of rhododendrons (April - June) and Sir Charles Barry's parterre terrace, complete with box scrolls and seasonal bedding. Harewood Bird Garden has one of the most comprehensive collections of rare and exotic species in the country including many endangered birds from Africa, America and Australia.

Special events include open air concerts, car rallies and 'behind the scenes' visits to the Old Kitchen. Telephone for details.

❖

CONTACT

Claire Saunderson
Moor House
Harewood Estate
Harewood
Leeds
West Yorkshire
LS17 9LQ

Tel: (0113) 288 6331

Fax: (0113) 288 6467

LOCATION

OS Ref. SE311 446

A1 N or S to Wetherby.

A659 via Collingham, Harewood is on A61 between Harrogate and Leeds. Easily reached from A1, M1, M62 and M18 .

15 mins from centre of Leeds or Harrogate.

Rail: Leeds Station 7m.

Bus: No. 36 from Leeds or Harrogate.

ℹ️ 2 Shops and plant centre. Grand piano, clay pigeon shooting, cricket and football pitch, ballooning, jousting, cricket matches arranged. Marquees can be accommodated, concerts (175 max) and product launches.

❌ Ideal for corporate entertaining including drinks receptions, buffets and wedding receptions.

♿ Visitors may alight at entrance. Parking in allocated areas. Most facilities accessible. Wheelchair available at house and bird garden. WC. Special concessions apply to disabled groups.

☕ Café.

🅿️ Ample. Cars 400 yds from house. 50+ coaches 500 yds from house.

🚶 Audio tour of house, £1.50. Lectures by arrangement.

👫 Educational programme.

🐕 Dogs on leads in grounds, guide dogs only in house or bird garden.

CONFERENCE/FUNCTION

ROOM	SIZE	MAX CAPACITY
State Dining Rm.		32
Gallery		96
Courtyard Suite		120
Courtyard Marquee	20' x 24'	400

OPENING TIMES

SUMMER
17 March - 1 November
Closed 5 June.

Bird Garden & Grounds
Daily from 10am.

House
Daily from 11am.

Café
10.30am - 4.30pm.

Harewood is closed to the public 5 June, 1998.

WINTER
November - March
house closed.
November/December:
Grounds & Gardens
open weekends
(ring to confirm times).
Certain rooms available
for corporate entertaining
plus Courtyard Suite for
conferences/product
launches.

ADMISSION

All attractions
Adult £6.75
Child/Student.........£4.50
OAP.........................£6.00
Groups of 15+
Adult £5.50
OAP.........................£5.25
Child (4 - 15yrs)....... Free*

* If accompanied

Bird Garden & Grounds
Adult £5.50
OAP.........................£4.50
Child (4-15)............£3.00
Student...................£3.00
Family (2+3) £16.75

HOVINGHAM HALL
York

Hovingham Hall is a Palladian country house in the heart of Yorkshire, overlooking the oldest private cricket ground in England. Built in warm local limestone, its unique design reflects the twin interests of its builder Thomas Worsley, architecture and horses. The house is entered through a huge Riding School; extensive halls, originally designed as stables, lead into the gracious family rooms. Portraits of many generations look down.

Hovingham Hall remains a family home in the heart of an agricultural estate famous for its woodlands. It is the birthplace of HRH The Duchess of Kent, sister of Sir Marcus Worsley who now lives in the Hall.

The gardens at Hovingham Hall reflect their long history. Great yew hedges planted in the 18th century give a framework to lawns and borders with a wide variety of plants new and old. A former kitchen garden has been laid out as an ornamental orchard, where golden hops reflect its ancient name, the Hop Garden. Roses are a particular family favourite and provide the background to matches on the cricket ground which gives the Hall its setting.

As the house is only opened for pre-booked groups it is possible to have exclusive use for corporate entertaining, overseas touring groups, car launches etc.

❖

CONTACT

Mrs Lamprey
Hovingham Hall
York
YO6 4LU

Tel: (01653) 628206
Fax: (01653) 628668

LOCATION

OS Ref. SE666 756

London A1/M1, A64 then to Hovingham 3^{1}/$_{2}$ hrs.
Leeds 50mins.

Rail: York 17m.

Air: Leeds/Bradford airport 40m. Teesside airport 40m.

Taxi: Rydale Taxis, Malton, North Yorkshire
Tel: 01653 600030.

OPENING TIMES

SUMMER
April - end September
Tue, Wed, Thur
11am - 7pm

Open for groups of 15 or more by written appointment only.

WINTER
Closed.

ADMISSION

House and Garden

Groups only (15+)
  Adult £3.50
  Child* £1.50

  min. payment........£52.50

* under 16yrs.

CONFERENCE/FUNCTION		
ROOM	SIZE	MAX CAPACITY
Ballroom	40' x 40'	130
Ionic Rm	40' x 20'	90
Hunting Hall	36' x 21'	100
Dining Rm	35' x 19'	24

ℹ️ Shop. Conference facilities, corporate hospitality, No photography.

✗ Lunches.

♿ Partially suitable.

☕ Tearoom, must pre-book.

🚶 Visits are by guided tour only.

🅿️ Ample. Park at entrance in centre of village.

🐕 Guide dogs only.

NEWBY HALL & GARDENS
Ripon

NEWBY HALL, the Yorkshire home of Mr and Mrs Robin Compton, is a late 17th century house built in the style of Sir Christopher Wren. William Weddell, an ancestor of Mr Compton, made the Grand Tour in the 1760s, and amongst the treasures he acquired were magnificent classical statuary and a superb set of Gobelin Tapestries. To house these treasures, Weddell commissioned Robert Adam to create the splendid domed Sculpture Gallery and Tapestry Room that we see today. The Regency dining room and billiard room were added later. There is much fine Chippendale furniture and in recent years Mrs Compton has restored the decoration of the house, painstakingly researching colour and decor of the Adam period.

GARDENS

25 acres of glorious gardens contain rare and beautiful shrubs and plants. Newby's famous double herbaceous borders, flanked by great bastions of yew hedges, sweep down to the River Ure. Formal gardens such as the Autumn and Rose Gardens - each with splashing fountains - a Victorian rock garden, the tranquillity of Sylvia's Garden, pergolas and even a tropical garden, make Newby a 'Garden for all Seasons'. Newby holds the National Collection of the Genus Cornus and in 1987 won the Christie's/ HHA Garden of the Year Award. The gardens also incorporate an exciting children's adventure garden and miniature railway.

❖

CONTACT

The Opening
Administrator
Newby Hall
Ripon
North Yorkshire
HG4 5AE

Tel: (01423) 322583
Fax: (01423) 324452

LOCATION

OS Ref. SE348 675

Midway between London and Edinburgh, 4m W of A1, towards Ripon. S of Skelton 2m NW of (A1) Boroughbridge. 4m SE of Ripon

Taxi: Ripon Taxi Rank (01765) 601283.

Bus: On Ripon - York route.

CONFERENCE/FUNCTION		
ROOM	SIZE	MAX CAPACITY
Grantham Room	90' x 20'	200

i Shop. Suitable for filming and for special events, craft and country fairs, vehicle rallies etc, promotions and lectures. No photography inside the house. Allow a full day for viewing house and gardens.

✗ Wedding receptions & special functions.

♿ 5 wheelchairs available. Access around ground floor of house and key areas in gardens. WC.

☕ Garden restaurant, teas, hot and cold meals. Pre-booked parties in Grantham Room. Menus/rates on request.

P Ample. Hard standing for coaches.

👥 Welcome. Rates on request. Grantham Room for use as wet weather base subject to availability. Woodland discovery walk, adventure gardens and train rides on 10$^{1}/_{4}$" gauge railway.

🐕 Guide dogs only.

OPENING TIMES

SUMMER

House
Easter - end September
Daily except Mon
(BH Mon only) 12 - 5pm
Last admission 4.30pm.

Garden
Easter - end September
Daily except Mon.
(BH Mons only)
October: Suns and
$^{1}/_{2}$ term week.
11am - 5.30pm
Last admission 5pm.

WINTER
October - end March
Closed.

ADMISSION

House & Garden
Adult £6.00
Child (4-16yrs)..........£3.60
OAP.........................£5.00
Disabled..................£3.60
Group (20+)
Adult £5.00
Child* £3.40

Garden only
Adult £4.30
Child (4-16yrs)..........£2.00
OAP.........................£3.70
Disabled　　　　£2.90
Group (20+)
Adult £3.70
Child* £2.60

Additional charge for train.

* Details from Administrator

SPECIAL EVENTS

• **MAY 10:**
Spring Plant Fair

• **JUN 6/7:**
Craft Fair

• **JUL 19:**
North East Club for Pre-War Austins Historic Vehicle Rally

• **SEPT 20:**
Autumn Plant Fair

Matthew Antrobus

NOSTELL PRIORY
Wakefield

This Palladian mansion is still the family home of Lord and Lady St Oswald. Inside you can see superb plasterwork ceilings in the state rooms designed and decorated in the middle of the 18th century.

Chippendale, England's most famous cabinet maker, designed furniture especially for the house. Only at Nostell can you find his furniture in such a variety of styles: the magnificent mahogany library table and richly lacquered green and gold 'chinoiserie' furniture.

Nostell is also home to many art treasures: the Brussels tapestries by Van der Borcht, and the famous paintings of *The Family of Sir Thomas More* and *The Procession to Calvary* by Pieter Breughel the Younger. These are just some of the many collections that you can enjoy. Can you imagine who might have played with the remarkable six foot high 18th century doll's house? It is still complete with its original fittings and furniture and is always a great attraction for our visitors.

You can test your knowledge of roses in the old walled garden, where many varieties are laid out in ornamental beds originally designed by the renowned architect Robert Adam as a soft fruit garden. A gentle lakeside walk leads you to the secluded summer house from where the beautiful flowering magnolia trees can be enjoyed in early summer.

The craft centre in the stable block is where you can find crafts people demonstrating and selling samples of their work. Close by, is Wragby church which is also open to visitors. Next to the adventure playground is a picnic area, an ideal place to enjoy lunch.

CONTACT

Visitor Services Manager
Nostell Priory
Wakefield
W. Yorks. WF4 1QE

Tel: (01924) 863892

Fax: (01924) 865282

Conference &
Function facilities:
Visitor Services Manager
Tel: (01924) 863892

LOCATION

OS Ref. SE403 175

6m SE of Wakefield, off A638 Wakefield to Doncaster road.

J40/M1 to Wakefield, then A638.

J38/A1(M) then A638.

Take junction off M62 to Pontefract A628/A638.

OPENING TIMES

4 April - 1 November

April - June, September and October:
Sat & Sun, 12 - 5pm.

1 July - 3 September:
Daily except Fri,
12 - 5pm
BH Mons, 12 - 5pm.

Closed Good Fri.

ADMISSION

House & Grounds
Adult £4.00
Child £2.00
Family £9.50

Grounds only
Adult £2.50
Child £1.50
Family £6.50

Groups of 30+
Special rates available.

SPECIAL EVENTS

Contact property for up to date information.

CONFERENCE/FUNCTION		
ROOM	SIZE	MAX CAPACITY
Old Riding School	22m x 12m	202
Old Coach House	10m x 17m	120

ℹ️ Two shops. Craft centre. Events throughout the year, eg craft fairs, field events. The Old Riding School and the Old Coach House available for concerts, dinner dances, exhibitions, conferences, workshops and training days.

✖️ Wedding receptions.

♿ Tactile books, taped guides, braille guides, Batricar, WCs, lift and wheelchairs.

🍽️ Light refreshments and afternoon teas in the stable tearoom.

🚶 Weekdays, for special group bookings only.

🅿️ Ample. Coaches may set down and pick up at entrance. Please advise if delayed.

👨‍👩‍👧 Welcome. Please pre-book - group rates.

Oakwell Hall

RED HOUSE MUSEUM &
OAKWELL HALL COUNTRY PARK
Gomersal / Batley

CONTACT

Red House Museum
Oxford Road
Gomersal
West Yorkshire
BD19 4JP

Tel: (01274) 335100

Fax: (01274) 335105

Oakwell Hall
Nutter Lane
Birstall
Batley
West Yorkshire
WF17 9LG

Tel: (01924) 326240

Fax: (01924) 326249

LOCATION

OS Ref. SE210 260
Red House:
On A651 in Gomersal.
M62/J27, follow A62 to
wards Huddersfield to
Birstall, follow brown
tourist signs.

OS Ref. SE217 271
Oakwell Hall:
On A652 in Birstall. Take
J27/A62 towards
Huddersfield to Birstall.

OAKWELL HALL:

CONFERENCE/FUNCTION		
ROOM	SIZE	MAX CAPACITY
Barn		120
Classroom		15-25

RED HOUSE MUSEUM

This delightful house was once home to the Taylor family, merchant clothiers. Not only is the house beautifully displayed with original and reproduction furnishings of the 1830s, it has a very important literary connection with Charlotte Brontë who was a regular visitor to the house and friend to the Taylor family.

See the painting and stained glass windows described by Charlotte Brontë in '*Shirley*', then wander to the kitchen and see the dresser piled high with jelly moulds, pewter and pots.

The shop includes delightful period gifts and there is a small garden with period herbs, flowers and shrubs.

Red House Museum

RED HOUSE MUSEUM

ℹ️ Shop. Brass band concerts, etc. Various exhibitions. Charlotte Brontë exhibition due to open in 1998.

♿ Large print notes, braille info, WCs. Lower floor only.

☕ Self-serve hot and cold drinks in exhibition room.

🚶 Charged extra for booked groups only.

🅿️ Turn into car park is difficult unless travelling south on A651 towards Dewsbury. Groups should book.

👥 Booking essential. Teachers info and staff assistance (extra charge).

OAKWELL HALL COUNTRY PARK

Elizabethan Manor house set in period gardens and over 100 acres of country park.

The house is furnished as the Batt family home of the 1690s, giving visitors a unique insight into gentry life at the time – from the elegant painted chamber to the domestic equipment of the kitchen. The house was visited by Charlotte Brontë who describes it as Fieldhead in her historical novel '*Shirley*'.

The site boasts excellent visitor facilities, a delightful garden, café and well-stocked shop. An innovative exhibition on the environment of the country park opened in 1996.

❖

Red House Museum

OAKWELL HALL COUNTRY PARK

ℹ️ Shop. Various events during the year, concerts, fairs, etc. Allow ½ day for visit. Adventure playground.

♿ Ground floor only. RADAR WC, braille guide, large print guide.

☕ Café.

🚶 Available to pre-booked groups at extra charge.

🅿️ Ample. Groups should book.

👥 Booking essential. Teacher resource pack.

🐕 Guide dogs only.

💒 Civil Wedding Licence.

OPENING TIMES

ALL YEAR

Both properties:

Mon – Fri
11am - 5pm.

Sat & Sun
12 - 5pm.

ADMISSION

Red House
Free all year.

Oakwell Hall
(1997 prices)

SUMMER
Adult £1.20
Child 50p
Family £2.50
Groups (max 10)
Discounts available for
pre-booked parties.

WINTER
FREE ENTRY.

**Both properties are
owned by Kirklees
Cultural Services.**

Northern Counties England

RIPLEY CASTLE
Harrogate

RIPLEY CASTLE has for twenty-four generations been the home of the Ingilby family and it retains that 'much loved and very much alive' feeling of a family home. The guides whilst being very knowledgeable, all have an excellent sense of humour, and the tours which take approximately one hour, are not only informative but great fun. The Castle contains fine portraits, paintings, furnishing and chandeliers and in the old (1555) tower, some splendid armour, books, panelling and a priests' secret hiding place.

The extensive walled gardens have recently been transformed and now house The National Hyacinth Collection and fabulous Ripley tropical plant collection, which includes many rare and exotic species. 120,000 spring flowering bulbs create a blaze of colour in April/May, and are followed by the bluebells and rhododendrons, delphiniums, roses and herbaceous borders. Ripley village, on the Castle's doorstep is a model estate village, with many interesting shops, an art gallery and farm museum.

CONTACT

Tours: Elizabeth Liddle
Meetings/Dinners:
Chloe Evans
Ripley Castle
Ripley
Harrogate
North Yorkshire
HG3 3AY

Tel: (01423) 770152

Fax: (01423) 771745

LOCATION

OS Ref. SE283 605

W edge of village. Just off A61, 3$\frac{1}{2}$ m N of Harrogate, 8m S of Ripon. M1 18m S, M62 20m S.

Rail: London - Leeds/York 2hrs. Leeds/York - Harrogate 30mins

Taxi: Blueline taxis Harrogate 503037.

CONFERENCE/FUNCTION		
ROOM	SIZE	MAX CAPACITY
Morning Rm	27' x 22'	80
Large Drawing Rm	30 'x 22'	80
Library	31 x 19'	75
Tower Rm	33' x 21'	75
Map Rm	19' x 14'	20
Dining Rm	23' x 19'	30

OPENING TIMES

SUMMER
Castle & Gardens
April, May - June,
September & October:
Thur - Sun
July & August:
Daily, Mon - Fri,
10.30am - 4.30pm.
Sat & Sun, 10.30am - 3pm.

Gardens only
March: Thur - Sun
11am - 4pm.
April - October:
Daily, 11am - 5pm.

November - 23 December
Daily, 11am - 3.30pm.

WINTER
Pre-booked groups of 15+.
(except 25 December)
10.30am - 7.30pm.

ADMISSION

ALL YEAR
Castle & Gardens
Adult £4.50
Child (5-16yrs) £2.00
OAP........................£3.50
Groups (min 15, max 500)
Adult £3.50
Child (5-16yrs) £1.75

Gardens only
Adult £2.25
Child (5-16yrs) £1.00
OAP........................£1.75
Groups (min 15, max 500)
Adult £1.75
Child (5-16yrs) £1.00

SPECIAL EVENTS

- **JUN 11 - 14:**
  Homes & Gardens Magazine
  Grand Summer Sale.

- **JUL 5:**
  Performing Arts Lakeside
  Concert.

ℹ️ Shop. Management training courses. No photography inside castle unless by prior written consent. Parkland ideal for outdoor activities and concerts. Murder mystery weekends and dry ski slope. Corporate hospitality.

✕ VIP lunches and dinners (max. 66): unlimited in marquees. Full catering service, wedding receptions banquets and medieval banquets.

♿ 5/7 rooms accessible. Gardens accessible (except Tropical Collection). WCs. Parking 50 yds.

☕ Cromwell's Eating House (seats 80) outside castle walls. Pub lunches or dinner at hotel (100 yds). Groups of 15+ must book in advance for both establishments.

🚶 Included in price. Tour time 75 mins.

🅿️ 290 cars - 300 yds from castle entrance. Coach park 50 yds. Free.

👫 Welcome by prior arrangement, between 10.30am - 7.30pm. Teachers' pack.

🐕 Guide dogs only.

🅰️ Boar's Head Hotel (RAC****) 100 yds. Owned and managed by the estate.

💒 Civil Wedding Licence.

SKIPTON CASTLE
Skipton

CONTACT

Judith Parker
Skipton Castle
Skipton
North Yorkshire
BD23 1AQ

Tel: (01756) 792442

Fax: (01756) 796100

www: http//www.
yorkshirenet.co.uk/
skiptoncastle

Guardian of the gateway to the Yorkshire Dales for over 900 years, this is one of the most complete and well-preserved medieval castles in England. From 1310 stronghold of the Cliffords, two Lords of Skipton went out from here to die on Roses battlefields. In the Civil War this was the last Royalist bastion in the North, falling after a three year siege.

Every phase of this turbulent history has left its mark, from the Norman entrance arch and gateway towers to the beautiful early Tudor courtyard built in the heart of the castle by 'The Shepherd Lord'; it was there in 1659, that Lady Anne Clifford planted a yew tree (in whose shade you can sit today) to mark the completion of her repairs after the Civil War. Thanks to her, and to Cromwell, who permitted them on condition that the roofs should not be able to support cannon – the castle is still fully roofed,

making a visit well worthwhile at any time of year. A delightful picnic area has been created on the Chapel Terrace with views over the town and woods.

The gatehouse of the castle contains the Shell Room, decorated in 1620 with shells and Jamaican coral said to have been brought home by Lady Anne's father, George Clifford, 3rd Earl of Cumberland, Champion to Queen Elizabeth and one of her Admirals against the Armada; he lies beneath a splendid tomb in Skipton's parish church, a few yards from the castle gates.

On leaving the castle, the visitor is at once in the town's bustling High Street, with its four market days every week (and lots of other good shopping) and a great variety of pubs and restaurants. Close by, the Leeds and Liverpool canal presents a lively scene.

LOCATION

OS Ref. SD992 520

In the centre of Skipton, at the N end of High Street.

Skipton is 20m W of Harrogate on the A59 and 26m NW of Leeds on A65.

Rail: Regular services from Leeds & Bradford.

Daily
(except 25 December)

from 10am
(Sun from 12pm).

Last admissions 6pm
(October - February 4pm).

ADMISSION

Adult	£3.80
OAP	£3.20

with illustrated tour sheet.

Child (5 - 18yrs)	£1.90

with badge & illustrated tour sheet.

Child (0 - 4yrs)	Free

Groups of 15+
Adult	less 10%

School Groups
Student	£1.90
Teacher	Free

Groups welcome:
Guides available for booked groups at no extra charge.

i Shop.

Soft drinks, ice creams sold in shop. Wide choice of cafés and pubs in town. Indoor and outdoor picnic areas.

P Large public coach and car park off nearby High Street. Coach drivers' rest room at Castle.

Welcome. Guides available. Teachers free.

WHITE SCAR CAVE
Ingleton

White Scar Cave is the longest show cave in Britain. The guided tour covers one mile, and takes about 80 minutes. The highlight of the tour is the impressive 200,000 year old Battlefield Cavern. Over 330 feet long, with its roof soaring in places to 100 feet, this is one of the largest caverns in Britain. It contains thousands of delicate stalactites, which hang from the roof in great clusters.

The tour begins near the original entrance found by Christopher Long, the student who discovered the cave in 1923. The path winds its way past cascading waterfalls, between massive banks of flowstone, and through galleries decorated with cream and carrot-coloured stalactites and stalagmites. Under the steel-grid walkways you can see the stream rushing and foaming on its way. Your guide will show you curious cave formations, including the Devil's Tongue, the Arum Lily and the remarkably lifelike Judge's Head.

There is electric lighting throughout, and the principal features are floodlit. White Scar Cave is part of a Site of Special Scientific Interest. It enjoys a spectacular location in the Yorkshire Dales National Park on the slopes of Ingleborough Hill (2372 ft).

CONTACT

John Connaughton
White Scar Cave
Ingleton
North Yorkshire
LA6 3AW

Tel: (015242) 41244

Fax: (015242) 41700

LOCATION

OS Ref. SD713 745

1 1/2 m from Ingleton on B6255 road to Hawes.

OPENING TIMES

ALL YEAR
Daily, 10am
Last tour at 5.30pm.
Closed 25 December.

ADMISSION

Adult £5.95
Child.....................£3.25

Groups
  Adult £4.76
  Child £2.45

i Shop.

♿ Partially suitable.

☕ Café.

🚶 Guided tours only.

P Ample.

👪 Fact sheets.

🐌 In grounds on leads.

ABBEY HOUSE MUSEUM

Tel: 01532 755821

Abbey Road, Kirkstall, Leeds, Yorkshire LS5 3EH

Owner: Leeds City Council   **Contact:** S Flavin

The house, which still includes the Norman Hall, enables visitors to explore the life of the people of Leeds at work and play. Shops and Georgian and Victorian streets recreated.

Location: OS Ref. SE260 363. On A65 3m NW of Leeds city centre.

Opening Times: Tue - Sat: 10am - 5pm. Sun 1 - 5pm. Closed Mons. Closed for major refurbishment for 18 months from 19 April, 1998.

Admission: Adult £2, Child 50p, Conc./Groups £1.

[i] Shop.   [♿] Ground floor suitable.   [☕] By arrangement.

ALDBOROUGH ROMAN TOWN ⚏

Tel: 01423 322768

High Street, Boroughbridge, North Yorkshire YO5 9ES

Owner: English Heritage   **Contact:** The Custodian

The principle town of the largest Roman town in Britain. The delightfully located remains include Roman defences and two mosaic pavements, a small museum displays finds.

Location: OS99 Ref. SE405 661. Close to Boroughbridge off A1.

Opening Times: 1 Apr - 1 Nov: daily, 10am - 6pm (dusk in Oct). Closed 1 - 2pm.

Admission: Adult £1.70, Child 90p, OAP/Student £1.30. 15% discount for groups of 11+.

[♿] Grounds suitable.   [🐕] In grounds, on leads.

ALLERTON PARK 🏛

See page 275 for full page entry.

AMPLEFORTH COLLEGE JUNIOR SCHOOL

Tel: 01439 788238 **Fax:** 01439 788538

The Castle, Gilling East, York, Yorkshire YO6 4HP

Owner: Ampleforth Abbey Trustees   **Contact:** Fr Jeremy Sierla

Not suitable for wheelchairs. No public toilets.

Location: OS Ref. SE610 768. W of Gilling East village. 20m N of York on B1363.

Opening Times: House: term time, 10am - 12 noon & 2 - 4pm. Gardens - all year: dawn - dusk.

Admission: Gardens: Adult £1, House: Free (Great Hall & Entrance Hall only).

[♿] Not suitable.   [🐕] Guide dogs only.

ASKE HALL

See opposite.

BENINGBROUGH HALL & GARDENS 🌿

Tel: 01904 470666

Shipton-by-Beningbrough, North Yorkshire YO6 1DD   **Fax:** 01904 470002

Owner: The National Trust   **Contact:** The Assistant Property Manager

Imposing 18th century house with over 100 portraits from the National Portrait Gallery. Exciting newly restored walled garden, children's playground.

Location: OS Ref. SE516 586. 8m NW of York, 3m W of Shipton, 2m SE of Linton-on-Ouse, follow signposted route.

Opening Times: 4 Apr - 1 Nov: Sat - Wed & Good Fri also Fri in Jul & Aug. House: 11am - 5pm. Last admission 4.30pm.

Admission: House & Garden: Adult £5, Child £2.50. Garden: Adult £3, Child £1.50, Family £12.50.

[i] Shop.   [♿] Partially suitable. WC.   [☕] Restaurant.   [🐕] No dogs.

[💒] Civil Wedding Licence.

BISHOPS HOUSE

Tel: 01142 557701

Meersbrook Park, Norton Lees Lane, Sheffield, Yorkshire S8 9BE

Owner: Sheffield City Council   **Contact:** Ms K Streets

Built around 1500, this beautiful timber-framed farmhouse is set in parkland and commands panoramic views over the city of Sheffield. Period rooms and displays contain local furniture, plasterwork and embroidery, and explore everyday life in Tudor and Stuart times. Temporary exhibitions and events programme on local historical themes throughout the year.

Location: OS Ref. SK348 843. A61, 2m S of city centre E of the Chesterfield Road.

Opening Times: All year: Wed - Sat, 10am - 4.30pm. Sun 11am - 4.30pm.

Admission: Adult £1, Child/OAP 50p, UB40 free.

[♿] Ground floor & grounds suitable.   [🐕] Guide dogs only.

BOLTON ABBEY

Tel: 01756 710227

Skipton, Yorkshire BD23 6EX

Owner: Trustees of the Chatsworth Settlement   **Contact:** J M Sheard

The Yorkshire estate of the Duke and Duchess of Devonshire. An Augustine Priory founded in 1154. The estate is renowned for its bird life and rare plants.

Location: OS Ref. SE074 542. On B6160, N from the junction with A59 Skipton - Harrogate road, 23m from Leeds.

Opening Times: All year.

Admission: £3 car park charge, £1.50 for disabled.

[i] Shop.   [✗] Wedding receptions.   [♿] Suitable.   [☕] Tearoom & restaurant.

[👥] Educational programme.   [P] Ample.   [🐕] In grounds, on leads.

ASKE HALL

RICHMOND, NORTH YORKSHIRE DL10 5HJ

Owner: The Marquess of Zetland   *Contact:* The Administrator

Tel: 01748 850391 **Fax:** 01748 823252

Nestling in 'Capability' Brown landscaped parkland, Aske has been the family seat of the Dundas family since 1763. This Georgian treasure house boasts exquisite 18th century furniture, paintings and porcelain, including work by Robert Adam, Chippendale, Gainsborough, Raeburn and Meissen.

Aske is an architectural kaleidoscope. There is the original 13th century Pele Tower and remodelled Jacobean tower. John Carr's stable block built in 1765 was later converted into a chapel with Italianate interior. A coach house with clock tower houses the family's carriage. There are follies and a lake as well as the new three tier terraced garden.

Location: OS Ref. NZ179 035. 2m SW of A1 at Scotch Corner, 1m from the A66, on the outskirts of Richmond, on the Gilling West road (B6274)

Opening Times: All year for groups of 15+ by appointment only. Telephone for programme of special events.

Admission: House & grounds: £4 per person.

[i] Conferences. Corporate hospitality.   [✗] Available.   [🏃] By arrangement.

BOLTON CASTLE

LEYBURN, NORTH YORKSHIRE DL8 4ET

Owner: Hon Mr & Mrs Harry Orde-Powlett   *Contact: Hon Mr & Mrs Harry Orde-Powlett*

Tel: 01969 623981   **Fax:** 01969 623332

A palatial baronial manor house/fortress completed in 1399, with a wealth of history. Home of the Scrope family. Mary Queen of Scots was imprisoned here for 6 months. The medieval garden includes 2 separate walled gardens (herb garden and vineyard), a formal rose garden, maze, camomile lawn and a wild flower meadow.

Location: OS Ref. SE034 918 Approx 6m from Leyburn. 1m NW of Redmire.

Opening Times: Mar - Nov: daily, 10am - 5pm or dusk. Dec - 1 Mar: open to pre-booked groups only.

Admission: Adult £3, Child/OAP £2. 10% reduction for pre-booked groups of 25+.

| i | Shop. | X | Wedding receptions. | ♿ | Partially suitable. | ☕ | Tearoom. |
| P | Ample. | | Teachers' pack. | | In grounds, on leads. | | Civil Wedding Licence. |

BRAMHAM PARK

WETHERBY, WEST YORKSHIRE LS23 6ND

Owner: George Lane Fox   *Contact: Estate Office, Bramham Park*

Tel: 01937 844265   **Fax:** 01937 845923

A splendid Palladio-style Florentine villa set in 66 acres of French palace garden. Uniquely unaltered layout of water gardens, cascades, follies and monuments, with 25ft clipped beech avenues, leads to grand vistas stretching out to 100 acres of geometrically designed woodland pleasure grounds. Three centuries on, the family still lives in the house, surrounded by fine collections of furniture, porcelain and paintings.

Location: OS Ref. SE410 416. Half way from London to Edinburgh, 1m W of A1, 5m S of Wetherby, 10m NE of Leeds, 15m SW of York.

Opening Times: Garden only: Easter, May Day & May BH weekends, 1.15 - 5.30pm. House & Garden: 11-14 Jun (Country Fair), 21 Jun - 6 Sept inc: Sun, Tue, Wed & Thur, 1.15 - 5.30pm. Last admission 5pm.

Admission: Garden only: Adult £2.50, Child £1, OAP £2. House & Garden: Adult £4, Child £2, OAP £3. Discount available for groups of 20+.

| ♿ | Grounds suitable. WC. | | Compulsory (weekdays). | | In grounds, on leads. |

SPECIAL EVENTS
JUN 11-14: Bramham International Horse Trials & Yorkshire Country Fair.

BRODSWORTH HALL & GARDENS ⊞

NPI Award 1997:
Winner - Best Overall Property

BRODSWORTH, NR DONCASTER, YORKSHIRE DN5 7XJ

Owner: English Heritage   *Contact: The Custodian*

Tel: 01302 722598   **Fax:** 01302 337165

The mysterious Chevaliere Casentini designed the house for Charles Sabine Augustus Thellusson in an Italianate classical style which was unusual for its day. It was built between 1861 and 1863. Brodsworth Hall and its contents have survived almost intact. An extraordinary time capsule which has been carefully conserved by English Heritage to preserve its faded grandeur.

Brodsworth conveys a vivid picture of daily life in a country house. The decoration and furnishings reflect not only the function of the rooms but the class, sex and even the age of the people who used them. The elegance of the ladies' drawing rooms contrasts with the more masculine atmosphere of the billiard room, the luxury of the family rooms with the plainer quarters of the servants' wing and the practical equipment of the great kitchens.

The design of the gardens is also unchanged, with formal gardens, croquet lawns and a quarry garden, rich in wildlife and garden history.

Location: OS Ref. SE505 070. In Brodsworth, 6m NW of Doncaster on B6422. W of A1 between A635 and A628.

Opening Times: 1 Apr - 1 Nov: Tue - Sun & BHs only. House: 1 - 5pm. Gardens: 12 - 6pm. Winter: Gardens, Shop & Tearoom only: 7 Nov - 28 Mar: Sat & Sun, 11am - 4pm.

Admission: Summer: House: Adult £4.50, Child £2.30, Conc. £3.40. Groups: Adult £3.80, Child £1.95, Conc. £2.89. Gardens: Adult £2.50, Child £1, Conc. £1.90. Groups: Adult £2.12, Child £1.10, Conc. £1. Winter: Adult £1.50, Child free, Conc. £1. Groups: Adult £1.20, Child free, Conc. 85p. (Child 5 - 15yrs).

| i | Shop. Exhibitions. | ♿ | Partially suitable. WC. | ☕ | Tearoom. |
| | Pre-booked groups: 10am - 1pm. | P | Ample. | | Available. | | No dogs. |

BRONTË PARSONAGE MUSEUM   **Tel:** 01535 642323 **Fax:** 01535 647131

Church St, Haworth, Keighley, West Yorkshire BD22 8DR

Owner: The Brontë Society   **Contact:** The Director

The Brontës were an extraordinary literary family and Haworth Parsonage was their lifelong home. Charlotte, Emily and Anne wrote some of the greatest novels in the English language: *Jane Eyre* (1847), *Wuthering Heights* (1847) and *The Tenant of Wildfell Hall* (1848). The Brontës were an intensely close-knit family and their parsonage home formed the heart of their world from early childhood until the ends of their brief lives. The Yorkshire moorland setting provided the Brontës with inspiration for their writing. The Brontë Society, founded in 1893, cares for their home, which opened as a museum in 1928, and the magnificent collection of books, manuscripts, paintings and personal memorabilia which it contains. A special programme of exhibitions and events celebrating the 150th anniversary of Emily's death will run from February 1998.

Location: OS Ref. SE029 373. 8m W of Bradford, 3m S of Keighley.

Opening Times: Summer: 1 Apr - 30 Sept: daily 10am - 5pm, Weds in Aug until 7pm. Winter: 1 Oct - 31 Mar: daily, 11am - 4.30pm. Closed 12 Jan - 6 Feb & 24 - 27 Dec inclusive.

Admission: Adult £3.80, Child £1.20, Conc. £2.80, Family £8.80. Discounts for pre-booked groups.

[i] Shop.   [Av] Available.   [dog] Guide dogs only.

SPECIAL EVENTS

FEB 6 '98 - JAN 10 '99: 'No Coward Souls: Emily, Anne and Branwell Brontë' commemmorating the 150th anniversaries of the deaths of Emily and Branwell and the publication of Anne's second novel: *The Tenant of Wildfell Hall.*

BROUGHTON HALL   See page 276 for full page entry.

BURTON AGNES HALL   [icon]

DRIFFIELD, YORKSHIRE YO25 0ND

Owner: *Burton Agnes Hall Preservation Trust Ltd*   **Contact:** *Mrs Susan Cunliffe-Lister*

Tel: 01262 490324 **Fax:** 01262 490513

A lovely Elizabethan Hall containing treasures collected by the family over four centuries from the original carving and plasterwork to modern and Impressionist paintings. The Hall is surrounded by lawns and topiary yew. The old walled garden has been recently redeveloped and now contains a maze, potager, jungle garden, campanula collection and colour gardens incorporating giant game boards. Children's corner.

Location: OS Ref. TA103 633. Off A166 between Driffield and Bridlington.

Opening Times: 1 Apr - 31 Oct: daily, 11am - 5pm.

Admission: House & Gardens: Adult £4, Child £2, OAP £3.50. Grounds only: Adult £2, Child £1, OAP £1.75. 10% reduction for groups of 30+.

[i] Shop. Plant sales.   [&] Ground floor & grounds.   [café] Café. Ice-cream parlour.

Registered Charity No. 272796.

BURTON AGNES MANOR HOUSE [icon]   **Tel:** 0191 261 1585

Burton Agnes, Bridlington, Humberside

Owner: English Heritage   **Contact:** The North Regional Office

A rare example of a Norman house, altered and encased in brick in the 17th & 18th centuries.

Location: OS Ref. TA103 633. Burton Agnes village, 5m SW of Bridlington on A166.

Opening Times: 1 Apr - 1 Nov: daily, 10am - 6pm or dusk if earlier. 2 Nov - 31 Mar: daily, 10am - 4pm. Closed 24 - 26 Dec, 1 Jan.

Admission: Free.

BURTON CONSTABLE HALL   [icon]

NR. HULL, EAST YORKSHIRE HU11 4LN

Owner: *Burton Constable Foundation*   **Contact:** *Mrs P Connelly*

Tel: 01964 562400 **Fax:** 01964 563229

Burton Constable, a magnificent 16th century house set in a 'Capability' Brown landscape. The collections include pictures, English furniture and scientific instruments and guns collected in the 18th century by William Constable. With nearly 30 rooms open, a unique insight is possible into the patronage of the Constable family who have lived here since it was built.

Location: OS Ref. TA193 369. 14m E of Beverley via A165 Bridlington Road, follow Historic House signs. 7m NE of Hull via B1238 to Sproatley then follow Historic House signs.

Open: Easter Sun - 31 Oct: Sat - Thur. Grounds & tearoom open 12 noon. Hall: 1 - 4.15pm (last admission).

Admission: Adult £4, Child £1.50, OAP £3.25. Group rates available.

BYLAND ABBEY [icon]   **Tel:** 01347 868614

Coxwold, Helmsley, North Yorkshire YO6 4BD

Owner: English Heritage   **Contact:** The Custodian

Hauntingly beautiful ruin, set in peaceful meadows in the shadow of the Hambleton Hills. It illustrates later development of Cistercian churches, including a beautiful floor of mosaic tiles.

Location: OS100 Ref. SE549 789. 2m S of A170 between Thirsk and Helmsley, NE of Coxwold village.

Opening Times: 1 Apr - 1 Nov: daily 10am - 6pm, dusk if earlier in Oct. Closed 1 - 2pm.

Admission: Adult £1.50, Child 80p, Student £1.10. 15% discount for groups of 11+.

[&] Suitable. WCs.   [P] Limited.   [dog] On leads.

CANNON HALL MUSEUM   **Tel:** 01226 790270

Cawthorne, Barnsley, South Yorkshire S75 4AT

Owner: Barnsley Metropolitan Borough Council   **Contact:** The Keeper

Late 17th century house, remodelled in the 1760s by John Carr of York. Contains decorative arts collections including fine furniture, paintings, pottery and glassware. Also the Regimental Museum of the 13th/18th Hussars. Situated in an 18th century park landscaped by Richard Woods.

Location: OS Ref. SE272 084. 6m NW of Barnsley of A635.

Opening Times: 1 Nov - 31 Mar: Sat, 10.30am - 5pm. Sun, 12 - 5pm. 1 Apr - 31 Oct: Tue - Sat, 10.30am - 5pm. Sun, 12 - 5pm. Closed Christmas and New Year's Day. Winter 1998 times subject to variations. Please contact before your visit.

Admission: Adults £1, Child/Conc. 50p, (1997 prices). Groups of 10+ 50p ea.

[i] Shop. Corporate hospitality.   [&] Partially suitable. WC.
[café] Tearoom (seasonal).   [P] Ample.   [Av] Education programme, teachers' pack.
[dog] In grounds, on leads.

CASTLE HOWARD [icon]   See page 277 for full page entry.

CLIFFORD'S TOWER ⊞
Tel: 01904 646940

Clifford Street, York, Yorkshire YO1 1SA

Owner: English Heritage   **Contact:** The Custodian

A 13th century tower on one of two mottes thrown up by William the Conqueror to hold York. There are panoramic views of the city from the top of the tower.

Location: OS105 Ref. SE 605 515. York city centre.

Opening Times: 1 Apr - 1 Nov: daily 10am - 6pm (dusk if earlier in Oct). Open to 7pm in Jul/Aug. 2 Nov - 31 Mar: daily 10am - 4pm. Closed 24 - 26 Dec.

Admission: Adult £1.70, Child 90p, Conc. £1.30. 15% discounts available for groups of 11+.

🅸 Shop.   ♿ Not suitable.   🐾 In grounds, on leads.

CONISBROUGH CASTLE ⊞
Tel: 01709 863329

Conisbrough, Yorkshire

Owner: English Heritage   **Contact:** The Administrator

The oldest circular keep in England and one of the finest medieval buildings.

Location: OS111 Ref. SK515 989. 4½ m SW of Doncaster.

Opening Times: 1 Apr - 30 Sept: daily 10am - 5pm (6pm at weekends & BHs). 10 Oct - 31 Mar: daily, 10am - 4pm.

Admission: Adults £2.75, Child £1.25, Conc. £1.75. Group: Adult £1.90.

🅸 Shop. Visitor centre.   🚶 Guides in costume.

CONSTABLE BURTON HALL GARDENS 🏛
Tel: 01677 450428

Leyburn, North Yorkshire DL8 5LJ

                         Fax: 01677 450622

Owner: M C A Wyvill Esq   **Contact:** M C A Wyvill Esq

A delightful terraced woodland garden of lilies, ferns, hardy shrubs, roses and wild flowers attached to a beautiful Palladian house designed by John Carr (not open). Near to the entrance drive is a stream, bog garden and rockery. Impressive spring display of daffodils, aconites and snowdrops.

Location: OS Ref. SE164 913. 3m E of Leyburn off the A684.

Opening Times: Garden only: 24 Mar - 20 Oct: daily, 9am - 6pm.

Admission: Adult £2, Child (under 16) 50p, OAP £1.50.

DUNCOMBE PARK 🏛
See page 278 for full page entry.

EASBY ABBEY ⊞
Tel: 0191 261 1585

Nr. Richmond, North Yorkshire

Owner: English Heritage   **Contact:** The Custodian

Substantial remains of the medieval abbey buildings stand by the River Swale near Richmond.

Location: OS92 Ref. NZ185 003. 1m SE of Richmond off B6271.

Opening Times: 1 Apr - 1 Nov: daily, 10am - 6pm or dusk in Oct.

Admission: Adult £1.50, Child 80p, Student/OAP £1.10. 15% discount for groups of 11+.

♿ Grounds suitable.   🅿 Limited.   🐾 In grounds, on leads.

EAST RIDDLESDEN HALL 🌿
Tel: 01535 607075 **Fax:** 01535 691462

Bradford Road, Keighley, West Yorkshire BD20 5EL

Owner: The National Trust   **Contact:** Assistant Property Manager

Homely 17th century merchant's house with beautiful embroideries, Yorkshire carved oak furniture, fine ceilings and stonework. Explore the magnificent Great Barn or feed the hungry ducks. Delightful flower and herb borders. Special events throughout the year.

Location: OS104 SE079 421. 1m NE of Keighley on S side of A650 in Riddlesden. 50yds from Leeds/Liverpool Canal. Bus: Frequent services from Skipton, Bradford and Leeds. Railway station at Keighley 1m.

Opening Times: 1 Apr - 1 Nov: Sat - Wed & Good Fri, also Thurs in Jul & Aug, 12 - 5pm, Sat 1 - 5pm.

Admission: Adult £3.30, Child £1.80, Family £8.

🅸 Shop.   ♿ Partially suitable. WC.   ☕ Tearoom.   🚶 Costumed tours.
👪 Available.   🐕 No dogs.   💒 Civil Wedding Licence.

EPWORTH OLD RECTORY
Tel: 01427 872268

1 Rectory Street, Epworth, Doncaster, South Yorkshire DN9 1HX

Owner: World Methodist Council   **Contact:** C J Barton (Warden)

1709 Queen Anne period house, John and Charles Wesley's boyhood home. Portraits, period furniture, Methodist memorabilia. Garden, picnic facilities, cinematic presentation. Teachers' pack for Epworth Wesley Trail will be available in early 1998.

Location: OS Ref. SE785 036. Epworth lies on A161, 3m S M180/J2. 10m N of Gainsborough.

Opening Times: 1 Mar - 31 Oct. Mar, Apr & Oct: Mon - Sat, 10am - 12pm & 2 - 4pm, Sun, 2 - 4pm. May - Sept: Mon - Sat, 10am - 4.30pm, Sun, 2 - 4.30pm.

Admission: Adult £2, Children in full-time education £1.

🅸 Shop.   ♿ Ground floor & grounds suitable.   ☕ Tearoom.
🚶 Compulsory.   🅿 Limited.   👪 Teachers' pack.   🐾 Guide dogs only.
🅰 2 doubles.

FAIRFAX HOUSE 🏛
See page 279 for full page entry.

FOUNTAINS ABBEY & STUDLEY ROYAL 🌿
See page 280 for full page entry.

THE GEORGIAN THEATRE ROYAL
Tel: 01748 823710 **Fax:** 01748 823710

Richmond, Yorkshire DL10 4DW

Owner: Georgian Theatre Royal Trust   **Contact:** Bill Sellars

Brochure on request. Built in 1788, this is the country's oldest theatre in original form.

Location: OS Ref. NZ174 013. 6m from Scotch Corner. In Richmond.

Opening Times: Museum: 1 Apr - 31 Oct: Mon - Sat, 10.30am - 4.30pm. Sun 11am - 2pm.

Admission: Museum: Adult £1.50, Child 75p, Conc £1. Theatre: £3 - £8.

HAREWOOD HOUSE
See page 281 for full page entry.

HARLOW CARR BOTANICAL GARDENS
Tel: 01423 565418

Crag Lane, Harrogate, North Yorkshire HG3 1QB

                         Fax: 01423 530663

Owner: Northern Horticultural Society   **Contact:** The Administrator

68 acre headquarters of the Northern Horticultural Society. Vegetable, fruit and flower trials; rock, foliage, winter and heather gardens; alpines; herbaceous beds; streamside; woodland and arboretum. National collections; exhibitions and displays; guided walks; lectures. Museum of Gardening; model village; children's play area. Shelters and seating.

Location: OS Ref. SE285 543. Off Otley Rd (B6162). 1½ m W from town centre.

Opening Times: Daily from 9.30am. Last admission 6pm or dusk if earlier.

Admission: Adult £3.50, Child free, OAP/Groups £2.60 .

🅸 Shop. Plant centre.   ✗ Available.   ♿ Grounds suitable. WC.   ☕ Restaurant.
🚶 Guided walks.   🅿 Ample.   🐾 Guide dogs only.

HELMSLEY CASTLE ⊞
Tel: 014397 70442

Helmsley, North Yorkshire YO6 5AB

Owner: English Heritage   **Contact:** The Custodian

Close to the market square, with a view of the town, is this 12th century castle. Spectacular earthworks surround a great ruined Norman keep. Exhibition and tableau on the history of the castle.

Location: OS100 SE611 836. In Helmsley town.

Opening Times: 1 Apr - 1 Nov: daily 10am - 6pm (or dusk if earlier in Oct). 2 Nov - 31 Mar: Wed - Sun, 10am - 4pm, Closed 1 - 2pm. (Closed 24 - 26 Dec).

Admission: Adult £2.20, Child £1.10, Conc £1.70. 15% discount for groups of 11+.

HELMSLEY WALLED GARDEN

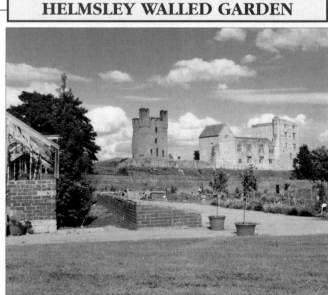

CLEVELAND WAY, HELMSLEY, NORTH YORKSHIRE YO6 5AH

Owner: Helmsley Walled Garden Ltd   *Contact:* Mrs Alison Ticehurst

Tel: 01439 771427 **Fax:** 01439 788002

A 5 acre walled garden under restoration. Historic glasshouses rescued, awaiting repair. Bedecked with couch and ivy in 1994, paths and ponds are renovated, walls repointed, wondrous borders developing including a rainbow border. Vegetables and fruit are prominent and part of the working walled garden theme. Pigs, geese and other small animals provide manure in this natural environment. All plants are homegrown.

Location: OS100 SE611 836. 25m N of York, 15m from Thirsk. In Helmsley follow signs to Cleveland Way.

Open: 1 Apr - 31 Oct: daily, 10.30am - 5pm. Nov - Mar: Fri, Sat & Sun, 1 - 4pm.

Admission: Adult £2, Child free, Conc. £1.

🅸 Shop. Plant centre. (Craft Workshops).   ♿ Suitable. WC.   ☕ Café.
🚶 By arrangement.   🅿 Cleveland Way car park.   👪 Educational programme.
🐾 In grounds, on leads.

HOVINGHAM HALL
See page 282 for full page entry.

KIRKHAM PRIORY ⌗
Tel: 01653 618768

Kirkham, Whitwell-on-the-Hill, Yorkshire YO6 7JS

Owner: English Heritage   **Contact:** The Custodian

The ruins of this Augustinian priory include a magnificent carved gatehouse.

Location: OS100 Ref. SE735 657. 5m SW of Malton on minor road off A64.

Opening Times: 1 Apr - 30 Sept: daily 12 - 5pm.

Admission: Adult £1.50, Child 80p, Conc. £1.10. 15% discount for groups of 11+.

ⓘ Shop.   Ⓟ Limited.   🐕 On leads.

KNARESBOROUGH CASTLE
Tel: 01423 503340 **Fax:** 01423 840026

Knaresborough, North Yorkshire HG1 2RY

Owner: Duchy of Lancaster   **Contact:** Ms Mary Kershaw

Ruins of 14th century castle standing high above the town. Local history museum housed in Tudor Courthouse. Gallery devoted to the Civil War.

Location: OS Ref. SE349 569. 5m E of Harrogate, off A59.

Opening Times: Easter BH w/e, 1 May - 30 Sept: daily 10.30am - 5pm.

Admission: Adult £1.75, Child/OAP £1, Family £4.50, Groups (10+) £1.25. Local residents free.

LOTHERTON HALL
Tel: 0113 281 3259 **Fax:** 0113 281 2100

Aberford, Leeds, Yorkshire LS25 3EB

Owner: Leeds City Council   **Contact:** The Supervisor

Magnificent former home of the Gascoigne family. Fine furniture, paintings, silver, pottery, porcelain and displays of costume.

Location: OS Ref. SE450 360. Just E of A1. 12m NE of Leeds city centre.

Opening Times: Mar: Tue - Sat 10am - 4pm. Sun 12 - 4pm. 1 Apr - 31 Oct: Tues - Sat, 10am - 5pm. Sun 1 - 5pm. 1 Nov - 31 Dec: Tue - Sat 10am - 4pm. Sun 12 - 4pm. (Closed Mons, except BHs & throughout Jan & Feb '98).

Admission: Adult £2, Child accompanied by adults 50p (Leeds schools free), Conc £1.

MARKENFIELD HALL
Tel: 01609 780306

Hell Wath Lane, Ripon, Yorkshire HG4 3AD

Owner: The Lady Grantley   **Contact:** Strutt & Parker

Fine example of an English Manor House.

Location: OS Ref. SE294 672. Local access from gate on W side A61, 3m S of Ripon.

Opening Times: Apr - Oct: Mons only, 10am - 12.30pm and 2.15 - 5pm.

Admission: Adult £3, Child £1.50. Exterior and outside courtyard free.

MERCHANT ADVENTURERS' HALL

FOSSGATE, YORK YO1 2XD

Owner: The Company of Merchant Adventurers   *Contact:* The Clerk

Tel/Fax: 01904 654818

The finest medieval guild hall in Europe, built in 1357/62 and substantially unaltered. In it the Merchants transacted their business, as their successors still do today. On the ground floor was their hospice, where they cared for the poor, and their private chapel, a unique survival in England. There are good collections of early portraits, furniture, silver and other objects used by the Merchants over the centuries, when their wealth and influence helped to make York the second city in England after London.

Location: OS Ref. SE606 518. Main entrance in Piccadilly, other entrance in Fossgate.

Opening Times: 14 Mar - 14 Nov: daily, 8.30am - 5pm. 15 Nov - 12 Mar 1999 (except Sun) 8.30am - 3.30pm. Closed Christmas/New Year week.

Admission: Adult £1.90, Child 60p, OAP/Student £1.60.

☒ Wedding receptions.   ♿ Ground floor & grounds suitable. WCs.

🚶 By arrangement.   👥 Teachers' pack available.

🐕 In grounds, on leads.   Civil Wedding Licence.

MIDDLEHAM CASTLE ⌗
Tel: 01969 623899

Middleham, Leyburn, Yorkshire DL8 4RJ

Owner: English Heritage   **Contact:** The Custodian

This childhood home of Richard III stands controlling the river that winds through Wensleydale. There is a massive 12th century keep with splendid views of the surrounding countryside from the battlements. Wheelchairs in grounds only.

Location: OS99 Ref. SE128 875. At Middleham, 2m S of Leyburn of A6108.

Opening Times: 1 Apr - 1 Nov: daily, 10am - 6pm (or dusk if earlier in Oct). 2 Nov - 31 Mar: Wed - Sun, 10am - 4pm (closed 24 - 26 Dec). Closed 1 - 2pm.

Admission: Adult £2.20, Child £1.10, Conc. £1.70. 15% discount for groups of 11+.

ⓘ Shop.   ♿ Grounds suitable.   🐕 In grounds, on leads.

Cricket:

A game of Saxon origin, called creag and played with a bent wooden bat. The first recorded organised game was in 1711, when Kent played All England. The Hambledon Club in Hampshire (1750) was the first organised club and the cradle of the modern game. The Hambledon was disbanded in 1791 and the Marylebone (1787) took the lead, from its grounds in Dorset Square, London; by 1814 it had moved to St John's Wood, to grounds belonging to Thomas Lord, hence Lord's. The first 'Gentlemen versus Players' match took place at Mr Lord's ground in 1806, the last in 1962. In the nineteenth and early twentieth centuries it was a popular country house pastime to put together a scratch team to play against a village or other country house team.

Extract from; "Life in the Country House" by David N Durant (published by John Murray), PB£15.99, see page twelve at the front of the book.

CIVIL WEDDING VENUES

See the front section for full list.

Northern Counties England

MOUNT GRACE PRIORY

National Trust Photographic Library

SADDLE BRIDGE, NORTH YORKSHIRE DL6 3JG

Owner: *National Trust*   **Managed by:** *English Heritage*   **Contact:** *The Custodian*

Tel: 01609 883494

Hidden in tranquil wooded countryside at the foot of the Cleveland Hills, one of the loveliest settings of any English Priory, and the best preserved Carthusian monastery in England. Monks lived as hermits in their cells and one cell, recently restored, is furnished to give a clear picture of their austere routine of work and prayer. Visitors enter through the manor built by Thomas Lascelles in 1654 on the site of the monastery guest house. It was rebuilt at the turn of the century using traditional techniques, typical of the Arts and Crafts movement.

Location: OS Ref. SE449 985. 12m N of Thirsk, 7m NE of Northallerton on A19.

Opening Times: 1 Apr - 1 Nov: daily 10am - 6pm (or dusk if earlier in Oct). 2 Nov - 31 Mar: Wed - Sun, 10am - 4pm (closed 1 - 2pm). Closed 24 - 26 Dec.

Admission: Adult £2.70, Child £1.40, Conc. £2. 15% discount for groups of 11+.

ⓘ Shop.   ♿ Ground floor & grounds suitable.   ☕ Available.   P Ample.

NEWBURGH PRIORY   **Tel:** 01347 868435

Coxwold, Yorkshire YO6 4AS

Owner: Sir George Wombwell Bt   **Contact:** Sir George Wombwell

Augustinian priory founded in 1145 converted into Tudor mansion, and again later in 18th century. Beautiful water garden.

Location: OS Ref. 541 764. 7m SE Thirsk. 1/2 m SE of Coxwold.

Opening Times: Apr - end Jun: Wed & Sun: House: 2.30 - 4.45pm, Garden: 2 - 6pm. Guided tours approx 60 mins. (Best to check first).

NEWBY HALL & GARDENS   See page 283 for full page entry.

NORTON CONYERS   **Tel:** 01765 640333   **Fax:** 01765 692772

Nr. Ripon, North Yorkshire HG4 5EQ

Owner: Sir James and Lady Graham   **Contact:** Lady Graham

Visited by Charlotte Brontë in 1839, Norton Conyers is an original of the 'Thornfield Hall' in *Jane Eyre* and a family legend was an inspiration for the mad Mrs Rochester. Building is late medieval with Stuart and Georgian additions. Friendly atmosphere, resulting from over 370 years of occupation by the Grahams. 18th century walled garden near house, with orangery and herbaceous borders. Small plant sales area specialising in unusual hardy plants. Pick your own fruit in season.

Location: OS Ref. SF319 763. 4m N of Ripon. 3¹/₂m from the A1.

Opening Times: House: BH Sun & Mon; Sun 7 Jun - 13 Sept; daily 20 - 25 July, 2 - 5pm. Garden: Sun & BH Mon, 12 Apr - 13 Sept: 11.30am - 5pm; also daily 20 - 25 July, 2 - 5pm.

Admission: House: Adult £2.95, Child (10 - 16) £2.50, Conc. £2. Groups (20+) by arrangement. Garden is free, donations are welcome, but charges are made at charity openings.

ⓘ Shop. Plant sales. No photography. No stilettos in house.   ♿ Partially suitable. WC.

🕊 By arrangement.   P Ample.   🐕 In grounds, on leads.

NOSTELL PRIORY   See page 284 for full page entry.

NUNNINGTON HALL   **Tel:** 01439 748283   **Fax:** 01439 748284

Nunnington, North Yorkshire YO6 5UY

Owner: National Trust   **Contact:** The Visitor Manager

16th century manor house with fine panelled hall and staircase. Carlisle collection of miniature rooms on display, walled garden with peacocks, orchard and clematis collection.

Location: OS Ref. SE670 795. In Ryedale, 4¹/₂m SE of Helmsley, 1¹/₂m N of B1257.

Opening Times: 1 Apr - 1 Nov: daily except Mon & Tue (but open BH Mon and every Tue during Jun, Jul & Aug) 1.30 - 6pm (1.30 - 5.30pm Apr & Oct). Open Good Fri.

Admission: House and Garden: Adult £4, Child £2. Family £10. Garden only: Adult £1, Child free.

ⓘ Shop.   ♿ Ground floor & grounds suitable. WC.   ☕ Tearoom.   🐕 Guide dogs only.

THE OLD GRAMMAR SCHOOL   **Tel:** 01482 613902   **Fax:** 01482 613710

Market Place, Hull

Owner: Hull City Council   **Contact:** S R Green

Housed in the Old Grammar School this history resource centre offers hands on activities for the public and schools alike.

Location: OS Ref. TA099 285. 50 yds SW of the Church at centre of the Old Town.

Opening Times: School holidays and weekends open to the public. Please phone for details.

Admission: £1, Child under 13yrs free.

ⓘ Shop.   ♿ House suitable.   P No parking.   🐕 Guide dogs only.

THE ORANGERY AT SETTRINGTON

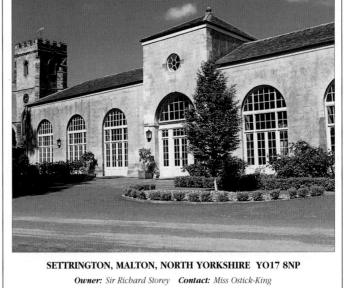

SETTRINGTON, MALTON, NORTH YORKSHIRE YO17 8NP

Owner: *Sir Richard Storey*   **Contact:** *Miss Ostick-King*

Tel: 01944 768345 or 01944 768440 - out of hours   **Fax:** 01944 768484

An outstanding and versatile venue in a beautifully converted 18th century building, standing in the magnificent grounds of Settrington House. From Civil Weddings to conferences, product launches to dinner dances, concerts and exhibitions. The Orangery is the exclusive setting for every occasion with seating from 50 to 300.

Location: OS Ref. SE840702. Between York and Scarborough.

Opening Times: Privately booked functions

Admission: Please telephone for prices.

ⓘ Conference facilities.   ✗ Wedding receptions, private functions.

♿ Suitable. WCs.   ☕ Licensed.   P Ample.

🐕 Guide dogs only.   🔔 Civil Wedding Licence.

ORMESBY HALL   **Tel:** 01642 324188

Church Lane, Ormesby, Middlesbrough TS7 9AS

Owner: National Trust   **Contact:** The House Manager

A mid 18th century house with opulent decoration inside, including fine plasterwork by contemporary craftsmen. A Jacobean doorway with a carved family crest survives from the earlier house on the site. The stable block, attributed to Carr of York, is a particularly fine mid 18th century building with an attractive courtyard leased to the Mounted Police; also an attractive garden with holly walk.

Location: OS Ref. NZ530 167. 3m SE of Middlesbrough.

Opening Times: 1 Apr - 1 Nov: Tue, Wed, Thur, Sun, BH Mon & Good Fri, 2 - 5.30pm.. Last adm. 5pm. Tues guided tours only. Last tour 3.30pm. Garden tours, last Thur of some months. (Please enquire for further details).

Admission: House, garden, railway and exhibitions: Adult £3, Child £1.50, Family £7.50. Garden, railway and exhibitions: Adult £2, Child £1.

ⓘ Shop.   ♿ Ground floor & grounds suitable. WC.   ☕ Tearoom.

PARCEVALL HALL GARDENS
Tel: 01756 720311

Skyreholme, Skipton, Yorkshire BD23 6DE   **Contact:** Jo Makin (Administrator)

Owner: Walsingham College (Yorkshire Properties) Ltd.

Location: OS Ref. SE068 613. E side of Upper Wharfedale, 1¹/₂ m NE of Appletreewick. 12m NNW of Ilkley by B6160 and across Barden Bridge.

Opening Times: Good Fri - 31 Oct: 10am - 6pm.

Admission: £2, Child 50p.

i Picnic area.	**&** Not suitable.	☕ Café.	🏃 Guided tours.
P Ample for cars, limited for coaches.		☕ In grounds, on leads.	

PICKERING CASTLE ⚜
Tel: 01751 474989

Pickering, Yorkshire YO18 7AX

Owner: English Heritage   **Contact:** The Custodian

A splendid motte and bailey castle, once a royal ranch. It is well preserved, with much of the original walls, towers and keep, and there are spectacular views over the surrounding countryside. There is an exhibition on the castle's history.

Location: OS100 Ref. SE800 845. In Pickering, 15m SW of Scarborough.

Opening Times: 1 Apr - 1 Nov: daily, 10am - 6pm (or dusk if earlier in Oct). 2 Nov - 31 Mar: Wed - Sun, 10am - 4pm (closed 1 - 2pm). Closed 24 - 26 Dec.

Admission: Adult £2.20, Child £1.10, Conc. £1.70. 15% discount for groups of 11+.

i Shop.	**&** Ground floor & grounds suitable.	**P** Limited.	☕ In grounds, on leads.

RED HOUSE MUSEUM & OAKWELL HALL COUNTRY PARK
See page 285 for full page entry.

RIEVAULX ABBEY ⚜

RIEVAULX, NR. HELMSLEY, NORTH YORKSHIRE YO6 5LB
Owner: English Heritage   **Contact:** The Custodian

Tel: 01439 798228

In a deeply wooded valley by the River Rye you can see some of the most spectacular monastic ruins in England, dating from the 12th century. The church has the earliest large Cistercian nave in Britain. A fascinating exhibition shows how successfully the Cistercians at Rievaulx ran their many businesses and explains the part played by Abbot Ailred, who ruled for twenty years.

Location: OS100 Ref. SE577 849. 2¹/₄ m W of Helmsley on minor road off B1257.

Opening Times: 1 Apr - 1 Nov: daily, 10am - 6pm (or dusk if earlier in Oct). 2 Nov - 31 Mar: daily, 10am - 4pm. Closed 24- 26 Dec.

Admission: Adult £2.90, Child £1.50, Conc. £2.20. 15% discount for groups of 11+.

i Shop.	**&** Ground floor & grounds suitable.	🏃 Audio tour.	**P** Ample.

RICHMOND CASTLE ⚜

RICHMOND, NORTH YORKSHIRE DL10 4QW
Owner: English Heritage   **Contact:** The Custodian

Tel: 01748 822493

A splendid medieval fortress, with a fine 12th century keep and 11th century remains of the curtain wall and domestic buildings. There are magnificent views from the 100 feet high keep.

Location: OS92 Ref. NZ174 006. In Richmond.

Opening Times: 1 Apr - 1 Nov: daily, 10am - 6pm (or dusk if earlier in Oct). 2 Nov - 31 Mar: daily, 10am - 4pm (closed for lunch 1 - 2pm). Closed 24- 26 Dec.

Admission: Adult £2.20, Child £1.10, Conc. £1.70. 15% discount for groups of 11+.

i Shop.	**&** Ground floor & grounds suitable.	☕ In grounds, on leads.

RIEVAULX TERRACE AND TEMPLES 🌿
Tel: 01439 798340

Rievaulx, Helmsley, North Yorkshire YO6 5LJ

Owner: The National Trust   **Contact:** The Visitor Manager

A ¹/₂ m long grass-covered terrace and adjoining woodlands with vistas over Rievaulx Abbey and Rye valley to Ryedale and the Hambleton Hills. There are two mid 18th century temples: the Ionic Temple has elaborate ceiling paintings and fine 18th century furniture. A permanent exhibition in the basement is on English landscape design in the 18th century. An abundance of wild flowers clothe the terrace in spring and summer.

Location: OS Ref. SE579 848. 2¹/₂ m NW of Helmsley on B1257. E of the Abbey.

Opening Times: 1 Apr - 1 Nov. Apr & Oct: daily, 10.30am - 5pm. May, Jun - Sept: daily, 10.30am - 6pm. Last admission 1hr before closing.

Admission: Adult £2.80, Child £1.40, Family £7.

i Shop.	**&** Grounds suitable. WCs.	☕ Tearoom.	☕ In grounds, on leads.

RIPLEY CASTLE 🏛
See page 286 for full page entry.

RIPON CATHEDRAL
Tel: 01765 604108 (information on tours etc.)

Ripon, Yorkshire HG4 1QR

                Contact: Canon Keith Punshon

One of the oldest crypts in Europe (672). Marvellous choir stalls and misericords (500 years old). Almost every type of architecture. Treasury.

Location: OS Ref. SE314 711. 5m W signposted off A1, 12m N of Harrogate.

Opening Times: All year: 8am - 6pm.

Admission: Donations. £2 per head pre-booked guided tours.

i Shop.	**&** Ground floor & grounds suitable.	🏃 By arrangement.
👥 Educational programme.	☕ Guide dogs only.	

Northern Counties England

ROCHE ABBEY

Tel: 01709 812739

Maltby, Rotherham, South Yorkshire S66 8NW

Owner: English Heritage   **Contact:** The Custodian

This Cistercian monastery, founded in 1147, lies in a secluded landscaped valley sheltered by limestone cliffs and trees. Some of the walls still stand to their full height and excavation has revealed the complete layout of the abbey.

Location: OS111 Ref. SK544 898. 1m S of Maltby off A634.

Opening Times: 1 Apr - 1 Nov: daily, 10am - 6pm (or dusk if earlier in Oct). Closed 1 - 2pm.

Admission: Adult £1.50, Child 80p, Conc. £1.10. 15% discount for groups of 11+.

- i   Ground floor & grounds suitable.
- Audio tour.
- P   Limited.
- In grounds, on leads.

ST WILLIAM'S COLLEGE

Tel: 01904 637134   **Fax:** 01904 642157

5 College Street, York, Yorkshire YO1 2JF

Owner: The Dean and Chapter of York   **Contact:** Sandie Clarke

15th century medieval home of Minster Chantry Priests. Three large medieval halls, available for functions, conferences, weddings, medieval banquets, etc. Halls open to view when not in use. Information Centre.

Location: OS Ref. SE605 522. College Street, York.

Opening Times: 10am - 5pm.

Admission: Adult 60p, Child 30p. For further details please telephone.

- i   Shop. Conferences. Corporate hospitality.
- X   Full facilities. Medieval banquets.
- Licensed restaurant/café/tearoom.
- P   No parking.
- Educational programme.
- Guide dogs only.

SCAMPSTON HALL

Tel: 01944 758224   **Fax:** 01944 758700

Scampston, Malton, North Yorkshire YO17 8NG

Owner: Sir Charles Legard Bt   **Contact:** Sir Charles Legard Bt

Opened for the first time in 1997, this country house has remained in the same family since it was built towards the end of the 17th century. The house was extensively remodelled in 1801 by the architect Thomas Leverton and has fine Regency interiors. It houses an important collection of works of art including pictures by Gainsborough, Marlow, Scott and Wilson. The park was laid out under the guidance of 'Capability' Brown and includes 10 acres of lakes and a Palladian bridge. The garden features a recently restored 19th century walk in rock and water garden with a collection of alpines, some of which are available for sale.

Location: OS100 Ref. SE865 755. 5m E of Malton, off A64.

Opening Times: 24 May - 5 Jun & 26 Jul - 7 Aug (closed Sat), 1 - 5pm. Last admission 4.30pm.

Admission: House & Garden: £5, Garden £2, no concessions. Groups and coaches by appointment only. Prices for groups by arrangement.

- i   Plant sales.
- Ground floor & grounds suitable.
- Tearoom.
- Guided tours only.
- No dogs.

SCARBOROUGH CASTLE

Tel: 01723 372451

Castle Road, Scarborough, North Yorkshire YO11 1HY

Owner: English Heritage   **Contact:** The Custodian

Spectacular coastal views from the walls of this enormous 12th century castle. The buttressed castle walls stretch out along the cliff edge and remains of the great rectangular stone keep still stand to over three storeys high. There is also the site of a 4th century Roman signal station. The castle was frequently attacked, but despite being blasted by cannons of the Civil War and bombarded from the sea during World War I, it is still a spectacular place to visit.

Location: OS101, Ref. TA050 893. Castle Road, E of town centre.

Opening Times: 1 Apr - 1 Nov: daily, 10am - 6pm (or dusk if earlier in Oct). 2 Nov - 31 Mar: Wed - Sun, 10am - 4pm (closed 1 -2 pm). Closed 24 - 26 Dec.

Admission: Adult £2.20, Child £1.10, Conc. £1.70. 15% discount for groups of 11+.

- i   Shop.
- Partially suitable.
- Inclusive taped tour.
- In grounds, on leads.

SEWERBY HALL & GARDENS

Tel: 01262 677874   **Fax:** 01262 674265

Church Lane, Sewerby, Nr. Bridlington, East Yorkshire YO15 1EA

Owner: East Riding of Yorkshire Council   **Contact:** Principal Museums Officer

Situated in a dramatic cliff-top position, forming the gateway to the Flamborough Heritage Coast, Sewerby Hall and Gardens, set in 50 acres of early 19th century parkland, enjoys spectacular views over Bridlington Bay. The Hall contains the magnificent orangery, period rooms, art and photographic galleries, the History of East Yorkshire permanent display, Mayor's parlour and Mayoral Regalia displays and the Amy Johnson room displays a collection of her awards, trophies and mementoes. The gardens are amongst the best in the region.

Location: OS Ref. TA203 690. 2m N of Bridlington in Sewerby village.

Opening Times: 7 Mar - 7 Apr: Sat - Tue, 11am - 4pm. 10 Apr - 1 Nov: daily, 10am - 6pm. 2 Nov - 22 Dec: Sat - Tue, 11am - 4pm.

Admission: Adult £2.60, Child £1, OAP £2.10, Family (2 + 3) £6.50. Groups half price. Prices may change during 1998. Please ring for details.

- i   Shop.
- X   Wedding receptions.
- Suitable. WC.
- Licensed tearoom.
- P   Ample.
- Teachers' pack.
- In grounds on leads.
- Civil Wedding Licence.

SHANDY HALL

Tel: 01347 868465

Coxwold, York YO6 4AD

Owner: The Laurence Sterne Trust   **Contact:** Mrs J Monkman

Built as a timber-framed hall in the 15th century. A lived-in house surrounded by attractive gardens. Former home of author Laurence Sterne.

Location: OS Ref. SE531 773. W end of Coxwold village, 4m E of A19 & 20m N of York, via Easingwold.

Opening Times: Jun - Sept: Wed, 2 - 4.30pm. Sun, 2.30 - 4.30pm. Other times by appointment. Garden: May - Sept: Sun - Fri, 11am - 4.30pm.

Admission: Adult £3, Child £1.50. Garden only: £2.

- i   Plant sales.

SHIBDEN HALL

Tel: 01422 352246   **Fax:** 01422 348440

Lister's Road, Halifax, West Yorkshire HX3 6XG

Owner: Calderdale MBC   **Contact:** Ms R Westwood

A half-timbered manor house, the home of Anne Lister set in a landscaped park. Oak furniture, carriages and an array of objects make Shibden an intriguing place to visit.

Location: OS Ref. SE107 262. 1¹/₂ m E of Halifax off A58.

Opening Times: 1 Mar - 30 Nov: Mon - Sat, 10am - 5pm. Sun, 12 - 5pm. Last admission 4.30pm. Closed Dec - Feb.

Admission: Adult £1.60, Child 75p, Conc. 80p, Family £4.50.

- i   Shop.
- Ground floor & grounds suitable.
- Café.
- P   Ample.
- Education programme, teachers' pack.
- Guide dogs only.

SION HILL HALL

KIRBY WISKE, THIRSK, NORTH YORKSHIRE YO7 4EU

Owner: H W Mawer Trust   *Contact:* John D Bridges

Tel: 01845 587206   **Fax:** 01845 587486

Charming, Edwardian mansion designed by Brierley – the 'Lutyens of the North' – has RIBA accolade for outstanding architectural merit. This award winning mansion houses the Mawer antique collection of furniture, porcelain, paintings and clocks. Period Costume and Dolls exhibitions. The most comprehensive display in the north. Birds of prey in the Victorian walled garden and daily flying displays.

Location: OS Ref. SE373 844. B44 Signed off A167. 6m S of Northallerton, 4m NW of Thirsk, 8m E of A1 via A61.

Opening Times: 22 Mar - 31 Oct: Wed - Sun, 12.30 - 5pm. Groups any time by arrangement.

Admission: Hall: Adult £4, Child/Student £2, Conc. £3.50. Birds: Adult £4, Child £2, Conc. £3.50.

- i   Shop. Plant centre. No photography.
- Partially suitable. WC.
- Licensed tearoom.
- P   Ample.
- In grounds, on leads.

SKIPTON CASTLE   See page 287 for full page entry.

SLEDMERE HOUSE

SLEDMERE, DRIFFIELD, EAST YORKSHIRE YO25 0XG

Owner: Sir Tatton Sykes Bt   *Contact:* Mrs Anne Hines

Tel: 01377 236637 **Fax:** 01377 236500

Sledmere House is the home of Sir Tatton Sykes, 8th Baronet. There has been a manor house at Sledmere since medieval times. The present house was designed and built by Sir Christopher Sykes, 2nd Baronet, a diary date states 'June 17th, 1751 laid the first stone of the new house at Sledmere.' Sir Christopher employed a fellow Yorkshireman, Joseph Rose, the most famous English plasterer of his day to execute the decoration of Sledmere. Rose's magnificent work at Sledmere was unique in his career. A great feature at Sledmere is the 'Capability' Brown parkland and the beautiful 18th century walled rose gardens. Also worthy of note is the recently laid out knot-garden.

Location: OS Ref. SE931 648. Off the A166 between York and Bridlington.

Opening Times: 10 Apr - 14 Apr & 2 May - 27 Sept: Closed Sat & Mon but open BH Sat & Mon: 11.30am - 4.30pm.

Admission: House & Gardens: Adult £4, Child £2, OAP £3.50. Gardens & Park: Adult £1.50, Child £1.

[i] Shop, museum & exhibition centre.   [café] Café.

SPOFFORTH CASTLE ⊞   **Tel:** 0191 261 1585

Harrogate, Yorkshire

Owner: English Heritage   **Contact:** The North Regional Office

This manor house has some fascinating features including an undercroft built into the rock. It was once owned by the Percy family.

Location: OS Ref. SE360 511. 3¹/₂ m SE of Harrogate on minor road off A661 at Spofforth.

Opening Times: 1 Apr - 30 Sept: daily, 10am - 6pm. 1 - 31 Oct: daily, 10am - 6pm or dusk if earlier. 1 Nov - 31 Mar: 10am - 4pm.

Admission: Free.

[&] Grounds suitable.   [P] No parking.   [dog] In grounds, on leads.

Scarborough Castle, Yorkshire.

STOCKELD PARK

WETHERBY, YORKSHIRE LS22 4AH

Owner: Mr and Mrs P G F Grant   *Contact:* Mrs L A Saunders

Tel: 01937 586101 **Fax:** 01937 580084

Stockeld is a beautifully proportioned Palladian villa designed by James Paine in 1763, featuring a magnificent cantilevered staircase in the central oval hall. Stockeld is still very much a family home, with a fine collection of 18th and 19th century furniture and paintings. The house is surrounded by lovely gardens of lawns, large herbaceous and shrub borders, fringed by woodland, and set in 100 acres of fine parkland in the midst of an extensive farming estate.

Location: OS Ref. SE376 497. York 12m, Harrogate 5m, Leeds 12m.

Opening Times: 2 Apr - 8 Oct: Thur only, 2 - 5pm. Groups please book.

Admission: Adult £3, Child £1.50, OAP £2. Group prices on application.

[&] House only.   [person] Compulsory.   [dog] No dogs.

STUDLEY ROYAL: ST MARY'S CHURCH ⊞   **Tel:** 01765 608888

Ripon, Yorkshire

Owner: English Heritage   **Contact:** The Custodian

A magnificent Victorian church, designed by William Burges in the 1870s with a highly decorated interior. Coloured marble, stained glass, gilded and painted figures and a splendid organ.

Location: OS Ref. SE278 703. 2¹/₂ m W of Ripon off B6265, in grounds of Studley Royal estate.

Opening Times: 1 Apr - 30 Sept: daily, 1 - 5pm.

Admission: Free.

[&] Not suitable.   [P] Ample.   [dog] In grounds, on leads.

Historic Scotland

SPECIAL EVENTS
1998 See the front section for full list.

SUTTON PARK

SUTTON-ON-THE-FOREST, NORTH YORKSHIRE YO6 1DP

Owner: Sir Reginald & Lady Sheffield   *Contact:* Mrs A Wilkinson

Tel: 01347 810249/811239 **Fax:** 01347 811251

The Yorkshire home of Sir Reginald and Lady Sheffield. Charming example of early Georgian architecture. Magnificent plasterwork by Cortese. Rich collection of 18th century furniture, paintings, porcelain, needlework, beadwork. All put together with great style to make a most inviting house. Award winning gardens attract enthusiasts from home and abroad.

Location: OS Ref. SE583 646. 8m N of York on B1363 Helmsley Road.

Opening Times: House: Easter Sun & Mon & all BH Sun & Mons. Conducted tours take place from 1.30pm. Gardens: Easter - end Sept, daily, 11am - 5pm. Private parties in house welcome any day of the week by prior arrangement.

Admission: Adult £4, Child £2.50, OAP £3.50. Groups: Adult £5. Groups of 25+: £4.50pp.

- ℹ️ Corporate hospitality. No photography.
- ✕ Hosted lunches & dinners
- ☕ Tearoom on BHs and for pre-booked groups
- 🚶 Compulsory.
- 🅿️ Ample.
- 🐕 No dogs.
- 🅰️ 3 double with ensuite bathrooms.

TEMPLE NEWSAM HOUSE

Tel: 0113 2647321 **Fax:** 0113 2602285

Leeds, West Yorkshire LS15 0AE

Owner: Leeds City Council   **Contact:** Miss D Lawson

Tudor and Jacobean mansion with extensive collections of decorative arts in their original room settings, including incomparable Chippendale collection.

Location: OS Ref. SE358 321. 5m E of city centre, 1m S of A63 Leeds to Selby Road.

Opening Times: Early Mar - end Dec: daily (except Mon), 10am - 5pm (or dusk). Sun only 1 - 5pm (or dusk). Last adm. 45 mins before closing. Please check before visiting.

Admission: Adult £2, Child 50p, Conc. £1, Pre-booked groups £1.

- ℹ️ Shop.
- ♿ Partially suitable. WC.
- ☕ Tearoom.
- 🚶 By arrangement.
- 🅿️ Ample.
- 👪 Educational programme.
- 🐕 On grounds, on leads.

THORP PERROW ARBORETUM

Tel: 01677 425323 **Fax:** 01677 425323

Bedale, North Yorkshire DL8 2PR

Owner: Sir John Ropner Bt   **Contact:** Louise McNeill

A collection of over 1,000 varieties of trees and shrubs. The home of three National Collections: ash, lime and walnut.

Location: OS Ref. SE258 851. Bedale - Ripon road, S of Bedale., 4m from Leeming Bar on A1.

Opening Times: All year: dawn - dusk.

Admission: Adult £3.50, Child £2, OAP £2.50, Family (2+4) £14, (2+2) £10.

- ☕ Shop. Plant centre. Corporate hospitality.
- ♿ Suitable.
- ☕ Tearoom. Picnic area.
- 🚶 By arrangement.
- 🅿️ Ample.
- 👪 Educational programme.
- 🐕 In grounds, on leads.

TREASURER'S HOUSE 🌿

Tel: 01904 624247

Minster Yard, York, North Yorkshire YO1 2JD

Owner: The National Trust   **Contact:** The Property Manager

An elegant townhouse situated in the tranquil surroundings of the Minster Close. A series of period rooms is the setting for a fine collection of furniture and paintings given to the National Trust by Yorkshire industrialist Frank Green, who lived here from 1897 to 1930. Introductory video and exhibition.

Location: OS Ref. SE604 523. The N side of York Minster. Entrance on Chapter House St.

Opening Times: 28 Mar - 1 Nov: daily except Fri, 10.30am - 5pm. Last admission 4.30pm.

Admission: Adult £3.50, Child £1.75. Family £8. Groups by arrangement.

- ♿ Ground floor suitable. WC.
- ☕ Licensed restaurant.
- 💍 Civil Wedding Licence.

WAKEFIELD CATHEDRAL

Tel: 01924 373923 **Fax:** 01924 215054

Northgate, Wakefield, West Yorkshire WF1 1HG

Owner: Church of England   **Contact:** Mr M E Ledger, Chapter Clerk

Built on the site of a previous Saxon church, this 14th century Parish Church became a cathedral in 1888 and was extended by Pearson and completed by his son. It also boasts, at 247ft, the highest spire in Yorkshire.

Location: OS Ref. SE333 208. Wakefield city centre. M1/ J39-41, M62/J29W, J30 E.

Opening Times: Mon - Sat: 8am - 5pm. Sun: between services only. Sunday Services: Holy Communion: 8am. Parish Eucharist: 9.15am. Solemn Eucharist: 11am. Choral Evensong (Winter): 4pm. Choral Evensong (Summer): 6.30pm. Daily Services: Holy Communion: Daily, 8am plus 10.30am on Wed & Sat and 12.30pm on Fri. Choral Evensong: Thur, 6.30pm. Said Evensong: Mon - Wed & Fri & Sat, 5pm.

Admission: Free admission. Donations welcome.

- ℹ️ Bookshop. Corporate hospitality.
- ♿ Grounds suitable. WC.
- 🚶 By arrangement.
- 🅿️ Limited.
- 👪 Educational programme.

WHITBY ABBEY

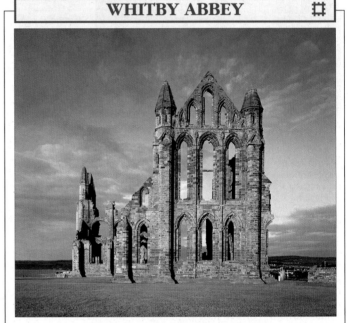

WHITBY, NORTH YORKSHIRE YO22 4JT

Owner: English Heritage   *Contact:* The Custodian

Tel: 01947 603568

An ancient holy place, once a burial place of kings and an inspiration for saints. A religious community was first established at Whitby in 657 by Abbess Hilda and was the home of Caedmon, the first English poet. The remains we can see today are of a Benedictine church built in the 13th and 14th centuries, and include a magnificent three-tiered choir and north transept. It is perched high above the picturesque harbour town of Whitby.

Location: OS94, Ref. NZ904 115. On cliff top E of Whitby.

Opening Times: 1 Apr - 1 Nov: daily 10am - 6pm (or dusk if earlier in Oct). 2 Nov - 31 Mar: 10am - 4pm. Closed 24 - 26 Dec.

Admission: Adult £1.70, Child 90p, Conc. £1.30. 15% discounts for groups of 11+.

- ℹ️ Shop.
- ♿ Ground floor suitable.
- 🐕 In grounds, on leads.

WHITE SCAR CAVE

See page 288 for full page entry.

WILBERFORCE HOUSE

Tel: 01482 613902 **Fax:** 01482 613710

High Street, Hull, Yorkshire HU1 1EP

Owner: Hull City Council   **Contact:** S R Green

Built c1656 the house has been a museum to the memory of William Wilberforce, slavery abolitionist, since 1906.

Location: OS Ref. TA102 286. High Street, Hull.

Opening Times: Mon - Sat, 10am - 5pm. Sun 1.30 - 4.30pm. Closed Good Fri & Christmas Day.

Admission: £1. Child under 13yrs free.

YORK MINSTER

Tel: 01904 639347 **Fax:** 01904 613049

Dean Gate, York YO1 2JN

Owner: Dean and Chapter of York   **Contact:** Dorothy Lee, Visitors' Officer

The largest gothic church north of the Alps housing the largest collection of medieval stained glass in England.

Location: OS Ref. SE603 522. Centre of York.

Opening Times: Nov - Mar: 7am - 6pm, Apr: 7am - 6.30pm, May: 7am - 7.30pm, Jun - Aug: 7am - 8.30pm, Sept: 7am - 8pm, Oct: 7am - 7pm, daily.

Admission: Free. Donation appreciated.

The Regions of
SCOTLAND

Scotland is divided into nine regions to coincide with Scotland's Area Tourist Boards.

The Regions of Scotland

Historic Houses Association Member, offering access under HHA Friends Scheme.

Property owned by The National Trust for Scotland.

Property in the care of Historic Scotland.

Outer
Islands

Outer
Islar

Outer
Islands

Highlands
& Skye

Gramp

West
Highlands

Perthshire/
Fife

Edinburgh

Greater
Glasgow

Border

South West

The Regions of Scotland

River Coladoir & Ben More, Isle of Mull. Argyll, the Isles, Loch Lomond, Stirling & Trossachs Tourist Board.

301

BOWHILL HOUSE & COUNTRY PARK
Selkirk

CONTACT

Mrs M Carter
Buccleuch Heritage Trust
Bowhill House &
Country Park
Bowhill
Selkirk
TD7 5ET

Tel/Fax: (01750) 22204

LOCATION

OS Ref. NT426 278

3m W of Selkirk off A708
Moffat Road,
A68 from Newcastle,
A7 from Carlisle
or Edinburgh.

Bus: 3m Selkirk.

Taxi: (01750) 20354.

Scottish Borders home of the Duke and Duchess of Buccleuch, dating mainly from 1812 and christened 'Sweet Bowhill' by Sir Walter Scott in his *Lay of the Last Minstrel*.

Many of the works of art were collected by earlier Montagus, Douglases and Scotts or given by Charles II to his natural son James, Duke of Monmouth and Buccleuch. Paintings include Canaletto's *Whitehall*, works by Guardi, Claude, Ruysdael, Gainsborough, Raeburn, Reynolds, Van Dyck and Wilkie. Superb French furniture, Meissen and Sèvres porcelain, silver and tapestries.

Historical relics include Monmouth's saddle and execution shirt, Sir Walter Scott's plaid and

some proof editions, Queen Victoria's letters and gifts to successive Duchesses of Buccleuch, her Mistresses of the Robes.

There is also a completely restored Victorian Kitchen, 19th century horse-drawn fire engine, 'Bowhill Little Theatre', a lively centre for the performing arts and where, prior to touring the house, visitors can see 'The Quest for Bowhill', a 20 minute audio-visual by Dr Colin Thompson.

Conference centre, arts courses, education service, visitor centre. Shop, tearoom, adventure playground, woodland walks, nature trails, picnic areas. Garden and landscape designed by John Gilpin.

❖

ℹ️ Shop. Fashion shows, air displays, archery, clay pigeon shooting, equestrian events, charity garden parties, shows, rallies, filming, lecture theatre. House is open by appointment outside public hours to groups led by officials of a recognised museum, gallery or educational establishment. No photography inside house.

✖️ Inside caterers normally used but outside caterers considered.

♿ Visitors may alight at entrance. WC. Wheelchair visitors free.

☕ Restaurant. Parties can book in advance, special rates for groups, menus on request.

🚶 Available for groups. Tour time 1¼ hrs.

🅿️ 60 cars and 6 coaches within 50yds of house.

👨‍👩‍👧 Welcome. Projects in Bowhill House and Victorian kitchen, Education Officers (service provided free of charge), schoolroom, ranger-led nature walks, adventure playground.

CONFERENCE/FUNCTION

ROOM	SIZE	MAX CAPACITY
Bowhill Little Theatre		72

OPENING TIMES

SUMMER
25 April - 31 Aug

Country Park
Daily except Fri
(open Fri in July)
12 - 5pm.

House
1 - 31 July
Daily: 1 - 4.30pm.

WINTER

By appointment only, for educational groups.

ADMISSION

SUMMER

House & Country Park
Adult £4.00
Child (5 - 16yrs)..........£1.00
OAP/Student...........£3.50
Group (min. 20).........£3.50

Country Park only
All ages......................£1.00

WINTER

House & Country Park
Adult £5.00
Child (5 - 16yrs)..........£1.00

Pre-booked educational groups over 20 persons welcomed.

FLOORS CASTLE
Kelso

CONTACT

Philip Massey
Director of Operations
Roxburghe Estates Office
Kelso
Roxburghshire
Scotland
TD5 7SF

Tel: (01573) 223333

Fax: (01573) 226056

LOCATION

OS Ref. NT711 347

From South A68, A698.

From North A68, A697/9
In Kelso follow signs.

Bus: Kelso Bus Station 1m.

Rail: Berwick 20m.

FLOORS CASTLE, home of the Duke and Duchess of Roxburghe is situated in the heart of the Scottish Border Country. It is reputedly the largest inhabited castle in Scotland. Designed by William Adam, who was both masterbuilder and architect, for the first Duke of Roxburghe, building started in 1721.

It was the present Duke's great-great-grandfather James, the 6th Duke, who embellished the plain Adam features of the building. In about 1849 Playfair, letting his imagination and talent run riot, transformed the Castle, creating a multitude of spires and domes.

The apartments now display the outstanding collection of French 17th and 18th century furniture, magnificent tapestries, Chinese and European porcelain and many other fine works of art. Many of the treasures in the castle today were collected by Duchess May, American wife of the 8th Duke.

The castle has been seen on cinema screens worldwide in the film *Greystoke*, as the home of Tarzan, the Earl of Greystoke.

Gardens

The extensive parkland and gardens overlooking the Tweed provide a variety of wooded walks. The walled garden contains splendid herbaceous borders and in the outer walled garden a summerhouse built for Queen Victoria's visit in 1867 can still be seen. An excellent children's playground and picnic area are very close to the castle.

SUMMER
10 April - 25 October
Daily: 10am - 4.30pm.

Last admission 4pm.

WINTER
November - March
Closed to the general public.

ADMISSION

SUMMER

Adult	£4.50
OAP	£3.75
Child (5 - 15yrs)	£2.50
Family	£12.00

Groups
Adult	£3.50
OAP	£3.25
Child (5 - 15yrs)	£2.00

CONFERENCE/FUNCTION		
ROOM	SIZE	MAX CAPACITY
Dining Rm	18m x 7m	150
Ballroom	21m x 8m	150

ℹ️ Shop. Gala dinners, conferences, product launches, incentive groups, 4 x 4 driving, highland games and other promotional events. Extensive park, helicopter pad, fishing, clay pigeon and pheasant shooting. No photography inside the castle.

♿ Visitors may alight at the entrance. WC.

🍴 Self-service, licensed restaurant, seating 125 opens 10am. Groups can book.

🚶 On request for up to 100. Tour time 1¼ hrs.

🅿️ Unlimited for cars, 100 yds away, coach park 50 yds. Coaches can be driven to the entrance, waiting area close to restaurant exit. Lunch or tea for coach drivers.

👨‍👩‍👧 Welcome, guide provided. Playground facilities.

🐕 In grounds, on leads.

MANDERSTON
Duns

MANDERSTON, together with its magnificent stables, stunning marble dairy and 56 acres of immaculate gardens, forms an ensemble which must be unique in Britain today.

The house was completely rebuilt between 1903 and 1905, with no expense spared.

Visitors are able to see not only the sumptuous State Rooms and bedrooms, decorated in the Adam manner, but also all the original domestic offices, in a truly 'upstairs downstairs' atmosphere. Manderston boasts a unique and recently restored silver staircase.

There is a special museum with a nostalgic display of valuable tins made by Huntley and Palmer from 1868 to the present day. Winner of the AA/NPI Bronze Award UK 1994.

GARDENS

Outside, the magnificence continues and the combination of formal gardens and picturesque landscapes is a major attraction: unique amongst Scottish houses.

The stables, still in use, have been described by *Horse and Hound* as "probably the finest in all the wide world."

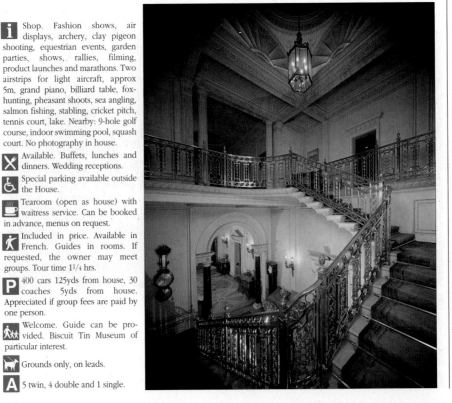

CONTACT

The Lord or Lady Palmer
Manderston
Duns
Berwickshire
Scotland
TD11 3PP

Tel: (01361) 883450
(01361) 882636

Fax: (01361) 882010

www: http://www.twisel.co.uk/borders/shomes/manderston.html

LOCATION

OS Ref. NT810 544

From Edinburgh
47m, 1hr.
1½ m E of Duns on
A6105.

Bus: 400 yds.

Rail: Berwick Station 12m.

Taxi: Chirnside 818216.

Airport: Edinburgh or Newcastle both 60m or 80 mins.

CONFERENCE/FUNCTION		
ROOM	SIZE	MAX CAPACITY
Dining Rm	22'x 35'	100
Ballroom	34' x 21'	150
Hall	22' x 38'	130
Drawing Rm	35' x 21'	150

i Shop. Fashion shows, air displays, archery, clay pigeon shooting, equestrian events, garden parties, shows, rallies, filming, product launches and marathons. Two airstrips for light aircraft, approx 5m, grand piano, billiard table, foxhunting, pheasant shoots, sea angling, salmon fishing, stabling, cricket pitch, tennis court, lake. Nearby: 9-hole golf course, indoor swimming pool, squash court. No photography in house.

Available. Buffets, lunches and dinners. Wedding receptions.

Special parking available outside the House.

Tearoom (open as house) with waitress service. Can be booked in advance, menus on request.

Included in price. Available in French. Guides in rooms. If requested, the owner may meet groups. Tour time 1¼ hrs.

P 400 cars 125yds from house, 30 coaches 5yds from house. Appreciated if group fees are paid by one person.

Welcome. Guide can be provided. Biscuit Tin Museum of particular interest.

Grounds only, on leads.

A 5 twin, 4 double and 1 single.

OPENING TIMES

SUMMER
Mid May - end September
Thur & Sun
2 - 5.30pm.

BH Mon, late May
& August
2 - 5.30pm.

Groups welcome
by appointment.

WINTER
September - May
Group visits welcome
by appointment.

ADMISSION

House & Grounds
Adult £5.00
Child £2.00
Groups (min 20 on open days)
Per person £4.00
School child............£2.00
(min Student group £60.00)

Grounds only
Including Stables &
Marble Dairy
Adult £3.00
Child £1.00
Groups (min 20)
Per person £2.50

On days when the house is closed to the public, parties viewing by appointment will have personally conducted tours. The Gift Shop will be open. On these occasions reduced party rates (except for school children) will not apply. Group visits other than open days are £5pp (min £100). Cream teas on open days only.

CONTACT

Ms C Maxwell Stuart
Traquair House
Innerleithen
Peeblesshire
EH44 6PW

Tel: (01896) 830323

Fax: (01896) 830639

e-mail: traquair.house
@scotborders.co.uk

LOCATION

OS Ref. NY330 354

From Edinburgh 1 hr,
Glasgow 1½ hrs,
Carlisle 1½ hrs,
Newcastle 2½ hrs.
On B709 near
junction with A72.

Rail: Edinburgh
Waverley 30m.

Bus: Hourly bus service
from Edinburgh to
Innerleithen.
Enquiries: Lowland
Omnibuses (0131) 558 1616.

Taxi: Leithen Valley Taxis
(01896) 831308

CONFERENCE/FUNCTION		
ROOM	SIZE	MAX CAPACITY
Dining Rm	33' x 18'	30
Drawing Room	27' x 24'	60

TRAQUAIR
Innerleithen

TRAQUAIR, situated amidst beautiful scenery and close by the River Tweed, is the oldest inhabited house in Scotland – visited by twenty-seven kings. Originally a Royal Hunting Lodge, it was owned by the Scottish Crown until 1478 when it passed to a branch of the Royal Stuart family whose descendants still live in the House today.

From a single tower block the building grew, reflecting the growth and importance of the Stuarts of Traquair and no exterior alterations were made after the end of the 17th century. At the end of the tree-lined avenue leading to the House are the famous Bear Gates closed since 1745 when the last person to pass through them

was Bonnie Prince Charlie (not to be opened again until the restoration of the Stuarts).

Nearly ten centuries of Scottish political and domestic life can be traced from the collection of treasures in the House. It is particularly rich in associations with the Catholic Church in Scotland, Mary Queen of Scots and the Jacobite Risings.

GARDEN

70 acres of grounds with peacocks, ducks and other wildlife. In spring there is a profusion of daffodils followed by rhododendrons, wild flowers and herbaceous plants. A maze in beech/leylandii cyprus is behind the House.

i Shop. Meetings and dinners, product launches, filming, archery, clay-pigeon shooting, theatre, son et lumière. 18th century fully operational Brewhouse, ale tasting every Fri, 3 - 4pm. 17th century harpsichord in drawing room, croquet (mallets can be hired). Lectures provided on the property, contents, history and grounds. No photography in House. Guide book translations in French, Spanish, German, Dutch, Swedish, Japanese and Italian.

X Marquee (lined and floored) available for wedding receptions, etc., in the gardens or courtyard. Lunches and dinners in dining room from £30pp by special arrangement.

& Visitors may alight at entrance. WCs.

Licensed self-service 1745 Cottage Tearoom. On fine days lunches and teas can be taken outdoors. Groups of up to 45 can be served in the Bear Cottage.

K Tours only outside opening hours £4.50pp (£80 min). Introductory talks can be given to groups. Out of hours visits with meals/refreshments by prior arrangement.

P Ample, 85 yds from House. Coaches preferably booked in advance. Drivers please apply for vouchers on arrival.

Dogs on leads in grounds.

A Traquair offers 2 fourposter suites with bathroom on a bed and breakfast basis.

OPENING TIMES

SUMMER
11 April - 30 September
Daily: 12.30 - 5.30pm.

June, July & August
10.30am - 5.30pm
Last admission 5pm.

October:
Fri - Sun: 12.30 - 5.30pm.

Restaurant: 12 - 5.30pm
June, July & August
from 11am.

WINTER
1 November - Easter
open by arrangement.

ADMISSION

SUMMER
House & Garden
Adult £4.50
Child* £2.25
Groups**
Adult £3.50
Child* £1.80

Garden only
Adult £1.75
Child* £1.25

* Under 15 years.
** Minimum payment £70 when House open, £90 when closed.

WINTER
£6.00 per person.

Includes glass of wine/whisky/Traquair Ale and shortbread.
Minimum charge £100.

SPECIAL EVENTS

• **APR 12:**
Easter Egg Extravaganza

• **MAY 23/24**
Scottish Beer Festival

• **AUG 1/2:**
Traquair Fair

• **SEPT 12/13:**
Traquair Needlework Weekend

Scotland
Borders

ABBOTSFORD HOUSE

MELROSE, ROXBURGHSHIRE TD6 9BQ

Owner: *Mrs P Maxwell-Scott OBE*   **Contact:** *Mrs P Maxwell-Scott OBE*

Tel: 01896 752043   **Fax:** 01896 752916

Sir Walter Scott purchased the Cartley Hall farmhouse on the banks of the Tweed in 1812. Together with his family and servants he moved into the farm which he renamed Abbotsford. Scott had the old house demolished in 1822 and replaced it with the main block of Abbotsford as it is today. Scott was a passionate collector of historic relics including an impressive collection of armour and weapons and over 9,000 rare volumes in his library.

Location: OS Ref. NT508 343. 35m S of Edinburgh. Melrose 3m, Galashiels 2m.

Opening Times: 16 Mar - 31 Oct: Mon - Sat, and Suns (Jun - Sept only) 10am - 5pm. Also Suns Mar - May and Oct, 2 - 5pm. Other dates by arrangement.

Admission: Adult £3.50, Child/Student £1.80. Groups: Adult £2.50, Child £1.30.

[i] Shop.   [&] House suitable. WC.   [☕] Tearoom.   [🐕] Guide dogs only.

AYTON CASTLE

AYTON, EYEMOUTH, BERWICKSHIRE TD14 5RD

Owner: *D I Liddell-Grainger of Ayton*   **Contact:** *The Curator*

Tel: 018907 81212 or 018907 81550

Built in 1846 by the Mitchell-Innes family and designed by the architect James Gillespie Graham. Over the last ten years it has been fully restored and is now a family home. It is a unique restoration project and the quality of the original and restored workmanship is outstanding. The castle stands on an escarpment surrounded by mature woodlands containing many interesting trees and has been a film-making venue due to this magnificent setting.

Location: OS Ref. NT920 610. 7m N of Berwick-on-Tweed on Route A1.

Opening Times: 10 May - 13 Sept: Sun, 2 - 5 pm or by appointment.

Admission: Adult £2, Child under 5 free.

AIKWOOD TOWER & JAMES HOGG EXHIBITION

Tel: 01750 52253

Ettrick Valley, Nr. Selkirk TD7 5HJ   **Fax:** 01750 52261

Owner: Lord & Lady Steel of Aikwood   **Contact:** Judy Steel

A fine 16 century pele tower and exhibition of James Hogg.

Location: OS Ref. NT419 260. SE side of B7009, 4 m SW of Selkirk.

Opening Times: Apr - Sept: Tue, Thur & Sun, 2 - 5pm.

Admission: £1.50.

BOWHILL [🏛]

See page 302 for full page entry.

BUGHTRIG GARDEN

Tel: 01890 840678   **Fax:** 01890 840509

Bughtrig, Coldstream, Berwickshire TD12 4JP

Owner: Major General C A Ramsay   **Contact:** The Secretary

Bughtrig is a classic Georgian family house c1785 with later additions. The formal garden is hedged and close to the house, surrounded by fine specimen trees which provide remarkable shelter. Its $2^1/_2$ acres contain an interesting combination of herbaceous plants, roses, shrubs, annuals, fruit, vegetables and tree nursery.

Location: OS Ref. NT797 447. $^1/_4$ mile east of Leitholm Village on B6461.

Opening Times: Garden: Jun - Sept: daily 11am - 5pm. House: by appointment only.

Admission: Adult £1.50, Child 50p, OAP £1. Rates for House or accommodation by arrangement.

[&] Partially suitable.   [P] Limited for cars.   [🐕] Guide dogs only.

[A] 4 twin bedrooms/3 bathrooms.

DAWYCK BOTANIC GARDEN

Tel: 01721 760254   **Fax:** 01721 760214

Stobo, Peeblesshire EH45 9JU   **Contact:** The Curator

Renowned historic arboretum. Follow the landscaped walks to discover Dawyck's secrets. Amongst mature specimen trees – some over 40 metres tall – are a variety of flowering trees, shrubs and herbaceous plants. Explore the world's first Cryptogamic Sanctuary and Reserve for 'non-flowering' plants.

Location: NT168 352. 8m SW of Peebles on B712.

Opening Times: 1 Mar - 31 Oct: daily, 9.30am - 6pm.

Admission: Adult £3, Child £1, Family £7, Conc. £2.50, Group discounts available.

[i] Shop. Plant centre.   [&] Partially suitable. WC.   [☕] Tearoom.

[🐕] Guide dogs only.   [P] Ample for cars. Limited for coaches.

Caryatids:

Supports and brackets in architecture (and furniture) in the form of female figures, often used instead of columns to support an entablature. Especially popular in Britain during the baroque period (1660–1720) and in the late eighteenth century Greek Revival. The male equivalents are known as Atlantes (literally, Atlas-figures, from the god Atlas carrying the globe).

Extract from; "Life in the Country House" by David N Durant (published by John Murray), PB£15.99.

DRUMLANRIG'S TOWER

Tel: 01450 373457 **Fax:** 01450 373993

Hawick Museum and Scott Gallery, Wilton Lodge Park, Hawick TD9 7JL

Owner: Scottish Borders Council   **Contact:** The Curator

A fortified tower of the 1550s.

Location: OS Ref. NT502 144. In Hawick town centre at W end of the High Street.

Opening Times: Late Mar - Oct: Sun, 12 - 5pm. Late Mar - May & Oct: Mon - Sat, 10am - 5pm. Jun & Sept: Mon - Sat, 10am - 5.30pm. Jul & Aug: Mon - Sat, 10am - 6pm.

Admission: Adult £2, Conc. £1. Free for local residents.

DRYBURGH ABBEY

Tel: 01835 822381

St Boswells, Melrose

Owner: Historic Scotland   **Contact:** The Custodian

The ruins of Dryburgh Abbey are remarkably complete. The burial place of Sir Walter Scott and Field Marshal Earl Haig. Perhaps the most beautiful of all the Border abbeys.

Location: OS Ref. NT591 317. 5m SE of Melrose off B6356. 1 1/2 m N of St Boswells.

Opening Times: 1 Apr - 30 Sept: daily 9.30am - 6.30pm. Last ticket 6pm. 1 Oct - 31 Mar: Mon - Sat 9.30am - 4.30pm, Sun, 2 - 4.30pm, last ticket 4pm.

Admission: Adult £2.30, Child £1, Conc. £1.75.

DUNS CASTLE

DUNS, BERWICKSHIRE TD11 3NW

Owner: *Alexander Hay of Duns*   **Contact:** *Mrs Aline Hay*

Tel: 01361 883211 **Fax:** 01361 882015

This historical 1320 pele tower has been home to the Hay family since 1696, and the current owners Alexander and Aline Hay offer it as a welcoming venue for individuals, groups and corporate guests to enjoy. They have renovated it to produce the highest standards of comfort while retaining all the character of its rich period interiors. Wonderful lakeside and parkland setting.

Location: OS Ref. NT777 544. 10m off A4. Rail: Berwick station 16m. Airports: Newcastle & Edinburgh, 1 hr.

Opening Times: Not open to the public except by arrangement and for individuals, groups and companies for day or residential stays. Available all year.

Admission: Rates for private and corporate visits, wedding receptions, filming by arrangement.

A 4 x 4-poster, 3 x double, 3 x twin (all with bathrooms), 2 single.

FERNIEHIRST CASTLE

JEDBURGH, ROXBURGHSHIRE TD8 6NX

Owner: *The Marquess of Lothian*   **Contact:** *Mrs J Fraser*

Tel: 01835 862201 **Fax:** 01835 863992

Ferniehirst Castle – Scotland's Frontier Fortress. Ancestral home of the Kerr family. Restored by the 12th Marquess of Lothian 1984/1987. Unrivalled 16th century Border architecture. Grand Apartment and Turret Library. A 16th century Chamber Oratory. The Kerr Chamber – Museum of Family History. A special tribute to Jedburgh's Protector to Mary Queen of Scots – Sir Thomas Kerr. Riverside walk by Jed Water. Archery Field opposite the Chapel where sheep of Viking origin still graze as they did four centuries ago.

Location: OS Ref. NT653 181. 2m S of Jedburgh on the A68.

Opening Times: July: Tue - Sun (closed Mons), 11am - 4pm.

Admission: Adult £3, Child £1.50. Groups (max. 50) by prior arrangement (01835 862201).

i Shop.

& Partially suitable. WCs.

k Guided tours only, groups by arrangement.

P Ample for cars and coaches.

In grounds, on leads.

FLOORS CASTLE 🏛
See page 303 for full page entry.

HALLIWELL'S HOUSE MUSEUM
Tel: 01750 20096 **Fax:** 01750 23282

Halliwell's Close, Market Place, High Street, Selkirk

Owner: Scottish Borders Council **Contact:** Ian Brown

Re-creation of buildings, formerly used as a house and ironmonger's shop.

Location: OS Ref. NT472 286. In Selkirk town centre.

Opening Times: Easter - 31 Oct: Mon - Sat, 10am - 5pm, Sun 2- 4pm. Jul & Aug open until 6pm.

Admission: Free

HERMITAGE CASTLE 🏛
Tel: 01387 376222

Liddesdale, Newcastleton

Owner: Historic Scotland **Contact:** The Custodian

Eerie fortress at the heart of the bloodiest events in the history of the Borders. Mary Queen of Scots made her famous ride here to visit her future husband.

Location: OS Ref. NY497 961. In Liddesdale 5½ m NE of Newcastleton, B6399.

Opening Times: 1 Apr - 30 Sept: daily, 9.30am - 6.30pm, last ticket 6pm.

Admission: Adult £1.50, Child 75p, Conc. £1.10.

THE HIRSEL GARDENS, COUNTRY PARK & HOMESTEAD MUSEUM
Tel: 01890 882834 **Fax:** 01890 882834

Owner: Lord Home of the Hirsel **Contact:** Peter Goodall

Coldstream, Berwickshire TD12 4LP **Contact:** Hirsel Estate Office

Wonderful spring flowers and rhododendrons. Homestead museum and crafts centre. Displays of estate life and adaption to modern farming.

Location: OS Ref. NT838 393. Immediately W of Coldstream off A697.

Opening Times: Grounds: daily, during daylight hours. Museum & Craft Shop: weekdays, 10am - 5pm. Weekends, 12 - 5pm.

Admission: Parking charge only, winter £1, Easter - 31 Oct £2.

ℹ️ Craft shop. ♿ Partially suitable. WC.

JEDBURGH ABBEY 🏛

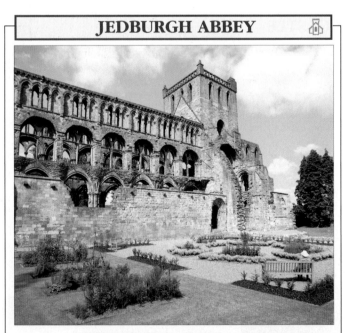

4/5 ABBEY BRIDGEND, JEDBURGH TD8 6JQ

Owner: Historic Scotland *Contact:* The Steward

Tel: 01835 863925

Founded by David I in about 1138 for Augustinian Canons. The church is mostly in the Romanesque and early Gothic styles and is remarkably complete. The award winning visitor centre contains the priceless 12th century 'Jedburgh Comb' and other artefacts found during archaeological excavations.

Location: OS Ref. NT650 205. In Jedburgh on the A68.

Opening Times: Apr - Sept: daily, 9.30am - 6.30pm. Oct - Mar: Mon - Sat, 9.30am - 4.30pm, Sun 2 - 4.30pm. Last ticket sold 30 mins before closing. 10% for groups over 10.

Admission: Adult £2.80, Child £1, OAP/Student £2.10.

ℹ️ Shop and picnic area. ♿ Partially suitable. WC. 🅿️ Ample.

🚌 Free pre-booked school visits. Teachers' pack. 🐕 Guide dogs only.

MANDERSTON 🏛
See page 304 for full page entry.

MARY QUEEN OF SCOTS' HOUSE
Tel: 01835 863331 **Fax:** 01450 378506

Jedburgh, Roxburghshire

Owner: Scottish Borders Council **Contact:** The Curator

16th century fortified bastel house. Telling the story Scotland's tragic Queen.

Location: OS Ref. NT652 206. In Queen Street between High Street and A68.

Opening Times: Mar - Nov: Mon - Sat, 10am - 4.30pm, Sun 12 - 4.30pm. Jun - Aug: Sun 10am - 4.30pm.

Admission: Adult £2, Conc. £1.

MELLERSTAIN HOUSE 🏛

MELLERSTAIN, GORDON, BERWICKSHIRE TD3 6LG

Owner: The Earl of Haddington *Contact:* Mr A Ashby

Tel: 01573 410225 **Fax:** 01573 410636

www. http://www.caligrafix.co.uk/mellerstain

One of Scotland's great Georgian houses and a unique example of the work of the Adam family; the two wings built in 1725 by William Adam, the large central block by his son, Robert 1770-78. Rooms contain fine plasterwork, colourful ceilings and marble fireplaces. The library is considered to be Robert Adam's finest creation. Many fine paintings and period furniture.

Location: OS Ref. NT648 392. From Edinburgh A68 to Earlston, turn left 5m, signed.

Opening Times: Easter weekend (Fri - Mon), 1 May - 30 Sept, daily except Sat, 12.30 - 5pm. Groups at other times by appointment.

Admission: Adult £4.50, Child £2, Conc. £3.50. Groups (min. 20) £3.50. Grounds only: £2.

ℹ️ Shop. ♿ Ground floor & grounds suitable. ☕ Tearoom. 🐕 In grounds.

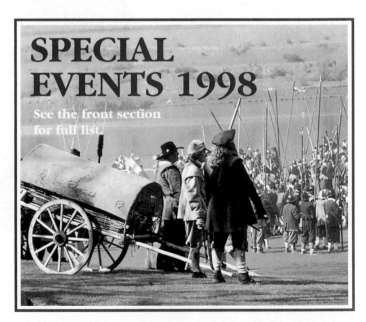

SPECIAL EVENTS 1998

See the front section for full list.

MELROSE ABBEY

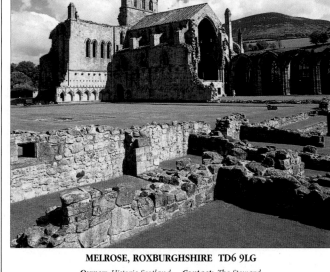

MELROSE, ROXBURGHSHIRE TD6 9LG

Owner: Historic Scotland   *Contact:* The Steward

Tel: 01896 822562

The Abbey was founded about 1136 by David I as a Cistercian Abbey and at one time was probably the richest in Scotland. Richard II's English army largely destroyed it in 1385 but it was rebuilt and the surviving remains are mostly 14th century. Burial place of Robert the Bruce's heart. Local history displays.

Location: OS Ref. NT549 342. In the centre of Melrose off the A68 or A7.

Opening Times: Apr - Sept: daily, 9.30am - 6.30pm. Oct - Mar: Mon - Sat 9.30am - 4.30pm, Sun 2 - 4.30pm. Last ticket 30 mins before closing.

Admission: Adult £2.80, Child £1, OAP/Student £2.10. 10% discount for groups 10+.

- ℹ️ Shop. Picnic area.
- ⚒️ Free audio tours.
- ♿ Tape for visitors with learning difficulties.
- 🅿️ Ample.
- Teachers' pack.
- Guide dogs only.

MERTOUN GARDENS

Tel: 01835 823236   **Fax:** 01835 822474

St Boswells, Melrose, Roxburgh TD6 0EA

Owner: The Duke of Sutherland   **Contact:** Miss Miller

26 acres of beautiful grounds. Walled garden and well preserved circular dovecote.

Location: OS Ref. NT617 318. Entrance off B6404 2m NE of St Boswells.

Opening Times: Apr - Sept: weekends and Public Holiday Mons only, 2 - 6pm. Last admission 5.30pm.

Admission: Adult £1.50, Child 50p. Groups by arrangement: Adult £1.35, Child 45p.

- ⚒️ By arrangement.
- 🅿️ Ample.
- No dogs.

MONTEVIOT HOUSE GARDEN

Tel: 01835 830380 (mornings only)

Jedburgh, Roxburghshire TD8 6UQ

Fax: 01835 830288
Contact: The Administrator

Rose garden, Herbaceous shrub borders, Water garden of islands linked by bridges. Beautiful views of the River Teviot. Greenhouse and plant stall. Limited disabled access. Parking and WCs. Dogs on leads only.

Location: OS Ref. NT648 247. 3m N of Jedburgh. S side of B6400 (to Nisbet). 1m E of A68.

Opening Times: Apr - Oct: Mon - Fri, 12 - 5pm & first Sat/Sun of these months. Coach parties by prior arrangement.

Admission: Adult £2, under 14s free, OAP £1.

- ♿ Partially suitable. WCs.
- ⚒️ By arrangement.
- 🅿️ Ample.
- In grounds, on leads.

NEIDPATH CASTLE

Tel/Fax: 01721 720333

Peebles, Scottish Borders EH45 8NW

Owner: Wemyss and March Estates   **Contact:** The Custodian

Authentic 14th century castle converted to tower house (17th century) home of Fraser, Hay and Douglas families. Pit prison, Laigh Hall with displays, Great Hall with 'Life of Mary Stuart - Queen of Scots' in Batik. Wonderful setting in wooded gorge of River Tweed.

Location: OS Ref. NT237 405. In Tweeddale 1m W of Peebles on A72.

Opening Times: Thur before Easter - 30 Sept: Mon - Sat, 11am - 5pm, Sun 1 - 5pm. Group bookings in Oct.

Admission: Adult £2.50, Child £1, Conc. £2, Family (2+3) £6.50. 10% discount for groups of 20+ . School rate available, 1 teacher free every 10 children.

- ℹ️ Shop.
- ♿ Ground floor & grounds suitable.
- 🅿️ Ample.
- In grounds, on leads.

OLD GALA HOUSE

Tel: 01750 20096

Scot Crescent, Galashiels TD1 3JS

Owner: Mr Ian Brown   **Contact:** Mr Ian Brown

Dating from 1583 the former house of the Laird of Gala includes displays on the history of the house and its inhabitants and the early growth of Galashiels. Particularly memorable is the painted ceiling dated 1635.

Location: OS Ref. NT492 357. S of town centre, signed from A7.

Opening Times: Late Mar - early Nov: Tues - Sat 10am - 4pm.

- ℹ️ Shop.
- ♿ Partially suitable. WCs.
- ☕ Tearoom.
- ⚒️ By arrangement.
- 🅿️ Limited for cars.
- Guide dogs only.

PAXTON HOUSE

BERWICK-UPON-TWEED TD15 1SZ

Owner: The Paxton Trust   *Contact:* Martin Purslow

Tel: 01289 386291   **Fax:** 01289 386660

'Highly Commended' by the Scottish Tourist Board, 1998. Built in 1756 by John and James Adam, the house boasts the pre-eminent collection of Chippendale furniture on view in Scotland, the largest picture gallery in a Scottish country house, designed by Robert Reid in 1818, which now functions as an outstation for the National Galleries of Scotland, and a fine collection of Regency furniture by Trotter of Edinburgh. Other features include over 80 acres of woodland, parkland, gardens and riverside walks to explore, temporary exhibitions, highland cattle and croquet. Function suite for hire.

Location: OS Ref. NT931 520. 3m off the A1 Berwick-upon-Tweed on B6461.

Opening Times: Good Fri, 10 Apr - 31 Oct: Grounds: 10am - sunset. House: 11am - 5pm. Last house tour 4.15pm. Open to groups/ schools all year by appointment.

Admission: Adult £4, Child £2. Grounds only: Adult £2, Child £1.

- ℹ️ Shop. Plant centre.
- ✖️ Conferences. Wedding receptions
- ♿ Partially suitable.
- ☕ Licensed tearoom.
- 🅿️ Ample.
- Educational programme.
- In grounds, on leads.

PRIORWOOD GARDEN & DRIED FLOWER SHOP

Melrose TD6 9PX

Tel: 01896 822493

Owner: The National Trust for Scotland   **Contact:** Mrs Cathy Ross

Overlooked by the Abbey's 15th century ruins is this unique garden, where most of the plants are suitable for drying. With the aid of volunteers, Priorwood Garden markets a wide variety of dried flower arrangements through its own dried flower shop.

Location: OS Ref. NT549 341. In the Border town of Melrose, beside the Abbey.

Opening Times: 1 Apr - 30 Sept: Mon - Sat 10am - 5.30pm, Sun 1.30 - 5.30pm. 1 Oct - 24 Dec: Mon - Sat 10am - 4pm, Sun 1.30 - 4pm.

Admission: Honesty box £1.

- ℹ️ Shop.
- ♿ Grounds suitable. WC.
- 🅿️ No parking.
- Guide dogs only.

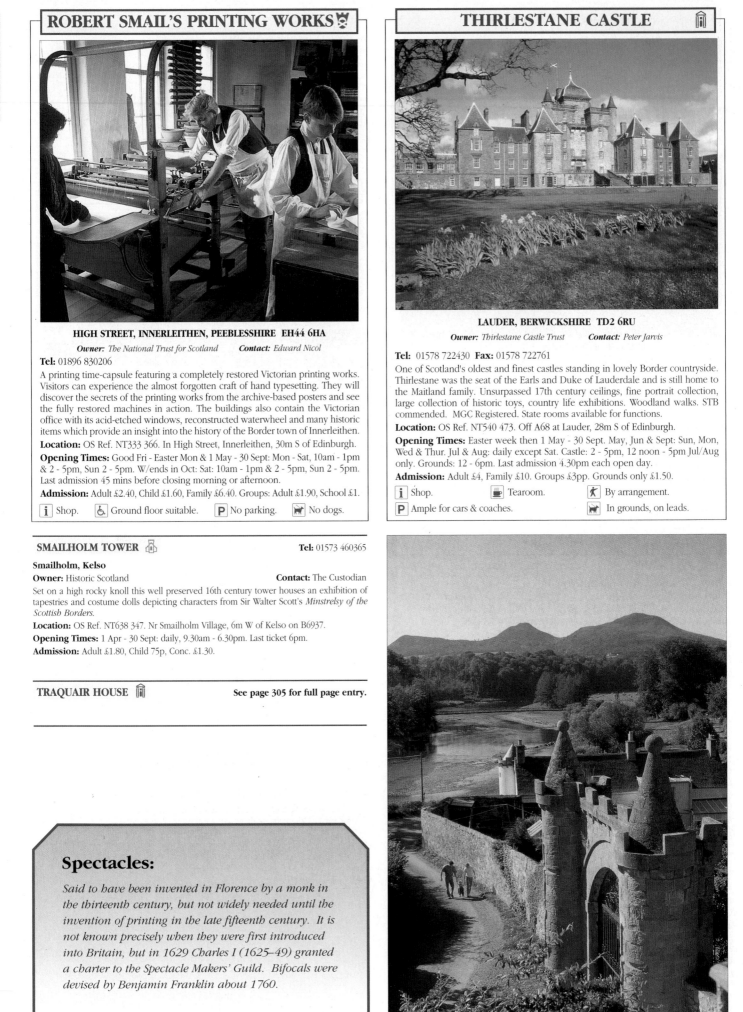

ROBERT SMAIL'S PRINTING WORKS

HIGH STREET, INNERLEITHEN, PEEBLESSHIRE EH44 6HA

Owner: *The National Trust for Scotland*   ***Contact:*** *Edward Nicol*

Tel: 01896 830206

A printing time-capsule featuring a completely restored Victorian printing works. Visitors can experience the almost forgotten craft of hand typesetting. They will discover the secrets of the printing works from the archive-based posters and see the fully restored machines in action. The buildings also contain the Victorian office with its acid-etched windows, reconstructed waterwheel and many historic items which provide an insight into the history of the Border town of Innerleithen.

Location: OS Ref. NT333 366. In High Street, Innerleithen, 30m S of Edinburgh.

Opening Times: Good Fri - Easter Mon & 1 May - 30 Sept: Mon - Sat, 10am - 1pm & 2 - 5pm, Sun 2 - 5pm. W/ends in Oct: Sat: 10am - 1pm & 2 - 5pm, Sun 2 - 5pm. Last admission 45 mins before closing morning or afternoon.

Admission: Adult £2.40, Child £1.60, Family £6.40. Groups: Adult £1.90, School £1.

i Shop.	& Ground floor suitable.	P No parking.	No dogs.

SMAILHOLM TOWER   **Tel:** 01573 460365

Smailholm, Kelso

Owner: Historic Scotland   **Contact:** The Custodian

Set on a high rocky knoll this well preserved 16th century tower houses an exhibition of tapestries and costume dolls depicting characters from Sir Walter Scott's *Minstrelsy of the Scottish Borders.*

Location: OS Ref. NT638 347. Nr Smailholm Village, 6m W of Kelso on B6937.

Opening Times: 1 Apr - 30 Sept: daily, 9.30am - 6.30pm. Last ticket 6pm.

Admission: Adult £1.80, Child 75p, Conc. £1.30.

TRAQUAIR HOUSE   See page 305 for full page entry.

Spectacles:

Said to have been invented in Florence by a monk in the thirteenth century, but not widely needed until the invention of printing in the late fifteenth century. It is not known precisely when they were first introduced into Britain, but in 1629 Charles I (1625–49) granted a charter to the Spectacle Makers' Guild. Bifocals were devised by Benjamin Franklin about 1760.

Extract from; "Life in the Country House" by David N Durant (published by John Murray), PB£15.99.

THIRLESTANE CASTLE

LAUDER, BERWICKSHIRE TD2 6RU

Owner: *Thirlestane Castle Trust*   ***Contact:*** *Peter Jarvis*

Tel: 01578 722430 **Fax:** 01578 722761

One of Scotland's oldest and finest castles standing in lovely Border countryside. Thirlestane was the seat of the Earls and Duke of Lauderdale and is still home to the Maitland family. Unsurpassed 17th century ceilings, fine portrait collection, large collection of historic toys, country life exhibitions. Woodland walks. STB commended. MGC Registered. State rooms available for functions.

Location: OS Ref. NT540 473. Off A68 at Lauder, 28m S of Edinburgh.

Opening Times: Easter week then 1 May - 30 Sept. May, Jun & Sept: Sun, Mon, Wed & Thur. Jul & Aug: daily except Sat. Castle: 2 - 5pm, 12 noon - 5pm Jul/Aug only. Grounds: 12 - 6pm. Last admission 4.30pm each open day.

Admission: Adult £4, Family £10. Groups £3pp. Grounds only £1.50.

i Shop.	Tearoom.	K By arrangement.
P Ample for cars & coaches.		In grounds, on leads.

River Tweed, Nr. Dryburgh.

SOUTH WEST SCOTLAND

HUDSON'S

SOUTH WEST SCOTLAND
Dumfries & Galloway, Ayrshire and the Isle of Arran

Scotland
South West

BLAIRQUHAN CASTLE
Maybole

CONTACT

James Hunter Blair
Blairquhan Castle
Maybole
Ayrshire
KA19 7LZ

Tel: (01655) 770239

Fax: (01655) 770278

LOCATION

OS Ref. NS366 055

From London M6 to
Carlisle, A75 to
Crocketford, A712 to
A713 nr New Galloway,
B741 to Straiton,
B7045 to Ayr.
Turn left $^1/_4$ m
beyond village.
6m SE of Maybole
off B7045.

Rail: Maybole 7m.

Air: Prestwick Airport,
15m. Direct flights to
London, Belfast & Dublin.
Executive Travel: contact
(01655) 882666

BLAIRQUHAN is the home of James Hunter Blair, the great-great-grandson of Sir David Hunter Blair, 3rd Baronet for whom it was designed by William Burn and built in 1821-24.

All the Regency furniture bought for the house remains, and the house has not been altered except discreetly to bring it up-to-date. There are ten double bedrooms including four four-poster beds, with en-suite bathrooms, five singles, and many public rooms which can be used for conferences and every sort of occasion.

The castle is approached by a 3 mile private drive along the River Girvan and is situated in one of the most charming parts of south west Scotland. There is a well-known collection of pictures. It is particularly suitable for conferences because the house is entirely at your disposal.

A five minute walk from the Castle are the walled gardens, laid out around the 1800s and recently replanned and replanted.

Blairquhan is only 50 miles from Glasgow. It is within about half an hour's drive of the world famous golf courses of Prestwick, Troon and Turnberry, the last two of which are venues for the British Open Golf Championships.

OPENING TIMES

SUMMER

18 July - 16 August
inclusive
Daily except Mon
2.00 - 4.45pm
Last admission 4.45pm.

Open at all other times
by appointment.

WINTER

Open by appointment.

ADMISSION

House & Garden

Adult £3.50
Child (5 - 14yrs)........£2.00
OAP.......................£2.50

Groups*
Negotiable

* Minimum payment £20.

SPECIAL EVENTS

• **EVENTS EVERY WEEKEND INCLUDING:**

Archery and model aeroplane flying

Battle re-enactments.

CONFERENCE/FUNCTION		
ROOM	SIZE	MAX CAPACITY
Drawing Rms	1200 sq ft	100
Dining Rm	750 sq ft	100
Library	400 sq ft	25
Saloon	600 sq ft	100
Meeting Rm	255 sq ft	50

ℹ️ Shop. Fashion shows, air displays, archery, shooting, equestrian events, garden parties, shows, rallies, filming, grand piano, snooker, fishing. Slide projector, overhead projector, screen, and secretarial assistance for meetings. No photography in castle.

✖️ Available. Wedding receptions.

♿ Visitors may alight at the entrance. WC.

☕ Restaurant, teas, lunches, buffets and dinners. Groups can book in advance, special rates for groups.

🚶 At no extra charge, up to 100, tour time 1hr, also available in French.

🅿️ Unlimited.

👨‍👩‍👧 Welcome, guide and schoolroom provided, cost negotiable.

🅰️ 10 doubles (4 4-posters) with bathrooms en-suite, 5 singles. The Dower House at Milton has 8 doubles, 2 singles, 5 bathrooms. 7 holiday cottages on the Estate.

Scotland
South West

DRUMLANRIG CASTLE
Thornhill

DRUMLANRIG CASTLE, Gardens and Country Park, the home of the Duke of Buccleuch and Queensberry KT was built between 1679 and 1691 by William Douglas, 1st Duke of Queensberry. Drumlanrig is rightly recognised as one of the first and most important buildings in the grand manner in Scottish domestic architecture. James Smith, who made the conversion from a 15th century castle, made a comparable transformation at Dalkeith a decade later.

The castle, of local pink sandstone, offers superb views across Nithsdale. It houses a renowned art collection, including work by Leonardo, Holbein, and Rembrandt, as well as cabinets made for Louis XIV's Versailles, relics of Bonnie Prince Charlie and a 300 year old silver chandelier.

The story of Sir James Douglas, killed in Spain while carrying out the last wish of Robert Bruce, pervades the castle in the emblem of a winged heart. Douglas family historical exhibition. The gardens, now being restored to the plan of 1738, add to the overall effect. The fascination of Drumlanrig as a centre of art, beauty and history is complemented by its role in the Queensberry Estate, a model of dynamic and enlightened land management.

CONTACT

A Fisher
Drumlanrig Castle
Thornhill
Dumfriesshire
DG3 4AQ

Tel: (01848) 330248

Fax: (01848) 600244

LOCATION

OS Ref. NX851 992

18m N of Dumfries,
3m NW of Thornhill
off A76.
16m from M74 at
Elvanfoot.
Approx. 1 1/2 hrs
by road from Edinburgh,
Glasgow and Carlisle.

CONFERENCE/FUNCTION		
ROOM	SIZE	MAX CAPACITY
Visitors' Centre	6m x 13m	50

i Shop. No photography inside the castle.

Welcome. Please enquire about facilities before visit.

Tearoom in castle. Snacks, lunches and teas during opening hours.

Available in the early season and by prior arrangement.

P Adjacent to the castle.

Children's quiz and work-sheets. Ranger-led activities, including woodlands and forestry. Adventure playground. Bird of prey centre.

OPENING TIMES

SUMMER

Castle
2 May - 23 August
Guided tours 12 - 4pm
(limited tours 10-12 July)

11am - 12pm available for pre-booked groups - school groups by appointment from 9.30am.

24 - 31 August
by appointment only.

Country Park, Gardens & Adventure Woodland
2 May - 31 August
Daily: 11am - 5pm

WINTER

By appointment only.

ADMISSION

Castle and Country Park

Adult £6.00
Child £2.00
OAP.........................£4.00
Family (2+4) £14.00
Wheelchairs ....free

Pre-booked groups
Special time................£8.00
Normal time £6.00

Country Park only
Adult £3.00

ARBIGLAND GARDENS

KIRKBEAN, DUMFRIES & GALLOWAY DG2 8BQ

Owner: *Capt & Mrs Beauchamp Blackett* **Contact:** *Capt & Mrs Beauchamp Blackett*

Tel: 01387 880283 **Fax:** 01387 880344

Formal woodland and water gardens which have evolved through three centuries. The ideal family outing garden as the gardens run down to a sheltered sandy bay where the younger members (and dogs) can let off steam. 400 yards from the John Paul Jones Birthplace Museum, his father created the gardens circa 1750.

Location: OS Ref. NX990 574. 15m S of Dumfries off A710 'Solway Coast Road'.

Opening Times: 1 May - 30 Sept: Tue - Sun plus BH Mon 2 - 6pm. House open 22 - 31 May by appointment.

Admission: Adult £2, Child 50p, OAP £1.50, Toddlers free.

[i] Shop. [♿] Grounds suitable. WC. [☕] Tearoom. [🐕] In grounds, on leads.

SPECIAL EVENTS

EASTER - 30 SEPT: John Paul Jones Birthplace Museum open.

BARDROCHAT

COLMONELL, AYRSHIRE KA26 0SG

Owner: *A McEwen*   **Contact:** *A McEwen*

Tel: 01465 881242 **Fax:** 01465 881330

Built by Robert Lorimer in 1893 for the present owner's grandfather. The house stands high on the south side of the Stinchar Valley. The house sleeps up to 16 for garden tours in May, golf on the many local great golf courses or salmon fishing. The price is all inclusive.

Location: OS Ref. NX140 850. Nr Colmonell, 10m S of Girvan off the A77.

Opening Times: Apr - Sept: Mon - Fri, 9am - 5pm.

Admission: Dinner, overnight accommodation, breakfast: £110pp. Open day prices: Adult £2.50, Child £2.

[i] Corporate hospitality. [X] Wedding receptions. [♿] Partially suitable.

[⚅] By arrangement. [🐕] In grounds, on leads.

[A] 2 single, 6 double all with ensuite bathrooms.

ARDWELL GARDENS   **Tel:** 01776 860227

Ardwell, Nr. Stranraer, Dumfries and Galloway

Owner: Mr Francis Brewis   **Contact:** Mrs Terry Brewis

The gardens surround an 18th century house and include a formal garden, wild garden and woodland.

Location: OS Ref. NX102 455. A716 10m S of Stranraer.

Opening Times: 1 Apr - 1 Oct: daily, 10am - 5pm.

Admission: Adult £1.50, Child/Conc. 75p.

[i] Plant centre. [♿] Partially suitable. WCs. [🐕] In grounds, on leads.

[P] Ample for cars. Limited parking and poor access for coaches.

BACHELORS' CLUB ♟   **Tel:** 01292 541940

Sandgate Street, Tarbolton KA5 5RB

Owner: The National Trust for Scotland   **Contact:** David Rodger

17th century thatched house in which poet Robert Burns and friends formed a debating society in 1780. Burns' mementos and relics, period furnishings.

Location: OS Ref. NS430 270. In Tarbolton, B744, 7¹/₂ m NE of Ayr, off B743.

Opening Times: Good Fri - 30 Sept: daily 1.30 - 5.30pm. Weekends in Oct: 1.30 - 5pm. Last admission 5pm.

Admission: Adult £2, Conc. £1.30, Family £5.30. Groups: Adult £1.60, School £1.

[♿] Ground floor suitable. [🐕] No dogs.

BARGANY GARDENS   **Tel:** 01465 871249 **Fax:** 01465 714191

Girvan, Ayrshire KA26 9QL

Owner: Mr John Dalrymple Hamilton   **Contact:** Mr John Dalrymple Hamilton

Lily pond, rock garden and a fine collection of hard and softwood trees.

Location: OS Ref. NS250 001. 4m ENE of Girvan by B734. After 2¹/₂ m keep ahead on to minor road to Dailly.

Opening Times: 1 Mar - 31 Oct: 10am - 7pm.

Admission: Contributions box.

[♿] Suitable. [P] Limited for coaches. [🐕] In grounds, on leads.

Douglas Macgregor

Brodick Castle and Country Park, Isle of Arran.

313

BRODICK CASTLE & COUNTRY PARK

Harvey Wood

ISLE OF ARRAN KA27 8HY

Owner: The National Trust for Scotland   *Contact:* Veronica Woodman

Tel: 01770 302202   **Fax:** 01770 302312

This is a castle you will never forget! The tall, stately building beckons you with the glow of its warm red sandstone. The setting is staggering, fronted by the sea, bedecked with gardens and overlooked by the majestic mountain of Goatfell. The castle was built on the site of a Viking fortress and dates from the 13th century. The contents are magnificent and include superb silver, porcelain, paintings and sporting trophies. The woodland garden ranks as one of Europe's finest.

Location: OS Ref. NS010 360. Isle of Arran. Ferries from Ardrossan & Claonaig and Kintyre. Ferry enquiries: 01475 650100

Opening Times: Castle: 1 Apr - 31 Oct: daily 11.30am - 5pm. Last admission 4.30pm. Reception Centre and shop (dates as castle) 10am - 5pm; restaurant 11am - 5pm. Garden & Country Park: All year, daily 9.30am - sunset. Goatfell open all year.

Admission: Castle: Adult £4.80, Child £3.20. Groups: Adult £3.80, School £1, Family £12.80. Garden & Country Park: Adult £2.40, Child £1.60. Groups: Adult £1.90, School £1.

[i] Shop.   [&] Suitable. WC.   [☕] Licensed restaurant.   [🐕] In grounds, on leads.

BROUGHTON HOUSE & GARDEN

HIGH STREET, KIRKCUDBRIGHT DG6 4JX

Owner: The National Trust for Scotland   *Contact:* Frances Scott

Tel: 01557 330437

This fascinating 18th century house in the pleasant coastal town of Kirkcudbright was the home and studio from 1901 - 1933 of the artist E A Hornel, one of the 'Glasgow Boys'. It contains many of his works, along with paintings by other contemporary artists, and an extensive collection of rare Scottish books, including valuable editions of Burns's works.

Location: OS Ref. NX684 509. Off A711 / A755, in Kirkcudbright, at 12 High St.

Opening Times: House & Garden: 1 Apr - 31 Oct, daily, 1 - 5.30pm. Last admission 4.45pm.

Admission: Adult £2.40, Child £1.60, Family £6.40. Groups: Adult £1.90, School £1.

[&] Not suitable.   [🚶] By arrangement.   [P] Limited.   [🐕] No dogs.

BLAIRQUHAN CASTLE 🏛   See page 311 for full page entry.

BURNS COTTAGE   **Tel:** 01292 441215

Alloway, Ayrshire KA7 4PY   **Contact:** J Manson

Thatched cottage, birthplace of Robert Burns in 1759. Now a museum.

Location: OS Ref. NS335 190. 2m SW of Ayr.

Opening Times: Apr - Oct: daily, 9am - 6pm. Nov - Mar: daily 10am - 4pm (Sun 12 - 4pm).

Admission: Adult £2.50, Child £1.25, OAP £1.85, Family £6. Admission charge includes entry to Burns' Monument and Gardens.

CAERLAVEROCK CASTLE

GLENCAPLE, DUMFRIES DG1 4RU

Owner: Historic Scotland   *Contact:* The Steward

Tel: 01387 770244

One of the finest castles in Scotland on a triangular site surrounded by moats. Its most remarkable features are the twin-towered gatehouse and the Renaissance Nithsdale lodging. The site of two famous sieges. Children's park, replica siege engine and nature trail to site of earlier castle.

Location: OS84 NY025 656. 8m S of Dumfries on the B725.

Opening Times: Apr - Sept: daily, 9.30am - 6.30pm. Oct - Mar: Mon - Sat, 9.30am - 4.30pm, Sun 2 - 4.30pm. Last ticket sold 30 mins before closing.

Admission: Adult £2.30, Child £1, OAP/Student £1.75. 10% discount for groups 10+.

[i] Shop.   [&] Partially suitable. WCs.   [☕] Tearoom.

[P] Ample but limited for coaches.   [👫] Teacher's pack.   [🐕] In grounds, on leads.

CARDONESS CASTLE 🗝   **Tel:** 01557 814427

Gatehouse of Fleet

Owner: Historic Scotland   **Contact:** The Custodian

Well preserved ruin of a four storey tower house of 15th century standing on a rocky platform above the Water of Fleet. Ancient home of the McCullochs. Very fine fireplaces.

Location: OS Ref. NX591 553. 1m SW of Gatehouse of Fleet, beside the A75.

Opening Times: 1 Apr - 30 Sept: daily 9.30am - 6.30pm. Last ticket 6pm. 1 Oct - 31 Mar: Sat 9.30am - 4.30pm, Sun 2 - 4.30pm. Last ticket 4pm.

Admission: Adult £1.80, Child 75p, Conc. £1.30.

CARLYLE'S BIRTHPLACE 🏠   **Tel:** 01576 300666

Ecclefechan, Dumfriesshire

Owner: The National Trust for Scotland   **Contact:** The Manager

Thomas Carlyle was born here in The Arched House in 1795, the year before Burns died. Carlyle was a brilliant essayist, historian, social reformer, visionary and literary giant. When he was 14 he walked the 84 miles to Edinburgh University - taking three days. Upstairs is the bedroom in which Carlyle was born. There is also a little museum with a notable collection of photographs, manuscripts and other documents.

Location: OS Ref. NY193 745. Off M74, 6m SE of Lockerbie. In Ecclefechan village.

Opening Times: 1 May - 30 Sept: Fri - Mon 1.30 - 5.30pm. Last admission 5pm.

Admission: Adult £2, Child £1.30, Family £5.30. Groups: Adult £1.60, School £1.

[&] Not suitable.   [🚶] By arrangement.   [P] Limited.   [🐕] No dogs.

CASTLE KENNEDY GARDENS
Tel: 01776 702024 **Fax:** 01776 706248

Stair Estates, Rephad, Stranraer, Dumfries and Galloway DG9 8BX
Owner: The Earl & Countess of Stair   **Contact:** The Earl of Stair
75 acres of gardens, originally laid out in 1730. Features include rhododendrons, pinetum, walled garden and circular lily pond.
Location: OS Ref. NX109 610. 3m E of Stranraer on A75.
Opening Times: Apr - Sept: daily.
Admission: Adult £2, Child £1, OAP £1.50.

CRAIGDARROCH HOUSE
Tel: 01848 200202

Moniaive, Dumfriesshire DG3 4JB
Owner: Mr Alexander Sykes   **Contact:** Mr Alexander Sykes
Location: OS Ref. NX741 909. S side of B729, 2m W of Moniaive, 19m WNW of Dumfries.
Opening Times: Jul: daily, 2 - 4pm.
Admission: £2pp.

[i] No WC facilities.

CRAIGIEBURN GARDEN
Tel: 01683 221250

Craigieburn House, Nr. Moffat, Dumfriesshire DG10 9LF
Owner: Janet Wheatcroft   **Contact:** Janet Wheatcroft
A plantsman's garden with a huge range of rare and unusual plants surrounded by natural woodland.
Location: OS Ref. NT117 053. NW side of A708 to Yarrow & Selkirk, $2^1/_2$ m E of Moffat.
Opening Times: Easter - Oct: Tue - Sun, 12.30 - 8pm.
Admission: Adult £1.50, Child free.

CROSSRAGUEL ABBEY
Tel: 01655 883113

Maybole, Strathclyde
Owner: Historic Scotland   **Contact:** The Custodian
Founded in the early 13th century by the Earl of Carrick. Remarkably complete remains include church, cloister, chapter house and much of the domestic premises.
Location: OS Ref. NS275 083. 2m S of Maybole on the A77.
Opening Times: 1 Apr - 30 Sept: Mon - Wed, Sat & Sun, 9.30am - 6.30pm, Thur 9.30am - 12 pm, Fri closed. Last ticket 6pm.
Admission: Adult £1.50, Child 75p, Conc. £1.10.

CULZEAN CASTLE & COUNTRY PARK

John K Wilkie

MAYBOLE KA19 8LE
Owner: *The National Trust for Scotland*   **Contact:** *Jonathan Cardale*

Tel: 01655 760274   **Fax:** 01655 760615
Robert Adam's 18th century masterpiece, a real 'castle in the air', is perched on a cliff high above the crashing waves of the Firth of Clyde. Arrow slits and mock battlements give medieval touches to the sturdy exterior, and on the seaward-side front is the imposing drum tower. The interior is the epitome of disciplined elegance, crowned by the spectacular oval staircase ascending through ornamental pillars and ironwork balustrading. Adam also designed many interior fittings. The exterior grounds encompass Scotland's first country park.
Location: OS Ref. NS240 100. 12m SW of Ayr, on A719, 4m W of Maybole.
Opening Times: Castle, Visitor Centre, licensed restaurants and shops: 1 Apr - 31 Oct: daily 10.30am - 5.30pm. Last admission 5pm. Other times by appointment. Country Park: All year, daily 9.30am - sunset.
Admission: Country Park only: Adult £3.50, Child £2.40, Family £9. Groups: Adult £3, Child/school £1, School coach £20. Castle & Park combined ticket: Adult £6.50, Child £4.40, Family £17. Groups: Adult £5.50, Child/school £2.

[i] Shops. [&] Suitable. WC. [tea] Licensed restaurants. [dog] In grounds, on leads.

DALGARVEN MILL
Tel: 01294 552448

Dalry Road, Kilwinning, Ayrshire K13 6PL
Owner: Dalgarven Mill Trust   **Contact:** The Administrator
Water-driven flour mill and country life museum.
Location: OS Ref. NS295 460. On A737 2m from Kilwinning.
Opening Times: All year: Easter - end Oct: Mon - Sat, 10am - 5pm. Sun, 11am - 5pm. Winter closes at 4pm, may not be open Mon/Tues - ring to check.
Admission: Adult £2.50, Conc. £1.50, Family £6.

DEAN CASTLE COUNTRY PARK
Tel: 01563 522702

Dean Road, Kilmarnock, Strathclyde KA3 1XB
Owner: East Ayrshire Council   **Contact:** Andrew Scott-Martin
Set in 81 hectares of Country Park.
Location: OS Ref. NS437 395. E of B7038 to Glasgow, $1^1/_4$ m NNE of town centre.
Opening Times: Country Park: All year. Castle: All year (except 25/26 Dec & 1/2 Jan), 12 noon - 4.30pm. Visitor Centre: as Castle dates but 11am - 5pm summer, 11am - 4pm winter.
Admission: Adult £2.50, Conc. £1.25. East Ayrshire residents free.

DRUMLANRIG CASTLE [icon]
See page 312 for full page entry.

DUNDRENNAN ABBEY [icon]
Tel: 01557 500262

Kirkcudbright
Owner: Historic Scotland   **Contact:** The Custodian
Mary Queen of Scots spent her last night on Scottish soil in this 12th century Cistercian Abbey founded by David I. The Abbey stands in a small and secluded valley.
Location: OS Ref. NX749 475. $6^1/_2$ m SE of Kirkcudbright on the A711.
Opening Times: 1 Apr - 30 Sept: Mon - Wed, Sat & Sun, 9.30am - 6.30pm, Thur 9.30am - 12 pm, Fri closed. Last ticket 6pm.
Admission: Adult £1.50, Child 75p, Conc. £1.10.

GALLOWAY HOUSE GARDENS
Tel: 01988 600680

Garlieston, Newton Stewart, Wigtownshire DG8 8HF
Owner: Galloway House Gardens Trust   **Contact:** D Marshall
Created in 1740 by Lord Garlies, currently under restoration.
Location: OS Ref. NX478 453. 15m S of Newton Stewart on B7004.
Opening Times: 1 Mar - 31 Oct: 9am - 5pm.
Admission: Adult £1, Child/Conc. 50p, Family £2.50.

GLENLUCE ABBEY [icon]
Tel: 01581 300541

Glenluce
Owner: Historic Scotland   **Contact:** Historic Scotland
A Cistercian Abbey founded in 1190. Remains include a handsome 16th century Chapter House.
Location: OS Ref. NX185 587. 2m NW of Glenluce village off the A75.
Opening Times: 1 Apr - 30 Sept: daily 9.30am - 6.30pm. Last ticket 6pm. 1 Oct - 31 Mar: Sat 9.30am - 4.30pm, Sun 2 - 4.30pm. Last ticket 4pm.
Admission: Adult £1.50, Child 75p, Conc. £1.10.

GLENWHAN GARDENS
Tel: 01581 400222 **Fax:** 01581 400295

Dunragit, Stranraer, Wigtownshire DG9 8PH
Owner: Mrs Tessa Knot   **Contact:** Mrs Tessa Knot
12 acre garden overlooking Luce Bay and the Mull of Galloway.
Location: OS Ref. NX150 580. N side of A75, 6m E of Stranraer.
Opening Times: All year: daily 10am - 5pm.
Admission: Adult £2, Child over 14yrs £1, Conc. £1.50.

[i] Plant centre.   [tea] Licensed tearoom.

KELBURN CASTLE [icon]
See page 326 for full page entry.

LOGAN BOTANIC GARDEN
Tel: 01776 860231 **Fax:** 01776 860333

Port Logan, Stranraer, Wigtownshire DG9 9ND
Owner: Royal Botanic Garden Edinburgh   **Contact:** The Curator
Scotland's most exotic garden. Take a trip to the south west of Scotland and experience the southern hemisphere! The exceptionally mild climate allows a colourful array of tender exotics to thrive out of doors - tree ferns, cabbage palms, unusual shrubs, climbers and tender perennials.
Location: OS Ref. NX097 430. 14m S of Stranraer on B7065.
Opening Times: 1 Mar - 31 Oct: daily, 9.30am - 6pm.
Admission: Adult £3, Child £1, Conc. £2.50, Family £7. Group discount available.

[i] Shop. Plant centre.   [X] Wedding receptions.   [&] Partially suitable. WCs.
[tea] Licensed restaurant.   [K] By arrangement.   [P] Ample.   [dog] Guide dogs only.

SOUTH WEST SCOTLAND
Dumfries & Galloway, Ayrshire and the Isle of Arran

HUDSON'S

SOUTH WEST SCOTLAND

Scotland
South West

MACLELLAN'S CASTLE

Tel: 01557 331856

Kirkcudbright

Owner: Historic Scotland   **Contact:** The Custodian

A handsome castellated mansion, built in 1577 using stone from an adjoining ruined monastery by the then Provost. Elaborately planned with fine architectural details, it has been a ruin since 1752.

Location: OS Ref. NX683 511. Centre of Kirkcudbright on the A711.

Opening Times: 1 Apr - 30 Sept: daily, 9.30am - 6.30pm. Last ticket 6pm.

Admission: Adult £1.20, Child 50p, Conc. 90p.

MAXWELTON HOUSE

Tel: 01848 200385

Moniaive, Thornhill, Dumfries & Galloway DG3 4DX

Owner: Maxwelton House Trust   **Contact:** Roderick Stenhouse

Glencairn Castle, now Maxwelton House, dates back to 1370s and is the home of the Earls of Glencairn. Stephen Laurie bought Glencairn Castle in 1611 and changed the name to Maxwelton. Annie Laurie was born here in 1682. The Stenhouse family purchased Maxwelton from the Laurie family in 1968 and carried out one of the largest restorations to a private house within Scotland. The restoration took three years and the continuing labour of no less than 65 men. It was completed in 1972. House, museum, Chapel.

Location: OS Ref. NX822 898. Entrances on B729 near Wallaceton or A702 near Penpont. 13m NW of Dumfries.

Opening Times: Last Sun in May - end Sept: Sun - Fri (closed Sat) 11am - 5pm. Apr/May open for groups only. Last admission ¹/₂ hr before closing.

Admission: Adult £4, Child (up to 16yrs) £2, Conc. £3. Groups: £3pp. Garden only: £2.

ℹ️ Shop.   ☕ Tearoom.   🚶 Compulsory.   🅿️ Free parking.   🐕 In grounds, on leads.

NEW ABBEY CORN MILL

Tel: 01387 850260

New Abbey Village

Owner: Historic Scotland   **Contact:** The Custodian

This carefully renovated 18th century water-powered oatmeal mill is in full working order and regular demonstrations are given for visitors in the summer.

Location: OS Ref. NX962 663. 8m S of Dumfries on the A710. Close to Sweetheart Abbey.

Opening Times: 1 Apr - 30 Sept: daily 9.30am - 6.30pm. Last ticket 6pm. 1 Oct - 31 Mar: Mon - Wed & Sat 9.30am - 4.30pm, Thur 9.30am - 12 noon, Fri closed, Sun 2 - 4.30pm. Last ticket 4pm.

Admission: Adult £2.30, Child £1, Conc. £1.75. Joint entry ticket with Sweetheart Abbey: Adult £2.80, Child £1.25, Conc. £2.10.

RAMMERSCALES

Tel: 01387 810229/811988 **Fax:** 01387 810940

Lockerbie, Dumfriesshire DG11 1LD

Owner: Mr M A Bell Macdonald   **Contact:** Mr M A Bell Macdonald

Georgian house.

Location: OS Ref. NY080 780. W side of B7020, 3m S of Lochmoben.

Opening Times: Last week in Jul, 1st three weeks in Aug: daily (excluding Sats), 2 - 5pm.

Admission: Adult £5, Conc. £2.50.

SHAMBELLIE HOUSE & GARDENS

Tel: 01387 850375

New Abbey, Dumfries, Dumfriesshire EH1 1JF

Owner: National Museums of Scotland   **Contact:** Sheila Watt

Mature Victorian gardens in a woodland setting.

Location: OS Ref. NX960 665. 7m S of Dumfries on A710.

Opening Times: 1 Apr - 31 Oct: daily, 11am - 5pm.

Admission: Adult £2.50, Conc. £1.50.

SORN CASTLE

Tel: 01290 551555

Ayrshire KA5 6HR

Owner: Mrs R G McIntyre   **Contact:** Mrs R G McIntyre

Originally 14th century castle. James V visited the castle then owned by the Earl of Winton in 1598. The castle has been enlarged several times, most recently in 1908.

Location: OS Ref. NS555 265. 4m E of Mauchline on B743.

Opening Times: By appointment.

♿ Grounds suitable.   🚶 Compulsory.   🐕 In grounds, on leads.

SOUTER JOHNNIE'S COTTAGE

Tel: 01655 760603

Main Road, Kirkoswald KA19 8HY

Owner: The National Trust for Scotland   **Contact:** Ms Jan Gibson

The home of John Davidson, original 'Souter' (cobbler) of Robert Burns' famous narrative poem *Tam O' Shanter*. Burns mementos and restored cobbler's workshop. Life-sized stone figures in adjacent 'ale-house'.

Location: OS Ref. NS240 070. On A77, in Kirkoswald village, 4m SW of Maybole.

Opening Times: Good Fri - 30 Sept: daily 11.30 - 5pm. Weekends in Oct: 11.30 - 5pm (last admission 4.30pm).

Admission: Adult £2, Child £1.30, Family £5.30. Groups: Adult £1.60, School £1.

♿ House suitable.   🅿️ Limited.   🐕 No dogs.

SWEETHEART ABBEY

Tel: 01387 850397

New Abbey Village

Owner: Historic Scotland   **Contact:** The Custodian

Cistercian abbey founded in 1273 by Devorgilla, in memory of her husband John Balliol. The principal feature is the well preserved precinct wall enclosing 30 acres. She also founded Balliol College, Oxford.

Location: OS Ref. NX965 663. In New Abbey Village, on A710 8m S of Dumfries.

Opening Times: 1 Apr - 30 Sept: daily 9.30am - 6.30pm. Last ticket 6pm. 1 Oct - 31 Mar: Mon - Wed & Sat 9.30am - 4.30pm, Thur 9.30am - 12 noon, Fri closed, Sun 2 - 4.30pm. Last ticket 4pm.

Admission: Adult £1.20, Child 50p, Conc. 90p. Joint entry ticket with New Abbey Corn Mill: Adult £2.80, Child £1.25, Conc. £2.10.

THREAVE CASTLE

Tel: 01831 168512

Castle Douglas

Owner: The National Trust for Scotland   **Contact:** Historic Scotland

Built by Archibald the Grim in the late 14th century, early stronghold of the Black Douglases. Around its base is an artillery fortification built before 1455 when the castle was besieged by James II. Ring the bell and the custodian will come to ferry you over. Long walk to property. Owned by The National Trust for Scotland but under the guardianship of Historic Scotland.

Location: OS Ref. NX739 623. 2m W of Castle Douglas on the A75.

Opening Times: 1 Apr - 30 Sept: daily 9.30am - 6.30pm. Last ticket 6pm.

Admission: Adult £1.80, Child 75p, Conc. £1.30. Charges include ferry trip.

THREAVE GARDEN

Tel: 01556 502575 **Tel:** 01556 502683

Castle Douglas DG7 1RX

Owner: The National Trust for Scotland   **Contact:** Trevor Jones

The garden has a wide range of features and a good collection of plants. There are peat and woodland garden plants and a colourful rock garden. Summer months bring a superb show from the herbaceous beds and borders. The heather gardens give a splash of colour, along with bright berries in the autumn. Truly a garden for all seasons.

Location: OS Ref. NX752 605. Off A75, 1m SW of Castle Douglas.

Opening Times: Estate & garden: All year, daily 9.30am - sunset. Walled garden and glasshouses: all year 9.30am - 5pm. Visitor Centre, Exhibition, & Shop: 1 Apr - 31 Oct: daily, 9.30am - 5.30pm. Restaurant: 10am - 5pm.

Admission: Adult £4, Child £2.70. Groups: Adult £3.20, School £1. Family £10.70.

ℹ️ Shop.   ♿ Grounds suitable. WC.   ☕ Restaurant.

WHITHORN PRIORY

Tel: 01988 500508

Whithorn

Owner: Historic Scotland   **Contact:** The Project Manager

Part of the 'Whithorn Cradle of Christianity' attraction. The site of the first Christian church in Scotland. Founded as 'Candida Casa' by St Ninian in the early 5th century it later became the cathedral church of Galloway. In the museum is a fine collection of early Christian stones including the Monreith Cross. Visitor Centre and archaeological dig.

Location: OS Ref. NX445 403. At Whithorn on the A746.

Opening Times: Please telephone 01988 500700 for details.

Admission: Joint ticket by Whithorn Trust gives entry to Priory, Priory Museum and archaeological dig.

Castle Kennedy Gardens, Stranraer.

EDINBURGH

HUDSON'S

EDINBURGH
City, Coast & Countryside

Scotland
Edinburgh

CONTACT

Mrs L Morison
Dalmeny House
South Queensferry
Edinburgh
EH30 9TQ

Tel: (0131) 331 1888

Fax: (0131) 331 1788

LOCATION

OS Ref. NT167 779

From Edinburgh A90,
B924, 7m N,
A90 $\frac{1}{2}$ m.

On south shore
of Firth of Forth.

Bus: From St Andrew
Square to Chapel Gate
1m from House.

Rail: Dalmeny railway
station 3m.

Taxi: Hawes Landing
(0131) 331 1077
Caledonian Private Hire
(0131) 331 3321.

CONFERENCE/FUNCTION

ROOM	SIZE	MAX CAPACITY
Library	10.4 x 7m	20
Dining Rm	11.2 x 7.4m	100
Garden Restaurant	12.7 x 9m	200
Rosebery Rooms		150

DALMENY HOUSE
South Queensferry

Dalmeny House rejoices in one of the most beautiful and unspoilt settings in Great Britain, yet it is only seven miles from Scotland's capital, Edinburgh, fifteen minutes from Edinburgh airport and less than an hour's drive from Glasgow. It is an eminently suitable venue for group visits, business functions, meetings and special events, including product launches and outdoor activities such as off-road driving.

Dalmeny Estate, the family home of the Earls of Rosebery for over 300 years, boasts superb collections of porcelain and tapestries, fine paintings by Gainsborough, Raeburn, Reynolds and Lawrence, together with the exquisite Mentmore Rothschild collection of 18th century French furniture. There is also the Napoleonic collection, assembled by the 5th Earl of Rosebery, Prime Minister, historian and owner of three Derby winners.

The Hall, Library and Dining Room will lend a memorable sense of occasion to corporate receptions, luncheons and dinners. Alternatively, there are the recently renovated areas of the former kitchen and servants' hall (now named the Rosebery Rooms) and the new Courtyard Restaurant, with facilities specifically designed for business meetings, small conferences, promotions, exhibitions and product launches. A wide range of entertainment can also be provided, from piano recitals to a floodlit pipe band Beating the Retreat.

OPENING TIMES

SUMMER

July and August
Sun, 1 - 5.30pm.
Last admission 4.45pm.

Mon & Tue
12 - 5.30pm.
Last admission 4.45pm.

WINTER

Open at other times by appointment only.

ADMISSION

SUMMER

Adult	£3.60
Child*	£2.00
OAP	£3.20
Student	£2.80
Groups (min 20)	£3.00

* 10 - 16 years

---

i Fashion shows, product launches, archery, clay pigeon shooting, equestrian events, shows, filming, background photography, small meetings and special events. Lectures on House, contents and family history. Screen and projector. Helicopter landing area. House is centre of a $4\frac{1}{2}$ m shore walk from Forth Rail Bridge to small foot passenger ferry at Cramond (ferry 9am - 1pm, 2 - 7pm in summer, 2 - 4pm winter, closed Fri). No fires, picnics or cameras.

X Conferences and functions, buffets, lunches, dinners.

♿ Visitors may alight at entrance. WC.

☕ Teas and lunches, groups can book in advance.

🚶 Special interest tours can be arranged outside normal opening hours.

P 60 cars, 3 coaches. Parking for functions in front of house.

🐕 No dogs.

CONTACT

Rozi Spurway
Harburn House
Harburn
West Calder
West Lothian
EH55 8RN

Tel: (01506) 461818
Fax: (01506) 416591

e-mail:
Harburn@compuserve.com

www:
http//www.harburnhouse.com

HARBURN HOUSE
Nr Livingston

HARBURN HOUSE offers its guests the perfect alternative to a first class hotel. This privately owned Georgian mansion, surrounded by its own 3000 acre sporting and leisure estate, is ideally situated offering unparalleled accessibility.

Harburn is essentially small and very personal. It is therefore frequently taken over exclusively for conferences, incentive travel, training seminars and product launches, etc. In this way guests may enjoy the luxury of a five star hotel, combined with the comfort and privacy of their own home.

The policies and lawns of Harburn are ideal for

larger events and these can be complemented by our own fully lined and floored marquee.

A stay at Harburn is a very relaxed and informal affair. The staff are first class and the atmosphere is one of a private house party.

The estate provides the full range of sporting and leisure activities including, golf, game shooting, fishing, clay pigeon shooting, tennis, riding and archery to name but a few.

The complete privacy and outstanding scenery, so accessible to the major cities and beauty spots, makes Harburn the ultimate choice for the discerning event or conference organiser.

❖

LOCATION

OS Ref. NT045 608

Off B7008, 2^1/$_2$ m S of A71. 2m N of A70. 20m SW of Edinburgh. Almost equidistant between Glasgow and Edinburgh, within 1hr of Perth, Stirling, Dundee and the Border country.

CONFERENCE/FUNCTION

ROOM	SIZE	MAX CAPACITY
Conference Room	30' x 18'	20
Drawing Rm	30' x 18'	40
Dining Rm	30' x 18'	40
Library	14' x 12'	15
Morning Rm	16' x 15'	20
Whole house		80
Marquee	120' x 40'	500

i Filming, conferences, activity days, product launches, golf, riding, fishing, archery, buggies, game shooting, falconry, etc. Golf and Country Club nearby.

X High quality in-house catering by our own top chef and fully trained staff. Prices and menus on request. Wedding receptions.

♿ Ground floor bedroom, dining room and drawing room.

P Parking for 300 cars and 10 coaches in summer, 100+ 10 in winter. Follow one way system and 20 mph speed limit, vehicles should not park on grass verges.

🐕 On leads.

A 17 bedrooms, all with their own bathrooms, exclusive to one group at a time.

OPENING TIMES

All year by appointment.

ADMISSION

The exclusive use of House and Grounds for activity days (without accommodation).

Per day £700.00

Accommodation Rates

Double with bath
Per person..............£90.00

Dinner, bed & breakfast
Per person............£110.00

Day Delegate Rate

Per person..............£38.00

24 hour rate

Per person............£115.00

VAT is not included in the above rates.

HOPETOUN HOUSE
Edinburgh

Hopetoun House is a unique gem of Europe's architectural heritage and undoubtedly 'Scotland's Finest Stately Home'. Situated on the shores of the Firth of Forth, it is one of the most splendid examples of the work of Scottish architects Sir William Bruce and William Adam. The interior of the house, with opulent gilding and classical motifs, reflects the aristocratic grandeur of the early 18th century, whilst its magnificent parkland has fine views across the Forth to the hills of Fife. The house is approached from the Royal Drive, used only by members of the Royal Family, notably King George IV in 1822 and Her Majesty Queen Elizabeth II in 1988.

Hopetoun is really two houses in one, the oldest part of the house was designed by Sir William Bruce and built between 1699 and 1707. It shows some of the finest examples in Scotland of carving, wainscoting and ceiling painting. In 1721 William Adam, by now a renowned Scottish architect, started enlarging the house by adding the magnificent façade, colonnades and grand State apartments which were the focus for social life and entertainment in the 18th century.

The house is set in 100 acres of rolling parkland including fine woodland walks, the red deer park, the spring garden with a profusion of wild flowers, and numerous picturesque picnic spots.

Hopetoun has been home of the Earls of Hopetoun, later created Marquesses of Linlithgow, since it was built in 1699 and in 1974 a charitable trust was created to preserve the house with its historic contents and surrounding landscape for the benefit of the public for all time.

CONTACT

Miss Lois Dunn
Hopetoun House
South Queensferry
Edinburgh
West Lothian
EH30 9SL

Tel: (0131) 331 2451

Fax: (0131) 319 1885

LOCATION

OS Ref. NT089 790

2¹/₂ m W of Forth Road
Bridge.

12m W of Edinburgh
(25 mins. drive).

34m E of Glasgow
(50 mins. drive).

OPENING TIMES

SUMMER

10 April - 27 September
Daily
10am - 5.30pm
Last admission 4.30pm.

WINTER

28 September - April
Closed except for group
visits by prior arrangement.

ADMISSION

Adult	£4.70
Child	£2.60
OAP	£4.20
Student	£4.20

Group
Adult £4.20

Winter prices on request.

CONFERENCE/FUNCTION		
ROOM	SIZE	MAX CAPACITY
Ballroom	92' x 35'	300
Tapestry Rm	37' x 24'	100
Red Drawing Rm	44' x 24'	100
State Dining Rm	39' x 23'	20

i Shop. Private functions, special events, antique fairs, concerts, Scottish gala evenings, conferences, grand piano, boules (petanque) piste, croquet lawn, helicopter landing. No smoking or flash photography in house.

✗ Receptions, gala dinners.

♿ Restaurant and exhibitions on ground floor. WC.

☕ Licensed restaurant, groups (up to 250) can book in advance, menus on request (Tel: 0131 331 4305).

🚶 Can be arranged in advance. Foreign language guides usually available.

P Free parking close to the house for cars and coaches. Book if possible, allow 1-2hrs for visit (min).

👪 Holders of 2 Sandford Awards for Heritage Education. Special tours of house and/or grounds for different age/interest groups. Teachers' information pack.

🐕 No dogs in house but welcome (on leads) in grounds.

SPECIAL EVENTS

• **FEB 20 / 21 / 22:**
Homes & Gardens
Interiors Fair

• **MAR 13 / 14 / 15:**
Antiques Fair

• **MAY 23:**
RNIB Son et Lumière concert
with BBC Scottish Symphony
Orchestra

• **JUN 5 / 6:**
Summer Concerts:
A Musical Feast

• **JUL 26:**
Hopetoun Country Fair

319

ARNISTON HOUSE

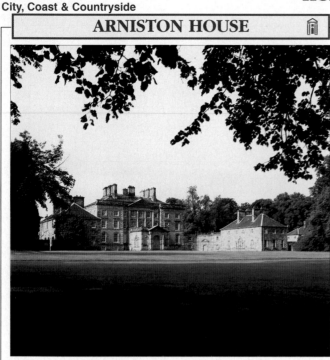

GOREBRIDGE, MIDLOTHIAN EH23 4RY

Owner: Mrs A Dundas-Bekker   *Contact: Miss H Dundas-Bekker*

Tel: 01875 830515 **Fax:** 01875 830515

Magnificent William Adam mansion started in 1726. Fine plasterwork, Scottish portraiture, period furniture and other fascinating contents. Beautiful country setting beloved by Sir Walter Scott.

Location: OS Ref. NT326 595. Off B6372, 1m from A7, Temple direction.

Opening Times: 2 Jul - 15 Sept: Sun, Tue & Thur, 2 - 5pm. Guided tours. Pre-arranged groups 10 - 50 people accepted throughout the year.

Admission: Adult £3, Child under school age free.

Tearoom.   Compulsory.   In grounds, on leads.

ARTHUR LODGE

Tel: 0131 667 5163

60 Dalkeith Road, Edinburgh EH16 5AD

Owner: S Roland Friden   **Contact:** S Roland Friden

A neo-classical 'Greek Revival' villa, designed by Thomas Hamilton in 1827, Arthur Lodge is a vision of a gentleman's country residence in town. In a beautiful setting, which includes a White Garden and an Italianate sunken garden, the house itself has been imaginatively restored and decorated. Unique in Edinburgh, Arthur Lodge offers visitors the opportunity to experience an exquisite, and often surprising, private residence.

Location: OS Ref. NT268 724. Edinburgh southside, opposite the Commonwealth Pool.

Opening Times: Jun - Jul: Wed & Sat afternoons. Aug - Sept: Wed afternoon only. Tours at 12pm, 1pm and 2pm. Other times by appointment.

Admission: Visits by guided tour only: Adult £3, Conc. £2, including tour.

No dogs.

BLACKNESS CASTLE

Tel: 01506 834807

Blackness

Owner: Historic Scotland   **Contact:** The Custodian

One of Scotland's most important strongholds. Built in the 14th century and massively strengthened in the 16th century as an artillery fortress, it has been a Royal castle and a prison armaments depot and film location for *Hamlet*. It was restored by the Office of Works in the 1920s. It stands on a promontory in the Firth of Forth.

Location: OS Ref. NT055 803. 4m NE of Linlithgow on the Firth of Forth, off the A904.

Opening Times: 1 Apr - 30 Sept: daily, 9.30am - 6.30pm, last ticket 6pm. 1 Oct - 31 Mar: Mon - Sat, 9.30am - 4.30pm, Sun 2 - 4.30pm, last ticket 4pm. Closed Thur pm & Fri in winter.

Admission: Adult £1.80, Child 75p, Conc. £1.30.

CRAIGMILLAR CASTLE

Tel: 0131 661 4445

Edinburgh

Owner: Historic Scotland   **Contact:** The Custodian

Mary Queen of Scots fled to Craigmillar after the murder of Rizzio and it was here that the plot was hatched for the murder of her husband Lord Darnley. This handsome structure with courtyard and gardens covers an area of one and a quarter acres. Built around an L-plan tower house of the early 15th century including a range of private rooms linked to the hall of the old tower.

Location: OS Ref. NT285 710. 2$^{1}/_{2}$ m SE of Edinburgh off the A68.

Opening Times: 1 Apr - 30 Sept: daily, 9.30am - 6.30pm, last ticket 6pm. 1 Oct - 31 Mar: Mon - Sat, 9.30am - 4.30pm, Sun 2 - 4.30pm, last ticket 4pm. Closed Thur pm & Fri in winter.

Admission: Adult £1.80, Child 75p, Conc. £1.30.

CRICHTON CASTLE

Tel: 01875 320017

Pathhead

Owner: Historic Scotland   **Contact:** The Custodian

A large and sophisticated castle with a spectacular façade of faceted stonework in an Italian style added by the Earl of Bothwell between 1581 and 1591 following a visit to Italy. Mary Queen of Scots attended a wedding here.

Location: OS Ref. NT380 612. 2$^{1}/_{2}$ m SSW of Pathhead off the A68.

Opening Times: 1 Apr - 30 Sept: daily, 9.30am - 6.30pm, last ticket 6pm.

Admission: Adult £1.50, Child 75p, Conc. £1.10.

DALKEITH PARK

Tel: 0131 663 5684

Dalkeith, Midlothian EH22 2NJ

Contact: J C Manson

Extensive grounds of Dalkeith Palace. 18th century bridge and orangery. Interpretation area.

Location: OS Ref. NT333 679. 7m SE of Edinburgh.

Opening Times: Mar - Oct: 10am - 6pm.

Admission: Adult £2, Child £2, Family £7, Groups £1.

Shop.   Partially suitable. WCs.   Tearoom.   By arrangement.
Ample.   Educational programme available. Teachers' pack.
In grounds, on leads.

DIRLETON CASTLE & GARDEN

DIRLETON, EAST LOTHIAN EH39 5ER

Owner: Historic Scotland   Contact: The Steward

Tel: 01620 850330

The oldest part of this romantic castle dates from the 13th century, when it was built by the De Vaux family. The renowned gardens, first laid out in the 16th century, now include magnificent Arts and Crafts herbaceous borders and a re-created Victorian Garden. In the picturesque village of Dirleton.

Location: OS Ref. NT516 839. In Dirleton, 7m W of North Berwick on the A198.

Opening Times: Apr - Sept: daily, 9.30am - 6.30pm. Oct - Mar: Mon - Sat, 9.30am - 4.30pm, Sun 2 - 4.30pm. Last ticket 30 mins before closing.

Admission: Adult £2.30, Child £1, OAP/Student £1.75. 10% discount for groups of 10+. Free pre-booked school visits, teachers' pack available.

Shop.   Partially suitable.   Ample.   Guide dogs only.

DALMENY HOUSE

See page 317 for full page entry.

DUNGLASS COLLEGIATE CHURCH

Tel: 0131 668 8800

Cockburnspath

Owner: Historic Scotland

Founded in 1450 for a college of canons by Sir Alexander Hume. A handsome cross-shaped building with vaulted nave, choir and transepts.

Location: OS Ref. NT767 719. 1m NW of Cockburnspath. SW of A1.

Opening Times: All Year.

Admission: Free.

EDINBURGH CASTLE

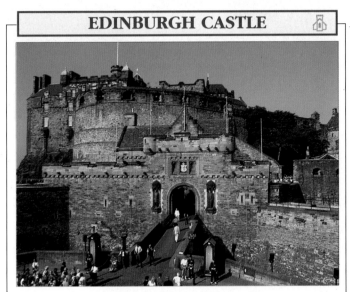

CASTLEHILL, EDINBURGH EH1 2NG

Owner: Historic Scotland   Contact: Neil Young

Tel: 0131 225 9846 **Fax:** 0131 220 4733

Scotland's most famous castle, dominating the capital's skyline and giving stunning views of the city and countryside. Home to the Scottish crown jewels, the Stone of Destiny and Mons Meg. Other highlights include St Margaret's Chapel, the Great Hall and the Scottish National War Memorial.

Location: OS Ref. NT252 736. At the top of the Royal Mile in Edinburgh.

Opening Times: Apr - Sept: daily, 9.30am - 6pm. Oct - Mar: daily, 9.30am - 5pm. Last ticket 45 mins before closing.

Admission: Adult £6, Child £1.50, OAP/Student £4.50. Pre-booked school visits available free, except Jun - Aug.

i Shop. Corporate hospitality.	Private evening hire of restaurant.
Partially suitable. WCs. Courtesy vehicle.	Licensed restaurant. Café.
Free audio guide in 6 languages. Guided tours available.	
P Ample (except Jun-Oct)	Teachers' pack.	Guide dogs only.

The Georgian House, 7 Charlotte Square, Edinburgh.

THE GEORGIAN HOUSE

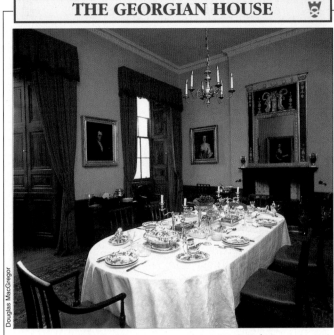

Douglas MacGregor

7 CHARLOTTE SQUARE, EDINBURGH EH2 4DR

Owner: The National Trust for Scotland   Contact: Jacqueline Wyer

Tel/Fax: 0131 226 3318

The north side of Charlotte Square is Robert Adam's masterpiece of urban architecture - a splendid example of the neo-classical 'palace front'. The three floors of No.7, The Georgian House, are delightfully furnished as they would have been around 1796. There is a fascinating array of china and silver, pictures and furniture, gadgets and utensils from the decorative to the purely functional.

Location: OS Ref. NT247 740. In Edinburgh's city centre, NW of Princes St.

Opening Times: 1 Apr (or Good Fri if earlier) - 31 Oct: Mon - Sat, 10am - 5pm, Sun, 2 - 5pm. Last admission 4.30pm.

Admission: Adult £4.20, Child £2.80, Family £11.20. Groups: Adult £3.40, School £1.

i Shop.	P No parking.	No dogs.

GLADSTONE'S LAND

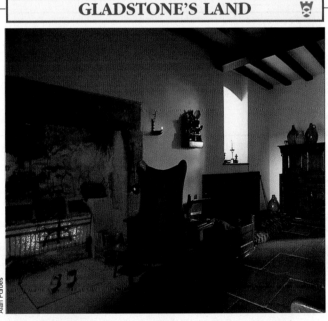

Alan Forbes

477b LAWNMARKET, ROYAL MILE, EDINBURGH EH1 2NT

Owner: The National Trust for Scotland   Contact: Pat Wigston

Tel: 0131 226 5856 **Fax:** 0131 226 4851

Gladstone's Land was the home of a prosperous Edinburgh merchant in the 17th century. On the Royal Mile, near the Castle, it is decorated and furnished with great authenticity to give visitors an impression of life in Edinburgh's Old Town some 300 years ago. Features of the 6-storey building are the painted ceilings and the reconstructed shop both complete with replicas of 17th century goods.

Location: OS Ref. NT255 736. In Edinburgh's Royal Mile, near the castle.

Opening Times: 1 Apr (or Good Fri if earlier) - 31 Oct: Mon - Sat, 10am - 5pm, Sun, 2 - 5pm, last admission 4.30pm.

Admission: Adult £3, Child £2, Family £8. Groups: Adult £2.40, School £1. Groups visits must be booked.

i Shop.	Ground floor suitable.	P No parking.	No dogs.

GOSFORD HOUSE

LONGNIDDRY, EAST LOTHIAN EH32 0PX

Owner: The Earl of Wemyss   *Contact:* The Earl of Wemyss

Tel: 01875 870201 **Fax:** 01875 870376

Robert Adam designed the central block and wings. These wings were later demolished. Two wings were rebuilt in 1890 by William Young. The Big Saloon was burnt in 1940 during military occupation and although unrestored, a new roof was constructed in 1987. The south wing is the family home and contains the famous Marble Hall (Staffordshire alabaster). Parts of the south wing are open. There is a fine collection of paintings and works of art. Surrounding gardens are being redeveloped, extensive policies, artificial ponds, geese and other wildfowl breeding. Greylag geese approach house closely.

Location: OS Ref. NT453 786. Off A198 2m NE of Longniddry.

Opening Times: Jun & Jul: Wed, Sat & Sun, 2 - 5pm.

Admission: Adult £2.50, Child 75p.

♿ Grounds suitable.   **P** Limited   🐕 In grounds, on leads.

HOUSE OF THE BINNS

LINLITHGOW, WEST LOTHIAN EH49 7NA

Owner: The National Trust for Scotland   *Contact:* Tam & Kathleen Dalyell

Tel: 01506 834255

A 17th century house, the home of the Dalyells, one of Scotland's great families, since 1612. Here in 1681, General Tam Dalyell raised the Royal Scots Greys Regiment, named after the colour of their uniforms. The house contains fine Italian-style plasterwork and an outstanding collection of family paintings.

Location: OS Ref. NT051 786. Off A904, 15m W of Edinburgh. 3m E of Linlithgow

Opening Times: House: 1 May - 30 Sept: daily except Fri, 1.30 - 5.30pm, last admission 5pm. Parkland: 1 Apr - 31 Oct: daily, 9.30am - 7pm. 1 Nov - 31 Mar: daily, 9.30am - 4pm, last admission 30mins before close.

Admission: Adult £3.70, Child £2.50, Family £9.90. Groups: Adult £3, School £1. Group visits must be booked.

♿ Ground floor & grounds suitable. WCs.   **P** Limited.   🐕 Guide dogs only.

HAILES CASTLE

Tel: 0131 668 8800

East Linton

Owner: Historic Scotland

Beautifully-sited ruin incorporating a fortified manor of the 13th century. It was extended in the 14th and 15th centuries. There are two vaulted pit prisons.

Location: OS Ref. NT575 758. 1½ m SW of East Linton. 4m E of Haddington. S of A1.

Opening Times: All year.

Admission: Free.

HARBURN HOUSE

See page 318 for full page entry.

HOPETOUN HOUSE

See page 319 for full page entry

INVERESK LODGE GARDEN

Tel: 01721 722502

24 Inveresk Village, Musselburgh, East Lothian EH21 7TE

Owner: The National Trust for Scotland   **Contact:** Head Gardener

Small garden in grounds of 17th century house, with large selection of plants. House closed.

Location: OS Ref. NT348 718. A6124, S of Musselburgh, 6m E of Edinburgh.

Opening Times: 1 Apr - 30 Sept: Mon - Fri, 10am - 4.30pm, Sat & Sun 2 - 5pm. 1 Oct - 31 Mar: Mon - Fri, 10am - 4.30pm, Sun 2 - 5pm.

Admission: £1 (honesty box).

♿ Grounds suitable.   **P** Limited.   🐕 No dogs.

LAURISTON CASTLE

Tel: 0131 336 2060 **Fax:** 0131 312 7165

Cramond Road South, Edinburgh EH4 5QD

Owner: City of Edinburgh Council   **Contact:** Robin Barnes

A beautiful house overlooking the Firth of Forth. The oldest part is a 16th century tower house. William Burn designed the early 19th century additions, which were modernised and furnished around 1900 by the important Edinburgh interior designer William Reid. The Reids also used the house to display their collections of furnishings.

Location: OS Ref. NT203 761. Between Davidsons Mains and Cramond, NW Edinburgh.

Opening Times: 1 Apr - 31 Oct: daily except Fri, 11am - 1pm and 2 - 5pm. 1 Nov - 31 Mar: Sat & Sun, 2 - 4pm. Admission by guided tour only.

Admission: Adult £4, Conc. £3.

♿ Grounds suitable. WC.   🚶 Compulsory.   🐕 Guide dogs only.

House of the Binns, Linlithgow.

Harvey Wood

LENNOXLOVE HOUSE

HADDINGTON, EAST LOTHIAN EH41 4NZ

Owner: His Grace the Duke of Hamilton   Contact: House Administrator

Tel: 01620 823720   **Fax:** 01620 825112

Home of the Duke of Hamilton. The 14th century keep houses a death mask said to be that of Mary Queen of Scots, a silver casket which once contained incriminating letters that helped send Mary to her death, and a sapphire ring given to her by Lord John Hamilton. The 17th century part of the house contains the Hamilton Palace collection of pictures, furniture and porcelain.

Location: OS Ref. NT515 721. 20m SE of Edinburgh, near Haddington.

Opening Times: Easter - end Oct: Wed, Sat & Sun, 2 - 4.30pm. Guided tours. Please check if house is open on a Sat before arriving.

Admission: Adult £3.50, Child £1.75. Group charges on application.

i Shop. No photography.	**X** Wedding receptions.	☕ Tearoom.
🕴 Compulsory.	**P** Ample.	

NEWLISTON
Tel: 0131 333 3231   **Fax:** 0131 335 3596

Kirkliston, West Lothian EH29 9EB

Owner: Mrs Caroline Maclachlan   **Contact:** Mrs C Maclachlan

Late Robert Adam house. Costumes on display. 18th century designed landscape, rhododendrons, azaleas and water features. On Sundays tea is in the Edinburgh Cookery School in the William Adam Coach House. Also on Sundays there is a ride-on steam model railway from 2 - 5pm.

Location: OS Ref. NT110 735. 8m W of Edinburgh, 3m S of Forth Road Bridge, off B800.

Opening Times: 1 May - 4 Jun: Wed - Sun, 2 - 6pm. Also by appointment.

Admission: Adult £1, Child/OAP 50p, Student £1.

♿ Grounds suitable.	☕ Available.	🐕 In grounds, on leads.

PALACE OF HOLYROODHOUSE
Tel: 0131 556 1096 (24hrs)

Edinburgh EH8 8DX

Owner: HM The Queen   **Contact:** The Superintendent

The Palace stands against the backdrop of Salisbury Crag. The Palace retains a modern appeal appropriate to a Royal residence still in regular use.

Location: OS Ref. NT269 739. Central Edinburgh, E end of Royal Mile.

Opening Times: 1 Apr - 31 Oct: daily, 9.30am - 5.15pm (last adm.). 1 Nov - 31 Mar: daily 9.30am - 3.45pm (last adm.). Closed: 10 Apr, 12 - 23 May, 24 Jun - 7 Jul, 25/26 Dec.

Admission: Adult £5.30, Child (under 17) £2.60, OAP £3.70, Family £13.

i Shop.	♿ House suitable.	**P** Ample.	🐕 Guide dogs only.

PARLIAMENT HOUSE
Tel: 0131 225 2595

Parliament Square, Royal Mile, Edinburgh   **Contact:** Reception Desk at Door 11

Supreme Court for Scotland, adjacent exhibition detailing the history of Pparliament House and its important features.

Location: OS Ref. NT258 736. In the centre of Edinburgh's Royal Mile.

Opening Times: All year: Mon - Fri, 9am - 6pm.

Admission: Free.

LINLITHGOW PALACE

LINLITHGOW, WEST LOTHIAN EH49 7AL

Owner: Historic Scotland   Contact: The Steward

Tel: 01506 842896

The magnificent remains of a great royal palace set in its own park and beside Linlithgow Loch. A favoured residence of the Stewart monarchs, James V and his daughter Mary Queen of Scots were born here. Bonnie Prince Charlie stayed here during his bid to regain the British crown.

Location: OS Ref. NT003 774. In the centre of Linlithgow off the M9.

Opening Times: Apr - Sept: daily, 9.30am - 6.30pm. Oct - Mar: Mon - Sat, 9.30am - 4.30pm, Sun 2 - 4.30pm. Last ticket 30 mins before closing.

Admission: Adult £2.30, Child £1, OAP/Student £1.75. 10% discount for groups of 10+. Free pre-booked school visits.

i Shop. Picnic area.	**X** Private evening hire.	♿ Partially suitable.
🕴 By arrangement.	**P** Ample for cars.	👥 Teachers' pack.
🐕 In grounds, on leads.		

PRESTON MILL

EAST LINTON, EAST LOTHIAN EH40 3DS

Owner: The National Trust for Scotland   Contact: Property Manager

Tel: 01620 860426

For centuries there has been a mill on this site and the present one operated commercially until 1957. While the interior of the mill is exciting, the exterior is extremely evocative and much favoured by artists who come from near and far to paint the attractive old buildings, with their red pantile roofs, fringed by the tranquillity of the mill pond with its ever present ducks.

Location: OS Ref. NT590 770. Off the A1, in East Linton, 23m E of Edinburgh.

Opening Times: Good Fri - Easter Mon, 1 May - 30 Sept: Mon - Sat, 11am - 1pm and 2 - 5pm, Sun 1.30 - 5pm. Weekends in Oct: 1.30 - 4pm, last admission 20mins before close morning and afternoon.

Admission: Adult £2, Child £1.30, Family £5.30. Group: Adult £1.60, School £1. Group visits must book.

i Shop.	♿ Grounds suitable. WC.	**P** Limited.	🐕 Guide dogs only.

Scotland
Edinburgh

ROSSLYN CHAPEL

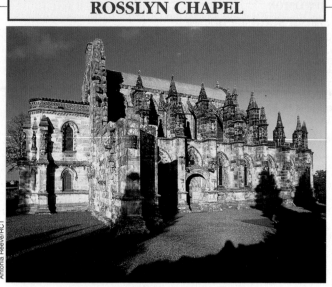

Antonia Reeve/RCT

ROSLIN, MIDLOTHIAN EH25 9PU

Owner: The Earl of Rosslyn   *Contact: Stuart Beattie*

Tel: 0131 440 2159 **Fax:** 0131 440 1979 **e-mail:** rosslynch@aol.com
www: rosslynchapel.org.uk

This most remarkable of churches was founded in 1446 by William St Clair, Prince of Orkney. Set in the woods of Roslin Glen and overlooking the River Esk, the Chapel is renowned for its richly carved interior and world famous apprentice pillar. Visitors to the chapel can enjoy a walk in some of Scotland's most romantic scenery. As Sir Walter Scott wrote, 'A morning of leisure can scarcely be anywhere more delightfully spent than in the woods of Rosslyn'. The chapel is available for weddings throughout the year.

Location: OS Ref. NT275 630. 6m S of Edinburgh off A701. Follow B7006.

Opening Times: All year: Mon - Sat, 10am - 5pm, Sun, 12 - 4.45pm.

Admission: Adult £2.50, Child £1, Conc. £2. 10% discount for groups of 20-40.

| i | Shop | ও | Chapel. Grounds suitable. WC. |
| | Tearoom. | P | Limited for coaches. |

ROYAL BOTANIC GARDEN   **Tel:** 0131 552 7171 **Fax:** 0131 552 0382

20A Inverleith Row, Edinburgh EH3 5LR   **Contact:** Angela Kilday

Scotland's premier garden. Discover the wonders of the plant kingdom in over 70 acres of beautifully landscaped grounds including the world-famous Rock Garden, the Pringle Chinese Collection and the amazing Glasshouse Experience featuring Britain's tallest palmhouse.

Location: OS Ref. NT249 751. Off A902, 1m N of city centre.

Opening Times: Daily (except 25 Dec & 1 Jan): open from 9.30am. Closing: Feb 5pm; Mar 6pm; Apr - Aug 7pm; Sept 6pm; Oct 5pm; Nov - Jan 4pm.

Admission: Free. Donations welcome.

i	Shop. Plant centre. Conference facilities. Corporate hospitality.	X	Wedding receptions.
ও	Grounds suitable.		Licensed restaurant.	⋏	Compulsory.	P	Ample.
	Educational programme. Teachers' pack.		Guide dogs only.

ST GILES' CATHEDRAL   **Tel:** 0131 225 9442 **Fax:** 0131 220 4763

Royal Mile, Edinburgh EH1 1RE
Owner: St Giles' Cathedral   **Contact:** Mrs Kirsty Nicol

St Giles' Cathedral dates from the twelfth century and is central to Scotland's turbulent history. This beautiful building was the church of John Knox during the Reformation and has many forms and royal connections. It is notable for its fine stained glass, magnificent organ and the exquisite Thistle Chapel. Guides on duty at all times for formal and informal visits.

Location: OS Ref. NT258 736. In the centre of Edinburgh's Royal Mile.

Opening Times: Easter - Mid Sept: Mon - Fri, 9am -7pm, Sat, 9am - 5pm, Sun 1 - 5pm. Mid Sept - Easter: Mon - Sat, 9am - 5pm, Sun, 1 - 5pm.

Admission: Admission free - donation of £1 per head suggested.

| i | Shop. | ও | Partially suitable. | ⋏ | By arrangement. | P | Public parking close by. |
| | Dogs welcome in the church. | | Religious wedding ceremonies. |

ST MARY'S CATHEDRAL   **Tel:** 0131 225 6293 **Fax:** 0131 225 3181

Edinburgh EH12 5AW   **Contact:** Cathedral Secretary

Neo-Gothic grandeur in the classical new town.

Location: OS Ref. NT241 735. ½m W of west end of Princes Street.

Opening Times: 7.30am - 6pm. Sun services: 8am, 10.30am and 3.30pm. Weekday services: 7.30am, 1.05pm and 5.30pm. Sat service: 7.30am.

Admission: Free

| ও | Suitable. WCs. | P | No parking. | | Guide dogs only. |

SCOTTISH NATIONAL PORTRAIT GALLERY   **Tel:** 0131 624 6200

1 Queen Street, Edinburgh EH2 1JD   **Contact:** Ronald Kerr

Unique visual history of Scotland.

Location: OS Ref. NT256 742. At E end of Queen Street, 300yds N of Princes Street.

Opening Times: All year: Mon - Fri, 10am - 5pm. Sun, 2 - 5pm.

Admission: Free.

| i | Shop. | ও | Suitable. WCs. | | Café. | | Guide dogs only. |

STEVENSON HOUSE   **Tel:** 01620 823217

Haddington, East Lothian EH41 4PU
Owner: Brown Dunlop Country Houses Trust   **Contact:** Mr A C H Dunlop

The house dates from the 13th century, partially destroyed on several occasions. Restored about 1560 and the present house dates mainly from this period.

Location: OS Ref. NT544 748. 20m from Edinburgh. 1½ m S of A1, 2m E of Haddington.

Opening Times: 4 Jul - 2 Aug 1998: daily except Fris: Guided tours lasting approx 1 hr at 3pm. Other times by arrangement.

Admission: Adult £2, Child (under 14) £1. Garden: £1 (payable into box at gate).

TANTALLON CASTLE

BY NORTH BERWICK, EAST LOTHIAN EH39 5PN

Owner: Historic Scotland   *Contact: The Steward*

Tel: 01620 892727

Set on the edge of the cliffs, looking out to the Bass Rock, this formidable castle was a stronghold of the powerful Douglas family. The castle has earthwork defences and a massive 80-foot high 14th century curtain wall. Interpretive displays include a replica gun.

Location: OS67 Ref. NT595 850. 3m E of North Berwick off the A198.

Opening Times: Apr - Sept: daily, 9.30am - 6.30pm. Oct - Mar: Mon - Sat, 9.30am - 6.30pm (but closed Thur pm & all day Fri), Sun 2 - 4.30pm.

Admission: Adult £2.30, Child £1, Conc. £1.75. 10% discount for groups of 10+.

| i | Shop. Picnic area. | ও | Partially suitable. | P | Ample. |
| | Pre-booked school visits free. Teachers' pack. | | In grounds, on leads. |

EDINBURGH

HUDSON'S

EDINBURGH
City, Coast & Countryside

Scotland
Edinburgh

Pele Towers:

A current term for a defensive tower house. In fourteenth century Scotland a pele was a defence ditch with an earth and timber rampart, and from this a new form of building evolved: the tower house, in which the usual rooms of the period were unconventionally arranged – the floor plan was upended, to become vertical instead of horizontal – for ease of defence. Some 150 tower houses survive in Cumberland and Northumberland; they consist of three storeys, with a vaulted basement for cattle or storage, an attached ground floor hall, a chamber on the first floor, and a smaller chamber above. Most were built around the time of the accession of James I (1603–25) and abandoned after the final Act of Union with Scotland of 1707. Pele houses, often known as bastle houses, were scaled-down versions of tower houses, built by farmers during the same period.

Tower houses were not confined to the Scottish borders: Longthorpe in Cambridgeshire dates from c.1250; one at Halloughton in Nottinghamshire was built c.1400; and Prior Overton built a brick tower house at Repton, Derbyshire in 1437 as part of a priory of Austin Canons. Curiously, these English examples share the common factor of having been built for clerics; the reason (if any) is so far undiscovered.

Extract from; "Life in the Country House" by David N Durant (published by John Murray), PB£15.99.

WINTON HOUSE

PENCAITLAND, TRANENT, EAST LOTHIAN EH34 5AT

Owner: *The Winton Trust*   **Contact:** *Francis Ogilvy*

Tel: 01620 824986   **Fax:** 01620 823961

A masterpiece of the Scottish Renaissance with famous stone twisted chimneys and magnificent plaster ceilings. A family home, still after 500 years with many treasures inside, including paintings by some of Scotland's most notable artists, fine furniture and a family exhibition of costumes and photographs. Specimen trees and terraced gardens.

Location: OS Ref. NT439 695. 14m SE of Edinburgh off the A1 at Tranent. Lodge gates S of New Winton (B6355) and in Pencaitland (A6093).

Opening Times: Open Day 18 April, 2 - 6pm and other times by prior arrangement.

Admission: Adult £3.50, Child/Conc. £2. Groups should pre-book (min. 10+).

i Plant centre. Corporate hospitality.	**✗** Wedding receptions.
& Suitable. WCs.	**∆** Guided tours only.	**P** Ample.
ᴧ Educational programme available.	**⚇** In grounds, on leads.

SPECIAL EVENTS:
THROUGHOUT THE YEAR: Musical evenings, dinners, product launches, etc.

Charlotte Square, Edinburgh.

KELBURN
Largs

KELBURN has been the home of the Boyle family, later the Earls of Glasgow, since the 13th century and it continues to be used as a family home.

The original Norman Keep was extended in 1580, and the magnificent 1700 William and Mary Mansion House was added by the 1st Earl of Glasgow, whose title was bestowed as reward for his role in the Act of Union. The final addition is the Victorian wing of 1879 with its original William Morris wallpapers.

The essential charm of the castle is its intimate lived-in atmosphere, its varied styles and stunning location.

The beautiful and extensive grounds are used for the Country Centre, and include the dramatic glen with woodland trails, waterfalls, and deep gorges. The peaceful walled garden 'The Plaisance' is dominated by two 1,000 year old yew trees and its exotic shrubs benefit from the Gulf Stream climate. Historical features include the Robert Adam Monument, 18th century Sundial and an Ice House.

For the active, there is horse riding, adventure courses, young children's stockade and soft play area.

The Secret Forest provides a series of exotic follies and fairytale features, "a unique attraction and a delight for all ages".

CONTACT

David Shields - Development Manager Kelburn Castle & Country Centre South Offices Fairlie, Nr Largs, Ayrshire KA29 0BE

Tel: Country Centre: (01475) 568685

Castle: (01475) 568204

Fax: Country Centre: (01475) 568121

Castle: (01475) 568328

LOCATION

OS Ref. NS210 580

M8 Edinburgh to Glasgow, M8 Glasgow to Greenock, A78 to Largs, 2m S of Largs.

Rail: Largs Station 2m.

Air: Glasgow 25m. Prestwick International 28m.

Bus: A78 main bus route to Ayr, stop adjacent to property.

Taxis: A2B taxis (01475) 673976.

CONFERENCE/FUNCTION		
ROOM	SIZE	MAX CAPACITY
Drawing Rm	33' x 24'	70
Dining Rm	30' x 20'	60

i Shop. Corporate events, clay pigeon shoots, exhibitions, business meetings, conferences, fashion shows, filming, product launches, nature activities and barbecues. Helicopter landing pad. Additional rooms for non-plenary sessions.

Full catering facilities for functions / conferences.

Visitors may alight at the entrance. WC. Some stairs.

Licensed restaurant and a tearoom. Groups can book, (special rates).

Max. 25, no additional cost, tour time 45 mins. Lectures on castle, grounds and history if booked. Ranger tour of grounds.

P Ample. Coach passengers can alight at the forecourt, coach park 5 - 10 mins walk.

Welcome. Teachers free, ratio of 1:10. Ranger service for guided walks and nature activities. Worksheets, pets' corner, pony rides/treks, adventure play areas.

In grounds, on leads.

A 1 single & 7 double.

OPENING TIMES

SUMMER

Castle

July, August & September Tours: 1.45pm, 3pm & 4.15pm. (Except when there are afternoon functions).

Tours can be arranged at other times of the year.

Country Centre & Gardens

Easter - end October Daily: 10am - 6pm.

WINTER

Castle

By arrangement only.

Country Centre

End October - Easter 11am - 5pm Grounds only.

ADMISSION

SUMMER

Castle tours

Per person £1.50
Student...................£1.20

(Does not include entry to Centre)

Country Centre

Adult £4.50
Child £3.00
Conc.......................£2.50
Groups (min 12)
Adult £3.00
Child £2.00
Conc.......................£1.75

SPECIAL EVENTS

• **APR 25 - 26:**
Woodcraft & Forestry Fair.

• **MAY 10:**
Horse Show & Gymkhana.

• **MAY 23 - 25:**
Festival of Flight.

BOTANIC GARDENS

Tel: 0141 334 2422   **Fax:** 0141 339 6964

730 Great Western Road, Glasgow G12 0UE

Owner: Glasgow City Council   **Contact:** The General Manager

Location: OS Ref. NS568 674.

Opening Times: All year: 7am - dusk. For glasshouse opening times please ring.

Admission: Free.

- Suitable. WCs.
- By arrangement.
- No parking.
- Educational programme available. Teachers' pack.
- In grounds, on leads.

BOTHWELL CASTLE

Tel: 01698 816894

Uddingston, Strathclyde

Owner: Historic Scotland   **Contact:** The Custodian

The largest and finest 13th century stone castle in Scotland, much fought over during the Wars of Independence. Part of the original circular keep survives, but most of the castle dates from the 14th and 15th centuries. In a beautiful setting overlooking the Clyde.

Location: OS Ref. NS688 593. 1m NW of Bothwell. At Uddingston off the B7071.

Opening Times: 1 Apr - 30 Sept: daily, 9.30am - 6.30pm, last ticket 6pm. 1 Oct - 31 Mar: Mon - Sat, 9.30am - 4.30pm, Sun, 2 - 4.30pm, last ticket 4pm. Closed Thur pm & Fri in winter.

Admission: Adult £1.80, Child 75p, Conc £1.30.

BURRELL COLLECTION

Tel: 0141 331 1854

Pollok Country Park, 2060 Pollokshaws Road, Glasgow G2 3EH

Owner: Glasgow Museums   **Contact:** Mr John Robertson

An internationally renowned, outstanding collection of art.

Location: OS Ref. NS560 615.

Opening Times: All year: Mon - Sat, 10am - 5pm. Sun, 11am - 5pm (closed Tuesdays).

Admission: Free.

- Shop. Conference facilities. No photography.
- Wedding receptions.
- Partially suitable. WCs.
- Licensed restaurant.
- By arrangement.
- Ample.
- Educational programme available.
- Guide dogs only.

CHATELHERAULT HUNTING LODGE   **Tel:** 01698 426213 **Fax:** 01698 4215327

Ferniegair, by Hamilton ML3 7UE

Owner: South Lanarkshire Council   **Contact:** Morvern Anderson

Built for James, 5th Duke of Hamilton, designed by William Adam, completed around 1744. Set in 500 acre country park.

Location: OS Ref. NS737 540. W side of A72, 1¹/₂ m SE of Hamilton.

Opening Times: Mon - Sat, 10am - 5pm. Sun 12 noon - 5pm (Easter Sun - end Sept, 5.30pm). Closed Christmas and New Year.

- Shop. Plant centre. Conference facilities. Corporate hospitality.
- Wedding receptions.
- Ground floor & grounds suitable. WCs.
- Tearoom.
- By arrangement.
- Ample.
- Educational programme available.
- In grounds, on leads. Guide dogs only in house.

COLZIUM HOUSE & WALLED GARDEN

Tel/Fax: 01236 823281

Colzium-Lennox Estate, off Stirling Road, Kilsyth G65 0RZ

Owner: North Lanarkshire Council   **Contact:** Charlie Whyte

A walled garden with an extensive collection of conifers, rare shrubs and trees. Kilsyth Heritage Museum, curling pond, tearoom, picnic tables, pitch and putt, woodland walks.

Location: OS Ref. NS762 786. Off A803 Banknock to Kirkintilloch Road. ¹/₂ m E of Kilsyth.

Opening Times: Walled garden: Easter - Sept: daily, 12 - 7pm. Sept - Mar: Sat/Sun, 12 - 4pm. Pitch and putt: Apr - Sept, daily.

Admission: Free. Charge for pitch and putt.

COREHOUSE

Tel: 01555 663126 or 0131 667 1514

Lanark ML11 9TQ

Owner: The Trustees of the late Lt Col A J E Cranstoun MC   **Contact:** Estate Office

Designed by Sir Edward Blore and built in the 1820s, Corehouse is a pioneering example of the Tudor Architectural Revival in Scotland.

Location: OS Ref. NS882 416. On S bank of the Clyde above the village of Kirkfieldbank.

Opening Times: 5 - 20 Aug: for guided tours at 1 & 2pm. 29 Aug - 16 Sept: for guided tours at 11am & 4pm. Closed Mon & Tue.

Admission: Adult £4, Child (under 14) £2, OAP £2.

CRAIGNETHAN CASTLE

Tel: 01555 860364

Lanark, Strathclyde

Owner: Historic Scotland   **Contact:** The Custodian

In a picturesque setting overlooking the River Nethan and defended by a wide and deep ditch with an unusual caponier, a stone vaulted artillery chamber, unique in Britain.

Location: OS Ref. NS815 463. 5¹/₂ m WNW of Lanark off the A72. ¹/₂ m footpath to W.

Opening Times: 1 Mar - 31 Oct: daily, 9.30am - 6.30pm. Closed Thur pm & Fri in Mar & Oct.

Admission: Adult £1.80, Child 75p, Conc. £1.30.

FINLAYSTONE

LANGBANK, RENFREWSHIRE PA14 6TJ

Owner: Mr Arthur MacMillan   *Contact:* Mrs Jane MacMillan

Tel: 01475 540285   **Fax:** 01475 540285

Overlooking the River Clyde, Finlaystone was the home of the Earls of Glencairn for 4 centuries and is now the home of the Chief of the Clan MacMillan. Visitors to this delightful country estate can explore beautiful gardens and woodlands, and have the opportunity to view a unique doll collection in the visitor centre which also houses natural history, Celtic art and Clan MacMillan displays and information. Fun for all the family with children's play areas and ranger service.

Location: OS Ref. NS390 730. On A8, 7m W of Glasgow airport.

Opening Times: House: Apr - Aug: Sun pm guided tours or groups any time by appointment. Grounds; all year, 10.30am - 5pm. Refreshments & visitor centre: Apr - Sept: daily, 11am - 4.30pm.

Admission: Grounds: Adult £2.40, Child/Conc. £1.40. Extra for House: Adult £1.50, Child/Conc. £1. 'Dolly Mixture': 50p.

- Shop. Corporate hospitality.
- Ground floor & grounds suitable. WC.
- Tearoom.
- By arrangement.
- Ample.
- Educational programme available.
- In grounds, on leads.

GLASGOW CATHEDRAL

Tel: 0141 552 6891

Glasgow

Owner: Historic Scotland   **Contact:** The Custodian

The only Scottish mainland medieval cathedral to have survived the Reformation complete. Built over the tomb of St Kentigern. Notable features in this splendid building are the elaborately vaulted crypt, the stone screen of the early 15th century and the unfinished Blackadder Aisle.

Location: OS Ref. NS603 656. E end of city centre. In central Glasgow.

Admission: Free.

Glasgow Cathedral.

GREENBANK

CLARKSTON, GLASGOW G76 8RB

Owner: The National Trust for Scotland　　*Contact:* Mr Jim May

Tel: 0141 639 3281

Be allured by the beautiful bronze water nymph 'Foam' whose exquisite form complements the circular pool and surrounding greenery. There are several small gardens including a parterre layout illustrating different aspects of gardening. The larger borders contain a wide range of shrub roses and perennial and annual flowers.

Location: OS Ref. NS563 566. Flenders Road, off Mearns Road, Clarkston. Off M77 and A726, 6m S of Glasgow city centre.

Opening Times: All year: daily, 9.30am - sunset, closed 25/26 Dec & 1/2 Jan. Shop & tearoom: 1 Apr - 31 Oct, daily, 11am - 5pm. 1 Nov - 31 Mar: Sat & Sun, 2 - 4pm. House: 1 Apr - 31 Oct: Sun only 2 - 4pm & during special events (subject to functions in progress).

Admission: Adult £3, Child £2, Family £8. Groups: Adult £2.40, School £1.

ⓘ Shop.   ♿ Grounds suitable. WC.   ☕ Tearoom.   🐕 In grounds, on leads.

Greenbank, Glasgow.

John K Wilkie

NEWARK CASTLE 🏛 　　**Tel:** 01475 741858

Port Glasgow, Strathclyde

Owner: Historic Scotland　　**Contact:** The Custodian

The oldest part of the castle is a tower built soon after 1478 with a detached gatehouse, by George Maxwell. The main part was added in 1597 - 99 in a most elegant style. Enlarged in the 16th century by his descendent, the wicked Patrick Maxwell who murdered two of his neighbours.

Location: OS Ref. NS329 744. In Port Glasgow on the A8.

Opening Times: 1 Apr - 30 Sept: daily, 9.30am - 6.30pm. Last ticket 6pm.

Admission: Adult £1.80, Child 75p, Conc. £1.30.

HUTCHESONS' HALL ♛ 　　**Tel:** 0141 552 8391 **Fax:** 0141 552 7031

158 Ingram Street, Glasgow G1 1EJ

Owner: The National Trust for Scotland　　**Contact:** Carla Sparrow

Described as one of Glasgow city centre's most elegant buildings, the Hall by David Hamilton, replaced the earlier 1641 hospice founded by George and Thomas Hutcheson. Reconstructed in 1876, the building is now 'A-Listed' as being of national importance.

Location: OS Ref NS594 652. Glasgow city centre, near SE corner of George Square.

Opening Times: Visitor centre/shop/function hall: all year (except BHs & 24 Dec - 6 Jan), Mon - Sat, 10am - 5pm. (Hall on view subject to functions in progress). Shop closed for stocktaking 2/3 Nov.

Admission: Free.

ⓘ Shop. Conferences.   ✗ For up to 120.   ♿ Stairlift. WC.   🚶 By arrangement.

MOTHERWELL HERITAGE CENTRE 　　**Tel:** 01698 251000

High Street, Motherwell

Owner: North Lanarkshire Council　　**Contact:** The Manager

Multimedia exhibition and other displays of local history.

Location: OS Ref. NS750 570.

Opening Times: All year: Mon - Sat, 10am - 6pm. Sun, 12 - 5pm. (closed 25/26 Dec & 1 Jan).

Admission: For Multimedia only: Adult £2, Child £1 for. Rest of building free.

ⓘ Shop. Conferences.   ♿ Suitable. WC.   ✗ Not available.   Ⓟ Ample.

🚸 School visits welcome.   🐕 Guide dogs only.

MUGDOCK COUNTRY PARK 　　**Tel:** 0141 956 6100

Craigallian Road, Milngavie, Glasgow G62 8EL

Owner: Stirling and East Dunbartonshire Councils　　**Contact:** Ian Amott

740 acres. Visitor Centre.

Location: OS Ref. NS560 770. 8m NNW of Glasgow, 1/2m W of A81.

Opening Times: All year: daily.

Admission: Free. Car park: Summer, 9am - 9pm. Winter, 9am - 5.30pm.

ⓘ Shop. Conference facilities.   ✗ Wedding receptions.   ♿ Suitable. WC.

☕ Tearoom.   🚶 By arrangement.   Ⓟ Ample.

🚸 Educational programme available. Teachers' pack available.

🐕 In grounds, on leads.

NEW LANARK

NEW LANARK MILLS, LANARK, S. LANARKSHIRE ML11 9DB

Owner: New Lanark Conservation Trust　　*Contact:* Owen Mullen

Tel: 01555 661345 **Fax:** 01555 665738

The historic village of New Lanark is a nominated World Heritage Site. Surrounded by woodlands, and the Falls of Clyde, this cotton spinning village was founded in 1785 and made famous by social pioneer Robert Owen. Beautifully restored as both a living community and attraction, its history is interpreted in the award-winning Visitor Centre. Accommodation available, please ring.

Location: OS Ref. NS880 426. 1m S of Lanark.

Opening Times: All year: daily, 11am - 5pm (except 25 Dec & 1/2 Jan).

Admission: Visitor Centre: Adult £3.75, Child/OAP £2.50. Groups: 1 free/10 booked.

ⓘ Shop. Conference facilities. Corporate hospitality.   ✗ Wedding receptions.

♿ Partially suitable. WC. Visitor Centre is wheelchair friendly.   ☕ Restaurant.

🚶 By arrangement.   Ⓟ Ample (5 min walk)   🐕 In grounds, on leads.

POLLOK HOUSE

Tel: 0141 649 7151 **Fax:** 0141 649 0823

Glasgow G43 1AT

Owner: City of Glasgow District Council   **Contact:** The Administrator

Early 18th century house, containing the remarkable Stirling Maxwell collection of Spanish paintings. Nearby in Pollok Park is the Burrell Collection.

Location: OS Ref. NS550 616. 2m SW of Glasgow city centre via M77 & A736.

Opening Times: Unconfirmed for 1998, please ring before visiting.

Admission: Free.

ST MARY'S CATHEDRAL

Tel/Fax: 0141 339 6691

300 Great Western Road, Glasgow G4 9JB   **Contact:** Rev Griff Dines

Fine Gothic Revival church by Sir George Gilbert Scott, with outstanding contemporary murals by Gwyneth Leech. Regular concerts and exhibitions.

Location: OS Ref. NS578 669. $^{1}/_{4}$ m after the Dumbarton A82 exit from M8 motorway.

Opening Times: Mon - Fri, 9.30am - 5.45pm, Sat, 9.30am - 12 noon. Sun services: 8.30am, 10am, 12 noon & 6.30pm. Weekday services: please telephone. Bookshop: Mon - Fri, 10am - 5pm.

| i | Bookshop. | ♿ | Partially suitable. | △ | By arrangement. | P | Limited for cars. |

⚔ School visits by arrangement.

Glasgow and Clyde Valley TB.

THE TENEMENT HOUSE

145 BUCCLEUCH STREET, GLASGOW G3 6QN

Owner: The National Trust for Scotland   *Contact:* Miss Lorna Hepburn

Tel: 0141 333 0183

A typical Victorian tenement flat of 1892, and fascinating time capsule of the first half of the 20th century. It was the home of an ordinary Glasgow shorthand typist, who lived up this 'wally close' for more than 50 years. It is exceptional as the gaslit flat retains many of its original fittings and items such as her mother's sewing machine.

Location: OS Ref. NS583 662. Garnethill, (three streets N of Sauchiehall Street, near Charing Cross), Glasgow.

Opening Times: 1 Mar - 31 Oct; daily, 2 - 5pm, last admission 4.30pm. Weekday morning visits by educational and other groups (max 15) by booking only.

Admission: Adult £3, Child £2, Family £8. Groups: Adult £2.40, School £1.

| ♿ | Not suitable. | P | Very limited. |

WEAVER'S COTTAGE

Tel: 01505 705588

Shuttle Street, Kilbarchan, Renfrew PA10 2JG

Owner: The National Trust for Scotland   **Contact:** Grace Murray

Typical cottage of an 18th century handloom weaver contains looms, weaving equipment and domestic utensils. Attractive cottage garden. Regular weaving demonstrations.

Location: OS Ref. NS402 633. Off A740 (off M8) and A737, at The Cross, Kilbarchan, (nr Johnstone, Paisley) 12m SW of Glasgow.

Opening Times: Good Fri - 30 Sept; daily, 1.30 - 5.30pm. Weekends in Oct: 1.30 - 5.30pm. Last admission 5pm.

Admission: Adult £2, Child £1.30, Family £5.30. Groups: Adult £1.60, School £1.

City Chambers, Glasgow.

SUMMERLEE HERITAGE PARK

Tel: 01236 431261

Heritage Way, Coatbridge, North Lanarkshire ML5 1QD

Owner: North Lanarkshire Council   **Contact:** The Manager

22 acre site, replica mine, miners' cottages, steam trains and exhibitions.

Location: OS Ref. NS730 650.

Opening Times: All Year: daily, 10am - 5pm. (closed 25/26 Dec & 1/2 Jan).

Admission: Free. Tram ride: Adult 50p, Child 30p.

i	Shop. Conference facilities.	X	Functions, not weddings.	&#9855;	Suitable. WCs.
&#9749;	Tearoom.	&#9651;	By arrangement.	P	Ample.
&#9876;	Teachers' pack available.	&#128021;	Guide dogs only.		

The Tenement House, Glasgow.

BLAIR CASTLE
Pitlochry

BLAIR CASTLE has been the ancient home and fortress of the Earls and Dukes of Atholl for over 725 years. Its central location makes it easily accessible from all major Scottish centres in less than two hours.

The Castle has known the splendour of Royal visitations, submitted to occupation by opposing forces on no less than four occasions, suffered siege and changed its architectural appearance to suit the taste of successive generations.

Today 32 rooms of infinite variety display beautiful furniture, fine collections of paintings, arms, armour, china, costumes, lace and embroidery, masonic regalia, Jacobite relics and other unique treasures giving a stirring picture of Scottish life from the 16th to 20th centuries.

The Duke of Atholl has the unique distinction of having the only remaining private army in Europe - The Atholl Highlanders.

GARDENS

Blair Castle is set in extensive parklands. Near the car and coach parks, there is a picnic area, a deer park and a unique two acre plantation of large trees known as 'Diana's Grove.' It has been said that "it is unlikely that any other two acres in the world contain such a number of different conifers of such heights and of such small age." A restored 18th century garden re-opened to visitors in 1996.

❖

CONTACT

Geoff G Crerar
Tourism Administrator
Blair Castle
Blair Atholl
Pitlochry
Perthshire
PH18 5TL

Tel: (01796) 481207

Fax: (01796) 481487

LOCATION

OS Ref. NN880 660

From Edinburgh 80m, M90 to Perth, A9, follow signs for Blair Castle. 1½ hrs. Trunk Road A9 2m.

Bus: Bus stop 1m in Blair Atholl.

Train: 1m, Blair Atholl Euston-Inverness line.

Taxi: Elizabeth Yule, (01796) 472290.

FUNCTION

ROOM	SIZE	MAX CAPACITY
Ballroom	89' x 35'	400
State Dining Rm	36' x 25'	200
Library	27' x 15'	40

i Fashion shows, garden parties, equestrian events, shows, rallies, filming, highland and charity balls, piping championships, grand piano, helicopter pad, cannon firing by Atholl Highlanders, resident piper, needlework displays. No smoking.

X Buffets, dinners, wedding receptions and banquets.

& Visitors may alight at the entrance. WC and wheelchair.

☕ Two restaurants (no smoking) for tea, snacks and lunches.

K In English, German and French at no extra cost. Max group size 25, tour time 1½ hrs.

P 200 cars, 20 coaches. Coach drivers and couriers free, plus free meal and free prize draw, information pack.

K Welcome, £4 each, primary schools £3 each. Nature walks, deer park, children's games, pony trekking.

🐕 No dogs.

OPENING TIMES

SUMMER
1 April - 30 October
Daily, 10am - 6pm
Last admission 5pm.

WINTER
Closed from
31 October - 31 March.

ADMISSION

House
Adult	£5.50
Child*	£4.00
OAP/Student	£4.50
Family	£17.00
Disabled	£2.00

Groups (min 20, max 40)
Adult	£5.00
Child/Student*	£4.00
OAP	£4.00
Disabled	£2.00

* (Age 5 - 16yrs)

Grounds & Parking
Cars	£2.00
Mini Buses	£5.00
Coaches	£10.00

SPECIAL EVENTS

- **MAY 23:**
  Atholl Highlanders' Parade
- **MAY 24:**
  Blair Castle Highland Games
- **AUG 21 - 24:**
  Bowmore Blair Castle
  International Horse Trials
- **OCT 2 - 4:**
  Special Needlelace Exhibition
- **OCT 31 - NOV 1:**
  Glenfiddich World Piping
  Championships

GLAMIS CASTLE
Glamis, by Forfar, Angus

GLAMIS CASTLE is the family home of the Earls of Strathmore and Kinghorne and has been a royal residence since 1372. It is the childhood home of Her Majesty Queen Elizabeth The Queen Mother, the birthplace of Her Royal Highness The Princess Margaret and the legendary setting of Shakespeare's play *Macbeth*. Although the Castle is open to visitors it remains a family home lived in and loved by the Strathmore family.

The castle, a five-storey 'L' shaped tower block, was originally a royal hunting lodge. It was remodelled in the 17th century and is built of pink sandstone. It contains the Great Hall,

with its magnificent plasterwork ceiling dated 1621, a beautiful family Chapel constructed inside the Castle in 1688, an 18th century billiard room housing what is left of the extensive library once at Glamis, a 19th century dining room containing family portraits and the Royal Apartments which have been used by Her Majesty Queen Elizabeth The Queen Mother.

The castle stands in an extensive park, landscaped towards the end of the 18th Century, and contains the beautiful Italian Garden which reflects the peace and serenity of the castle and grounds.

CONTACT

Lt Col P J Cardwell Moore
(The Administrator)
Estates Office
Glamis Castle
Glamis
by Forfar
Angus
DD8 1RJ

Tel: (01307) 840393

Fax: (01307) 840733

LOCATION

OS Ref. NO386 480

From Edinburgh M90,
A94, 81m.
From Forfar A94, 6m.
From Glasgow 101m.

Motorway: M90.

Rail: Dundee Station 12m.

Air: Dundee Airport 12m.

Taxi: B Morrison
(01575) 572988.

CONFERENCE/FUNCTION		
ROOM	SIZE	MAX CAPACITY
Dining Rm	84 sq.m.	120
Restaurant	140 sq.m.	100
16th century Kitchens		50

ℹ️ Shopping complex. Plant centre. Corporate hospitality. Fashion shoots, archery, clay pigeon shooting, equestrian events, shows, rallies, filming, product launches, highland games, new cricket pavilion, grand piano. No photography in the castle.

✕ The State Rooms are available for grand dinners, lunches and wedding receptions.

♿ Disabled visitors may alight at entrance. Those in wheelchairs will be unable to tour the castle but may visit the two exhibitions. WC.

☕ Self-service, licensed restaurant. Morning coffees, light lunches, afternoon teas.

🚶 All visits are guided, tour time 50 - 60 mins. Tours leave every 10 - 15 mins. Tours in French, German, Italian and Spanish by appointment at no additional cost. Three exhibitions.

🅿️ 500 cars and 20 coaches 200 yds from castle. Coach drivers and couriers admitted free. Beware narrow gates; they are wide enough to take buses (10ft wide).

👨‍👧 Welcome, one teacher free for every 10 children. Nature trail, family exhibition rooms, dolls' house, play park. Glamis Heritage Education Centre in Glamis village. Education pack.

🐕 In grounds, on leads.

OPENING TIMES

29 March - 25 October
Daily, 10.30am - 5.30pm.

July - August
opens 10am

Last admission 4.45pm.

At other times groups welcome, by appointment.

WINTER

By arrangement.

ADMISSION

SUMMER

House & Grounds

Adult	£5.20
Child (5 - 16yrs)	£2.70
OAP/Student	£4.00
Family	£14.00

Groups (min 20)

Adult	£4.70
Child (5 - 16yrs)	£2.40
OAP/Student	£3.50

Grounds only

Adult	£2.40
Child (5 - 16yrs)	£1.30
OAP	£1.30
Disabled	FREE

Groups: Prices as above.

SPECIAL EVENTS

• **JUL:**
Strathmore Vintage
Vehicle Club

• **JUL:**
A Grand Scottish Prom and outdoor picnic concert with spectacular fireworks

PERTHSHIRE
Angus & Dundee and The Kingdom of Fife

HUDSON'S

PERTHSHIRE

Scotland
Perthshire/Fife

SCONE PALACE
Perth

SCONE PALACE, just outside Perth, is the home of the Earls of Mansfield. Here Kenneth MacAlpine united Scotland and in 838AD, placed the stone of Scone upon the Moot Hill which became the Crowning Place of Scottish Kings, including Macbeth and Robert the Bruce. Edward I moved the Coronation Stone to Westminster in 1296.

The Abbey of Scone and the Bishops' Palace were ransacked and burned in 1559. The Gowries built a new Palace in 1580, which was enlarged and embellished around 1804 by the Third Earl and houses a fabulous collection of French furniture, clocks, 16th Century needlework (including bed hangings worked by Mary Queen of Scots),

ivories, objets d'art and Vernis Martin and one of the finest collections of porcelain in the country.

GARDENS

Scone's famous pinetum is a unique collection of rare pines, some of which are over 150 feet high and still growing. There are pleasant walks through 100 acres of wild garden which offer the visitor magnificent displays of daffodils, rhododendrons and azaleas.

There is a fine picnic area, adventure playground and a collection of veteran machinery. A cricket pitch and pavilion in an attractive setting are ideal for a variety of outdoor functions.

CONTACT

The Administrator
Scone Palace
Perth
PH2 6BD
Tel: (01738) 552300
Fax: (01738) 552588

LOCATION

OS Ref. NO114 266

From Edinburgh Forth Bridge M90, A93 1 hr.

Bus: Regular buses from Perth (including open-top tours).

Rail: Perth Station 3m.

Motorway: M90 from Edinburgh.

Taxi: (01738) 636777.

OPENING TIMES

SUMMER
10 April - 12 October
Daily: 9.30am - 5.15pm.

Last admission 4.45pm

Evening tours by appointment.

WINTER
13 October - 1 April 1999
By appointment only.

ADMISSION

SUMMER
Palace & Garden
Adult £5.20
Child* £3.00
OAP........................£4.40
Family £16.00
Groups (min. 20)
Adult £4.70
Child* £2.60
OAP........................£4.00

Grounds only
Adult £2.60
Child* £1.50

*Age 5 - 16yrs

WINTER
Per person................£12.00
(£240 min. payment)

CONFERENCE/FUNCTION		
ROOM	SIZE	MAX CAPACITY
Long Gallery	140' x 20'	200
Queen Victoria's Rm	20' x 20'	35
Drawing Rm	50' x 24'	100

i Shop. Receptions, fashion shows, war games, archery, clay pigeon shooting, equestrian events, garden parties, shows, rallies, filming, shooting, fishing, floodlit tattoos, product launches, highland games, parkland, cricket pitch, airfield, helicopter landing, croquet, speciality lectures, racecourse, polo field, firework displays, adventure playground.

X Grand dinners in state rooms, buffets, receptions, wedding receptions, cocktail parties.

All state rooms on one level, wheelchair access to restaurants. Visitors may alight at entrance. WC.

Two restaurants, teas, lunches, dinners, can be booked, menus upon request, special rates for groups.

Free, guides in rooms, tour time 45 mins. French and German guides available by appointment.

P 500 cars and 15 coaches, groups please book, couriers and coach drivers free meal and admittance.

ABERDOUR CASTLE

Tel: 01383 860519

Aberdour, Fife

Owner: Historic Scotland   **Contact:** The Custodian

A 14th century castle built by the Douglas family. The gallery on the first floor gives an idea of how it was furnished at the time. The castle has a 14th century tower extended in the 16th and 17th centuries, a delightful walled garden and a circular dovecote.

Location: OS Ref. NT193 854. In Aberdour 5m E of the Forth Bridge on the A921.

Opening Times: 1 Apr - 30 Sept: daily, 9.30am - 6.30pm, last ticket 6pm. 1 Oct - 31 Mar: Mon - Sat, 9.30am - 4.30pm, Sun, 2 - 4.30pm, last ticket 4pm. Closed Thur pm & Fri in winter.

Admission: Adult £1.80, Child 75p, Conc. £1.30.

ANGUS FOLK MUSEUM

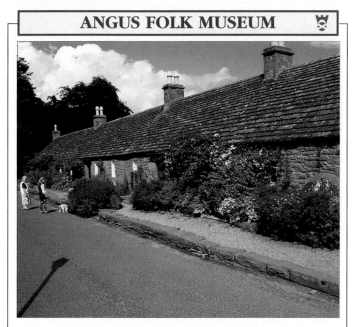

KIRKWYND, GLAMIS, FORFAR, ANGUS DD8 1RT

Owner: The National Trust For Scotland   *Contact:* Kathleen Ager

Tel: 01307 840288   **Fax:** 01307 840233

Where will you find cruisie lamps, pirn winders, cloutie rugs, bannock spades and a thrawcrook? All these fascinating items, and many more, are to be found in the Angus Folk Museum, one of Scotland's finest. The domestic section is housed in six charming 18th century cottages in Kirkwynd, and the agricultural collection is in the farmsteading opposite. The displays inside the building explain and illustrate changes in the Angus countryside in the last 200 years.

Location: OS Ref. NO385 467 Off A94, in Glamis, 5m SW of Forfar.

Opening Times: Good Fri - Easter Mon, 1 May - 30 Sept; daily, 11am - 5pm. Weekends in Oct: 11am - 5pm, last admission 4.30pm.

Admission: Adult £2.40, Child £1.60, Family £6.40. Groups: Adult £1.90, School £1.

ℹ Shop.   ♿ House suitable. WC.   🅿 Limited.   🐕 No dogs.

A Forbes

Angus Folk Museum.

ARBROATH ABBEY

Tel: 01241 878756

Arbroath, Tayside

Owner: Historic Scotland   **Contact:** The Custodian

The substantial ruins of a Tironensian monastery, notably the gate house range and the abbot's house. Arbroath Abbey holds a very special place in Scottish history. It was here in 1320 that Scotland's nobles swore their independence from England in the famous 'Declaration of Arbroath'.

Location: OS Ref. NO644 414. In Arbroath town centre on the A92.

Opening Times: 1 Apr - 30 Sept: daily 9.30am - 6.30pm, last ticket 6pm. 1 Oct - 31 Mar: Mon - Sat, 9.30am - 4.30 pm, Sun 2 - 4.30pm, last ticket 4pm.

Admission: Adult £1.80, Child 75p, Conc. £1.30.

BALGONIE CASTLE

Tel: 01592 750119   **Fax:** 01592 753103

Markinch, Fife KY7 6HQ

Owner: The Laird of Balgonie   **Contact:** The Laird of Balgonie

14th century tower, additions to the building up to 1702. Still lived in by the family. 14th century chapel.

Location: OS Ref. NO313 006. 1/2 m S of A911 Glenrothes - Leven road at Milton of Balgonie on to B921.

Opening Times: All year: daily, 10am - 5pm.

Admission: Adult £3, Child £1.50, OAP £2.

ℹ Corporate hospitality.   ✗ Wedding receptions.   ♿ Partially suitable.

🚶 Compulsory.   🅿 Ample.   👥 Teachers' pack.

🐕 Strictly no dogs. Resident deerhounds.

BALHOUSIE CASTLE (BLACK WATCH MUSEUM)

Tel: 01738 621 281

Hay Street, North Inch Park, Perth

Owner: MOD   **Contact:** Major McKinnell

Regimental museum housed in the castle.

Location: OS Ref. NO115 244. 1/2 m N of town centre, E of A913 road to Dunkeld.

Opening Times: May - Sept: Mon - Sat, 10am - 4.30pm. Oct - Apr: Mon - Fri, 10am - 3.30pm. Closed 23 Dec - 5 Jan & last Sat in June.

Admission: Free.

ℹ Shop.   ♿ Not suitable.   🚶 By arrangement.

🅿 Limited.   🐕 Guide dogs only.

BARRIE'S BIRTHPLACE

Tel: 01575 572646

9 Brechin Road, Kirriemuir, Angus DD8 4BX

Owner: The National Trust for Scotland   **Contact:** Karen Gilmour or Mrs Sheila Philip

'Do you believe in fairies?' The creator of the eternal magic of *Peter Pan*, J M Barrie, was born here in 1860. He was the ninth of ten children born to David Barrie, a handloom weaver and his wife Margaret Ogilvy. See the imaginative exhibition about this famous novelist and dramatist with life-size figures, miniature stage sets, dioramas, theatre posters and stage costumes, while a darting light, 'Tinkerbell', moves around the room!

Location: OS Ref. NO388 542. On A926/B957, in Kirriemuir, 6m NW of Forfar.

Opening Times: Good Fri - Easter Mon, 1 May - 30 Sept: Mon - Sat 11am - 5.30pm, Sun 1.30 - 5.30pm. Weekends in Oct: Sat 11am - 5.30pm, Sun 1.30pm - 5.30pm, last adm. 5pm.

Admission: Adult £2, Child £1.30, Family £5.30. Groups: Adult £1.60, School £1.

♿ Stairlift.   ☕ Tearoom.   🅿 No parking.   🐕 No dogs.

BARRY MILL

Tel: 01241 856761

Barry, Carnoustie, Angus DD7 7RJ

Owner: The National Trust for Scotland   **Contact:** Peter Ellis

19th century meal mill. Demonstrations and displays. Waymarked walks. Picnic area.

Location: OS Ref. NO533 349. N of village between A92 & A930, 2m W of Carnoustie.

Opening Times: Good Fri - Easter Mon, 1 May - 30 Sept; daily, 11am - 5pm. Weekends in Oct: 11am - 5pm.

Admission: Adult £2, Child £1.30, Family £5.30. Groups: Adult £1.60, School £1.

BLAIR CASTLE

See page 330 for full page entry.

BOLFRACKS GARDEN

Tel: 01887 820207

Aberfeldy, Perthshire PH15 2EX

Owner: Mr J D Hutchison   **Contact:** Mr J D Hutchison

A garden for all seasons overlooking the Tay Valley. Approximately 4 acres with a walled garden including a good collection of roses and walks along the burn garden with rhododendrons, azaleas, meconopsis and primulas.

Location: OS Ref. NN822 481. 2m W of Aberfeldy on A827 towards Kenmore.

Opening Times: 1 Apr - 31 Oct; daily, 10am - 6pm.

Admission: Adult £2, Child (under 16 years) free.

🐕 No dogs.

BRANKLYN GARDEN

Tel: 01738 625535

Dundee Road, Perth PH2 7BB

Owner: The National Trust for Scotland   **Contact:** Steve McNamara

Small but magnificent garden with an impressive collection of rare and unusual plants. Among the most breathtaking are the Himalayan blue poppy, *Meconopsis* x *sheldonii*. There is a rock garden with purple maple and the rare golden *Cedrus*. Seasonal highlights in May and June are the alpines and rhododendrons and in autumn the fiery red *Acer palmatum*.

Location: OS Ref. NO125 225. On A85 at 116 Dundee Road, Perth.

Opening Times: 1 Mar - 31 Oct; daily, 9.30am - sunset.

Admission: Adult £2.40, Child £1.60, Family £6.40. Groups: Adult £1.90, School £1.

ℹ Shop. Plant centre.   ♿ Grounds suitable, but limited access.   🐕 No dogs.

CAMBO GARDENS

Tel: 01333 450054 **Fax:** 01333 450987

Cambo Estate, Kingsbarns, St Andrews, Fife KY16 8QD

Owner: Peter Erskine Esq   **Contact:** Catherine Erskine

Enchanting traditional walled garden in bloom from snowdrops to Autumn crocus. Blossoms, bulbs, lilies and 200 varieties of roses are a speciality. Gardened with joy to make it more fun than fossilised.

Location: OS Ref. NO603 114. 3m N of Crail. 7m SE of St Andrews.

Opening Times: All year; daily except Christmas and New Year 10am - dusk.

Admission: Adult £2, Child free.

| ⓘ Conferences. | ♿ Suitable. | 🐕 In grounds, on leads. | Ⓐ Available. |

CASTLE MENZIES

Tel: 01887 820982

Weem, Aberfeldy, Perth PH15 2JD

Owner: Menzies Charitable Trust   **Contact:** R A Adam

Magnificent example of a 16th century 'Z' plan fortified tower house, seat of the Chiefs of Clan Menzies for over 400 years. "Bonnie Prince Charlie" was given hospitality here in 1746. Visitors can explore the whole building, together with part of 19th century addition. Small clan museum and gift shop.

Location: OS Ref. NN838 497. 1^1/$_2$ m from Aberfeldy on B846.

Opening Times: 1 Apr - 17 Oct: Mon - Sat 10.30am - 5pm, Sun 2 - 5pm, last entry 4.30pm.

Admission: Adult £3, Child £1.50, Conc. £2.50, Groups (min 20): Adult £2.70.

| ⓘ Shop. | ♿ Ground floor suitable. WC. | ☕ Tearoom. | 🐕 Guide dogs only. |

CHARLETON HOUSE

Tel: 01333 340249 **Fax:** 01333 340583

Colinsburgh, Leven, Fife KY9 1HG

Location: OS Ref. NO464 036. Off A917. 1m NW of Colinsburgh. 3m NW of Elie.

Opening Times: Sept: 12 - 3pm. Admission every ^{1}/$_2$ hr with guided tours only.

Admission: Standard £5.

CLUNY HOUSE GARDENS

Tel: 01887 820795

Aberfeldy, Perthshire PH15 2JT   **Contact:** W Mattingley

Good woodland garden including many rare Himalayan species.

Location: OS Ref. NN879 513. 3^1/$_2$ m NW of Aberfeldy on the Weem to Strathtay Road.

Opening Times: 1 Mar - 31 Oct: 10am - 6pm.

Admission: Adult £2, Child under 16 free, Groups: £2 per person (guided tour).

| ⓘ Plant centre. | ♿ Not suitable. | 🚶 By arrangement. | Ⓟ Limited. | 🐕 No dogs. |

CULROSS PALACE

CULROSS, FIFE KY12 8JH

Owner: The National Trust For Scotland   *Contact:* Michael Ford

Tel: 01383 880359   **Fax:** 01383 882675

Relive the domestic life of the 16th and 17th centuries at this Royal Burgh fringed by the River Forth. Here the old buildings and cobbled streets create a time warp for visitors as they explore the old town. Enjoy too the Palace, dating from 1597 and the medieval garden.

Location: OS Ref. NS985 860. Off A985. 12m W of Forth Road Bridge and 4m E of Kincardine Bridge, Fife.

Opening Times: Palace: 1 Apr - 30 Sept; daily 11am - 5pm, last admission 4pm. Town house & study: same dates, 1.30 - 5pm and weekends in Oct: 11am - 5pm. Groups other times by appointment. Tearoom (in Bessie Bar Hall) dates as Town house, 10.30am - 4.30pm.

Admission: Adult £4.20, Child £2.80, Family £11.20. Groups: Adult £3.40, School £1.

| ♿ WC. | ☕ Tearoom. | 🚶 By arrangement. | Ⓟ Ample. | 🐕 No dogs. |

DRUMMOND CASTLE GARDENS

MUTHILL, CRIEFF, PERTHSHIRE PH5 2AA

Owner: Grimsthorpe & Drummond Castle Trust   *Contact:* Joe Buchanan

Tel: 01764 681257 **Fax:** 01764 681550

Scotland's most important formal gardens, among the finest in Europe. The terraces overlook a magnificent parterre, celebrating the saltire and family heraldry, surrounding the famous multiplex sundial by John Milne, Master Mason to Charles I. Featured in the United Artists' film *Rob Roy*.

Location: OS Ref. NN844 181. 2m S of Crieff off the A822.

Opening Times: Easter then 1 May - 31 Oct: 2 - 6pm, last entry 5pm.

Admission: Adult £3, Child £1.50, OAP £2.

| ♿ Partially suitable. | Ⓟ Ample. | 🐕 In grounds, on leads. |

SPECIAL EVENTS
AUG 2: Open Day, 2 - 5pm, entertainments, teas, raffle.

DUNFERMLINE ABBEY & PALACE

Tel: 01383 739026

Dunfermline, Fife

Owner: Historic Scotland   **Contact:** The Custodian

The remains of the Benedictine abbey founded by Queen Margaret in the 11th century. The foundations of her church are under the 12th century Romanesque-style nave. Robert the Bruce was buried in the choir. Substantial parts of the Abbey buildings remain, including the vast refectory.

Location: OS Ref. NY090 873. In Dunfermline off the M90.

Opening Times: 1 Apr - 30 Sept: daily, 9.30am - 6.30pm, last ticket 6pm. 1 Oct - 31 Mar: Mon - Sat, 9.30am - 4.30pm, Sun, 2 - 4.30pm, last ticket 4pm. Closed Thur pm and Fri in winter.

Admission: Adult £1.80, Child 75p, Conc. £1.30.

EDZELL CASTLE AND GARDEN

Tel: 01356 648631

Edzell, Angus

Owner: Historic Scotland   **Contact:** The Custodian

The beautiful walled garden at Edzell is one of Scotland's unique sights, created by Sir David Lindsay in 1604. The 'Pleasance' is a delightful formal garden with walls decorated with sculptured stone panels, flower boxes and niches for nesting birds. The fine tower house, now ruined, dates from the last years of the 15th century. Mary Queen of Scots held a council meeting in the castle in 1562 on her way north as her army marched against the Gordons.

Location: OS Ref. NO585 691. At Edzell, 6m N of Brechin on B966. 1m W of village.

Opening Times: 1 Apr - 30 Sept: daily, 9.30am - 6.30pm, last ticket 6pm. 1 Oct - 31 Mar: Mon - Sat, 9.30am - 4.30pm, Sun, 2 - 4.30pm, last ticket 4pm. Closed Thur pm and Fri in winter.

Admission: Adult £2.30, Child £1, Conc. £1.75.

ELCHO CASTLE

Tel: 0131 668 8800

Perth

Owner: Historic Scotland

This handsome and complete fortified mansion of 16th century date has four projecting towers. The original wrought-iron grilles to protect the windows are still in place.

Location: OS Ref. NO164 211. On the Tay, 3m SE of Perth.

Opening Times: Tel: 0131 668 8800 for details.

Admission: Adult £1.50, Child 75p, Conc. £1.10.

FALKLAND PALACE

FALKLAND KY15 7BU

Owner: *The National Trust for Scotland*   **Contact:** *Mrs Margaret Marshall*

Tel: 01337 857397   **Fax:** 01337 857980

The Royal Palace of Falkland, set in the heart of a unique medieval village, was the country residence and hunting lodge of eight Stuart monarchs, including Mary Queen of Scots. Built between 1502 and 1541, the Palace is an extremely fine example of Renaissance architecture. It includes the exceptionally beautiful Chapel Royal, and is surrounded by internationally known gardens, laid out in the 1950s. The Royal Tennis Court, reputedly the world's oldest, is still used today.

Location: OS Ref. NO253 075. A912, 11m N of Kirkcaldy.

Opening Times: Palace & Garden: 1 Apr - 31 Oct: Mon - Sat 11am - 5.30pm, Sun 1.30 - 5.30pm, last admission to Palace 4.30pm, to Garden 5pm. Groups at other times by appointment. Town Hall by appointment only.

Admission: Adult £4.80, Child £3.20. Groups: Adult £3.80, School £1. Family £12.80. Garden only: Adult £2.40, Child £1.60. Groups: Adult £1.90, School £1.

| i | Shop. | ♿ | Grounds suitable. | 🐕 | No dogs. |

GLAMIS CASTLE 🏛   See page 331 for full page entry.

GLENEAGLES   **Tel:** 01764 682388

Auchterarder, Perthshire PH3 1PJ

Owner: Gleneagles 1996 Trust   **Contact:** J Martin Haldane of Gleneagles

Gleneagles had been the home of the Haldane family since the 12th century. The 18th century pavilion is open to the public by written appointment.

Location: OS Ref. NS931 088. Auchterarder.

Opening Times: By written appointment only.

Falkland Palace.

HILL OF TARVIT MANSIONHOUSE

CUPAR, FIFE KY15 5PB

Owner: *The National Trust for Scotland*   **Contact:** *Mrs June Pratt*

Tel: 01334 653127

This fine house was rebuilt in 1906 by Sir Robert Lorimer, the renowned Scottish architect, for a Dundee industrialist, Mr F B Sharp. The house still presents a perfect setting for Mr Sharp's notable collection of superb French, Chippendale and vernacular furniture. Fine paintings by Raeburn and Ramsay and a number of eminent Dutch artists are on view together with Chinese porcelain and bronzes. Don't miss the restored Edwardian laundry behind the house which is set in the midst of a delightful garden.

Location: OS Ref. NO379 118. Off A916, 2¹/₂ m S of Cupar, Fife.

Opening Times: House: Good Fri - Easter Mon & 1 May - 30 Sept: daily, 1.30 - 5.30pm. Weekends in Oct: 1.30 - 5.30pm, last admission 4.45pm. Tearoom: same dates but opens 12.30pm. Garden & grounds: All year, daily, 9.30am - 9pm.

Admission: Adult £3.70, Child £2.50, Family £9.90. Groups: Adult £3, School £1.

| i | Shop. | ♿ | Ground floor & grounds suitable. WC. | ☕ | Tearoom. |
| 🚶 | By arrangement. | P | Ample. | 🐕 | No dogs. |

HOUSE OF DUN

MONTROSE, ANGUS DD10 9LQ

Owner: *The National Trust for Scotland*   **Contact:** *Property Manager*

Tel: 01674 810264   **Fax:** 01674 810722

This beautiful Georgian house, overlooking the Montrose Basin, was designed by William Adam and built in 1730 for David Erskine, Lord Dun. Lady Augusta Kennedy-Erskine was the natural daughter of William IV and Mrs Jordan and House of Dun contains many royal mementos. The house features superb plasterwork by Joseph Enzer.

Location: OS Ref. NO670 599. 3m W Montrose on A935.

Opening Times: House & shop: Good Fri - Easter Mon, 1 May - 30 Sept; daily, 1.30 - 5.30pm. Weekends in Oct: 1.30 - 5.30pm, last admission 5pm. Restaurant: same dates but opens 12.30pm. Garden & grounds: all year, daily 9.30am - sunset.

Admission: Adult £3.70, Child £2.50, Family £9.90, Groups: Adult £3, School £1. Gardens & grounds: Honesty box £1.

| i | Shop. Conferences. | ♿ | Ground floor & basement suitable. WC. |
| ☕ | Restaurant. | 🐕 | In grounds, on leads. Special dog walk. |

Douglas MacGregor

PERTHSHIRE
Angus & Dundee and The Kingdom of Fife

HUDSON'S

PERTHSHIRE

Scotland
Perthshire/Fife

HUNTINGTOWER CASTLE
Tel: 01738 627231

Perth

Owner: Historic Scotland   **Contact:** The Custodian

The splendid painted ceilings are especially noteworthy in this castle, once owned by the Ruthven family. Scene of a famous leap between two towers by a daughter of the house who was nearly caught in her lover's room. The two towers are still complete, one of 15th - 16th century date, the other of 16th century origin. Now linked by a 17th century range.

Location: OS Ref. NO084 252. 3m NW of Perth off the A85.

Opening Times: 1 Apr - 30 Sept: daily, 9.30am - 6.30pm, last ticket 6pm. 1 Oct - 31 Mar: Mon - Sat, 9.30am - 4.30pm, Sun, 2 - 4.30pm, last ticket 4pm. Closed Thur pm & Fri in winter.

Admission: Adult £1.80, Child 75p, Conc. £1.30.

INCHCOLM ABBEY
Tel: 01383 823332

Inchcolm, Fife

Owner: Historic Scotland   **Contact:** The Custodian

Known as the 'Iona of the East'. This is the best preserved group of monastic buildings in Scotland, founded in 1123. Includes a 13th century octagonal chapter house.

Location: OS Ref. NT190 826. On Inchcolm in the Firth of Forth. Reached by ferry from South Queensferry (30 mins) tel. 0131 331 4857, and from North Queensferry (weather permitting).

Opening Times: 1 Apr - 30 Sept: daily 9.30am - 6.30pm, last ticket 6pm.

Admission: Adult £2.30, Child £1, Conc. £1.75. Additional charge for ferries.

INCHMAHOME PRIORY
Tel: 01877 385294

Port of Menteith

Owner: Historic Scotland   **Contact:** The Custodian

A beautifully situated Augustinian priory on an island in the Lake of Menteith founded in 1238 with much of the building surviving. The five year old Mary Queen of Scots was sent here for safety in 1547.

Location: OS Ref. NN574 005. On an island in Lake of Menteith. Reached by ferry from Port of Menteith, 4m E of Aberfoyle off A81.

Opening Times: 1 Apr - 30 Sept: daily 9.30am - 6.30pm, last ticket 6pm.

Admission: Adult £2.80, Child £1, Conc. £2.10. Charge includes ferry trip.

House of Dun, Angus.

LOCH LEVEN CASTLE
Tel: 01786 450000

Loch Leven, Kinross

Owner: Historic Scotland   **Contact:** The Regional Custodian

Mary Queen of Scots endured nearly a year of imprisonment in this 14th century tower before her dramatic escape in May 1568. During the First War of Independence it was held by the English, stormed by Wallace and visited by Bruce.

Location: OS Ref. NO138 018. On island in Loch Leven reached by ferry from Kinross off the M90.

Opening Times: 1 Apr - 30 Sept: daily 9.30am - 6.30pm, last ticket 6pm.

Admission: Adult £2.80, Child £1, Conc. £2.10. Prices include ferry trip.

MEGGINCH CASTLE GARDENS
Tel: 01821 642222   Fax: 01821 642708

Errol, Perthshire PH2 7SW

Owner: Captain Drummond of Megginch and Lady Strange

15th century castle, 1,000 year old yews, flowered parterre, double walled kitchen garden, topiary, astrological garden, pagoda dovecote in courtyard. Part used as a location for the film *Rob Roy* released in 1995.

Location: OS Ref. NO241 245. 8m E of Perth on A90.

Opening Times: Apr - Oct: Wed. Aug: daily 2.30 - 6pm.

Admission: Adult £2.50, Child £1.

ℹ️ Corporate hospitality.   ✗ Wedding receptions.   ♿ Partially suitable.

🚶 By arrangement.   🅿 Ample for cars, limited for coaches.   🐕 In grounds, on leads.

MEIGLE SCULPTURED STONE MUSEUM
Tel: 01828 640612

Meigle

Owner: Historic Scotland

A remarkable collection of 25 sculptured monuments of the Celtic Christian period. This is one of the finest collections of Dark Age sculpture in Western Europe.

Location: OS Ref. NO287 446. In Meigle on the A94.

Opening Times: 1 Apr - 30 Sept: daily, 9.30am - 6.30pm, last ticket 6pm.

Admission: Adult £1.50, Conc. £1.10, Child 75p.

MONZIE CASTLE
Tel: 01764 653110

Crieff, Perthshire PH7 4HD

Owner: Mrs C M M Crichton   **Contact:** Mrs C M M Crichton

Built in 1791. Destroyed by fire in 1908 and rebuilt and furnished by Sir Robert Lorimer.

Location: OS Ref. NN873 244. 2m NE of Crieff.

Opening Times: 16 May - 14 Jun: daily, 2 - 5pm. By appointment at other times.

Admission: Adult £3, Child £1. Groups: Adult £2.50.

KELLIE CASTLE & GARDEN

PITTENWEEM, FIFE KY10 2RF

Owner: The National Trust for Scotland   *Contact: Mr John Oatts*

Tel: 01333 720271   **Fax:** 01333 720326

This very fine example of domestic architecture in Lowland Scotland dates from the 14th century and was sympathetically restored by the Lorimer family in the late 19th century. The castle contains magnificent plaster ceilings and painted panelling as well as fine furniture designed by Sir Robert Lorimer. Of particular interest are the Victorian nursery and the old kitchen. The late Victorian garden features a fine collection of old fashioned roses and herbaceous plants which are cultivated organically.

Location: OS Ref. NO519 051. On B9171, 3m NW of Pittenweem, Fife.

Opening Times: Castle: Good Fri - Easter Mon & 1 May - 30 Sept: daily, 1.30 - 5.30pm. Weekends in Oct: 1.30 - 5.30pm, last admission 4.45pm. Garden & grounds: All year, daily, 9.30am - sunset.

Admission: Adult £3.70, Child £2.50, Family £9.90. Groups: Adult £3, School £1.

ℹ️ Shop.   ♿ Ground floor & grounds suitable.   ☕ Tearoom.   🐕 No dogs.

PERTHSHIRE

HUDSON'S

PERTHSHIRE
Angus & Dundee and The Kingdom of Fife

Scotland
Perthshire/Fife

ST ANDREWS CASTLE

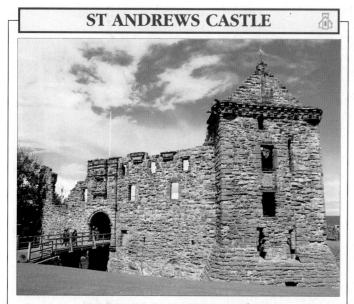

THE SCORES, ST ANDREWS, KY16 9AR

Owner: Historic Scotland   Contact: The Steward

Tel: 01334 477196

This was the castle of the Bishops of St Andrews and has a fascinating mine and counter-mine, rare examples of medieval siege techniques. There is also a bottle dungeon hollowed out of solid rock. Cardinal Beaton was murdered here and John Knox was sent to the galleys when the ensuing siege was lifted.

Location: OS Ref. NO513 169. In St Andrews on the A91.

Opening Times: Apr - Sept: daily 9.30am - 6.30pm. Oct - Mar: Mon - Sat 9.30am - 4.30pm; Sun 2 - 4.30pm. Last ticket 30 mins before closing. Joint ticket with St Andrews Cathedral available.

Admission: Adult £2.30, Child £1, OAP/Student £1.75. 10% discount for groups over 10. Free pre-booked school visits.

i Shop. Visitor centre.	X Private evening hire.	♿ Partially suitable. WCs.
By arrangement.	P On street only.	Teachers' pack.
Guide dogs only.		

ST ANDREWS CATHEDRAL   **Tel:** 01334 472563

St Andrews, Fife

Owner: Historic Scotland   **Contact:** The Administrator

The remains still give a vivid impression of the scale of what was once the largest cathedral in Scotland along with the associated domestic ranges of the priory. The precinct walls are particularly well preserved. Climb St Rule's Tower for a magnificent view of the town and visit the cathedral's collection of celtic and medieval carved stones and other relics found on the site.

Location: OS Ref. NO514 167. In St Andrews.

Opening Times: 1 Apr - 30 Sept: daily 9.30am - 6.30pm, last ticket 6pm. 1 Oct - 31 Mar: Mon - Sat 9.30am - 4.30pm, Sun 2 - 4.30pm, last ticket 4pm.

Admission: Adult £1.80, Child 75p, Conc. £1.30. Joint entry ticket available with St Andrews Castle: Adult £3.50, Conc. £2.70, Child £1.25.

SCONE PALACE   See page 332 for full page entry.

See page 332 for full page entry.

SCOTLAND'S SECRET BUNKER   **Tel:** 01333 310301 **Fax:** 01333 312040

Troywood, St Andrews KY16 8QH   **Contact:** General Manager

100ft underground is the secret bunker where the Government would have gone in the event of a nuclear war. Operations room. Cinemas. Restaurants. A unique family day out.

Location: OS Ref. NO562 090. Off the B940, 6m S of St Andrews. Thistle signs.

Opening Times: 1 Apr - end Oct: daily 10am - 5pm.

Admission: Adult £5.95, Child £3.25, Conc. £4.95, Family £16. Curator's tours by arrangement.

Scone Palace.

WEST HIGHLANDS & ISLANDS
Loch Lomond, Stirling & Trossachs

HUDSON'S

WEST HIGHLANDS & ISLANDS

Scotland
W.Highlands/Stirling

ARGYLL'S LODGING
Stirling

ARGYLL'S LODGING, the residence of the Earls of Argyll in Stirling, is the finest and most complete surviving example in Scotland of a 17th century town residence. Set back behind a screen wall on the upper approaches to Stirling Castle, its fine architecture marks it out as a town house intended for the household of a great nobleman serving the Royal Stewart Court within the Castle. The principal rooms within the lodging – including the Laigh Hall, Dining Room, Drawing Room and Bedchamber – have recently been restored and furnished as they would have been when the 9th Earl of Argyll lived there in 1680. The Earl was executed for treason in 1685.

CONTACT

Jon MacNeil
Argyll's Lodging
Castle Wynd
Stirling
FK8 1EJ

Tel: 01786 450000
Fax: 01786 464678

LOCATION

OS Ref. NS793 938

At the top and on E side of Castle Wynd in Stirling.

Train: Stirling.

Air: Edinburgh or Glasgow.

OPENING TIMES

April - September:
9.30am - 6pm.

October - March:
9.30am - 5pm.

ADMISSION

Adult	£2.50
Child*	£1.00
Student	£1.90
OAP	£1.90

*(up to 16 years)

FUNCTION

ROOM	SIZE	MAX CAPACITY
Laigh Hall	11 x 6m	60 for reception
High Dining Room	11 x 6m	26 for dinner
Both rooms: 120 for receptions		

i Shop. Corporate hospitality. Interpretation scheme includes computer animations; joint ticket with Stirling Castle available.

X Evening receptions/dinners.

Partially suitable. No wheelchair access to upper floor.

No guided tours.

P Ample parking for coaches and cars on Stirling Castle Esplanade.

Free pre-booked school visits scheme.

Guide dogs only.

WEST HIGHLANDS & ISLANDS

HUDSON'S

WEST HIGHLANDS & ISLANDS
Loch Lomond, Stirling & Trossachs

Scotland
W.Highlands/Stirling

INVERARAY CASTLE
Inveraray

The Duke of Argyll's family have lived in Inveraray since the early 15th century. The present Castle was built between 1740 and 1790.

The ancient Royal Burgh of Inveraray lies about 60 miles north west of Glasgow by Loch Fyne in an area of spectacular natural beauty combining the ruggedness of highland scenery with the sheltered tidal loch 90 miles from the open sea.

The Castle is the home of the Duke and Duchess of Argyll. Its fairytale exterior belies the grandeur of its gracious interior. The building was designed by Roger Morris and decorated by Robert Mylne, the clerk of works being William

Adam, father of Robert and John, who did much of the laying out of the present Royal Burgh, an unrivalled example of an early planned town.

Visitors may see the famous Armoury Hall containing some 1300 pieces, French tapestries made especially for the Castle, fine examples of Scottish, English and French furniture together with a wealth of other works of art including china, silver and family artifacts, all of which form a unique collection spanning the generations which are identified by a magnificent genealogical display in the Clan Room.

❖

CONTACT

The Factor
Dept HHD
Argyll Estates Office
Cherry Park
Inveraray
Argyll
PA32 8XE

Tel: (01499) 302203

Fax: (01499) 302421

LOCATION

OS Ref. NN100 090

From Edinburgh
2$^{1}/_{2}$ - 3 hrs via Glasgow.

Just NE of Inveraray
on A83. W shore
of Loch Fyne.

Bus: Bus route stopping
point within $^{1}/_{2}$ m.

OPENING TIMES

SUMMER
4 April - 11 October

April, May, June,
September & October:
Mon, Tue, Wed,
Thur & Sat:
10am - 1pm & 2 - 5.45pm
Fri: Closed
Sun: 1 - 5.45pm.

July - August
Daily: 10am - 5.45pm
(including Friday)
Sun: 1 - 5.45pm.

Last admissions
12.30 & 5pm.

**The Castle will be closed
on Sat 18th April, 1998.**

ADMISSION

SUMMER
House only
Adult £4.50
Child (under 16yrs)......£2.50
OAP/Student...........£3.50
Family (2+2) £12.00
Groups (min. 20)
20% discount

WINTER
Closed

ℹ️ Shop. No photography. Guide books in French, Italian, Japanese and German translations.

♿ Visitors may alight at the entrance to the castle. Wheelchair ramp to Castle plus two steps. All main public rooms suitable but two long flights of stairs to the smaller rooms upstairs. WCs.

☕ Tearoom, seats up to 50. Menus available on request. Groups book in advance. Tel: (01786) 813317.

🚶 Available for up to 100 people at no additional cost. Groups please book in advance. Tour time: 1 hr.

🅿️ 100 cars. Separate coach park close to Castle

👨‍👩‍👧 Welcome. £1.50 per child. A guide can be provided. Areas of interest include a nature walk.

🐕 Guide dogs only.

ACHAMORE GARDENS

Tel: 01583 505254/505267

Isle of Gigha, Argyll PA41 7AD

Owner: Mr and Mrs Derek Holt   **Contact:** Mr William Howden

Gardens only open. Sub-tropical gardens created by Sir James Horlick who bought Gigha in 1944.

Location: OS Ref. NR650 500. Off the Mull of Kintyre. Ferry from Tayinloan.

Opening Times: Dawn until dusk every day.

Admission: Adult £2, Child £1.

Grounds suitable.   By arrangement.   Ample.

Educational programme available.   In grounds, on leads.

4 single, 8 double. Ensuite available.

ANGUS'S GARDEN

Tel: 01866 21254 **Fax:** 01866 21652

Barguillean, Taynuilt, Argyll, West Highlands PA35 1HY

Owner: Mr Sam MacDonald   **Contact:** Mr Sam MacDonald

Garden of peace, tranquility and reconciliation.

Location: OS Ref. NM999 298.

Opening Times: All year: daily, 9am - 5pm.

Admission: £2.

ARDENCRAIG GARDENS

Tel/Fax: 01700 504225

Ardencraig, Rothesay, Isle of Bute, West Highlands PA20 9BP

Owner: Argyll and Bute Council   **Contact:** Martin Deighan

Walled garden, greenhouses.

Location: OS Ref. NS105 645. 2m from Rothesay.

Opening Times: May - Sept: Mon - Fri, 10am - 4.30pm, Sat and Sun, 1 - 4.30pm.

Admission: Free.

ARDUAINE GARDEN

Harvey Wood

ARDUAINE, BY OBAN, ARGYLL PA34 4XQ

Owner: The National Trust for Scotland   *Contact:* Maurice Wilkins

Tel/Fax: 01852 200366

A haven of tranquillity nestling on the west coast, Arduaine Garden is most spectacular in the late spring and early summer when the rhododendrons and azaleas are at their glorious best. With informal perennial borders giving a delightful display of colour throughout the season, the garden offers pleasant surroundings for a relaxing walk through the woodland garden to the coastal viewpoint, or simply an opportunity to sit and enjoy the peaceful atmosphere of the water garden.

Location: OS Ref. NM798 105. On A816, 20m S of Oban and 17m N of Lochgilphead.

Opening Times: All year: daily 9.30am - sunset.

Admission: Adult £2.40, Child £1.60, Family £6.40. Groups: Adult £1.90. School £1.

By arrangement.   Ample.   Guide dogs only.

ARGYLL'S LODGING

See page 338 for full page entry.

AUCHINDRAIN

Tel: 01499 500235

Auchindrain, Inveraray, Argyll PA32 8XN

Owner: Auchindrain Trust   **Contact:** John McDonald

Open-air museum of an original West Highland township with restored buildings to give a fascinating experience of what life was really like for the Highlander in past centuries.

Location: OS Ref. NN050 050. On A83, 6m SW of Inveraray.

Opening Times: April - Sept: daily 10am - 5pm.

Admission: Adult £3, Child £1.50, OAP £2.50.

Shop.   Ample.   In grounds, on leads.

BALLOCH CASTLE COUNTRY PARK

Tel: 01389 758216 **Fax:** 01389 755721

Balloch, Dunbartonshire G83 8LX

Contact: Loch Lomond Park Authority Ranger Service

A 200 acre country park on the banks of Loch Lomond. This ancient seat of the Lennox offers the visitor a chance to blend the wild, natural beauty of Scotland with the formal glory of the ornamental gardens and splendid trees of former estate days. Balloch Castle, now the Visitor Centre, was built in 1808 in the 'castle-gothic' style.

Location: OS Ref. NS390 830. SE shore of Loch Lomond, off A82 for Balloch or A811 for Stirling.

Opening Times: Visitor Centre: Easter - Oct: daily, 10am - 5.30pm. Country Park: All year, dawn - dusk.

Admission: Free for both Visitor Centre and Country Park.

Shop. Visitor Centre.   Partially suitable. WCs.   Limited for coaches.

Educational programme.   In grounds, on leads.

BANNOCKBURN HERITAGE CENTRE

Tel: 01786 812664
Fax: 01786 810892

Glasgow Road, Stirling FK7 0LJ

Owner: The National Trust for Scotland   **Contact:** Judith Fairley

In 1314 from this battlefield the Scots 'sent them homeward to think again', when Edward II's English army was soundly defeated by King Robert the Bruce. Inside the Heritage Centre there is a life-size statue of William Wallace, Bruce on his throne, a display enriched with replicas, vignettes of Scottish life and a panorama of historical characters.

Location: OS Ref. NS810 910. Off M80 & M9/J9, 2m S of Stirling.

Opening Times: Site: All year: daily. Heritage Centre & Shop: 1 - 31 Mar and 1 Nov - 23 Dec: daily 11am - 3pm. 1 Apr - 31 Oct: daily 10am - 5.30pm (last visual show $\frac{1}{2}$ hr before closing). Shop closed 1 - 6 Nov for stocktaking.

Admission: Adult £2.40, Child £1.60, Family £6.40. Groups: Adult £1.90, School £1.

Shop.   Suitable. WC.   Ample.   In grounds, on leads.

BONAWE IRON FURNACE

Tel: 01866 822432

Taynuilt, Argyll

Owner: Historic Scotland   **Contact:** The Custodian

Founded in 1753 by Cumbrian iron masters this is the most complete remaining charcoal fuelled ironworks in Britain. Displays show how iron was once made here.

Location: OS Ref. NN005 310. By the village of Taynuilt off the A85.

Opening Times: 1 Apr - 30 Sept: daily, 9.30am - 6.30pm, last ticket 6pm.

Admission: Adult £2.30, Child £1, Conc. £1.75.

CASTLE CAMPBELL

Tel: 01259 742408

Dollar Glen, Central District

Owner: The National Trust for Scotland   **Contact:** Historic Scotland

Known as 'Castle Gloom' this spectacularly sited 15th century fortress was the lowland stronghold of the Campbells. Stunning views from the parapet walk.

Location: OS Ref. NS961 993. At head of Dollar Glen, 10m E of Stirling on the A91.

Opening Times: 1 Apr - 30 Sept: daily 9.30am - 6.30pm, last ticket 6pm. 1 Oct - 31 Mar: Mon - Sat 9.30am - 4.30pm (closed Thur pm & Fri all day) Sun 2 - 4.30pm, last ticket 4pm.

Admission: Adult £2.30, Child £1, Conc. £1.75.

CASTLE STALKER

Tel: 01883 622768 **Fax:** 01883 626238

Portnacroish, Appin, Argyll PA38 4BA

Owner: Mrs M Allward   **Contact:** Messrs R & A Allward

Early 15th century Tower House and ancient seat of the Stewarts of Appin. Picturesquely set on a rocky islet approx 400 yds off the mainland on the shore of Loch Linnhe. Reputed to have been used by James IV as a hunting lodge. Garrisoned by Government troops during the 1745 rising. Restored from a ruin by the late Lt Col Stewart Allward following acquisition in 1965 and now retained by his family.

Location: OS Ref. NM930 480. Approx. 20m N of Oban on the A828. On islet $\frac{1}{4}$ m off-shore.

Opening Times: Apr - Sept for 25 days. Telephone for details. Times variable depending on tides and weather.

Admission: Adult £6, Child £3.

Not suitable for coach parties.   Not suitable.

DOUNE CASTLE   **Tel:** 01786 841742

Doune

Owner: Earl of Moray (leased to Historic Scotland)   **Contact:** The Custodian

A formidable 14th century courtyard castle, built for the Regent Albany. The striking keep-gatehouse combines domestic quarters including the splendid Lord's Hall with its carved oak screen, musicians' gallery and double fireplace.

Location: OS Ref. NN720 020. In Doune, 8m S of Callendar on the A84.

Opening Times: 1 Apr - 30 Sept: daily, 9.30am - 6.30pm. 1 Oct - 31 Mar: Mon - Wed & Sat 9.30am - 4.30pm, Thur 9.30am - 12 noon, Fri closed, Sun 2 - 4.30pm, last admission $^1/_2$ hr before closing.

Admission: Adult £2.30, Child £1, Conc. £1.75.

DUART CASTLE

ISLE OF MULL, ARGYLL PA64 6AP

Owner: Sir Lachlan Maclean Bt   *Contact:* Sir Lachlan Maclean Bt

Tel: 01680 812309 or 01577 830311

Duart Castle has been a Maclean stronghold since the 12th century. The keep was built by Lachlan Lubanach, 5th Chief, in 1360. Burnt by the English in 1758, the castle was restored in 1912 and today is still the home of the Chief of the Clan Maclean. It has a spectacular position overlooking the Sound of Mull.

Location: OS Ref. NM750 350. Off A849 on the east point of the Isle of Mull.

Opening Times: 1 May - 11 Oct: 10.30am - 6pm.

Admission: Adult £3.50, Child £1.75, OAP/Student £3, Family £8.75.

i Shop. Corporate Hospitality.	Not suitable.	Tearoom.
By arrangement.	P Ample. Free of charge.	In grounds, on leads.

DUMBARTON CASTLE   **Tel:** 01389 732167

Dumbarton, Strathclyde

Owner: Historic Scotland   **Contact:** The Custodian

Location: OS Ref. NS401 744. In Dumbarton on the A82.

Opening Times: 1 Apr - 30 Sept: daily 9.30am - 6.30pm, last ticket 6pm. 1 Oct - 31 Mar: Mon - Wed & Sat 9.30am - 4.30pm, Thur 9.30am - 12 noon, Fri Closed, Sun 2 - 4.30pm, last ticket 4pm.

Admission: Adult £1.80, Child 75p, Conc £1.30.

DUNBLANE CATHEDRAL   **Tel:** 01786 823388

Dunblane

Owner: Historic Scotland   **Contact:** The Custodian

One of Scotland's noblest medieval churches. The lower part of the tower is Romanesque but the larger part of the building is of the 13th century. It was restored in 1889 - 93 by Sir Rowand Anderson.

Location: OS Ref. NN782 015. In Dunblane.

Opening Times: All year.

Admission: Free.

DUNSTAFFNAGE CASTLE

BY OBAN, ARGYLL PA37 1PZ

Owner: Historic Scotland   *Contact:* The Steward

Tel: 01631 562465

A very fine 13th century castle built on a rock with a great curtain wall. The castle's colourful history stretches across the Wars of Independence to the 1745 rising. The castle was briefly the prison of Flora Macdonald. Marvellous views from the top of the curtain wall. Close by are the remains of a chapel with beautiful architectural detail.

Location: OS49 NM882 344. By Loch Etive, $3^1/_2$ m from Oban on the A85.

Opening Times: Apr - Sept: daily, 9.30am - 6.30pm, last ticket $^1/_2$ hr before closing.

Admission: Adult £1.80, Child 75p, OAP/Student £1.30. 10% discount for groups 10+.

i Shop.	Partially suitable.	By arrangement.
P Ample.	Free school visits.	In grounds, on leads.

GLENCOE

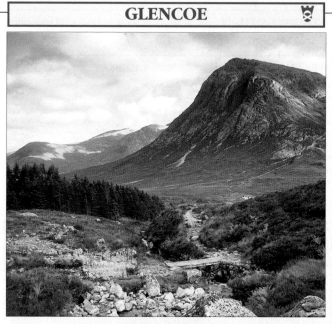

BALLACHULISH, ARGYLL PA39 4HX

Owner: The National Trust for Scotland   *Contact:* Derrick Warner

Tel: 01855 811307 or 811729 (during closed season)   **Fax:** 01855 811772

This is a breathtaking, dramatic glen with jagged peaks incised on either side by cascading water. In 1692 many of the MacDonald clan were massacred by soldiers of King William's army, to whom they had given hospitality. Wildlife abounds and herds of red deer, wildcat and golden eagle enjoy this wilderness area.

Location: OS Ref. NN100 590. Off A82, 17m S of Fort William.

Opening Times: Site: All year, daily. Visitor Centre & Snack Bar: 1 Apr - 18 May and 1 Sept - 31 Oct: daily, 10am - 5pm. 19 May - 31 Aug: daily, 9.30am - 5.30pm, last admission $^1/_2$ hr before closing.

Admission: Adult 50p, Child 30p.

i Shop.	Ground floor suitable. WC.	Kiosk.	Guide dogs only.

THE HILL HOUSE

UPPER COLQUHOUN STREET, HELENSBURGH G84 9AJ

Owner: The National Trust for Scotland   *Contact:* Mrs Anne Ellis

Tel: 01436 673900   **Fax:** 01436 674685

Certainly the finest domestic creation of the famous Scottish architect and artist, Charles Rennie Mackintosh. He set this 20th century masterpiece high on a hillside overlooking the Firth of Clyde. Mackintosh also designed furniture, fittings and decorative schemes to complement the house, and suggested a layout for the garden which has been renovated by the Trust.

Location: OS Ref. NS300 820. Off B832, between A82 & A814, 23m NW of Glasgow.

Opening Times: 1 Apr - 31 Oct; daily, 1.30 - 5.30pm, last admission 5pm. Tearoom: 1.30 - 4.30pm. Increasing visitor numbers are placing great strain on the structure of The Hill House, which was designed for domestic purposes. Access may be restricted at peak times and at the discretion of the Property Manager.

Admission: Adult £5.80, Child £3.90, Family £15.50. Groups must pre-book.

ℹ️ Shop.   ☕ Tearoom.

INVERARAY CASTLE 🏛️

See page 339 for full page entry.

INVERARAY JAIL

Tel: 01499 302381   **Fax:** 01499 302195

Church Square, Inveraray, Argyll PA32 8TX

Owner: Visitor Centres Ltd   **Contact:** J Linley

A living 19th century prison! Uniformed prisoners and warders, life-like figures, imaginative exhibitions, sounds, smells and trials in progress, bring the 1820 courtroom and former county prison back to life. New exhibition now open. A comparison of life 'In Prison Today'.

Location: OS Ref. NN100 090. Church Square, Inveraray, Argyll.

Opening Times: Apr - Oct: 9.30am - 6pm, last adm. 5pm. Nov - Mar: 10am - 5pm, last adm. 4pm.

Admission: Adult £4.30, Child £2.10, OAP £2.75, Family £11.75. Groups: £3.50, OAP £2.25.

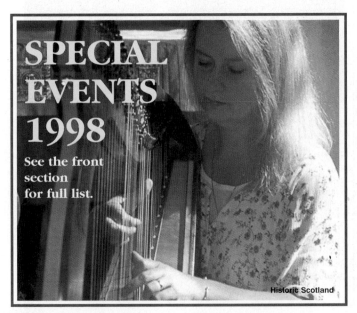

SPECIAL EVENTS 1998

See the front section for full list.

Historic Scotland

MOUNT STUART HOUSE & GARDENS

ISLE OF BUTE PA20 9LR

Owner: The Mount Stuart Trust   **Contact:** The Administrator

Tel: 01700 503877   **Fax:** 01700 505313

Spectacular High Victorian Gothic house, ancestral home of the Marquesses of Bute. Splendid interiors, art collection and architectural detail. Set in 300 acres of stunning woodlands, mature Victorian pinetum, arboretum and exotic gardens. Countryside Ranger Service. Scottish Tourism Oscar winner.

Location: OS Ref. NS100 600. 5m S of Rothesay Pierhead, local bus service to house. Frequent ferry service from Wemyss Bay, Renfrewshire & Colintraive, Argyll. 1 hr from Glasgow Airport.

Opening Times: 10 - 13 April and 1 May - 18 Oct: daily except Tue & Thur. Gardens: 10am - 5pm. House: 11am - 4.30 pm.

Admission: House & Gardens: Adult £6, Child £2.50, Family £15. Gardens: Adult £3.50, Child £2, Family £9. Conc. & group rates given. Pre-booked guided tours available.

ℹ️ Shop. Picnic area.   ♿ Suitable. WC.   ☕ Tearoom.   🐕 No dogs.

ROTHESAY CASTLE

Tel: 01700 502691

Rothesay, Isle of Bute

Owner: Historic Scotland   **Contact:** The Custodian

A favourite residence of the Stuart Kings, this is a wonderful example of a 13th century circular castle of enclosure with 16th century forework containing the Great Hall. Attacked by Vikings in its earlier days.

Location: OS Ref. NS088 646. In Rothesay, Isle of Bute. Ferry from Wemyss Bay on the A78.

Opening Times: 1 Apr - 30 Sept: daily 9.30am - 6.30pm, last ticket 6pm. 1 Oct - 31 Mar: Mon - Wed & Sat 9.30am - 4.30pm, Thur 9.30am - 12 noon, Fri closed, Sun 2 - 4.30pm, last ticket 4pm.

Admission: Adult £1.80, Child 75p, Conc. £1.30.

ST BLANE'S CHURCH

Tel: 0131 668 8800

Kingarth, Isle of Bute

Owner: Historic Scotland

This 12th century Romanesque chapel stands on the site of a 12th century Celtic monastery.

Location: OS Ref. NS090 570. At the S end of the Isle of Bute.

Opening Times: All year: daily.

Admission: Free.

Glyn Satterley

Arduaine Garden, by Oban.

STIRLING CASTLE

CASTLE WYND, STIRLING FK8 1EJ

Owner: *Historic Scotland*   **Contact:** *Jon MacNeil*

Tel: 01786 450000 **Fax:** 01786 464678

Stirling Castle has played a key role in Scottish history, dominating the North–South and East–West routes through Scotland. The battles of Stirling Bridge and Bannockburn were fought in its shadow and Mary Queen of Scots lived here as a child. Marvellous Renaissance architecture and interpretive displays.

Location: OS Ref. NS790 941. At the top of Castle Wynd in Stirling.

Opening Times: Apr - Sept: 9.30am - 6pm. Oct - Mar: 9.30am - 5pm, last ticket 45 mins before closing.

Admission: Adult £4.50, Child £1.20, OAP/Student £3.50. 10% discount for groups of 10+. Free pre-booked school visits, except July & August.

- i Shop. Picnic area. Joint ticket with Argyll's Lodging.
- X Private hire.
- & Partially suitable. WC.
- Licensed café.
- Available.
- P Ample.
- Teachers' pack.
- Guide dogs only.

Stirling Castle.

TOROSAY CASTLE & GARDENS

CRAIGNURE, ISLE OF MULL PA65 6AY

Owner: *Mr Chris James*   **Contact:** *Mr Chris James*

Tel: 01680 812421 **Fax:** 01680 812470

Torosay Castle and Gardens set on the magnificent Island of Mull, was completed in 1858 by the eminent architect David Bryce in the Scottish baronial style, and is surrounded by 12 acres of spectacular gardens which offer an exciting contrast between formal terraces, impressive statue walk and informal woodland, also rhododendron collection, alpine, walled, bog and Japanese gardens. The house offers family history, portraits, scrapbooks and antiques in an informal and relaxed atmosphere.

Location: OS Ref. NM730 350. 1$\frac{1}{2}$ m SE of Craignure by A849. 2m W of Duart Castle.

Opening Times: House: Easter - Oct: Mon - Sun, 10.30am - 5.30pm, last admission 5pm. Gardens: all year, daily during daylight hours.

Admission: Adult £4.50, Child £1.50, Conc. £3.50. Groups: Adult £3.50, Child £1, Conc. £3.50.

- i Shop.
- & Grounds suitable. WC.
- Tearoom.
- In grounds, on leads.

YOUNGER BOTANIC GARDEN BENMORE

Tel: 01369 706261
Dunoon, Argyll PA23 8QU   **Fax:** 01369 706369
Contact: The Curator

A botanical paradise. Enter the magnificent avenue of giant redwoods and follow trails through the Formal Garden and hillside woodlands to a viewpoint with its spectacular outlook over the Holy Loch and the Eachaig Valley. World famous collections of rhododendrons and conifers.

Location: OS Ref. NS150 850. 7m N of Dunoon on A815.

Opening Times: 1 Mar - 31 Oct: daily, 9.30am - 6pm.

Admission: Adult £3, Child £1, Conc. £2.50, Family £7. Group discounts available.

- i Shop. Plant centre. Corporate hospitality.
- X Wedding receptions.
- & Suitable. WCs.
- Licensed café.
- By arrangement.
- P Ample.
- In grounds, on leads.

Harvey Wood.

Glencoe.

DUFF HOUSE
Banff

Duff House is one of the most imposing and palatial houses in Scotland, with a strong classical façade and a grand staircase leading to the main entrance. It remained in the hands of the Duffs, Dukes of Fife, until 1906 when the family presented the estate to Banff and Macduff, consigning its contents to the saleroom.

Since then it has had a colourful history as an hotel, sanatorium and prisoner-of-war camp, before being taken into the care of Historic Scotland in 1956. After a comprehensive programme of structural repairs and extensive conservation and restoration, Duff House opened to the public as an outstation of the National Galleries of Scotland in April 1995.

Set in acres of parkland, by the banks of the River Deveron, Duff House is one of the glories of the North East. Designed by William Adam for William Duff (1st Earl Fife), it is dramatically sited next to the Royal Burgh of Banff and the fishing port of Macduff and is a splendid example of Scottish Baroque architecture.

Drawn from the rich holdings of the National Galleries, highlights of the picture display include El Greco's St Jerome in Penitence, J G Cuyp's Dutch Family Group; and Allan Ramsay's magnificent full length portrait of Elizabeth Cunyngham has been transformed by recent cleaning, revealing a wonderfully subtle range of colours.

❖

CONTACT

The Chamberlain
Duff House
Banff
AB45 3SX
Tel: (01261) 818181
Fax: (01261) 818900

LOCATION

OS Ref. NT691 634

Banff. 47m NE of
Aberdeen on A947

OPENING TIMES

SUMMER

1 April - 30 September
Daily: 11am - 4pm.

WINTER

1 October - 31 March
Thur - Sun
11am - 4pm.

ADMISSION

Adult	£3.00
Conc	£2.00
Family	£7.00
Groups* (10+)	£2.00

* per person.

Free admission to shop, tearoom, grounds and woodland walks.

Free wedding photography permitted in grounds. Wedding photography permitted in vestibule for fee of £50.

CONFERENCE/FUNCTION

ROOM	MAX CAPACITY
Long Gallery	100
Vestibule	65
Dining Room Salon	80
North Drawing Room	40

ℹ️ Shop. Audio-visual room, baby changing facilities, playground, assault course, woodland walks. Croquet and French Boules equipment available for hire.

✗ Available for special functions, corporate hospitality, conferences.

♿ Access and parking, lift to gallery floor, wheelchairs. WC.

☕ Tearoom serving light lunches. Open: 11am - 4pm.

🅿️ Car and coach parking free, 4 coach spaces, coaches to book.

👫 Schools admitted free, teachers' pack, education suite, teachers encouraged to pre-visit free.

GRAMPIAN HIGHLANDS

HUDSON'S

GRAMPIAN HIGHLANDS
Aberdeen & North East Coast

Scotland
Grampian

ARBUTHNOTT HOUSE

Tel: 01561 361226 **Fax:** 01561 320476

Arbuthnott, Laurencekirk AB30 1PA

e-mail: keith@arbuth.u-net.com

Owner: The Viscount of Arbuthnott

Contact: The Master of Arbuthnott

Arbuthnott family home for 800 years with formal 17th century walled garden on unusually steep south facing slope. Well maintained grass terraces, herbaceous borders, shrubs and greenhouses.

Location: OS Ref. NO796 751. Off B967 between A90 and A92, 25m S of Aberdeen.

Opening Times: House: 11 - 13 Apr, 4/5 & 24/25 May, 26/27 Jul, 2/3/ & 30/31 Aug: 2 - 5pm. Guided tours: 2 - 5pm. Garden: All year, 9am - 5pm.

Admission: House: £3 Garden: £2.

♿ Ground floor suitable. ♯ Compulsory. P Ample. 🐕 No dogs.

BALFLUIG CASTLE

Tel: 0171 624 3200

Alford, Aberdeenshire AB33 8EJ

Owner: Mark Tennant of Balfluig

Contact: Mark Tennant of Balfluig

Small 16th century tower house in farmland, restored in 1967.

Location: OS Ref. NJ586 151. Alford, Aberdeenshire.

Opening Times: By written appointment only to M I Tennant Esq, 30 Abbey Gardens, London NW8 9AT.

♿ Not suitable. 🐕 No dogs. A 1 single, 4 double.

BALMORAL CASTLE (GROUNDS & EXHIBITIONS)

Tel: 013397 42334
Fax: 013397 42271

Balmoral, Ballater, Aberdeenshire AB35 5TB

Owner: Her Majesty The Queen

Contact: Captain J R Wilson

Holiday home of the Royal Family, bought by Prince Albert in 1852. Grounds, gardens and exhibition of paintings and works of art in the ballroom.

Location: OS Ref. NO256 951. Off A93 between Ballater and Braemar. 50m W of Aberdeen.

Opening Times: 10 Apr - 30 May: Mon - Sat, 10am - 5pm. 1 Jun - 2 Aug: daily 10 - 5pm.

Admission: Adult £3.50, Child (5-16yrs) £1, OAP £2.50.

♿ House & grounds suitable. WC. ☕ Tearoom. 🐕 In grounds, on leads.

BALVENIE CASTLE

Tel: 01340 820121

Dufftown

Owner: Historic Scotland

Contact: The Custodian

Picturesque ruins of 13th century moated stronghold originally owned by the Comyns. Visited by Edward I in 1304 and by Mary Queen of Scots in 1562. Occupied by Cumberland in 1746.

Location: OS Ref. NJ326 408. At Dufftown on A941.

Opening Times: 1 Apr - 30 Sept: daily, 9.30am - 6.30pm, last ticket 6pm.

Admission: Adult £1.20, Child 50p, Conc. 90p.

BRAEMAR CASTLE

Tel/Fax: 01339 741219

Braemar, Aberdeenshire AB5 4EX

Owner: Invercauld Estate

Contact: B McCudden

Turreted stronghold built in 1628 by the Earl of Mar and burnt by Farquharson of Inverey in 1689. Rebuilt in 1748 when garrisoned by Hanoverian troops. Now a fully furnished family residence.

Location: OS Ref. NO156 924. $^{1}/_{2}$ m NE of Braemar on A93.

Opening Times: Easter - Oct: Sat - Thur, 10am - 6.pm.

Admission: Adult £2, Child £1, OAP/Coach £1.50.

i Shop. ♿ Not suitable. ♯ By arrangement. P Ample. 🐕 Guide dogs only.

Douglas MacGregor

NPI Award 1997:
Winner - Best National Trust for Scotland Property,
& Best Overall Property *Family* Award.

Brodie Castle.

BRODIE CASTLE

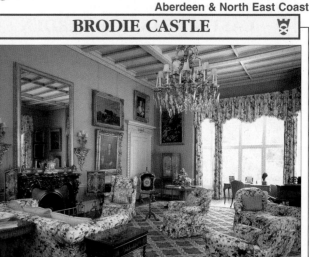

NPI Award 1997: Winner

FORRES, MORAY IV36 0TE

Owner: The National Trust for Scotland   *Contact:* Dr Stephanie Blackden

Tel: 01309 641371 **Fax:** 01309 641600

This imposing Castle stands in rich Morayshire parkland. The lime harled building is a typical 'Z' plan tower house with ornate corbelled battlements and bartizans, with 17th & 19th century additions. The interior has unusual plaster ceilings, a major art collection, porcelain and fine furniture. There is a woodland walk by a large pond with access to wildlife observation hides. In springtime the grounds are carpeted with many varieties of daffodils for which Brodie Castle is rightly famous.

Location: OS Ref. NH980 577. Off A96 4$^{1}/_{2}$ m W of Forres and 24m E of Inverness.

Opening Times: Castle: 1 Apr - 30 Sept: Mon - Sat, 11am - 5.30pm. Sun, 1.30 - 5.30pm, weekends in Oct: Sat, 11am - 5.30pm, Sun, 1.30 - 5.30pm. Last admission 4.30pm. Other times by appointment. Grounds: all year, daily, 9.30am - sunset.

Admission: Adult £4.20, Child £2.80, Family £11.20. Groups: Adult £3.40, Schools £1.

i Shop. ♿ Suitable. WCs. ☕ Tearoom. 🐕 In grounds, on leads.

CANDACRAIG GARDEN & GALLERY

Tel: 01975 651226 **Fax:** 01975 651391

Candacraig Gardens, Strathdon AB36 8XT

Owner: Harry Young

Contact: Harry Young

1820s B listed walled display garden, art gallery and specialist plant nursery. Civil wedding licence holder, ceremonies conducted in beautiful Victorian Gothic marriage room, offering full wedding facilities. Marquees in garden for receptions, garden parties, picnics, barbecues and small business conferences. Telephone, fax and video facilities. Floodlights in evening.

Location: OS Ref. NJ339 110. On A944 1$^{1}/_{2}$m SW of Strathdon, 20m from Alford.

Opening Times: 1 May - 30 Sept: daily, 10am - 6pm.

Admission: Donation box. Pre-arranged groups: Adult £1, Child free.

i Plant centre. Corporate hospitality. X Wedding receptions. ♿ Suitable. WC.
♯ By arrangement. P Ample, limited for coaches. 🐕 Guide dogs only.
A 1 single, 1 double (self-catering).

CASTLE FRASER & GARDEN

SAUCHEN, INVERURIE AB51 7LD

Owner: *The National Trust for Scotland*   *Contact:* *Eric Wilkinson*

Tel: 01330 833463

Over 400 years of history could be told if the stout walls of Castle Fraser could speak. Begun in 1575 by the 6th Laird, Michael Fraser, the two low wings contribute to the scale and magnificence of the towers rising above them, combining to make this the largest and most elaborate of the Scottish castles built on the 'Z' plan. The stunning simplicity of the Great Hall, which occupies the entire first floor of the main block, with its striking fireplace, almost 3 metres wide, immediately creates for the visitor the atmosphere of past centuries.

Location: OS Ref. NJ723 125. Off A944, 4m N of Dunecht & 16m W of Aberdeen.

Opening Times: Castle: Good Fri - Easter Mon, 1 May - 30 Jun & 1 - 30 Sept: daily, 1.30 - 5.30pm. 1 Jul - 31 Aug: daily, 11am - 5.30pm, weekends in Oct, 1.30 - 5.30pm, last adm. 4.45pm. Tearoom; as castle but 12.30pm when castle opens 1.30pm. Garden: all year, daily, 9.30am - 6pm. Grounds: all year, daily, 9.30 - sunset.

Admission: Adult £4.20, Child/Conc. £2.80. Groups: Adult £3.40. School £1. Family £11.20. Garden & grounds only: Adult £2, Child £1.30, Groups: Adult £1.60, Child/School £1.

ⓘ Shop. Plant sales.   ♿ Suitable. WC.   ☕ Tearoom.

CRATHES CASTLE

BANCHORY AB31 3QJ

Owner: *The National Trust for Scotland*   *Contact:* *William Bowman*

Tel: 01330 844525   **Fax:** 01330 844797

Fairytale-like turrets, gargoyles of fantastic design, superb painted ceilings and the ancient Horn of Leys given in 1323 to Alexander Burnett by King Robert the Bruce, are just a few of the exciting features at this most picturesque castle. The building of the castle began in 1553 and took 40 years to complete. Just over 300 years later, Sir James and Lady Burnett began developing the walled garden and created not just one but eight superb gardens which now provide a riot of colour throughout the summer.

Location: OS Ref. NO733 969. On A93, 3m E of Banchory and 15m W of Aberdeen.

Opening Times: Castle, visitor centre, shop & restaurant: 1 Apr - 31 Oct: daily, 11am - 5.30pm, last admission to castle 4.45pm. Plant sales: same dates except weekends only in Oct. Other times by appointment only. Garden & grounds: all year, daily, 9.30am - sunset. Timed tickets - limited number available each day.

Admission: Adult £4.80, Child £3.20, Family £12.80. Group: Adult £3.80, School £1. Grounds only: Adult £2, Child £1.30.

ⓘ Shop. Plant sales.   ♿ Suitable. WCs.   ☕ Restaurant.

CORGARFF CASTLE

Tel: 013398 83635

Strathdon

Owner: Historic Scotland   **Contact:** The Custodian

A 16th century tower house converted into a barracks for Hanoverian troops in 1748. Its last military use was to control the smuggling of illicit whisky between 1827 and 1831. Still complete and with star-shaped fortification.

Location: OS Ref. NJ255 086. 8m W of Strathdon on A939. 14m NW of Ballater.

Opening Times: 1 Apr - 30 Sept: daily, 9.30am - 6.30pm. 1 Oct - 31 Mar: Sat 9.30am - 4.30pm. Sun 2 - 4.30pm, last admission ½ hr before closing.

Admission: Adult £2.30, Child £1, Conc. £1.75.

CRAIGSTON CASTLE

Tel: 01888 551228

Turriff, Banff, Aberdeenshire Grampian Highlands

Owner: William Pratesi Urquhart of Craigston   **Contact:** Mrs Urquhart of Craigston

Built in 1607 by John Urquhart is unique in style and includes a sculptured balcony on top of a central arch.

Location: OS Ref. NJ762 550. On B9105, 4¹/₂m NE of Turrif. 8m SE of Banff.

Opening Times: 20 - 28 Jun & 18 Jul - 2 Aug: 10am - 4pm.

Admission: £2.50. Concessions available.

CRUICKSHANK BOTANIC GARDEN

Tel: 01224 272704 **Fax:** 01224 272703

St Machar Drive, Aberdeen AB24 3UU

Owner: University of Aberdeen   **Contact:** R B Rutherford

Extensive collection of shrubs, herbaceous and alpine plants and trees. Rock and water gardens.

Location: OS Ref. NJ938 084. In old Aberdeen.

Opening Times: All year: Mon - Fri, 9am - 4.30pm. May - Sept: Sat and Sun only 2 - 5pm.

Admission: Free.

♿ Grounds suitable.   Ⓟ No parking.   In grounds, on leads.

DALLAS DHU DISTILLERY

Tel: 01309 676548

Forres

Owner: Historic Scotland   **Contact:** The Custodian

A completely preserved time capsule of the distiller's craft. Wander at will through this fine old Victorian distillery then enjoy a dram. Visitor centre, shop and audio-visual theatre.

Location: OS Ref. NJ035 566. 1m S of Forres off the A940.

Opening Times: 1 Apr - 30 Sept: daily, 9.30am - 6.30pm, last ticket 6pm. 1 Oct - 31 Mar: Mon - Sat, 9.30am - 4.30pm, Sun, 2 - 4.30pm, last ticket 4pm. Closed Thur pm and Fri in winter.

Admission: Adult £2.30, Child £1, Conc. £1.75.

DELGATIE CASTLE

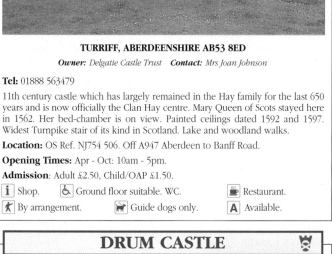

TURRIFF, ABERDEENSHIRE AB53 8ED

Owner: Delgatie Castle Trust   **Contact:** *Mrs Joan Johnson*

Tel: 01888 563479

11th century castle which has largely remained in the Hay family for the last 650 years and is now officially the Clan Hay centre. Mary Queen of Scots stayed here in 1562. Her bed-chamber is on view. Painted ceilings dated 1592 and 1597. Widest Turnpike stair of its kind in Scotland. Lake and woodland walks.

Location: OS Ref. NJ754 506. Off A947 Aberdeen to Banff Road.

Opening Times: Apr - Oct: 10am - 5pm.

Admission: Adult £2.50, Child/OAP £1.50.

i	Shop.	👤	Ground floor suitable. WC.	☕	Restaurant.
🚶	By arrangement.	🐕	Guide dogs only.	A	Available.

DRUM CASTLE

DRUMOAK, BY BANCHORY AB31 3EY

Owner: The National Trust for Scotland   **Contact:** *Mrs Krista Chisholm*

Tel: 01330 811204

The combination over the years of a 13th century square tower, a very fine Jacobean mansion house and the additions of the Victorian lairds make Drum Castle unique among Scottish castles. Owned for 653 years by one family, the Irvines, every stone and every room is steeped in history. Superb furniture and paintings provide a visual feast for visitors. In the 16th century Chapel, the stained glass windows, the font copied from the Saxon one in Winchester Cathedral and the Augsburg silver Madonna, all add immense interest for visitors.

Location: OS Ref. NJ796 004. Off A93, 3m W of Peterculter and 10m W of Aberdeen.

Opening Times: Castle: Good Fri - Easter Mon, 1 May - 30 Sept; daily, 1.30 - 5.30pm. Weekends in Oct: 1.30 - 5.30pm, last admission 4.45pm. Garden; same dates, daily 10am - 6pm. Grounds; all year, daily, 9.30 - sunset.

Admission: Adult £4.20, Child £2.80, Family £11.20. Groups: Adult £3.40, School £1. Group visits must book. Gardens & grounds only: Adult £2, Child £1.30. Groups: Adult £1.60, School £1.

DRUMMUIR CASTLE   **Tel:** 01542 810332 **Fax:** 01542 810302

Drummuir, by Keith, Banffshire AB55 5JE

Owner: The Gordon-Duff Family   **Contact:** Liz Robson

Castellated Victorian Gothic-style castle built in 1847 by Admiral Duff. 60ft high lantern tower with fine plasterwork. Family portraits, interesting artefacts and other paintings. Organic walled garden and plant sales.

Location: OS Ref. NO881 839. Midway between Keith (5m) and Dufftown, off the B9014.

Opening Times: 29/30 Aug, 5/6 Sept & 9 - 29 Sept: tours at 2pm & 3pm.

Admission: Adult £2, Child £1.50. Pre-arranged groups: Adult £2, Child £1.50.

i	Plant centre.	👤	Suitable. WC.	🚶	Guided tours only.	P	Ample.
🐕	In grounds on leads.						

DUFF HOUSE   See page 344 for full page entry.

DUNNOTTAR CASTLE   **Tel:** 01569 762173

The Lodge, Stonehaven AB3 2TL   **Contact:** P McKenzie

Spectacular ruin. Impregnable fortress to the Earls Marischals of Scotland. The site for the successful protection of the Scottish Crown Jewels against the might of Cromwell's army. A castle dreams are made of. A must for anyone who takes Scottish history seriously.

Location: OS Ref. NO881 839. Just off A92. $1^1/2$ m SE of Stonehaven.

Opening Times: Easter - Oct: Mon - Sat, 9am - 6pm. Sun 2 - 5pm. Nov - Easter: Mon - Fri, 9am - sunset. Closed weekends. Last admission: 30 mins before closing.

Admission: Adult £3, Child £1.

👤	Not suitable.	P	Ample.	🐕	In grounds, on leads.

DUTHIE PARK & WINTER GARDENS **Tel:** 01224 585310 **Fax:** 01224 210532

Polmuir Road, Aberdeenshire, Grampian Highlands, Aberdeen AB11 7TH

Owner: Duthie Park Trust   **Contact:** G Perk Esq

45 acres of parkland and gardens.

Location: OS Ref. NJ97 044. Just N of River Dee, 1m S of city centre.

Opening Times: All year: daily from 9.30pm.

Admission: Free.

i	Shop. Plant centre.	X	Wedding receptions.	👤	Suitable. WCs.
☕	Licensed restaurant, tearoom, café.	🚶	By arrangement.		
P	Ample for cars. Limited for coaches.	👥	Educational programme.		
🐕	Guide dogs only.				

ELGIN CATHEDRAL 🏛   **Tel:** 01343 547171

Elgin

Owner: Historic Scotland   **Contact:** The Custodian

When entire this was perhaps the most beautiful of Scottish cathedrals, known as the Lantern of the North. 13th century, much modified after almost being destroyed in 1390 by Alexander Stewart, the infamous 'Wolf of Badenoch'. The octagonal chapterhouse is the finest in Scotland. You can see the Bishop's home at Spynie Palace, 2m north of the town.

Location: OS Ref. NJ223 630. In Elgin on the A96.

Opening Times: 1 Apr - 30 Sept: daily, 9.30am - 6.30pm, last ticket 6pm. 1 Oct - 31 Mar: Mon - Sat, 9.30am - 4.30pm, Sun 2 - 4.30pm, last ticket 4pm. Closed Thur pm & Fri in winter.

Admission: Adult £1.80, Child 75p, Conc. £1.30. Joint entry ticket with Spynie Palace: Adult £2.80, Child £1.20, Conc. £2.10.

Drum Castle.

Scotland
Grampian

FASQUE

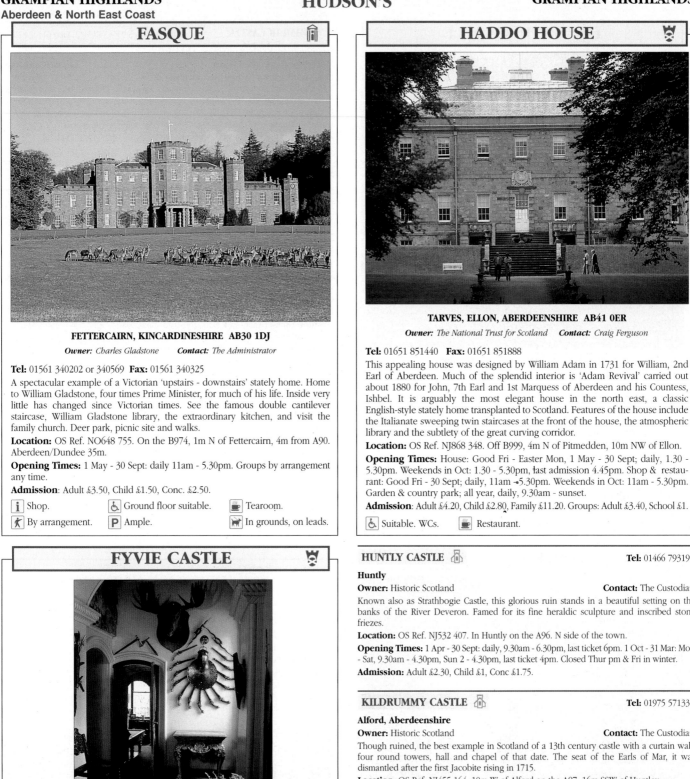

FETTERCAIRN, KINCARDINESHIRE AB30 1DJ

Owner: Charles Gladstone   *Contact:* The Administrator

Tel: 01561 340202 or 340569 **Fax:** 01561 340325

A spectacular example of a Victorian 'upstairs - downstairs' stately home. Home to William Gladstone, four times Prime Minister, for much of his life. Inside very little has changed since Victorian times. See the famous double cantilever staircase, William Gladstone library, the extraordinary kitchen, and visit the family church. Deer park, picnic site and walks.

Location: OS Ref. NO648 755. On the B974, 1m N of Fettercairn, 4m from A90. Aberdeen/Dundee 35m.

Opening Times: 1 May - 30 Sept: daily 11am - 5.30pm. Groups by arrangement any time.

Admission: Adult £3.50, Child £1.50, Conc. £2.50.

| ℹ️ Shop. | ♿ Ground floor suitable. | ☕ Tearoom. |
| 🚶 By arrangement. | 🅿️ Ample. | 🐕 In grounds, on leads. |

FYVIE CASTLE

TURRIFF, ABERDEENSHIRE AB53 8JS

Owner: The National Trust for Scotland   *Contact:* The Property Manager

Tel: 01651 891266 **Fax:** 01651 891107

The south front of this magnificent building employs a plethora of crow-stepped gables, turrets, sculpted dormers and finials in the form of musicians, to create a marvellous façade. The five towers of the castle bear witness to the five families who have owned it. Fyvie Castle boasts the finest wheel stair in Scotland and there is a superb collection of arms and armour and paintings, including works by Batoni, Raeburn, Romney, Gainsborough, Opie and Hoppner.

Location: OS Ref. NJ763 393. Off A947, 8m SE of Turriff, and 25m N of Aberdeen.

Opening Times: Castle: 1 Apr - 30 Jun, 1 - 30 Sept; daily 1.30 - 5.30pm. 1 Jul - 31 Aug; daily, 11am - 5.30pm. Weekends in Oct: 1.30 - 5.30pm, last admission 4.45pm. Tearoom, as castle but 12.30pm when castle opens at 1.30pm. Grounds: all year, daily, 9.30am - sunset.

Admission: Adult £4.20, Child £2.80, Family £11.20. Groups: Adult £3.40, School £1.

| ℹ️ Shop. | ♿ Suitable, WC. | ☕ Tearoom. |

HADDO HOUSE

TARVES, ELLON, ABERDEENSHIRE AB41 0ER

Owner: The National Trust for Scotland   *Contact:* Craig Ferguson

Tel: 01651 851440 **Fax:** 01651 851888

This appealing house was designed by William Adam in 1731 for William, 2nd Earl of Aberdeen. Much of the splendid interior is 'Adam Revival' carried out about 1880 for John, 7th Earl and 1st Marquess of Aberdeen and his Countess, Ishbel. It is arguably the most elegant house in the north east, a classic English-style stately home transplanted to Scotland. Features of the house include the Italianate sweeping twin staircases at the front of the house, the atmospheric library and the subtlety of the great curving corridor.

Location: OS Ref. NJ868 348. Off B999, 4m N of Pitmedden, 10m NW of Ellon.

Opening Times: House: Good Fri - Easter Mon, 1 May - 30 Sept; daily, 1.30 - 5.30pm. Weekends in Oct: 1.30 - 5.30pm, last admission 4.45pm. Shop & restaurant: Good Fri - 30 Sept; daily, 11am - 5.30pm. Weekends in Oct: 11am - 5.30pm. Garden & country park; all year, daily, 9.30am - sunset.

Admission: Adult £4.20, Child £2.80, Family £11.20. Groups: Adult £3.40, School £1.

| ♿ Suitable. WCs. | ☕ Restaurant. |

HUNTLY CASTLE   **Tel:** 01466 793191

Huntly

Owner: Historic Scotland   **Contact:** The Custodian

Known also as Strathbogie Castle, this glorious ruin stands in a beautiful setting on the banks of the River Deveron. Famed for its fine heraldic sculpture and inscribed stone friezes.

Location: OS Ref. NJ532 407. In Huntly on the A96. N side of the town.

Opening Times: 1 Apr - 30 Sept: daily, 9.30am - 6.30pm, last ticket 6pm. 1 Oct - 31 Mar: Mon - Sat, 9.30am - 4.30pm, Sun 2 - 4.30pm, last ticket 4pm. Closed Thur pm & Fri in winter.

Admission: Adult £2.30, Child £1, Conc £1.75.

KILDRUMMY CASTLE   **Tel:** 01975 571331

Alford, Aberdeenshire

Owner: Historic Scotland   **Contact:** The Custodian

Though ruined, the best example in Scotland of a 13th century castle with a curtain wall, four round towers, hall and chapel of that date. The seat of the Earls of Mar, it was dismantled after the first Jacobite rising in 1715.

Location: OS Ref. NJ455 164. 10m W of Alford on the A97. 16m SSW of Huntley.

Opening Times: 1 Apr - 30 Sept: daily, 9.30am - 6.30pm, last ticket 6pm.

Admission: Adult £1.80, Child 75p, Conc. £1.30.

KILDRUMMY CASTLE GARDEN   **Tel:** 01975 571203 / 571277

Kildrummy, Aberdeenshire   **Contact:** Alastair J Laing

Ancient quarry, shrub and alpine gardens renowned for their interest and variety. Water gardens below ruined castle.

Location: OS Ref. NJ455 164. On A97 off A944 10m SW of Alford. 16m SSW of Huntley.

Opening Times: Apr - Oct: daily, 10am - 5pm.

Admission: Adult £2, Child free.

| ℹ️ Plant centre. | ♿ Partially suitable. | ☕ Tearoom. | 🚶 By arrangement. |
| 🅿️ Ample. | 🐕 In grounds, on leads. | | |

LEITH HALL

HUNTLY, ABERDEENSHIRE AB54 4NQ

Owner: The National Trust for Scotland   *Contact:* Eileen Law

Tel: 01464 831216 **Fax:** 01464 831489

This mansion house is built around a courtyard and was the home of the Leith family for almost 400 years. With an enviable family record of military service over the centuries, the house contains a unique collection of military memorabilia displayed in an exhibition *'For Crown and Country'*. The graciously furnished rooms are a delight to wander through and present a fine impression of the lifestyle of the Leith family.

Location: OS Ref. NJ541 298. B9002, 1m W of Kennethmont, 7m S of Huntley.

Opening Times: House & tearoom: Good Fri - Easter Mon, 1 May - 30 Sept; daily, 1.30 - 5.30pm. Weekends in Oct: 1.30 - 5.30pm, last admission 4.45pm. Gardens & grounds; all year, daily, 9.30am - sunset.

Admission: Adult £4.20, Child £2.80, Family £11.20. Groups: Adult £3.40, School £1. Gardens & grounds: Adult £2, Child £1.30. Groups: Adult £1.60, School £1.

[&] Partially suitable. WC. [☕] Tearoom.

PITMEDDEN GARDEN

Doug Westland

ELLON, ABERDEENSHIRE AB41 0PD

Owner: The National Trust for Scotland   *Contact:* Douglas Westland

Tel: 01651 842352 **Fax:** 01651 843188

The centrepiece of this property is the Great Garden which was originally laid out in 1675 by Sir Alexander Seton, 1st Baronet of Pitmedden. The elaborate designs, inspired by the garden at the Palace of Holyroodhouse in Edinburgh, have been painstakingly recreated for the enjoyment of visitors. The 100-acre estate, contains the very fine Museum of Farming Life, which presents a vivid picture of the lives and times of bygone days when the horse was the power in front of the plough and farm machinery was less complicated than it is today.

Location: OS Ref. NJ885 280. On A920 1m W of Pitmedden village and 14m N of Aberdeen.

Opening Times: Garden, visitor centre, museum, grounds and other facilities: 1 May - 30 Sept; daily, 10am - 5.30pm, last admission 5pm.

Admission: Adult: £3.70, Child £2.50, Family £9.90. Groups: Adult £3, School £1.

[&] Suitable.

MONYMUSK WALLED GARDEN   **Tel:** 01467 651543

Home Farm, Monymusk, Aberdeen AB51 7HL

Owner: Mrs E Whyte   **Contact:** Mrs E Whyte

Mainly herbaceous plants in walled garden setting.

Opening Times: Nov - Mar: Mon, Wed, Fri & Sat, 10am - 3pm, Sun 12 noon - 3pm. Apr - Oct: Mon - Sat, 10am - 5pm, Sun 12 noon - 5pm.

Admission: Donations welcome.

Haddo House.

PLUSCARDEN ABBEY   **Tel:** 01343 890257 **Fax:** 01343 890258

Nr Elgin, Moray IV30 3UA

Owner: The Benedictine Community   **Owner:** Father Giles
Valliscaulian, founded 1230.

Location: OS Ref. NJ142 576. On a minor road 6m SW of Elgin. Follow B9010 for first mile.

Opening Times: 4.45am - 8.30pm. Shop open 8.30am - 5pm.

Admission: Free

[i] Shop. Retreats. [X] Not available. [&] Partially suitable. WCs. Won access award.

[K] By arrangement. [P] Ample. [👥] Teachers' pack. [🐕] In grounds, on leads.

[A] 24 singles. No ensuite.

Fyvie Castle.

GRAMPIAN HIGHLANDS
Aberdeen & North East Coast

HUDSON'S

GRAMPIAN HIGHLANDS

Scotland
Grampian

PROVOST SKENE'S HOUSE

45 GUEST ROW, OFF BROAD STREET, ABERDEEN AB10 1AS

Owner: Aberdeen City Council   *Contact: Christine Rew*

Tel: 01224 646333 **Fax:** 01224 632133

Built in the 16th century, Provost Skene's House is one of Aberdeen's few remaining examples of early Bugh architecture. Splendid room settings include a suite of Georgian rooms, an Edwardian nursery, magnificent 17th century plaster ceilings and wood panelling. The painted gallery houses the most important cycle of religious painting in North East Scotland.

Location: OS Ref. NJ943 064. Aberdeen city centre, off Broad Street.

Opening Times: All year: Mon - Sat, 10am - 5pm (except 25/26 Dec & 1/2 Jan).

Admission: Free.

i Shop. No photography.	X Small functions.	& Not suitable.
Tearoom.	By arrangement.	P Car parks nearby.
Educational programme.	Guide dogs only.	

SPECIAL EVENTS 1998

See the front section for full list.

ST MACHAR'S CATHEDRAL TRANSEPTS

Tel: 0131 668 8800

Old Aberdeen

Owner: Historic Scotland

The nave and towers of the Cathedral remain in use as a church, and the ruined transepts are in care. In the south transept is the fine altar tomb of Bishop Dunbar (1514 - 32).

Location: OS Ref. NJ939 088. In old Aberdeen. $1/2$ m N of King's College.

Admission: Free.

SPYNIE PALACE

Tel: 01343 546358

Elgin

Owner: Historic Scotland   **Contact:** The Custodian

Spynie Palace was the residence of the Bishops of Moray from the 14th century to 1686. The site is dominated by the massive tower built by Bishop David Stewart (1461-77) and affords spectacular views across Spynie Loch.

Location: OS Ref. NJ231 659. 2m N of Elgin off the A941.

Opening Times: 1 Apr - 30 Sept: daily, 9.30am - 6.30pm. 1 Oct - 31 Mar: Sat, 9.30am - 4.30pm, Sun, 2 - 4.30pm. Last ticket 30 mins before closing.

Admission: Adult £1.80, Child 75p, Conc. £1.30. Joint entry ticket with Elgin Cathedral: Adult £2.80, Child £1.20, Conc. £2.10.

TOLQUHON CASTLE

Tel: 01651 851286

Aberdeenshire

Owner: Historic Scotland   **Contact:** The Custodian

Tolquhon was built for the Forbes family. The early 15th century tower was enlarged between 1584 and 1589 with a large mansion around the courtyard. Noted for its highly ornamented gatehouse and pleasance.

Location: OS Ref. NJ874 286. 15m N of Aberdeen on the A920. 6m N of Ellon.

Opening Times: 1 Apr - 30 Sept: daily, 9.30am - 6.30pm. 1 Oct - 31 Mar: Sat, 9.30am - 4.30pm, Sun, 2 - 4.30pm. Last ticket 30 mins before closing.

Admission: Adult £1.50, Child 75p, Conc. £1.10.

J Henderson.

Crathes Castle.

CAWDOR CASTLE
Nairn

CONTACT

The Secretary
Cawdor Castle
Nairn
Scotland
IV12 5RD

Tel: (01667) 404615

Fax: (01667) 404674

e-mail:
cawdor.castle@btinternet.com

LOCATION

OS Ref. NH850 500

From Edinburgh
A9, 3¹/₂ hrs,
Inverness 20 mins,
Nairn 10 mins.
Main road: A9, 14m.

Rail: Nairn Station
5m.

Bus: Inverness to Nairn
bus route 200 yds.

Taxi: Nairn Taxis
(01667) 455342

Air: Inverness Airport 5m.

This splendid romantic castle dating from the late 14th century was built as a private fortress by the Thanes of Cawdor, and remains the home of the Cawdor family to this day. The ancient medieval tower was built around the legendary holly tree.

Although the house has evolved over 600 years, later additions mainly of the 17th century were all built in the Scottish vernacular style with slated roofs over walls and crow-stepped gables of mellow local stone. This style gives Cawdor a strong sense of unity, and the massive, severe exterior belies an intimate interior that gives the place a surprisingly personal, friendly atmosphere.

Good furniture, fine portraits and pictures, interesting objects and outstanding tapestries are arranged to please the family rather than to echo fashion or impress. Memories of Shakespeare's *Macbeth* give Cawdor an elusive, evocative quality that delights visitors.

GARDENS

The flower garden also has a family feel to it, where plants are chosen out of affection rather than affectation. This is a lovely spot between spring and late summer. The walled garden has been restored with a holly maze, paradise garden, knot garden and thistle garden. The wild garden beside its stream leads into beautiful trails through a spectacular mature mixed woodland, through which paths are helpfully marked and colour-coded.

OPENING TIMES

SUMMER

1 May - 11 October
Daily, 10am - 5.30pm.

Last admission 5pm.

WINTER

12 October - 30 April
Closed.

ADMISSION

SUMMER
House & Garden

Adult £5.20
Child* £2.80
OAP/Student...........£4.20
Family (2+5) £14.00

Groups (Min 20)
Adult £4.70
Child* £2.30
OAP/Student...........£4.20

Garden only
Per person £2.80

*Age 5 - 15

SPECIAL EVENTS

• **JUNE 6/7:**
Special Garden Weekend.
Guided tours of gardens and
Cawdor Big Wood.

---

i Gift, book and wool shops. Conferences, 9 hole golf course, putting green, golf clubs for hire, whisky tasting, musical entertainments, specialised garden visits. No photography, video taping or tripods inside.

✗ Lunches, sherry or champagne receptions.

♿ Visitors may alight at the entrance. WC. Only ground floor accessible.

☕ Licensed buttery, May-Oct, groups should book.

P 250 cars and 25 coaches. Two weeks' notice for group catering, coach drivers/couriers free.

👨‍👩‍👧 Welcome, £2.30 per child. Room notes, quiz and answer sheet can be provided. Ranger service and nature trails.

🐕 No dogs.

CONFERENCE/FUNCTION		
ROOM	SIZE	MAX CAPACITY
Cawdor Hall		40

DUNVEGAN CASTLE
Isle of Skye

DUNVEGAN is unique. It is the only Great House in the Western Isles of Scotland to have retained its family and its roof. It is the oldest home in the whole of Scotland continuously inhabited by the same family - the Chiefs of the Clan Macleod. A Castle placed on a rock by the sea - the curtain wall is dated before 1200 A.D. - its superb location recalls the Norse Empire of the Vikings, the ancestors of the Chiefs.

Dunvegan's continuing importance as a custodian of the Clan spirit is epitomised by the famous Fairy Flag, whose origins are shrouded in mystery but whose ability to protect both Chief and Clan is unquestioned. To enter Dunvegan is to arrive at a place whose history combines with legend to make a living reality.

GARDENS
The gardens and grounds extend over some ten acres of woodland walks, peaceful formal lawns and a water garden dominated by two spectacular natural waterfalls. The temperate climate aids in producing a fine show of rhododendrons and azaleas, the chief glory of the garden in spring. Always one is aware of the proximity of the sea and many garden walks finish at the Castle Jetty, from where traditional boats make regular trips to view the delightful Seal Colony.

CONTACT

The Administrator
Dunvegan Castle
Isle of Skye
Scotland
IV55 8WF

Tel: (01470) 521206
Fax: (01470) 521205

LOCATION

OS Ref. NG250 480

1m N of village. NW corner of Skye.

From Inverness A82 to Invermoriston, A887 to Kyle of Lochalsh 82m. From Fort William A82 to Invergarry, A87 to Kyle of Lochalsh 76m.

Kyle of Lochalsh to Dunvegan 45m via Skye Bridge (toll).

Ferry: To the Isle of Skye, 'roll-on, roll-off', 30 minute crossing.

Rail: Inverness to Kyle of Lochalsh 3 - 4 trains per day - 45m.

Bus: Portree 25m, Kyle of Lochalsh 45m.

Gift and craft shop. Boat trips to seal colony. Loch cruises, charter and fishing trips, pedigree Highland cattle. No photography in castle.

Visitors may alight at entrance. WC.

Licensed restaurant, (cap. 70) special rates for groups, menus upon request. Tel: (01470) 521310. Open late peak season for evening meals.

By appointment in English or Gaelic at no extra charge. If requested owner may meet groups, tour time 45mins.

120 cars and 10 coaches. Do not attempt to take passengers to Castle Jetty (long walk). If possible please book. Seal boat trip dependent upon weather.

Welcome by arrangement. Guide available on request.

In grounds only, on lead.

4 self-catering units, 3 of which sleep 6 and 1 of which sleeps 7.

OPENING TIMES
SUMMER

23 March - 31 October
Daily: 10am - 5.30pm.
Last admission 5pm.

WINTER

11am - 4pm.

ADMISSION
SUMMER

Castle
Adult £5.00
Child (under 16) £2.50
OAP/Student...........£4.50
Group £4.50

Garden
Adult £3.50
Child (under 16) £2.00

Seal Boats
Adult £3.80
Child (under 16) £2.50

Loch Cruises
Adult £8.00
Child/Conc. £6.00

WINTER

11am - 4pm.
No boat trips.

ATTADALE GARDENS

By STRATHCARRON, ROSS-SHIRE IV54 8YX

Owner: Mr & Mrs Ewen Macpherson   *Contact:* Mr & Mrs Ewen Macpherson

Tel: 01520 722217

The garden and woodland walks were planted by the Schroder family from 1890 onwards with species rhododendrons, azaleas and southern hemisphere plants made possible by the warm gulf stream. Spectacular water gardens with primula, iris and giant gunnera. Hill walks with views of Skye and the sea. Victorian sunken garden by the house. Waterproof shoes recommended.

Location: OS Ref. NG920 400. On A890 between Strathcarron and South Strome. 12m N of A87.

Opening Times: 1 Apr - 31 Oct: Mon - Sat, 10am - 5.30pm.

Admission: Adult £2, Child £1. Coaches/guided tours by prior arrangement.

♧ WC.   ☺ One mile away.   P Ample.   In grounds, on leads.

BALLINDALLOCH CASTLE 🏛

GRANTOWN-ON-SPEY, BANFFSHIRE AB37 9AX

Owner: Mr & Mrs Russell   *Contact:* Mrs Clare Russell

Tel: 01807 500206   **Fax:** 01807 500210

Ballindalloch is a much loved family home and one of the few castles lived in continuously by its original owners, the Macpherson-Grants, since 1546. Filled with family memorabilia and a magnificent collection of 17th century Spanish paintings, it is home to the famous breed of Aberdeen Angus cattle. Beautiful rock and rose garden, river walks.

Location: OS Ref. NJ178 366. 14m NE of Grantown-on-Spey on A95, 22m S of Elgin on A95.

Opening Times: Good Fri - 30 Sept: 10am - 5pm.

Admission: Adult £4.50, Child (under 5) free (6 - 16) £2.50, Disabled £2. Groups: (20+) Adult £4. Garden and grounds only: £2.

i Shop.   Ground floor & grounds. WC.   Tearoom.   P Ample.   Audio-Visual.   In grounds, on leads.

CAWDOR CASTLE 🏛   See page 351 for full page entry.

CLAN DONALD VISITOR CENTRE & ARMADALE CASTLE GARDEN

Armadale, Isle of Skye IV45 8RS   **Tel:** 01471 844305   **Fax:** 01471 844275

Owner: Clan Donald Lands Trust   **Contact:** R McDonald Parker

Part of Armadale Castle houses a visitor centre houses the "Museum of the Isles" telling the story of the Macdonalds and the Lords of the Isles.

Location: OS Ref. NG630 020. 1m N of the Mallaig - Armadale ferry terminal.

Opening Times: Apr - Oct: daily, 9.30am - 5.30pm.

Admission: Adult £3.40, Child £2.20, Conc./Groups £2.20.

i Shop.   X Wedding receptions.   Partially suitable. WCs.   Licensed restaurant, tearoom.   By arrangement.   P Ample.   Educational programme.   In grounds, on leads.

CROMARTY COURTHOUSE   **Tel:** 01381 600418   **Fax:** 01381 600408

Church Street, Cromarty IV11 8XA   **Contact:** David Alston

18th century town courthouse, visitor centre and museum.

Location: OS Ref. NH790 680. 25m N of Inverness.

Opening Times: Apr - Oct: 10am - 5pm.

Admission: Adult £3, Conc. £2.

Educational programme. Teachers' pack.

CULLODEN ⚜

CULLODEN MOOR, INVERNESS IV1 2ED

Owner: The National Trust for Scotland   *Contact:* Ross Mackenzie

Tel: 01463 790607   **Fax:** 01463 794294

No name in Scottish history evokes more emotion than that of Culloden, the bleak moor which in 1746 saw the hopes of the young Prince Charles Edward Stuart crushed, and the end of the Jacobite Rising, the 'Forty-Five'. The Prince's forces, greatly outnumbered by those of the brutal Duke of Cumberland, nevertheless went into battle with a courage which has passed into legend.

Location: OS Ref. NH745 450. On B9006, 5m E of Inverness.

Opening Times: Site; all year, daily. Visitor centre: 1 Feb - 31 Mar & 1 Nov - 30 Dec (except 25/26 Dec); daily, 10am - 4pm. 1 Apr - 31 Oct; daily, 9am - 6pm. Restaurant & audio visual; same dates but closes 30 mins earlier.

Admission: Adult £3, Child £2, Family £8. Groups: Adult £2.40, School £1.

i Shop (closed 1 - 6 Nov) & visitor centre.   Suitable. WC.   Restaurant.   Audio visual show.   In dog walking area only.

DOCHFOUR GARDENS

Tel: 01463 861218

Dochgarroch, Inverness IV3 6JY

Owner: The Hon. A J Baillie   **Contact:** Miss J Taylor

Victorian terraced garden near Inverness with panoramic views over Loch Dochfour. Magnificent specimen trees, naturalised daffodils, rhododendrons, water garden, yew topiary.

Location: OS Ref. NH620 610. 6m SW of Inverness on A82 to Fort William.

Opening Times: Gardens: Apr - Sept, Mon - Fri, 10am - 5pm. Jul - Aug also open Sat & Sun, 2 - 5pm. House not open.

Admission: Garden walk - £1.50.

DUNROBIN CASTLE

GOLSPIE, SUTHERLAND KW10 6SF

Owner: *The Sutherland Trust*   **Contact:** *Keith Jones, Curator*

Tel: 01408 633268 **Fax:** 01408 634081

Dates from the 13th century with additions in the 17th, 18th and 19th centuries. Wonderful furniture, paintings, library, ceremonial robes and memorabilia. Victorian museum in grounds with a fascinating collection including Pictish stones. Set in fine woodlands overlooking the sea. Magnificent formal gardens, one of few remaining French/Scottish formal parterres.

Location: OS Ref. NC850 010. 50m N of Inverness on A9. 1m NE of Golspie.

Opening Times: 1 Apr - 31 May & 1 - 15 Oct: Mon - Sat, 10.30am - 4.30pm. Sun, 12 - 4.30pm. 1 Jun - 30 Sept: Mon - Sat, 10.30am - 5.30pm. Sun, 12 - 5.30pm.

Admission: Adult £5, Child/Conc. £3.50. Groups: Adult £4.50, Child/Conc £3. Family (2+2) £15.

ⓘ Gift shop.   🍴 Restaurant.

DUNVEGAN CASTLE

See page 352 for full page entry.

EILEAN DONAN CASTLE

Tel: 01599 555202

Dornie, Kyle, Wester IV40 8DX   **Contact:** The Administrator

Picturesque castle on an islet dating back to 1220.

Location: OS Ref. NG880 260. On A87 8m E of Skye Ferry.

Opening Times: Easter - end Oct: 10am - 5.30pm.

Admission: Adult £3, Conc./Groups £1.50.

ⓘ Shop.   ♿ Not suitable.   ☕ Available.

Ⓟ Ample.   🐕 In grounds, on leads.

FORT GEORGE

ARDERSIER BY INVERNESS IV1 2TD

Owner: *Historic Scotland*   **Contact:** *Tommy Simpson*

Tel: 01667 462777 **Fax:** 01667 462698

Built following the Battle of Culloden to subdue the Highlands, Fort George never saw a shot fired in anger. One of the most outstanding artillery fortifications in Europe with reconstructed barrack room displays. The Queen's Own Highlanders' Museum.

Location: OS Ref. NH762 567. 11m NE of Inverness off the A96 by Ardersier.

Opening Times: April - Sept: daily, 9.30am - 6.30pm. Oct - Mar, Mon - Sat, 9.30am - 4.30pm; Sun 2 - 4.30pm. Last ticket sold 45 mins before closing.

Admission: Adult £3, Child £1, Conc. £2.30. 10% discount for groups over 10.

ⓘ Shop, picnic tables.   ✗ Private evening hire.   ☕ Tearoom in summer.

♿ Wheelchairs available. WCs.   Ⓟ Ample.   🧑‍🏫 Teachers' pack.

🐕 In grounds, on leads.

GLENFINNAN

INVERNESS-SHIRE PH37 4LT

Owner: *The National Trust for Scotland*   **Contact:** *Mrs Lillias Grant*

Tel/Fax: 01397 722250

The monument, situated on the scenic road to the Isles, is set amid superb Highland scenery at the head of Loch Shiel. It was erected in 1815 in tribute to the clansmen who fought and died in the Jacobite cause. Prince Charles Edward Stuart's standard was raised near here in 1745. Despite its inspired beginnings, the campaign came to a grim conclusion on the Culloden battlefield in 1746.

Location: OS Ref. NM906 805. On A830, 18m W of Fort William, Lochaber.

Opening Times: Site: all year, daily. Visitor centre & snack bar: 1 Apr - 18 May and 1 Sept - 31 Oct; daily, 10am - 1pm & 2 - 5pm. 19 May - 31 Aug; daily, 9.30am - 6pm (snack bar 10am - 6pm).

Admission: Adult £1.50, Child £1, Family £4.

ⓘ Shop. Visitor centre.   ♿ Grounds suitable. WC.   ☕ Snack bar.

Ⓟ Ample.   🐕 In grounds, on leads.

HUGH MILLER'S COTTAGE

Hugh Miller's Cottage.

CROMARTY IV11 8XA

Owner: *The National Trust for Scotland*   **Contact:** *Ms Frieda Gostwick*

Tel: 01381 600245

Furnished thatched cottage of c1698, birthplace of eminent geologist and writer Hugh Miller. Exhibition and video.

Location: OS Ref. NH790 680. Via Kessock Bridge & A832, in Cromarty, 22m NE of Inverness.

Opening Times: 1 May - 30 Sept: Mon - Sat, 11am - 1pm & 2 - 5pm. Sun 2 - 5pm.

Admission: Adult £2, Child £1.30, Family £5.30. Groups: Adult £1.60, School £1.

♿ Not suitable.   P Public parking at shore.   Guide dogs only.

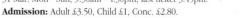

URQUHART CASTLE   **Tel:** 01456 450551

Drumnadrochit, Loch Ness

Owner: Historic Scotland   **Contact:** The Custodian

The remains of one of the largest castles in Scotland dominate a rocky promontory on Loch Ness. It fell into decay after 1689. Most of the existing buildings date from the 16th century. A popular viewpoint for monster spotting. Splendid views up and down the loch.

Location: OS Ref. NH531 286. On Loch Ness, 1½ m S of Drumnadrochit on A82.

Opening Times: 1 Apr - 30 Sept: Mon - Sun, 9.30am - 6.30pm, last ticket 5.45pm. 1 Oct - 31 Mar: Mon - Sun, 9.30am - 4.30pm, last ticket 3.45pm.

Admission: Adult £3.50, Child £1, Conc. £2.80.

INVEREWE GARDEN

Inverewe Garden, Ross & Cromarty.

POOLEWE, ROSS & CROMARTY IV22 2LQ

Owner: *The National Trust for Scotland*   **Contact:** *Keith Gordon*

Tel: 01445 781200   **Fax:** 01445 781497

Where in Scotland will you see the tallest Australian gum trees in Britain, sweetly scented Chinese rhododendrons, exotic trees from Chile and Blue Nile lilies from South Africa, all growing on a latitude more northerly than Moscow? The answer is Inverewe. Although you are in a remote corner of Wester Ross, you are also in a sheltered garden, blessed by the North Atlantic Drift. In a spectacular lochside setting among pinewoods, Osgood Mackenzie's Victorian dreams have produced a glorious 50 acre mecca for garden lovers.

Location: OS Ref. NG860 820. On A832, by Poolewe, 6m NE of Gairloch, Highland.

Opening Times: Garden: 15 Mar - 31 Oct; daily, 9.30am - 9pm. 1 Nov - 14 Mar; daily, 9.30 - 5pm. Visitor centre & shop: 15 Mar - 30 Sept; daily, 9.30am - 5.30pm. Restaurant; same dates, daily, 10am - 5pm. Guided walks: 1 Apr - 30 Oct: Mon - Fri at 1.30pm.

Admission: Adult £4.80, Child £3.20, Family £12.80. Groups: Adult £3.80, School £1.

i Shop & visitor centre.   ♿ Grounds suitable. WC.   Licensed restaurant. P Ample (no shade for dogs).   Guide dogs only.

Scotland
Outer Islands

BALFOUR CASTLE
Tel: 01856 711282 **Fax:** 01856 711283

Shapinsay, Orkney Islands KW17 2DY
Owner: Mrs Lidderdale   **Contact:** Mrs Lidderdale
Built in 1848.
Location: OS Ref. HY475 164 on Shapinsay Island, 3^1/2n NNE of Kirkwall.
Opening Times: Mid May - mid Sept: Wed and Suns, 2.30 - 5.30pm.
Admission: £13 including boat fare, guided tour of castle and gardens and afternoon tea.

BISHOP'S & EARL'S PALACES
Tel: 01856 875461

Kirkwall, Orkney
Owner: Historic Scotland   **Contact:** The Custodian
The Bishop's Palace is a 12th century hall-house with a round tower built by Bishop Reid in 1541-48. The adjacent Earl's Palace built in 1607 has been described as the most mature and accomplished piece of Renaissance architecture left in Scotland.
Location: Bishop's Palace: OS Ref. HY447 108. Earl's Palace: OS Ref. HY448 108. In Kirkwall on A960.
Opening Times: 1 Apr - 30 Sept: daily, 9.30am - 6.30pm, last ticket 6pm.
Admission: Adult £1.50, Child 75p, Conc. £1.10. Joint entry ticket available for all the Orkney monuments: Adult £9, Child £2.50, Conc. £7.

BLACK HOUSE
Tel: 01851 710395

Arnol, Isle of Lewis
Owner: Historic Scotland   **Contact:** The Custodian
A traditional Lewis thatched house, fully furnished, complete with attached barn, byre and stockyard. A peat fire burns in the open hearth.
Location: OS Ref. NB320 500. In Arnol village, 11m NW of Stornoway on A858.
Opening Times: 1 Apr - 30 Sept: Mon - Sat, 9.30am - 6.30pm, last ticket 6pm. 1 Oct - 31 Mar: Mon - Thurs & Sat, 9.30am - 4.30pm, last ticket 4pm.
Admission: Adult £1.80, Child 75p, Conc. £1.30.

BROCH OF GURNESS
Tel: 01831 579478

Aikerness, Orkney
Owner: Historic Scotland   **Contact:** The Custodian
Protected by three lines of ditch and rampart, the base of the broch is surrounded by a warren of Iron Age buildings.
Location: OS Ref. HY383 268. At Aikerness, about 14m NW of Kirkwall on A966.
Opening Times: 1 Apr - 30 Sept: daily, 9.30am - 6.30pm, last ticket 6pm.
Admission: Adult £2.30, Child £1, Conc. £1.75. Joint entry ticket available for all Orkney monuments: Adult £9, Child £2.50, Conc. £7.

CALANAIS STANDING STONES
Tel: 01851 621422

Calanais, Stornoway, Lewis, Outer Islands
Owner: Historic Scotland
A cross shaped setting of standing stones, unique in Scotland.
Location: OS Ref. NB213 330. 12m W of Stornaway off A859.
Opening Times: All year: daily, summer 10am - 7pm, winter 10am - 4pm. Visitor centre closed Sundays.
Admission: Adult £1.50, Child 50p, Conc. £1.

JARLSHOF PREHISTORIC & NORSE SETTLEMENT
Tel: 01950 460112

Shetland
Owner: Historic Scotland   **Contact:** The Custodian
Over 3 acres of remains spanning 3,000 years from the Stone Age. Oval shaped Bronze Age houses, Iron Age broch and wheel houses. Viking long houses, medieval farmstead and 16th century laird's house.
Location: OS Ref. HY401 096. At Sumburgh Head, 22m S of Lerwick on the A970.
Opening Times: 1 Apr - 30 Sept: daily, 9.30am - 6.30pm. Last adm. ^{1}/2 hr before closing.
Admission: Adult £2.30, Child £1, Conc. £1.75.

MAES HOWE
Tel: 01856 761606

Orkney
Owner: Historic Scotland   **Contact:** The Custodian
This world famous tomb was built in Neolithic times, before 2700 BC. The large mound covers a stone-built passage and a burial chamber with cells in the walls. Runic inscriptions tell of how it was plundered of its treasures by Vikings.
Location: OS Ref. NY318 128. 9m W of Kirkwall on the A965.
Opening Times: 1 Apr - 30 Sept: daily, 9.30am - 6.30pm. 1 Oct - 31 Mar: Mon - Wed & Sat, 9.30am - 4.30pm, Thursdays mornings only, Sun 2 - 4.30pm.
Admission: Adult £2.30, Child £1, Conc. £1.75. Joint entry ticket available for all Orkney monuments: Adult £9, Child £2.50, Conc. £7. Admission, shop and refreshments at nearby Tormiston Mill.

RING OF BRODGAR STONE CIRCLE & HENGE
Tel: 0131 668 8600

Stromness, Orkney
Owner: Historic Scotland   **Contact:** The Custodian
A magnificent circle of upright stones with an enclosing ditch spanned by causeways. Of late Neolithic date.
Location: OS Ref. HY294 134. 5m NE of Stromness.
Opening Times: Any reasonable time.
Admission: Free.

ST MAGNUS'S CATHEDRAL
Tel: 01856 873535

Broad Street, Kirkwell, Orkney
Owner: Orkney Islands Council   **Contact:** Mr Richard Welch
Location: OS Ref. HY447 109. Centre of Kirkwell.
Opening Times: 1 Apr - end Sept: Mon - Sat, 9am - 6pm, Sun, 2 - 6pm. 1 Oct - end Mar: Mon - Sat, 9am - 1pm & 2 - 5pm.
Admission: Free.

SKARA BRAE & SKAILL HOUSE

SANDWICK, ORKNEY
Owner: *Historic Scotland/Major M R S Macrae*   **Contact:** *The Steward*

Tel: 01856 841815
Skara Brae is one of the best preserved groups of Stone Age houses in Western Europe. Built before the Pyramids, the houses contain stone furniture, hearths and drains. New visitor centre opening in April 1998 with joint admission with Skaill House – 17th century home of the Laird who excavated Skara Brae.
Location: OS6 HY231 188. 19m NW of Kirkwall on the B9056.
Opening Times: Apr - Sept: daily, 9.30am - 6.30pm; Oct - Mar, Mon–Sat 9.30am - 4.30pm; Sun 2 - 4.30pm.
Admission: Apr - Sept: Adult £4, Child £1.20, Conc. £3. Oct - Mar: Adult £3.20, Child £1, Conc. £2.40. 10% discount for groups over 10. Joint ticket with other Orkney sites available. Free schools visit scheme (pre-booked).

ℹ️ Shop.   ♿ Partially suitable. WCs.   🅿 Ample.
👫 Teachers' pack.   🐕 Guide dogs only.

TANKERNESS HOUSE
Tel: 01856 873191 **Fax:** 01856 874615

Broad Street, Kirkwall, Orkney
Owner: Orkney Islands Council   **Contact:** Bryce S Wilson
A fine vernacular 16th century town house containing museum of Orkney history.
Location: OS Ref. HY446 109. In Kirkwall opposite W end of cathedral.
Opening Times: All year: Mon - Sat, 10.30am - 12.30pm and 1.30 - 5pm, Suns 2 - 5pm.
Admission: Adult £2, Conc. Free.

W A L E S

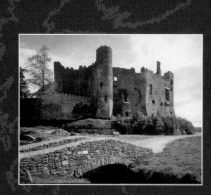

Wales

North Wales

South Wales

Historic Houses Association Member, offering access under HHA Friends Scheme.

Property owned by The National Trust.

Property in the care of CADW ~ Welsh Historic Monuments.

Wales

North and South

ABERCONWY HOUSE

Tel: 01492 592246

Castle Street, Conwy LL32 8AY

Owner: The National Trust

Contact: The Custodian

Dating from the 14th century, this is the only medieval merchant's house in Conwy to have survived the turbulent history of this walled town for nearly six centuries. Furnished rooms and an audio-visual presentation show daily life from different periods in its history.

Location: OS Ref. SH781 775. At junction of Castle Street and High Street.

Opening Times: 1 Apr - 1 Nov: daily except Tue, 10am - 5pm. Last adm. 30mins before close.

Admission: Adult £2, Child £1, Family (2+2) £5. Pre-booked groups (15+) £1.80pp.

ⓘ Shop (open all year). No indoor photography.　🕴 By arrangement. AV presentation.

🅿 Parking in town car parks only.　👫 Teachers' pack available.　🐕 Guide dogs only.

BEAUMARIS CASTLE ✠

BEAUMARIS, ANGLESEY LL58 8AP

Owner: CADW: Welsh Historic Monuments　*Contact: The Administrator*

Tel: 01248 810361

The most technically perfect medieval castle in Britain, standing midway between Caernarfon and Conwy, commanding the old ferry crossing to Anglesey. A World Heritage listed site.

Location: OS Ref. SH608 762. 5m NE of Menai Bridge (A5) by A545. 7m from Bangor.

Opening Times: Mar - Oct: daily, 9.30am - 6.30pm. Oct - Mar: Mon - Sat, 9.30am - 4pm. Sun, 11am - 4pm.

Admission: Adult £2.20, Child/Conc./OAP £1.70, Family £6.

ⓘ Shop.　♿ Suitable.　🕴 Available.　🅿 Ample.　🐕 Guide dogs only.

CADW: Welsh Historic Monuments. Crown Copyright

BODELWYDDAN CASTLE

Tel: 01745 584060　**Fax:** 01745 584563

Bodelwyddan, Denbighshire LL18 5YA

Owner: Denbighshire County Council

Contact: Karen Short

This magnificently restored Victorian mansion set in rolling parkland, displays extensive collections from the National Portrait Gallery, furniture from the Victoria and Albert Museum and John Gibson sculpture from the Royal Academy. There are exhibitions of Victorian Amusements and Inventions and a programme of temporary exhibitions and events takes place throughout the year.

Location: OS Ref. SH999 749. Follow signs off A55 expressway. 2m W of St Asaph, opposite Marble Church.

Opening Times: Apr - Oct: daily except Fri (daily during Jul & Aug) 10am* - 5pm. Nov - Easter: daily except Mon & Fri, 11am - 4pm. Last admission 1hr before closing. * Castle Gallery opens at 10.30am.

Admission: Adult £4.30, Child/Student/Disabled £2.70, OAP/UB40 £3.80, Family (2+3) £13. Group: Adult £3.70, Child/Student/Disabled £2.30, OAP/UB40 £3.25. Season Ticket: Adult £12.60, Child/Student/Disabled £8.40, OAP/UB40 £10.50, Family £27.30.

ⓘ Shop. Corporate hospitality.　♿ Partially suitable. WCs.　☕ Tearoom.

🕴 By arrangement.　🅿 Ample.

👫 Educational programme. Teachers' pack.　🐕 Guide dogs only.

BODNANT GARDEN ✿

Tel: 01492 650460　**Fax:** 01492 650448

Tal-y-Cafn, Colwyn Bay LL28 5RE

Owner: The National Trust

Contact: The Secretary

The 32-ha garden at Bodnant is one of the finest in the world, situated above the River Conwy and looking across the valley towards the Snowdon range. The garden is in two parts. The upper part around the house consists of the Terrace Garden and informal lawns shaded by trees. The lower portion, The Dell, contains the Pinetum and Wild Garden. Masses of bulbs in spring make a colourful display. Rhododendrons, magnolias and camellias flower as well as splendid autumn colours.

Location: OS Ref. SH801 723. 8m S of Llandudno and Colwyn Bay, off A470. Signposted from A55.

Opening Times: 14 Mar - 31 Oct: daily, 10am - 5pm. Last admission 30 mins before close.

Admission: Adult £4.60, Child £2.30, Groups (20 +) £4.20pp.

ⓘ Shop. Plant centre.　♿ Partially suitable. WCs.　☕ Tearoom.

🕴 Not available.　🅿 Ample.　🐕 Guide dogs only.

Wales Tourist Board.

Rhuddlan Castle.

BODRHYDDAN

RHUDDLAN, CLWYD LL18 5SB

Owner: *Colonel The Lord Langford OBE DL* **Contact:** *Colonel The Lord Langford OBE DL*

Tel: 01745 590414

The home of Lord Langford and his family, Bodrhyddan is basically a 17th century house with 19th century additions by the famous architect, William Eden Nesfield, although traces of an earlier building exist. The house has been in the hands of the same family since it was built over 500 years ago. There are notable pieces of armour, pictures, period furniture, a 3,000 year old mummy, a formal parterre, a woodland garden and attractive picnic areas. Teas are available. Bodrhyddan is a Grade I listing making it one of few in Wales to remain in private hands.

Location: OS Ref. SJ045 788. On the A5151 midway between Dyserth and Rhuddlan, 4m SE of Rhyl.

Opening Times: Jun - Sept inclusive: Tue & Thur, 2 - 5.30pm.

Admission: Adult £3, Child £1.

X Receptions by special arrangement.   & Partially suitable.   Tearoom.
K Guided tours only.   P Ample.   By special arrangement.

BRYN BRAS CASTLE   **Tel/Fax:** 01286 870210

Llanrug, Caernarfon, Gwynedd LL55 4RE

Owner: Mr & Mrs N E Gray-Parry   **Contact:** Marita Gray-Parry

Built in the Neo-Romanesque style in 1830, on an earlier structure and probably designed by Thomas Hopper. Elegantly romantic family home with fine stained-glass, panelling, interesting ceilings and richly carved furniture. The Castle stands in the beautiful Snowdonian range and the extensive gardens include herbaceous borders, walled knot garden, woodland walks, stream and pools, 1/4 m mountain walk with superb views of Snowdon, Anglesey and the sea. Picnic area.

Location: OS Ref. SH543 625. 1/2 m off A4086 at Llanrug, 4 1/2 m E of Caernarfon.

Opening Times: Only for groups by prior appointment.

Admission: By arrangement. No young children please.

Tearoom.   No dogs.   **A** Self-catering apartments within Castle.

CAERNARFON CASTLE

CADW: Welsh Historic Monuments. Crown Copyright

NPI Award 1997: Runner Up

CASTLE DITCH, CAERNARFON LL55 2AY

Owner: *CADW: Welsh Historic Monuments*   **Contact:** *The Administrator*

Tel: 01286 677617

The most famous, and perhaps the most impressive castle in Wales. Taking nearly 50 years to build it proved the costliest of Edward I's castles. A World Heritage listed site.

Location: OS Ref. SH477 626. In Caernarfon, just W of town centre.

Opening Times: Mar - Oct: daily, 9.30am - 6.30pm. Oct - Mar: Mon - Sat, 9.30am - 4pm, Sun 11am - 4pm.

Admission: Adult £3.80, Child/Conc./OAP £2.80, Family £10.

i Shop.   & Suitable.   P Ample.   Guide dogs only.

Criccieth Castle.

CARREGLWYD

Tel: 01407 730551 **Fax:** 01407 730888

Llanfaethlu, Holyhead, Anglesey LL65 4NY

Owner: Tom Carpenter　　　　　　　**Contact:** Tom Carpenter

Built in 1634 by Dr William Griffiths who was Chancellor of St Asaph and Master of the Rolls to Charles I, the house is Grade II*. The grounds include a lake, woodland and marsh (with SSI designation).

Location: OS Ref. SH308 878. Anglesey.

Opening Times: Grounds: May, daily, 1 - 5pm except Fri & Mons 11/18 May. 31Aug: 1.30 - 5.30pm. House: Upon request a guided tour of the house is available at 4pm each day.

Admission: Adults £3.50, Child, OAP £2. Groups by appointment.

🚶 Tours of house available on request.

CHIRK CASTLE

National Trust Photographic Library: Matthew Antrobus

CHIRK LL14 5AF

Owner: *The National Trust*　　**Contact:** *The Property Manager*

Tel: 01691 777701 **Fax:** 01691 774706

700 year old Chirk Castle, a magnificent marcher fortress, commands fine views over the surrounding countryside. Rectangular with a massive drum tower at each corner, the Castle has beautiful formal gardens with clipped yews, roses and a variety of flowering shrubs. The dramatic dungeon is a reminder of the Castle's turbulent history, whilst later occupants have left elegant state rooms, furniture, tapestries and portraits. The Castle was sold for five thousand pounds to Sir Thomas Myddelton in 1595, and his descendants continue to live in part of the Castle today.

Location: OS Ref. SJ269 380. 8m S of Wrexham off A483, 2m from Chirk village.

Opening Times: 1 Apr - 30 Sept: daily except Mon & Tue (open BH Mons). 3 Oct - 1 Nov: Sat & Sun only. Castle: 12 - 5pm. Garden: 11am - 6pm. Last admission 4.30pm.

Admission: Adult £4.60, Child £2.30, Family (2+2) £11.50. Pre-booked groups of 15+ £3.70. NT members free. Garden only: Adults £2.40, Child £1.20.

ℹ️ Shop. No indoor photography.　♿ Suitable. WCs.　🍽️ Licensed tearoom.
🚶 By arrangement.　🅿️ Ample.　👥 Educational programme.　🐕 Guide dogs only.

COCHWILLAN OLD HALL

Tel: 01248 364608

Talybont, Bangor, Gwynedd LL57 3AZ

Owner: R C H Douglas Pennant　　　　**Contact:** P Llewellyn

A fine example of medieval architecture with the present house dating from about 1450. It was probably built by William Gryffydd who fought for Henry VII at Bosworth. Once owned in the 17th century by John Williams who became Archbishop of York. The house was restored from a barn in 1971.

Location: OS Ref. SH606 695. 3½ m SE of Bangor. 1m SE of Talybont off A55.

Opening Times: By appointment.

Admission: Please telephone for details.

CONWY CASTLE ✠

CADW: Welsh Historic Monuments. Crown Copyright

CONWY LL32 8AY

Owner: *CADW: Welsh Historic Monuments*　　**Contact:** *The Administrator*

Tel: 01492 592358

Taken together the Castle and town walls are the most impressive of the fortresses built by Edward I, and remain the finest and most impressive in Britain. A World Heritage Listed Site.

Location: OS Ref. SH783 774. Conwy by A55 or B5106.

Opening Times: Mar - Oct: daily, 9.30am - 6.30pm. Oct - Mar: Mon - Sat, 9.30am - 4pm. Sun, 11am - 4pm.

Admission: Adult £3, Child/OAP £2, Family £8.

ℹ️ Shop.　🚶 By arrangement.　🅿️ Ample.　🐕 Guide dogs only.

CRICCIETH CASTLE ✠

Tel: 01766 522227

Castle Street, Criccieth, Gwynedd LL52 0DP

Owner: CADW: Welsh Historic Monuments　　　　**Contact:** The Administrator

Overlooking Cardigan Bay, Criccieth Castle is the most striking of the fortresses built by the native Welsh Princes. Its inner defences dominated by a powerful twin-towered gatehouse.

Location: OS Ref. SH500 378. A497 to Criccieth from Porthmadog or Pwllheli.

Opening Times: Mar - Jun: daily, 9.30am - 6.30pm. Jul - Sept: daily, 10am - 6pm. Oct - Feb: daily, 9.30am - 4pm.

Admission: Adult £2.20, Child/Conc./OAP £1.70, Family £6.

🐕 Guide dogs only.

CYMER ABBEY ✠

Tel: 01341 422854

Dolgellau, Gwynedd

Owner: CADW: Welsh Historic Monuments　　　　**Contact:** The Administrator

The modest little Abbey at Cymer, with its simple Church, stands amid remote and beautiful countryside. Situated near the head of the Mawddach estuary.

Location: OS Ref. SH722 195. 2m NW of Dolgellau on A470.

Opening Times: Telephone for opening hours.

Admission: (1997 prices) Adult £1.20, Conc. 70p, Family £3.

🅿️ Limited.

DENBIGH CASTLE ✠

Tel: 01745 813979

Denbigh, Clwyd

Owner: CADW: Welsh Historic Monuments　　　　**Contact:** The Administrator

Crowning the summit of a prominent outcrop dominating the Vale of Clwyd, the principal feature of this spectacular site is the great gatehouse dating back to the 11th century. Some of the walls can still be walked by visitors.

Location: OS Ref. SJ052 658. Denbigh via A525 or B5382.

Opening Times: Telephone for opening hours.

Admission: (1997 prices) Castle: Adult £1.70, Reduced £1.20, Family £4.

DOLWYDDELAN CASTLE ✠

Tel: 01690 750366

Blaenau Ffestiniog, Gwynedd

Owner: CADW: Welsh Historic Monuments   **Contact:** The Administrator

Standing proudly on a ridge, this stern building remains remarkably intact and visitors cannot fail to be impressed with the great solitary square tower, built by Llewelyn the Great in the early 13th century.

Location: OS Ref. SH722 522. A470(T) Blaenau Ffestiniog to Betws-y-Coed, 1m W of Dolwyddelan.

Opening Times: Late Mar - late Oct: daily, 9.30am - 6.30pm. Late Oct - late Mar: daily, 9.30am - 4pm. Closed 24 - 26 Dec & 1 Jan.

Admission: Adult £1.70, Child/Conc. £1.20, Family £4.

♿ Suitable.   P Ample.

DYFI FURNACE ✠

Tel: 01222 500200

Aberdyfi, Dyfed

Owner: CADW: Welsh Historic Monuments   **Contact:** The Administrator

This was built around 1755 and is probably the best preserved charcoal furnace in Britain. Set in beautiful woodland it also has a grand external water-wheel in working order.

Location: OS Ref. SN685 951. On the A487 near Eglwysfach, 6m SW from Machynlleth.

Opening Times: 1 May - 30 Sept: daily, 10am - 5pm.

Admission: Adult £1.70. Conc. £1.20. Family £4.

P Limited.

GLANSEVERN HALL GARDENS

Tel: 01686 640200   **Fax:** 01686 640829

Berriew, Welshpool, Powys SY21 8AH

Owner: Mr G and Miss M Thomas   **Contact:** Mr & Mrs R N Thomas

A classic Greek revival house romantically positioned on banks of River Severn. Over 15 acres of mature gardens notable for variety of unusual tree species. Also much new planting. Lakeside and woodland walks, water and rock gardens, grotto, walled rose garden.

Location: OS Ref. SJ195 001. On A483, 5m S of Welshpool, 1m SE of Berriew.

Opening Times: May - Sept: Fri, Sat and BH Mon, 12 - 6pm.

Admission: Adult £2, Child (under 16) free.

ⓘ Shop. Plant centre.   ♿ Grounds suitable.   Tearoom.   P Ample.

In grounds, on leads.

GYRN CASTLE

Tel/Fax: 01745 853500

Llanasa, Holywell, Flintshire CH8 9BG

Owner: Sir Geoffrey Bates BT   **Contact:** Sir Geoffrey Bates BT

Dating, in part, from 1700, castellated 1820. Large picture gallery, panelled entrance hall. Pleasant woodland walks and fantastic views to Mersey and Lake District.

Location: OS Ref. SJ111 815. 26m W of Chester, off A55, 4¹/₂m SE of Prestatyn.

Opening Times: All year by appointment.

Admission: £4. Discount for groups.

♿ Grounds suitable.   By arrangement.

ERDDIG

NR WREXHAM LL13 0YT

Owner: The National Trust   *Contact:* The Property Manager

Tel: 01978 355314 / 01978 313333

One of the most fascinating houses in Britain, not least because of the unusually close relationship that existed between the family of the house and their servants. The beautiful and evocative range of outbuildings includes kitchen, laundry, bakehouse, stables, sawmill, smithy and joiner's shop, while the stunning state rooms display most of their original 18th & 19th century furniture and furnishings, including some exquisite Chinese wallpaper. The large walled garden has been restored to its 18th century format design with Victorian parterre and yew walk, and also contains the National Ivy Collection. There is an extensive park with woodland walks.

Location: OS Ref. SJ326 482. 2m S of Wrexham.

Opening Times: 21 Mar - 1 Nov: daily except Thur & Fri, but open Good Fri. House: 12 - 5pm. Garden: 11am - 6pm (10am - 6pm during Jul & Aug). From 3 Oct: House: 12 - 4pm, Garden: 11am - 5pm. Last admission 1 hr before closing.

Admission: NT members free. All-inclusive ticket: Adult £5.60, Child £2.80, Family (2+2) £14. Pre-booked group of 15+ £4.60pp. Belowstairs (including outbuildings & Garden): Adult £3.60, Child £1.80, Family (2+2) £9, Pre-booked groups of 15+ £2.90pp.

ⓘ Shop. Plant sales.   ♿ Partially suitable. WCs.   Licensed restaurant.

✯ AV presentation.   P Ample.   Educational programme.   Guide dogs only.

HARLECH CASTLE ✠

HARLECH LL46 2YH

Owner: CADW: Welsh Historic Monuments   *Contact:* The Administrator

Tel: 01766 780552

Set on a towering rock above Tremadog Bay, this seemingly impregnable fortress is the most dramatically sited of all the castles of Edward I. A World Heritage listed site.

Location: OS Ref. SH581 312. Harlech, Gwynedd on A496 coast road.

Opening Times: Mar - Oct: daily, 9.30am - 6.30pm. Oct - Mar: Mon - Sat, 9.30am - 4pm. Sun, 11am - 4pm.

Admission: Adult £3, Child/OAP £2, Family £8.

ⓘ Shop.   P Ample.   Guide dogs only.

FFERM

Tel/Fax: 01352 770217

Pontblyddyn, Mold, Flintshire

Owner: Dr M Jones-Mortimer   **Contact:** Dr M Jones-Mortimer

17th century farmhouse. Viewing is limited to 7 persons at any one time. Prior booking is recommended. No toilets or refreshments.

Location: OS Ref. SJ279 603. Access from A541 in Pontblyddyn, 3¹/₂m SW of Mold.

Opening Times: 2nd Wed in every month, 2 - 5pm. Pre-booking is recommended.

Admission: £4.

No dogs.

HARTSHEATH

Tel/Fax: 01352 770217

Pontblyddyn, Mold, Flintshire

Owner: Dr M Jones-Mortimer   **Contact:** Dr M Jones-Mortimer

18th and 19th century house set in parkland. Viewing is limited to 7 persons at any one time. Prior booking is recommended. No toilets or refreshments.

Location: OS Ref. SJ287 602. Access from A5104, 3m SW of Mold between Pontblyddyn and Penyffordd.

Opening Times: 1st, 3rd & 5th Wed in every month (except 1st Jan), 2 - 5pm.

Admission: £4.

No dogs.

ISCOYD PARK

Nr Whitchurch, Shropshire SY13 3AT

Owner: Mr P C Godsal   **Contact:** Mr P C Godsal

18th century Grade II* listed redbrick house in park.

Location: OS Ref. SJ504 421. 2m W of Whitchurch on A525.

Opening Times: By written appointment only.

PENRHYN CASTLE

National Trust Photographic Library: Matthew Antrobus

BANGOR LL57 4HN

Owner: The National Trust   Contact: The Property Manager

Tel: 01248 353084

This dramatic neo-Norman castle sits between Snowdonia and the Menai Strait and was built by Thomas Hopper between 1820 and 1845 for the wealthy Pennant family, who made their fortune from the local slate quarries. The extraordinarily grand staircase and extravagant stone carving of the interior create an almost cathedral-like atmosphere. The castle contains fascinating 'Norman' furniture, panelling and plasterwork all designed by Hopper, and houses an outstanding collection of paintings by the old masters. There is also an industrial railway museum, a countryside exhibition, a Victorian terraced walled garden and an extensive tree and shrub collection, as well as attractive walks in the grounds.

Location: OS Ref. SH602 720. 1m E of Bangor, at Llandegai on A5122.

Opening Times: 25 Mar - 1 Nov: daily except Tue. Castle: 12 - 5pm (Jul & Aug_ 11am - 5pm). Grounds & Stableblock exhibitions: 11am - 5pm (Jul & Aug: 10am - 5.30pm). Last admission 30 mins before closing. Last castle audio tour 4pm.

Admission: All inclusive ticket: Adult £4.80, Child £2.40, Family (2+2) £12. Pre-booked groups of 15+ £3.80pp. Garden & Stableblock Exhibitions only: Adult £3, Child £1.50. NT members free. Audio tour: additional 50p pp including NT members.

ⓘ Shop.   ☕ Licensed tearoom.   👥 Educational programme.

PLAS BRONDANW GARDENS   Tel: 01766 770484 / 770814

Menna Angharad, Plas Brondanw, Llanfrothen, Gwynedd LL48 6SW

Italianate gardens with topiary.

Owner: Trustees of the Second Portmeirion Foundation

Location: OS Ref. SH618 423. 3m N of Penrhyndeudraeth off A4085, on Croesor Road.

Opening Times: All year: daily, 9am - 5pm.

Admission: Adult £1.50, Child 25p, Group £1 (if pre-booked).

🐕 No dogs.

Sugar-loaf:

The form in which cane sugar arrived in the kitchen; cone-shaped, white and crusty on the outside, it was broken into lumps by means of sugar nips. Near the centre the sugar was brown, with molasses in the centre. The shape was acquired after the cane was boiled and the sugar stacked up to dry. The name 'Sugar Loaf' is often given to cone-shaped hills, such as the Sugar Loaf outside Abergavenny in Wales.

Extract from; "Life in the Country House" by David N Durant (published by John Murray), PB£15.99.

PLAS MAWR

CADW: Welsh Historic Monuments. Crown Copyright

HIGH STREET, CONWY LL32 8EF

Owner: CADW: Welsh Historic Monuments   Contact: The Administrator

Tel: 01492 580167

The best preserved Elizabethan town house in Britain, the house reflects the status of its builder Robert Wynn. A fascinating and unique place allowing visitors to sample the lives of the Tudor gentry and their servants, Plas Mawr is famous for the quality and quantity of its decorative plasterwork.

Location: OS Ref. SH779 777. Conwy by A55 or B5106.

Opening Times: Mar - Oct: daily (except Mon), 10am - 6pm.

Admission: Adult £3, Child/OAP £2, Family £8.

🅿 Limited.   🐕 Guide dogs only.

PLAS NEWYDD

National Trust Photographic Library: Nick Meers

LLANFAIRPWLL, ANGLESEY LL61 6DQ

Owner: The National Trust   Contact: The Property Manager

Tel: 01248 714795   **Fax:** 01248 713673

Cradled in a landscape garden on the banks of the Menai Strait, this elegant 18th century country house by James Wyatt commands magnificent views of the Strait and the mountains of Snowdonia. The house contains Rex Whistler's largest wall painting and an exhibition on his work, as well as a military museum with relics of the battle of Waterloo. Superb rhododendron garden in the spring ($^3/_4$ m from the house). Pleasant new walk along banks of the Menai Strait.

Location: OS Ref. SH521 696. 2m S of Llanfairpwll and A5.

Opening Times: 1 Apr - 1 Nov: daily except Fri & Sat. House: 12 - 5pm. Gardens: 11am - 5.30pm. Last admission 30 mins before closing. Shop: daily, 11am - 5pm. Rhododendron Garden open from Apr - early Jun only.

Admission: Adult £4.20, Child £2.10, Family (2+2) £10.50. Pre-booked groups of 15+ £3.40pp. Garden only: Adult £2, Child £1. NT members free.

ⓘ Shop. No indoor photography.   ♿ Partially suitable. WCs.

☕ Licensed tearoom.   🚶 By arrangement.   🅿 Ample.   👥 Teachers' pack.

PLAS PENHELIG

Tel: 01654 767676 **Fax:** 01654 767783

Aberdovey, Gwynedd LL35 0NA

Owner: The Richardson Family **Contact:** David Richardson

Edwardian country house with views of Cardigan Bay and Dovey Estuary. Set amongst 7 acres of gardens with azaleas, rhododendrons and spring flowers, Formal walled garden with herbaceous beds, peaches, vines and nectarines.

Location: OS Ref. SN622 961. 1/2 m E of Aberdyfi on the A493 coast road. 10m W of Machynlleth.

Opening Times: 1 Apr - 31 Oct: Wed - Sun, 10.30am - 5.30pm.

Restaurant. In grounds, on leads.

PLAS YN RHIW

Tel/Fax: 01758 780219

Rhiw, Pwllheli LL53 8AB

Owner: The National Trust **Contact:** The Custodian

A small manor house, with garden and woodlands, overlooking the west shore of Porth Neigwl (Hell's Mouth Bay) on the Llyn Peninsula. The house is part medieval, with Tudor and Georgian additions, and the ornamental gardens have flowering trees and shrubs, divided by box hedges and grass paths, rising behind to the snowdrop wood.

Location: OS Ref. SH237 282. 12m SW of Pwllheli, 3m S of the B4413 to Aberdaron. No access for coaches.

Opening Times: 2 Apr - 18 May: daily except Tue & Wed. 20 May - 30 Sept: daily except Tue, 12 - 5pm. Last admission 30 mins before closing.

Admission: Adult £3.20, Child £1.60, Family (2+2) £8. Pre-booked groups of 15+, evenings (incl. guided tour) £4pp.

Shop. Plant centre. Partially suitable. WCs. By arrangement.

Limited. Guide dogs only.

PORTMEIRION

Tel: 01766 770228 **Fax:** 01766 771331

Portmeirion, Gwynedd LL48 6ET

Owner: Portmeirion Ltd **Contact:** Mr R Llywelyn

Fairy tale Italianate village on shores of Cardigan Bay built by the architect Sir Clough Williams Ellis.

Location: OS Ref. SH590 371. Off A487 at Minffordd between Penrhyndeudraeth and Porthmadog.

Opening Times: All year (except Christmas Day): daily, 9.30am - 5.30pm.

Admission: Adult £3.70, Child £1.90, OAP £3.20, Family £10.

Shop. Plant centre. Conference facilities. Corporate hospitality.

Wedding receptions. Partially suitable. Licensed restaurant. Café.

Ample. Strictly no dogs. 39 double. Ensuite available.

Civil Wedding Licence.

POWIS CASTLE

Tel: 01938 554338 **Fax:** 01938 554336

Nr. Welshpool Y21 8RF

Owner: The National Trust **Contact:** The Property Manager

Perched on a rock above the late 17th century garden terraces, this medieval castle contains the finest country house collection in Wales.

Location: OS Ref. SJ195 001. 1m W of Welshpool, 1m SE of Berriew, car access on A490.

Opening Times: 1 Apr - 1 Nov: daily, excl. Mon & Tues (Jul & Aug daily excl. Mon). Open every BH Mon throughout season. Castle & Museum: 1 - 5pm. Garden: 11am - 6pm. Last adm. to Garden, Castle & Museum 30 mins before closing.

Admission: Garden: Adult £5, Child £2.50, Family (2+2) £12.50. Pre-booked groups £4pp. All-inclusive (Castle, Museum & Garden): Adult £7.50, Child £3.75, Family £18.75. Pre-booked groups £6.50pp. No group rates on Sun & BH Mon.

Shop. Plant centre. No indoor photography. Licensed tearoom.

Limited for coaches. Guide dogs only.

RHUDDLAN CASTLE

Tel: 01745 590777

Castle Gate, Castle Street, Rhuddlan LL18 5AD

Owner: CADW: Welsh Historic Monuments **Contact:** The Administrator

Guarding the ancient ford of the river Clwyd, Rhuddlan was the strongest of Edward I's castles in North-East Wales. Linked to the sea by an astonishing deep water channel nearly 3 miles long, it still proclaims the innovative genius of its architect.

Location: OS Ref. SJ025 779. SW end of Rhuddlan via A525 or A547.

Opening Times: May - Sept: daily, 10am - 5pm.

Admission: Adult £1.70, Child/OAP £1.20, Family £4.

Ample. Guide dogs only.

ST ASAPH CATHEDRAL

Tel: 01745 583597

St Asaph, Denbighshire LL17 0RL **Contact:** The Dean

Britain's smallest ancient cathedral founded in 560AD by Kentigern, a religious community enclosed in a 'llan', hence Llanelwy. Present building dates from 13th century. Post reformation period, close association with the translators of the Welsh Prayer Book and Bible. A copy of the William Morgan Bible of 1588 can be seen. The Translators' Memorial, erected in 1888, stands outside. Within, a 17th century Spanish Madonna in ivory, stained glass, an exhibit of literary treasures, the only recumbent effigy, from 1268 - 93, an iron chest (1738) and four painted angels in the choir roof are just some of the things of interest. Housing an original Hill organ and home to the International North Wales Music Festival yearly, in September.

Location: OS Ref. SJ039 743. In St Asaph, S of A55.

Opening Times: Summer: 7.30am - 6pm. Winter: 7.30am - dusk. Sun services: 8am, 11am, 3.30pm.

Shop. Ground floor suitable. Guide dogs only.

TREWERN HALL

Tel: 01938 570243

Trewern, Welshpool, Powys SY21 8DT

Owner: Chapman Family **Contact:** Mrs Margaret Chapman

Trewern Hall is a Grade II* listed building standing in the Severn Valley. It has been described as 'one of the most handsome timber-framed houses surviving in the area'. The porch contains a beam inscribed RF1610, though it seems likely that parts of the house are earlier. The property has been in the ownership of the Chapman family since 1918.

Location: OS Ref. SJ269 113. Off A458 Welshpool - Shrewsbury Road, 4m from Welshpool.

Opening Times: During May: Mon - Fri, 2 - 5pm.

Admission: Adult £2, Child/OAP/Student £1.

Not suitable. No parking. No dogs.

VALLE CRUCIS ABBEY

Tel: 01978 860326

Llangollen, Clwyd

Owner: CADW: Welsh Historic Monuments **Contact:** The Administrator

Set in a beautiful valley location, Valle Crucis Abbey is the best preserved medieval monastery in North Wales, enhanced by the only surviving monastic fish pond in Wales.

Location: OS Ref. SJ205 442. B5103 from A5, 2m NW of Llangollen, or A542 from Ruthin.

Opening Times: Apr - Sept: daily, 10am - 5pm. Oct - Mar: daily, 9.30am - 4pm.

Admission: Adult £1.70, Child/Conc. £1.20. Family £4.

Suitable.

WERN ISAF

Tel: 01248 680437

Penmaen Park, Llanfairfechan LL33 0RN

Owner: Mrs P J Phillips **Contact:** Mrs P J Phillips

This Arts and Crafts house was built in 1900 by the architect H L North as his family home and it contains much of the original furniture and William Morris fabrics. It is situated in a woodland garden and is at its best in the Spring. It has extensive views over the Menai Straits and Conwy Bay. One of the most exceptional houses of its date and style in Wales.

Location: OS Ref. SH685 752.

Opening Times: Mar, Apr & Aug: Sat & Sun, 11am - 4pm, by appointment only.

Wales Tourist Board.

Rhuddlan Castle.

North Wales

The Gower Peninsula. Wales Tourist Board.

ABERDULAIS FALLS

Tel: 01639 636674

Aberdulais, Vale of Neath, Nr. Neath SA10 8EU

Owner: The National Trust   **Contact:** The Property Warden

For over 300 years this famous waterfall has provided the energy to drive the wheels of industry, from the first manufacture of copper in 1584 to present day remains of the tinplate works. It has also been visited by famous artists such as J M W Turner in 1796. The site today houses a unique hydro-electrical scheme which has been developed to harness the waters of the Dulais river. The Turbine House provides access to an interactive computer, fish pass and display panels. A special lift has been installed to allow disabled visitors access to the roof level, which affords excellent views of the Falls. The new water wheel, the largest currently used in Britain to generate electricity, makes Aberdulais Falls self-sufficient in environmentally friendly energy.

Location: OS Ref. SS772 995. On A4107, 3m NE of Neath. 4m from M4/J43.

Opening Times: March: Sat & Sun only. 1 Apr - 1 Nov: Mon - Fri, 10am - 5pm. Sat, Sun & BHs, 11am - 6pm. Last admission 30 mins before closing.

Admission: Adult £2.80, Child £1.40 (Jul & Aug - one child under 16 free with each adult). Pre-booked group (15+) £2.20pp, Child £1.10.

[i] Shop   [P] Limited.   Teachers' pack.

BLAENAVON IRONWORKS

Tel: 01495 792615

Nr Brecon Beacons National Park, Blaenavon, Gwent

Owner: CADW: Welsh Historic Monuments   **Contact:** The Administrator

The famous ironworks at Blaenavon were a milestone in the history of the Industrial Revolution. Visitors can view much of the ongoing conservation work as well as 'Stack Square' - a rare survival of housing built for pioneer ironworkers.

Location: OS Ref. SO248 092. Via A4043 follow signs to Big Pit Mining Museum and Blaenavon Ironworks. Abergavenny 8m. Pontypool 8m.

Opening Times: May - Sept: Mon - Sat, 11am - 5pm. Sun 2 - 5pm. Winter: Pre-bookings only.

Admission: Adult £1.20, Child/OAP 70p, Family £3.

[&] Partially suitable.   [P] Ample.   Guide dogs only.

CAE HIR GARDENS

Tel: 01570 470839

Cae Hir, Cribyn, Lampeter, Cardiganshire SA48 7NG

Owner: Mr W Akkermans   **Contact:** Mr W Akkermans

A garden with a difference, not typically British in style, yet thoroughly fitting into the Welsh countryside. A serendipitous find for the searcher, this transformed 19th century smallholding offers a succession of pleasant surprises and shows a quite different approach to gardening. Its originality has been acknowledged by television both nationally and locally in a variety of programmes.

Location: OS Ref. SN522 511. W on A482 from Lampeter, after 5m turn S on B4337. Cae Hir is 2m on left.

Opening Times: Daily, excluding Mon (open BH Mon), 1 - 6pm.

Admission: Adult £2, Child 50p, OAP £1.75. Groups (20+) £1.75 pp.

[&] Grounds partially suitable.   Available.   [P] Limited.   No dogs.

CAERLEON ROMAN BATHS & AMPHITHEATRE

Tel: 01633 422518

High Street, Caerleon NP6 1AE

Owner: CADW: Welsh Historic Monuments   **Contact:** The Administrator

Caerleon is the most varied and fascinating Roman site in Britain - incorporating fortress and baths, well preserved amphitheatre and a row of barrack blocks, the only examples currently visible in Europe.

Location: OS Ref. ST340 905. 4m ENE of Newport by B4596 to Caerleon, M4/J25.

Opening Times: Mar - Oct: daily, 9.30am - 6.30pm. Oct - Mar: Mon - Sat, 9.30am - 4pm. Sun, 2 - 4pm.

Admission: Adult £2, Child/OAP £1.20, Family £4.

[&] Suitable.   [P] Ample.   Guide dogs only.

Blaenavon Ironworks.

CAERPHILLY CASTLE

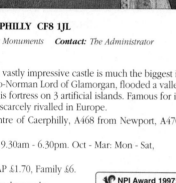

CAERPHILLY CF8 1JL

Owner: *CADW: Welsh Historic Monuments*   **Contact:** *The Administrator*

Tel: 01222 883143

Often threatened, never taken, this vastly impressive castle is much the biggest in Wales. 'Red Gilbert' de Clare, Anglo-Norman Lord of Glamorgan, flooded a valley to create the 30 acre lake, setting his fortress on 3 artificial islands. Famous for its leaning tower, its fortifications are scarcely rivalled in Europe.

Location: OS Ref. ST156 871. Centre of Caerphilly, A468 from Newport, A470, A469 from Cardiff.

Opening Times: Mar - Oct: daily, 9.30am - 6.30pm. Oct - Mar: Mon - Sat, 9.30am - 4pm. Sun, 11am - 4pm.

Admission: Adult £2.20, Child/OAP £1.70, Family £6.

[i] Shop.   [P] Limited.   Guide dogs only.   **NPI Award 1997: Winner**

CARDIFF CASTLE

Tel: 01222 878100

Castle Street, Cardiff CF1 2RB

Owner: City and County of Cardiff   **Contact:** Mrs Jean Brown

A large historic site with many levels of interest for the visitor.

Location: OS Ref. ST181 765. Cardiff city centre, signposted from M4

Opening Times: 1 Mar - 30 Oct: daily, 9.30am - 6pm. Nov - Feb: daily, 9.30am - 4.30pm. Closed Christmas and New Year.

Admission: Adult £4.80, Child/OAP £2.40.

[i] Shop.   Tearoom.   In grounds, on leads.   Civil Wedding Licence.

CAREW CASTLE & TIDAL MILL

Tel/Fax: 01646 651782

Tenby, Pembrokeshire SA70 8SL

Owner: Pembrokeshire Coast National Park   **Contact:** Mr G M Candler

A magnificent Norman castle which later became an Elizabethan country house. Royal links with Henry Tudor and the setting for the Great Tournament of 1507. The Mill is one of only four restored tidal mills in Britain. Introductory slide programme, automatic 'talking points' and special exhibition on 'The Story of Milling'.

Location: OS Ref. SN046 037. $\frac{1}{2}$ m N of A477, 5m E of Pembroke.

Opening Times: Easter - end Oct: daily, 10am - 5pm.

Admission: Adult £2.50, Child/OAP £1.60, Family £6.50.

[i] Shop.   [&] Partially suitable. WC.   By arrangement.   [P] Ample.   In grounds on leads.

CARREG CENNEN CASTLE

Tel: 01558 822291

Tir-y-Castell Farm, Llandeilo

Owner: CADW: Welsh Historic Monuments   **Contact:** The Administrator

Spectacularly crowning a remote crag 300 feet above the River Cennen, the castle is unmatched as a wildly romantic fortress sought out by artists and visitors alike. The climb from Rare Breeds Farm is rewarded by breathtaking views and the chance to explore intriguing caves beneath.

Location: OS Ref. SN668 190. Minor roads from A483(T) to Trapp village.

Opening Times: Mar - May & Sept - Oct: daily, 9.30am - 6.30pm. Jun - Aug: daily, 9.30am - 8pm. Oct - Mar: daily, 9.30am - 4pm.

Admission: Adult £2.20, Child/OAP £1.70, Family £6.

South Wales

CASTELL COCH ✠

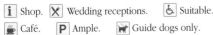

CADW: Welsh Historic Monuments. Crown Copyright

TONGWYNLAIS, CARDIFF CF4 7JS

Owner: CADW: Welsh Historic Monuments   *Contact: The Administrator*

Tel: 01222 810101

A fairytale castle in the woods, Castell Coch embodies a glorious Victorian dream of the Middle Ages. Designed by William Burges as a country retreat for the 3rd Lord Bute, every room and furnishing is brilliantly eccentric, including paintings of Aesop's fables on the drawing room walls.

Location: OS Ref. ST131 826. M4/J32, A470 then signposted.

Opening Times: Mar - Oct: daily, 9.30am - 6.30pm. Oct - Mar: Mon - Sat, 9.30am - 4pm. Sun, 11am - 4pm.

Admission: Adult £2.20, Child/OAP £1.70, Family £6.

i Shop.	**X** Wedding receptions.	**&** Suitable.	NPI Award 1997: Runner Up
Café.	**P** Ample.	Guide dogs only.	

THE CASTLE HOUSE

Tel: 01291 672563

Usk, Gwent NP5 1SD

Owner: J H L Humphreys   **Contact:** J H L Humphreys

Medieval Gatehouse with 19th century interior and 13th century castle ruins, set in a series of gardens providing seasonal interest (donations to NGS).

Location: OS Ref. SO376 011. Off Monmouth Road in Usk, opposite fire station.

Opening Times: Castle ruins on request. Gardens by appointment throughout the year. House: 2nd Wed every month & BHs, 2 - 5pm. Guided tours only, numbers limited to 5, prior booking recommended.

Admission: House & Garden: Adult £3.50, Family £8. Castle & Garden: Adult £2, Child free.

& Not suitable.	**↟** Compulsory.	**P** Limited.	In ground, on leads.

CHEPSTOW CASTLE ✠

Tel: 01248 624065

Chepstow, Gwent

Owner: CADW: Welsh Historic Monuments   **Contact:** The Administrator

This mighty fortress has guarded the route from England to South Wales for more than nine centuries. So powerful was this castle that it continued in use until 1690, being finally adapted for cannon and musket after an epic civil war siege. This huge, complex, grandiosely sited castle deserves a lengthy visit.

Location: OS Ref. ST533 941. Chepstow via A465, B4235 or A48. 1¹/₂ m N of M4/J22.

Opening Times: Mar - Oct: daily, 9.30am - 6.30pm. Oct - Mar: Mon - Sat, 9.30am - 4pm. Sun, 11am - 4pm.

Admission: Adult £3, Child/OAP £2, Family £8.

i Shop.	**&** Partially suitable.	**P** Ample.	Guide dogs only.

CILGERRAN CASTLE ✠

Tel: 01239 615007

Cardigan, Dyfed

Owner: CADW: Welsh Historic Monuments   **Contact:** The Administrator

Perched high up on a rugged spur above the River Teifi, Cilgerran Castle is one of the most spectacularly sited fortresses in Wales. It dates from the 11th - 13th centuries.

Location: OS Ref. SN195 431. Main roads to Cilgerran from A478 and A484. 3¹/₂ m SSE of Cardigan.

Opening Times: Mar - Oct: daily, 9.30am - 6.30pm. Oct - Mar: daily, 9.30am - 4pm.

Admission: Adult £1.70, Child/OAP £1.20, Family £4.

CLYNE GARDENS

Tel: 01792 401737

Mill Lane, Blackpill, Swansea SA3 5BD

Owner: City and County of Swansea   **Contact:** Julie Bowen

50 acre spring garden, large rhododendron collection, 4 national collections, extensive bog garden, native woodland.

Location: OS Ref. SS614 906. S side of Mill Lane, 500yds W of A4067 Mumbles Road, 3m SW of Swansea.

Opening Times: All year, daily.

Admission: Free.

& Not suitable.	**↟** By arrangement.	**P** Limited for cars.
Educational programme available.		In grounds, on leads.

COLBY WOODLAND GARDEN 🌿

Tel: 01834 811885 / 01558 822800

Amroth, Narbeth, Pembrokeshire SA67 8PP

Owner: The National Trust   **Contact:** The Centre Manager

An attractive woodland garden. The house is not open. There are walks through secluded valleys along open woodland pathways. Nearby is the coastal resort of Amroth.

Location: OS Ref. SN155 080. ¹/₂ m inland from Amroth beside Carmarthen Bay. Signs from A477.

Opening Times: 27 Mar - 31 Oct: daily, 10am - 5pm. Walled Garden: 1 Apr - 30 Oct: 11am - 5pm.

Admission: Adult £2.80, Child £1.40, Family (2+2) £7. Pre-booked groups (15+): Adult £2.30, Child £1.15.

i Shop. Plant centre.	**X** By arrangement.	Tearoom.	**↟** By arrangement.
P Ample.	Educational programme.		In grounds, on leads.

CRESSELLY

Fax: 01646 687045

Kilgetty, Pembrokeshire SA68 0SP

Owner: H D R Harrison-Allen Esq MFH   **Contact:** H D R Harrison-Allen Esq MFH

Home of the Allen family for 250 years. The house is of 1770 with matching wings of 1869 and contains good plasterwork and fittings of both periods. The Allens are of particular interest for their close association with the Wedgwood family of Etruria and a long tradition of foxhunting. Bed & Breakfast (dinner by arrangement). Wedding receptions and functions in house or marquee in gardens from 20 - 300 persons. Dinners and private or corporate events in historic dining room or panelled billiard room.

Location: OS Ref. SN065 065. In the Pembrokeshire National Park, off the A4075 between Canaston Bridge and Carew.

Opening Times: 28 days between May & Sept. Please write or fax for details.

Admission: Adult £3.50, no children under 12.

i Corporate hospitality.	**X** Wedding receptions.	**&** Gound floor only.
↟ Compulsory.	**P** Ample, coaches by arrangement.	No dogs.
A 2 double en-suite, 1 twin, 1 single (children by arrangement).		

CYFARTHFA CASTLE MUSEUM

Tel: 01685 723112

Brecon Road, Merthyr Tydfil, Mid Glamorgan CF47 8RE

Owner: Merthyr Tydfil County Borough Council   **Contact:** Mrs Claire Dovey-Evans

Castle originates from 1824/1825, now a museum and school. Shop. Conference facilities. Corporate hospitality. Suitable for disabled. Café. Guided tours by appointment. Ample parking. Educational programme available. Guide dogs only. Civil Wedding Licence.

Location: OS Ref. SO041 074. NE side of A470 to Brecon, ¹/₂ m NW of town centre.

Opening Times: 1 Apr - 1 Oct: Mon - Sun, 10am - 6pm, last admission 5.30pm. Winter: Mon - Fri, 10am - 3.30pm, Sat & Sun, 12 - 3.30pm, last admission 3pm.

Admission: Adult £1.50, Child/OAP 80p.

DINEFWR PARK 🌿

Tel: 01558 823902

Llandeilo SA19 6RT

Owner: The National Trust   **Contact:** The Property Manager

A Victorian Gothic mansion within an 18th century landscaped park. Parts of the ground floor and basement are open and a small exhibition explains the history of Dinefwr. There is a Victorian garden currently under restoration at the rear of Newton House, and an ancient deer park with White Park cattle. There is limited access to a privately owned walled garden. The Dinefwr White Park cattle and herd of fallow deer can be seen from vantage points. Access to Dinefwr Castle. Footpaths through parts of 162-ha estate and outstanding views of Towy Valley.

Location: OS Ref. SN615 225. 1m W of Llandeilo on A40. Take M4 from Swansea to Pont Abraham. A48 to Cross Hands and A476 to Llandeilo. Entrance by police station.

Opening Times: 2 Apr - 1 Nov: daily except Tue & Weds, 11am - 5pm. Last admission ¹/₂ hr before closing. Park open throughout winter in daylight hours.

Admission: Adult £2.80, Child £1.40. Pre-booked group (15+) Adult £2.60pp, Child £1.20.

X Corporate hospitality.	**&** Suitable. WCs.	Tearoom.	**↟** By arrangement.
P Ample. Limited for coaches.	Educational programme.		In grounds on leads.

THE DINGLE

Tel: 01437 764370

Crundale, Haverfordwest, Dyfed

Owner: Mrs J Jones   **Contact:** Mrs A Jones

18th century country gentleman's home, surrounded by gardens. Gardens only open.

Location: OS Ref. SM975 184. 2m NE of Haverfordwest off B4329.

Opening Times: Mar - Oct: Wed - Sun inclusive.

Admission: Adult £1, Child 50p.

DYFFRYN GARDENS

Tel: 01222 593328 **Fax:** 01222 591966

St Nicholas, Cardiff CF5 6SU

Owner: The Vale of Glamorgan Council   **Contact:** H J England

55 acres of landscaped gardens, beautiful at all times of year. Numerous small theme gardens, heather bank, arboretum and glass houses.

Location: OS Ref. ST095 723. 3m NW of Barry, J33/M4. 1¹/₂ m S of St Nicholas on A48.

Opening Times: Daily, 10am - dusk.

Admission: Adult £2, Child £1.50, Family £6, Conc. £1.50, Groups £1.50.

- i Shop & plant centre.
- & Grounds suitable. WC.
- Licensed restaurant.
- By arrangement.
- P Ample.
- In grounds, on leads.

FONMON CASTLE

RHOOSE, BARRY, SOUTH GLAMORGAN CF62 3ZN

Owner: Sir Brooke Boothby   *Contact:* Victoria Robinson

Tel: 01446 710206 **Fax:** 01446 711687

Occupied as a home since the 13th century, this medieval castle has the most stunning Georgian interiors and is surrounded by extensive gardens. Available for weddings, concerts, corporate entertainment and multi-activity days.

Location: OS Ref. ST047 681. 15m W of Cardiff, 1m W of Cardiff airport.

Opening Times: 1 Apr - 30 Sept: Tue & Wed, 2 - 5pm (last tour 4pm). Other times by appointment. Groups by appointment.

Admission: Adult £3.50, Child free. Groups: Adult £2.50, Child free.

- i Conferences.
- X By arrangement (up to 120)
- & Ground floor & grounds suitable. WC.
- P Ample.
- Guide dogs only.
- Civil Wedding Licence.

Laugharne Castle.

THE JUDGE'S LODGING

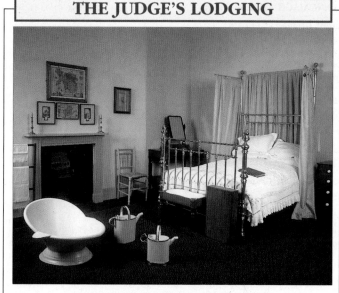

BROAD STREET, PRESTEIGNE, POWYS LD8 2AD

Owner: Powys County Council   *Contact:* Gabrielle Rivers

Tel: 01544 260650 **Fax:** 01544 260652

'The most commodious and elegant apartments for a judge in all England and Wales', Lord Chief Justice Campbell, 1855. The stunningly restored Judge's Lodging captures the 'upstairs, downstairs' heyday of a most unusual Victorian household - by gaslight, lamp and candle. An 'eavesdropping' audio tour features actor Robert Hardy - A Victorian Revelation.

Location: OS Ref. SO314 644. In town centre, off A44 and A4113. Easy reach from Herefordshire and mid-Wales.

Opening Times: 1 May - 31 Oct: 10am - 6pm. 1 Mar - 30 Apr: 10am - 4pm. Closed 1 Nov - 28 Feb.

Admission: Adult £3.50, Child/OAP/Student £2.50. Group (min 10, max 50): Adult £2.75, Child/OAP/Student £2.

- i Shop.
- X Available.
- & Partially suitable (access via lift)
- Audio tour.
- P Ample in town.
- Welcome.
- Guide dogs only.

KIDWELLY CASTLE ✠

Tel: 01554 890104

Kidwelly, West Glamorgan SA17 5BG

Owner: CADW: Welsh Historic Monuments   **Contact:** The Administrator

A chronicle in stone of Medieval fortress technology this strong and splendid castle developed during more than three centuries of Anglo-Welsh warfare. The half-moon shape stems from the original 12th century stockaded fortress, defended by the river Gwendraeth on one side and a deep crescent shaped ditch on the other.

Location: OS Ref. SN409 070. Kidwelly via A484. Kidwelly Rail Station 1m.

Opening Times: Mar - Oct: daily, 9.30am - 6.30pm. Oct - Mar: Mon - Sat, 9.30am - 4pm. Sun, 11am - 4pm.

Admission: Adult £2.20, Child/OAP £1.70, Family £6.

- & Suitable.
- By arrangement.
- P Ample.
- Guide dogs only.

LAMPHEY BISHOP'S PALACE ✠

Tel: 01646 672224

Lamphey, Dyfed

Owner: CADW: Welsh Historic Monuments   **Contact:** The Administrator

Lamphey marks the place of the spectacular Bishop's Palace but it reached its height of greatness under Bishop Henry de Gower who raised the new Great Hall. Today the ruins of this comfortable retreat reflect the power enjoyed by the medieval bishops.

Location: OS Ref. SN018 009. A4139 from Pembroke or Tenby.

Opening Times: 1 May - 30 Sept: daily, 10am - 5pm.

Admission: Adult £1.70, Child/OAP £1.20, Family £4.

LAUGHARNE CASTLE ✠

Tel: 01994 427906

King Street, Laugharne SA33 4SA

Owner: CADW: Welsh Historic Monuments   **Contact:** The Administrator

Picturesque Laugharne Castle stands on a low ridge overlooking the wide Taf estuary, one of a string of fortresses controlling the ancient route along the South Wales coast.

Location: OS Ref. SN303 107. A4066 from St Clears.

Opening Times: May - Sept: daily, 10am - 5pm.

Admission: Adult £1.70, Child/OAP £1.20, Family £4.

- Guide dogs only.

LLANCAIACH FAWR MANOR
Tel: 01443 412248 **Fax:** 01443 412688

Cardiff, Glamorgan CF1 1NU
Owner: Caerphilly County Borough Council   **Contact:** The Administrator
Tudor fortified manor dating from 1530 with Stuart additions.
Location: OS Ref. ST114 967. S side of B4254, 1m N of A472 at Nelson.
Opening Times: All year: Mon - Fri, 10am - 5pm. Sat, 10am - 6pm. Oct - Mar: Sun, 12 - 6pm. Rest of year: 10am - 6pm. Closed Christmas week.
Admission: Adult £4.10, Child £2.75, Conc. £2.85, Family £11.65.

| i | Shop. | & | Partially suitable. | ☕ | Licensed restaurant. Tearoom. | 🏃 | Compulsory. |
| P | Ample. | 👪 | Educational programme. | 🐕 | In grounds, on leads. |

LLANDAFF CATHEDRAL
Tel: 01222 561545

Llandaff, Cardiff, Glamorgan CF5 2YF
Owner: **Contact:** The Administrator
Oldest cathedral in the British Isles. Epstein's 'Christ in Majesty' and Rosetti's 'Seed of David'. Educational programme available.
Location: OS Ref. ST155 781. 2¹/₂ m NW of city centre, ¹/₄ m W of A48 ring road.
Opening Times: 7am - 6.45pm. Sun service: 8am, 9am, 11am, 12.15pm, 3.30pm and 6.30pm. Weekday service: 7.30am & 6pm.
Admission: Donation.

| P | Shop. | ☕ | Tearoom (seasonal). | 🏃 | By arrangement. | P | Limited. Public car park. |

MARGAM PARK
Tel: 01639 881635 **Fax:** 01639 895897

Port Talbot, Glamorgan SA13 2TJ
Owner: Neathport Talbot County Borough Council   **Contact:** Mr Ray Butt
Margam Orangery is the largest of its kind in Britain. Castle and Abbey ruins, 850 acres of parkland and forest, with waymarked signs.
Location: OS Ref. SS804 865. NE side of A48, 1m SE of M4/J38, 4m SE of Port Talbot.
Opening Times: Summer: daily, 10am - 5.30pm, last entry 4pm. Winter: Wed - Sun, 10am - 5pm, last entry 3pm.
Admission: Adult £3.50, Child £2.50

MUSEUM OF WELSH LIFE
Tel: 01222 573500

St Fagans, Cardiff
St Fagans Castle, a 16th century building built within the walls of a 13th century castle. The grounds have numerous reconstructed old farmhouses, cottages and other buildings which together with the museum building represent the life and culture of Wales.
Location: OS Ref. ST118 772. 4m W of city centre, 1¹/₂m N of A48, 2m S of M4/J33 off A4232.
Opening Times: All year. Oct - Jun: daily, 10am - 5pm. Jul - Sept: daily 10am - 6pm.
Admission: Summer: Adult £5.25, Child/OAP £3.75, Family £13.50. Winter: Adult £4.25, Child/OAP £2.50, Family £9.75.

NEATH ABBEY
Tel: 01792 812387

Neath, West Glamorgan   **Contact:** Mrs Roberts
Ruined Abbey. Limited parking - 6 cars only.
Location: OS Ref. SS738 974. 1m W of Neath, 300yds S of A4230, W of A474 roundabout. Gateway on N side of main street.
Opening Times: All year.
Admission: Free.

OXWICH CASTLE ✤
Tel: 01792 390359

c/o Oxwich Castle Farm, Oxwich SA3 1NG
Owner: CADW: Welsh Historic Monuments   **Contact:** The Administrator
Beautifully sited in the lovely Gower peninsula, Oxwich Castle is a striking testament to the pride and ambitions of the Mansel dynasty of Welsh gentry.
Location: OS159 Ref. SS497 864. A4118, 11m SW of Swansea, in Oxwich village.
Opening Times: May - Sept: daily, 10am - 5pm.
Admission: Adult £1.70, Child/OAP £1.20, Family £4.

| & | Suitable. | 🐕 | Guide dogs only. |

PEMBROKE CASTLE
Tel: 01646 681510 **Fax:** 01646 622260

Pembroke, Dyfed SA71 4LA
Owner: Trustees of Pembroke Castle   **Contact:** I B Ramsden
Early 13th century Norman castle with circular great tower or keep. The tower stands 75 ft high and dominates the castle. Birthplace of Henry VII. Interpretative exhibition of the Earls of Pembroke. Pembroke Yeomanry Exhibition. Introductory video.
Location: OS Ref. SM983 016. W end of the main street in Pembroke.
Opening Times: 1 Apr - 30 Sept: daily, 9.30am - 6pm. Mar & Oct: daily, 10am - 5pm. Nov - Feb: daily, 10am - 4pm. Closed Christmas Day, Boxing Day and New Year's Day.
Admission: Adult £3, Child/OAP £2. Group (min 20): Adult £2.60, OAP £1.70.

| i | Shop. | & | Suitable. WC. | ☕ | Café (summer only). | 🏃 | By arrangement. |
| 👪 | Education programme, teachers' pack. | 🐕 | In grounds on leads. |

PENHOW CASTLE 🏛

NR. NEWPORT, GWENT NP6 3AD
Owner: Stephen Weeks Esq   *Contact:* Miss Kathleen Bull

Tel: 01633 400800 **Fax:** 01633 400990
Wales' oldest lived-in Castle, the first home in Britain of the Seymour family. Now lovingly restored by the present owner, visitors explore the varied period rooms from battlements to kitchens. Discover the Norman bedchamber, 15th century Great Hall with minstrels' gallery, elegant panelled Carolean dining room, guided by the acclaimed 'Time Machine' audio tours included in the admission; also in French and German. Penhow holds 8 awards for careful restoration and imaginative interpretation. Exciting children's tours and school visits.
Location: OS Ref. ST423 908. Midway between Chepstow and Newport on the A48. Use M4/J24.
Opening Times: Summer: Good Fri - 30 Sept: Wed - Sun & BHs. Aug: daily, 10am - 5.15pm (last adm.) Winter: Wed, 10am - 4pm. Selected Sun, 1 - 4pm. Evening Candlelit Tours all year by arrangement. Christmas Tours 15 Nov - 5 Jan.
Admission: Adult £3.35, Child £2.05, Family (2+2) £8.75. Groups by arrangement all year, 10% discount for 20+.

| & | Not suitable. | ☕ | Kiosk. | 🏃 | Audio tours. | P | Limited. |
| 👪 | Educational programme available. | 🐕 | Guide dogs. |

PENPERGWM LODGE
Tel: 01873 840208

Abergavenny, Gwent
Owner: Mrs Catriona Boyle   **Contact:** Mrs Catriona Boyle
3 acre terraced garden including rose and vine walks.
Location: OS Ref. SO325 101. On B4598 to Usk, 3m SE of Abergavenny.
Opening Times: Mar - Oct: Thur - Sun, 2 - 6pm.
Admission: Adult £1.50, Child free.

| i | Plant centre. | 🏃 | By arrangement. | 🐕 | In grounds, on leads. |

CADW: Welsh Historic Monuments. Crown Copyright

Oxwich Castle.

South Wales

PICTON CASTLE

HAVERFORDWEST, PEMBROKESHIRE SA62 4AS

Owner: Picton Castle Trust   Contact: Mr D Pryse Lloyd

Tel/Fax: 01437 751326

Built around 1300, Picton has been occupied by descendants of the same family up to the present day. The home of the Philipps family was remodelled above the undercroft level in 1749 - 52 with fine plasterwork and panelling, sash windows and fine fireplaces. The Regency wing was added around 1800. The woodland gardens extend to 40 acres and have a unique collection of rhododendrons and azaleas bred over 35 years. There are mature trees and shrubs such as ancient oaks, giant redwoods, magnolia, myrtle, embothrium, eucriphia and a recently planted maze and picnic area. Wild flowers abound. The walled garden has roses, fernery, herbaceous borders, a large collection of herbs and a fish pond.

Location: OS Ref. SN011 135. 4m E of Haverfordwest just off the A40.

Opening Times: Castle: Jul - Sept (also Easter & BH Mon & Sun pm), Thur & Sun afternoon. Gardens: Apr - Oct: daily (except Mon), 10.30am - 5pm.

Admission: Woodland Gardens: Adult £2.50, OAP £2, Child £1. Castle and Woodland Gardens: Adult £4, OAP £3, Child £1. Reduction for castle tours and gardens for groups of 20+.

ℹ️ Shops. Art gallery.   ♿ Ground floor suitable. WC.   ☕ Licensed restaurant.

🚶 Compulsory for castle. No indoor photography.   🅿️ Ample.

🐕 In grounds, on leads.

RAGLAN CASTLE ✠

Tel: 01291 690228

Raglan NP5 2BT

Owner: CADW: Welsh Historic Monuments   **Contact:** The Administrator

Undoubtedly the finest late medieval fortress-palace in Britain, it was begun in the 1430s by Sir William ap Thomas who built the mighty 'Yellow Tower'. His son William Lord Herbert added a palatial mansion defended by a gatehouse and many towered walls. The high quality is still obvious today.

Location: OS Ref. SO415 084. Raglan, NE of Raglan village off A40 and signposted.

Opening Times: Jan - Dec: Mon - Sat, 9.30am - 4.30pm. Sun, 11am - 4pm.

Admission: Adult £2.20, Child/OAP £1.70, Family £6.

ℹ️ Shop.   ♿ Suitable.   🅿️ Ample.   🐕 Guide dogs only.

Raglan Castle.

ST DAVIDS BISHOP'S PALACE ✠

Tel: 01437 720517

St Davids, SA62 6PE

Owner: CADW: Welsh Historic Monuments   **Contact:** The Administrator

The city of St Davids boasts not only one of Britain's finest cathedrals but also the most impressive medieval palace in Wales. Built in the elaborate 'decorated' style of Gothic architecture, the palace is lavishly encrusted with fine carving.

Location: OS Ref. SM750 254. A487 to St. Davids, minor road past the Cathedral.

Opening Times: Late Mar - late Oct: daily, 9.30am - 6.30pm. Late Oct - late Mar: Mon - Sat, 9.30am - 4pm. Sun, 2 - 4pm.

Admission: Adult £1.70, Child/OAP £1.20, Family £4.

♿ Suitable.   🅿️ Ample.   🐕 Guide dogs only.

St Davids Bishop's Palace.

ST DAVIDS CATHEDRAL

Tel: 01437 720691   **Fax:** 01437 721885

St Davids, Dyfed SA62 6QW   **Contact:** Mr R G Tarr

St Davids is Britain's smallest city by Royal Charter, March 1994. Premier cathedral of church in Wales. Over eight centuries old. Many unique and 'odd' features. Reputed to be on site of St Davids 6th century monastery.

Location: OS Ref. SM751 254. 5-10 mins walk from car/coach parks: signs for pedestrians.

Opening Times: Daily: 7.30am - 6.30pm. Sun: 12.30 - 5.30pm, may be closed for services in progress. Sun services: 8am, 9.30am, 11.15am & 6pm. Weekday services: 7.30am, 8am & 6pm. Wed extra service: 10am.

Admission: Donations. Guided tours (Adult £2.50, Child £1) must be booked in advance.

STRATA FLORIDA ABBEY ✠

Tel: 01974 831261

Ystrad Meurig, Pontrhydfendigaid SY25 6BT

Owner: CADW: Welsh Historic Monuments   **Contact:** The Administrator

Remotely set in the green, kite-haunted Teifi Valley with the lonely Cambrian mountains as a backdrop, the ruined abbey has a wonderful doorway with Celtic spiral motifs and preserves a wealth of beautiful medieval tiles.

Location: OS Ref. SN746 658. Minor road from Pontrhydfendigaid reached from the B4340 or B4343.

Opening Times: Apr - Sept: daily, 10am - 5pm. Oct - Mar: open at all times.

Admission: Adult £1.70, Child/OAP £1.20, Family £4.

♿ Suitable.   🅿️ Ample.   🐕 Guide dogs only.

South Wales *(side tab)*

TINTERN ABBEY ✠

Tel: 01291 689251

Tintern NP6 6SE

Owner: CADW: Welsh Historic Monuments   **Contact:** The Administrator

Tintern is the best preserved abbey in Wales and ranks among Britain's most beautiful historic sites. Elaborately decorated in 'Gothic' architecture style this church stands almost complete to roof level. Turner sketched and painted here, while Wordsworth drew inspiration from the surroundings.

Location: OS Ref. SO533 000. Tintern via A466, from M4/J22. Chepstow 6m.

Opening Times: Mar - Oct: daily, 9.30am - 6.30pm. Oct - Mar: Mon - Sat, 9.30am - 4pm. Sun, 11am - 4pm.

Admission: Adult £2.20, Child/OAP £1.70, Family £6.

🛈 Shop.   ♿ Suitable.   🅿 Ample.   🐕 Guide dogs only.

TREDEGAR HOUSE & PARK 🏛

NEWPORT, SOUTH WALES NP1 9YW

Owner: Newport County Borough Council   *Contact: Marketing & Events Officer*

Tel: 01633 815880   **Fax:** 01633 815895

South Wales' finest country house, ancestral home of the Morgan family. Parts of a medieval house remain, but Tredegar owes its reputation to lavish rebuilding in the 17th century. Visitors have a lively and entertaining tour through 30 rooms, including glittering State Rooms and 'below stairs'. Set in 90 acres of parkland with formal gardens. Winner of Best Public Park and Garden in Great Britain 1997. Carriage rides, boating and craft workshops.

Location: OS Ref. ST290 852. M4/J28 signposted. From London 2¹/₂ hrs, from Cardiff 20 mins. 2m SW of Newport town centre.

Opening Times: Easter - Sept: Wed - Sun & BHs, 11am - 4pm. Evening tours by appointment. Oct: Sat & Sun, 11am - 4pm. Nov - Mar: Groups only by appointment.

Admission: Adult £3.95, Child £2, Conc. £3. Groups: Adult £3.65, Child £2, Conc. £2.75. £1 car parking charge.

🛈 Shop. Corporate hospitality. Conferences.   ♿ Partially suitable.WC.

☕ Tearoom.   🚶 Compulsory.   🅿 Ample.

👨‍🏫 Educational programme.   🐕 In grounds, on leads.   💒 Civil Wedding Licence.

SPECIAL EVENTS: Held throughout the year.

TREOWEN

Tel/Fax: 01600 712031

Wonastow, Nr Monmouth NP5 4DL

Owner: R A & J P Wheelock   **Contact:** John Wheelock

Early 17th century mansion built to double pile plan with magnificent well-stair to four storeys.

Location: OS Ref. SO461 111. 3m WSW of Monmouth.

Opening Times: May, Jun, Aug & Sept: Fri. Also Sat & Sun on 9/10 & 16/17 May also 12/13, 19/20 & 26/27 Sept: 10am - 4pm.

Admission: £4. £2.50 if appointment made. Groups by appointment only.

🅰 Entire house let, self catering. Sleeps 22+.

TRETOWER COURT & CASTLE ✠

Tel: 01874 730279

Tretower, Crickhowell NP8 2RF

Owner: CADW: Welsh Historic Monuments   **Contact:** The Administrator

A fine fortress and an outstanding medieval manor house, Tretower Court and Castle range around a galleried courtyard, now further enhanced by a beautiful recreated medieval garden.

Location: OS Ref. SO187 212. Signposted in Tretower Village, off A479, 3m NW of Crickhowell.

Opening Times: Mar: daily, 10am - 5pm. Apr - Oct: daily, 10am - 6pm.

Admission: Adult £2.20, Child/OAP £1.70, Family £6.

♿ Suitable.   🐕 Guide dogs only.

TUDOR MERCHANT'S HOUSE 🍂

Tel: 01834 842279

Quay Hill, Tenby SA70 7BX

Owner: The National Trust   **Contact:** The Administrator

A late 15th century town house, characteristic of the building tradition of south west Wales. The ground-floor chimney at the rear of the house is a fine vernacular example, and the original scarfed roof-trusses survive. The remains of early frescos can be seen on three interior walls. Access to small herb garden, weather permitting. Furniture and fittings re-create the atmosphere from the time when a Tudor family was in residence.

Location: OS Ref. SN135 004. Tenby.

Opening Times: 2 Apr - 30 Sept: Mon - Sat, excl. Wed, 10am - 5pm; Sun 1 - 5pm. 1 - 31 Oct: Mon, Tue, Thur & Fri, 10am - 3pm; Sun, 12 - 3pm.

Admission: Adult £1.80, Child 90p. Pre-booked group: Adult £1.40, Child 70p.

🛈 No indoor photography.   🅿 No parking.   👨‍🏫 Teachers' pack.

🐕 Guide dogs only.

WEOBLEY CASTLE ✠

Tel: 01792 390012

Weobley Castle Farm, Llanrhidian SA3 1HB

Owner: CADW: Welsh Historic Monuments   **Contact:** The Administrator

Perched above the wild northern coast of the beautiful Gower peninsula, Weobley Castle was the home of the Knightly de Bere family. Its rooms include a fine hall and private chamber as well as numerous 'garderobes' or toilets and an early Tudor porch block.

Location: OS Ref. SN477 928. B4271 or B4295 to Llanrhidian Village, then minor road for 1¹/₂ m.

Opening Times: Mar - Oct: daily, 9.30am - 6.30pm. Oct - Mar: Mon - Sat, 9.30am - 4pm. Sun, 2 - 4pm.

Admission: Adult £1.70, Child/OAP £1.20, Family £4.

☕ Tearoom.   🅿 Ample.   🐕 Guide dogs only.

WHITE CASTLE ✠

Tel: 01600 780380

Llantillio Crossenny, Gwent

Owner: CADW: Welsh Historic Monuments   **Contact:** The Administrator

With its high walls and round towers reflected in the still waters of its moat, White Castle is the ideal medieval fortress. It was rebuilt in the mid-13th century by the future King Edward I to counter a threat from Prince Llywelyn the Last.

Location: OS Ref. SO380 167. By minor roads 2m NW from B4233, A7 Llantilio Crossenny. 8m ENE of Abergavenny.

Opening Times: Telephone for opening hours.

Admission: Adult £1.70, Conc. £1.20, Family £4.

CADW: Welsh Historic Monuments. Crown

Tintern Abbey.

IRELAND

ALTAMONT

Tel/Fax: +353 503 59128

Tullow, Co. Carlow

Owner: Mrs C North   **Contact:** Mrs C North

Altamont dates back to the 1500s. 18th century plantings and layout - mix of formal and informal. One of Ireland's finest gardens.

Location: Off N81 between Tullow and Bunclody.

Opening Times: 1 Apr - 31 Oct: Sun & BHs, 2 - 6pm. Other days and times by request. Groups by appointment.

Admission: Adult £3, Child £1, Conc. £2.

ℹ️ Shop.   ♿ Partially suitable.   ☕ Tearoom.

ANNES GROVE GARDENS

Tel: +353 22 26145

Castletownroche, Co. Cork

Owner: R A Grove-Annesley   **Contact:** Mr P Annesley

The gardens around the 18th century house contain magnolias, eucryphias and hoherias of unusual size. Winding paths and riverside walks.

Location: 1.6 km N of Castletownroche.

Opening Times: 17 Mar - 30 Sept: Mon - Sat, 10am - 5pm; Sun, 1 - 6pm. Other times by arrangement.

Admission: Adult £2.80, Child £1, Student/OAP £1.50.

♿ Suitable.   🚶 Available.

ANTRIM CASTLE GARDENS

Tel: 01849 428000   **Fax:** 01849 460360

Antrim BT41 4LH

Owner: Antrim Borough Council   **Contact:** Sinead Holland

On a 15-ha site adjacent to the Sixmilewater River, the restored 17th century Anglo-Dutch water garden is maintained in a manner authentic to the period. Many woodland walks.

Location: Outside Antrim town centre off A26 on A6.

Opening Times: All year: Mon - Fri, 9.30am - 4.30pm; Sat, 9.30am - 5pm; Summer only: Sun, 2 - 5pm.

Admission: Free. Charge for guided group tours.

🚶 Available.

ARDGILLAN CASTLE

Tel: +353 1 849 2212   **Fax:** +353 1 849 2786

Balbriggan, Co. Dublin   **Contact:** Stephanie Burke

"Flúirse talamh is mara" – Rich in land and sea – part of the Fingal Region of North County Dublin crest and nowhere more true than in Ardgillan Demesne. 194 acres of parkland and gardens surround this early 18th century house.

Location: 30km N of Dublin, off the N1.

Opening Times: All year: 1 Apr - 30 Sept: Tue - Sun & Bhs, 11am - 6pm. 1 Oct - 31 Mar: Wed - Sun & BHs 11am - 4.30pm. 20 Dec - 31 Jan: Suns only 2 - 4pm. Gardens: Guided tours Jun/Jul/Aug: Thurs at 3.30pm.

Admission: Castle by guided tour only: Adult £2.75, Conc. £1.75, Family £6.50. Groups (10+) £1.50.

ℹ️ No photography.   ♿ Suitable. WCs.   ☕ Tearoom.

🚶 Castle by guided tours only. Gardens guided tour on Thurs in Jun/Jul/ Aug at 3.30pm.

🅿️ Ample.   🐾 Educational programme available.   🐕 In grounds, on leads.

ARDRESS 🌸

Tel: 01762 851236

64 Ardress Road, Portadown, Co Armagh BT62 1SQ

Owner: The National Trust   **Contact:** The Administrator

Originally a 17th century farmhouse, the main front and garden façades were added in the 18th century by the owner-architect George Ensor. The house contains some particularly fine neo-classical plasterwork as well as good furniture and pictures. There is a display of farm implements and livestock in the farmyard, an attractive garden and woodland walks.

Location: 7m from Portadown on Moy road B28, 5m from Moy, 3m from Loughgall intersection 13 on M1, 9m from Armagh.

Opening Times: Apr, May & Sept: Sat & Sun & BHs, 2 - 6pm; Easter: daily 2 - 6pm; Jun - end Aug: daily except Tue, 2 - 6pm.

Admission: Adult £2.30, Child £1.15, Family £5.75. Groups £2. Groups outside regular opening times £3pp.

♿ Ground floor suitable. WC.   🚶 Guided tours only.   🅿️ Ample.

THE ARGORY 🌸

Tel: 01868 784753   **Fax:** 01868 789598

Moy, Dungannon, Co Tyrone BT71 6NA

Owner: The National Trust   **Contact:** The Administrator

Set in over 130-ha of woodland overlooking the Blackwater River, the house dates from 1820 and remains substantially unchanged since the turn of the century. Fascinating furniture and contents, including an 1824 Bishop's barrel organ. Imposing stableyard with a coach house and carriages, harness room, laundry and acetylene gas plant. Also an interesting sundial garden and extensive walks.

Location: 4m from Moy, 3m from M1/J13 or J14.

Opening Times: Easter: daily. Apr, May & Sept: Sat, Sun & BHs. Jun - Aug: daily except Tue, 2 - 6pm (open 1 - 6pm on all BHs). Last tour 5.15pm.

Admission: Adult £2.50, Child £1.25, Family £6.25. Groups £2pp. Groups outside regular opening times £3pp. Estate: £1.50 per car. Coaches must book.

ℹ️ Shop.   ♿ Ground floor suitable. WC.   ☕ Tearoom.   🚶 Guided tours only.

BANTRY HOUSE

Tel: + 353 27 50047   **Fax:** +353 27 50795

Bantry, Co. Cork

Owner: Mr & Mrs Egerton Shelswell-White   **Contact:** Mr E Shelswell-White

House contains extensive art and tapestry collection.

Location: On outskirts of Bantry, 90km from Cork city.

Opening Times: Mar - Oct: daily, 9am - 6pm.

Admission: House & gardens: Adult £6, Groups (20+) £4. Gardens only: Adult £2, Groups (20+) £1.50.

ℹ️ Shop.   ♿ Suitable.   ☕ Tearoom.   🚶 Available.   🅰️ Available.

BARONSCOURT

Tel: 01662 661683   **Fax:** 01662 662059

Newtownstewart, Omagh, Co. Tyrone BT78 4EZ

Owner: Mount Castle Trust   **Contact:** The Agent

The home of the Duke and Duchess of Abercorn, Baronscourt was built in the late 18th century and subsequently extensively remodelled by William and Richard Morrison (1819 - 1841), Sir Albert Richardson (1947-49) and David Hicks (1975-76).

Location: 5km SW of Newtownstewart.

Opening Times: By appointment only.

Admission: Adult £4.50, Conc. £3. Groups max. 50.

ℹ️ Plant centre.   ♿ Partially suitable. WCs.   🚶 By arrangement.   🅿️ Ample.

🐾 Educational programme available.   🐕 Strictly no dogs.

BENVARDEN GARDEN

Tel: 012657 41331   **Fax:** 012657 41955

Dervock, Ballymoney, Co. Antrim

Owner: Mr H J Montgomery   **Contact:** Mr H J Montgomery

One of the oldest estates in the north of Ireland, dating back to the 1630s.

Location: 10 km from Giants Causeway on B67.

Opening Times: 1 Jun - 31 Aug: daily (except Mon), 2 - 6pm. Other times by arrangement.

Admission: Adult £2, Child £1. Group rates on request. Guided tours by arrangement.

ℹ️ Small museum. Plant sales.   ♿ Suitable.   ☕ Tearoom.

BIRR CASTLE DEMESNE

Tel: +353 509 20336   **Fax:** +353 509 21583

Birr, Co. Offaly

Owner: Lord & Lady Rosse   **Contact:** Mr Aldo Giordana

The gardens are particularly noted for their spring flowering magnolias, cherry and crab apple trees; autumn-colouring maples, chestnuts and weeping birch; also for the formal gardens, hornbeam allées and box hedges acknowledged as the tallest in the world. Castle dates back to 1620s and remains a private family home. Also on view is the famous giant 72" reflecting telescope erected in 1845.

Location: In town of Birr. 130km from Dublin; 90km from Shannon via Limmerick.

Opening Times: All year: 9am - 6pm or dusk if earlier.

Admission: Jan - Jun: Adult £3.50, Child £1.50. Jul - Dec: Adult £5, Child £2.50.

ℹ️ Shop.   ♿ Suitable.   ☕ Tearoom.   🚶 Available.

BLARNEY CASTLE

Tel: +353 21 382141   **Fax:** +353 21 382142

Blarney, Co. Cork

Owner: Sir Richard La T Colthurst Bart   **Contact:** Mervyn Johnston Esq

Site of the Blarney Stone.

Location: 7km from Cork city, off N20.

Opening Times: May & Sept: Mon - Sat, 9am - 6pm; Sun, 9.30am - 5.30pm. Jun - Aug: Mon - Sat, 9am - 7pm; Sun, 9.30am - 5.30pm, Oct - Apr: Mon - Sat, 9am - 5pm or sundown; Sun, 9.30am - sundown. Closed 24 - 25 Dec.

Admission: Adult £3, Conc. £2, Child £1.

ℹ️ Shop.   ♿ Grounds suitable.

SPECIAL EVENTS:
JUNE 4 - 7: International Horse Trials.

Porter:

A black beer brewed from malt partly charred or browned by drying at a high temperature, with a long fermentation, and heavily flavoured with hops. First brewed in London in the 1720s, it quickly became very popular throughout the country. It was exported to Ireland, where Arthur Guinness of Dublin established his own brew with such success that this was exported to London to the detriment of the local brewers there. Guinness remains the most famous porter to this day.

Extract from: "Life in the Country House" by David N Durant (published by John Murray), PB£15.99, see page twelve at the front of the book.

SHANNON HERITAGE

"A COMMON CELTIC PAST"
5000 YEARS OF MAGIC AND MYSTERY

8 EXCITING HERITAGE SITES
LOUGH GUR STONE AGE CENTRE
CRAGGAUNOWEN THE LIVING PAST
KILLALOE HERITAGE CENTRE
KING JOHN'S CASTLE
BUNRATTY CASTLE AND FOLK PARK
KNAPPOGUE CASTLE
CLIFFS OF MOHER
DUNGUAIRE CASTLE

4 WORLD FAMOUS EVENING
ENTERTAINMENTS
BUNRATTY CASTLE
MEDIAEVAL BANQUET
KNAPPOGUE CASTLE
MEDIAEVAL BANQUET
BUNRATTY CEILI
(TRADITIONAL IRISH NIGHT)
DUNGUAIRE CASTLE
MEDIAEVAL BANQUET
CENTRAL RESERVATIONS
BUNRATTY CASTLE & FOLK PARK
BUNRATTY, CO. CLARE IRELAND
TEL: 00353 61 360788
FAX: 00353 61 361020

CARRIGGLAS MANOR

Tel: +353 43 45165   Fax: +353 43 41026

Longford, Rep. of Ireland
Owner: Mr J Lefroy   **Contact:** Mrs J G Lefroy
Property of the year 1988. A romantic Tudor Gothic house.
Location: 4.8km from Longford town on T15/R194.
Opening Times: 3 Jun - 3 Sept (except Tue & Wed): daily, 2 - 6pm or by telephone appointment. House tours on the hour.
Admission: Stables, gardens & museum: Adult £2, Child under 7 free, Conc. £1.50. House: £3 extra. Pre-booked groups welcome (10+), Apr - Oct.

ⓘ Shop.   ☕ Tearoom.   🚶 Available.   Ⓐ Self-catering.

CASTLE COOLE 🌼

Tel: 01365 322690   Fax: 01365 325665

Enniskillen, Co Fermanagh BY74 6JX
Owner: The National Trust   **Contact:** The Administrator
This very fine neo-classical late 18th century house with colonnaded wings was designed by James Wyatt. It contains original decoration and furniture dating from before 1830, and is set in a landscaped parkland with mature oak woodland. State bedroom prepared for George IV in 1821. Exterior attractions include servants' tunnel, stables and nature display room in Grand Yard.
Location: ½ m SE of Enniskillen on A4, Belfast - Enniskillen road.
Opening Times: Easter (10 - 14 Apr): daily. Apr & Sept: Sat, Sun & BHs only. May - Aug: daily (except Thur), 1 - 6pm. Last tour 5.15pm. Grounds open during daylight hours.
Admission: Adult £2.80, Child £1.40, Family £7. Groups £2.50. Group after hours £3pp. Estate: £2 per car.

ⓘ Shop.   ♿ Partly suitable. WC.   ☕ Tearoom.   🐕 In grounds, on leads.

CASTLE LESLIE

Tel: +353 47 88109   Fax: +353 47 88256

Glaslough, Co. Monaghan
Owner: Samantha Leslie   **Contact:** Samantha Leslie
The present castle was built in 1878. Contains Italian and Spanish furniture, tapestries and carpets. The family home of the Leslies.
Location: 6 km N of Monaghan at Glaslough village.
Opening Times: 30 Apr - 31 Aug: Sun - Thur, 2 - 6pm.
Admission: Guided tour on the hour (min 4 persons). Adult £3, Child £1.50, Conc. £2. Garden only: Adults £1, Conc. 50p. Group rates on request.

CASTLE WARD 🌼

Tel: 01396 881204   Fax: 01396 881729

Strangford, Downpatrick, Co Down BT30 7LS
Owner: The National Trust   **Contact:** The Administrator
Castle Ward is set in a 285-ha country estate on the shores of Strangford Lough. This unique 18th century mansion has opposing façades in different styles. The west front is Classical and the east front Gothick. In the stableyard there is a Victorian laundry and theatre for visiting companies. Also formal and landscape gardens with specimen shrubs and trees, fortified towers, a sawmill and working cornmill. Strangford Lough Wildlife Centre, located on the water's edge, has audio visual shows. Caravan park, holiday cottages and a basecamp for young people.
Location: 1m W of Strangford on A25 Downpatrick - Strangford.
Opening Times: House: Sept & Oct: Sat & Sun, 1 - 6pm; Easter (10 - 19 Apr): daily, 1- 6pm; May - Aug: daily except Thur, 1 - 6pm. Estate & Grounds: All year, dawn - dusk. Shop & Restaurant: Open days as house: weekends & BHs, 1 - 6pm; weekdays 1 - 5pm. Strangford Lough Wildlife Centre: Open as house except May & June when open Sat, Sun & BHs only, 2 - 6pm.
Admission: Adult £2.60, Child £1.30, Family £6.50. Groups £2pp (after hours £3pp). Estate: £3.50per car.

ⓘ Shop.   ♿ Ground floor & grounds suitable.   ☕ Tearoom.   🐕 In grounds, on leads.

CLONALIS HOUSE

Tel: +353 907 20014

Castlerea, Co. Rosscommon

Owner: P O'Conor Nash Esq

Ancestral home of the O'Conors of Connaught, descendants of the last High Kings of Ireland.

Location: W of Castlerea town on T39.

Opening Times: 1 Jun - 15 Sept: daily, except Mon, 11am - 5pm. Open all year to groups by arrangement.

Admission: Adult £3.50, Child £2, Conc. £2.50.

ⓘ Shop.   Tearoom.   Available.   A Self-catering.

CRATLOE WOODS HOUSE

Tel: +353 61 327028   **Fax:** +353 61 327031

Cratloe, Co. Clare

Owner: Mr & Mrs G Brickenden   **Contact:** Mr & Mrs G Brickenden

House dates from the 17th century and is the only example of the Irish longhouse which is still a home.

Location: 8 km from Limerick and 16 km from Shannon airport.

Opening Times: 1 Jun - mid Sept: Mon - Sat, 2 - 6pm. Open other times by arrangement.

Admission: Adult £2.50, Child £1.50, Conc. £2.

♿ Suitable.   Tearoom.   A Available.

CROM

Tel: 013657 38174

Newtownbutler, Co. Fermanagh

Owner: The National Trust   **Contact:** The Administrator

One of the most important nature conservation sites owned by The National Trust.

Location: 5 km W of Newtownbutler.

Opening Times: 1 Apr - end Sept: Mon - Sat, 10am - 6pm; Sun, 12 - 6pm.

Admission: £3 per car or boat. Group rates available.

♿ Suitable.

DAMER HOUSE & ROSCREA CASTLE

Tel: +353 505 21850

Roscrea Heritage Centre, Roscrea, Co. Tipperary

Owner: Dept. of Arts & Culture and the Roscrea Heritage   **Contact:** Eimear Hughes

House dates back to the 18th century. Restored by Irish Georgian Society and Roscrea Heritage Society. 13th century castle.

Location: In Roscrea town.

Opening Times: Jun - Sept: daily, 9.30am - 6pm. Winter: Sat & Sun only, 10am - 5pm. Other dates & times by arrangement.

Admission: Adult £2.50, Child/Student £1, OAP £1.75. Family £6. Group (20+) £1.75pp.

🚶 Available.

DUBLIN'S WRITERS MUSEUM

Tel: +353 1 8222077   **Fax:** +353 1 8722231

18 Parnell Square, Dublin 1

Owner: Dublin Tourism Enterprises   **Contact:** Fiona McKiernan

Situated in a very fine 18th century mansion in the north city centre, the museum features the lives and works of Dublin's literary celebrities over the past 300 years. Swift, Sheridan, Shaw and Wilde, Yeats, Joyce and Beckett are among those represented through their books, letters, portraits and personal items.

Location: City Centre, N of O'Connell Street.

Opening Times: Jan - Dec: Mon - Sat, 10am - 5pm. Sun & BHs, 11am - 5pm. Jun - Aug: late opening Mon - Fri, 10am - 6pm.

Admission: Adult IR£2.95, Child (3-11yrs) IR£1.30, OAP/student (12-17yrs) IR£2.50.

DUNGUAIRE CASTLE

Tel: +353 61 360788   **Fax:** +353 61 361020

Kinvara, Co. Clare

Owner: Shannon Heritage   **Contact:** Central Reservations

16th century tower house and bawn built by descendants of the 7th century King of Connaught.

Location: On Clare/Galway road.

Opening Times: May - 6 Oct: daily, 9.30am - 5.30pm. Last adm 5pm.

Admission: Adult IR£2.75, Child (3-11yrs) IR£1.65, OAP/student (12-17yrs) IR£1.90, Family £6.80. Groups: Adult £2.45, Student £1.45.

ⓘ Shop.   Tearoom.   🚶 Available.

DUNKATHEL

Tel: +353 21 821014   **Fax:** +353 21 821023

Glanmire, Co. Cork

Owner: Mrs Elizabeth Russell   **Contact:** Mr Frankie Russell

House dates from around 1790. Contains splendid bifurcated staircase of Bath stone.

Location: 5 km from Cork off N25.

Opening Times: May - mid Oct: Wed - Sun, 2 - 6pm or by appointment.

Admission: Adult £2, Child £1, OAP/Student £1.50. Special group rate.

🚶 Available.

DUNLOE CASTLE HOTEL GARDENS

Tel: +353 64 44111   **Fax:** +353 64 44583

Beaufort, Killarney, Co. Kerry

Owner: The Liebherr Family   **Contact:** Mary Rose Hickey

Collection of trees, shrubs and plants from around the world.

Location: 13 km from Killarney.

Opening Times: May - Oct: Groups and tours by appointment.

Admission: Free. Catalogue £1.

♿ Suitable.   Tearoom.   🚶 Compulsory, by arrangement.   A Available.

Crom Boathouse, Ireland.

Mike Williams

FERNHILL
Tel: +353 1 295 6000

Sandyford, Co. Dublin

Owner: Mrs Sally Walker   **Contact:** Mrs Sally Walker

200 year old garden for all seasons. Fine trees, rare shrubs, Victorian kitchen garden, collection of roses and herbaceous plants.

Location: On the NE slope of the Three Rock mountain, 11 km S of the city centre on the Enniskerry Road. 6 km inland from Dun Laoghaire.

Opening Times: 1 Mar - 31 Oct: Tue - Sat & BH Mon, 11am - 5pm; Sun 2 - 6pm.

Admission: Adult £3, Child £1, Conc. £2. Groups £2.50pp.

🚶 By arrangement.   🐕 No dogs.

FLORENCE COURT
Tel: 01365 348249 **Fax:** 01365 348873

Enniskillen, Co Fermanagh BT92 1DB

Owner: The National Trust   **Contact:** The Administrator

One of the most important houses in Ulster, built in the mid-18th century by John Cole, father of 1st Earl of Enniskillen. Contents include fine rococo plasterwork and good examples of 18th century furniture. There are pleasure grounds with an ice house and water-powered sawmill, plus walled garden and fine views over surrounding mountains.

Location: 8m SW of Enniskillen via A4 Sligo road and A32 Swanlinbar road.

Opening Times: Easter (10 - 14 Apr): daily, 1 - 6pm. Apr & Sept: Sat, Sun, BH only. May - Aug: daily except Tue, 1 - 6pm. Last adm. 5.15pm. Grounds: All year, 10am - 7pm, Oct - Mar: 10am - 4pm. Closed 25 Dec.

Admission: House: Adult £2.80, Child £1.40, Family £7. Groups £2.50pp. Groups outside opening hours £3pp. Estate: £2 per car.

ℹ️ Shop.   ♿ Ground floor suitable. WC.   🚶 Compulsory.   🐕 In grounds, on leads.

THE FRY MODEL RAILWAY
Tel: +353 18 463779 **Fax:** +353 18462537

Malahide Castle, Demesne, Malahide, Co. Dublin

Owner: Dublin Tourism Enterprises   **Contact:** John Dunne

The Fry Model Railway is a unique collection of handmade models of Irish trains from the beginning of travel to modern times.

Location: 10m N of Dublin.

Opening Times: Apr - Oct (Closed Fris, Apr/May): Mon - Fri, 10am - 6pm, Sat 10am - 5pm, Sun & BHs 2 - 6pm. Nov - Mar: Sat, Sun & BHs, 2 - 5pm. Closed 1 - 2pm daily all year.

Admission: Adult IR£2.75, Child (3-11yrs) IR£1.60, OAP/student (12-17yrs) IR£2.10.

GLENVEAGH CASTLE & GARDENS
Tel: +353 7437088 **Fax:** +353 7437072

Glenveagh National Park, Churchill, Letterkenny, Co. Donegal

Owner: Dúchas - The Heritage Service **Contact:** Dr Cieran O'Keeffe, Park Superintendent

A Scottish baronial-style castle fully furnished, surrounded by wonderful gardens. Situated in the middle of thousands of acres of mountain bog and lake.

Location: Glenveagh National Park.

Opening Times: 14 - 17 Mar & 11 Apr - 1 Nov: daily 10am - 5pm. During Oct closed Fris.

Admission: Park & Gardens: Adult £2, Child/Student (up to 18yrs) £1, OAP £1.50, Family (2+4) £5. Groups (20+) £1.50. Castle: Adult £2, Child/Student (up to 18yrs) £1, OAP £1.50, Family (2+4) £5. Groups (20+) £1.50.

GRAY'S PRINTING PRESS
Tel: 01504 884094

49 Main Street, Strabane, Co. Tyrone BT82 8AU

Owner: The National Trust   **Contact:** The Administrator

An 18th century printing press, shop and stationers. It may be here that John Dunlap, the printer of the American Declaration of Independence, and James Wilson, grandfather of President Woodrow Wilson, learned their trade. There is a collection of 19th century hand printing machines and an audio visual display.

Location: Strabane centre.

Opening Times: Apr - Sept: daily, except Thur, Sun & BH, 2 - 5.30pm. At other times by prior arrangement.

Admission: Adult £1.50, Child 75p, Family £4.25. Group £1.

HAMWOOD HOUSE
Tel: +353 44 8255210

Dunboyne, Co. Meath

Owner: Major and Mrs Hamilton   **Contact:** Mrs Hamilton

Palladian-style house originally built in 1779, contains a fine collection of 18th century furniture.

Location: 2m from Dunboyne on Maynooth Rd.

Opening Times: 1 Feb - 31 Mar: Mon - Fri, 10am - 2pm. 1 May - 31 Aug: Mon - Fri. 2 - 6pm. 3rd Sun of each month, 2 - 6pm.

Admission: House: Adult £2. Garden: Adult £2. Groups by arrangement.

HEZLETT HOUSE
Tel: 01265 848567

107 Sea Road, Castlerock, Coleraine, Co. Londonderry BT51 4TW

Owner: The National Trust   **Contact:** The Administrator

A 17th century thatched house, with an interesting cruck truss roof construction. Furnished in late Victorian style. Small museum of farm implements.

Location: 5m W of Coleraine on Coleraine - Downhill coast road, A2.

Opening Times: Easter (10 - 14 Apr): daily. Apr, May & Sept: Sat, Sun & BH only. Jun - Aug: daily except Tue, 12 noon - 5pm. Guided tours. Groups must book in advance.

Admission: Adult £1.80, Child 90p, Family £4.50. Groups £1.30pp (outside hours £2pp).

♿ Ground floor suitable.   🚶 Compulsory.   🅿️ Ample.   🐕 In grounds, on leads.

HILTON PARK
Tel: +353 47 56007 **Fax:** +353 47 56033

Hilton Park, Clones, Co. Monaghan

Owner: Mr John Madden   **Contact:** Mr John Madden

Lakeside pleasure grounds, herb garden, parterre and herbaceous border in rolling parkland.

Location: 3m due S of Clones on L46, Ballyhaise Rd.

Opening Times: May - Sept: daily 2 - 6pm.

Admission: Adult £2.50.

A Available.

THE IRISH MUSEUM OF MODERN ART
Tel: + 353 1 612 9900

Royal Hospital, Military Rd, Kilmainham, Dublin 8

Fax: +353 1 612 9999

Owner: Irish Museum of Modern Art   **Contact:** Rowena Neville

The oldest surviving fully classical building in Ireland. Once the Royal Hospital.

Location: Near Heuston Station, 2km from city centre.

Opening Times: Tue - Sat, 10am - 5.30pm. Sun 12 noon - 5.30pm. Guided tours: Wed & Fri at 2.30pm, Sat at 11.30am. Other times by appointment.

Admission: Free.

♿ Suitable.   ☕ Tearoom.   🚶 Available.

JAMES JOYCE TOWER
Tel: +353 1 280 9265 **Fax:** +353 1 280 2641

Sandycove, Co. Dublin

Owner: Dublin Tourism Enterprises   **Contact:** Robert Nicholson

A martello tower containing the Joyce museum.

Location: Dun Laoghaire, S of Dublin.

Opening Times: Apr - Oct: Mon - Sat, 10am - 5pm. Closed 1 - 2pm. Sun & BHs, 2 - 6pm.

Admission: Adult £2.50, Conc. £2, Child £1.30. Group rates on request.

🚶 Available.

JAPANESE GARDENS
Tel: +353 45 521617 **Fax:** +353 45 522964

Tully, Co. Kildare

Owner: Irish National Stud   **Contact:** Pat Mullarkey Esq

Created 1906 - 1910, the Japanese Gardens symbolise the Life of Man from the Cave of Birth to the Gateway to Eternity.

Location: 1m from Kildare Town. 30m from Dublin off N7.

Opening Times: 12 Feb - 12 Nov: daily 9.30am - 6pm.

Admission: Adult £5, Child (under 12) £2, Conc. £3.50, Family (2+4) £12. One ticket includes National Stud and Japanese Garden.

Chris Hill

Mount Stewart, Co. Down.

KING HOUSE
Tel: +353 79 63242   **Fax:** +353 79 63243

Boyle, Co. Rosscommon

Owner: Rosscommon County Council   **Contact:** The Administrator
4 storey Georgian mansion dating from the early 18th century.

Location: In the centre of Boyle.

Opening Times: Apr - Oct: weekends & BHs, 10am - 6pm. May - Sept: daily, 10am - 6pm. Last admission 5pm.

Admission: Adult £3, Conc. £2.50. Child £2, Family (2+4) £8. Group rates on request.

ℹ️ Shop.   ♿ Suitable.   ☕ Tearoom.

KING JOHN'S CASTLE
Tel: +353 61 411201

Limerick City

Owner: Shannon Heritage   **Contact:** Central Reservations
13th century military castle.

Location: In Limerick city.

Opening Times: Apr - 31 Oct: daily, 9.30am - 5.30pm. Last adm. 4.30pm. Open on request for groups.

Admission: Adult £4, Child £2.50, Student/OAP £3.15, Family £10.50. Groups: Adult £3.60, Student £2.20.

ℹ️ Shop.   ♿ Suitable.   ☕ Tearoom.

KNAPPOGUE CASTLE
Tel: +353 61 360788

Quin, Co. Clare

Owner: Shannon Heritage   **Contact:** Central Reservations
Original 15th century castle.

Location: 10km SE of Ennis.

Opening Times: Apr - 6 Oct: daily, 9.30am - 5.30pm. Open on request for groups.

Admission: Adult £2.75, Child £1.65, Student/OAP £1.90, Family £6.80. Groups: Adult £2.45, Student £1.45.

KYLEMORE ABBEY

CONNEMARA, CO. GALWAY

Owner: Benedictine Nuns   *Contact:* Sister Magdalena

Tel: +353 95 41146   **Fax:** +353 95 41145   **e-mail:** enquiries@kylemoreabbey.ie

Set in the heart of the Connemara mountains. Kylemore is a premier tourist attraction, international girls' boarding school with a magnificent Gothic church, superb restaurant, pottery and one of the finest craft shops in Ireland. May 1998 sees the first public viewing of the 6 acre Victorian Walled Garden, currently undergoing restoration. The garden is today the largest walled garden in Ireland. The walls stretch for over half a mile to enclose: the kitchen garden, flower or pleasure garden, gardener's cottage, bothy and the glass (hot) house complex. The Benedictine Nuns at Kylemore continue to restore the estate and open it to the education and enjoyment of all who visit.

Location: Between Reccess & Letterfrack, West of Ireland.

Opening Times: Abbey Gate (Abbey reception rooms, lake walk, video & exhibition: All year (closed Good Fri & Christmas week). Shop & Restaurant: 17 Mar - Nov, (closed Good Fri). Garden Gate (Walled Garden, wilderness walk, Tea House, shop & exhibition): Easter - Nov.

Admission: Abbey: Adult £2.50, Conc. £2, Family £6. Groups: Adult £1.50. Gardens: Adult £3, Family £7.50, Conc. £2.50. Groups: Adult £1.75. Joint tickets available.

ℹ️ Shop.   ♿ Ground floor & grounds suitable. WC.   ☕ Restaurant.

LISMORE CASTLE GARDENS
Tel: +353 58 54424   **Fax:** +353 58 54896

Lismore, Co. Waterford

Owner: Trustees of the Lismore Estate   **Contact:** Michael Penruddock
Lismore Castle has been the Irish home of the Dukes of Devonshire since 1748 and at one time belonged to Sir Walter Raleigh. The beautifully situated walled and woodland gardens extend to 7 acres and contain a fine collection of magnolias, camellias, rhododendrons and a remarkable yew walk where Spenser is said to have written *The Faerie Queen*.

Location: In Lismore town.

Opening Times: 25 Apr - 27 Sept: daily, 1.45 - 4.45pm.

Admission: Adult £2.50, Child £1.50, Conc. £2.50. Groups: Adult £2.25, Child £1.30, Conc. £2.25. Group discount applies to NT members.

♿ Not suitable.   🐕 In grounds, on leads.

LISNAVAGH GARDENS
Tel: +353 503 61104   **Fax:** +353 503 61148

Lisnavagh, Rathvilly, Co Carlow, Ireland

Owner: Lord and Lady Rathdonnell   **Contact:** Lord and Lady Rathdonnell
Ten acres of outstanding trees and shrubs, mixed borders, rock garden and cruciform yew walk, with panoramic views of the Wicklow Hills and Mount Leinster. A large walled garden with peacocks strutting amongst old fruit trees. Also the informal peace of endless woodland walks with all sorts of wildlife.

Location: Situated 2m S of Rathvilly. Signposted.

Opening Times: Mid May - end Aug: Suns 2 - 6pm. Other times by appointment.

Admission: Adult £2, Child £1.50.

ℹ️ Shop. Plant centre.   ♿ Partially suitable.   ☕ Tearoom.   🚶 By arrangement.
P Limited.   🐕 Strictly no dogs.   A 1 single, 3 double. Ensuite available.

LISSADELL HOUSE
Tel: +353 71 63150   **Fax:** +353 71 66906

Drumcliffe, Co. Sligo

House built in the 1830s by Sir Robert Gore-Booth, and still the family home.

Location: 13km N of Sligo.

Opening Times: 1 Jun - mid Sept: (except Sun), 10.30am - 12.30pm & 2 - 4.30pm. Last admission 12.15pm & 4.15pm. Guided tours available.

Admission: Adult £3, Child £1. Group: (20+) £2.

LODGE PARK WALLED GARDEN & STEAM MUSEUM
Tel: +353 1 6273155

Straffan, Co. Kildare   **Fax:** +353 1 6273477

Contact: The Curator

The fine walled garden with brick lined North wall of 18C origian is a plantsman's delight. From the axis of the long walk it features garden rooms, extending to a delightful rosarie. The steam museum is housed in the Gt Southern & Western Railway Church, re-erected here from Inchicore, Dublin. The Richard Guinness Model Hall displays his collection of historic prototype locomotive models. The Power Hall displays restored engines working in steam. InterActive area for educational use. Memorabilia Gallery.

Location: 16m from Dublin, signposted off the N7 road at Kill junction traffic lights.

Opening Times: Apr - May: Suns & BHs, 2.30 - 5.15pm. Jun - Aug:Tues - Suns & BHs, 2 - 5.45pm. Sept: Suns & BHs 2.30 - 5.15pm.

Admission: Adult £4, Conc. £2, Family £10. Groups (10) less 10%. Garden only: £2. Tech Student + card free.

ℹ️ Shop.   ☕ Teahouse.

MALAHIDE CASTLE
Tel: +353 1 846 2184 / 846 2516   **Fax:** +353 1 846 2537

Malahide, Co. Dublin

Owner: Dublin Tourism Enterprises   **Contact:** Maria Morgan
Home of the Talbot family from 1185 until 1973, the castle is magnificently restored with beautiful period furniture together with an extensive collection of Irish portrait paintings. The castle has changed very little in 800 years and it and the surrounding parklands retain a unique sense of the history.

Location: 10m N of Dublin city.

Opening Times: Apr - Oct: Mon - Sat, 10am - 5pm. Sun & BHs 11am - 6pm. Closed 12.45 - 2pm daily. Nov - Mar: Mon - Fri, 10am - 5pm. Sat, Sun & BH, 2 - 5pm. Closed 12.45 - 2pm daily.

Admission: Adult IR£3, Child (3-11) IR£1.65, OAP/Student (12-17yrs) IR£2.50.

ℹ️ Shop.   ☕ Tearoom.   🚶 By arrangement.

MOUNT STEWART 🌿
Tel: 01247 788387 or 788487   **Fax:** 01247 788569

Newtownards, Co. Down   BT22 2AD

Owner: The National Trust   **Contact:** The Administrator
Fascinating 18th century house with 19th century additions, where Lord Castlereagh grew up. Gardens largely created by Edith, wife of 7th Marquess of Londonderry, with an unrivalled collection of plants, colourful parterres and magnificent vistas. The Temple of the Winds, James 'Athenian' Stuart's banqueting hall of 1785 overlooks Strangford Lough.

Location: 15m SE of Belfast on A20, 5m SE of Newtownards.

Opening Times: House: Apr - Oct: weekends only 1- 6pm, Easter (10 - 19 Apr): daily, 1 - 6pm; May - Sept: daily, except Tue including BHs, 1 - 6pm. Garden: Mar: Sun only, 2 - 5pm. 1 Apr - Sept: daily, 10.30am - 6pm; Oct: weekends only, 10.30am - 6pm. Temple of the Winds: same days as house, 2 - 5pm.

Admission: House, Garden & Temple: Adult £3.50, Child £1.75, Family £8.75, Group £3pp (after hours £5pp). Garden: Adult £3, Child £1.50, Family £7.50, Group £2.50pp (after hours £5pp).

MUCKROSS HOUSE & GARDENS   **Tel:** +353 64 31440   **Fax:** +353 64 633926

Killarney, Co. Kerry

Owner: Office of Public Works   **Contact:** Mr Paul Morgan

Muckross House, gardens and traditional farms; magnificent Victorian mansion, outstanding gardens and real life traditional farms depicting rural life in the 1930s. Craft workshops, audio-visual and nature trails.

Location: 6 km from Killarney on Kenmare road (N71).

Opening Times: All year: daily, 9am - 6pm. Jul & Aug: 9am - 7pm. (Farms: Mar - Oct)

Admission: House: Adult IR£3.80, Child IR£1.60, Conc. IR£2.70. Family/group rates available.

[i] Shop.   [&] Suitable.   [☕] Tearoom.   [🚶] Available.

NEWBRIDGE HOUSE   **Tel:** +353 1 843 6534   **Fax:** +353 1 846 2537

Donabate, Co. Dublin

This delightful 18th century manor is set in 350 acres of parkland 12 miles north of Dublin city. It boasts one of the finest Georgian interiors in the British Isles. Each room open to the public has its own style of antique and original furniture – indeed the house appears much as it did 150 years ago.

Location: 12m N of Dublin city.

Opening Times: Apr - Sept: Tue - Sat, 10am - 5pm, Sun & BHs, 2 - 6pm (closed Mons). Closed 1 - 2pm daily. Oct - Mar: Sat, Sun & BHs, 2 - 5pm.

Admission: Adult IR£2.85, Child (3 - 11yrs) IR£1.55, OAP/Student (12 - 17yrs) IR£2.50.

[i] Shop.   [☕] Tearoom.   [🚶] Available.

NEWMAN HOUSE   **Tel:** +353 1 706 7422   **Fax:** +353 1 706 7211

85/86 St Stephens Green, Dublin

Owner: University College, Dublin   **Contact:** Ruth Ferguson, Curator

Two Georgian houses containing examples of Dublin's finest 18th century plasterwork.

Location: Central Dublin.

Opening Times: Jun - Aug (inc) and by prior arrangement. Tue - Fri, 12 - 4pm. Sat, 2 - 4pm; Sun, 11am - 1pm. Guided tours only.

Admission: Adult £2, Conc. £1.

NUMBER TWENTY-NINE   **Tel:** +353 1 702 6165   **Fax:** +353 1 702 7796

Fitzwilliam Street Lower, Dublin 2

Owner: Electricity Supply Board & National Museum of Ireland   **Contact:** Delo Collier

Restored middle class house of the late 18th century.

Location: Merrion Square, central Dublin.

Opening Times: Tue - Sat, 10am - 5pm; Sun, 2 - 5pm. Closed two weeks before Christmas.

Admission: Adult £2.50, Conc. £1.

[i] Shop.   [☕] Tearoom.   [🚶] Available.

PALM HOUSE BOTANIC GARDENS   **Tel:** 01232 324902

Belfast City

Owner: Belfast City Council   **Contact:** Mr Reg Maxwell

Built by Richard Turner who later built the Great Palm House at Kew.

Location: Between Botanic Avenue & Stranmillis Road, South Belfast.

Opening Times: Palm House & Tropical Ravine: Apr - Sept. Mon - Fri, 10am - 12 noon & 1 - 5pm; Sat & Sun, 1 - 5pm. Oct - Mar: Mon - Fri, 10am - 12 noon & 1 - 4pm; Sat & Sun, 1 - 4pm. BHs as Sat & Sun. Park: 8am - sunset.

Admission: Free.

[i] Corporate hospitality.   [✗] Wedding receptions.   [&] Suitable.

[🚶] By arrangement.   [P] Limited.   [👥] Educational programme.

[🐕] In grounds, on leads.

POWERSCOURT ESTATE

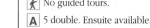

ENNISKERRY, CO. WICKLOW

Owner: *The Slazenger Family*   **Contact:** *The Estate office*

Tel: +353 1 204 6000   **Fax:** +353 1 286 3561   **e-mail:** +353 1 286 3561

One of the world's great gardens, situated in the foothills of the Wicklow Mountains. It is a sublime blend of formal gardens, sweeping terraces, statuary and ornamental lakes together with secret hollows, rambling walks, walled gardens and over 200 varieties of trees and shrubs. Powerscourt House incorporates an exhibition on the history of the estate. A terrace café overlooking the gardens and speciality shops. 5km from the gardens is Powerscourt Waterfall, the highest in Ireland.

Location: 12m S of Dublin City centre, off N11 adjacent to Enniskerry village.

Opening Times: 1 Mar - 31 Oct: daily, 9.30am - 5.30pm. 1 Nov - 28 Feb: daily, 10.30am - dusk. Closed 25/26 Dec.

Admission: Adult £5, Child £3, OAP/Student £4.50. Groups: Adult £4.50, Child £2.70, OAP/Student £4. Special winter prices. Groups (20+).

[i] Shop. Plant centre.   [&] Partially suitable. WCs.   [☕] Café.

[🚶] No guided tours.   [P] Ample.   [🐕] Guide dogs only.

[A] 5 double. Ensuite available.

POWERSCOURT TOWN HOUSE   **Tel:** +353 1 679 4144   **Fax:** +353 1 671 7505

South William St, Dublin 2

Owner: Clarendon Properties

Built for the 4th Viscount Powerscourt between 1771 and 1774.

Location: Central Dublin.

Opening Times: Daily, except Sun & BHs, 9am - 6pm.

Admission: Free.

[i] Shop.   [&] Suitable.   [☕] Tearoom.

RIVERSTOWN HOUSE   **Tel:** +353 21 821722

Glanmire, Co. Cork

Owner: Mr & Mrs D Dooley   **Contact:** Mrs D Dooley

Georgian House. Plaster work by Lafrancini Bros.

Location: 6km from Cork city on old Cork/Dublin Rd.

Opening Times: May - mid Sept: Wed - Sat, 2 - 6pm. Other times by appointment.

Admission: £2.

[&] Partially suitable.   [🚶] Available.   [P] Ample.

ROTHE HOUSE   **Tel/Fax:** +353 56 22893

Parliament St, Kilkenny

Owner: Kilkenny Archaeological Society   **Contact:** Mary Flood

Built 1594. Various exhibitions. Also houses the County Geneological Research Service.

Location: In Kilkenny city.

Opening Times: Apr - Oct: Mon - Sat, 10.30am - 5pm; Sun, 3 - 5pm. Nov - Mar: Mon - Sat, 1 - 5pm; Sun, 3 - 5pm.

Admission: Adult £2, Child £1, Student/OAP £1.50. Groups (20+): Adult £1.50pp.

[i] Shop.   [☕] Tearoom.   [🚶] Available.

Ireland

ROWALLANE GARDEN

Tel: 01238 510131   **Fax:** 01238 511242

Saintfield, Ballynahinch, Co. Down BT24 7LH

Owner: The National Trust   **Contact:** The Administrator

A unique tree and shrub garden, notable rock garden and wildflower meadows.

Location: 11m SE of Belfast, 1m S of Saintfield, W of the A7 Downpatrick road.

Opening Times: 1 Apr - Oct: daily, weekdays 10.30am - 6pm, Weekends 2 - 6pm. Nov - Mar 99: daily except Sat & Sun, 10.30am - 5pm. Closed 25, 26 Dec & 1 Jan.

Admission: Easter - Oct: Adult £2.50, Child £1.25, Family £6.25, Groups £1.75pp (after hours £3pp). Nov '98 - Mar 99: Adult £1.40, Child 70p. Groups 80p

♿ Grounds suitable. WC.   ☕ Tearoom.   In grounds, on leads.

RUSSBOROUGH

Tel: + 353 45 865239   **Fax:** +353 45 865054

Blessington, Co. Wicklow   **Contact:** The Administrator

A beautifully maintained 18th century house bought in 1952 housing the Beit collection, fine furniture, tapestries, carpets, porcelain, silver and bronzes.

Location: 30km from Dublin on N81. 3km S of Blessington.

Opening Times: Easter, Apr & Oct: Sun & BHs, 10.30am - 5.30pm. May & Sept: Mon - Sat, 10.30am - 2.30pm, Sun & BHs, 10.30am - 5.30pm. Jun - Aug: daily, 10.30am - 5.30pm.

Admission: Main rooms: Adult £3, Conc. £2, Child £1. Upstairs: £1.50.

ⓘ Shop.   ♿ Suitable.   ☕ Tearoom.   Guided tours only.

SEAFORDE GARDENS

SEAFORDE, CO. DOWN BT30 8PG

Owner: Patrick Forde   *Contact:* Patrick Forde

Tel: 01396 811225   **Fax:** 01396 811370

18th century walled garden and adjoining pleasure grounds, containing many rare and beautiful trees and shrubs; many of them tender. There are huge rhododendrons and the National Collection of Eucryphias. The oldest maze in Ireland is in the centre of the walled garden, which can be viewed from the Mogul Tower. The tropical butterfly house contains hundreds of beautiful highly coloured butterflies; also a collection of parrots, insects and reptiles. The nursery garden contains many interesting plants for sale.

Location: 20m S of Belfast on the main road to Newcastle.

Opening Times: Easter - end Sept: Mon - Sat, 10am - 5pm; Sun, 1 - 6pm. Oct - Mar: 10am - 5pm.

ⓘ Shop. Plant centre.	✗ Wedding receptions.	♿ Suitable.
☕ Restaurant.	🚶 By arrangement.	Ⓜ Ample.
Educational programme available.		Strictly no dogs.

Chris Hill

Rowallane, Co, Down.

SHAW BIRTHPLACE
Tel: + 353 1 4750854   **Fax:** +353 1 8722231

33 Synge Street, Dublin 8
Owner: Dublin Tourism Enterprises   **Contact:** Fiona McKiernan
The first home of the Shaw family and the renowned playwright has been restored to its Victorian elegance and charm. It has the appearance that the family has gone out for the afternoon. The neat terraced house is as much a celebration of Victorian Dublin domestic life as of the home of one of Dublin's Nobel Laureates for Literature.
Location: 10 mins from City centre.
Opening Times: May - Sept: Mon - Sat, 10am - 5pm, Sun & BHs 11am - 5pm. Closed for lunch 1 - 2pm.
Admission: Adult IR£2.50, Child (3 - 11yrs) IR£1.30, OAP/Student (12 - 17yrs) IR£2.

SPRINGHILL
Tel: 01648 748210

20 Springhill Road, Moneymore, Magherafelt, Co. Londonderry BT45 7NQ
Owner: The National Trust   **Contact:** The Administrator
17th century 'Planter' house with 18th and 19th century additions. Springhill was the home of ten generations of a family which arrived from Ayrshire in the 17th century and the house contains family furniture, a refurbished nursery, paintings, ornaments, curios and 18th century hand-blocked wallpaper. Outbuildings house an extensive costume collection and there are walled gardens and woodland walks.
Location: 1m from Moneymore on B18.
Opening Times: Easter (10 - 14): daily. Apr, May & Sept: Sat, Sun and BH only, 2 - 6pm. Jun - Aug: daily except Thur, 2 - 6pm.
Admission: Adult £2.50, Child £1.25, Family £6.25, Group £2pp (outside hours £3.50pp).

ⓘ Shop.   ♿ Partly suitable. WC.   ☕ Tearoom.   🦌 In grounds, on leads.

STROKESTOWN PARK HOUSE
Tel: +353 78 33013   **Fax:** +353 78 33712

Strokestown, Co. Roscommon
Owner: Westward Group   **Contact:** Declan Jones
The ancestral home of the Pakenham Mahon family. The Palladian style house is complete with its original contents.
Location: 114 km from Dublin on N5.
Opening Times: 1 Apr - 31 Sept: daily, 11.30am - 5.30pm. Tours, other times by appointment.
Admission: Adult £3, Child £1.25, Conc. 20% discount.

ⓘ Shop.   ✖ Wedding receptions.   ♿ Partially suitable. WCs.
☕ Licensed restaurant. Tearoom.   🚶 By arrangement.   Ⓟ Ample.
👨‍👩‍👧 Educational programme. Teachers' pack.

TEMPLETOWN MAUSOLEUM
Tel: 01238 510721

Templepatrick, Ballyclare, Co. Antrim
Owner: The National Trust   **Contact:** Regional Office
Built in 1783 by Robert Adam in memory of the Hon Arthur Upton.
Location: In Castle Upton graveyard at Templepatrick on Belfast - Antrim road A6.
Opening Times: All year during daylight hours.

TIMOLEAGUE CASTLE GARDENS
Tel: +353 23 46116

Timoleague, Bandon, Co. Cork
Charming gardens surround a 1920s house and ruined Norman tower.
Location: 11 km S of Bandon.
Opening Times: 1 Jun - 31 Aug: Mon - Sat, 11am - 5.30pm; Sun, 2 - 5.30pm. Other times by appointment.
Admission: Adult £2.50, Child £1, Conc. £2.

TULLYNALLY CASTLE & GARDENS
Tel: +353 44 61159   **Fax:** +353 44 61856

Castlepollard, Co. Westmeath
Owner: Thomas and Valerie Pakenham   **Contact:** Valerie Pakenham
Gothick revival castle dating from the 17th century, now probably the largest in Ireland to survive as a family home. Set in romantic 18th century parkland, with 10ha (approx) of woodland and walled gardens with follies, grotto and ornamental lakes.
Location: 1m from Castlepollard on Granard Road off N52, or N4 to Mullingar.
Opening Times: Castle: 15 Jun - 30 Jun: 2 - 6pm. Gardens: May - Sept: 2 - 6pm. Open to groups at other times by appointment. Tearoom open weekends & BHs.
Admission: Adult £4, Child £2. Groups: Adult £3.50, Child £2. Gardens only: Adult £2.50, Child £1.

♿ Suitable.   ☕ Tearoom.   🚶 Compulsory.   🦌 In grounds, on leads.

WELLBROOK BEETLING MILL
Tel: 01648 751735

20 Wellbrook Road, Corkhill, Cookstown, Co. Tyrone BT80 9RY
Owner: The National Trust   **Contact:** The Administrator
A hammer mill powered by water for beetling, the final process in linen manufacture. Original machinery is in working order. The mill is situated in an attractive glen, with wooded walks along the Ballinderry River and by the mill race.
Location: 4m W of Cookstown, 1/2 m off Cookstown - Omagh road, from Cookstown turn right at Kildress Parish Church or follow Orritor Road A53 to avoid town centre.
Opening Times: Easter (10 - 14 Apr): daily, 2 - 6pm. Apr, May, Jun & Sept: Sat, Sun & BH only, 2 - 6pm. Jul & Aug: daily except Tue, 2 - 6pm.
Admission: Adult £1.80, Child 90p, Family £4.50. Group £1.30pp (outside hours £2pp).

Prices for properties in Northern Ireland are given in £ Sterling.
Prices for properties in the Republic of Ireland are given in Irish Punt.

Springhill, Ireland.

Chris Hill.

Saltee
Islands

Point

Rosslare - Fishguard

Rosslare - Pembroke Dock

Strumble
Head

Dinas
Head

Cilgerran
Castle

Cae Hir
Gardens

A487

A496

A475

A482

A487

A478

A484

A485

PEMBROKESHIRE

CARMARTHENSHIRE

Dinefwr Park

A483

Carreg
Cennen Castle

St David's
Head

St Davids
Cathedral

A487

A40

Carmarthen

A40

A40

The
Dingle

Ramsey
Island

St Davids
Bishops Palace

Picton
Castle

A40

A48

Ammanford

St Brides
Bay

A40

A477

Skomer
Island

Milford
Haven

Cresselly

Colby
Woodland
Garden

Laugharne
Castle

Kidwelly
Castle

A476

A483

49

48

SWANSEA

CHERBOURG
LE HAVRE

Skokholm
Island

Carew
Castle &
Tidal Mill

A4076

A477

Tudor
Merchants
House

Carmarthen
Bay

Llanelli

M4

46

45

Abercar
Abbey

Neath

Pembroke
Castle

Lamphey
Bishop's
Palace

Swansea

A4118

42

41

Linney
Head

Pembroke

Caldey
Island

Weobley Castle

Clyne
Gardens

Port
Talbot

49

St Govan's
Head

A418

Oxwich
Castle

Mumbles
Head

39

Worms
Head

Swansea
Bay

Porthcawl

Map Key

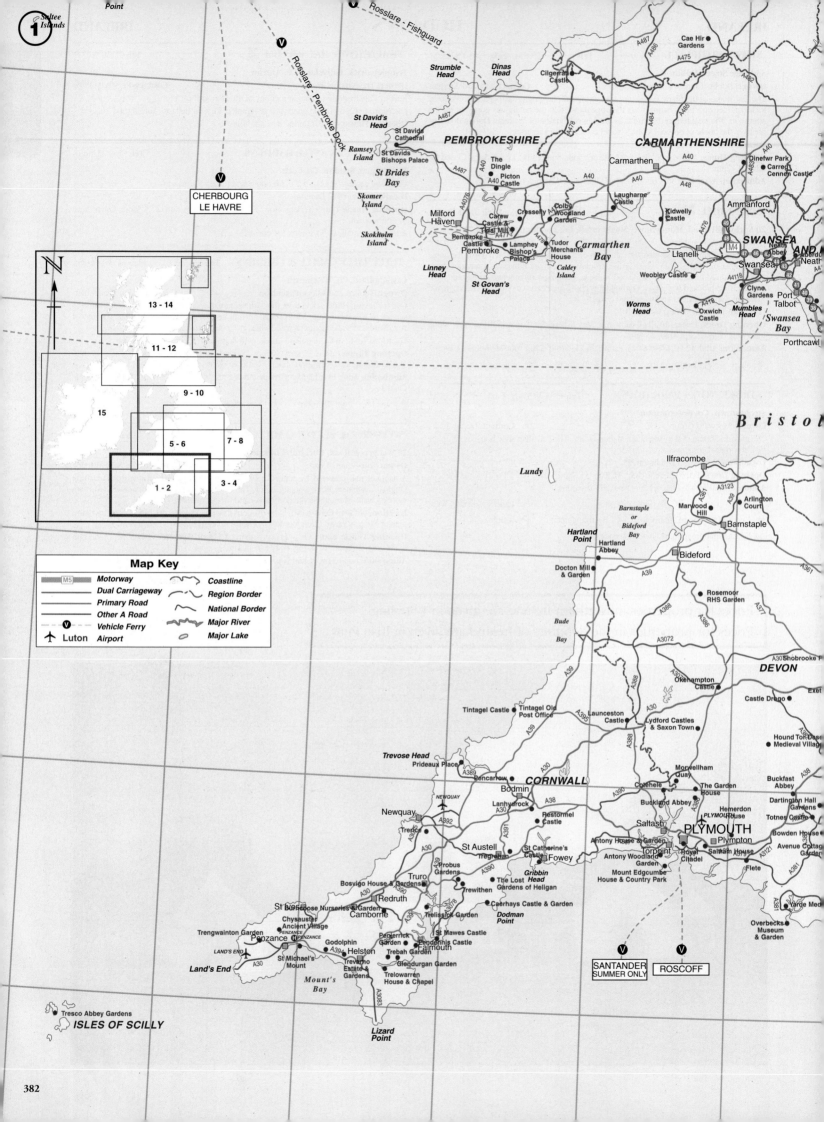

M5	Motorway		Coastline
	Dual Carriageway		Region Border
	Primary Road		National Border
	Other A Road		Major River
V	Vehicle Ferry		Major Lake
✈ Luton	Airport		

N

13 - 14

11 - 12

9 - 10

15

5 - 6

7 - 8

1 - 2

3 - 4

Bristol

Ilfracombe

Lundy

A3123

A361

Arlington
Court

Marwood
Hill

Barnstaple
or
Bideford
Bay

Barnstaple

A39

Bideford

A361

Hartland
Point

Hartland
Abbey

Docton Mill
& Garden

A39

Rosemoor
RHS Garden

A388

A386

A371

Bude
Bay

A3072

A30 Shobrooke

DEVON

Okehampton
Castle

A30

Exet

Tintagel Castle

Tintagel Old
Post Office

A395

Launceston
Castle

A30

Castle Drego

A39

Lydford Castles
& Saxon Town

A388

Hound Tor Dese
Medieval Village

Trevose Head

Prideaux Place

A389

Bencarrow

CORNWALL

A30

A388

Morwellham
Quay

Cotehele

The Garden
House

Buckfast
Abbey

Newquay

A392

Bodmin

A38

Buckland Abbey

A386

Dartington Hall
Gardens

Lanhydrock

A30

A390

Hemerdon
House

Totnes Castle

NEWQUAY

Trerice

Restormel
Castle

A391

Saltash

PLYMOUTH

PLYMOUTH

Plympton

Bowden House

St Austell

Tregrehan

St Catherine's
Castle Fowey

Antony House & Garden

Torpoint

Saltram House

Avenue Cottag

Probus
Gardens

Gribbin
Head

Antony Woodland
Garden

Royal
Citadel

Flete

Truro

Trewithen

The Lost
Gardens of Heligan

Mount Edgcumbe
House & Country Park

Yarde Med

Bosvigo House & Gardens

Caerhays Castle & Garden

Dodman
Point

St I Roseose Nurseries & Garden

Redruth

Trelissick Garden

Overbecks
Museum
& Garden

Chysauster
Ancient Village

Camborne

Godolphin

Pencarrick
Garden

St Mawes Castle

Trengwainton Garden

Penzance

PENZANCE

Helston

Pendennis Castle

Falmouth

LAND'S END

Trevarno
Estate &
Gardens

Trebah Garden

SANTANDER
SUMMER ONLY

ROSCOFF

Land's End

St Michael's
Mount

A394

Glendurgan Garden

Trelowarren
House & Chapel

Mount's
Bay

Tresco Abbey Gardens

A3083

ISLES OF SCILLY

Lizard
Point

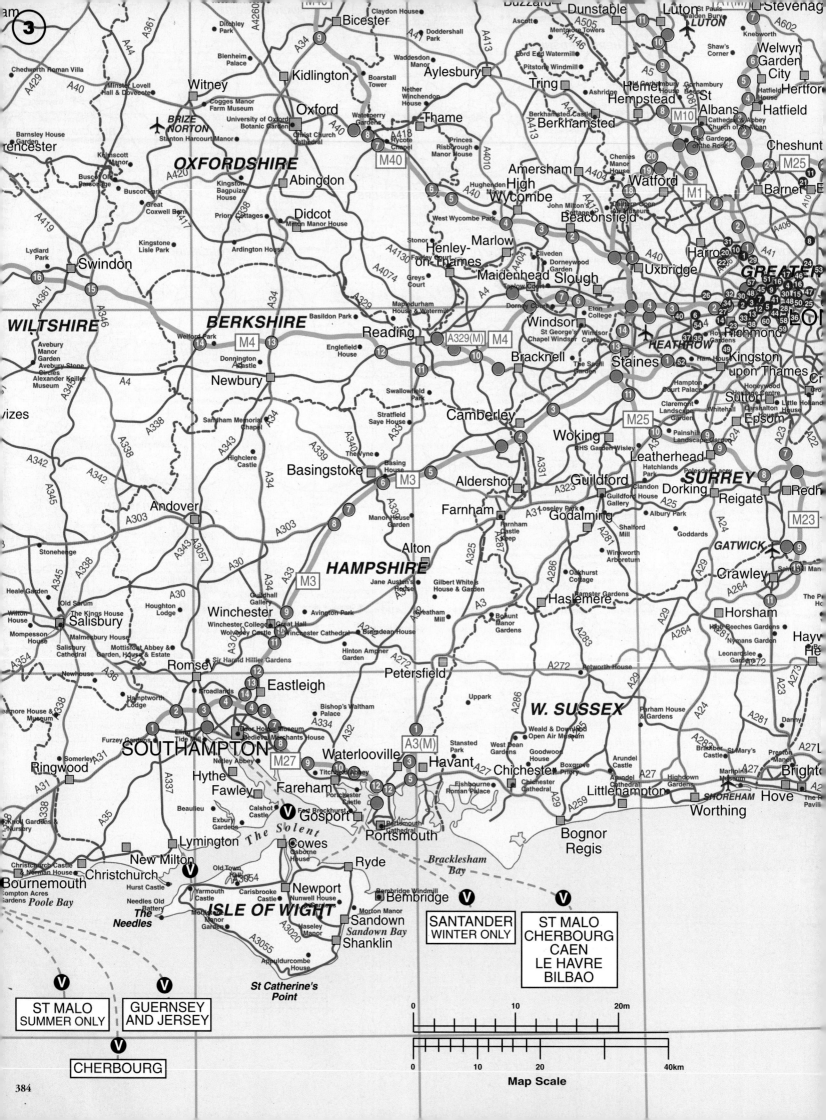

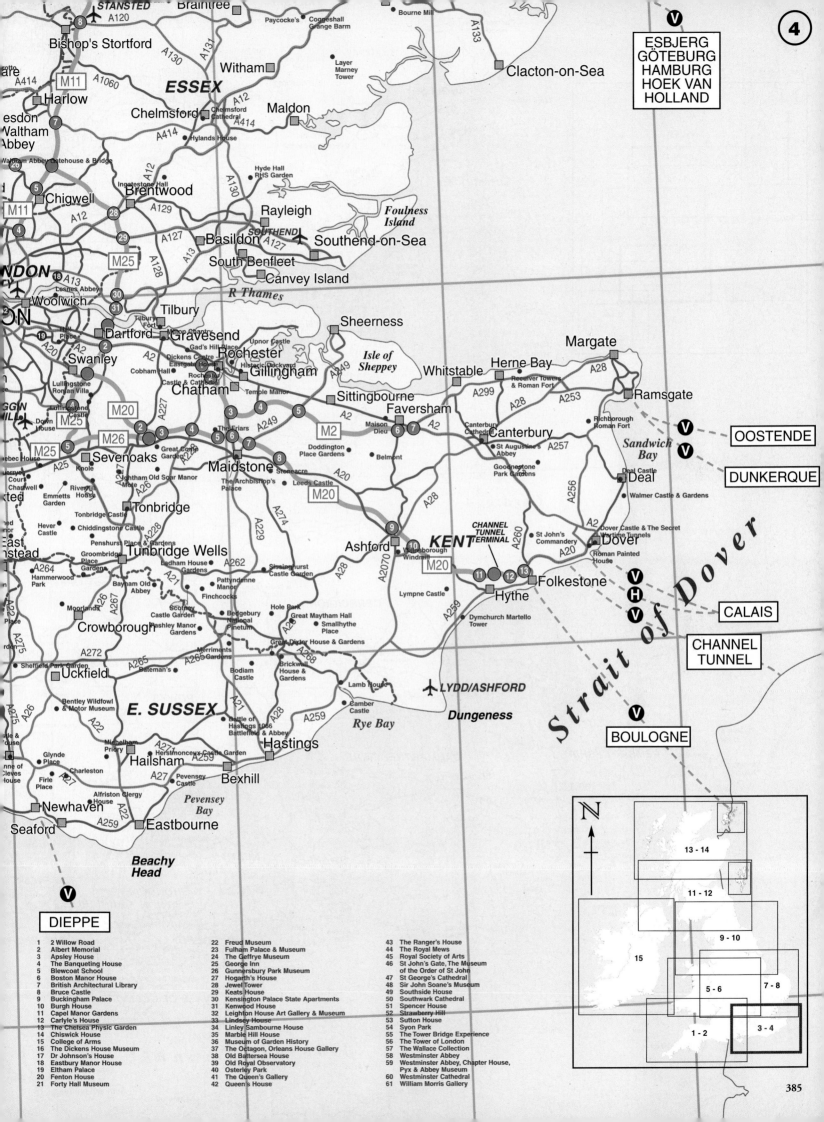

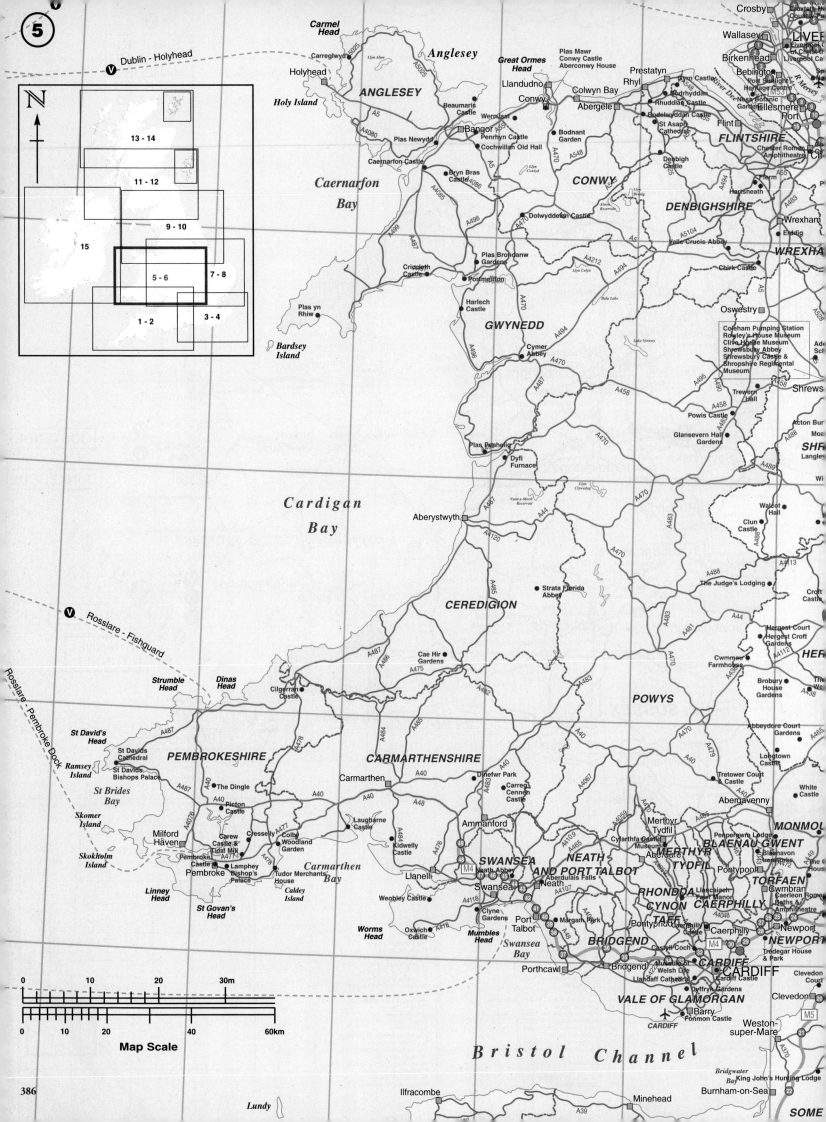

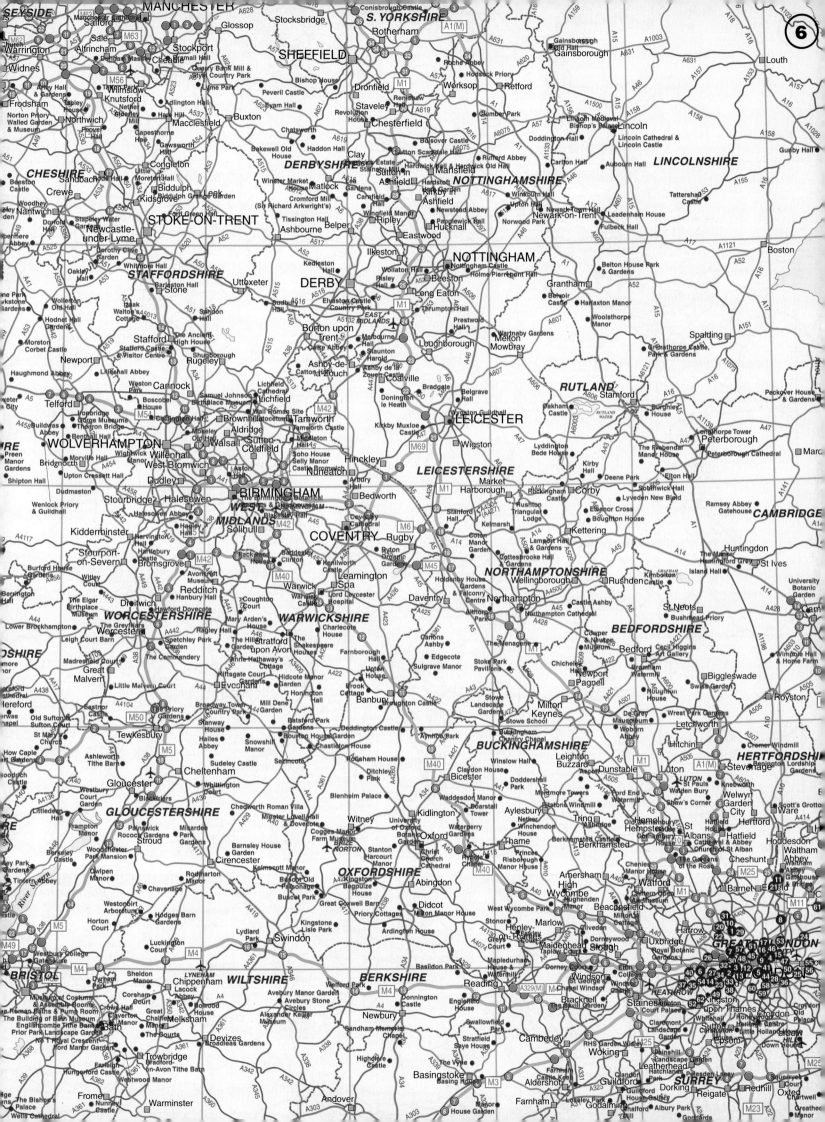

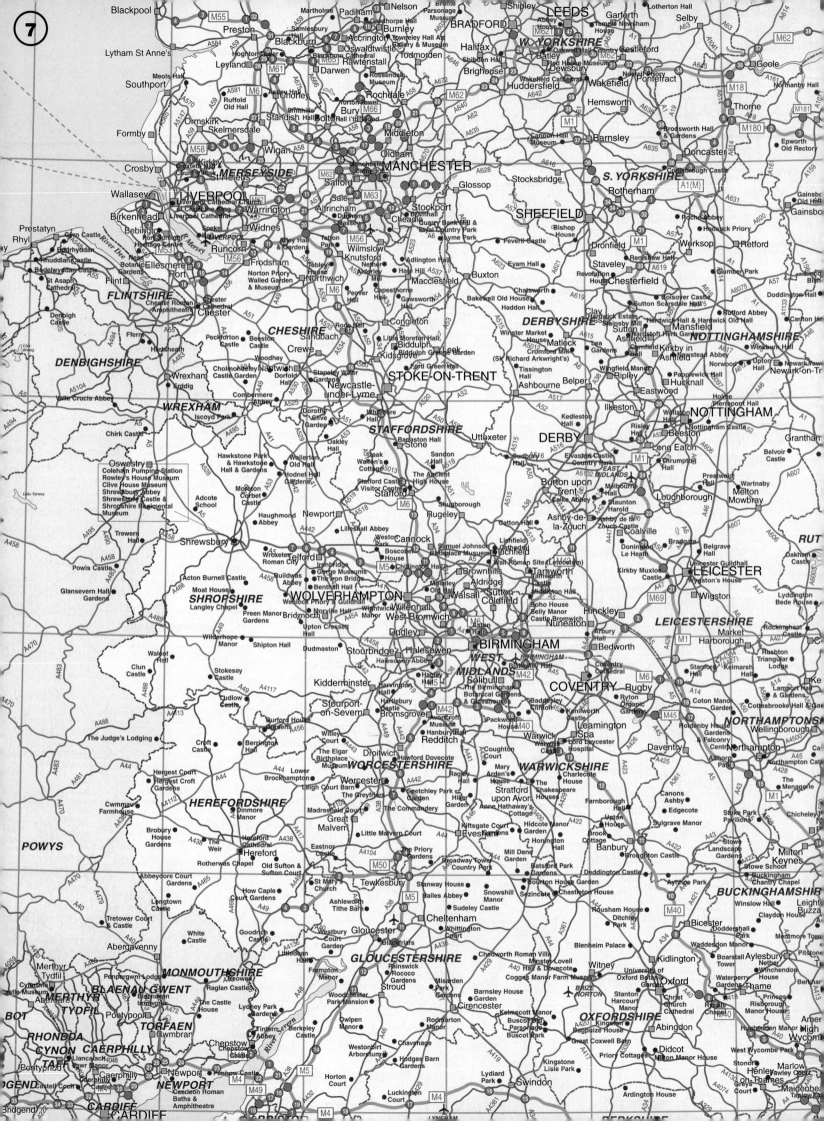

BERGEN
STAVANGER

GÖTEBORG
SUMMER ONLY

HAMBURG
SUMMER ONLY

AMSTERDAM
SUMMER ONLY

ROTTERDAM
(EUROPORT)
ZEEBRUGGE

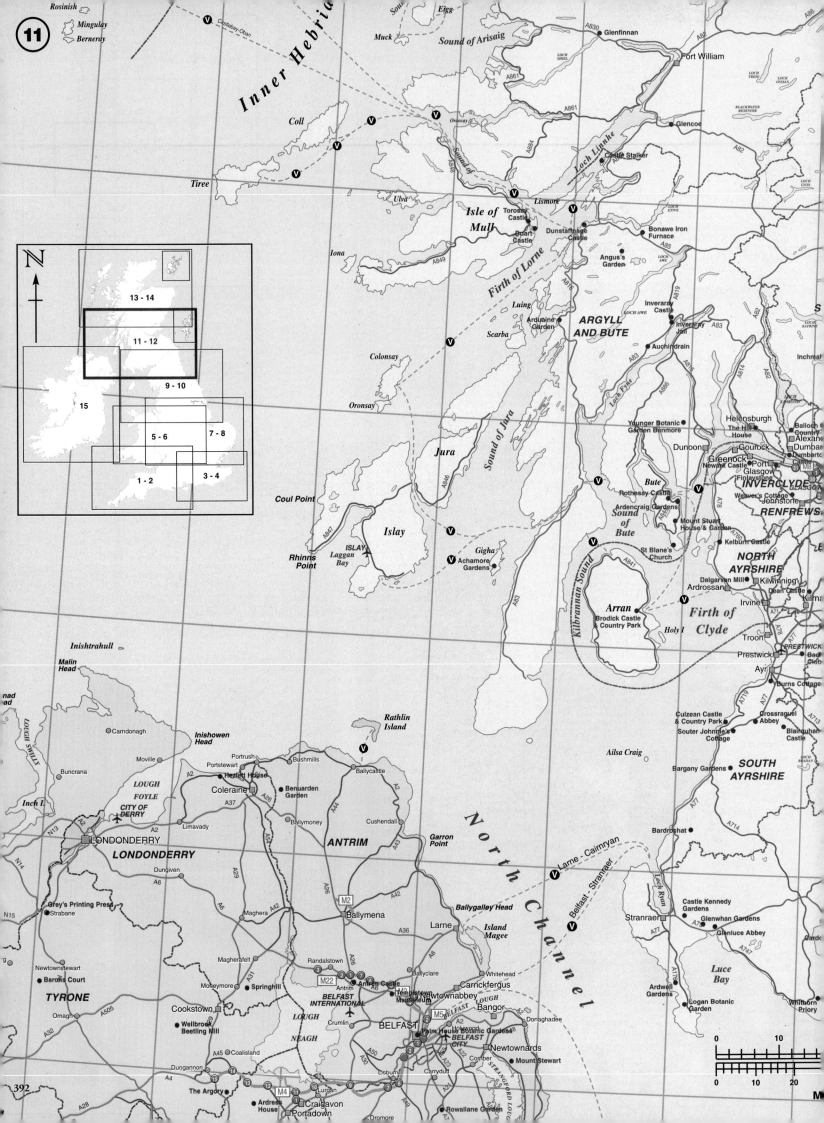

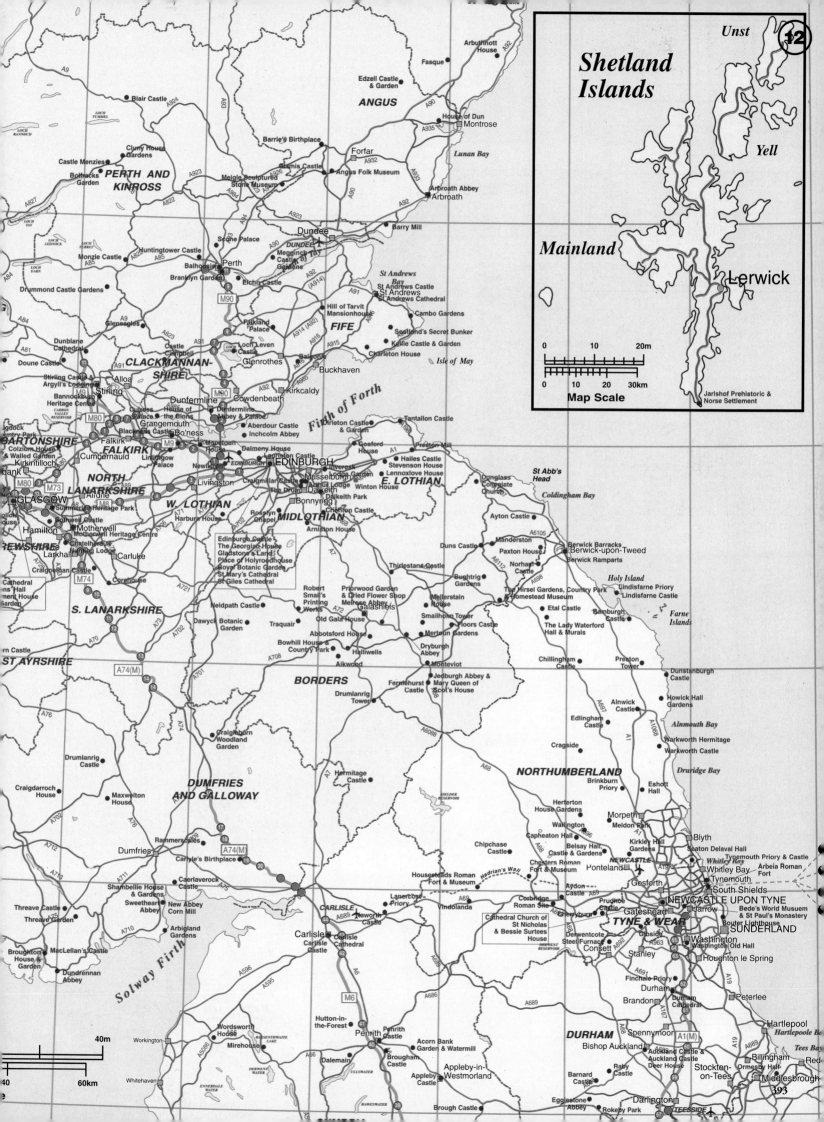

Shetland
Islands

Unst

Yell

Mainland

Lerwick

Map Scale

0   10   20m

0   10   20   30km

Jarlshof Prehistoric &
Norse Settlement

Arbuthnott
House

Fasque

Edzell Castle
& Garden

ANGUS

House of Dun
Montrose

Barrie's Birthplace

Lunan Bay

Forfar

Glamis Castle

Meigle Sculptured
Stone Museum

Angus Folk Museum

Arbroath Abbey
Arbroath

Blair Castle

Cluny House
Gardens

Castle Menzies

Bolfracks
Garden

PERTH AND
KINROSS

Huntingtower Castle

Monzie Castle

Scone Palace

Dundee

Meggineh
Castle
Gardens

Barry Mill

Drummond Castle Gardens

Perth

Balhousie

Branklyn Garden

Elcho Castle

St Andrews
Bay

St Andrews Castle
St Andrews
St Andrews Cathedral

Dunblane
Cathedral

Gleneagles

Castle
Campbell

Hill of Tarvit
Mansionhouse

Cambo Gardens

Doune Castle

CLACKMANNAN-
SHIRE

Falkland
Palace

FIFE

Scotland's Secret Bunker

Loch Leven

Kellie Castle & Garden

Stirling Castle &
Argyll's Lodging

Alloa

Glenrothes

Charleton House

Isle of May

Bannockburn
Heritage Centre

Stirling

CARRON
VALLEY
RESERVOIR

Dunfermline
Dunfermline
Abbey & Palace

Culross
Palace

House of
the Binns

Cowdenbeath

Kirkcaldy

Buckhaven

Blackness Castle

Grangemouth
Bo'ness

FALKIRK

Falkirk

Cumbernauld

Linlithgow
Palace

Hopetoun
House

Dalmeny House

Lauriston Castle

Newliston

EDINBURGH

Firth of Forth

Tantallon Castle

Dirleton Castle
& Garden

Aberdour Castle

Inchcolm Abbey

Gosford
House

Preston Mill

A1

Hailes Castle

Stevenson House

Lennoxlove House

St Abb's
Head

NORTH
LANARKSHIRE

Kirkintilloch

Colzium House
& Walled Garden

Airdrie

Summerlee Heritage Park

Livingston

Inveresk
Lodge Garden

W. LOTHIAN

Craigmillar Castle

The Drum

Musselburgh

Dalkeith

Arthur Lodge

Winton House

E. LOTHIAN

Dunglass
Collegiate
Church

Coldingham Bay

GLASGOW

Motherwell

Motherwell Heritage Centre

Bothwell Castle

Hamilton

Chatelherault

Hunting Lodge

Larkhall

Harburn House

Bonnyrigg

Dalkeith Park

Rosslyn
Chapel

MIDLOTHIAN

Crichton Castle

Arniston House

Ayton Castle

A6105

Manderston

Berwick Barracks
Berwick-upon-Tweed
Berwick Ramparts

A6112

Duns Castle

Paxton House

Craignethan Castle

Edinburgh Castle
The Georgian House
Gladstone's Land
Palace of Holyroodhouse
Royal Botanic Garden
St Mary's Cathedral
St Giles Cathedral

Neidpath Castle

Robert
Small's
Printing
Works

A7

Priorwood Garden
& Dried Flower Shop

Melrose Abbey
Galashiels

Thirlestane Castle

Bughtrig
Gardens

Norham
Castle

Holy Island

Lindisfarne Priory
Lindisfarne Castle

The Hirsel Gardens, Country Park
& Homestead Museum

Mellerstain
House

Etal Castle

Bamburgh
Castle

Farne
Islands

S. LANARKSHIRE

Corehouse

Dawyck Botanic
Garden

Traquair

Old Gala House

Abbotsford House

Smailholm Tower

Merton Gardens

Floors Castle

The Lady Waterford
Hall & Murals

Bowhill House &
Country Park

Dryburgh
Abbey

Chillingham
Castle

Preston
Tower

Halliwells

Aikwood

Monteviot

Jedburgh Abbey &
Mary Queen of
Scot's House

Dunstanburgh
Castle

ST AYRSHIRE

BORDERS

Fernieburst
Castle

A6088

Howick Hall
Gardens

Alnwick
Castle

Drumlanrig
Tower

Edlingham
Castle

A697

A1

A1068

Alnmouth Bay

Craigdarroch
House

Craiglieburn
Woodland
Garden

Drumlanrig
Castle

Maxwelton
House

DUMFRIES
AND GALLOWAY

Hermitage
Castle

A68

Cragside

NORTHUMBERLAND

Warkworth Hermitage
Warkworth Castle

Druridge Bay

Brinkburn
Priory

Eshott
Hall

Herterton
House Gardens

Morpeth

Meldon Park

Rammerscales

A74(M)

Wallington

Chipchase
Castle

Capheaton Hall

Belsay Hall,
Castle & Gardens

Blyth

Kirkley Hall
Gardens

Seaton Delaval Hall

Dumfries

Carlyle's Birthplace

Chesters Roman
Fort & Museum

Ponteland

NEWCASTLE

Whitley Bay

Tynemouth Priory & Castle
Whitley Bay
Arbeia Roman
Fort

Shambellie House
& Gardens

Caerlaverock
Castle

Housesteads Roman
Fort & Museum

Hadrian's Wall

Gosforth

Aydon
Castle

A69

Tynemouth
South Shields

Threave Castle

Threave Garden

Sweetheart
Abbey

New Abbey
Corn Mill

CARLISLE

Lanercost
Priory

Vindolanda

Corbridge
Roman Site

Cherryburn

Prudhoe
Castle

NEWCASTLE UPON TYNE

Gateshead

Jarrow

Bede's World Musuem
& St Paul's Monastery

Souter Lighthouse

Broughton
House & Garden

MacLellan's Castle

Dundrennan
Abbey

Arbigland
Gardens

Naworth
Castle

Carlisle

Carlisle
Cathedral

Cathedral Church of
St Nicholas &
Bessie Surtees
House

Derwentcote
Steel Furnace

Consett

Stanley

TYNE & WEAR

Gibside

Washington
Washington Old Hall

SUNDERLAND

Houghton le Spring

Solway Firth

A6

M6

Wordsworth
House

Hutton-in-
the-Forest

Penrith
Castle

Penrith

Acorn Bank
Garden & Watermill

Finchale Priory

Durham

Brandon

Durham
Cathedral

Peterlee

Hartlepool
Hartlepoole Be

40m

60km

Workington

Mirehouse

Dalemain

Brougham
Castle

Appleby
Castle

Appleby-in-
Westmorland

DURHAM

Bishop Auckland

Spennymoor

Auckland Castle &
Auckland Castle
Deer House

Raby
Castle

Stockton-
on-Tees

Billingham

Ormesby Hall

Middlesbrough

Whitehaven

Barnard
Castle

Egglestone
Abbey

Rokeby Park

Darlington

TEESSIDE

Tees Ba

Red

Brough Castle

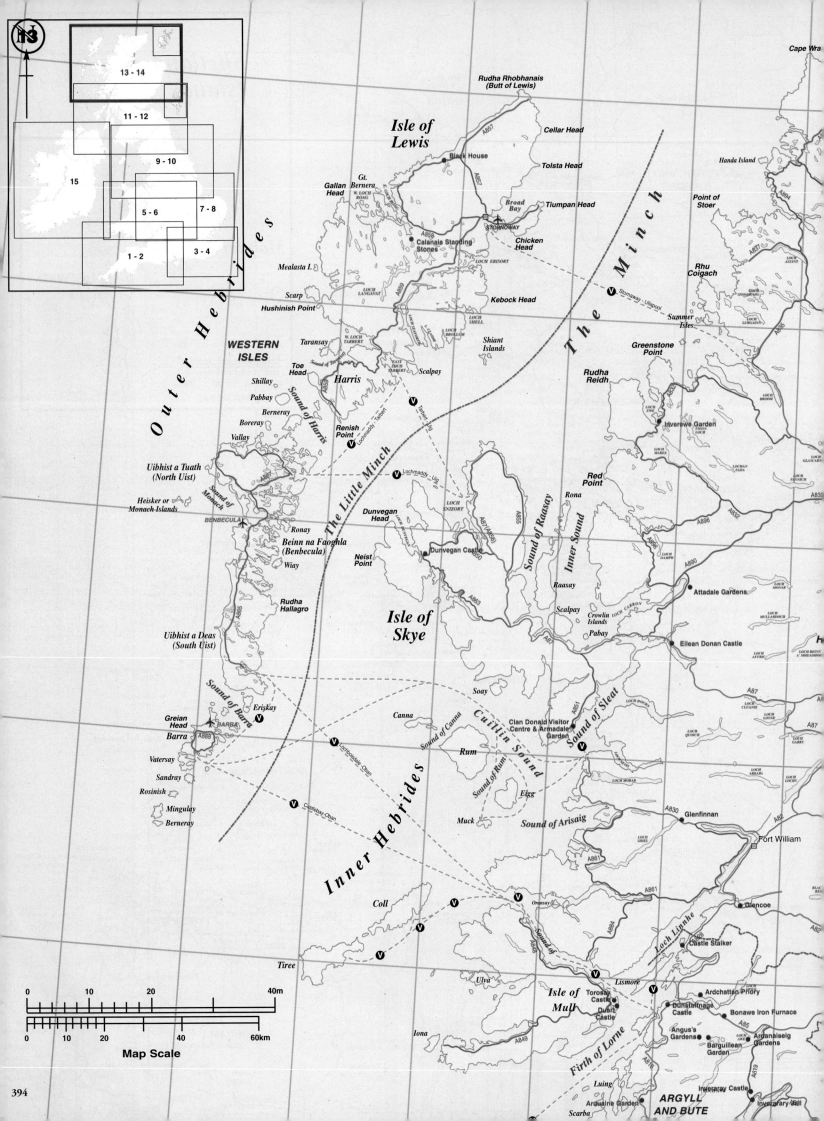

Pentland Firth

Whiten Head
Dunnet Head
Strathy Point
Island of Stroma
Duncansby Head

Noss Head
WICK

Orkney Islands

Mainland

Broch of Gurness

Ring of Brodgar
Stone Circles & Henge
Skara Brae
Maes Howe
Balfour Castle

Kirkwall

Tankerness House
Bishop's Palace
Earl's Palace
St Magnus' Cathedral

Hoy

Scotland

Dunrobin Castle

Dornoch Firth

Moray Firth

Hugh Miller's Cottage
Cromarty Courthouse
Spynie Palace
Fraserburgh

Elgin
Elgin Cathedral
Duff House
Craigston Castle

Fort George
Brodie Castle
Dallas Dhu Distillery
Pluscarden Abbey
Delgatie Castle

INVERNESS
MORAY
Drummuir Castle
A950
Peterhead

Inverness
Cawdor Castle
Culloden
Fyvie Castle

Dochfour Gardens
Ballindalloch Castle
Balvenie Castle
Huntly Castle
Haddo House

Urquhart Castle
Leith Hall
Tolquhon Castle
Pitmedden Garden

Kildrummy Castle
Kildrummy Castle Garden
ABERDEENSHIRE
Monymusk Walled Garden
To Stromness
To Lerwick

Candacraig Garden & Gallery
Castle Fraser & Garden
ABERDEEN
ABERDEEN CITY Aberdeen

Corgarff Castle

St Machar's Cathedral
Transepts
Cruickshank Botanic Garden
Provost Skene's House
Duthie Park & Winter Gardens

Crathes Castle
Drum Castle

Braemar Castle
Balmoral Castle

Dunnottar Castle

Arbuthnott House

Fasque
Edzell Castle & Garden

ANGUS

House of Dun
Montrose

Blair Castle

Lunan Bay

Cluny House Gardens
Barrie's Birthplace
Forfar

Castle Menzies
PERTH AND KINROSS
Glamis Castle
Angus Folk Museum

Bolfracks Garden
Meigle Sculptured Stone Museum

Arbroath Abbey
Arbroath

Barry Mill

Monzie Castle
Huntingtower Castle
Scone Palace
Dundee
DUNDEE

Perth
Megginch Castle Gardens
Barry Mill

Drummond Castle Gardens
Branklyn Garden
Elcho Castle

St Andrews Bay

STIRLING
Gleneagles
Dunblane Cathedral

Falkland Palace
Hill of Tarvit Mansionhouse
St Andrews Castle
St Andrews Cathedral

Cambo Gardens
Scotland's Secret Bunker
Kellie Castle & Garden
FIFE

395

Index

Index